Principles of
Modern Organic
Chemistry

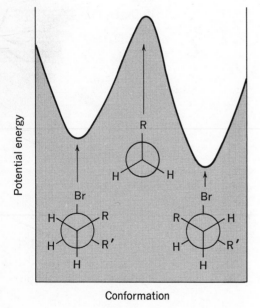

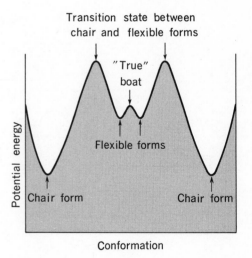

Principles of Modern Organic Chemistry

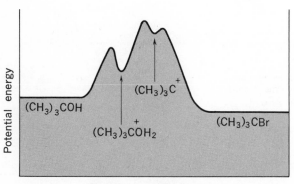

JAMES CASON

Professor of Chemistry
University of California, Berkeley

PRENTICE-HALL, Inc.
Englewood Cliffs, New Jersey

Library of Congress Catalog Card Number, 66-17374

Current printing (last digit):

10 9 8 7 6 5 4 3 2 1

PRINTED IN THE UNITED STATES OF AMERICA   C—70954

PRENTICE-HALL INTERNATIONAL, INC., *London*
PRENTICE-HALL OF AUSTRALIA, PTY. LTD., *Sydney*
PRENTICE-HALL OF CANADA, LTD., *Toronto*
PRENTICE-HALL OF INDIA (PRIVATE) LTD., *New Delhi*
PRENTICE-HALL OF JAPAN, INC., *Tokyo*

Preface

This book is developed around the concept that organic chemistry has become fundamentally a study of the geometry of molecules, and the physical and chemical properties which are a consequence of these geometric features. Thus, the concept of structure is introduced at the outset, and is made realistic by the inclusion of infrared and nuclear magnetic resonance spectra, as well as numerous photographs of molecular models. This is followed by a development of the dependence on energy relations of structural conformation, chemical reactions and types of chemical bonding. The interplay between energy relations and structure is developed at an early stage so that the groundwork is laid for a treatment in Chapter 7 of conformation in the six-membered ring and its important consequences in organic chemistry.

The study of chemical reactions is emphasized throughout this book. This study is organized around the types of chemical reactions which occur and the basic reasons for their occurrence. The importance of energy relations in determining the course of reactions is introduced at the beginning, and continued as the prime basis for control of the direction of reactions. Thus, energy diagrams are used freely to graphically demonstrate energy changes during the course of reactions. Reactions are studied on the basis of bond types in the reactants, rather than on the kinds of bonds formed in the reactions. This facilitates the demonstration of the dependence of reaction pathway on structure and energy relations. Thus, the several varieties of displacement reactions are introduced first, and these are followed by elimination and addition reactions, then radical reactions. Experience has indicated that this allows students to gain a clear understanding of the underlying factors that control reaction mechanisms at the same time that reactions are developed in a sequence which bears a reasonable relation to their importance. In addition, this approach is well adapted to a study of the classes of compounds in a natural sequence depending on their significance, with alcohols and alkyl halides first. This contrasts with the classical approach, which has survived in many modern texts, wherein early attention is directed towards halogenation of an alkane, one of the more complicated and least useful reactions. It would seem to be better pedagogy to first introduce a student to the more important and fundamental aspects of the subject matter, namely, structural concepts, energy relations and organic reactions of importance in synthesis.

The application of organic reactions to the synthesis of molecules is a subject of continuing emphasis, since the conversion of organic compounds into other desired ones is probably the most important goal of organic chemistry. Modern knowledge of structure, reaction mechanisms and energy relationships is focussed on the use of organic reactions in synthesis. The reasons for acquiring the knowledge in these respective areas, as well as the ultimate goals of the study of organic chemistry, are frequently summarized and correlated.

The treatment of aromatic chemistry may be regarded as "semi-integrated", in that it is introduced at points regarded as most appropriate to the underlying organization of subject matter. Thus, resonance stabilization in benzene and its effect on reaction type are introduced in Chapter 12, devoted to stabilization of organic molecules by electron delocalization, whereas a systematic study of aromatic substitution is deferred to later chapters. On account of the importance of primary aromatic amines, the systematic study of organic bases is introduced after the basic aspects of aromatic chemistry have been considered. The fundamental importance of electrical effects in aromatic chemistry is developed in some detail.

Relatively great emphasis is placed on heterocyclic chemistry, by way of a study in depth of the pyridine and quinoline ring systems. This material was first introduced into our teaching because the growing importance of heterocyclic chemistry seemed to render mandatory its inclusion in a properly balanced introductory course in organic chemistry. The material was expanded as it was realized that the study of pyridine and quinoline chemistry offers an invaluable opportunity to review and extend theoretical as well as practical aspects of both aliphatic and aromatic chemistry. The application of these basic principles in a different context offers the student the opportunity to consolidate and greatly improve his understanding of many of the more important aspects of organic chemistry.

The consideration of optical isomerism is thorough and rather extensive, for this is felt to be of basic importance in the elementary organic course. Failure to give a rigorous foundation in this area is likely to result in severe handicap to the student in future years. Thus, optical isomerism is introduced as soon as sufficient sophistication has been developed, and this is judged to be somewhat beyond the middle of the book. The principles of the sequence rule (assignment of *R*- and *S*-configurations) are introduced and subsequently used in discussions involving absolute configuration. It seems clear that this system of designating absolute configuration is so superior to the traditional system that future chemists should study the rather fuzzily-based D- and L-notation only in a historical perspective.

The study of carbohydrate chemistry is very greatly simplified, as well as modernized, by exclusive use of conformational formulas for pyranoside structures. Again, older systems of designation are described only as of historical interest. Classroom experience of the author has shown that use of conformational formulas removes most of the memory strain from the study of carbohydrate structures as well as reactions. The net gain in this area alone considerably more than compensates for the time required for a careful study of conformational analysis. Use of the R- and S-designations are an additional advantage in the study of carbohydrate chemistry.

Modern developments in nucleic acid and protein chemistry are introduced, and the remarkable significance of the spatial arrangement of atoms in these structures is emphasized. This consideration of the geometry of the components of living tissue may be regarded as a climax to the development of the ubiquitous importance of structure in organic chemistry.

Structural features are frequently emphasized by reference to absorption spectra, and to mass spectra. Near the end of the book there is a development of the basic principles of mass spectrometry, and applications of this important tool are used to emphasize its rapidly growing significance in determining the structures of organic molecules.

In order to stimulate the appetite of the more alert and ambitious students, selected references to original literature are included as footnotes in the text. In addition, the final chapter is designed to function as an introduction to use of the literature of organic chemistry. The objective of this approach is to make clear to the student that although the things regarded as most fundamental are described in the text, the horizon of organic chemistry is truly infinite. The source of additional information is ultimately the original research literature, written by those exploring on the frontiers.

The author wishes to express his real appreciation of the indispensable help received from many of his colleagues at Berkeley, as well as chemistry professors elsewhere. Contributions of particular importance include: careful review of important chapters constituting nearly half the manuscript by Professor F. E. Jensen of my department; critical review and up-dating of the carbohydrate chapters by Professor Clinton Ballou, and of the protein chapter by Professor David Cole, both of the Department of Biochemistry at Berkeley; critical review of the material on displacement reactions by Professor Donald Noyce of my department; numerous helpful suggestions for the chapters on heterocyclic chemistry by Professor Henry Baumgarten of the University of Nebraska; helpful and searching review of the entire manuscript by Professor N. L. Allinger of Wayne State University. The photographs of Framework Molecular Models are the product of the patience and skill of Mr. Jess Bravo of Norton Pearl Photography.

J. C.

Contents

4 **Alcohols as a Class of Organic Compounds 41**

5 **Systematic Nomenclature in Organic Chemistry 50**

6 **Displacement Reactions. Organic Syntheses 62
from Alcohols and Alkyl Halides**

7 **Cyclic Structures in Organic Compounds. 85
Geometrical Isomerism and Conformation**

16

17

18

19

Introduction

Since this book is devoted to a development of the essential principles of organic chemistry it is no doubt in order to consider, briefly, the historical developments leading to the classification of organic chemistry as one division of the broader science of chemistry. Such a consideration leads us back to the early part of the nineteenth century when the science of chemistry was emerging from the mysteries classified as alchemy. At the time, chemical substances were classified in two categories: organic compounds, produced by living organisms; inorganic compounds, found in minerals. The production of organic compounds by living organisms was a basic concept; it was held that such compounds could be produced only through the agency of a "vital force" present in living organisms. This concept was first challenged in 1828, when the German chemist Friedrich Wöhler reported that he had been able to convert ammonium cyanate, of recognized mineral origin, into urea. Since urea was recognized as an organic substance secreted by animals, this experiment had a profound effect on chemical thinking of that day. As is so often the case when a really revolutionary discovery is reported, advocates of the "well-established principles" vigorously resisted this "radical" idea, and questioned both the validity and significance of Wöhler's report. As is always true, however, the facts in the case cannot be dismissed, and after the lapse of some twenty years and the discovery of additional "syntheses" of organic compounds it became generally recognized that the original definition of organic chemistry was no longer meaningful.

During the period that the theory of the "vital force" was being discredited, development of methods of analytical chemistry had revealed that the substances of animal and plant origin, classified as organic compounds, always contained the element carbon. Hydrogen was usually present, oxygen was sometimes present, and a variety of elements was occasionally encountered, but carbon was always present in the compounds of natural origin that had been classified as organic compounds. This led to the definition of organic compounds as those containing carbon, regardless of their origin. This continues to be a rather accurate concept, so that **organic chemistry is** commonly defined as **the chemistry of the compounds of carbon.** In practice, the metallic cyanides and carbonates are excepted from the classification of organic compounds. These are included with the inorganic compounds, which are commonly defined as all compounds not containing carbon.

Since the compounds of carbon alone are classified as organic compounds, and all compounds not containing carbon are grouped together as inorganic, it would appear that there must be something rather special about carbon. Well, there is! Indeed, there are several rather unique characteristics of the element carbon. And these characteristics are so significant that *the total number of known organic compounds outnumbers the total number of known inorganic compounds by a factor of at least ten.* This refers, not to the compounds that are theoretically possible, but to compounds actually handled by experimental chemists. The number of organic compounds that is theoretically possible is truly without limit. The number of known organic compounds is so large that it cannot be assessed accurately; however, it is in excess of 2,000,000, and some 80,000 new organic compounds are added yearly to those known. Thousands of new organic compounds are described in the chemical journals each month, and it is not uncommon for an organic chemist to prepare, or supervise the preparation of, as many as one thousand new organic compounds during his career. Nearly all the things we eat and wear are organic compounds; in fact, the animal organism is composed largely of organic compounds and water. Also almost entirely organic are the paint on a house and the different kind of paint on an automobile, as well as the gasoline that drives the engine and the oil that lubricates it. With the exception of the metals and minerals, most of the things with which we come in daily contact are organic compounds.

Of the properties of carbon which make its compounds so numerous, the most important is its ability to join with itself to form rings and chains of great size. There appears to be no practical limit to the number of carbons that can combine to form a chain. Polymers are known that contain chains of many hundreds of carbon atoms. Furthermore, there may be branches in the chain, rings interposed in a chain, or other elements inserted in the chain or attached to its side. These atoms are usually held together by covalences, the most characteristic feature of the organic compounds. Atoms held together by covalences are not only a specific distance apart, but the valences form specific angles with each other. *It follows that the nature of chemical bonding, and the geometry of the covalently bonded compounds are of vital importance in the study of organic chemistry.* In fact, the geometry of the molecules is the most basic aspect governing their reactions, including the reactions vital in life processes. It is important to study early, and continually, in the science of organic chemistry, the nature of chemical bonding and the consequences of this bonding in terms of the geometry of the molecules, and the energy relations between the molecules involved in reactions. These factors determine the kinds of reactions which organic molecules will undergo, and they are basic to understanding the mechanisms by which these reactions occur.

Although it may be said that the scope of organic chemistry has been summarized above, this scope is very large indeed on account of the great variety of structures possible in organic compounds and the large number of types of chemical reactions that have been found possible with these structures. An effective elementary working knowledge of organic chemistry may be acquired in a year's study, however, if this study concentrates on the basic principles involved. Such a study is of obvious value as a foundation for more advanced work in chemistry; however, it can also be of great interest to anyone wishing to have some understanding of the many natural phenomena which he encounters daily. If the true definition of culture is knowledge of many things, so that one is stimulated by many things, and life becomes more interesting, what better path to culture than learning something about the natural phenomena that are around us all the time. They may be enjoyed at any time, without buying a ticket or getting dressed for the occasion.

As an aid in the study of organic chemistry, one particular characteristic of the science should be well understood. In general, each of the isolated theories or facts is rather simple; sometimes, they appear absurdly simple. Indeed, all things that one understands seem simple. As more of the knowledge is accumulated, however, the whole tends to become more complex, *especially if the simple parts have not been mastered* along the way. If the tyro learns the simple things as they are encountered, the whole is greatly simplified; if he waits for a period and then attempts to grapple with a large segment of the whole, the subject seems hopelessly complicated and beyond comprehension. If one sees an automobile or radio assembled, it proves to be made of very simple pieces which are joined together in a straightforward manner, but the completed article is a complex machine. This characteristic should be borne well in mind from the very beginning of, and throughout, a study of organic chemistry. It can make the difference between success (and pleasure in the study) and failure (with complete disappointment in the study), with the same amount of effort applied.

Since the first part of a study of organic chemistry consists of a running encounter with a series of new concepts and facts, it is imperative that these things be learned. The oft-heard excuse, "I am poor at organic chemistry because I can't memorize," is merely a poor excuse, for there is no way to acquire knowledge except by memorization, however the process may be decorated for improvement of palatability. The critical characteristic of organic chemistry is that the science is very highly structured, perhaps the most highly structured of any science. This is the reason that one who does not acquire the basic information is lost. The foundation must be acquired before one can build on it, and the upper floors are built upon the lower ones. If any floor is weak, all that is above it collapses—and the collapse is likely to crush that which is below. Thus, an initial investment must be made in studying the first principles, and this investment must be protected by continuing to accumulate the basic knowledge. If this is done, intriguing deductions can be made, and a variety of challenging problems may be solved. But one can think intelligently only if he has something to think about.

The Concept of Structure in Organic Chemistry

Physical Properties of Organic Compounds

Compounds whose atoms are held together by electrovalences do not have a definite sequence and position for the atoms, except in a crystal lattice in the solid state. In contrast, there is a definite sequence and position for the atoms in a molecule held together by covalences, regardless of whether the physical state be gas, liquid, or solid. The order in which the atoms are joined to each other is known as the **structure** of the molecule. In the present chapter, we will consider some of the consequences of structure in covalently bonded molecules, especially in terms of physical properties. In the next chapter we will consider the nature of the covalent chemical bond which is so important in determining the nature of organic molecules. After chemical bonding will come the study of the geometrical shapes of organic molecules, and the energy relations which determine the course of organic reactions. These studies are necessary before one can consider with understanding the chemical reactions of organic molecules.

The concept of structure may be profitably introduced by considering a simple molecule in the manner that a chemist approaches the elucidation of the structure of a molecule whose structure has not previously been determined. For this purpose, ethyl alcohol, a substance of considerable importance as a raw material in the chemical industry, is satisfactory. In spite of the long-standing controversy concerning the merits of ethyl alcohol as a beverage, there is no disagreement concerning its importance as a starting material for synthesis of many of the compounds of carbon.

Composition of Ethyl Alcohol

In the case of a new compound of unknown structure, it is first necessary to obtain the compound in a pure condition, otherwise, its study is extremely difficult, if at all possible. Next, the number and kind of atoms in the molecule are determined. These investigations usually follow a specific sequence.

1. Isolation, purification, and proof of purity. Classical methods of separation of organic compounds depended largely on the processes of crystallization and distillation; however, these methods have now been supplemented by methods classified as chromatography,[1] which have enormously increased the chemist's ability to separate organic compounds and to test the purity of the compounds separated. Since these methods are ordinarily the subject of detailed study in the experimental part of a chemistry course they will not be considered at this time. After the compound has been separated, it may be recognized by its physical properties; furthermore, if additional efforts at purification do not cause a change in physical properties this is regarded as the best evidence that the compound is indeed homogeneous, i.e., pure.

2. Physical properties. The physical properties of a compound, like the physical properties of people or other things, may be used in order to recognize the compound. As is the case for methods of purification, physical properties useful for recognition of a compound have become rather different during

---

[1] The technique now known as chromatography was first applied to adsorption of colored substances from a solution passed through a column of an adsorbent contained in a glass tube. As more solvent was poured through the tube, the colored substances separated into bands as they migrated down the tube at different rates dependent on their relative strengths of adsorption. This appearance of colored bands gave rise to the name chromatography, which is now applied to a wide variety of separations which depend on a distribution of some sort. Most of the things to which the process is applied are colorless. The original technique of adsorption chromatography depends on distribution of a compound between a solution and adsorption on a surface. Separations depend on differences in strength of adsorption, and this has proved a potent method of separating certain types of compounds. Other types of chromatography which have been found effective include distribution between two liquid phases, between a gas phase and an adsorbed phase, and between a gas phase and a solution. The latter type, known as gas-liquid partition chromatography or simply gas chromatography, has proved remarkably effective. It has made possible clean separations which are otherwise entirely impossible. Furthermore, the rate at which a substance passes through a given gas chromatography column is an important physical constant useful for recognition of the substance.

Numerous books have been devoted to various types of chromatography. Nearly all the more useful types are described by H. G. Cassidy, in A. Weissberger's *Technique of Organic Chemistry*, Vol. X, *Fundamentals of Chromatography* (New York: Interscience, 1957).

the middle of the twentieth century. Of course the properties have not changed, but man's ability to observe these properties has been enhanced many-fold by the introduction of new devices for observing certain properties. Although compounds have such properties as color, odor and macroscopic crystal form, these characteristics are of use only in limited numbers of cases. The most important properties for the description of organic compounds have been the melting point and boiling point; however, these properties have now become less definitive than the use of **absorption spectra.** Instruments have become available, although they are expensive, for easy and rapid determination of absorption of various kinds of radiant energy. A record of the amount of absorption as a function of the wavelength (or other parameter) of the radiation is termed an **absorption spectrum** (plural, as above, spectra).

Features of structure in a molecule will cause strong absorption at certain specific wavelengths. **Absorption maxima** in the ultraviolet and visible regions of the spectrum are due to excitation of electronic vibrations in the molecule, while maxima in the infrared region of the spectrum occur from resonance with molecular vibrations dependent on the structure of the molecule. These and other types of spectra will be discussed later in this chapter in connection with structure determinations, but for the present the spectra are introduced as physical properties of molecules. Many compounds may have the same boiling point, or melting point, and a few may have both of these properties the same. It is much more rare, however, for two compounds to have the same absorption spectrum in a given region of wavelength; and it is virtually impossible for two different compounds to be identical in two or three different types of spectra. Thus, a compound may be identified with great reliability if its absorption spectrum is observed by use of an appropriate instrument.

To return to the compound under consideration, ethyl alcohol, a pure sample will be a colorless liquid with a boiling point of 78°. Its infrared absorption spectrum will show a strong absorption band at a wavelength of about 3.0 μ. The significance of this spectral feature will be developed later in connection with the structure of the molecule.

3. Qualitative analysis for elements. If the compound in question is indeed an organic compound, then it must contain carbon. The presence of carbon may be tested by burning a sample and testing the evolved gases for presence of carbon dioxide. Nearly all organic compounds burn more or less readily, in contrast with inorganic compounds, many of which cannot be burned at all under ordinary conditions. In addition, most covalently bonded compounds have relatively low boiling points and melting points (below 400°); however, some inorganic compounds are covalently bonded. An example is stannic chloride which has a boiling point of 114° and a melting point of −30°.

Hydrogen is nearly always present in organic compounds, and there is no simple qualitative test for it. Oxygen is frequently present in organic compounds, but there is no simple qualitative test for it. The elements commonly present in organic compounds for which there are simple qualitative tests are halogens, nitrogen, sulfur and phosphorus. These can be determined by the simple tests of inorganic chemistry *only after they have been converted to suitable ions after rupture of the covalent bonds in the organic molecule.* This can be accomplished only by such vigorous treatment as fusion with molten sodium.

In the case of ethyl alcohol, tests prove negative for halogen, nitrogen, sulfur, and phosphorus; therefore, it is concluded that only carbon, hydrogen, and oxygen may be present.

4. Quantitative analysis. Experimentally, quantitative analysis for the elements in organic compounds requires specific training in the particular technique involved, so an organic chemist rarely carries out such analyses. He refers any needed analyses to a trained analyst who not only has the necessary experimental skill but also keeps abreast of the rapid developments in this field. It has become possible to secure analyses accurate to about 0.3% on samples of material less than 1 mg.

In theory, obtaining of quantitative analytical data is usually simple. For example, in the case of ethyl alcohol, an accurately weighed sample could be burned quantitatively to carbon dioxide and water, and these would be collected and weighed. Calculation of composition by usual methods would involve, for example, for carbon:

$$\text{wt. of } CO_2 \times \frac{C}{CO_2} = \text{wt. of C in sample}$$

where the fraction C/CO_2 is $\frac{12}{44}$. Also,

$$\frac{\text{wt. of C in sample}}{\text{wt. of sample}} \times 100 = \text{per cent of C in sample}$$

If the sum of the percentages of all elements known to be present is less than 100, the difference is assumed to be oxygen. Only in rare cases is the rather troublesome analysis for oxygen performed.

Although experimental figures are always subject to some limitation in accuracy, the ratio of atoms in the molecule may usually be calculated exactly unless the molecular weight is moderately large (more than a dozen carbon atoms in the molecule). Representative data for ethyl alcohol are presented in the following tabulation:

Calculation of Empirical Formula for Ethyl Alcohol

Atom	Per cent	Atomic wt.	Atomic ratio	Integral ratio of atoms
C	52.07 (by analysis)	12.01	4.34	2
H	13.07 (by analysis)	1.008	12.94	6
O	34.86 (by difference)	16.00	2.18	1

These data give an **empirical formula** for ethyl alcohol of C_2H_6O. The empirical formula is thus defined as a formula showing the *kind* and *ratio* of atoms present in the molecule, but not the total number of atoms per molecule.

5. Molecular weight. The final step in the analysis is determination of the molecular weight, in order to assign the total number of atoms in a molecule, i.e., determine the number by which the empirical formula must be multiplied in order to get the molecular formula. In theory, this can be done by any of several methods of physical chemistry. For example, a known volume of the vapor of the substance may be weighed at a known temperature and pressure. From this may be calculated the gram molecular weight of the substance, i.e., the weight of 22.4 liters of the vapor at $0°$ and 760 mm. pressure. In the case of ethyl alcohol, this gives a molecular weight of 46, hence the **molecular formula** is C_2H_6O, the same as the empirical formula. If the molecular weight had proved to be 92, then the molecular formula would have been $(C_2H_6O)_2$ or $C_4H_{12}O_2$.

In practice, precise determination of molecular weight is quite difficult, if at all possible, unless there be invoked the modern method known as **mass spectrometry.** This type of spectrometry is rather different from other techniques termed spectrometry, in that the substance is bombarded, in a high vacuum, with a stream of electrons of sufficient velocity to knock electrons out of the organic molecule. This causes breaking of bonds in the molecule so that charged fragments are produced in addition to formation of the **molecular ion,** which is the molecule minus an electron. These positive ions are accelerated in an electric field and deflected in a magnetic field. The amount of deflection in the magnetic field is a function of the mass of the ion, and this measurement of mass proves susceptible to great refinement. In a "single-focussing" mass spectrometer, the type in most common use, the mass of an ion may be determined with a precision of one unit at a mass of 800. In general, the ion of highest mass is the molecular ion, so the molecular weight may be determined with great precision. A study of the ions from fragmentation has become a powerful tool for determining structure, and the basic principles of the method are discussed in Chapter 34. Application of mass spectral data to the structure of ethyl alcohol will be included in the following section.

The Structure of Ethyl Alcohol

The determination of composition, as outlined above, culminating in the assignment of the molecular formula, does not establish the identity of an organic molecule. Indeed, the problem is just beginning to unfold, for there remains the matter of structure, the order in which the atoms are joined together. Since the covalence holds the atoms firmly in definite positions, it follows that two different molecules may contain the same atoms arranged in different orders. Illustrative of this possibility, let us consider the substance dimethyl ether, which is similar to but not the same as diethyl ether which is used as an anesthetic. Dimethyl ether is a poisonous gas at room temperature, whereas ethyl alcohol is a liquid of boiling point $78°$, so the compounds are obviously different substances. Nevertheless, if we subject dimethyl ether to the same investigation outlined for ethyl alcohol, we arrive at C_2H_6O as the molecular formula. Such compounds as ethyl alcohol and dimethyl ether, which have the same molecular formula, are known as **isomers,** and the phenomenon relating them is termed **isomerism.**

The phenomenon of isomerism is responsible, in major part, for the large numbers of organic compounds. For the relatively simple formula, $C_6H_{14}O$, twenty-six isomers are known. Since isomers differ from each other only in the order in which the atoms are arranged, if a formula is to specify one, and only one, organic compound, it is clear that the structure must be indicated. A formula which indicates structure is known as a **structural formula,** and we may write the structural formula for ethyl alcohol only after additional facts have been ascertained. If there are considered certain rules of valence, to be described below, the structure of ethyl alcohol may be established by either *chemical or physical methods*, i.e., by a study of chemical reactions or physical properties. Both these methods will be described since they are commonly used in conjunction with each other to determine the structures of more complicated molecules.

Certain Chemical Reactions of Ethyl Alcohol

Let us consider two chemical reactions known to occur with ethyl alcohol and the reactions of water with the same reagents. These reactions are shown in Eqs. 1 through 4. It is evident that in Eq. 3 sodium has replaced a hydrogen,

$$2C_2H_6O + 2Na \longrightarrow 2NaOC_2H_5 + H_2 \tag{1}$$

$$3C_2H_6O + PBr_3 \longrightarrow 3C_2H_5Br + H_3PO_3 \tag{2}$$

$$2H_2O + 2Na \longrightarrow 2NaOH + H_2 \tag{3}$$

$$3H_2O + PBr_3 \longrightarrow 3HBr + H_3PO_3 \tag{4}$$

whereas in Eq. 4 bromine has replaced the hydroxyl group, OH. It follows that water has the structural formula H—O—H. It may be added that the atoms in water are bound in this order by covalences, and this is why water, an inorganic compound, has physical properties ordinarily associated with covalently bonded molecules. An inspection of Eqs. 1 and 2 leads to the conclusion that ethyl alcohol differs from water only in having the group C_2H_5 rather than H. Thus, we have arrived at a partial structural formula for ethyl alcohol, C_2H_5—O—H. Before applying the rules of valence in order to deduce the structure of C_2H_5, let us consider how the same partial structural formula may be determined by simple application of physical methods.

Certain Physical Properties of Ethyl Alcohol

Infrared spectrum. As has already been mentioned, ethyl alcohol has a moderately strong absorption in the infrared (an **absorption band**) at a wavelength of about 3 μ. It has been well established that most compounds having a hydroxyl group in their structures exhibit infrared absorption in this region, while compounds not having a hydroxyl group do not exhibit strong absorption near 3 μ. It may be concluded with confidence, therefore, that ethyl alcohol has such a group in its structure.

Although the rapid determination of the presence of hydroxyl in ethyl alcohol is possible only because infrared spectra have been observed for many compounds whose structures had previously been determined by chemical methods, nevertheless, this method is now available, rapid and reliable. The chemist no longer uses chemical methods in instances where past structural determinations allow application at the present time of the rapid and effective physical methods.

In order to make familiar the form in which an infrared spectrum is received, a recorder tracing of the spectrum of ethyl alcohol is reproduced in Fig. 1. The strong band centered at 3.05 μ, characteristic of hydroxyl, may be noted.[2] The exact position of the hydroxyl absorption band depends on whether the molecules are associated with each other by hydrogen bonding, a phenomenon which will be discussed in some detail in Chapter 13. In the 0.1-molar solution used for the spectrum shown in Fig. 1, most of the molecules are associated, and this is the species responsible for the absorption at 3.05 μ. The small fraction of unassociated alcohol gives the weak band at about 2.80 μ.

Another characteristic absorption in ethyl alcohol is the split band with maxima at 3.40 and 3.55 μ, but this absorption is characteristic of organic compounds in general, for it is due to absorption by the carbon-hydrogen bond structure. Since absence of carbon-hydrogen bonds in an organic molecule is very rare indeed, absorption near 3.5 μ is regarded as an excellent criterion that a molecule is organic in nature. Since different types of carbon-hydrogen bonds absorb at slightly different wavelengths, this band is usually split, even in as simple a molecule as ethyl alcohol.

A third characteristic band in the spectrum shown in Fig. 1 is the weak absorption at 7.25 μ, characteristic of the methyl group, which is carbon with three hydrogens attached to it. Although this is a rather weak band, its location varies very little in different structures, so it is of considerable diagnostic value. The intensity of this band is also of use for determining how many methyl groups are present in a structure.

The strong band centered at about 9.5 μ is characteristic of the C—O linkage, whether in an ether or alcohol, but the diagnostic value of this band is limited by the frequency with which skeletal vibrations (cf. next paragraph) occur in the same location.

Much of the infrared absorption beyond about 8 μ is caused by skeletal vibrations of the molecule as a whole, and is quite difficult to assign to specific structures. The nature of this "long-wavelength absorption" is quite sensitive to the total structure of a molecule, however, and is especially valuable for determining whether two samples of a chemical compound are indeed the same substance. For example, if a substance isolated from a natural product has the

---

[2] Since water contains hydroxyl, its absence must be assured if interpretation of the spectrum is to be reliable. The sample of alcohol used for the spectrum recorded in Fig. 1 had been distilled from sodium metal in order to assure its dryness.

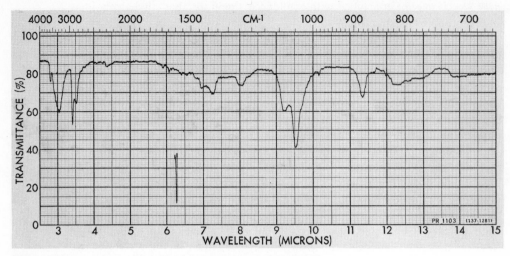

Fig. 1. Recorder tracing of the infrared absorption of ethyl alcohol in 0.1-molar solution in carbon tetrachloride. Cell thickness was 0.1 mm. and cell windows were sodium chloride. The spectrograph translates to an electrical potential the energy received by an infra-red-sensing device. This potential is supplied to a recorder which traces such a pattern as shown. When energy is absorbed by the organic molecule at a particular wavelength, less radiation is received by the sensing device, so the potential fed to the recorder becomes less and the pen drops on the chart. The "wiggling" of the tracing is the result of static ("noise") in the electronic systems in the spectrograph and recorder. The more sensitive the measurement desired, the lower must the noise level be.

A spectrum may be taken on a very thin film of a liquid but, when a solution is used, any absorption by the solvent "blacks out" that region of the spectrum where the solvent absorbs. Since carbon tetrachloride has absorption above about 12 μ, this region of the spectrum is blacked out in Fig. 1. This region is not of interest in ethyl alcohol, but if it were desired, solution in another appropriate solvent could be used. A thin film of ethyl alcohol is difficult to keep dry.

The sharp band traced below the ethyl alcohol spectrum is recorded from a polystyrene film, as a calibration point for the spectrum. The true location of this band is 6.24 μ, and it is at about 6.26 μ in this recording; so the spectrum is located almost exactly correctly. Any correction indicated by the calibration band is applied whenever a spectrum is read.

same melting point as a known compound, this is tentative evidence that the structure of the natural product is that of the known compound; however, if the infrared absorption in the long-wavelength region of the infrared is the same for two samples, identity is virtually assured. For this reason, this wave-length region is known as the **fingerprint region.**

Mass spectrum. The presence of hydroxyl in ethyl alcohol may also be determined by application of mass spectrometry. It is now known that com-pounds containing the hydroxyl group are easily fragmented in the electron beam to give water (mass 18) and a positively charged ion of 18 mass units less than the molecular weight. Indeed, this fragmentation is so easy that the molecular ion (M) is much less abundant in the mass spectrum than the ion with mass $M - 18$. In some instances, the molecular ion is scarcely observable. Thus, the mass spectrum of ethyl alcohol shows a very prominent ion at mass 28 $(46 - 18)$ and a very weak ion at mass 46, so the presence of OH is revealed.

Rules of Valence

Much of chemical behavior could be understood for the first time when there were formulated, during the middle part of the nineteenth century, certain rules of valence, sometimes called Kekulé's rules. These rules were established empirically by correlating reactions of a large number of organic compounds. By considering the two most important of these rules, we may deduce the structure of C_2H_5 in ethyl alcohol:

(a) Carbon has a valence of four, hydrogen one, oxygen two (occasionally four), nitrogen three or five, and halogen one.

(b) Carbon may be joined to itself in chains or rings.

Although these rules seem simple, many years of careful study by many scholars were necessary before they could be formulated. The second of these observed facts, resulting in part from the position of carbon near the middle of the periodic table, is a major factor contributing to the large number of organic compounds. No other atom exhibits this property to an extent approaching carbon. Even silicon, adjacent to carbon in the periodic table, is able to form stable compounds with only a few silicon atoms joined directly to each other.

The structure of the grouping C_2H_5 follows directly from an application of these rules of valence. Since hydrogen has a valence of only one, all the atoms in C_2H_5 may be accommodated in a bonded whole only if the two carbons are joined together and the remaining carbon valences are occupied by hydrogen atoms. Thus we may write the completed structural formula for ethyl alcohol according to either of two conventions, where lines are used to indicate a single bond between atoms:

$$
\begin{array}{cc}
\mathrm{H\ \ H} & \\
\mathrm{|\ \ \ |} & \\
\mathrm{H-C-C-O-H} & \qquad \mathrm{CH_3-CH_2-OH} \\
\mathrm{|\ \ \ |} & \\
\mathrm{H\ \ H} &
\end{array}
$$

Expanded structural   Condensed structural
formula   formula

Expanded structural formulas are used only in special cases, for condensed structural formulas ordinarily convey all the essential information of which this type of formula is capable. For illustration of certain things, such as specific features of a chemical reaction, a part of a structural formula may be expanded. It should be *emphasized*, however, that *the condensed structural formula is definitive, for the conventional structural formula can indicate, and is intended to indicate, only the order in which the atoms are attached to each other, not their positions in space.* It follows that all the following formulas are entirely equivalent to each other and to the above formulas, for the order of the atoms is the same:

$$
\begin{array}{ccc}
\text{H} \quad \text{H} & \text{H} \quad \text{H} & \text{HO} \quad \text{H} \\
| \quad | & | \quad | & | \quad | \\
\text{H—C—C—H} & \text{HO—C—C—H} & \text{H—C—C—H} \\
| \quad | & | \quad | & | \quad | \\
\text{H} \quad \text{OH} & \text{H} \quad \text{H} & \text{H} \quad \text{H}
\end{array}
$$

Planar projections of three-dimensional formulas, necessary to indicate the positions of atoms in space, will be discussed in the next chapter and frequently thereafter. The actual geometrical shapes of organic molecules are a very important factor determining much of their physical and chemical behavior. Thus, numerous conventions and devices have been elaborated for indicating solid geometry on a planar surface.

General Determination of Structure

Although the structures of many organic compounds isolated from natural sources are sufficiently complicated to resist the best efforts of chemists for many years, most of them eventually become elucidated. Prior to about 1945 this was usually accomplished by "degradation" of the complicated molecule. This process involved carrying out chemical reactions whose course was known, in order to break the larger molecule down to smaller ones and eventually to arrive at structures which had been previously elucidated by such basic chemical methods as have been described in this chapter. Since 1945 the introduction of instruments for rapid and accurate measurement of physical properties has revolutionized the matter of structure determination. Illustrations of the use of infrared spectra and mass spectra have been mentioned. An additional very powerful tool, widely used since about 1960, is nuclear magnetic resonance spectroscopy (NMR).

Nuclear Magnetic Resonance Spectroscopy

This type of spectroscopy depends on the fact that many elements have a nuclear structure which causes them to behave as tiny magnets. Carbon-12 does not have such a nuclear structure but hydrogen-1 does, and this property of hydrogen has been of great use for determining its environment in an organic molecule. When a hydrogen atom (in an organic molecule) is placed in a powerful magnetic field a small percentage of the "nuclear magnets" will be aligned with the magnetic field. When an electromagnetic field is also applied, these aligned nuclei can absorb just the amount of energy (a quantum) required to flip them over so that their polarity is opposed to that of the applied magnetic field. The exact amount of energy required to accomplish this flip proves to vary slightly as a function of the environment of that hydrogen with respect to other atoms in the molecule. In particular, a given hydrogen is affected by the magnetic fields of other hydrogens that are quite close to it. In turn, the size of the quantum of energy absorbed is a function of the frequency of the applied electromagnetic field. Thus, a hydrogen in one environment will absorb energy at one frequency, while another hydrogen in a different environment will absorb energy at a different frequency. Signals are received at the various frequencies at which the several hydrogen nuclei are "in resonance" with the field. Furthermore, and especially important, the magnitude of the signal at a given frequency is linearly proportional to the number of hydrogens in resonance at that frequency. Remarkably accurate instruments have been developed for NMR spectroscopy so that the frequency at which energy is absorbed can be measured with a precision of about 0.01 part per million.

In the NMR spectrum of ethyl alcohol, three kinds of hydrogen will be observed, in that absorption of energy will occur at three different frequencies. Furthermore, the relative intensities of the signals at the three frequencies will be in the ratio of 3:2:1; that is, there are three hydrogens in one environment (those on the methyl), two in another environment (on the methylene, hence next to the oxygen), and one in the third environment (attached to oxygen). The range of frequencies at which hydrogens in the various environments will be in resonance with the electromagnetic field have been established, as well as the types of interaction of neighboring hydrogens, so that both the number and environment of the hydrogens can be ascertained from the NMR spectrum. Indeed, a 5-mg. sample of ethyl alcohol may be identified conclusively in a few minutes by the single device of examining its NMR spectrum.

The NMR spectrum of ethyl alcohol, as presented in Fig. 2, makes apparent the reliability with which the data summarized in the preceding paragraph may be evaluated. Hydrogen attached to oxygen is at lowest field, and it appears as the sharp peak[3] at δ 4.45. The presence of oxygen adjacent to carbon on which hydrogens are located makes the hydrogen in resonance at lower field than if the electron-rich oxygen were not nearby. Thus, the hydrogens on —CH_2— (methylene) occur at lower field than those on —CH_3 (methyl) in ethyl alcohol. Furthermore, the hydrogens on each of these carbons are affected

---

[3] The location of the position of resonance of a hydrogen atom is determined with reference to hydrogen in a standard substance, and this difference is expressed in parts per million (ppm) by which the electromagnetic field varies from that at which the reference substance shows resonance. The reference nearly always used is tetramethylsilane, $(CH_3)_4Si$, which has only one kind of hydrogen in it. The point of resonance of the hydrogen in tetramethylsilane (TMS) is at very high field; very few substances give peaks at higher field. Two systems of expressing the field difference from TMS are in use. In one, utilized in this discussion, the location is given as ppm below TMS, and the number is preceded by the Greek letter δ. In the other system, known as use of the tau scale (Greek letter τ), TMS is given the location of 10, with zero on the lower field side of TMS. Thus, the location of the hydrogen on oxygen in ethyl alcohol is at δ 4.45 or τ 5.55 (10 − 4.45), each value in ppm. It is unfortunate, but true, that the two systems have been applied in a manner that causes the δ values to increase with decreasing field, while the τ values increase with increasing field.

by the neighboring hydrogens in a predictable manner, and this effect causes the "splitting" of the peaks which is apparent in Fig. 2.

The splitting of the peaks when there are adjacent hydrogens is caused by the effect on one hydrogen of the other acting as a tiny magnet (recall that the basic NMR phenomenon depends on the nucleus of the atom acting as a magnet). Since the behavior of a nucleus as a magnet is ascribed to "spin"

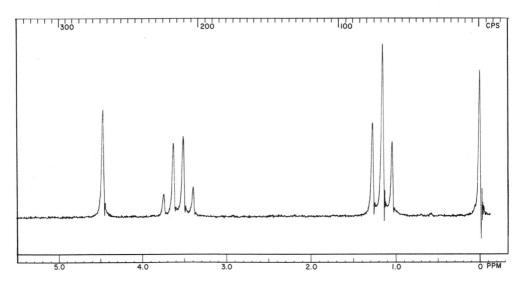

Fig. 2. The NMR spectrum of ethyl alcohol in carbon tetrachloride solution. Units indicated on the abscissa below the graph are parts per million (ppm) in electromagnetic field below the point of resonance of tetramethylsilane (TMS). A small amount of TMS was included in the solution (a common practice), then the instrument was adjusted so that the signal from TMS fell at zero. Units indicated on the abscissa above the graph are cycles per second in electromagnetic field. The ordinate is in arbitrary units of intensity of response, so that the area under the tracing in a given peak is proportional to the concentration of hydrogen atoms giving that particular resonance response. Thus, the total area of the triplet (due to methyl hydrogens) is three times that of the singlet (hydrogen on oxygen), while the total area of the quartet (methylene hydrogens) is twice that of the singlet.

in the nucleus, the phenonemon causing splitting of the peaks is termed **spin–spin coupling.** In more complicated molecules, especially those with asymmetric structures, the analysis of spin-spin coupling becomes rather complicated, and capable of revealing fine details of structure; however, in relatively simple molecules an approximate analysis of spin-spin coupling can be accomplished rather easily. In symmetrical structures, all the hydrogens on a single carbon appear in a single peak, and there is no splitting caused by their interaction with each other. Hydrogens on an adjacent carbon, however, cause splitting, and the number of peaks into which each major peak is split is equal to one plus the number of equivalent hydrogens on adjacent carbons. Thus, the signal from the two hydrogens on the methylene group is split into a quartet (three adjacent hydrogens), while the methyl hydrogens give a triplet. Furthermore, since these sets of hydrogen are "splitting each other" (causing split peaks), the separation of the peaks in the fine structure of the two peaks must be the same. Inspection of the figure will reveal that the separation between the central peak and the side peaks in the triplet from the methyl is the same as the separation between the peaks in the quartet from the methylene. This separation is called the **coupling constant** (termed J), and is normally given in the cycles per second (cps) by which the positions in the electromagnetic field differ. In Fig. 2, the coupling constant will be noted as about 7 cps (each division on the abscissa is 5 cps). The hydrogen on oxygen is not involved in coupling because this hydrogen exchanges rapidly from one molecule of alcohol to another.

Structure of methyl alcohol. Methyl alcohol, the poisonous substance sometimes called wood alcohol, proves to have the molecular formula CH_4O. Since the methods mentioned in connection with ethyl alcohol show the presence of a hydroxyl group, the only structure which may be assigned is CH_3—OH, which differs from ethyl alcohol in the nature of the group attached to hydroxyl.

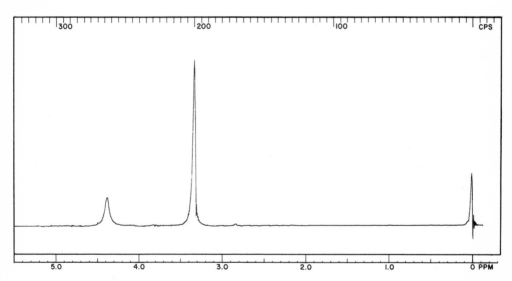

Fig. 3. The NMR spectrum of methyl alcohol in carbon tetrachloride solution, with TMS included as internal reference standard.

The NMR spectrum of methyl alcohol (Fig. 3) will stand alone as a complete identification of the compound. The hydrogen on oxygen, at about the same position as the corresponding hydrogen in ethyl alcohol, gives the area represented by a single hydrogen. The sharp peak at δ 3.32 contains an area corresponding to three hydrogens, and is in the correct position for hydrogens on a methyl attached to oxygen. Thus, this spectrum will reliably identify methyl alcohol, even without knowledge of the molecular formula.

Structure of dimethyl ether. This structure may be established by chemical methods since the molecule fails to react with sodium or phosphorus tribromide, reactions shown in Eqs. 1 and 2. This demonstrates absence of the hydroxyl group. Since the molecular formula for dimethyl ether is C_2H_6O, as previously stated, application of the rules of valence leads to a single possible structure, CH_3—O—CH_3.

The structure of dimethyl ether may also be established by physical methods. The infrared spectrum shows no absorption in the hydroxyl region (near 3 μ), hence absence of the hydroxyl group is indicated. Furthermore, the NMR spectrum shows the presence of only one kind of hydrogen in a sharp peak at the same location as the methyl hydrogens in methyl alcohol (refer to Fig. 3). Thus, again the NMR spectrum identifies the compound.

The potency of NMR spectroscopy is illustrated by the above considerations of simple molecules, but its great utility lies in elucidation of complicated structures involving dozens of carbon and hydrogen atoms. After the NMR spectrum has been analyzed for the number and kinds of hydrogen atoms present, an attempt is next made to fit the pieces of the puzzle together so as to give a coherent molecule.

Terminology

Numerous terms used in the present chapter, and defined either directly or by the context in which they were used, must become a routine part of any discussion of organic chemistry, so they should be well understood and remembered so well that the meanings are known intuitively. Certain additional definitions should be developed at this point.

In Eqs. 1 and 2, we have seen that the group C_2H_5— remains intact during attack of chemical reagents on ethyl alcohol, whereas the hydroxyl group, —OH, is altered or replaced during the reactions. Methyl alcohol behaves similarly. This difference in reactivity (susceptibility to attack by other chemical reagents) is caused by several factors which will be discussed subsequently; however, it may be stated at the outset that a major factor is that the *energy required to break certain bonds is greater than that required to break others.* Much more energy is usually required to break a bond between carbon and hydrogen than is required for rupture of the bond between carbon and oxygen. Since the covalent bond must be ruptured in order to secure reaction of organic molecules, the energy content of bonds and of molecules is a matter of great significance and is a continuing and integral part of the study of organic chemistry. In any molecule, if an atom or group of atoms is attached to the adjacent atom (usually carbon) by an easily ruptured bond, then this group "reacts" readily with other reagents. It is called the **functional group.** Thus, in ethyl alcohol the hydroxyl group is the functional group. The grouping C_2H_5— usually survives a chemical reaction intact and is called a **radical.** This particular radical is the **ethyl radical,** whereas CH_3— is the **methyl radical.** Both of these radicals may be expressed by the general formula C_nH_{2n+1}, and all radicals whose formulas may be expressed by this general formula are termed **alkyl radicals.** Other alkyl radicals are C_3H_7, C_4H_9, etc., ad infinitum.

Any group of compounds having a common functional group is called a **class of compounds.** Methyl alcohol and ethyl alcohol belong to the class of compounds known as **alcohols,** and any compound having a hydroxyl group attached to an alkyl radical is an alcohol. Similarly, dimethyl ether and diethyl ether belong to the class known as ethers (write the structural formula of diethyl ether!). Since the chemical behavior of an organic compound is that of its functional group it is obviously an advantage to study compounds by classes. It should be noted at the outset, however, that the reactions of the functional group, especially the **rates** of its reactions, are influenced by the nature of the remainder of the molecule. Thus, different alcohols give similar reactions, but not identical ones by any means, so these factors must be considered in connection with the study of any class of compounds.

EXERCISES

1. Give the general characteristics of a compound whose atoms are joined by covalences, as compared to one containing electrovalences.

2. A compound of empirical formula C_3H_7O, when fragmented by an electron beam in a mass spectrometer, gave a fragmentation pattern in which the highest mass ion was 118. This ion of highest mass was in very low intensity compared to one of mass 100. To what class of compounds does this substance belong? Discuss features you would expect to observe in the infrared absorption spectrum of this compound.

3. Another compound of empirical formula C_3H_8O, showed a moderate intensity for the highest mass ion at 60, and no ion of significant intensity could be observed at mass 42. Write the structural formula for this molecule. (It can be done on this evidence alone!) After reference to Figs. 2 and 3, draw the NMR spectrum you would predict for this compound.

4. How many kinds of hydrogen atoms should be detected in diethyl ether by use of the NMR spectrum? Predict the approximate location of the bands in the field and the splitting expected in each.

5. Define or clearly illustrate all the terms used in Chapter 2 with which you were previously unfamiliar.

Concerning the Nature of Chemical Bonds

Conclusions concerning the most probable nature of chemical bonds are based largely on experimental observations and mathematical deductions contributed by chemists exploring the frontiers in those particular areas of chemistry. Other chemists have found, however, that they may very profitably use the conclusions that have been reached, for chemical bonding is of basic importance to all branches of chemistry, especially organic chemistry. In particular, organic chemists have found that the molecular orbital theory of chemical bonding is very useful for correlating many experimental observations. Moreover, this theory and deductions based on it have made it possible to predict certain types of chemical behavior which was later verified experimentally. It has not yet become possible to predict all types of chemical behavior, by any means, nor have all the predictions been correct; nevertheless, the score has been adequately high to justify careful attention to basic theories of chemical bonding. The present chapter is designed to present qualitatively a working knowledge of present concepts of the chemical bond. Although these concepts have their origins in the wave-mechanical treatment of atoms and molecules, it seems entirely feasible and proper to dispense with any mathematical treatment at this time, and to consider certain more generally useful results of the theory.

The Structure of Atoms

An atom may be regarded as a positively charged nucleus surrounded by one or more negatively charged electrons. The stability of such an atom may be ascribed, then, to the electrostatic attraction between the positive nucleus and the negative electrons. Each electron carries a unit electric charge; in fact, the charge on an electron is defined as one unit of electric charge. In the neutral atom, the number of units of positive charge on the nucleus is equal to the number of electrons around the nucleus, hence the over-all electrical neutrality of the atom. If one electron is removed from an atom, a singly charged positive ion is generated; if one electron is added to an atom, a singly charged negative ion is generated. The charge on the nucleus of an atom, which is equal to the number of electrons surrounding the nucleus, is the *atomic number* of the atom. Hydrogen, with one charge on the nucleus, has an atomic number of one. Next is helium with an atomic number of two. Carbon, the most important element to the organic chemist, has the atomic number of six, hence six extranuclear electrons.

Although nearly all the mass of an atom resides in the nucleus, the formation of chemical bonds is concerned only with the extranuclear electrons; therefore our discussion will be concerned with the *electron cloud* surrounding the nucleus. Each of these electrons must be at a specific **energy level**[1] and may not have various random amounts of energy. The possible energy levels are classified into **principal energy levels,** and **sublevels.** The principal energy levels are numbered consecutively, 1, 2, 3, etc., and the higher numbers indicate higher energy levels (with a few exceptions, with which we will not be concerned). Within each principal energy level the sublevels are denoted by the letters, *s, p, d,* and *f.* The sublevels with which we will be concerned are the *s* and *p* levels, whose energies increase in the order named. The electrons at each energy level are regarded as in constant motion[2] but confined to a certain space. The space to which an electron is confined has a definite shape, to be mentioned subsequently, and this space is termed an **atomic orbital.** It is important to understand that an orbital is a space in which the electron will be found. The position of the electron changes with time, but if we could see the electron at a given moment it would be somewhere within this space termed its orbital. The term orbital has no such significance as is associated with the term orbit, which defines a particular path of movement, as a planet around a sun. An orbital is simply a space with a definite geometrical shape, and the electron may be at any place within its orbital although it may spend more time in certain parts of the orbital than in others. *Furthermore, no more than two electrons may occupy one orbital.* The pair of electrons in an orbital must have opposite spins in order to be accommodated in the single orbital. In this situation, the spins are said to be

---

[1] Just as a level of altitude is the distance above or below the position defined as zero (usually sea level), a level of energy is the amount above or below the position defined as zero.

[2] Actually, in mathematical treatments, the electrons are treated as wave motions, but in our treatment it is more convenient to visualize them as particles with kinetic energy.

coupled. Two electrons with the same spin must go into different orbitals. Uncoupling of a pair of electrons (changing from opposite spins to the same spin) is a process which requires an input of energy, thus the system becomes of higher energy, therefore less stable.

The consecutive numbering of the principal energy levels is very convenient,[3] for it helps us to remember how many sublevels may occur in each principal energy level and how many orbitals there may be in each principal energy level. The number of sublevels in a given principal energy level is equal to the number of that level, and the total number of atomic orbitals in a principal energy level is equal to the square of the number of that level. For example, in the second principal energy level there are two sublevels (the s and the p levels) and four (2^2) atomic orbitals. Since no more than two electrons may occupy a single orbital, it follows that *the first principal energy level may accommodate only two electrons, but the second principal energy level may accommodate eight electrons.* The development of this important conclusion is the major objective of the present section, and its significance will become apparent in the discussion of valence.

The Geometrical Forms of Atomic Orbitals

The first ten elements (atomic numbers of 1–10) include hydrogen (1), carbon (6), nitrogen (7), and oxygen (8), which are the elements occurring most often in organic compounds. Among these elements, the largest charge on the nucleus is ten; so the electrons are in only two principal energy levels (two in the first level, eight in the second). In the second principal energy level there can be only two sublevels, the s and p levels; so our discussion may properly be confined to the shapes of the atomic orbitals occupied by the s and p electrons.

The s atomic orbital is spherical in form and is simply represented as in Fig. 1. Since the space occupied by the nucleus is very small compared with the size of the electronic orbitals, the nucleus is ordinarily represented by a point or a plus charge. The s orbital is spherically symmetrical about the nucleus, so there can be only one such orbital of a given size. There can be spheres of different sizes,[4] and indeed, there is one s orbital at each principal energy level; for the higher energy level, the orbital is larger. Thus the $1s$ orbital lies entirely within

---

[3] The principal energy levels are sometimes designated by the capital letters, K, L, M, etc., but we will not use this terminology on account of the greater utility of numbering the levels.

[4] The exact size of the orbital is not so important as the shape. Indeed, the size is somewhat arbitrary, in that the volume in space termed an orbital is that volume in which there is a very high probability (usually set at 85–90%) of finding the electron. The boundary defined for an orbital is determined by calculating the locus of a point where the probability of finding an electron is constant. The lower this probability is set, the larger the orbital, but the shape remains the same. The locus of a point defining the limits of an orbital may be likened to the contours on a topographic map, except that probability of finding the electron is involved in setting the orbital's bounds, whereas a contour line defines the contour of the land by indicating altitude above sea level.

Fig. I. Geometrical form of the s atomic orbital. The nucleus, at the center of the orbital, is indicated by +.

the 2s orbital. In the mathematical derivations leading to the spaces known as orbitals, there proves to be no restriction against two or more orbitals occupying the same space.

The p atomic orbitals. The p orbitals have the shape shown in Fig. 2, that is, there is a position at the center, termed a *node*, where the space available to the electron becomes smaller and smaller until it approaches zero as a limit.

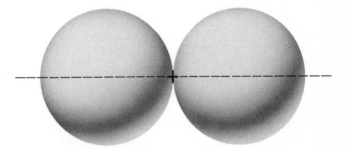

Fig. 2. Geometrical form of the p atomic orbital. The line is the long axis of the orbital, and the location of the nucleus is indicated by +.

This does not mean that the electron is confined to one or the other loop of the orbital, but it does mean that the probability of finding the electron at the node approaches zero. Since this type of orbital is not spherically symmetrical about the nucleus, there may be more than one of them. An additional requirement for this particular type of orbital is that each orbital be perpendicular to the others; so there are three of them, one directed along each of the three perpendicular axes indicated in Fig. 3. The existence of the three p orbitals is indicated

Fig. 3. Relative directions of p atomic orbitals. All three orbitals have a common node at intersection of the lines which represent the long axes of the orbitals. (Cf. Fig. 2.)

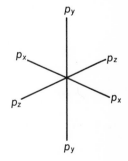

by referring to them as the p_x, p_y, and p_z orbitals. The subscripts do not imply any difference in energy, but simply indicate that the p orbitals have *direction* as well as form.

Electronic Configurations of the Atoms

It has been stated, in the preceding sections of this chapter, that electrons in atoms must fall into certain specific energy levels. Certain characteristics of these levels may be profitably summarized at this point:

1. The principal energy levels are numbered consecutively, 1, 2, etc. For the first three, which are those of concern to us, this is the order of increasing energy.
2. The number of a principal energy level is also the number of sublevels included in that principal level.
3. The square of the number of a principal level is the number of atomic orbitals in that level.
4. There may be only one s orbital in a principal energy level, but there may be three p orbitals.
5. No more than two electrons may occupy a single orbital.

The combination of these principles results in there being a maximum of two s electrons (that is, in s orbitals) in the first principal energy level, whereas there may be in the second principal energy level a maximum of two s electrons and six p electrons (two in each p orbital). The atom neon, which has an atomic number of 10, hence ten electrons, has all the orbitals in the first two energy levels filled. The shorthand method for describing this electronic configuration of neon is as follows: $1s^2$; $2s^2$; $2p_x{}^2$; $2p_y{}^2$; $2p_z{}^2$. Thus the letters indicate the type of orbital, the coefficients indicate the principal energy level in which the orbital occurs, and the superscripts indicate the number of electrons in that orbital.

For convenient reference and for illustration, the electronic configuration of neon is shown in Fig. 4.

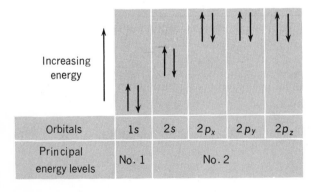

Increasing energy

| Orbitals | 1s | 2s | 2p$_x$ | 2p$_y$ | 2p$_z$ |

| Principal energy levels | No. 1 | No. 2 | | | |

Fig. 4. Electronic configuration of neon. Each arrow represents one electron. The arrows in a pair point in opposite directions to denote that the electrons in a pair occupying an orbital must have opposite spins.

If we introduce two additional rules or principles, we may immediately write the electronic configurations of all the elements below neon.[5] These rather logical rules are:

(a) An electron will go into the lowest energy level available to it (if an s orbital is open, the electron will not go into a p orbital; electrons will not go into the second principal energy level until the first is filled).[6]

(b) Two electrons will not go into a single orbital until each orbital of that energy level contains one electron (we do not get two p_x electrons until each of the three p orbitals contains one electron).

The electronic configurations, as deduced from these considerations, of the first ten elements are summarized in Table 1. It should be noted that superscripts

Table I. Electronic Configurations

Element	At. No.	Electronic configuration	Number of unpaired electrons
H	1	$1s$	1
He	2	$1s^2$	0
Li	3	$1s^2, 2s$	1
Be	4	$1s^2, 2s^2$	0
B	5	$1s^2, 2s^2, 2p_x$	1
C	6	$1s^2, 2s^2, 2p_x, 2p_y$	2
N	7	$1s^2, 2s^2, 2p_x, 2p_y, 2p_z$	3
O	8	$1s^2, 2s^2, 2p_x^2, 2p_y, 2p_z$	2
F	9	$1s^2, 2s^2, 2p_x^2, 2p_y^2, 2p_z$	1
Ne	10	$1s^2, 2s^2, 2p_x^2, 2p_y^2, 2p_z^2$	0

denote number of electrons in that orbital; therefore addition of the superscripts for a given element yields the number of electrons in that element, which is its atomic number. The significance of the unpaired electrons will be developed in connection with the following discussion of valence.

Bond Formation and Valence

Although the nature of the chemical bond has not yet been mentioned specifically, this topic follows rather directly once the electronic structures in atoms are understood. *Atoms tend to combine with other atoms to form molecules if this process results in a lowering of their energy, for the most stable condition is that with the lowest energy.* **An atom is in its most stable condition when it does not have a principal energy level whose orbitals are only partially filled with electrons.** It may be seen from an inspection of Table 1 that helium and neon

---

[5] Atoms of greater atomic number may be treated similarly if higher energy levels are considered, but the present discussion is adequate for our purposes.

[6] This statement should not be extrapolated to higher principal energy levels. For example, $3d$ electrons are at a slightly higher energy level than $4s$ electrons.

have all available orbitals filled, for the first principal energy level may have two electrons and the second eight. This is why these substances are *inert*, and do not tend to combine with other atoms. The atoms themselves are already in the most stable condition; therefore they cannot increase their stabilities (lower their energies) by combining with other atoms in the usual way.[7] The remaining atoms in Table 1 do not have filled energy levels; so they can improve their stabilities by combining with other atoms in such manner as to fill their orbitals or come nearer to doing so. This improvement in stability can be accomplished in two ways: (a) by donating or receiving electrons, (b) by sharing electrons. These two processes result in different types of chemical bonds.

I. The electrovalence. If a lithium atom should donate its single electron to a fluorine atom there would result a positively charged lithium ion and a negatively charged fluorine ion.[8] Lithium would be left with its only remaining principal energy level filled with electrons, and fluorine would have both of its principal energy levels filled with electrons. Thus a gain in stability would be accomplished; so lithium fluoride is a stable chemical compound consisting of lithium ions and fluorine ions. If two such ions are held together, it is by electrostatic force, and such a chemical bond is termed an electrovalence or electrostatic bond. In solution in certain solvents, notably water, the ions may move about more or less independently of each other. The electrostatic force is exerted equally in all directions; so such a bond has no particular direction. Some such electrovalent compounds, for example, sodium chloride, have been shown to exist in the gas phase as ion pairs held together by electrostatic attraction. Other compounds, such as hydrogen fluoride or hydrogen chloride, "dissociate" into ions in water solution, but are held together by covalent bonds in the gas state.

2. The covalence. This is of much more importance in organic compounds, and results from two atoms *sharing* electrons in order to fill their energy levels. In such a situation, the shared electrons go into *molecular orbitals*, that is, orbitals encompassing two positive nuclei. As is the case in atomic orbitals, only one pair of electrons can occupy a single molecular orbital which encompasses two nuclei. It might be expected, from logical reasoning, that such a combination would result in a decrease of energy (increase in stability), for the shared electrons are attracted by two positive nuclei instead of one as in an

---

[7] Inorganic chemists have recently succeeded in forming compounds with certain of the "inert" gases. Bonding no doubt becomes possible by virtue of "promotion" of electrons into higher energy orbitals, then regaining by bonding the energy required for the "promotion." This process bears some resemblance to the type of bonding in carbon, as discussed below.

[8] In this discussion and other similar ones, there is intended no inference that there is available to the lithium atom a device by which it can *directly* donate an electron to fluorine; that is, it is not necessarily true that atomic lithium will react under known conditions with atomic fluorine. In many instances, a given pair of atoms will not directly combine with each other. It is often necessary to accomplish the ultimate combination by passing through several intermediate compounds.

atom. In order for this favorable situation to exist, however, the two nuclei must remain together. Indeed, the stability is greatest for certain precise distances between the nuclei; and this value remains approximately constant for a given pair of atoms. If the nuclei are separated, the bond is broken, and this requires an input of energy equal to the difference in energy between the bonded atoms and the separated atoms. This is the *bond energy* and is a measure of the "strength" of the bond. In connection with the reactions of ethyl alcohol (Chap. 2), it was mentioned that some bonds are stronger than others.[9] It should be noted that **the bond energy is the energy which the molecule does not have** as a result of formation of the bond. It is the amount the stability of the system is increased by bond formation.

When electrons are shared in a molecular orbital, each of the sharing atoms may utilize all the shared electrons in filling its energy levels. If two hydrogen atoms share electrons with each other there results a hydrogen molecule, H_2, held together by the covalence resulting from the electrons forming a molecular orbital. Since each atom utilizes both shared electrons to fill its respective energy level, each has two *s* electrons, its energy level is filled, and a stable molecule results. Since a molecular orbital has a pair of electrons, one from each atom, it might be deduced that the valence of an atom is equal to the number of unpaired electrons it has available for sharing (see Table 1). This is precisely the situation with such elements as hydrogen, lithium, nitrogen, oxygen, and fluorine. It will be noted that a common valence of these elements is equal to the number of unshared electrons in the atoms. With beryllium, boron, and carbon, which have "unused" *p* orbitals, more electrons are made available by the formation of "hybridized orbitals," which will be discussed in connection with the types of molecular orbitals which may be formed.

Molecular Orbitals

I. Molecular orbitals from *s* electrons. A molecular orbital is formed when two atomic orbitals overlap so that the electrons come to occupy a common orbital which encompasses two nuclei. In the case of an *s* atomic orbital, which is spherically symmetrical, this overlap can occur equally well in any direction; so there is no direction to an *s* bond. As mentioned previously, the electrostatic bond also is not directional; however, the electrostatic bond does not involve a molecular orbital in which a pair of electrons is associated with two positive nuclei. In Fig. 5, the *s-s* molecular orbital, such as occurs in the

---

[9] Since a covalent bond must be broken in order for an atom to be replaced by another in an organic molecule, the combined energy of the two reacting species must be great enough to accomplish this bond rupture just at the moment they collide. If the energy is not great enough to rupture this bond, the molecules merely bounce; no reaction occurs. It follows that the stronger the bond, the less likely is a reaction from a given collision. For this reason, nearly all organic reactions occur much more slowly than ionic reactions where reaction always occurs when the ions meet. *Rates* of organic reactions are of much interest and will be mentioned frequently in subsequent chapters. The *mechanisms* by which the old bond may be broken and the new one formed will also be the subject of recurrent discussions.

Fig. 5. Geometrical form of the s-s molecular orbital, such as occurs in the hydrogen molecule.

hydrogen molecule, H_2, is shown. The two electrons of the hydrogen molecule now occupy the larger molecular orbital. As previously discussed,[4] there is a significant probability of finding an electron at the very edge of this orbital; however, probability of finding electrons is highest in a region more or less between the two nuclei, for in this region they are attracted equally by both nuclei. The *electron density* (probability of finding an electron at a given time) is greatest, then, between the two nuclei, but there is some chance of finding electrons at other places within the molecular orbital.

2. Molecular orbitals from *p* electrons. Since the *p* atomic orbital has the shape shown in Fig. 2, it can overlap another orbital best along the direction of the long axis of the orbital; in fact, the energy is so much lower for this direction that *a molecular orbital formed from a p electron* has direction in relation to other *p* orbitals in the atom. A bond having direction in this sense is termed a **sigma bond.** Since the angle between the bonding directions for *p* orbitals is 90° (see Fig. 3), it follows that in water (Fig. 6) the angle to be expected between the two valences to hydrogen is 90°. For such small atoms as oxygen, it turns out that the attached hydrogens are so close together that there is repulsion between them which spreads the valence angle; however, any such

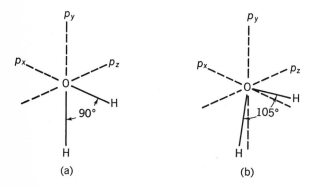

(a) (b)

Fig. 6. (a) Theoretical direction of valences from oxygen to hydrogen in water. If all three atoms are regarded as in the p_x-p_y plane, the orbital of the non-bonding pair of *p* electrons has its long axis at right angles to this plane, as indicated by p_z. Both pairs of s electrons in the oxygen ($1s^2$ and $2s^2$) are in spherical orbitals. (b) Actual angle between the valence directions in water, as caused by repulsion between the hydrogen atoms. All three atoms are in the p_x-p_y plane.

distortion of the normal valence angle increases the energy of the molecule and makes it less stable than it would be in absence of the distortion. Thus there is a finite force tending to hold the valence angle to that giving the lowest energy. In hydrogen sulfide, where the larger sulfur atom allows the hydrogens to be farther apart, the observed valence angle is 92° 20′.

Although it is connoted in the above discussion, it may be mentioned that an s atomic orbital and a p atomic orbital may overlap or combine to form an s-p molecular orbital, even though the atomic orbitals in the two atoms are in different principal energy levels.

3. Hybridized orbitals. In atoms such as beryllium, boron, and carbon (cf. Table 1), there are "unused" p orbitals, for the electrons go into the orbitals of lowest energy and thus give the most stable state for the atom. It has also been pointed out that bonding between atoms by means of molecular orbitals lowers the energy in respect to the separated atoms; this is the origin of the strength of a covalent bond. In the normal state of the carbon atom, only two such energy-lowering bonds may be formed, since only the two p electrons are unpaired. If one of the s electrons were "promoted" into the vacant higher-energy p orbital, this would cause an increase in energy; however, this would also result in there being *four* unpaired electrons which could form bonds. It turns out that the lowering of energy resulting from formation of two additional bonds is more than that necessary to promote an electron from an s orbital to a p orbital in the second principal energy level. It follows that although the isolated carbon atom is most stable with two $2s$ electrons and two $2p$ electrons, the most stable compounds of carbon result when all four electrons in the second energy level are in separate orbitals and may thus form four covalent bonds. When this situation makes both s and p electrons available for bond formation they do not form different types of bonds.[10] Instead, each bond is the same as the others, for the orbitals become "hybridized." This concept may be well illustrated by considering carbon, which has available for bond formation one $2s$ electron and three $2p$ electrons, since "promotion" of one $2s$ electron is energetically profitable as explained above. Each orbital then becomes the average resulting from a combination or "hybridization" of the four orbitals available. This may be visualized by considering each orbital as three-fourths p orbital and one-fourth s orbital. Such an orbital is described as an *sp³ orbital* (spoken as "*sp* three"). The inference is that such an orbital is the result of adding up three p orbitals and one s orbital, then dividing by four; and this is approximately what is done mathematically in order to get the properties of such a hybrid orbital. Such an orbital has a shape differing somewhat from that of a p orbital, in that the lobe on one side of the node (cf. Fig. 2) is larger than the lobe on the other side. Overlap with another orbital, to form a bond, naturally occurs with the larger lobe. The most important characteristics of the $sp³$

---

[10] An exception to this statement occurs if there are more bonds than one between two atoms, for example, if there is a "double" bond between two carbon atoms. Multiple bonds will be discussed in Chapter 8.

orbitals are that there are four of them, and *the angles between them are approximately 109.5°*. This relationship between the valences in carbon must be indicated in three dimensions, as in Fig. 7. If the valences are regarded as radiating from the nucleus of the carbon atom, their directions are toward the points of a regular tetrahedron. For this reason, reference is sometimes made

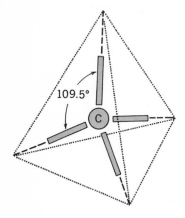

Fig. 7. Directions of valence forces in carbon. The heavy lines indicate the directions of the long axes of the sp^3 orbitals, hence the preferred directions in which the valence forces extend.

to the "tetrahedral configuration" of the carbon atom, but this term is not recommended, since its connotations are not at all representative of the actual situation. The important consideration is that the forces constituting valence bonds are symmetrically distributed in space so that the angle between any two of them is about 109.5°. These angles may be distorted by such forces as are operative in a water molecule (cf. Fig. 6), but such distortions lead to decreased stability. If this distortion becomes excessive the bond will become unstable (easily broken), eventually to the point where no bond can be formed.

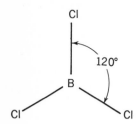

Fig. 8. Valence directions in boron trichloride. The lines indicate the directions of the long axes of the sp^2 orbitals, all of which lie in a plane; hence all four atoms lie in a plane.

In boron (cf. Table 1), promotion of one $2s$ electron makes available for bonding one $2s$ and two $2p$ electrons. These combine to form **three sp^2 hybridized orbitals.** The long axes of these orbitals *lie in a plane, with 120° between them*; so all the atoms in boron trichloride lie in a plane as shown in Fig. 8. This relationship is in marked contrast to the situation existing in carbon (Fig. 7). If a plane is placed to include carbon and two of the atoms attached to it, the remaining two atoms lie one on each side of this plane. The covalent nature of boron trichloride is evidenced by its physical properties; at room temperature it is a gas which condenses to a liquid on cooling to 13°. Its freezing point is −107°.

In beryllium, promotion of one 2s electron makes available for bonding one 2s and one 2p electron, and these form **two hybridized *sp* orbitals,** whose long axes make an angle of 180° with each other. In other words, if beryllium dichloride is a covalent compound, the three atoms in it are all in a straight line in space (180° is half of a full circle). The melting point of 440° is rather high for a covalent compound, but does not rule out the possibility that beryllium dichloride is a linear covalent compound.

Spatial Formulas and Interatomic Distances

Although many discussions of chemical compounds and their reactions may be referred to ordinary condensed or expanded structural formulas, it is sometimes profitable to indicate the relative positions of the atoms in space. For many purposes, it is satisfactory to represent this rather simply as in Fig. 9.

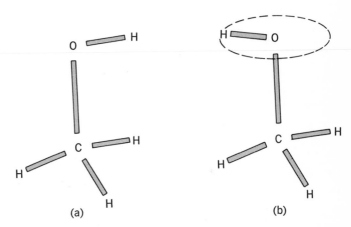

Fig. 9. Simple representation of the positions in space of the atoms in methyl alcohol. In (a) and (b) are shown two of the infinite number of possible positions for the hydrogen attached to oxygen. As oxygen rotates around the direction of its bond with carbon, the hydrogen follows in the path indicated by the dotted circle in (b). In all these positions, the distance between this hydrogen and carbon remains constant.

This follows directly from the representation in Fig. 7. Since atoms are more or less free to rotate around the direction of their valence bonds, the two positions shown for the hydroxyl group are two of the infinite number of possible positions resulting from rotation of the oxygen around the direction of its valence bond to carbon. In all these possible positions, however, the interatomic distance between oxygen and hydrogen remains the same. As has already been stated, the most stable molecular orbitals are formed when the nuclei of the atoms are a fixed distance from each other. This distance varies only small amounts on account of such molecular vibrations as cause absorption of infrared radiation. The interatomic distance varies for different atoms, but is relatively constant for the same atoms in different molecules.

The interatomic distances between atoms may actually be measured by the techniques of x-ray diffraction or microwave spectroscopy. A few such interatomic distances, of particular interest in organic chemistry, are listed in Table 2.

Table 2. Interatomic Distances

Atoms	Interatomic distances	Atoms	Interatomic distances
C—C	1.54 Å	C—Cl	1.77 Å
C—H	1.09	C—Br	1.91
C—O	1.51	O—H	1.06
C—N	1.51	S—H	1.36

These distances are most properly regarded as measured between the centers of the nuclei; however, this distance varies only slightly from the internuclear distances. Although most of the mass of an atom is in the nucleus, most of the space is occupied by the orbitals in which the electrons are found. Since molecular dimensions are so small in comparison with ordinary units of length, the unit of measurement used for such lengths is the Ångstrom unit (abbreviated Å.), which is 10^{-8} centimeter.

Molecular Models

Although there will be discussed, in this chapter and later, devices for projecting three-dimensional formulas on a plane surface, the shapes of molecules are best understood by examination of molecular models. In fact, molecular models are indispensable for acquiring a sense of the true shapes of organic molecules and observing how the shape varies as atoms are "rotated" around valence bonds. Of the several types of molecular models that have been developed, the *ball and stick models* and the *framework models* are best adapted to student use, so these types will be discussed at the present time.

If different colored balls are used to indicate the atoms, and these are joined together by match sticks, we may construct a molecular model of such appearance as shown in Fig. 10. Such models are much better if the balls are joined by moderately stiff springs, of different lengths to indicate different interatomic distances. Since the springs may be turned in the holes in the balls, effects of rotation around a valence direction may be examined. Furthermore, the springs will yield to pressure, thus giving the effect of slightly distorting valence direction. It should be remembered that the bonds represented by the springs are in the directions of the long axes of the molecular orbitals resulting from combinations of atomic orbitals.

One feature of the ball and stick models, necessary for their construction but not really representative of molecular geometry, is the relatively large size of

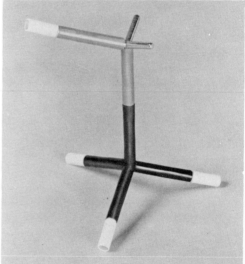

Fig. 11. Framework Molecular Model of methyl alcohol. Models of a convenient size result when a distance of one inch is used to represent one Ångstrom unit. A bond between two atoms consists of a combination of lengths of tubing of appropriate colors representing the atomic radii of the respective atoms. Atomic radii can be easily calculated from the interatomic distances in Table 2. For example, since the interatomic distance between two carbon atoms is 1.54 Å., the carbon radius is 0.77 Å. and would be represented by a piece of black tubing 0.77 in. in length. If the carbon radius is subtracted from the C—H interatomic distance (1.09 Å.), there results the radius for hydrogen, so a piece of white tubing 0.32 in. in length represents the hydrogen radius. The C—H bond, then, is a combination of 0.77 in. of black tubing and 0.32 in. of white tubing. Similarly, the C—O bond is represented by a piece of tubing consisting of 0.77 in. of black tubing and 0.74 in. of red tubing. Construction of a model with the metal pieces and tubing gives the geometrical shape of the molecule, with the atoms proportionately spaced, hence the name Framework Molecular Models.

the balls representing nuclei. Although nearly all the mass of a molecule is in the nucleus the space occupied by it is small compared to the interatomic distances. Of course, these distances between the nuclei are not just open space; they contain the orbitals in which the electrons are found. The **Framework Molecular Models,** as shown in Fig. 11, use metal pieces as the nuclei so that their size is not over-exaggerated.[11] These metal nuclei are joined by pieces of plastic tubing of different colors and lengths to indicate different atoms at the proper interatomic distances. The tubing is of a convenient stiffness to indicate the valence direction, yet it can be bent to form molecules in which the valence directions are somewhat distorted. Other features include the possibility of indicating the unshared pairs of electrons on oxygen by the additional metal pins (cf. Fig. 11). Bonds between different atoms are indicated by junction of two colors of tubing representing the two atoms joined. The length of a given color of tubing represents the *atomic radius* (half its interatomic distance) for the atom which that color represents.

Planar Projections of Molecular Models

If the model of methyl alcohol, such as shown in Fig. 10, is considered in a position such that the hydroxyl is extending straight up, two hydrogens forward and to each side, and the third hydrogen back, a projection may be written as in Fig. 12(a). Such projections, in which the central atom is written as a circle depicting a cross section of a ball and the other atoms are indicated by their symbols, are known as Alexander projections.[12] The extension to ethyl alcohol is shown in Fig. 12(b), where the three lower atoms (like the feet on a tripod) are extending down from the lower carbon, while the upper three atoms extend up. As will be developed in future chapters, these projections are very useful in studying the relative positions of atoms in molecules.

Another type of projection, known as the Newman projection,[13] is shown in Fig. 13. This projection results from viewing the ethyl alcohol molecule from above, looking "down the bond" joining the two carbon atoms. It is especially useful in the interpretation of reaction mechanisms, for it emphasizes an important feature of a molecule. If the hydrogens in ethyl alcohol were actually directly opposite each other, as depicted in Fig. 12, the highly positive hydrogen atoms would be closer to each other and repel each other more than if they were "staggered" in the manner shown in Fig. 13 (remember expansion of the valence angle in water, Fig. 6). Although rotation about the C—C bond results in an infinite number of relative positions of the hydrogen atoms with respect to each

---

[11] The Framework Molecular Models are sold in kits from which all molecules of interest in most work can be constructed. The price is considerably less than that of a textbook, and the utility is at least as great as a textbook. They are highly recommended.

[12] Elliot P. Alexander was a promising young assistant professor of organic chemistry at the University of Illinois when he was killed in a light plane accident.

[13] Melvin S. Newman, professor of chemistry at The Ohio State University, has been active in the study of dependence of chemical behavior on the geometry of molecules.

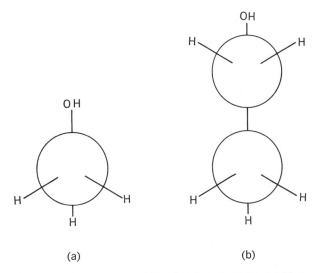

(a)   (b)

Fig. 12. Alexander projections. (a) Methyl alcohol. (b) Ethyl alcohol. When the valence line extends into the circle this indicates that the attached atom is extending forward, and to one side. A short line to the edge of the circle (as to lower H) indicates that the atom is extending behind. A long line to the edge of the circle indicates that the atom is standing straight above the central carbon, as the OH in (a). Such projections may be understood immediately if studied in connection with models such as shown in Fig. 10 or Fig. 11.

other (cf. Fig. 9), the molecule will spend much more time with the hydrogens in the staggered position, the position of lower energy. In fact, it is believed that the molecule spends most of its time vibrating back and forth on each side of the staggered position, and only occasionally turns through the high energy position with the hydrogens directly opposed.

Fig. 13. Newman projection of ethyl alcohol. The model projected in Fig. 12(b) is viewed from the top so that one is looking straight down in the direction of the bond between the carbon atoms. The atoms attached to the top carbon are then joined by lines which meet in the center, while the atoms attached to the bottom carbon are joined by lines extending to the edge of the circle. Rotation of the top atom would then place the OH in various positions. When the hydrogens are directly above each other, this is the position of highest energy, thus lowest stability.

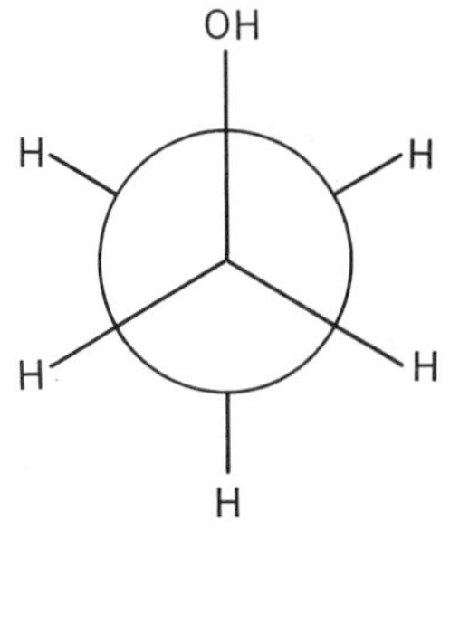

Electronic Formulas

In our discussions thus far, the covalent bond has been indicated in structural formulas by a short line between the atoms sharing the electrons. This line indicates a single covalent bond, whether it be formed by electrons in

sp, sp^2, or sp^3 orbitals; and in the ordinary structural formulas no effort is made to indicate the relative positions in space of the bond directions or the distances between the atoms. Only in projections of molecular models are the positions of the atoms indicated. In addition, there is no designation in structural formulas of any electrons not occupied in bonding. In "electronic" formulas, again no effort is made to indicate spatial relationships, but each electron in the highest level (valence electron) is designated by a dot, regardless of whether the electron is actually engaged in bond formation. Those electrons which are engaged in bonding are placed as a pair between the atoms sharing them. Thus, the condensed structural formula and the electronic formula for methyl alcohol are

$$
\text{CH}_3\text{—OH}
\qquad
\begin{array}{c}
\text{H} \\
\ddots \;\; \ddots \\
\text{H}:\text{C}:\overset{\cdot\cdot}{\underset{\cdot\cdot}{\text{O}}}:\text{H} \\
\ddots \;\; \\
\text{H}
\end{array}
$$

In case there are two or three bonds between two atoms, as is often the case and will be studied later, this is indicated by the appropriate number of pairs of electrons. In illustration of this usage, we may consider the structural and electronic formulas for the molecule ethylene:

$$
\text{H}_2\text{C}=\text{CH}_2
\qquad
\begin{array}{c}
\text{H} \quad\; \text{H} \\
\ddots \;\;\; \ddots \\
\text{H}:\text{C}::\text{C}:\text{H}
\end{array}
$$

The most stable configurations result when there are two electrons in the first energy level and eight in the second; therefore, if an electronic formula is written correctly, there should be two electrons associated with hydrogen and eight associated with other low atomic weight elements. All these are indicated, whether or not they are involved in bonding, as in the formula above for methyl alcohol. Remember that electrons in molecular orbitals (shared electrons) are "counted" for each of the atoms sharing them. This type of formula is very convenient for depicting certain types of valence, as will be discussed in the next sections.

The coordinate covalence. The simple covalence consists of a pair of shared electrons, and each of the atoms involved has donated one of the electrons. In this instance, two negative electrons are equally shared by two nuclei; therefore it seems reasonable to regard the net electric charge associated with each atom as unchanged. What an atom loses in negative charge by sharing an electron, it regains from the shared electron donated by the other atom. In an atom such as nitrogen (cf. Table 1), three covalent bonds may be formed by this process to give such compounds as ammonia and nitrous acid.

$$
\begin{array}{c}
\text{H} \\
\ddots \\
\text{H}:\text{N}:\text{H} \\
\ddots
\end{array}
\qquad\qquad
\begin{array}{c}
\ddots \\
\text{H}:\overset{\cdot\cdot}{\text{O}}:\text{N}::\overset{\cdot\cdot}{\text{O}}: \\
\ddots \;\; \ddots \;\; \ddots
\end{array}
$$

Ammonia   Nitrous acid

In the electronic formulas for these substances, it may be noted that nitrogen has an unshared pair of electrons, but is in a stable condition, for it has an octet of eight electrons in the highest energy level. It might be suspected that nitrogen in these molecules would be inert to further bonding as is the neon atom, for its highest energy level has all its orbitals full. It turns out to be the case, however, that nitric acid, $HONO_2$, is a well-known and stable compound in which nitrogen has a valence of five.

The structure of nitric acid may be explained by considering the possibility that nitrogen might form a covalent bond with oxygen if nitrogen should donate both the electrons for this bond. This is possible because this would not increase the number of electrons around nitrogen, and oxygen can accommodate two electrons before its octet is filled. In this case, however, nitrogen has lost one unit of electric charge, for it was neutral before it shared two of its electrons. Conversely, oxygen now has an equal share in two additional electrons, or an increase of one in negative charge. This situation is indicated by the following electronic formula:

$$H:\overset{\cdot\cdot}{\underset{\cdot\cdot}{O}}:\overset{\cdot\cdot\ +}{N}::\overset{\cdot\cdot}{\underset{\cdot\cdot}{O}}:$$
$$:\overset{}{\underset{\cdot\cdot}{O}}:\_$$

Thus nitrogen has a covalence of four and an electrovalence of one, while one of the oxygens has a covalence of one and an electrovalence of one. The creation of this sort of situation may, perhaps, be understood better if *hypothetical steps* in conversion of nitrous acid and oxygen to nitric acid are considered, as follows:

(a) $H:\overset{\cdot\cdot}{\underset{\cdot\cdot}{O}}:\overset{\cdot\cdot}{N}::\overset{\cdot\cdot}{\underset{\cdot\cdot}{O}}: + :\overset{\cdot\cdot}{\underset{\cdot\cdot}{O}}:$ (both neutral)

(b) $H:\overset{\cdot\cdot}{\underset{\cdot}{O}}:\overset{\cdot\cdot\ +}{N}::\overset{\cdot\cdot}{\underset{\cdot\cdot}{O}}: + :\overset{\cdot}{\underset{\cdot\cdot}{O}}:^{-}$ (electron transfer as in formation of ions)

(c) $H:\overset{\cdot\cdot}{\underset{\cdot\cdot}{O}}:\overset{\cdot\cdot\ +}{N}::\overset{\cdot\cdot}{\underset{\cdot\cdot}{O}}:$ (formation of covalence by sharing of electrons)
$$:\overset{}{\underset{\cdot\cdot}{O}}:\_$$

This combination of a covalence and an electrovalence between the same atoms is sometimes called a **semipolar double bond,** but more often, perhaps, called a **coordinate covalence.** In any case, it is actually a double bond of a different type than the ordinary double bond in which two pairs of electrons are shared (cf. Chap. 8). Since electronic formulas are tedious to write and used only for special purposes, the coordinate covalence is indicated in line formulas by an arrow pointing toward the negative end of the bond, or occasionally by a line plus the charges. Thus nitric acid is written

$$H—O—N{=}O \qquad or \qquad H—O—\overset{+}{N}{=}O$$
$$\quad\;\downarrow \qquad\qquad\qquad\qquad\quad |$$
$$\quad\;O \qquad\qquad\qquad\qquad\quad O^{-}$$

Both sulfur and oxygen have electron pairs to be donated for formation of coordinate covalences, and sulfur may form either one or two such bonds; so sulfur may have a total valence of two, four, or six.

$$
\begin{array}{ccc}
 & & \text{O} \\
 & & \uparrow \\
\text{H—S—H} & \text{HO—S—OH} & \text{HO—S—OH} \\
 & \downarrow & \downarrow \\
 & \text{O} & \text{O} \\
\text{Hydrogen} & \text{Sulfurous} & \text{Sulfuric} \\
\text{sulfide} & \text{acid} & \text{acid}
\end{array}
$$

It should be noted that formation of a coordinate covalence increases the valence in jumps of two. Nitrogen never has a valence of four, always three or five.

Ammonium Salts

Nitrogen has a valence of five in ammonium salts, and the bonds involved are the same as in compounds with a coordinate covalence, *except that the covalence and electrovalence are not to the same atoms.* This type of bond formation may also be presented as a series of hypothetical steps, as follows:

(a) $\text{H} : \overset{\displaystyle \text{H}}{\underset{\displaystyle \text{H}}{\text{N}}} : \text{H} + \text{H}^+ + \; : \overset{..}{\underset{..}{\text{Cl}}} :^-$ (neutral molecule and two ions)

(b) $\text{H} : \overset{\displaystyle \text{H}}{\underset{\displaystyle \cdot}{\overset{..+}{\text{N}}}} : \text{H} + \text{H} \cdot + \; : \overset{..}{\underset{..}{\text{Cl}}} :^-$ (electron transfer; neutral atom and two ions; same total charge)

(c) $\text{H} : \overset{\displaystyle \text{H}}{\underset{\displaystyle \text{H}}{\overset{..+}{\text{N}}}} : \text{H} + \; : \overset{..}{\underset{..}{\text{Cl}}} :^-$ (formation of covalence by sharing of electrons)

Ammonium   Chloride
ion   ion

Thus nitrogen has four covalences and one electrovalence, but the electrovalences are associated with atoms not otherwise joined. Ammonium chloride may dissociate in solution just as does sodium chloride. Furthermore, the ammonium and chloride ions cannot associate except by electrostatic attraction. There is no opportunity for a covalence to be formed between nitrogen and chlorine.

Measurement of the valence angles in ammonium salts has shown that the orbitals by which nitrogen forms four covalences are sp^3 **hybridized orbitals.** Since the unshared pair in trivalent nitrogen is in a $2s$ orbital, the electron donated in step (b) above is one of these $2s$ electrons. Thus the electronic configuration of pentavalent nitrogen is the same as that of the bonding carbon atom, and formation of sp^3 hybridized orbitals is reasonable and to be expected.

Acids and Bases in the Lewis Sense

In the discussion above, it may be noted that ammonia acts as a base which neutralizes hydrochloric acid by virtue of being able to donate an electron. Conversely, the hydrogen ion acts as an acid by being able to accept an electron. In accord with this mechanism of neutralization, G.N. Lewis proposed that in the broadest sense an acid is a species capable of receiving electrons, while a base is a species capable of donating a pair of electrons for bond formation. This concept of acids and bases is very useful, indeed, in organic chemistry where reactions are usually carried out in nonaqueous media and bases rarely function as such by virtue of forming hydroxyl ions. It is to be noted that the Lewis definition does include orthodox acids and bases as well as those not functioning by way of hydrogen or hydroxyl ions.

Onium Salts

In the Lewis sense, water, $H:O:H$, which has electrons to donate should be regarded as a base. As a matter of fact, ionization of electrovalent compounds in water is regarded as caused in large measure by *hydration* of the ions. More than one water molecule may be held by electrostatic forces, but one water molecule may well hold a positive ion by a covalent bond via a mechanism similar to formation of ammonium hydroxide by solution of ammonia gas in water.

$$H:N:H + H:O:H \rightleftharpoons H:N:H + \ {}^{-}:O:H \tag{1}$$

Ammonium
ion

$$H:O:H + H:Cl: \rightleftharpoons H:O:H + :Cl: \tag{2}$$

Hydronium
ion

Many organic molecules are bases in the Lewis sense, but weaker bases than water. For example, diethyl ether will form a salt with a strong acid in absence of water:

$$H_5C_2-O-C_2H_5 + HCl \rightleftharpoons H_5C_2-\overset{+}{O}-C_2H_5 + Cl^- \tag{3}$$
$$\overset{|}{H}$$

Such a salt, formed by various oxygen-containing organic compounds such as alcohols and ethers, is called an **oxonium salt. In these salts oxygen has a valence of four.** Many naturally occurring pigments, known as anthocyanins, are oxonium salts of ethers of rather complicated structure. They are responsible for many of the blue and purple colors in the flowers, fruits, leaves, and stems of plants.

Since an understanding of the structures of the molecules is of fundamental importance to understanding organic chemistry, this chapter and Chapter 8 should be fixed well in mind and reviewed at intervals.

EXERCISES

1. For the third principal energy level, how many of each of the following may there be?

(a) Sublevels of energy.
(b) Atomic orbitals.
(c) Electrons.

2. Why may there be three p atomic orbitals in the second principal energy level, but only one s atomic orbital in this level?

3. Explain why atoms with atomic numbers of 2 and 10 are inert to bond formation. Also, use your answer to Exercise 1 to predict the atomic number of the next atom which should be inert to bond formation.

4. Define or clearly illustrate the following terms.

(a) Bond energy of a covalent bond.
(b) An electrovalence.
(c) A molecular orbital.
(d) An interatomic distance.
(e) A p atomic orbital.
(f) The valence angle of an atom.
(g) A hybridized orbital.

5. Explain how a carbon atom may form four covalences in a molecule, although the uncombined carbon atom is regarded as having only two unshared electrons.

6. Write electronic formulas, showing all electrons and charges, for the following.

(a) Sulfuric acid.
(b) The nitrate ion.
(c) The salt of dimethyl ether and nitric acid.
(d) Ammonium sulfate.

7. Explain how pentavalent nitrogen may be bonded by hybridized sp^3 orbitals, but must have one electrovalence.

8. If a plane be passed through the two carbon atoms in ethyl alcohol, how many hydrogen atoms may lie in this plane at the same time? "At the same time" means for a given position of rotation around the carbon-carbon bond.

Alcohols as a Class of Organic Compounds

Alcohols are among the more important classes of organic compounds and are especially important as basic raw materials in the chemical industry. As has been mentioned in Chapter 2, a *class* of compounds is characterized by a common functional group. In the case of alcohols, this is the hydroxyl group, —OH. Since alcohols consist of the hydroxyl group attached to an alkyl radical, the *general formula* for alcohols is $C_nH_{2n+1}OH$. Since *n* may have any value, an infinite number of alcohols is theoretically possible, and thousands are actually known to chemists. Certain characteristics of ten of the more simple alcohols are listed in Table 1. In this table, each alcohol is named by placing the name of the alkyl radical as a separate word preceding the term alcohol. *Since the radical names are basic units in organic nomenclature, they should be learned.* Systematic development of organic nomenclature will be the subject of the next chapter. It will be noted that each radical name except the first two carries a hyphenated, italicized "*n*" as prefix. This stands for "normal", and is read not as "*n*" but as "normal." It means that the carbon atoms in this alkyl radical are attached to each other in a linear fashion, with no branches in the "chain," and attachment to the functional group is at the end of the chain. Isomerism in the alkyl radical will be discussed subsequently.

Table I. Characteristics of Certain Alcohols

Name	Formula	Boiling point	Increment in B.P.	Melting point	Increment in M.P.
Methyl alcohol	CH_3—OH	64°			
			14°		
Ethyl alcohol	CH_3—CH_2—OH	78°			
			20°		
n-Propyl alcohol	CH_3—CH_2—CH_2—OH	98°		−127°	
			20°		37°
n-Butyl alcohol	CH_3—$(CH_2)_3$—OH	118°		−90°	
			20°		11°
n-Amyl alcohol	CH_3—$(CH_2)_4$—OH	138°		−79°	
			19°		28°
n-Hexyl alcohol	CH_3—$(CH_2)_5$—OH	157°		−51°	
			19°		17°
n-Heptyl alcohol	CH_3—$(CH_2)_6$—OH	176°		−34°	
			19°		18°
n-Octyl alcohol	CH_3—$(CH_2)_7$—OH	195°		−16°	
			20°		11°
n-Nonyl alcohol	CH_3—$(CH_2)_8$—OH	215°		−5°	
			18°		11.5°
n-Decyl alcohol	CH_3—$(CH_2)_9$—OH	233°		+6.5°	

Homologous Series

It may be noted in Table 1 that each formula in the list differs from the one before it, as well as the one after it, by the unit —CH_2—. The —CH_2— grouping is termed a **methylene group.** A series of compounds in which the structural formula of each differs from the immediately preceding and following ones by a methylene group, and in no other way, is known as a **homologous series.** Any compound in such a series is termed a **homolog** of the others. Thus n-propyl alcohol and n-hexyl alcohol are homologs, while n-butyl alcohol is the **next higher homolog** of n-propyl alcohol. The relationship between members of a homologous series is termed **homology.**

Variation of Properties within a Homologous Series

The concept of the homologous series is quite useful in studying organic compounds, for all the members of a homologous series usually give the same chemical reactions; these reactions are those exhibited by the particular functional group characteristic of that homologous series. It should be emphasized that members of a homologous series differ *only* in the number of methylene groups present. This distinction is quite significant, for compounds differing in other ways, such as isomerism in the alkyl group, frequently give rather different chemical reactions.

Since organic reactions involve the breaking and making of covalent bonds (cf. Chap. 3, footnote 9), these reactions are not infinitely rapid, as are the ionic reactions characteristic of inorganic compounds. It is common for organic reactions to be completed only after hours or days, and the *rates* of reactions are a subject of much interest to organic chemists. This subject will be discussed in various connections, but it may be mentioned, at present, that the rate of a given reaction in a homologous series in which the alkyl group is normal decreases with addition of each methylene group up to a total of four carbons. Above this molecular weight, the rate remains constant. Knowledge of this sort of predictable behavior is of obvious utility to a chemist who wants to know how long will be required to complete a given reaction. If the rate of the particular reaction is known for one member of a homologous series, a close approximation can be reached for any other member of the series.

Physical properties also vary in a more or less regular manner in a homologous series. This regular variation continues throughout the series, although the difference between successive members becomes less as molecular weight increases. This is reasonable since the percentage change resulting from the increment of a methylene group is less as the molecular weight becomes greater. Although this regular variation is observed for any physical property, it may be conveniently illustrated by consideration of the values for boiling point recorded in Table 1. For compounds containing as many as ten carbons, the *increment of about 20° per methylene group* remains approximately constant, but it should be mentioned that for compounds containing about twenty carbons the increment per methylene group has dropped to about 10°. The values recorded in this table are believed to be the best available in the chemical literature; however, the increment of 20° between *n*-octyl and *n*-nonyl alcohols suggests that a careful measurement might well reveal a small error in the boiling point of *n*-nonyl alcohol.[1]

It is of interest that the *melting point increments* in the homologous series of normal alcohols decrease more rapidly with molecular weight than do the increments of boiling point. Although the increase in melting point is much less systematic than is that in boiling point, there may be noted an **alternation** in the size of the increment; for the even-carbon alcohols melt higher, in relation to molecular weight, than do the odd-carbon alcohols. This alternation of properties for the even- and odd-carbon compounds is very common in various homologous series for properties involving the *solid state*. Such behavior is not characteristic of the liquid state. The greater regularity in variation of properties of the liquid state is also a rather general phenomenon.

Isomerism Involving the Alkyl Group

In Chapter 2 there was discussed isomerism resulting from a different arrangement of atoms giving rise to different functional groups. Isomerism

---

[1] This point is mentioned at this time chiefly to call attention to the fact that the precision of physical measurements is always subject to some limit, and recorded values are simply those regarded as the best thus far reported. It is not uncommon for more careful measurements with currently modern equipment to reveal small or large errors in previously reported values.

may also result from a different order of attachment of the carbon atoms to each other or to the functional group, even though the same functional group is present in both instances. Such isomerism may occur in any compound having alkyl groups of three or more carbons. Examination will reveal that in the ethyl radical there is no alternative way of arranging the two carbon atoms or of attaching the functional group (refer to different ways of presenting this formula in Chap. 2). In the case of propyl alcohol, however, there is an alternative arrangement; the hydroxyl group may be attached to the center carbon atom:

$$CH_3—CH_2—CH_2—OH \qquad\qquad CH_3—\underset{\underset{OH}{|}}{CH}—CH_3 \text{ or } CH_3—\underset{\underset{CH_3}{|}}{CH}—OH$$

$$\textit{n-}Propyl \text{ alcohol} \qquad\qquad\qquad \text{Isopropyl alcohol}$$

Since any radical which has the terminal grouping $CH_3—\underset{\underset{CH_3}{|}}{CH}—$ is termed

"iso," the propyl alcohol with hydroxyl attached to the center carbon is called isopropyl alcohol. It may be emphasized at this point that the two propyl alcohols are definitely different compounds, as is evidenced by a difference in physical properties. For example, n-propyl alcohol has a boiling point of 98°, whereas isopropyl alcohol has a boiling point of 82°.

In the butyl radical, there may be not only a difference in point of attachment of the hydroxyl but also a different arrangement of the carbon atoms. There are four butyl alcohols:

$$CH_3—CH_2—CH_2—CH_2—OH \qquad\qquad CH_3—\underset{\underset{CH_3}{|}}{CH}—CH_2—OH$$

$$\textit{n-}Butyl \text{ alcohol} \qquad\qquad\qquad \text{Isobutyl alcohol}$$
$$\text{B.P. } 118° \qquad\qquad\qquad\qquad \text{B.P. } 108°$$

$$CH_3—CH_2—\underset{\underset{CH_3}{|}}{CH}—OH \qquad\qquad CH_3—\underset{\underset{CH_3}{\overset{CH_3}{|}}}{\overset{|}{C}}—OH$$

$$\textit{sec-}Butyl \text{ alcohol} \qquad\qquad\qquad \textit{tert-}Butyl \text{ alcohol}$$
$$\text{B.P. } 100° \qquad\qquad\qquad\qquad \text{B.P. } 83°$$

The hyphenated prefix *sec-* stands for "secondary" and is so read. Similarly, *tert-* stands for tertiary. It should be noted that "isobutyl" in not hyphenated. If the definition of homology is re-examined at this point, it will be noted that neither *sec*-butyl nor isobutyl alcohols are homologs of *n*-propyl alcohol, for they differ in other respects than addition of a methylene group. Either of these two butyl alcohols differs from isopropyl alcohol by one methylene group; however, the *homology exists between isopropyl alcohol and sec-butyl alcohol*, for they are the *same type of alcohol*—and hence give similar chemical reactions. Isopropyl alcohol and isobutyl alcohol are not homologs, for one is a secondary alcohol and the other is primary. A better name is *sec*-propyl alcohol; unfortunately, isopropyl alcohol is in much more frequent usage.

Types of Alcohols

Since the valence of carbon is four, in an alcohol the carbon to which the hydroxyl is attached may be attached to one, two, or three additional carbon atoms. Since these differences in structure give rise to certain differences in chemical behavior, it is useful to classify these three types of alcohols as primary, secondary (*sec*), and tertiary (*tert*). On this basis, it will be noted that the four butyl alcohols include two primary alcohols, one secondary alcohol, and one tertiary alcohol. In particular, it should be noted that isobutyl alcohol is a primary alcohol, not a secondary alcohol, for the carbon attached to two other carbons is not the carbon attached to hydroxyl. Further, isopropyl alcohol is a secondary alcohol, whereas all other iso alcohols are primary alcohols.

The use of the terms, primary, secondary, and tertiary is widespread in organic nomenclature. Since it is applied to radical names, it is a *fundamental part of all nomenclature based on radical names;* therefore it should be well understood. The rather different reactions given by compounds in which the functional group is attached in a primary, secondary, or tertiary position will be discussed in Chapter 6, wherein the study of organic reactions will be initiated.

Industrial Availability of Alcohols

Although we are presently concerned less with chemical technology than with the fundamental principles of chemistry, several of the alcohols are such important raw materials that a brief mention of their sources seems in order.

Methyl alcohol. Methyl alcohol has long been a readily available article of commerce, and prior to 1923 was obtained by the "destructive distillation" of wood (hence the name "wood alcohol"). This process consisted of heating wood in absence of air until it was thermally decomposed. The tarry distillate contains, among several other things, methyl alcohol. Nearly all the wood distillation plants have been put out of business today by introduction of better methods for making the things previously obtained from "wood tar." Methyl alcohol is obtained by a catalytic process from hydrogen and carbon monoxide.[2]

$$CO \ + \ 2H_2 \xrightarrow[\text{ZnCr}_2\text{O}_4 \text{ catalyst}]{400°, \text{ high pressure}} CH_3OH \tag{1}$$

Carbon
monoxide

Ethyl alcohol can be obtained from ethylene by a process which will be discussed in Chapter 9, but the major industrial source of this alcohol is

---

[2] Carbon probably has a valence of four in carbon monoxide, as it does in other compounds. The electronic structure of this compound and other compounds in which multiple bonds occur will be discussed in Chapter 8.

fermentation of sugars. This complicated process gives several compounds, but the formation of ethyl alcohol may be represented as in Eq. 2.

$$C_6H_{12}O_6 \xrightarrow{\text{zymase}} 2C_2H_5OH + 2CO_2 \qquad (2)$$

A sugar

Zymase is a mixture of the complicated organic compounds known as **enzymes.** An enzyme may be regarded as a catalyst of biological origin. Since enzymes are made only by living organisms, they are reminiscent of the mysterious "vital force" which early organic chemists regarded as necessary for formation of organic compounds. The particular enzyme, zymase, is made by growing yeast cells, and the fermentation of sugars is carried out by yeast.

A by-product of sugar fermentation is a mixture of higher alcohols known as **fusel oil.** Since these higher alcohols are quite toxic, their separation from ethyl alcohol to be used as a beverage is very important, and accomplished satisfactorily only with the expensive distillation equipment used in the chemical industry. Although some *n*-**propyl alcohol** is separated from fusel oil and marketed, fusel oil is not a significant source of pure higher alcohols.

n-**Butyl alcohol.** Many chemical compounds other than ethyl alcohol are produced industrially by biological processes which employ the enzymes from various microorganisms. These include such highly publicized substances as penicillin, streptomycin, and cortisone, as well as more prosaic but very important compounds such as *n*-butyl alcohol. The fermentation of corn starch to yield acetone (to be studied later) was developed during World War I, by use of the organism, *clostridium acetobutylicum*. *n*-Butyl alcohol was a by-product. Since that time, other methods have been developed for manufacture of acetone, but the fermentation process has been developed into a major industrial source of *n*-butyl alcohol.

Higher alcohols. Various primary, secondary, and tertiary alcohols with eight or fewer carbons are commercially available, and the primary straight-chain alcohols with an *even* number of carbons are available up to C_{18}. Sources of these compounds will be discussed in later chapters. There will also be discussed in later chapters synthetic methods for preparation of alcohols of nearly any desired structure.

Conventions Used in Writing Equations

A given compound, or compounds, will often react in any of several different ways to give different products, depending on the specific conditions under which the reaction is carried out. Thus the conditions (temperature, catalyst, concentrations, etc.) under which a reaction is carried out are a very important part of the reaction and should be learned as a part of the equation. These conditions are frequently written on the arrow, as in Eq. 1. Conditions, such as concentration, which apply specifically to one of the reagents may be written in parentheses beneath that particular reagent.

It is rarely the case that a set of conditions can be discovered under which two or more chemical reagents will react in only one way. Usually the best we can do is choose conditions which favor formation of the compound or compounds which we desire; nevertheless, it is customary to write a balanced equation, such as Eq. 1, yielding the desired compounds. Under the particular conditions specified, the *yield* of methyl alcohol is quite good, and this is an entirely practical method for making methyl alcohol; however, numerous higher alcohols are formed at the same time in relatively small quantity, and these are actually separated and marketed as pure compounds or useful mixtures. The reaction leading to the principal product is often called the **main reaction**, while reactions leading to other products in smaller amount are called **side reactions.** The products of these side reactions are termed **side products** or **by-products.** Since formation of by-products is often unavoidable, they must be separated from the main product. They may be simply discarded, but on an industrial scale this is not only wasteful but creates a problem of disposal. They may be burned as fuel, but some commercial use for by-products is always sought. For example, one of the by-products of the methyl alcohol synthesis is *n*-propyl alcohol, and this constitutes a major commercial source of this important alcohol. The practicality of an industrial process may depend on the usefulness of the by-products. One critic has remarked that organic chemistry is the study of side reactions and by-products.

Characteristics of Industrial Processes and Laboratory Processes

It is probably in order to set forth at this time a general comparison of processes suitable for industrial use and those suitable for laboratory use. Industrial processes are responsible for production of nearly all organic chemicals if the measurement is in *weight of chemicals.* If, however, we consider *numbers of compounds*, the principal production is in the laboratory. If an industrial organization is attempting the discovery of an insecticide which will do a specific job, dozens or hundreds of compounds may be synthesized in the laboratory for testing. If one or more of them proves suitable for the desired purpose, the next problem is development of a suitable process for producing the substance in ton quantities at a price which is practical.

Since laboratory synthesis is usually aimed at producing large numbers of compounds in small quantity for testing of some kind, laboratory apparatus must be versatile and relatively simple; therefore it is desirable, although not absolutely necessary, that laboratory processes not involve extreme conditions such as very high temperatures or very high pressures. It is especially important that laboratory processes give a rather good yield of the desired compound not admixed with by-products which are inseparable or separable only with great difficulty or elaborate equipment. The cost of starting materials in laboratory syntheses is usually unimportant, for small quantities are usually desired. Also, a multistep synthesis is tolerable in the laboratory provided each step gives a reasonable yield of the desired compound in a pure condition.

Industrial synthesis is aimed at quantity production for a specific purpose at a competitive price; therefore most of the considerations of importance in laboratory syntheses do not apply. Use of extreme temperatures and pressures increases the initial cost of the equipment, but the plant will turn out the compound on a 24-hour basis for as long as there is a market for it. Thus maintenance and operating expense become major factors. Since cost is all-important, the starting materials should be cheap and abundant, and the number of steps involved in the process should be as few as possible. Although some industrial uses, such as those in the polymer and drug industries, require pure compounds, many others may satisfactorily utilize impure compounds or suitable mixtures. Furthermore, a process which gives several compounds which are separable is satisfactory if a market can be found for all the compounds. For this latter reason, many aspects of the chemical industry are interlocked, and there is a delicate balance of price between superficially unrelated compounds. The economics of the chemical industry is often as complicated as the chemistry.

Since our present study is concerned largely with the principles of organic chemistry, our major attention will be directed towards laboratory syntheses. After the principles of the science have been studied, the scientist is then in a position to continue to the matters of engineering and economics involved in industrial production. In our study of reactions, however, we will always consider the matter of whether the reactions yield a major amount of a single compound. This is important knowledge, fundamental in one way or another to any type of application of the reactions. Knowledge of the *mechanisms of reactions* also becomes important for this reason. If one is familiar with the details of the mechanisms of chemical conversion, it often becomes possible to alter conditions so as to increase the ratio of the desired product at the expense of the undesired ones. We will also consider industrial availability of important starting materials, as we have for the alcohols, for any new synthesis of a known or unknown compound must eventually start with something which can, on the day the synthesis is started, be taken out of a bottle, a drum, or a tank car.

EXERCISES

1. Write the condensed structural formula for the next higher homolog of each of the following compounds.

(a) Isohexyl alcohol.
(b) *tert*-Butyl alcohol.
(c) *n*-Octyl alcohol.

2. From the data in Table 1 and the boiling points given for the isomeric butyl alcohols, estimate the boiling points of the two branched-chain compounds mentioned in the preceding question.

3. Write condensed structural formulas for the following.

(a) Two isomers with different functional groups.
(b) Two isomers with the same functional group.
(c) Five primary hexyl alcohols, two secondary hexyl alcohols, and two tertiary hexyl alcohols.

4. Write condensed structural formulas for all the secondary amyl alcohols. How many secondary butyl alcohols are there?

5

Systematic Nomenclature in Organic Chemistry

Since both the number and diversity of organic compounds are very large indeed, a systematic approach to the naming of the compounds is essential. There are in use a limited number of "common" or "trivial" names of organic compounds which were applied in the early days of the development of organic chemistry, and have survived to the present time. Other compounds of very complicated structure are given "common" names in order to obviate the use of a very long and involved name. When common names are in regular use for relatively important compounds, it is necessary, of course, to learn these names as the compounds are studied; however, the major effort in nomenclature will be directed to systematic nomenclature.

It would seem best and most logical, at first consideration, to have a single system of nomenclature; however, there are in use at least three basic systems of nomenclature, and each is used sufficiently that one is lost if he attempts to study organic chemistry without understanding all these systems of naming compounds. The most widely applicable, and most important system of nomenclature is that which has been developed during many years by committees of the International Union of Pure and Applied Chemistry. As might be surmised, from the origin of the system, it is used in all languages in which there is significant chemical literature. This system of nomenclature is commonly termed the **IUPAC System,** or shortened to **IUC System,** but may be called the

International System or the Geneva System (from the city in which early meetings were held). The two other comprehensive systems which we will study may be termed: (a) naming as a derivative of the simplest member of the series, (b) naming as a derivative of a straight-chain acid. The latter system, whose study will be deferred until we encounter the carboxylic acids, is rather similar to the IUC system and probably should be classified as the forerunner of the IUC system. Each of these additional systems is rather widely used, partly because they preceded the IUC system and became entrenched, partly because some types of compounds are more easily or more clearly named by one of the alternate systems.

Regardless of the rationale behind the alternate systems of nomenclature, it is imperative that the organic chemist understand the more important systems. Even if one learns hardly anything about organic chemistry, if he understands nomenclature he can learn things from the literature. If one does not understand nomenclature, it becomes difficult, perhaps impossible, to learn a significant amount of organic chemistry. There are not many things that one must know in order to understand nomenclature, but *these things he must know well.* The situation may be likened to mathematics, wherein algebra is quite difficult for one who does not know how to add. It is imperative that the basics of nomenclature, as described in this chapter, be learned unusually well, and supplemented by the occasional additional items added from time to time.

Basic Names for Normal Hydrocarbons

The **saturated aliphatic hydrocarbons, or alkanes,** are the compounds containing only carbon and hydrogen (as implicit in the name) with no multiple bonds between carbon atoms. In view of the absence of any functional group (group whose bonding is relatively easily broken), the alkanes are quite unreactive chemically; in fact, the principal use of alkanes, chief constituents of petroleum, is for burning as a fuel. In order to secure chemical reaction, it is necessary to break the very stable C—C or C—H linkages. Except for the rough conditions applicable for combustion, which results in relatively indiscriminate attack, the only important reaction of alkanes is the free radical type of reaction, to be described in Chapter 11.

The same simplicity of structure which renders alkanes of minor significance in the study of chemical reactions makes them the logical basis for both systems of nomenclature to be studied at this time. The names of the normal (straight-chain) saturated hydrocarbons up to C_{20} are recorded in Table 1, along with additional names from which all other names may be deduced. These names are the first and *most basic* items of nomenclature. It may be noted that all these names end in *-ane*, as does the class name, *alkane*. The first four names are rather arbitrary ones inherited from the early days of chemistry, but all the remainder are formed by adding the ending *-ane* to the root based on the Greek word for the number corresponding to the number of carbons in the molecule. This circumstance relieves the burden of memory to some extent, for it proves necessary to learn only those hydrocarbon names up to C_{15} and then the names for C_{20}, C_{30}, etc. The remaining names may be obtained by simple combinations of the Greek root words for the numerals. There should be noted the concession to euphony, which results in the jettisoning of *ei-* from the C_{22} to C_{29} names. It is rarely that there arises the occasion to name a compound with more than a twenty-carbon chain, but all the information needed to do so is included in the last column of Table 1.

Table I. Basic Names for Normal Hydrocarbons

C_1	methane	C_{11}	hendecane (undecane)	C_{21}	heneicosane
C_2	ethane	C_{12}	dodecane	C_{22}	docosane
C_3	propane	C_{13}	tridecane	C_{23}	tricosane
C_4	butane	C_{14}	tetradecane	etc.	to
C_5	pentane	C_{15}	pentadecane	C_{30}	triacontane
C_6	hexane	C_{16}	hexadecane	C_{31}	hentriacontane
C_7	heptane	C_{17}	heptadecane	C_{32}	dotriacontane
C_8	octane	C_{18}	octadecane	etc.	to
C_9	nonane	C_{19}	nonadecane	C_{40}	tetracontane
C_{10}	decane	C_{20}	eicosane	C_{90}	nonacontane

It may be noted by reference to Table 1, Chapter 4, that **the basic radical names**, with a single exception at the C_5 level, differ from the basic hydrocarbon names only in that the characteristic ending for a radical name is *-yl*, while that for a hydrocarbon is *-ane*. It follows that Table 1 also contains all the information necessary for constructing the name for any normal radical. The radical names are also used in all systems of nomenclature, including the relatively limited system (cf. Table 1, Chap. 4) of combining the radical name with that of the functional group.

Naming as a Derivative of the Simplest Member of the Series

This system is most commonly applied to hydrocarbons and alcohols, especially alcohols, so these two applications will be discussed. Extension to other classes of compounds, such as carboxylic acids, requires essentially no additional information.

Alkanes. Methane, obviously, is the simplest member of this series, so higher molecular weight alkanes with branching chains are named as derivatives of methane according to the following:

1. The carbon atom attached to the largest number of other carbon atoms is selected as the "methane carbon," and each radical attached to this

carbon is named. The combination of these names is used as a prefix to methane, and the resultant combination is written as a single word.

2. The radicals are arranged in order according to either of two principles: (a) alphabetically or (b) according to size, with the smallest first.
3. Two of the same radical are indicated by the prefix *di-*, three by *tri-* and four by *tetra-*.

That is all one needs to know in order to understand this system of nomenclature, but a few examples may be considered in order to clarify certain points that arise.

$$CH_3-CH-CH_2-CH_3$$
$$|$$
$$CH_3$$

Dimethylethylmethane

$$CH_3-CH-CH_2-CH-CH_2-CH_3$$
$$|\qquad\qquad|$$
$$CH_3\qquad\quad CH_3$$

Ethylisobutylmethylmethane

$$\qquad\qquad C_2H_5$$
$$\qquad\qquad |$$
$$CH_3-CH_2-CH_2-C-CH_2-CH_2-CH_3$$
$$\qquad\qquad |$$
$$\qquad\qquad CH_3$$

Ethyldi-*n*-propylmethylmethane

$$\qquad\quad CH_3$$
$$\qquad\quad |$$
$$CH_3-C-CH_3$$
$$\qquad\quad |$$
$$\qquad\quad CH_3$$

Tetramethylmethane

In these names the radicals have been listed in alphabetical order, as preferable for use in an alphabetical listing such as an index. The reason for selecting as the "methane carbon" the one carrying the most *substituents*, that is, the one to which the most branches are attached, is that this makes the radicals as simple as possible. In any structure having more than a single branch, the carbon at any branch may be chosen as the basis for the name, but in practice one chooses the position of branching so as to simplify the naming of the radicals. For example, if the compound on the upper right had been named with the choice of the second carbon from the left end as the methane to serve as basis for the name, the radical on the right would present a problem in naming. In fact, this radical can be named only by applying the IUC system of naming radicals, to be discussed later. We have, therefore, an illustration of a limitation of this system of naming. Unless it be combined with the IUC system, the radicals to be named must be either normal or have a common name (such as isobutyl).

Alcohols. The simplest member of the series of alcohols is methyl alcohol, but for application of the presently considered system of nomenclature, the name *-carbinol* is used to designate the first member of the series. For this reason, this system of naming alcohols is sometimes termed the **Carbinol System.** No additional information is needed to apply this system of nomenclature, as is illustrated in the following:

$$CH_3-CH-CH-OH$$
$$\qquad\qquad |\quad\; |$$
$$\qquad\; CH_3\; C_2H_5$$
Ethylisopropylcarbinol

$$\qquad\qquad\qquad CH_3$$
$$\qquad\qquad\qquad |$$
$$CH_3-CH-CH_2-C-OH$$
$$\qquad\quad |\qquad\qquad |$$
$$\qquad\; CH_3\qquad\; CH_3$$
Dimethylisobutylcarbinol

$$CH_3-CH_2-CH-CH_2-CH_3$$
$$\qquad\qquad\qquad |$$
$$\qquad\qquad\qquad OH$$
Diethylcarbinol

$$\qquad\quad C_2H_5$$
$$\qquad\quad |$$
$$C_2H_5-C-C_2H_5$$
$$\qquad\quad |$$
$$\qquad\quad OH$$
Triethylcarbinol

$$\qquad\qquad\qquad C_2H_5$$
$$\qquad\qquad\qquad |$$
$$CH_3-CH-C\quad\;\;-CH-CH_3$$
$$\qquad\quad |\quad\; |\qquad |$$
$$\qquad\; CH_3\; OH\quad CH_3$$
Diisopropylethylcarbinol

$$\qquad\qquad\qquad\qquad C_2H_5$$
$$\qquad\qquad\qquad\qquad |$$
$$CH_3-CH_2-CH_2-C-CH_2-CH_2-CH_2-CH_3$$
$$\qquad\qquad\qquad\qquad |$$
$$\qquad\qquad\qquad\qquad OH$$
n-Butylethyl-n-propylcarbinol

This system can be applied to a primary alcohol, but it is most commonly applied to secondary and tertiary alcohols. Rather complicated alcohols may be named, but there remains the limitation that it must be possible to name all the radicals attached to the carbinol carbon (the carbon to which hydroxyl is attached).

The IUPAC System of Nomenclature

The importance of learning the basic rules needed to apply this system of naming cannot be overemphasized, for it is the only system capable of application to any type of compound of any complexity. Most of the principles may be developed by consideration of the naming of alkanes; extension to other classes of compounds usually requires only the learning of the ending characteristic of that class.

Alkanes. The characteristic suffix denoting a saturated hydrocarbon is -*ane*, so alkane is actually the IUC class name of the saturated hydrocarbons. There will be presented the basic rules for naming an alkane by the IUC system, then they will be applied in the naming of some compounds.

1. The longest continuous chain of carbon atoms is selected as the basis for the name, and this chain is named according to the basic names given in Table 1.
2. The carbon atoms in this chain are numbered consecutively, starting at the end nearest a branch.
3. The branching alkyl groups are located by the number of the atom to which they are attached in the basic chain. They are named according to the alkyl radical names derived from the basic hydrocarbon names in Table 1. More complicated radicals may be named by application of the IUC system to radicals, as will be described below after consideration of the basic principles is concluded.

4. When two or more of the same substituent occur, the number of them must be indicated by the appropriate prefix (di-, tri-, tetra-, etc.), and the location of each on the main chain is indicated by number.

5. The numbers locating the radicals (or other substituents) are placed immediately before the names of the respective substituents and *hyphens are placed before and after the numbers*. When two or more numbers occur together, *commas are placed between them*.

6. In listing for purposes of indexing, names of substituents are placed in alphabetical order. For all other purposes it is satisfactory to place the substituents in order of increasing molecular weight or complexity or number on the chain. The order in which substituents are placed does not affect the formula represented; only the numbers and names do this.

7. The name of the alkane results from placing the combination of numbers and radical names as a prefix to the basic hydrocarbon name. The whole is written as one word.

Let us consider the application of these rules to naming of the following rather complex alkane.

$$\overset{1}{CH_3}-\overset{2}{CH_2}-\overset{3}{CH}-\overset{4}{CH}-\overset{5}{CH_2}-\overset{6}{CH_2}-\overset{7}{CH}-\overset{8}{CH_2}-\overset{9}{CH_3}$$

with substituents CH_3, C_2H_5 on carbons 3,4 and CH_3 on carbon 7.

First: The longest chain has nine carbons, hence is nonane.

Second: Although there is a branch on the third carbon from each end, at one end there is also a branch on the fourth carbon; so numbering is started at the end containing two branches. In such cases, numbering is started at the end which will make the sum of the numbers of the substituents as small as possible.

Third: There are methyl groups on carbons 3 and 7, hence these will be named and numbered thus -3,7-dimethyl.

Fourth: There is an ethyl group at position 4, thus, -4-ethyl.

Fifth: The name is assembled as one word, thus, 3,7-dimethyl-4-ethyl-nonane. Note that when the name is assembled, the hyphen at the beginning of the resultant word in dropped.

The following names illustrate certain additional points:

$$\overset{2}{CH_3}-\overset{3}{CH}-CH-CH_2-\overset{5}{CH}-CH_2-CH_2-\overset{8}{CH}-C_4H_9$$

with substituents CH_3, CH_3 on carbons 2,3; $CH-CH_3$ (with CH_3) on carbon 5; CH_3 on carbon 8.

2,3,8-Trimethyl-5-isopropyldodecane

$$CH_3-\underset{CH_3}{\overset{CH_3}{C}}-CH_2-\underset{CH-CH_3}{CH}-CH_2-CH_2-\underset{C_2H_5}{\overset{CH_3}{C}}-C_{10}H_{21}$$

with C_2H_5 substituent.

2,2,7-Trimethyl-7-ethyl-4-sec-butylheptadecane

In any radical where no structure is indicated, as $-C_{10}H_{21}$, the normal radical $-(CH_2)_9-CH_3$ is understood. Note that "iso" and "*sec*" are written as previously described and that the number is repeated when two of the same substituent are on the same carbon. The *sec*-butyl radical is actually the only radical that can be named definitively as a secondary radical, except for *sec*-propyl which is commonly termed isopropyl. For higher alkyl groups, there are two or more secondary radicals. Thus, *sec*-amyl may be either of two structures (see below) and is, therefore, *not an acceptable name*.

Cyclic alkanes. Cyclic structures are of such importance in organic chemistry that their geometry and properties will be considered in some detail in Chapter 7; however, the naming of such compounds may be introduced at this time by considering the **cycloalkanes.** Rings of any size, including three-atom rings, are possible, indeed occur in nature, but the five- and six-atom rings are most easily formed and will be used for illustration. The five- and six-membered ring compounds are especially abundant in petroleum in certain locations such as the San Joaquin Valley in California.

The naming of cycloalkanes follows, in all details, the principles discussed for open-chain alkanes, except that the ring is the basic unit on which the name is based, and the cyclic structure is indicated by the prefix cyclo-, as in the class name cycloalkane. The following formulas illustrate the basic use of the system:

Cyclopentane   Cyclohexane   Methylcyclohexane

In the case of a single substituent, there is obviously no need for a number. In order to reduce the labor of writing cyclic formulas, without loss of clarity, *line formulas* such as that shown for methylcyclohexane are nearly always used. Each "corner" is understood to be the location of a carbon atom, and each carbon is assumed to be attached to two hydrogen atoms unless some other substituent is indicated as replacing one or both hydrogen atoms. Replacement of one hydrogen atom is illustrated in methylcyclohexane.

When more than one substituent is present in the ring, each substituent must be numbered. Numbering is started with a carbon bearing a substituent, and proceeds around the ring in the direction which makes the sum of the numbers smaller. In case a choice is available, numbering is started on the carbon giving numbers whose sum is smaller. The following formulas are illustrative:

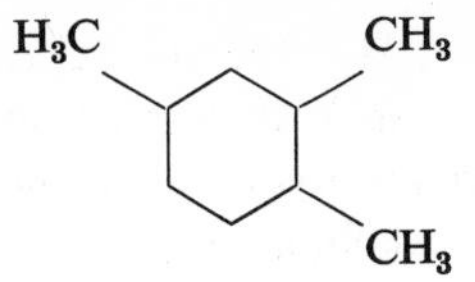

H$_3$C   CH$_3$

CH$_3$

1,2,4-Trimethylcyclohexane

CH$_2$—CH$_2$—CH—CH$_3$

CH$_3$

H$_3$C

C$_2$H$_5$

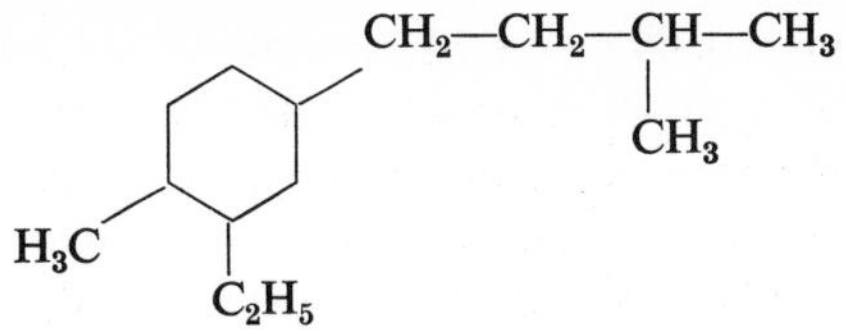

1-Methyl-2-ethyl-4-
isoamylcyclohexane

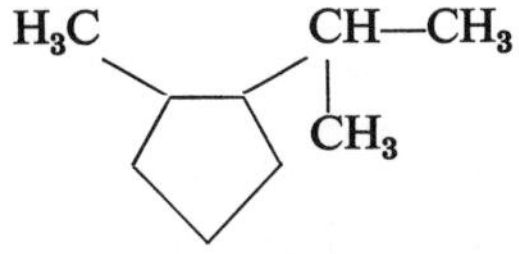

H$_3$C   CH—CH$_3$

CH$_3$

1-Methyl-2-isopropylcyclopentane
or
1-Isopropyl-2-methylcyclopentane

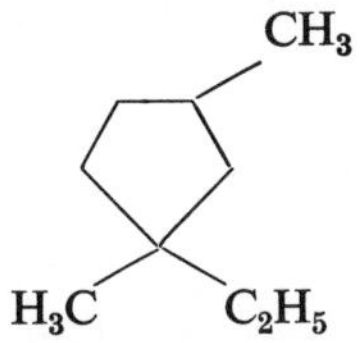

CH$_3$

H$_3$C   C$_2$H$_5$

1,3-Dimethyl-1-ethylcyclo-
pentane

Examples of *incorrect* numbering are: 1,4,6-trimethylcyclohexane (upper left-hand formula), 1,3-dimethyl-3-ethylcyclopentane (lower right-hand formula).

Radicals. Complex radicals may be named by only minor additions to the guides for naming of alkanes:

1. The carbon by which the radical is attached to the rest of the molecule is numbered one.
2. The radical is named strictly according to the rules used for naming alkanes. To avoid ambiguity, the completed radical name may be placed in parentheses. The following formulas are illustrative:

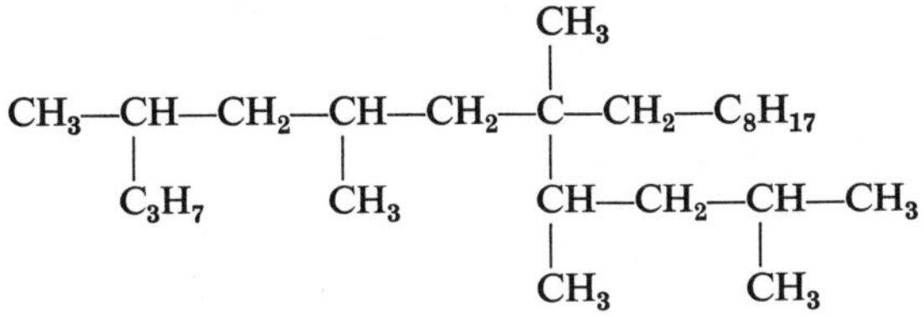

$$CH_3$$

CH$_3$—CH—CH$_2$—CH—CH$_2$—C—CH$_2$—C$_8$H$_{17}$

C$_3$H$_7$ CH$_3$ CH$_3$ CH—CH$_2$—CH—CH$_3$

CH$_3$ CH$_3$

4,6,8-Trimethyl-8-(1,3-dimethylbutyl)heptadecane

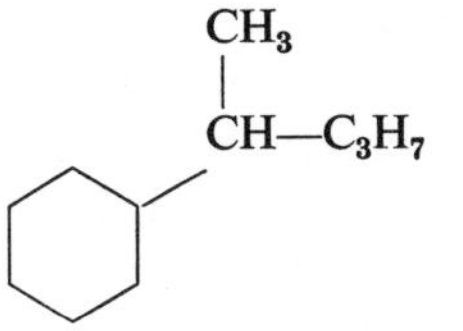

CH$_3$

CH—C$_3$H$_7$

1-Methylbutylcyclohexane

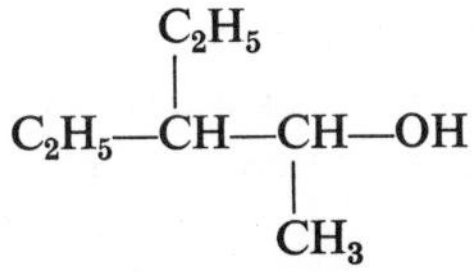

C$_2$H$_5$

C$_2$H$_5$—CH—CH—OH

CH$_3$

(1-Ethylpropyl)methylcarbinol

It should be noted that a name such as 2-pentylcyclohexane (lower left-hand formula) is not strictly correct, for it violates the first rule cited for naming of radicals. Cyclic structures may also be named as radicals. For example, an *alternate name* for the lower left formula is *2-cyclohexylpentane*.

Alcohols. The lower right-hand formula just above illustrates the use of the IUC system for naming radicals, but the carbinol system is used for naming the alcohol. As will prove to be the case in each instance, only limited additional information is needed to apply IUC nomenclature to alcohols:

1. The *characteristic ending* indicating an alcohol is *-ol*. This is substituted in the basic chain name (cf. Table 1) instead of -e, which is the characteristic ending for an alkane.

2. The carbon to which the functional group (hydroxyl) is attached is indicated by the number which results when the basic chain is numbered from the end which will make the number of the carbon bearing the functional group smaller. The position of this number in the name is subject to some variation (it is sometimes placed just before *-ol*); however, the position immediately preceding the basic chain name is usually preferred, as shown in the accompanying illustrations.

The eight isomeric amyl alcohols are named as follows:

$CH_3-(CH_2)_3-CH_2-OH$

1-Pentanol

$CH_3-CH-C_3H_7$
$\qquad\quad |$
$\qquad\quad OH$

2-Pentanol

$C_2H_5-CH-C_2H_5$
$\qquad\quad |$
$\qquad\quad OH$

3-Pentanol

$CH_3-CH-CH_2-CH_2-OH$
$\qquad\quad |$
$\qquad\quad CH_3$

3-Methyl-1-butanol

$C_2H_5-CH-CH_2-OH$
$\qquad\quad |$
$\qquad\quad CH_3$

2-Methyl-1-butanol

$CH_3-CH-CH-CH_3$
$\qquad\quad |\quad\ |$
$\qquad\quad CH_3\ OH$

3-Methyl-2-butanol

$\qquad\quad CH_3$
$\qquad\quad |$
CH_3-C-CH_2-OH
$\qquad\quad |$
$\qquad\quad CH_3$

2,2-Dimethyl-
1-propanol

$\qquad\quad CH_3$
$\qquad\quad |$
C_2H_5-C-OH
$\qquad\quad |$
$\qquad\quad CH_3$

1,1-Dimethyl-
1-propanol

The IUC name for the carbinol used as an earlier illustration is 3-ethyl-2-pentanol, obviously superior to the name in the carbinol system.

Cyclic compounds having a functional group are numbered so that the carbon bearing the functional group is numbered one, so it is unnecessary to specify this in the name:

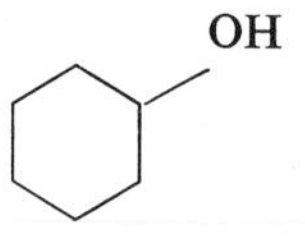

Cyclohexanol

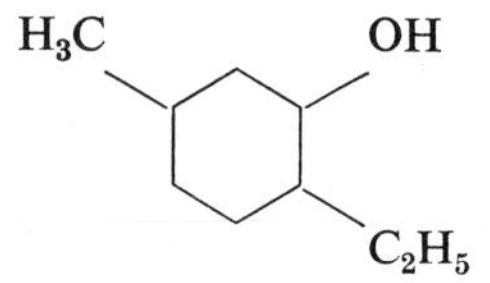

2-Ethyl-5-methylcyclohexanol

3-Methyl-6-ethylcyclohexanol would be an *incorrect name.*

When there occur **more than one of a functional group,** the groups are located by numbers as usual, while di-, tri-, etc., are used to indicate the number of the functional groups present. For example, the common trihydroxy alcohol whose common name is glycerol or glycerin may be named conveniently by the IUC system:

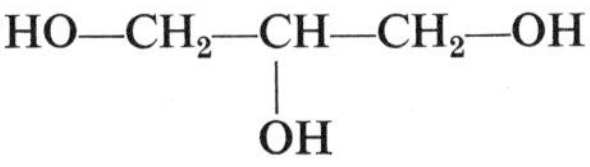

$$HO-CH_2-CH-CH_2-OH$$
$$|$$
$$OH$$

1,2,3-Propanetriol

Naming of substituents. Thus far, the only substituent groups considered have been alkyl radicals. Any group may be named as a substituent; however, some groups are nearly always named as substituents. This applies especially to the **halogens** which, as substituents, are termed fluoro, chloro, bromo, iodo, halo. Illustrative haloalkanes are:

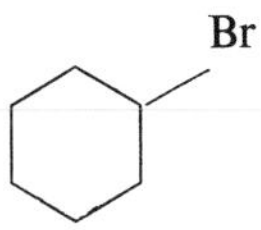

$$\begin{array}{c} I \\ | \\ C_{15}H_{31}-CH-C_2H_5 \end{array}$$

3-Iodooctadecane

Bromo-
cyclohexane

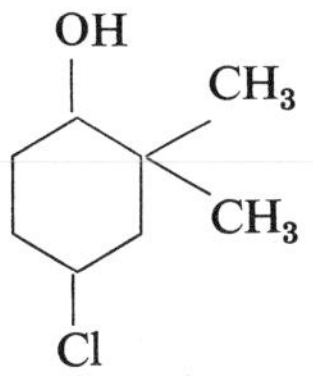

4-Chloro-2,2-
dimethylcyclohexanol

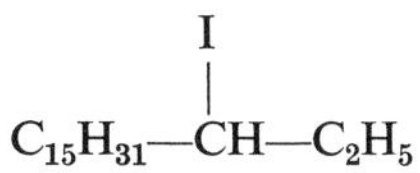

$$CH_3-(CH_2)_8-Br$$

1-Bromononane

The only other common system for naming halogen compounds is by combining radical names with the name of the halide. This system is satisfactory for relatively simple compounds. Thus, *alternate names* for formulas above are cyclohexyl bromide and *n*-nonyl bromide. The haloalkanes as a class of compounds may be termed **alkyl halides.**

Ethers may be named by use of radical names in the case of simple compounds such as dimethyl ether and diethyl ether (cf. Chap. 2). In more complicated structures, however, it is much more widely applicable to name an **alkoxy group** as a substituent. As indicated in the term alkoxy, such a name is formed from the radical name by replacing -*yl* with -*oxy*. Although the IUC system may be used for naming any type of complicated radical, such structures are rarely encountered for both radicals in ethers. Typical structures containing alkoxy groups as substituents are the following:

$$CH_3-O-CH_2-CH_2-Cl$$

1-Chloro-2-methoxyethane

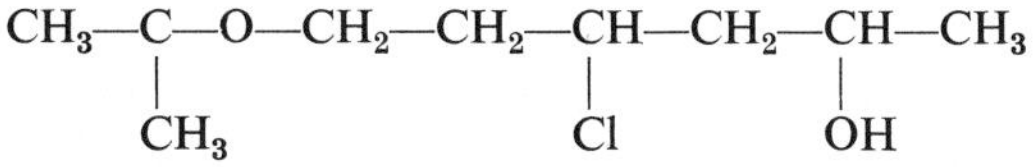

$$CH_3-\overset{\displaystyle CH_3}{\underset{\displaystyle |}{C}}-O-CH_2-CH_2-\overset{\displaystyle Cl}{\underset{\displaystyle |}{CH}}-CH_2-\overset{\displaystyle OH}{\underset{\displaystyle |}{CH}}-CH_3$$

4-Chloro-6-isopropoxy-2-
hexanol

The formula on the right illustrates the usage that alkoxy and halogen are normally regarded as substituents in naming, rather than as functional groups used as the basis for the name. *Any functional group that is present, other than halogen and alkoxy, is used as the basis for the name and the compound is named as a member of that class of compounds.* The other functional groups may be properly named as substituents, e.g., hydroxy, only if another functional group (other than halogen and alkoxy) is present and is used as the basis for the name. Since this principle arises whenever polyfunctional compounds are named, it should be well understood.

EXERCISES

1. Write the names for the normal primary alcohols having the following numbers of carbon atoms: 19, 25, 33, 42, 56, 67.

2. (a) How many normal secondary dodecanols are there? (b) How many alcohols are there which may be formed by substituting a hydrogen with —OH in 2,4-dimethylhexane. (c) Name each of the alcohols in (b) and classify each as primary, secondary, or tertiary.

3. Write structural formulas and one name for each of the bromomethylcyclopentanes (not forgetting cyclopentylbromomethane).

4. Write two names for each of the following structures.

(a)

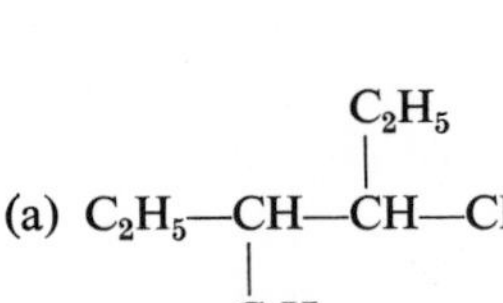

$$C_2H_5-\overset{\overset{\displaystyle C_2H_5}{|}}{C}H-\overset{\overset{\displaystyle }{|}}{C}H-C_4H_9$$
$$\underset{\underset{\displaystyle CH_3}{|}}{}$$

(b)

$$CH_3-\overset{\overset{\displaystyle C_2H_5}{|}}{C}H-\overset{\overset{\displaystyle }{|}}{C}H-OH$$
$$\underset{\underset{\displaystyle C_2H_5}{|}}{}$$

(c)

$$CH_3-\overset{\overset{\displaystyle C_3H_7}{|}}{C}H-CH_2-\overset{\overset{\displaystyle }{|}}{C}-OH$$
$$\underset{\underset{\displaystyle CH_3 \quad C_2H_5}{|}}{}$$

5. Write the IUC name for each of the following structures.

(a) $C_2H_5-\overset{\overset{\displaystyle C_2H_5}{|}}{C}H-\overset{}{C}H-CH_2-\overset{}{C}H-CH_2-OH$
  $\quad\quad\quad \underset{C_3H_7}{|} \quad\quad\quad\quad \underset{O-(CH_2)_3-CH_3}{|}$

(b) $HO-CH_2-\overset{}{C}H-CH_2-CH_2-CH_2OCH_3$
  $\quad\quad\quad\quad \underset{OH}{|}$

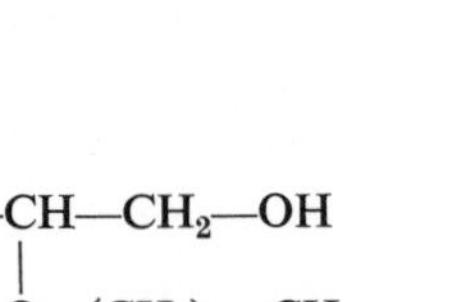

(c)

$CH_3-\overset{}{C}-C_7H_{15}$
$\quad\quad \underset{C_5H_{11}}{|}$
with Br substituent on ring

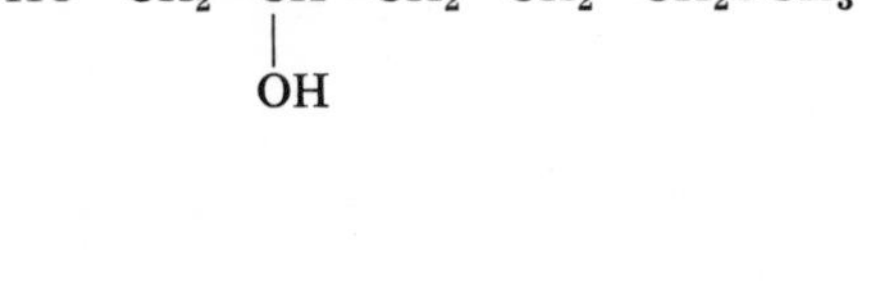

(d)

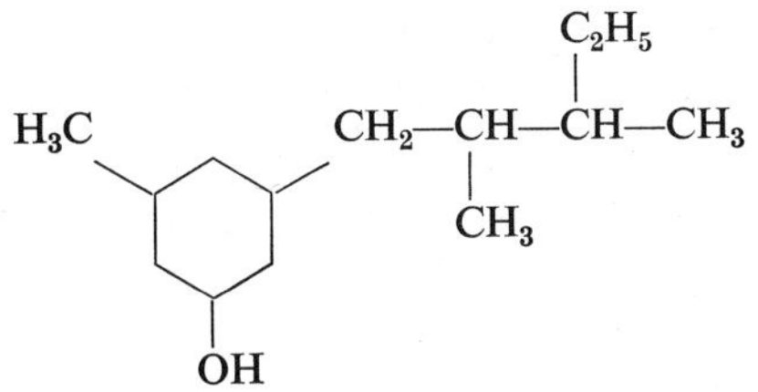

$$\underset{\text{OH}}{\overset{\text{H}_3\text{C}}{\bigcirc}} \quad \underset{\text{CH}_3}{\overset{\text{C}_2\text{H}_5}{\text{CH}_2\text{—CH—CH—CH}_3}}$$

(e) 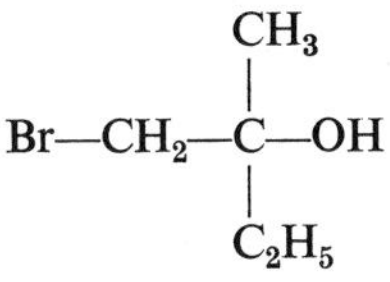 $\underset{\text{C}_2\text{H}_5}{\overset{\text{CH}_3}{\text{Br—CH}_2\text{—C—OH}}}$

(f) 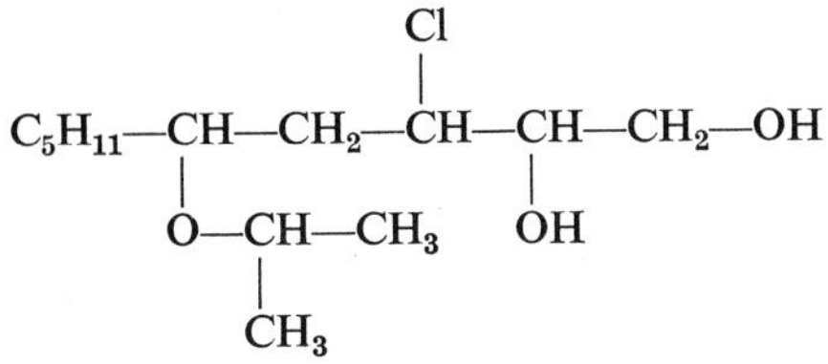 $\text{C}_5\text{H}_{11}\text{—CH—CH}_2\text{—CH—CH—CH}_2\text{—OH}$
  with O—CH—CH_3 below first CH, Cl above third CH, OH below fourth CH, and CH_3 below O—CH—CH₃

(f) $\underset{\underset{\underset{\text{CH}_3}{|}}{\text{O—CH—CH}_3}}{\text{C}_5\text{H}_{11}\text{—CH}}\text{—CH}_2\text{—}\overset{\overset{\text{Cl}}{|}}{\text{CH}}\text{—}\underset{\underset{\text{OH}}{|}}{\text{CH}}\text{—CH}_2\text{—OH}$

(g) 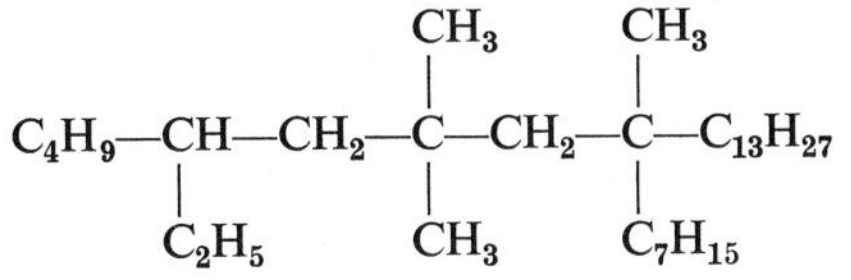 $\text{C}_4\text{H}_9\text{—CH—CH}_2\text{—C—CH}_2\text{—C—C}_{13}\text{H}_{27}$ with C_2H_5 below first CH, CH_3 above and CH_3 below first C, CH_3 above and C_7H_{15} below second C

6. Write the structural formula for each of the following compounds.

(a) 2,5-Dimethyl-3-hexanol.
(b) 2-Chloro-7-bromononadecane.
(c) 2,3,5-Trimethyl-3,4-diethyl-4-octanol.
(d) 2,2-Dimethyl-3,3-diethyl-1-pentanol.
(e) 3,4,5-Trimethyl-4-methoxyheptane.
(f) 2-Chloro-6-(1-methylhexyl)-hexadecane.
(g) 3-Iodo-5-methylcycloheptane.
(h) 3-Methoxy-1,2-propanediol.

7. For each of the following, write a structural formula and name the compound whose structure is written.

(a) A bromohexane in which the bromine is attached at a tertiary position.
(b) A cyclohexanediol, containing also an ethyl group, and with one hydroxyl secondary and the other tertiary.
(c) A secondary carbinol with one secondary alkyl and one tertiary alkyl on the carbinol carbon.
(d) A six-carbon methoxy alcohol, with a single branch in the carbon chain, but with both the methoxy and hydroxy groups at primary positions.

6

Displacement Reactions
Organic Syntheses from Alcohols and Alkyl Halides

Much of the significance of organic chemistry, whether in the manufacture of organic chemicals or in applications to medicine and biochemistry, depends on organic syntheses, conversions of organic compounds into other compounds. By such conversions, a relatively few simple compounds ultimately obtainable from natural products may be converted into the millions of known organic compounds. In some cases, rather complicated natural products are converted cheaply into relatively simple compounds of great utility as starting materials in organic synthesis. The fermentation processes are notable examples of the latter types of conversion. The industrial production of ethyl alcohol and *n*-butyl alcohol (Chap. 4) are illustrative. Since the production of such large numbers of useful compounds depends on chemical reactions, it is obviously of fundamental importance to know what reactions can be accomplished and to understand the basic mechanisms that guide the course of these reactions.

Displacement Reactions

In spite of the large numbers of species that may be used in organic reactions, the number of basic types of reactions is not large. The most important reaction in saturated compounds (compounds not containing double bonds) is the displacement reaction—the displacement of one functional group by another. The basic type of reaction occurs according to several somewhat different detailed mechanisms, but two modifications are of major importance in the saturated compounds. These are the **simple displacement reaction** and the **assisted displacement reaction.**

Simple displacement reactions. The name for this reaction is highly descriptive of precisely what happens. A group in the molecule is displaced by the entry of another group. A typical net reaction of this type is illustrated (Eq. 1) by the displacement of the halogen in an alkyl halide by the cyanide ion

$$CH_3—CH_2—CH_2—Br + {}^-CN \longrightarrow CH_3—CH_2—CH_2—CN + {}^-Br \qquad (1)$$

(ordinarily supplied as sodium or potassium cyanide). The mechanics of the process by which the bromide ion leaves the molecule and the cyanide ion enters are rather interesting. A matter of prime interest is that the energy required to form the species of highest energy in this conversion is substantially less than the energy input required to break the carbon-bromine bond, i.e., the carbon-bromine bond energy. Thus, we may say at the outset that breaking the carbon-bromine bond is facilitated by the entry of the cyanide ion.

The importance of the simple displacement reaction has resulted in sufficient study of it to allow a good understanding of the details of the process, i.e., the mechanism. An abundance of evidence supports the concept that the *entering group* approaches the carbon carrying bromine on the side directly opposite the position of attachment of the bromine. As the entering group approaches carbon and begins to form a bond, the *leaving group* moves further away as its bond weakens and becomes longer than the stable bond distance, finally becomes no bond at all when the group has left. As energy is required to break the old bond it is supplied by the energy released on simultaneous formation of the new bond. During the process, the valence directions on the reacting carbon "flip" from one direction to the other, like an umbrella in a high wind. This process is outlined and the change in geometry is shown in Fig. 1.

The situation shown in Fig. 1(b), where the molecule is "flipping" would be expected to be the point at which the potential energy of the system is the highest,[1] for the bond directions are deformed a maximum amount. This species, with the highest potential energy, least stable geometry, is termed the **transition state.** By its very nature, the point of highest energy, the transition state is present during a reaction only momentarily. The total time span of the reaction, from first lengthening of the bond with the leaving group to complete

---

[1] The point where the energy is highest may not be *exactly* at the stage where the three groups are in a plane. If the bond energies of the leaving and entering groups are quite different, the two groups would be expected to be associated with the reacting (inverting) atom to a somewhat different extent at the point of maximum energy. At the point of maximum energy (minimum stability) in such instances, the other three groups might well be somewhat out of a plane.

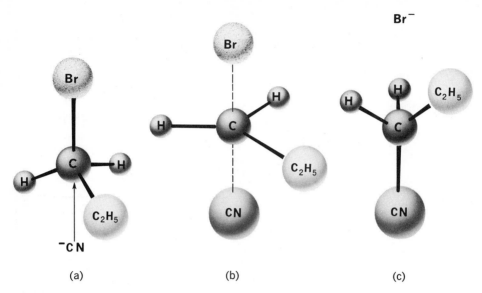

Fig. I. Mechanics of a displacement reaction. (a) "Backside" attack by cyanide on carbon in *n*-propyl bromide. (b) Midpoint in breaking of old bond and forming new bond; note three valences approximately in a plane. This is the point of highest energy, the transition state. (c) Reaction product, with cyanide attached to carbon and the bromide ion completely displaced.

formation of the bond with the entering group, is much less than a millionth of a second; therefore, the lifetime of the transition state is indeed a fleeting moment. Energy relations involved during a displacement reaction are shown in Fig. 2. Amplification of certain aspects of this **energy diagram** are in order.

The plot along the reaction coordinate in Fig. 2 represents the progress of the reaction during the extremely brief interval of time during which the reactants pass to products. If we consider the displacement shown in Eq. 1 and in Fig. 1, at the beginning of the plot shown in Fig. 2 cyanide ion is approaching from the back side of the carbon bearing halogen, but is sufficiently far away that the combined potential energy of the two species is that of the ground state. As the cyanide comes sufficiently close that the carbon-bromine bond is becoming longer and the carbon-cyanide bond begins to form, the other three valence directions to carbon begin to move towards being in a common plane. This distortion of the normal valence directions results in an increase in potential energy which reaches a maximum at the transition state [Fig. 1(b)]. Beyond the transition state, potential energy decreases until the new bond with cyanide has been formed, the bromide ion has become too far away to affect the energy of the propyl cyanide formed, and the valence directions have inverted to the normal ones for the product [Fig. 1(c)]. *The increase in potential energy required to reach the transition state must be supplied by a conversion of the kinetic energy of the reacting species.* It follows that the kinetic energy of the specific molecules involved in a given reaction must be high enough to allow the supplying of the activation energy, otherwise no reaction

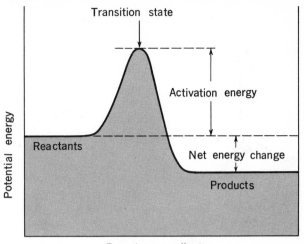

Fig. 2. Energy relationships in a simple displacement reaction.

can occur. In practice, a reaction proceeds at a moderate rate, but not explosively, when a very few per cent of the total molecules have sufficient total energy that the kinetic energy can supply the activation energy required for reaction. As temperature is raised, the energy distribution changes in favor of a larger percentage of the total number of molecules being in the higher energy group; therefore, reaction rate increases as the temperature is raised.

As molecules collide with each other, in moving about at high speed in solution or the gas phase, there may be an exchange of kinetic energy so that the total energy of a given molecule varies with time as it passes from one collision to the next. In order for reaction to result from a collision, not only must the reacting species collide with each other, but at least two other conditions must be met at the moment of collision: total energy must be high enough to allow the activation energy to be supplied by a conversion of kinetic energy; the orientation of the collision must be proper to allow a backside displacement to occur as depicted in Fig. 1. The minimum activation energy is that required when the entering group (cyanide in Fig. 1) approaches directly in line with the valence direction to the leaving group (carbon-bromine bond in Fig. 1). As the approach deviates from this line, the activation energy becomes higher. When the angle becomes great enough, even the most energetic molecule present at the temperature involved cannot supply the activation energy, so no reaction can occur. In nearly all organic reactions, there are many collisions per reaction.

In general, any reaction may be regarded as potentially reversible, that is, the products, as shown in Fig. 2, may go to the transition state and thence to the components described as reactants in Fig. 2. It is apparent that if the energy of the products is lower than that of the reactants, the activation energy of the reverse reaction is larger than that of the forward reaction. Further, a lower percentage of the molecules will have the amount of energy necessary to reach the transition state, so the reverse reaction will be slower. The **equilibrium constant** for a reaction, K, is defined as the ratio of products to reactants at equilibrium. In kinetic terms, the equilibrium constant may also be described in terms of the ratio of the forward and back reactions:

$$K = \frac{\text{rate constant of forward reaction}}{\text{rate constant of back reaction}}$$

If the net energy change in the reaction is sufficiently large, then the reverse reaction does not occur at all, and we refer to the reaction as *irreversible*. In the case of the displacement of bromide by cyanide (Eq. 1), the energy change is sufficiently large that the reaction is not reversible.

Important factors determining the **size of the activation energy** in a displacement reaction are the tendency of the **leaving group** to depart and the potency of the **entering group** in pushing into the molecule. A group with a great tendency to be displaced is called a **good leaving group.** Major factors affecting this tendency are the bond strength and the stability of the ion after it has left. For a given ion, this stability is greatly influenced by solvent. For example, the polar water molecules around a negative ion greatly stabilize the ion, an effect known as *solvation*. The variation in stability from ion to ion, however, is a function of the nature of the ion. It turns out that halogen atoms have such a strong electron-attracting tendency that the negative ions are relatively stable; in fact, halogen is one of a *very small list of ions sufficiently stable* to be a good enough leaving group to engage in a simple displacement reaction. It is, by all criteria, the best leaving group that gives easily purified molecules that are readily synthesized. It follows, inevitably, that the *alkyl halides are very useful molecules in organic synthesis*, hence our consideration of them as initial examples of molecules giving useful synthetic reactions.

The entering group is a negative species which is attacking the nucleus of the reacting carbon, hence it is known as a **nucleophilic group** or a **nucleophile** (from the Greek, $\phi\iota\lambda\epsilon\omega$, to love). The potency of a nucleophile in effecting a displacement is termed its **nucleophilicity** or nucleophilic strength. Nucleophilicity is intimately involved with the tendency of the group to donate electrons, for it is donating the electrons to make the new bond, and *good nucleophiles are always Lewis bases* (cf. Chap. 3). There are other factors involved in nucleophilicity besides basicity, however, so there is not a linear relationship between nucleophilicity and basicity. The nature of the other factors has been the subject of considerable study, but there is not agreement on their nature and relative significance. It is frequent practice to lump the "other factors" together and term this quantity the "polarizability" of the nucleophile.

The simple displacement reaction involves two species, the nucleophile and the molecule in which the displacement occurs; therefore, it is a **second order reaction,** i.e., its rate will depend on the concentration of each of the two species. Thus, the simple displacement reaction is a second order nucleophilic substitution of one group by the other, and there has become widely used the terminology S_N2 **Reaction** (substitution, nucleophilic, 2nd order). In the most general sense, the S_N2 reaction is one in which the transition state for the slowest step involved in the conversion is formed from two species. In the assisted displacement reaction, also classified as S_N2 and to be discussed soon, additional species are involved in steps prior to the slowest step. In these instances, the over-all kinetic order is normally greater than two; nevertheless, the reaction is termed S_N2 if two species are involved in the step giving the transition state.

Synthetically Useful S_N2 Reactions

As has been mentioned, the halide ion is the principal group of use in simple displacements. In ease of leaving, the halides rank: $I > Br > Cl > F$. In practice, fluoride is so difficult to displace that special conditions are usually required, and the fluorides have little use in displacement reactions, especially since synthesis of fluorides is also difficult. Although iodide is the best leaving group, synthesis of alkyl iodides is less satisfactory than bromides or chlorides, and iodides are much more expensive. Thus, the alkyl bromides and chlorides are most widely used in synthesis; the bromides are more reactive and favored in research work, while the chlorides are cheaper and generally used in industrial syntheses. Synthesis of the alkyl halides will be discussed later, in connection with the concerted displacement reactions.

There prove to be numerous groups that are sufficiently good nucleophiles to displace halogen under conditions that are convenient in the organic laboratory (a few hours at temperatures below $100°$). The cyanide ion has already been mentioned, and the alkyl cyanides (or alkanenitriles) are useful compounds which will be studied further, especially in Chapter 14. Other useful S_N2 reactions are shown in Eqs. 2 through 4. These reactions are useful in synthesis, but it should be emphasized that their usefulness varies for many reasons, of

$$C_3H_7\text{—}Br + {}^-OH \longrightarrow C_3H_7\text{—}OH + Br^- \tag{2}$$

$$C_3H_7\text{—}Br + {}^-OCH_3 \longrightarrow C_3H_7\text{—}O\text{—}CH_3 + Br^- \tag{3}$$

$$C_3H_7 : \overset{..}{\underset{..}{Br}} : + H : \overset{..}{\underset{H}{N}} : H \longrightarrow C_3H_7 : \overset{H}{\underset{H}{\overset{..+}{N}}} : H \quad : \overset{..}{\underset{..}{Br}} : ^- \tag{4}$$

n-Propylammonium
bromide

which important ones are: (a) the product may be made more easily in other ways; (b) the product may have limited usefulness; (c) there may be serious side reactions (other products formed under the same conditions). The reaction in Eq. 2 is of very limited use because of criteria (a) and (c), especially (a)—the bromide is usually made from the alcohol (see below).

The reaction in Eq. 3 is an effective synthesis of ethers; however, dialkyl ethers have limited uses except as solvents, and the more expensive **mixed ethers** (two different groups on oxygen) are less likely to be used than the simple ethers (same groups on oxygen) which may be obtained readily by a reaction to be described later. The methoxide ion shown as the nucleophile in Eq. 3 is obtained by ionization in a polar solvent, such as an alcohol, of sodium or potassium methoxide prepared from reaction of the metal with the alcohol (cf. Eq. 2-1).[2] Other metallic alkoxides may be prepared by similar reactions with other alcohols. The alkoxides are useful strong bases, but must be prepared and used in anhydrous media, for they give a rapid reaction with water (Eq. 5), with the equilibrium displaced well forward.

$$NaOC_3H_7 + HOH \rightleftarrows NaOH + HOC_3H_7 \qquad (5)$$

The reaction shown in Eq. 4 is of interest for several reasons, one of which is that the nucleophile is not a negative ion. It is, however, a Lewis base (has electrons to donate) and is a moderately good nucleophile. Since the nitrogen donated the electron pair for the C—N bond and was neutral before the reaction, it becomes positive after the electron pair is donated for the bond (cf. Chap. 3). The resultant cation differs from the ammonium ion only in that one hydrogen has been replaced by an alkyl radical. Thus we have the salt of the organic base C_3H_7—NH_2, which is *n*-propylamine, a typical organic base. As will be developed in a later chapter, this reaction constitutes an important method of synthesis of such organic bases.

Since halogen is a moderately good nucleophile, one halide ion can displace another. Treatment of an alkyl bromide with potassium iodide, for example, yields an equilibrium mixture of the alkyl bromide and alkyl iodide. Although this might appear to be a rather useless type of reaction, it proves to be a commonly used method for making iodides. This synthesis, carried out as depicted in Eq. 6, is an illustration of a device used to drive an equilibrium to

$$C_4H_9\text{—}Br + K^+I^- \xrightarrow[\text{solvent}]{\text{ethanol}} C_4H_9\text{—}I + \underline{KBr} \qquad (6)$$

| *n*-Butyl bromide | | *n*-Butyl iodide | (ppt.) |

completion in the desired direction. Whereas potassium iodide is moderately soluble in ethyl alcohol, potassium bromide is sparingly soluble, so its precipitation displaces the equilibrium to the right so effectively that the reaction becomes essentially non-reversible.

---

[2] Reference to equations in the same chapter will be by equation number only, whereas references to equations in other chapters will include the chapter number followed by a hyphen and the number of the equation.

Assisted Displacement Reactions

The best synthesis of alkyl halides is from the corresponding alcohol; however, hydroxyl is such a poor leaving group that it is not displaced by strong nucleophiles (Eqs. 7 and 8). It is of interest, therefore, that hydrogen bromide

$$C_4H_9-OH + KBr \xrightarrow[\text{for dissolution}]{\text{suitable solvent}} \text{No Reaction} \qquad (7)$$

1-Butanol

$$C_4H_9-OH + KCN \longrightarrow \text{No Reaction} \qquad (8)$$

will react with 1-butanol to give 1-bromobutane (Eq. 9), and use of excess of the relatively cheap halogen acid will displace the equilibrium forward sufficiently well to give a useful yield. The same considerations apply to other primary

$$C_4H_9-OH + HBr \rightleftharpoons C_4H_9-Br + HOH \qquad (9)$$

(excess)

alcohols; *n*-butyl alcohol is chosen as an illustration. Since no reaction occurs under the reaction conditions shown in Eq. 7, whereas a rapid reaction occurs with the reagents shown in Eq. 9, it is apparent that the synthesis of the bromide in Eq. 9 does not depend on a simple displacement reaction. It might be immediately suspected that the proton in hydrogen bromide has become involved in the reaction, and this has been well established as the actual fact.

As has already been mentioned in Chapter 3, alcohols react with strong acids to give an oxonium salt (Eq. 10), and this is the species which is readily displaced by the bromide ion (Eq. 11). Since the oxonium salt has a positive

$$C_4H_9-OH + H^+ \rightleftharpoons C_4H_9-\overset{+}{\underset{H}{O}}H \qquad (10)$$

$$C_4H_9-\overset{+}{\underset{H}{O}}H + Br^- \rightleftharpoons C_4H_9-Br + HOH \qquad (11)$$

charge on oxygen, this should attract more towards oxygen the electron pair bonding it to carbon—*electrostatic attraction* of a negative electron pair by a positive center. In order for the OH to leave by displacement, the electron pair must go with it; therefore, the HOH should be displaced more readily from the oxonium salt than is OH from the alcohol. This is, of course, the experimental fact as regards displacement of the hydroxyl group, and this type of reasoning leads to prediction of the correct results in numerous similar situations.

It is of considerable interest to observe how much information concerning reactions can be clearly depicted in an energy diagram, as is illustrated in Fig. 3. This diagram conveys the following information:

1. The unattainable transition state for Eq. 7 may be circumvented by the process of first converting the poor leaving group (hydroxyl) to a better leaving group which may be displaced in a much lower-energy transition state.

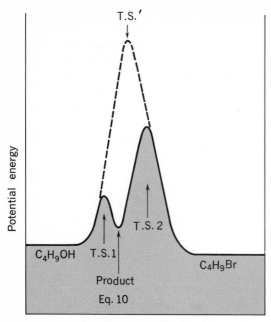

Fig. 3. Energy diagram for conversion of *n*-butyl alcohol to *n*-butyl bromide. T.S.I is the transition state for Eq. 10, while T.S.2 is the transition state for Eq. 11. T.S.′ is the extremely high-energy transition state which results because hydroxyl is such a poor leaving group and which prevents the occurrence of the reaction shown in Eq. 7. The product from Eq. 10 is likely to exist for a very long time (in terms of the time elapsing during a reaction), or even return to butyl alcohol, before it encounters a bromide ion under conditions that will get over the energy hump represented by T.S.2 and thus go to butyl bromide. The reaction coordinate is not supposed to represent a linear time scale, however, but rather to represent the progress of the reaction, so a plot of the type shown is most useful for this purpose.

2. The process in Eq. 10 has a low energy of activation, hence proceeds rapidly, but the product is of higher energy than the reactants so the equilibrium constant is small.

3. The activation energy for Eq. 11 is much higher than that for Eq. 10 (although much lower than that for Eq. 7), so the reaction in Eq. 11 is much slower than that in Eq. 10; however, the equilibrium constant for Eq. 11 is much larger than that for Eq. 10.

4. The rate-determining step for the over-all conversion is the second step, which is a second order reaction, so this process is classified as an $S_N 2$ reaction. The first step is also second order, but it is the faster step, hence not rate-determining.

5. The net energy change for the sequence of two reactions is small, hence the equilibrium constant for the over-all process is only slightly greater than unity. It follows that some means of displacing the

equilibrium forward must be utilized if a good yield is to be obtained in the conversion.

Since halide can displace hydroxyl only when it is *assisted* by the proton forming an oxonium salt, the terminology assisted displacement is descriptive of this type of S_N2 reaction. Since we may say that the proton is pulling the hydroxyl out at the same time that the bromide is pushing it out from the backside, this type of reaction is also known as a **concerted displacement reaction.**[3]

Certain predictions may be made on the basis of Eqs. 10 and 11; indeed, such things have been used as a test of the validity of this mechanism. For example, let us consider the effect of adding sulfuric acid to the reaction between the alcohol and halogen acid. The first, and principal, ionization of sulfuric acid is to give a single proton and the acid sulfate anion (Eq. 12). The latter is such a poor nucleophile that ordinarily it does not engage in a displacement reaction. On the other hand, *addition of the sulfuric acid speeds up the displacement by bromide ion.*[4] The increase in rate is proportional to the concentration

$$
\begin{array}{cccc}
\text{HO} & \text{O} & {}^-\text{O} & \text{O} \\
\diagdown \nearrow & & \diagdown \nearrow & \\
\text{S} & \longrightarrow & \text{S} & + \text{H}^+ \\
\diagup \searrow & & \diagup \searrow & \\
\text{HO} & \text{O} & \text{HO} & \text{O}
\end{array} \qquad (12)
$$

of sulfuric acid. This follows logically from the fact that protons from whatever source displace the equilibrium in Eq. 10 forward, thus increase the concentration of one reactant in Eq. 11. For this reason, sulfuric acid is commonly used in synthesis of *n*-alkyl halides; it not only speeds up the rate but increases yield by inactivating water and displacing the equilibrium.[4]

In connection with assisted displacement reactions, it is of interest to consider the possibility of direct synthesis of an alkyl cyanide from an alcohol. As already stated (Eq. 8), hydroxyl cannot be displaced directly. Furthermore, if the assisted displacement is attempted by treatment with cyanide in acid solution, this fails also, for hydrogen cyanide is formed, and this is such an extraordinarily weak acid (ionization constant is 7.2×10^{-10}) that the concentration of cyanide ions approaches zero. Thus, *synthesis of an alkyl cyanide from an alcohol must proceed in two steps*: conversion of the alcohol to the

---

[3] This term is also descriptive since concerted means "planned together" or "mutually contrived." There has also been used the equally descriptive and more vivid terminology, "push-pull reaction."

[4] Increase in rate should be clearly distinguished from displacement of equilibrium. Addition of protons displaces the equilibrium in the very rapid reaction in Eq. 10 by the law of mass action, and this increases the rate of Eq. 11 (a slower reaction) by increasing the concentration of one reactant. The final equilibrium in the two-step process will also be shifted forward. As a separate effect, the equilibrium in Eq. 11 is displaced by the fact that sulfuric acid combines with and inactivates water, so effectively removes it from the reaction.

alkyl halide (Eq. 9), followed by reaction of the halide with a metal cyanide (Eq. 1).

n-Alkyl iodides and chlorides may be synthesized (Eqs. 13 and 14) by

$$C_4H_9\text{—}OH + HI \rightleftarrows C_4H_9\text{—}I + HOH \qquad (13)$$

$$C_4H_9\text{—}OH + HCl \underset{ZnCl_2}{\rightleftarrows} C_4H_9\text{—}Cl + HOH \qquad (14)$$

concerted displacement reactions analogous to the synthesis of n-alkyl bromides. Sulfuric acid must not be used in iodide synthesis, for hydrogen iodide is oxidized by sulfuric acid to iodine. Zinc chloride is found to be very effective as a dehydrating agent in synthesizing chlorides, and it also accelerates the reaction, for it forms an oxonium salt by virtue of being a Lewis acid (cf. Chap. 3), as follows:

$$\overset{\bar{}}{ZnCl_2}$$
$$C_4H_9 : \overset{..}{\underset{..}{O}} : H$$
$$\overset{}{+}$$

Since a Lewis acid is an electron acceptor it may form an oxonium salt, in similar manner to a proton, except that the metal in the Lewis acid becomes negatively charged from accepting the electron pair.

Phosphorus trihalides may also be used for conversion of alcohols to n-alkyl halides. In this process, the displacement occurs on the oxonium salt of the phosphite ester, a type of compound formed by displacement of halogen from phosphorus by the alcohol, which is a Lewis base and a nucleophile (cf. Eq. 15). As in the case of displacement by nitrogen (cf. Eq. 4), the oxygen

$$C_4H_9\text{—}OH + PBr_3 \longrightarrow C_4H_9\text{—}\overset{+}{\underset{\underset{H}{|}}{O}}\text{—}PBr_2 \overset{Br^-}{\longrightarrow} \begin{array}{l}\text{displacement of}\\\text{second and}\\\text{third bromine}\end{array} \qquad (15)$$

$$C_4H_9\text{—}O\text{—}PBr_2 + H^+Br^-$$

species becomes a cation. This is in equilibrium with the Lewis base and the halogen acid, just as if the salt had been formed from these latter compounds; however, it is the oxonium cation in which the assisted displacement occurs, as shown in Eq. 16. It is of interest that both the nucleophile and the species in

$$C_4H_9\text{—}\overset{+}{\underset{H}{O}}\text{—}PBr_2 + Br^- \longrightarrow C_4H_9\text{—}Br + HOPBr_2 \qquad (16)$$

which displacement occurs are generated in Eq. 15. Similar sequences occur with the second and third halogens, so that the balanced over-all equation[5] is that shown in Eq. 17. A similar process using phosphorus triiodide is also successful

$$3C_4H_9-OH + PBr_3 \longrightarrow 3C_4H_9-Br + H_3PO_3 \qquad (17)$$

and *constitutes a good synthesis of n-alkyl iodides*; however, *alkyl chlorides are not formed from an alcohol and phosphorus trichloride.* Chlorine is not sufficiently nucleophilic to accomplish the displacement shown in Eq. 16, so the end product of the reaction is the phosphite ester (Eq. 18). This is a striking

$$3C_4H_9-OH + PCl_3 \longrightarrow C_4H_9O-P-OC_4H_9 \qquad (18)$$
$$\overset{|}{OC_4H_9}$$

Tri-*n*-butyl phosphite

illustration of the manner in which the different nucleophilicities of the halogens (I > Br > Cl) can radically change the products of the reactions.

Although an alcohol is a poor nucleophile (halogen is very easily displaced from phosphorus, Eq. 15), it can be used in displacement of the oxonium ion if a rather high temperature is used and better nucleophiles are absent. These conditions are met if the oxonium ion is formed with sulfuric acid, where the accompanying anion is an extremely poor nucleophile. The reaction[6] is

$$C_4H_9-OH + H_2SO_4 \rightleftarrows C_4H_9-\overset{+}{O}H_2 + {}^-OSO_2OH$$
$$140° \Big| C_4H_9-OH \qquad\qquad (19)$$
$$\downarrow$$
$$C_4H_9-O-C_4H_9 + HOH + H^+$$

shown in Eq. 19. This process is the best and easiest way to **synthesize the simple ethers** used as solvents. Diethyl ether (boiling point 37°) is made in particularly large quantity by this process, primarily for use as a solvent.

The process shown in Eq. 19 is *not suitable* for making *mixed ethers* unless a mixture of mixed ethers is satisfactory. This results from the reversibility shown in the top line of Eq. 19 (also refer to Fig. 3). It is not possible

---

[5] The inorganic product of this reaction is not written $P(OH)_3$, for the structure of this

$$\overset{H}{\underset{\downarrow}{\overset{|}{HO-P-OH}}}$$
$$O$$

compound has been shown to be $HO-P-OH$, properly called phosphonic acid rather than phosphorous acid (cf. Chap. 34). The esters formed from PCl_3 and an alcohol do have the phosphite structure, as shown in Eq. 18.

[6] An alcohol also reacts with sulfuric acid to give the mono-ester, $R-O-SO_2-OH$, an alkyl hydrogen sulfate, or at higher temperature the di-ester, $R-O-SO_2-O-R$, a dialkyl sulfate. The oxonium ions from these esters are displaced quite readily; in fact, the sulfate anion is one of the few ions displaced as readily as halogen. Thus, the alkyl hydrogen sulfate may be the intermediate in at least part of the reactions leading to the ether, but this does not change the basic mechanism of the reaction.

to convert one alcohol, say *n*-butyl alcohol, entirely to the oxonium salt, then add ethyl alcohol in order to get ethyl butyl ether as a sole product. There would also be formed dibutyl ether and diethyl ether.

Ethers are very inert, chemically, for the alkoxy group is a very poor leaving group, even when protonated. The only common reaction is cleavage at elevated temperature with a strong acid whose anion is a good nucleophile. Although hydrobromic acid is sometimes effective, hydriodic acid is usually preferred on account of the greater nucleophilicity of the iodide ion. The sequence of reactions occurring is shown in Eq. 20, wherein R is used to indicate an alkyl group, and the symbol Δ is used to indicate that the reaction must be heated if a practical rate is to be realized. In case a mixed ether is subjected to

$$\text{R—O—R} + \text{HI} \underset{\Delta}{\overset{\Delta}{\rightleftarrows}} \underset{\underset{\text{H}}{|}}{\overset{+}{\text{R—O—R}}} \text{ I}^- \longrightarrow \text{RI} + \text{ROH} \Bigg\downarrow \text{HI} \tag{20}$$

$$\text{RI} + \text{HOH}$$

this procedure, of course two alkyl iodides are obtained. The cleavage of ethers has only occasional application in synthesis, but is frequently used for degradation of a natural product of unknown structure (cf. Chap. 2). The nature of the ether becomes known if the structures of the cleavage products can be ascertained.

It may be noted that the above discussions have been confined to primary alcohols. There is an important reason for this, in that the reactions become more involved, at least in part, with secondary and tertiary alcohols. These ramifications will be discussed in the next section, as a background necessary for understanding the reactions of the secondary and tertiary alcohols.

Substitution via Ionization

In the case of the assisted displacement reaction on alcohols, the proton is pulling the hydroxyl group and thus making it considerably more easily displaced. In principle, it would appear possible that the carbon-oxygen bond could be weakened sufficiently that actual dissociation would occur, to give an organic ion, without participation of the entering group. In actual practice, this can indeed happen in many types of structure, to give water and a positive ion with the plus charge on carbon. *Such an occurrence requires a structure in which there is not only weakening of the carbon-oxygen bond but also interference with approach of the entering group.*

An organic ion with the plus charge on carbon is known as a **carbonium ion,** and it is a much more reactive, unstable species than the usual inorganic ions or organic ions with the charge on oxygen or nitrogen. All types of carbonium ions are high energy species, but some are of higher energy (less stable) than others. This is a case in which there is a rather large energy difference between the primary, secondary, and tertiary structures, with stability being in the order tertiary > secondary > primary (the reverse of the energy content).

The butyl carbonium ions, in the order of their stability, are the following:

$$CH_3-\underset{\underset{\displaystyle CH_3}{|}}{\overset{\overset{\displaystyle CH_3}{|}}{C^+}} \qquad CH_3-CH_2-\underset{\underset{\displaystyle CH_3}{|}}{CH^+} \qquad CH_3-CH_2-CH_2-CH_2^+$$

In these structures, there is an open orbital around carbon, with no electrons in it, so the valence bonds are of sp^2 type. This means that all three valence directions are in a plane, with about 120° angles between the bond directions. The more stable (lower energy) the carbonium ion from a dissociation, the lower the activation energy for the dissociation is likely to be. With a lower energy of activation, a larger fraction of the molecules can reach this energy in a given time; therefore, there *results a higher rate of dissociation for the oxonium cation of the secondary alcohol*, compared to the primary one, and a *still higher rate for the tertiary alcohol*.

In the case of a tertiary alcohol the activation energy for the dissociation of the oxonium salt becomes significantly lower than that for the S_N2 reaction, so dissociation becomes the only route for conversion of the alcohol to the bromide. In this process, there is actually a sequence of three steps, with the energy relations those shown in Fig. 4. In comparing this energy diagram with

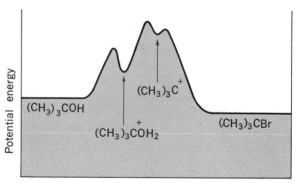

Fig. 4. Energy diagram for the reaction sequence by which *tert*-butyl alcohol is converted to *tert*-butyl bromide:

$$(CH_3)_3COH + HBr \rightleftarrows (CH_3)_3C\overset{+}{O}H_2 + Br^- \rightleftarrows HOH + (CH_3)_3C^+ + Br^- \rightleftarrows (CH_3)_3CBr$$

$$\left| \text{net reaction} \atop \xrightarrow{\hspace{2cm}} (CH_3)_3CBr + HOH \right.$$

that in Fig. 3, it may be noted that the oxonium salt forms similarly, but that the tertiary oxonium salt dissociates via a lower-energy transition state than that for the displacement reaction in Fig. 3. The carbonium ion, product of the second step in the sequence, is a very high-energy species, only slightly below the energy of the transition state for its formation; therefore, this cation is a highly reactive species. Activation energy for reaction of the carbonium ion is insignificant, so that relatively few ions are of too low energy to react on collision. A reaction intermediate of such high energy as the usual carbonium ion is a highly transitory species during the reaction. In very unusual structures, however, some of which will be discussed in Chapter 18, energy of the carbonium ion can be lowered sufficiently to make it stable enough for isolation.

In addition to a dissociation being energetically more favored in the secondary and tertiary structures, there is a second factor which interferes with approach of the entering group and thus allows more time for the dissociation to occur. This feature, known as **steric hindrance,** is a blocking of the backside approach of the nucleophile by the groups attached to the reacting carbon. It is evident from an examination of the structures of the butyl alcohols that the *n*-butyl alcohol has the three valences forming the tripod on the opposite side from hydroxyl occupied by two hydrogens (very small atoms) and one alkyl group. In the *sec*-butyl alcohol, there are two alkyls and one hydrogen, while in the tertiary structure there are three alkyls. The blocking capability of the alkyls is evident when models are examined, and it may be visualized to some extent from the picture (Fig. 5) of Framework Molecular Models of the *n*-butyl and *tert*-butyl alcohols. Since the atoms are rotating or vibrating around the axes constituting the valence directions, the nucleophile attempting a backside attack on the tertiary alcohol is confronted with a problem that may be likened to the effort to penetrate a set of propellers spinning at very high speed.

Since the secondary and tertiary ions are progressively more stable, and backside attack is progressively more blocked sterically, tendency towards carbonium ion formation becomes rapidly greater. Indeed, there is *no evidence that either a simple or assisted displacement reaction can be accomplished in a tertiary system.* Even in a *tert*-alkyl bromide, where there is no "pull" on the halogen other than solvation of the bromide ion by a polar solvent, there appears to be no displacement. Action of hydroxide ion yields some *tert*-butyl alcohol, but the mechanism of the reaction is by way of dissociation, as outlined in Eq. 21. One evidence of this route of reaction is that *the rate of the reaction is*

$$
\begin{array}{c}
\underset{\underset{CH_3}{|}}{\overset{\overset{CH_3}{|}}{CH_3-C-Br}} \;\rightleftharpoons\; \underset{\underset{CH_3}{|}}{\overset{\overset{CH_3}{|}}{CH_3-C^+}} + Br^- \\
\end{array}
\qquad (21)
$$

$$
\xrightarrow{\;^-OH\;} CH_3-\underset{\underset{CH_3}{|}}{\overset{\overset{CH_3}{|}}{C}}-OH
$$

independent of the concentration of hydroxide ion. The slow step, or *rate-determining step,* is the dissociation; as soon as the highly reactive carbonium ion is formed it reacts quite rapidly with hydroxide (or any other negative species in the solution). Thus, kinetically, the reaction is unimolecular, involves only the single molecule *tert*-butyl bromide, so this type of substitution has become

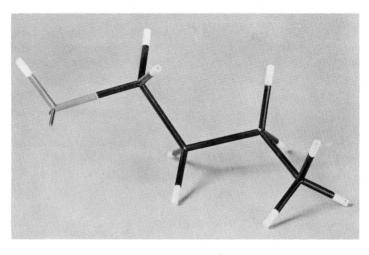

(a)

Fig. 5. Framework Molecular Models of (a) *n*-butyl alcohol and (b) *tert*-butyl alcohol. Rapid rotation or vibration occurs about the axes constituting the valence directions between the atoms. Relatively low-energy positions have been chosen for the atoms in the illustrations, i.e., positions where the atoms are a maximum distance apart; so this probably does not reflect the maximum steric interference that is actually operative.

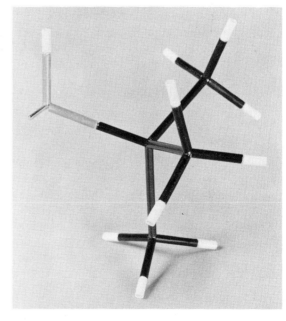

(b)

known as an **S_N1 Reaction (substitution, nucleophilic, first order for the slowest step).** Although this terminology is accurate from the kinetic viewpoint if one considers only the species shown in Eq. 21, it ignores the fact that solvation of the ions is an important factor in causing the dissociation. In the absence of a polar solvent, the reaction is extremely slow, if it occurs at all, whereas a small amount of water in the reaction medium tremendously accelerates the reaction.

Indeed, the rate becomes a function (not a simple one) of the concentration of water. Similarly, in the assisted S_N1 reaction of the type shown in Fig. 4, rate is affected by the concentration of acid.

In the case of **secondary alkyl structures,** where the carbonium ion is of higher energy and the steric hindrance is less, the displacement reaction can occur; however, ionization is also possible. In many reactions in secondary structures, the two types of reaction occur concurrently; some of the product is formed by way of displacement, while some is formed by way of ionization. In the case of the ionization route, there arises the unpleasant liability known as rearrangement, which must be discussed next.

Molecular Rearrangement of Carbonium Ions

Although the carbonium ion combines with any negative groups available, at a high rate, rearrangement is so rapid that this becomes the dominant, or exclusive, reaction in those cases where a more stable ion is available by rearrangement. Even an ion of equal stability is formed extremely rapidly. In short, there appears to be essentially no activation energy for the process of carbonium ion rearrangement. The term **rearrangement** *refers to migration of atoms in a molecular moiety which ordinarily passes through reactions unchanged.* Such a process is a basic contradiction to the concept that the functional group is altered in a reaction and the remainder of the molecule survives intact. Modern methods of organic chemistry have made it possible, however, to discover that rearrangements occur with sufficient frequency that an early and continuing study of them is necessary. If one is attempting the synthesis of pure compounds of known structure, he must know what conditions and structures are likely to lead to rearrangement and how to decrease the likelihood. At the least, he should know the nature of the rearranged products.

Since the energy differences between the primary, secondary, and tertiary carbonium ions are rather large, there is no tendency for the more stable tertiary ion to rearrange to a secondary or primary ion, even with no activation energy as a barrier. The product of such a reaction would have a much higher energy than the reactant. For this reason, the expected products are obtained from an S_N1 reaction in a tertiary system, as illustrated in Eq. 22, even though the carbonium ion is an intermediate.

$$
\begin{array}{ccc}
\quad\quad \text{CH}_3 & & \quad\quad \text{CH}_3 \\
\quad\quad | & & \quad\quad | \\
\text{C}_2\text{H}_5\text{—C—OH} + \text{HBr} & \longrightarrow & \text{C}_2\text{H}_5\text{—C—Br} + \text{HOH} \\
\quad\quad | & & \quad\quad | \\
\quad\quad \text{CH}_3 & & \quad\quad \text{CH}_3
\end{array}
\qquad (22)
$$

2-Methyl-2-butanol   2-Methyl-2-bromobutane

In a **secondary system,** if a carbonium ion forms it is likely to rearrange, for nearly all such structures (excepting the simple *sec*-butyl structure) have adjacent secondary positions at which the carbonium ion is of about the same energy.

This may be illustrated by the results obtained when 2-pentanol is converted to the bromide by use of "normal" conditions that have been discussed (Eq. 23).

$$CH_3-CH_2-CH_2-\underset{\underset{OH}{|}}{CH}-CH_3 + HBr \longrightarrow CH_3-CH_2-CH_2-\underset{\underset{Br}{|}}{CH}-CH_3 + HOH$$

and

$$CH_3-CH_2-\underset{\underset{Br}{|}}{CH}-CH_2-CH_3 \quad (23)$$

$$CH_3-CH_2-CH_2-\underset{\underset{+OH_2}{|}}{CH}-CH_3$$

$$CH_3-CH_2-CH_2-\overset{+}{CH}-CH_3 \rightleftarrows CH_3-CH_2-\overset{+}{CH}-CH_2-CH_3$$
$$+ \; HOH$$

If the reaction is carried out without heating, the product bromide is 10–20% 3-bromopentane. Since the two carbonium ions should have equal energy and react at the same rate, and since rearrangement is believed to occur very rapidly in comparison with displacement, we may reach the conclusion that a majority of the molecules react by the S_N2 route. It is not practical, however, to get a pure sample of 2-bromopentane in this way, for the 2- and 3-bromopentanes are nearly impossible to separate. If dissociation is encouraged by heating or by use of sulfuric acid, the S_N1 route becomes dominant, so there is a statistical distribution (2:1) between the 2- and 3-bromopentanes. It has been found that if phosphorus tribromide is used for the conversion (cf. Eqs. 15 through 17), at temperatures of 0° or below, there is only a minor amount of ionization, and a nearly pure sample of unrearranged bromide is obtained. If a strictly pure sample of a secondary bromide is required, either highly specialized purification methods must be used or else a different type of synthesis of a rather specialized nature must be used (cf. Eq. 18-23).

In a **primary system** which is **unhindered,** there is very little tendency for the high energy primary carbonium ion to form. In the conversion shown in Eq. 9, there is no dissociation even if sulfuric acid is used and the mixture is heated. In a system that is sterically hindered, however, dissociation can occur, and of course the highly unstable primary carbonium ion is especially prone to rearrange to a more stable secondary or tertiary ion. In a primary system with a single branch adjacent to the reacting carbon, such as 2-methyl-1-butanol, *hindrance leads to some dissociation only if sulfuric acid is used or the reaction mixture is heated.* Under such unfavorable conditions, the product consists of some tertiary bromide, 2-methyl-2-bromobutane, in addition to the expected

$$CH_3-CH_2-\underset{\underset{CH_3}{|}}{CH}-CH_2-OH \qquad CH_3-CH_2-\underset{\underset{CH_3}{|}}{CH}-CH_2-Br \qquad CH_3-CH_2-\underset{\underset{CH_3}{|}}{\overset{\overset{Br}{|}}{C}}-CH_3$$

2-Methyl-1-butanol 2-Methyl-1-bromobutane 2-Methyl-2-bromobutane primary bromide. An alkyl group can migrate readily in the carbonium ion rearrangement (see below); however, the hydrogen will migrate preferentially for it leads to a tertiary carbonium ion. Migration of methyl in the 2-methylbutyl carbonium ion would lead to a secondary carbonium ion, of higher energy than the tertiary ion resulting from hydrogen migration.

If there are **two substituents** on the carbon adjacent to the reacting carbon, hindrance becomes comparable to that in a tertiary system (cf. Framework Molecular Model in Fig. 6). An assisted displacement becomes impossible— ionization is the only reaction pathway. The simple displacement occurs only at

Fig. 6. Framework Molecular Model of 2,2-dimethyl-1-propanol (neopentyl alcohol).

an impractically slow rate under drastic conditions arranged so as to offer no encouragement to the ionization (strictly anhydrous medium). The reaction of neopentyl alcohol (2,2-dimethyl-1-propanol) with halogen acid is shown in

$$
\begin{array}{c}
\underset{\underset{\displaystyle CH_3}{|}}{\overset{\overset{\displaystyle CH_3}{|}}{CH_3-C-CH_2-OH}} + HBr \longrightarrow \underset{\underset{\displaystyle CH_3}{|}}{\overset{\overset{\displaystyle Br}{|}}{CH_3-C-CH_2-CH_3}} + HOH
\end{array}
$$

2-Methyl-2-bromobutane

$\uparrow\downarrow H^+$ $\qquad\qquad\qquad\qquad\qquad\qquad\qquad\qquad$ $\uparrow Br^-$ $\qquad$ (24)

$$
\underset{\underset{\displaystyle CH_3}{|}}{\overset{\overset{\displaystyle CH_3}{|}}{CH_3-C-CH_2-\overset{+}{O}H_2}} \rightleftarrows HOH + \underset{\underset{\displaystyle CH_3}{|}}{\overset{\overset{\displaystyle CH_3}{|}}{CH_3-C-CH_2{}^+}} \rightleftarrows \underset{\underset{\displaystyle CH_3}{|}}{\overset{\overset{\displaystyle CH_3}{|}}{CH_3-\overset{+}{C}-CH_2-CH_3}}
$$

Eq. 24, wherein the reaction pathway is shown in the lower line. Note that the product of this reaction is the same as that obtained by rearrangement from 2-methyl-1-butanol.

The driving force behind the carbonium ion rearrangement, resulting in a negligible activation energy, may be presumed to be the attraction to the open orbital of a negative group from an adjacent atom. The migrating group is either a hydrogen atom with its electron pair or an alkyl group with its electron pair. The former, $H:^-$, is the **hydride ion,** while the latter, $R:^-$, is known as a **carbanion.** This descriptive name refers to an anion in which the unbonded pair of electrons is associated with carbon. In the carbonium ion rearrangement, the migrating group does not dissociate from one carbon, then become attached to another carbon. Rather, it shifts from one carbon to an adjacent one, forms the new bond as the old one collapses. A group does not "jump" from one carbon to a distant one; however, in some instances, consecutive migrations have been found to occur so that the over-all result is shift of a group to a carbon more remote than its next neighbor.

Summary of Synthetic Reactions Using Alcohols as Starting Materials

1. Any of the three types of alcohols, primary, secondary, or tertiary, may be converted to the corresponding alkyl halides by reaction with halogen acid (Eqs. 9, 13, 14). In the secondary alcohol, however, substantial rearrangement occurs when halogen acid is used, and rearrangement is minimized when phosphorus tribromide or triiodide is used at low temperature (Eq. 17). With tertiary alcohols, however, phosphorus trihalides fail completely (probably because of failure of the displacement reaction, Eq. 16). Phosphorus trichloride fails to give alkyl chlorides with any type of alcohol, due to failure of the displacement reaction with the poorly nucleophilic chloride ion; good yields of trialkyl phosphites are obtained.

2. Simple ethers may be formed by a displacement reaction of an alcohol on its oxonium cation (Eq. 19).

3. Primary and secondary alkyl halides, other than severely hindered ones, may be used successfully in displacement reactions to yield other halides (Eq. 6), ethers (Eq. 3), amine salts (Eq. 4), or alkyl cyanides (Eq. 1). Alcohols may be obtained, but the reverse conversion (alcohol → alkyl halide) is that of synthetic utility.

4. Tertiary alkyl halides are too hindered to allow a displacement reaction. Substitution by the ionization route may occur, as in Eq. 21; however, side reactions proceed at such a high rate (alkene formation, cf. Chap. 9) that any type of substitution reaction with tertiary halides is defeated. If it were not for success of the reaction forming the Grignard reagent (next section), *tert*-alkyl halides would be of essentially no value in organic synthesis.

5. **The Grignard reagent.** All alkyl halides—primary, secondary, and tertiary; iodides, bromides, and chlorides—react with magnesium metal in an anhydrous ether as solvent to give the type of compound known as the Grignard

reagent.[7] Since this is virtually the only useful reaction of tertiary alkyl halides such a structure is used in the illustration in Eq. 25. It is possible to form Grignard reagents without use of an ether as solvent; however, practical

$$
\underset{\substack{\text{3-Bromo-3-methyl-}\\\text{pentane}}}{\overset{\overset{\displaystyle CH_3}{|}}{\underset{\underset{\displaystyle C_2H_5}{|}}{C_2H_5-C-Br}}} + Mg \xrightarrow[\text{as solvent}]{\text{diethyl ether}} \underset{\substack{\text{1-Ethyl-1-methyl-}\\\text{propylmagnesium bromide}}}{\overset{\overset{\displaystyle CH_3}{|}}{\underset{\underset{\displaystyle C_2H_5}{|}}{C_2H_5-C-Mg-Br}}} \tag{25}
$$

application of the Grignard reagent in synthesis is confined largely to reactions carried out in an ether as solvent. Except for some special purpose, the cheap and low-boiling diethyl ether is used. The function of this type of solvent, as well as the structure of the Grignard reagent, have been intensively investigated. There appears to be little doubt that in ether solution the Grignard reagent is actually an equilibrium between the species indicated in Eq. 26, along with

$$
2RMgX \rightleftharpoons R-Mg-R + MgX_2 \tag{26}
$$
$$
(R = alkyl; X = halogen)
$$

complexes of these components with each other.[8] In nearly all reactions of the Grignard reagent, $RMgX$ gives the same reactions as R_2Mg; so it is common practice to use the former in writing equations (perhaps due to ease of balancing).

There has appeared hardly any investigation of the mechanism by which an alkyl halide reacts with metallic magnesium to form the ether-soluble alkylmagnesium halide. A proposal concerning this mechanism appears in Chapter 22 (Eq. 22-8). It is well-known, however, that **no rearrangement occurs during formation of the Grignard reagent.** This is true even when the reagent is formed from such a hindered structure as 1-bromo-2,2-dimethylpropane (neopentyl bromide; for synthesis of this compound, see Chap. 11). Thus, in any structure where the alkyl halide may be obtained, the Grignard reagent may be employed for utilization of that structure in synthesis.

Applications of the Grignard reagent in synthesis, by virtue of its reaction with a variety of structures, will be discussed in subsequent chapters; however,

---

[7] This reagent, one of the most useful in organic synthesis, is named after the French chemist, Victor Grignard, who began his investigation of this type of compound while a graduate student, at the beginning of this century. His subsequent exploration of applications of the reagent in organic synthesis was recognized by award of the Nobel Prize in chemistry in 1912. Victor Grignard bears another distinction even more unique than the award of a Nobel Prize. Only one or two others, besides Grignard, have ever declined the invitation to teach at the University of Paris, the focal point of the university system in France. Grignard spent his fruitful career teaching at the Universities at Nancy and Lyon.

[8] It was proposed long ago by the German chemist, Schlenk, that there exists the equilibrium shown in Eq. 26; however, its existence was discredited by investigations published in the nineteen fifties. In 1965, however, additional investigation has established with some reliability that the Schlenk equilibrium does indeed exist.

it will be mentioned at this time that this reagent must be prepared in solutions completely free of compounds containing "active hydrogen." An "active" hydrogen is most conveniently defined as one reacting with a Grignard reagent! Most such compounds contain hydrogen attached to oxygen or nitrogen, although there occurs an occasional structure where an active hydrogen is attached to carbon (cf. Chap. 10). The result of this reaction of a Grignard reagent is a hydrocarbon, as illustrated in Eqs. 27 and 28. From these reactions

$$R—Mg—X + HOH \longrightarrow R—H + HO—Mg—X \tag{27}$$

$$R—Mg—X + CH_3OH \longrightarrow R—H + CH_3O—Mg—X \tag{28}$$

it is clear that the ether used as solvent must be free of both ethyl alcohol and water, impurities present in commercial ether. The net result of converting an alkyl halide to a Grignard reagent, then treating this reagent with water or an alcohol is replacement of the halogen with hydrogen—reduction of the halide to an alkane. This is a **useful synthesis of alkanes** in instances where (a) no other groups are present that react with the Grignard reagent, (b) use of the alkane justifies the expense of making it by the Grignard reaction (expensive principally because of the pure ether required).

EXERCISES

1. Define or clearly illustrate the following terms. Use any diagrams or formulas necessary for clarity.

(a) S_N2 reaction.
(b) S_N1 reaction.
(c) Carbonium ion.
(d) Carbanion.
(e) Hydride ion.
(f) Bond energy.
(g) Backside approach.
(h) Steric hindrance.
(i) Concerted reaction.
(j) Oxonium cation.

(k) Activation energy.
(l) Energy diagram for a reaction.
(m) Lewis acid.
(n) Equilibrium reaction.
(o) Leaving group.
(p) Nucleophilicity.
(q) Solvation.
(r) Grignard reagent.
(s) Phosphonic acid.

2. Indicate the ions to which you would expect each of the following carbonium ions to rearrange.

(a) $CH_3—CH_2—CH_2—CH_2{}^+$

(b) $CH_3—CH—\overset{+}{C}H—CH_2—CH_3$
 $\quad\quad\;\; |$
 $\quad\quad\; CH_3$

(c) $CH_3—\overset{+}{C}—\overset{CH_3}{\overset{|}{C}H}—CH_2—CH_3$
 $\quad\quad\;\; |$
 $\quad\quad\; CH_3$

(d)

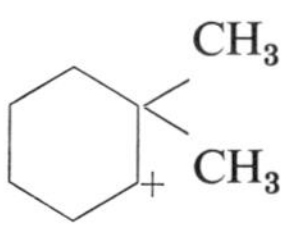

(e) $CH_3—\overset{CH_3}{\overset{|}{C}H}—CH_2—\overset{+}{C}H—CH_2—CH_3$

3. Write the IUPAC names for the neopentyl radical and for the *tert*-amyl radical.

4. Write equations showing all the ethers that would be formed if a mole of *n*-butyl alcohol mixed with a mole of sulfuric acid were heated and then treated with a mole of *n*-propyl alcohol.

5. Outline by equations, not necessarily balanced but with indication of all conditions and reagents necessary for success of the reactions, a method for converting *n*-hexyl alcohol to each of the following compounds. Any other reagents may be used so long as *n*-hexyl alcohol is converted to the desired compounds in a continuous sequence of steps.

(a) *n*-Hexyl cyanide.
(b) Di-*n*-hexyl ether.
(c) Methyl *n*-hexyl ether.
(d) Hexane.

(e) *n*-Hexyl iodide (without use of HI).
(f) *n*-Hexylammonium chloride.
(g) Tri-*n*-hexyl phosphite.

6. Write the formulas and names for all the alkyl halides that would be expected to result from heating the following alcohol with hydrobromic acid.

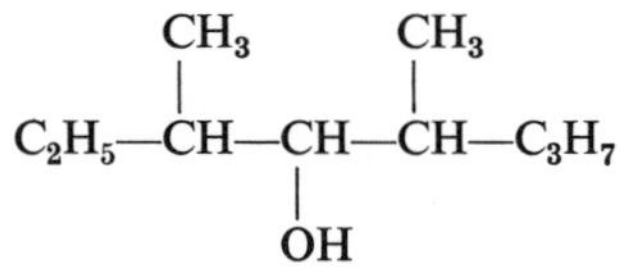

$$\underset{\displaystyle \text{OH}}{C_2H_5-CH-\underset{\displaystyle |}{CH}-CH-C_3H_7}$$

with CH$_3$ groups on the second and fourth carbons:

$$\begin{array}{ccc} CH_3 & & CH_3 \\ | & & | \\ C_2H_5-CH-CH-CH-C_3H_7 \\ & | \\ & OH \end{array}$$

Cyclic Structures in Organic Compounds

Geometrical Isomerism and Conformation

Cyclic compounds containing no atoms other than carbon in the ring structures are known as carbocyclic compounds, whereas those compounds having at least one ring atom which is not carbon are **heterocyclic** compounds. Both types of structures have attained great importance, especially in biochemistry and drug chemistry. The geometry of molecules is of basic importance in both biochemical function and the mechanism of chemical reactions, so the geometry of cyclic structures will be developed at this time. Since the carbocyclic compounds exhibit most of the characteristics of interest, they will be used as the basis of the present discussions. Many of the important heterocyclic compounds contain nitrogen, so they will be studied later, after the chemistry of nitrogen-containing compounds has been considered in some detail. The carbocyclic compounds include a host of well-known or important substances, such as camphor, vitamin D, sex hormones, growth factors, and oral contraceptives.

Since the normal unstrained bond angle in a saturated carbon atom, with bonds of the sp^3 type, is about 109°, rings containing five or six carbon atoms are formed most readily and with the least deformation of the normal bond angles. Rings of virtually any size are well known, but the five- and six-membered rings are in an overwhelming majority, so they will be examined in considerably more detail. The geometry in these two sizes of ring proves to be quite different.

(a)

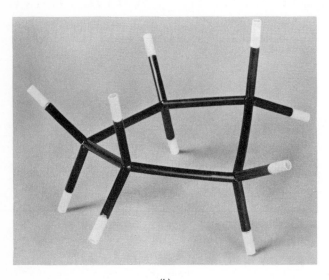

(b)

Fig. 1. Framework Molecular Models of the cyclopentane molecule. (a) The planar ring, with directly opposed hydrogen atoms. (b) An out-of-plane form, which allows a staggered position for adjacent hydrogen atoms.

Five-Atom Ring Structures

According to the principles discussed in Chapter 3, two valences of carbon lie in a plane and the other two lie in a second plane at right angles to the first. As a consequence of this structure and the bond angle of about 109°, a five-atom planar ring of carbon atoms may be formed with virtually no strain from the normal bond angles. In such a ring, however, the two hydrogen atoms on each carbon are directly opposite the hydrogen atoms on each adjacent carbon. The five hydrogen atoms on each side of the carbon ring would lie in a plane. In this position, the highly positive hydrogen atoms are in the closest proximity possible, hence repel each other a maximum amount. This situation can best be understood by examining a Framework Molecular Model of cyclopentane, arranged with all the carbons in a plane, as in Fig. 1(a). If the carbons in this ring are twisted out of a plane, the energy of the molecule increases on account of the bond deformation; however, the energy decreases on account of reduction of the repulsion between the hydrogen atoms. As a result of calculations of the effects of these two energetic factors, as well as actual experimental measurement of the locations of the atoms in some molecules, it has become established that a minimum in the energy (most stable position) occurs when the ring is twisted significantly out of a plane. The departure from a planar structure varies somewhat, depending on substituents in the ring, but the structure is similar to that shown in the model in Fig. 1(b).

For many purposes, the cyclopentane ring is written as a simple pentagon, as has been the practice in Chapter 5, and as is shown in the formula for methylcyclopentane on the left below. It is often profitable, however, and very simple, to draw a **projection formula,** as on the right, wherein lines are used to show all the valence directions, but hydrogen atoms are not included. Although the

angles are somewhat exaggerated in the projection formula, it gives a useful representation which is easily drawn. In particular, it becomes very easy to note whether two substituent groups are on the same side of the ring or opposite sides. Frequently, the lines showing valence directions to the hydrogen atoms are omitted.

Geometrical Isomerism

In the case of a molecule with two substituents in the ring, on different carbon atoms, two structures are possible. One structure has the groups on the same side, and is known as *cis*, while the other structure has the groups on opposite sides, and is known as *trans*. Examination of molecular models makes it apparent that these are different molecules. The structures may be represented effectively by projection formulas:

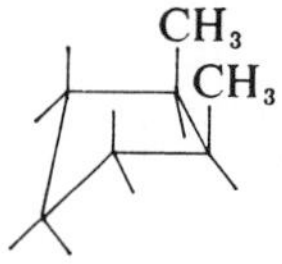

cis-1,2-Dimethylcyclo-
pentane

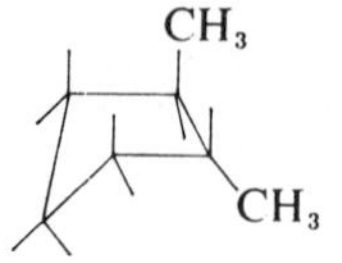

trans-1,2-Dimethylcyclo-
pentane

As a matter of convenience, the projected ring is orientated in the opposite direction to that shown for methylcyclopentane.

Molecules which differ from each other, not in the sequence in which the atoms are attached to each other (as in position isomers), but only in the relative positions in space of the atoms, are known as **geometrical isomers.** Geometrical isomerism is one type of **stereoisomerism** (cf. Chap. 22 for optical isomerism). A formula showing the positions of the atoms in space is known as a **stereochemical formula,** and such a formula is said to show the **configuration** of the molecule. Configuration may also be indicated by adopting a convention with the formula using a simple pentagon. One such convention employs solid lines to groups in front of the plane of the ring (which is in the plane of the paper) and dashed lines to groups behind the plane of the ring. Configuration in the 1,2-dimethylcyclohexanes would be indicated thus:

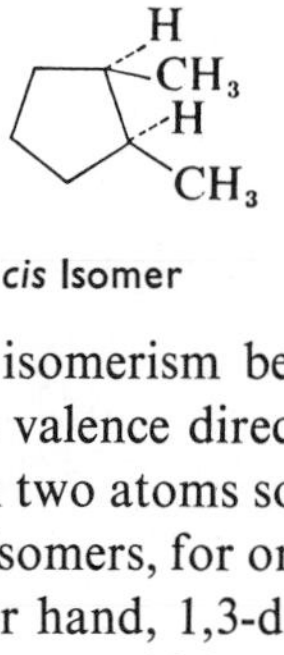

cis Isomer

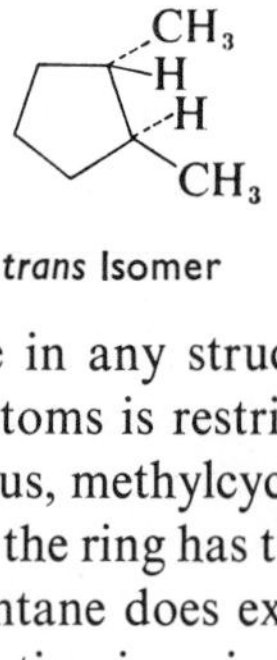

trans Isomer

Geometrical isomerism becomes possible in any structure in which free rotation about the valence direction between atoms is restricted, and there are different groups on two atoms so restricted. Thus, methylcyclopentane does not have cis and trans isomers, for only one atom in the ring has two different groups on it. On the other hand, 1,3-dibromocyclopentane does exist as cis and trans isomers. One structure which prevents free rotation is a ring, and the phenomenon occurs in a ring of any size. The five-membered ring has been used as an illustration. As will be developed in the next chapter, the double bond between carbon atoms also prevents free rotation and thus generates the possibility of geometrical isomerism.

Six-Membered Rings

In instances where detailed specification of geometry is unnecessary, the six-atom carbocyclic ring is usually written as a simple hexagon, as has been the practice in Chapter 5; however, in reality, a ring of six carbon atoms cannot be formed in a single plane without considerable deformation of the valence angles. A *multiplanar ring* may be formed with virtually no strain of the valence angles; furthermore, two relatively low-energy forms for this unstrained ring are possible, as shown in the molecular models in Fig. 2. In these models, it may be noted (especially if the models are actually constructed and handled) that in the chair form hydrogens on adjacent carbons are not directly opposite each other. In this form of the ring the hydrogens on one carbon are located between or to one side of those on adjacent carbons. In contrast, when one methylene group is on the same side of the ring as the opposite methylene group, as in the boat form, four pairs of hydrogen are directly opposite those on adjacent carbons. Even more serious interference occurs between the two hydrogens directly opposing each other "across the top of the boat." In about 1950 it was realized that the "true boat" would have a higher energy than a "twisted boat form" in which the hydrogens opposing each other across the top of the true boat are twisted out of opposition at the same time that the pairs of opposing hydrogens are shifted somewhat. The more the boat is twisted the more the repulsion between the nearby hydrogens is relieved; however, this twisting increases energy on account of deformation of normal valence angles. The lowest energy (probably 1–2 kcal. per mole below the "true boat") occurs when the "true boat" is twisted slightly, as shown in Fig. 2(c). This position for the ring, usually known as the **flexible form,** is normally of the lowest energy except for the chair form in which there is negligible hydrogen repulsion or bond deformation. Two of the hydrogens in 1- and 3-positions relative to each other are directly opposed in the chair form, but the distance between these hydrogens is great enough so that there is only a small effect on the energy content of the molecule. When larger groups are in the 1- and 3-positions, interference can occur, and this matter will be discussed at some length later in this chapter.

Conformation. Since atoms are free to rotate or vibrate about the directions of the valence bonds, there may be equilibration between the chair and flexible forms in a cyclohexane derivative unless the activation energy for the transition state between the two forms is excessively high. In actuality, this energy barrier proves to be of such a height as to give a discreet and separate existence to the chair and flexible forms, but with rapid equilibration between them. The manner in which this interconversion occurs is readily observed in a molecular model, and may be visualized by considering the photographs in Fig. 2. If the methylene group at the lower right [Fig. 2(a)] is pulled upward by turning the appropriate pins in the tubes, this methylene will pass through the plane of the four methylenes in a common plane (transition state) and thence to the other side of that plane. This gives either the flexible form or the "true boat" form [Fig. 2(b) or (c)]. Molecules which differ from each other only as a result of rotation about the directions of valence bonds are called **conformers.** They differ from each other in **conformation.** The difference between conformers and isomers should be clearly recognized. Conformers differ from each other by twisting about bond directions, and this occurs in a given molecule as time goes by. Isomers cannot be changed one to the other except by the breaking and making of bonds.

Energy relations amongst the various conformers of a cyclohexane derivative may be best understood by reference to Fig. 3, in which the potential

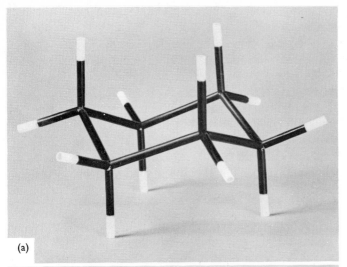

(a)

(b)

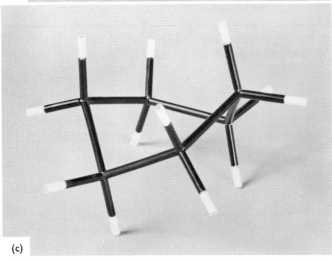

(c)

Fig. 2. Conformations of the cyclohexane ring. (a) The chair form, (b) the "true boat" form, (c) the twisted boat or flexible form. The flexible form differs from a "true boat" form in that the ring is twisted somewhat so that the hydrogens are not directly opposing each other, especially the two in direct opposition across the "top of the boat." In the literature prior to about 1955, only the chair and boat forms of the cyclohexane ring are recognized, but the "true boat" form is now known to exist only in compounds in which additional constraint is introduced by such factors as another ring joining the two carbons opposing each other across the "top of the boat" [cf. structure for camphor (Fig. 4) later in this chapter]. *It is probably desirable to abandon use of the term "boat form," in favor of "flexible form,"* to indicate the non-chair form in which cyclohexane derivatives actually exist to some extent. The true shape of the flexible form, which actually does not have the rigidity of the chair form, bears no resemblance to the shape of a boat [refer to Fig. 2(c) or, better, to a model].

energy of the molecule is plotted as a function of conformation. The chair form [Fig. 2(a)], in which there is no bond strain and no interference between opposing hydrogen atoms on adjacent carbons, is the lowest-energy form. If bond deformation occurs, as a result of vibrations in the molecule, the potential energy rises, finally reaches a maximum, then decreases as the methylene "flips" to the other side of the plane containing four methylene groups. The flexible

Fig. 3. Energy relations amongst the conformers of cyclohexane. For the unsubstituted cyclohexane, the energy of the flexible form is 5–6 kcal. per mole higher than that of the chair form; therefore, in the equilibrium mixture at room temperature, only one molecule in about a thousand will be in the flexible form. The term "flexible form" is sometimes used to refer to all positions of relatively low energy between the transition states to the chair forms.

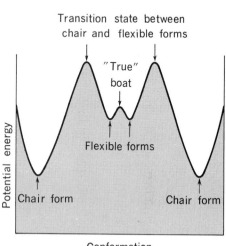

form, the lowest-energy conformation with the two methylenes on the same side, is twisted slightly out of a "true boat" conformation so that there is a minimum energy as a result of balance between hydrogen opposition and bond deformation. As shown in Fig. 3, there is a flexible form as the molecule becomes twisted in either direction from the "true boat"; true boat is the transition state between the two flexible forms. In the "true boat," bond deformation is at a minimum, but hydrogen repulsion increases the potential energy somewhat above that in the flexible form.

Projection formulas. In order to display geometrical features in compounds containing the six-atom ring, without calling upon the talents of an artist, rather useful projection formulas have been developed.[1] These formulas become especially informative if they are compared with a model. Projections of the cyclohexane molecule are drawn as follows:

Flexible form

Chair form

---

[1] There is available a Chemist's Triangle, containing stencils for many useful geometrical forms such as those used in this chapter.

The directions of the hydrogen valences are sometimes omitted, especially in parts of the molecule not under particular scrutiny.

Axial and equatorial bonds. If the methylene which was regarded as being flipped in the above discussion of conformation should flip back to its original position, then the molecule would pass back over the energy barrier to its original conformation (left side of Fig. 3). If we visualize the other methylene as flipping, however, and this is represented by the right side of Fig. 3, we again go to a chair form, but *this is a conformer of the chair form just discussed.* In unsubstituted cyclohexane, the energy of these conformers is identical, but in substituted ones, this is usually not the case because *the positions in space of the two bonds to hydrogen on a given carbon atom have changed.* If reference is made to the projection formulas below of the chair forms of cyclohexane (better to a molecular model):

it will be noted that half the bonds to hydrogen extend almost (but not exactly) in a horizontal plane while the others are in a vertical direction. These bonds have been labeled *a* and *e* because the two types are known as **axial** and **equatorial.** This designation has been adopted because the chair form of cyclohexane may be rather grossly likened to a flattened spherical shape, in which case the equator would be in a horizontal direction and the axis in a vertical direction.

In the two projection formulas above, it is of particular importance to note that if the chair form on the left is flipped to that on the right, *every equatorial bond in the conformer on the right is an axial bond in the conformer on the left.* The consequences of this change in bond type will be discussed in the next section.

It may be observed in a model that the axial bonds are indeed very near the vertical when the molecule is placed in the proper orientation. The model will sit on the lower three axial hydrogens like a three-legged stool. In view of this bond orientation, the placing of axial and equatorial bonds in a projection drawing is accomplished very easily and reliably by first drawing the axial bonds, three down and the alternate three up. An equatorial bond may then be drawn on each carbon, *with adjacent ones on opposite sides of the ring* (slanted above or below the horizontal). It is clear in the projection (and even more apparent in the model) that **axial bonds on adjacent carbons** point in opposite directions and, therefore, **are in the *trans* position.** It follows that **equatorial bonds on adjacent carbons are also in the *trans* position.** Finally, *cis* positions on adjacent carbons involve one equatorial bond and one axial bond.

Axial and equatorial substituents. The distinction of bond types in geometric isomers becomes of considerable importance in cyclohexane derivatives. In the unsubstituted cyclohexane ring, one might assume that the two conformers which have been projected above are identical, since the one on the right may be rotated 180° about an axis vertical to the paper and thus be shown to be congruent with the projection on the left. This is not the actual situation, however, for the projection on the left is not merely the one on the right in a different position in space; it results from *flipping* the one on the right in the manner discussed. The change in bond type from axial to equatorial, or vice versa, on flipping of the molecule is quite apparent if a model is flipped; however, it may also be illustrated reasonably well by projections of a substituted cyclohexane, such as methylcyclohexane.

Methyl equatorial   Methyl axial
Conformers of Methylcyclohexane

In these projections, only bond directions pertinent to the discussion have been drawn. It is clear that in the right-hand projection the methyl is axial, whereas in the left-hand projection it is equatorial. This result is inevitable since no bonds are broken.

Relative stability of axial and equatorial conformers. In the chair form of cyclohexane, there is no short-range repulsion between hydrogen atoms of the sort encountered in the boat form; however, the axial hydrogens on alternate carbon atoms are directly opposed to each other (refer to projection formulas or models). These hydrogens are not sufficiently close to each other to generate a major interference; however, if a larger group, even the methyl group, is present, this **1,3-diaxial interference** becomes rather significant. In the projections of methylcyclohexane, it may be noted that when the methyl occupies the axial position there are axial hydrogens in positions to interfere with the methyl on each of the alternate carbons. *In the projections, the distance in the horizontal direction is exaggerated*; but in the model it may be observed that the two axial hydrogens in the 3-positions to the axial methyl are equidistant from this methyl. If the above reasoning is correct, then the energy of the conformer with axial methyl should be higher than that of the conformer with equatorial methyl. This energy difference can be determined by measuring the equilibrium between the two conformers, and the energy change for the equilibrium has been found to be about 1.7 kcal. per mole. This means that methylcyclohexane is about 95 % in the form of the conformer with equatorial methyl.

Relative stabilities of geometric isomers in the cyclohexane series. The relative stabilities of dimethylcyclohexanes have been studied with some care, and they serve as an illustration of the factors involved in determining energy contents of the isomers.

Projections of the 1,2-dimethylcyclohexanes show the following geometry:

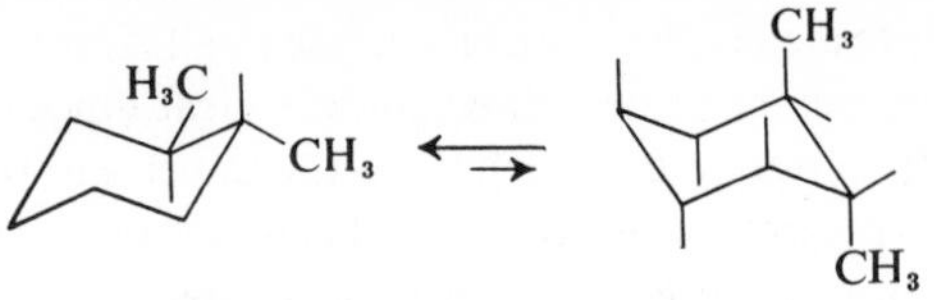

trans-1,2-Dimethylcyclohexane

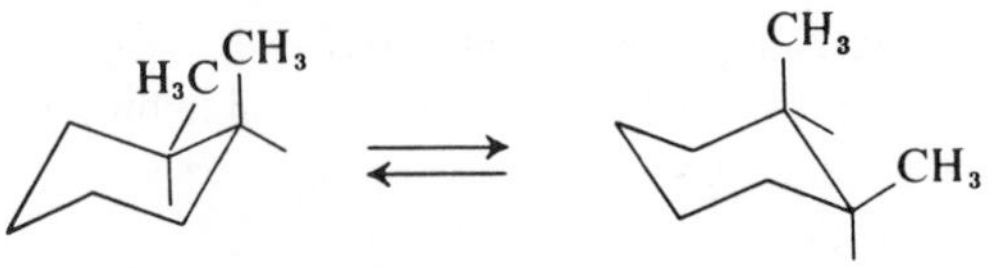

cis-1,2-Dimethylcyclohexane

It becomes immediately apparent, on examination of the projections, that the *trans* isomer would exist predominantly in the form with both methyls equatorial. In the other conformer, there is 1,3-diaxial interference between each methyl group and hydrogens in the 3-positions. In actuality, this isomer exists to the extent of about 99 % as the di-equatorial conformer. In the *cis* isomer, there is an axial methyl in each conformer, so neither would be favored in the equilibrium. Furthermore, the *cis* isomer should be of substantially higher energy than the *trans* isomer, for the latter has available a conformer with no axial methyl group. This proves to be the case. The *trans*-1,2-dimethylcyclohexane is more stable than the *cis* isomer by about 1.6 kcal. per mole.

Before the relatively recent development of **conformational analysis** (the process being discussed), it was known that the *trans*-1,2-dimethylcyclohexane is of substantially lower energy than the *cis* isomer, and this was explained on the simple basis that groups on the same side of the ring would exert interference. This explanation was deemed adequate in the case of the 1,2-isomer; however, considerable confusion resulted when it was learned that the *cis isomer is more stable in* 1,3-*dimethylcyclohexane*, while the *trans isomer is again more stable in* 1,4-*dimethylcyclohexane*. The simple concept of steric interference with each other of groups that are *cis* is clearly incapable of explaining these phenomena. Not only is the relative stability in the wrong direction for the 1,3-isomer; it can hardly be expected that groups in the 1- and 4-positions are sufficiently close together to interfere with each other. It is of interest that conformational analysis predicts the correct answer!

Examination of the projections of the more stable conformers of 1,3-dimethylcyclohexane reveals that the situation is indeed directly opposite to that encountered in the 1,2-isomer. It is the *trans* isomer in which both conformers

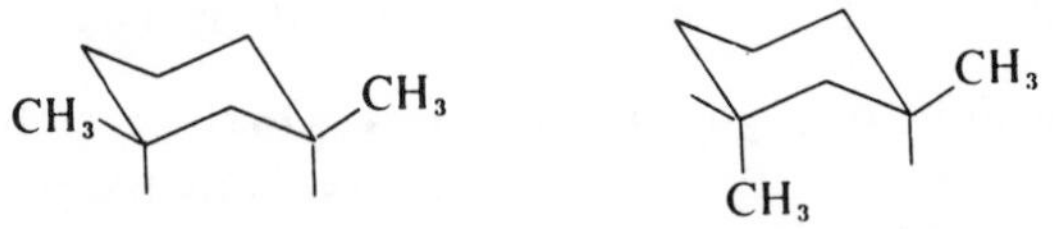

cis Isomer   trans Isomer

1,3-Dimethylcyclohexanes

have one axial methyl group. It is, of course, arbitrary as to whether these projections are drawn as shown or with the right end up and the left end down. The more stable conformer of the *cis* isomer would still be that with both methyl groups equatorial. It proves to be a considerable aid to the memory, however, if there is adopted the practice of always drawing the more stable conformer in the same way in instances where both conformers are not being drawn. The method adopted above is that most convenient in connection with the study of sugars (Chap. 23).

It is probably worthwhile to again emphasize that it is quite easy to decide which bond directions are *cis* or *trans* if one uses the axial bonds for reference. For example, in the 1,3-dimethylcyclohexanes, it is apparent that the 1- and 3-axial positions are on the same side of the ring, therefore *cis*; consequently, the 1- and 3-equatorial positions are also *cis*. Furthermore, there must be one axial and one equatorial position involved in the 1,3-*trans* relationship; for the 1- and 3-axial positions are *cis*.

In the 1,4-dimethylcyclohexanes, it follows, from the conformational analysis, that the *trans* isomer should be more stable since it may have both methyl groups in equatorial positions.

CH₃

CH₃   CH₃   CH₃

cis Isomer   *trans* Isomer

1,4-Dimethylcyclohexanes

With other substituents than methyl in the cyclohexane ring, energy differences between conformers or isomers will be different than those for methylcyclohexanes, as a function of the size of the group and its repulsion by the group in the 3-position. This is a quantitative difference, however, which will affect the exact position of the equilibrium between conformers. The conclusion as to which conformer or isomer is the more stable will remain the same.

Finally, it should be emphasized that the existence of conformers in cyclohexane derivatives is a very real phenomenon, and the consequences of it are frequently encountered in the study of organic compounds. An important example of the usefulness of the conformational concept will be encountered in the study of sugars (Chap. 23). Perhaps the most striking display of the reality of conformation follows from examination of the nuclear magnetic resonance spectrum of cyclohexane. As discussed in Chapter 2, this type of measurement is influenced by the environment of the hydrogen atom, so an axial hydrogen should exhibit resonance at a different frequency than an equatorial one. At room temperature, only a single broad band is observed, for the shift from one conformer to the other is so fast that a signal is received as an average of the positions of the hydrogen atoms. As the temperature is lowered, however, and the rate of equilibration is slowed down, the broad band begins to separate into a double band. At $-60°$, a clean separation into two signals is achieved, one from six axial hydrogens and one from six equatorial hydrogens!

Small Rings

It is apparent that the four-membered ring, with an average bond angle of 90°, can be formed only by a severe distortion of the normal sp^3 bond direction of 109°. This distortion is no doubt responsible for the fact that such rings are formed with considerable difficulty. Furthermore, the carbon-carbon bonds in the ring are rather easily broken, in contrast to the usual very strong carbon-carbon bond.

The cyclobutane ring proves to be not quite planar, presumably for the same reason discussed for the cyclopentane ring. Thus, this ring is sometimes represented as a projection of the type shown at right below, but for most purposes the four-membered ring is represented by a simple square, as on the

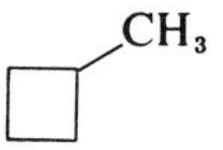

Methylcyclobutane

Bromocyclobutane (projection)

left. As in the case of other ring compounds, disubstituted compounds occur in *cis* and *trans* isomers, but there is no involvement with conformation, similarly to the case with cyclopentane.

Compounds with a three-carbon ring have proved to be more easily synthesized than those with a four-atom ring. From this evidence alone, it would be assumed that the bonding in the cyclopropanes is not simply strained sp^3 bonds, for the strain in angle seems excessive. Actually, the bonds in cyclopropane are a modified type of single bond, sometimes called "bent bonds," in that the greater electron density is believed to be somewhat outside the direct line between the atoms, in contrast with the normal sigma bond. The bonds actually have some of the character of the double bond (next chapter), and give several reactions characteristic of double bonds, e.g., reaction with bromine (Chap. 9). Since there is only the single bond in a cyclopropane, however, reaction with bromine opens the ring (Eq. 1). Such a facile rupture of the carbon-carbon bond is very uncommon, indeed.

$$\triangle + Br_2 \longrightarrow Br-CH_2-CH_2-CH_2-Br \tag{1}$$

Disubstituted cyclopropanes may also exist as *cis* and *trans* isomers, and the formulas may be written as for cyclopentanes. Since 1,1-dimethylcyclopropane

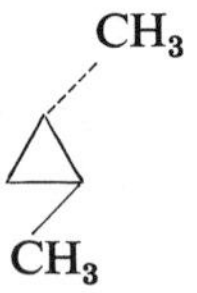

trans-Dimethylcyclopropane

cannot exist as *cis* and *trans* isomers it is unnecessary to specify *trans*-1,2-dimethylcyclopropane. There is only one *trans*-dimethylcyclopropane.

Chemical reactions of small rings, as well as large rings, are discussed briefly in Chapter 34.

Large Rings

Rings containing more than six atoms are frequently termed large rings, on account of the frequency of occurrence of the 5- and 6-atom rings. Further, the rings with 7–11 atoms are known as "medium-sized" rings. The 7-atom ring is formed less readily than the 6-atom ring, but it does not present serious difficulty in synthesis. Geometry and conformation in the cycloheptanes are probably rather similar to that in the cyclohexanes, but details of geometry in the 7-atom rings have been studied relatively little.

Rings of eight to eleven carbons are formed with considerable difficulty; in fact, special methods are required, especially reaction at very high dilution. A molecule containing functional groups that can react with each other to produce the desired ring size is subjected to reaction conditions in such dilute solution that a given molecule waits so long before seeing another that time is allowed for the occasional event where the carbon chain gets into the right conformation to give the medium-sized ring. These rings can assume various shapes in space so that their geometry as well as their reactions are a subject for advanced study.

Polycyclic Compounds

Since most of the cyclic compounds which are of biochemical importance contain more than a single ring, the basic geometry of the polycyclic compounds should be introduced at this time. The most abundant and important polycyclic compounds have adjacent carbons common to two rings, and the **decalins,** which have two six-membered rings, serve as useful illustrations. If the simple hexagonal formulas are used, decalin is written as two fused 6-atom rings, as on the left below. This formula does not specify, however, whether the rings are joined to

Decalin   *cis*-Decalin   *trans*-Decalin

each other in a *cis* or *trans* manner, and either junction is possible. Such a formula is commonly used to indicate a mixture of *cis* and *trans* isomers. A useful convention for showing geometry of the ring juncture in this type of simple formula is illustrated in the right-hand formulas. A large dot at the ring juncture means that the hydrogen atom at that point is "up" (above the plane of the paper), whereas the absence of such a conspicuous dot indicates that the hydrogen is "down". Since *trans*-decalin has one hydrogen on each side of the rings, it follows that its formula has a single dot. In *cis*-decalin, the representation could employ no dots, rather than two dots as shown, for this would mean that the molecule was turned over so that both hydrogens are "down." Since a formula with no dots is used when stereochemistry is not specified, it is customary to write a *cis* ring junction with two dots. The use of dots is entirely applicable in monocyclic compounds, and is sometimes employed. Examples are the following:

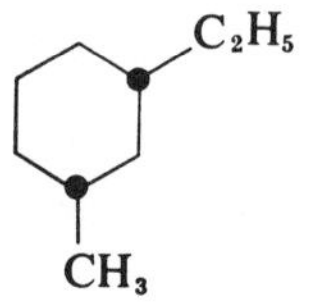

| *cis*-1-Ethyl-3-methyl-
cyclohexane | *trans*-1,2-Dibromo-
cyclohexane |

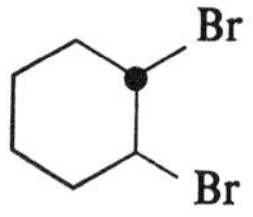

For the bicyclic compounds, the most definitive representations are the projections which show the conformation (conformational formulas). The more stable chair conformations for the decalins follow:

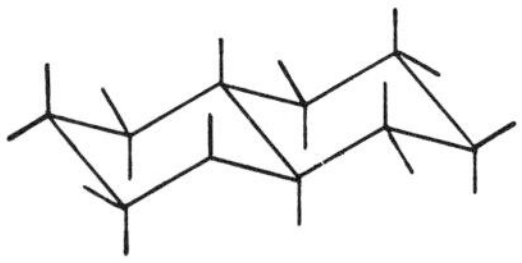

| *trans*-Decalin | *cis*-Decalin |

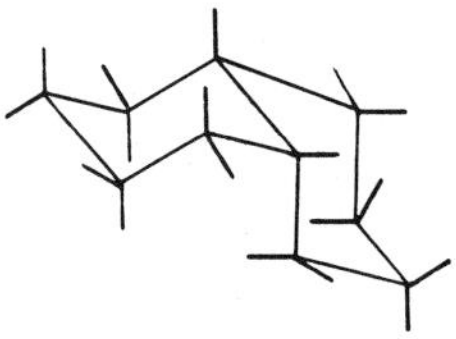

Striking features of these conformational formulas are the relatively linear shape of the *trans* ring juncture and the sharp angle in the formula with the *cis* ring juncture. This follows from the possibility of utilizing the *trans* equatorial positions for the *trans* juncture, whereas the *cis* juncture, as when substituents are involved, must utilize one equatorial and one axial position. Models of the decalins strikingly reveal these differences in geometry.

Bridged structures. When the atoms common to two rings are not adjacent, the structure is said to be bridged. Such structures are rather common in nature, and one of the more frequently occurring ring systems is the bicyclo[2.2.1]heptane system, which is illustrated in two projections below. The

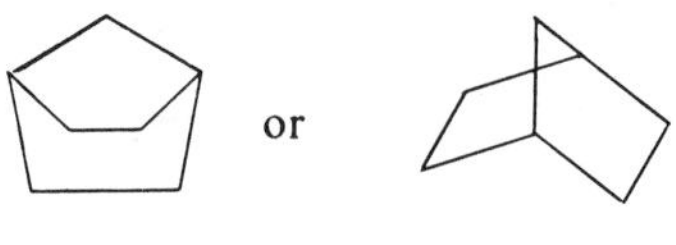

| Bicyclo[2.2.1]heptane | Camphor |

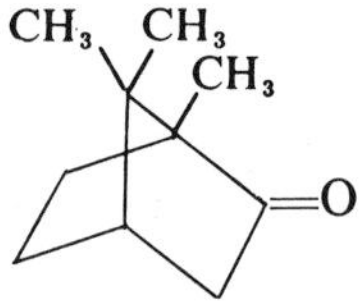

left-hand projection emphasizes the fact that this ring system consists of the boat form of cyclohexane joined by a one-carbon bridge across the top, while the other projection views this structure from the top and side. In this structure, the cyclohexane cannot assume the chair conformation. The right-hand option is the projection most commonly used, for it is possible to show substituent groups more easily. A common natural product having this structure is camphor, whose formula is shown. It is instructive to compare a Framework Molecular Model of camphor (Fig. 4) with the projection formula. The functional group in camphor, which is an oxygen doubly-bonded to carbon, is

Fig. 4. Framework Molecular Model of the camphor molecule.

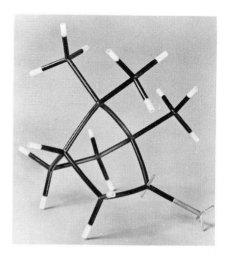

the carbonyl group. Its reactions and properties will be studied in several subsequent chapters.

Nomenclature will not be developed fully for the bicyclic systems, but the basic system of naming will be explained. The total number of carbons is used as the basis for the name, and the number of rings is indicated by the prefix bi-, meaning two. Thus, the above-described formula has seven carbons and two rings (a six-membered ring and a bridge), so it is a bicycloheptane. The numbers (which are separated by periods rather than commas and enclosed in brackets) specify the number of carbons in each "wing" of the rings. To amplify this, note that we may go from one side of the "bridgehead" to the other along three paths; two of these paths contain two carbons between the junction points, and the third has one carbon. Thus, this structure is the 2.2.1-isomer.

Two additional formulas are given to illustrate the system of nomenclature.

Bicyclo[3.1.1]heptane   Bicyclo[2.2.2]octane

EXERCISES

1. Draw two types of line formulas (one the projection formula) for *trans*-1,3-diethylcyclopentane. Why is there no compound named 1,4-diethylcyclopentane?

2. There are three geometrical isomers of 1,2,3-trimethylcyclohexane.

(a) Draw conformational formulas for the most stable conformer of each isomer.
(b) Label these formulas: 1-*trans*, 2-*trans*, all-*cis*; of course the names should be matched with the correct formulas.
(c) Which of these isomers should be of lowest energy?

3. Draw conformational formulas for the *cis* and *trans* isomers of the nine-carbon compound differing from decalin only in that one ring is of five atoms. The IUC name for this compound is bicyclo[4.3.0]nonane. Explain the construction of this name.

4. Draw projection formulas for the following.

(a) Bicyclo[3.3.2]decane.
(b) Bicyclo[3.2.1]octane.
(c) Bicyclo[2.1.1]hexane.
(d) Bicyclo[3.3.0]octane.
(e) 1-Ethyl-4-methylcyclooctane (use a regular octagon). No indication of geometric isomers is required.

5. Using formulas in which stereochemistry is indicated by dots, write all the geometrical isomers of the following structures.

(a)

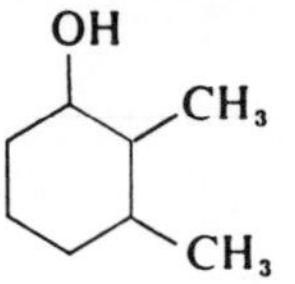

(b)

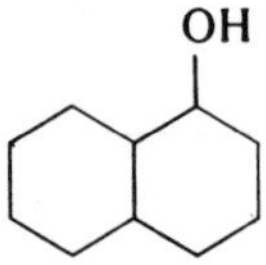

6. Write each conformation for both *cis* and *trans* isomers of 1,4-cyclohexanediol. For each isomer, indicate which conformation is the more stable.

7. Write a correct name for each of the following structures.

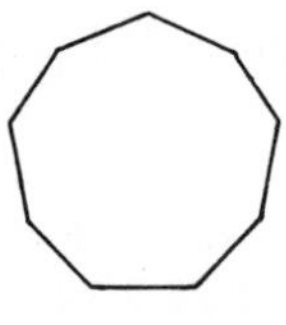

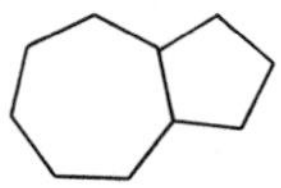

8. In the conformational formula for *trans*-decalin, label each hydrogen (as indicated by the bond direction) as either *a* or *e*.

Concerning the Nature of Multiple Bonds

Nomenclature for Alkenes and Alkynes

The types of chemical reactions to be studied next are the elimination reactions, by which multiple bonds are generated, and addition reactions, in which various moieties are added to the multiple bonds. It is appropriate, therefore, to extend our discussion of chemical bonding (Chap. 3) to include the double bond and triple bond. As already mentioned, compounds containing a carbon-carbon double bond are known as alkenes (Chap. 9). The compounds containing a carbon-carbon triple bond are known as alkynes (Chap. 10). The molecular orbital theory of chemical bonding (Chap. 3) is especially useful in the treatment of multiple bonds, so the basic principles of this theory, as set forth in Chapter 3, should be reviewed prior to study of the present chapter.

The Double Bond

The simplest compound containing a carbon-carbon double bond is ethylene, C_2H_4. Since each carbon in ethylene has two hydrogens attached to it, the remaining two valences of each carbon atom must be shared with the other carbon atom. In such a structure, it is energetically profitable, as usual, for the carbon atoms to promote one electron from the $2s$ to the $2p$ energy level so that four electrons (one $2s$, three $2p$) are available for valence formation in molecular orbitals; however, the hybridization of these electrons is different than is the case when four single bonds are formed. The difference is that one *p* electron does not become involved in hybridized orbitals, but remains in a separate *p* orbital. The remaining three electrons (one *s* and two *p*) in the second principal energy level do become hybridized; hence three *sp*²

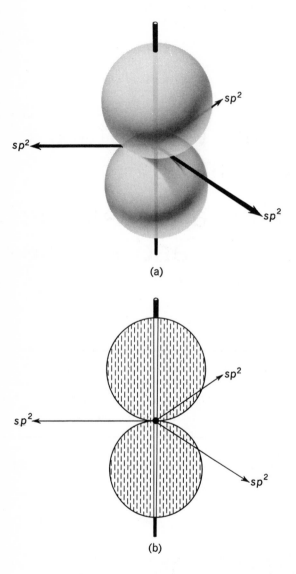

Fig. I. Carbon atom containing three hybridized *sp*² orbitals (only the long axes indicated) and one *p* orbital. In (a) the shape of the *p* orbital is shown, and in (b) is shown the cross section of this orbital in the plane at right angles to the plane of the *sp*² orbitals. The lines show the long axes of the orbitals.

(a)

(b)

orbitals are formed. As described in Chapter 3, the long axes (hence valence directions) of the *sp*² orbitals lie in a plane, with angles of 120° between them (cf. Fig. 3-8). The third, unhybridized *p* electron occupies a separate *p* orbital, which has its long axis at right angles to the plane of the *sp*² orbitals. The orientation of this orbital with respect to the *sp*² orbitals is shown in Fig. 1. It may be noted that the *p* orbital has the usual shape (cf. Fig. 3-2), but the plane at right angles to its long axis contains, not the axes of two additional *p* orbitals (cf. Fig. 3-3), but the long axes of the three *sp²* orbitals.

The π-bond. If two carbon atoms, whose valence electrons are in the configuration shown in Fig. 1, form a covalent bond with each other by sharing electrons in the *sp²* orbitals, one position of rotation of the carbon atoms about

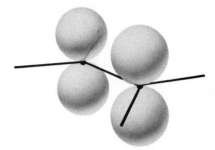

Fig. 2. Carbon atoms joined to each other by *sp²* bond, with remaining *sp²* bond directions in same plane. This places the *p* orbitals in the same plane, as shown.

this bond direction is that shown in Fig. 2. The significant feature of this position of rotation is that the axes of all the *sp²* orbitals are in the same plane; therefore the long axes of the remaining *p* orbitals on the two carbon atoms are also in a common plane, that at right angles to the plane of the *sp²* orbitals. When this is the case, the *p* electrons on the two carbon atoms may enter a type of molecular orbital known as a π-orbital (spoken as "pi-orbital"). This π-orbital consists of volumes above and below the plane containing the axes of the *sp²* orbitals, and

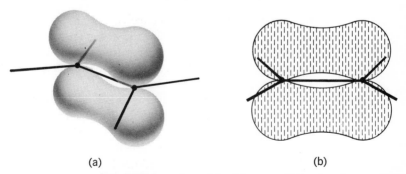

(a)   (b)

Fig. 3. Carbon atoms joined by one *sp²* bond and one π-bond resulting from overlapping and merging of the *p* orbitals of the two atoms. In (a) is shown the shape of the π-orbital; in (b) is shown its cross section.

its shape is that shown in Fig. 3. It should be emphasized that one electron is not confined above the plane dividing the orbital and one below. The only specification is that these volumes represent the orbital for the two electrons involved in the π-bond. At a given moment, both electrons might be on one side of the plane, and at another moment one on each side. The type of bond resulting from a pair of electrons in a molecular orbital of the π-type is quite logically called a π-bond.

Formation of the π-bond from the two p electrons is energetically profitable to the molecule for the same reason that formation of other types of bonds is profitable. The electrons have a lower energy, hence are in a more stable condition, when they are able to be associated with two positive nuclei in a molecular orbital, rather than with only one positive nucleus in their respective atomic orbitals. It may be seen from inspection of Figs. 2 and 3 that the two atomic orbitals can overlap to best advantage to form a molecular orbital when their respective long axes are in the same plane. If there is rotation around the carbon-carbon sp^2 bond so that these axes are not in the same plane, overlapping is less effective, and there is no overlapping at all if these axes are at right angles to each other, as shown in Fig. 4. In other words, the further the p orbitals turn

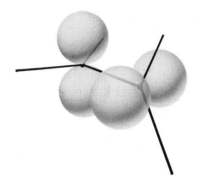

Fig. 4. Carbon atoms joined by an sp^2 bond, but rotated so that the p orbitals are at right angles to each other, hence unable to overlap and form a π-orbital. Maximum inability of the p orbitals to overlap in this position causes it to be the highest energy, hence least favored position.

out of a common plane the higher the energy until a maximum energy (minimum stability) is reached when they are at right angles. At this point, the π-bond may be regarded as "broken"; the energy input required for the molecule to reach this position (as in Fig. 4) is the bond energy of the π-bond. This means that there is a force exerted to hold the carbon atoms in the position shown in Fig. 3. As a result of thermal energy, there will be some oscillation back and forth around the sigma bond; but only at rather high thermal energy will this vibration be sufficiently vigorous to push over the high energy hump so that there is a half revolution around the carbon-carbon bond. Thus the effect of the π-bond is to cause *restricted rotation* around the carbon-carbon bond. This is in marked contrast to the situation existing when only a single covalence connects atoms, for atoms joined by a single covalence are relatively free to rotate around the direction of the valence bond (the long axis of the molecular orbital connecting them). The π-bond may be defined as a bond causing restriction of rotation on account of having one rotational position of lowest energy. Most π-bonds of interest to organic chemists are formed from p electrons, but this is not a necessary requirement.

Convention for writing the double bond. Since the restricted rotation caused by the π-bond holds all the sp^2 bonds in the same plane, the shape of the ethylene molecule is as represented in Fig. 5, where all the atoms

Fig. 5. The ethylene molecule.

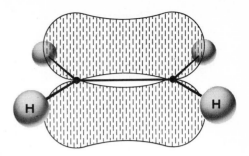

are in a common plane which is at right angles to the plane bisecting the π-orbital. The conventional manner of writing the formula for a doubly-bonded molecule such as ethylene has been to simply use two lines to indicate the two bonds, as in the following expanded and condensed structural formulas:

$$
\begin{array}{ccc}
\text{H} & & \text{H} \\
& \diagdown \quad \diagup & \\
& \text{C}\!=\!\text{C} & \\
& \diagup \quad \diagdown & \\
\text{H} & & \text{H}
\end{array}
\qquad\qquad
H_2C\!=\!CH_2
$$

This would appear to be a poor practice, since two entirely different kinds of bond are indicated by the same symbol; however, the usage became firmly entrenched prior to our present concept of the double bond. Since this device is also easier and faster to write than use of two different symbols to indicate

Fig. 6. Framework Molecular Model of the ethylene molecule. The side tubes define the extent of a cross section (as in Fig. 5) through the π-orbital, which is at right angles to the plane containing the centers of all the atoms.

the two different kinds of bond, it seems highly probable that the double bond will continue to be written as two identical short lines. The chemist should become accustomed, however, to visualization of the π-orbital, with realization that this prevents rotation about the bond direction unless at such high temperature that vibrational energy is sufficient to break the π-bond. This restriction of rotation, of course, leads to the possibility for geometrical isomerism, as discussed below.

In spite of the entrenched symbolism for writing formulas which do not make any indication of the nature of the π-bond, it is desirable to have molecular models which do provide a visual concept of the π-orbital. The **Framework Molecular Models** include this feature. In particular, they indicate the extent of the π-orbital with relation to the length of the sigma bond. Figure 6 depicts the Framework Molecular Model of ethylene, with plastic tubes attached to delineate the location and transverse extent of the π-orbital. This device also restricts rotation and makes apparent the existence of geometric isomers.

Geometrical Isomerism in Alkenes

The restricted rotation entailed by the nature of the carbon-carbon double bond gives rise to geometrical isomerism in alkenes having two different groups on each of the doubly bonded carbon atoms. Such a compound is the following dichloroethylene:

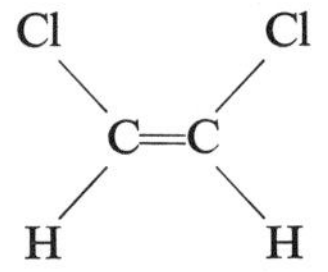

$$
\begin{array}{ccc}
\text{Cl} \qquad \text{Cl} & & \text{Cl} \qquad \text{H} \\
\diagdown \quad \diagup & & \diagdown \quad \diagup \\
\text{C}=\text{C} & & \text{C}=\text{C} \\
\diagup \quad \diagdown & & \diagup \quad \diagdown \\
\text{H} \qquad \text{H} & & \text{H} \qquad \text{Cl} \\
\textit{cis} \text{ Isomer} & & \textit{trans} \text{ Isomer}
\end{array}
$$

As in the case of geometrical isomers in the cyclic structures (Chap. 7), *cis* refers to two groups on the same side and *trans* (Latin, meaning "across") refers to groups on opposite sides. In the open-chain compounds, however, certain additional guides for naming become necessary, as will be discussed below.

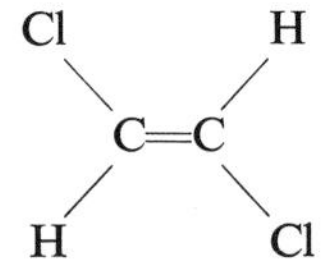

If only one doubly-bonded carbon has two different groups on it, as for chloroethylene, then geometrical isomers do not exist. If there should be 180°

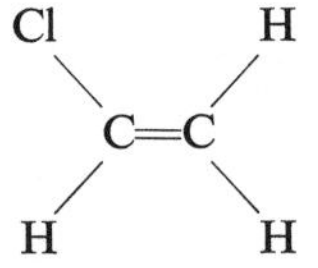

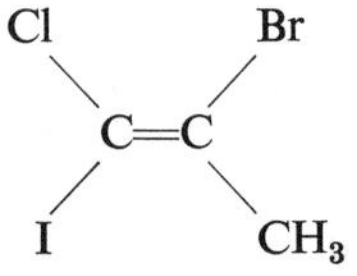

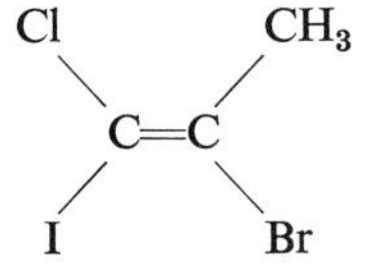

$$
\begin{array}{ccc}
\text{Cl} \quad \text{H} & \text{Cl} \quad \text{Br} & \text{Cl} \quad \text{CH}_3 \\
\diagdown \ \diagup & \diagdown \ \diagup & \diagdown \ \diagup \\
\text{C}=\text{C} & \text{C}=\text{C} & \text{C}=\text{C} \\
\diagup \ \diagdown & \diagup \ \diagdown & \diagup \ \diagdown \\
\text{H} \quad \text{H} & \text{I} \quad \text{CH}_3 & \text{I} \quad \text{Br}
\end{array}
$$

rotation about the axis of the double bond the chlorine would still be on the same side as a hydrogen atom, for the other carbon has hydrogen atoms on both sides. By the same token, only two geometrical isomers are possible, even if all the groups substituted on the doubly-bonded carbons are different. This is illustrated by the tetrasubstituted ethylene shown above.

As mentioned in connection with the discussion of the nature of the double bond, under ordinary laboratory conditions rotation about the axis of the double bond is prevented entirely. The *cis* and *trans* isomers of alkenes are stable compounds with different physical properties and can be separated by orthodox procedures such as distillation, crystallization, or gas chromatography. At sufficiently high temperatures, however, it is usually possible to secure rupture of the π-bond without breaking the sigma bond, so that **equilibration** of the isomers will occur without accompanying isomerism of other types. Such equilibration can also be secured by irradiating the molecule with light of energy which is absorbed by the double bond. By such methods it is possible to secure an equilibrium constant for the equilibration of the geometrical isomers, and from the equilibrium constant the difference in energy between the geometric isomers may be calculated. Such measurements have shown that steric interference between groups on the same side of the π-bond causes an increase in energy content of that isomer. Except in rare instances, as in molecules where there is an attractive force between groups of opposite polarity, **the *trans* isomer (or that isomer with its largest groups on opposite sides) is the lower-energy species.**

Synthesis of geometrical isomers. In reactions in which geometrical isomers are synthesized, some of each of the isomers is likely to be formed; however, the ratio between the isomers is controlled to a major extent by steric factors. In some instances, a synthesis will yield one isomer almost exclusively, and such a synthesis is termed **stereospecific.** In synthesis of compounds of biological significance, a pure geometric isomer is nearly always desired; therefore, either the mixture must be separated or a stereospecific synthesis must be used. For this reason, considerable attention will be devoted to the mechanisms and geometry of alkene synthesis in Chapter 9.

The Triple Bond

When a triple bond is formed between two carbon atoms, one of these bonds is an *sp* bond and the other two are π-bonds. Thus each carbon atom has only two of its valence electrons, one *s* and one *p*, in hybridized *sp* orbitals; so the angle between these valence directions is 180° (cf. Chap. 3). It follows that in acetylene, which has the molecular formula C_2H_2, the two hydrogens and two carbons all lie in a straight line, as has been previously described for beryllium chloride (cf. Chap. 3). The two π-orbitals, containing the unhybridized *p* electrons, lie in planes at right angles to each other and intersecting at the line connecting the four atoms. These relations are shown in Fig. 7. The 90°-angle between the π-orbitals follows from the fact that the angle between the *p* atomic orbitals is 90° (cf. Chap. 3). It may be noted in Fig. 7 that the electronic distribution in the π-orbitals is essentially symmetrical around the axis joining the carbon atoms.

In a triply-bonded compound, such as acetylene, there is no structural significance attached to rotation around the carbon-carbon *sp* bond. Such

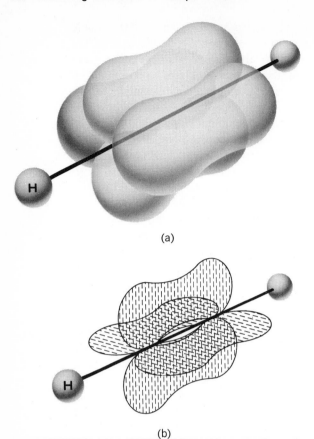

(a)

Fig. 7. Bond directions and π-orbitals in the acetylene molecule. In (a) are shown the shapes of the π-orbitals; in (b) the cross sections of the π-orbitals are shown in planes through their long axes.

(b)

Fig. 8. Framework Molecular Model for acetylene. The tubes delineate cross sections through the π-orbitals. The total π-orbital system is of cylindrical symmetry.

rotation does not give rise to geometrical isomerism, for the two atoms attached to the triply-bonded carbons are in line, and their position relative to each other is not changed by rotation about the carbon-carbon valence.

The triple bond is designated by three lines, in extension of the system used for the double bond; however, it should be remembered that one of these bonds is a sigma bond while the other two are pi bonds. The electron structure in the triple bond is symbolized in the Framework Molecular Models. The model for acetylene in Fig. 8 shows the linear nature of the molecule and the extent of the π-orbitals.

Nomenclature in Alkenes

Common names patterned after ethylene are occasionally used for specific compounds, such as the following:

$$CH_3—CH=CH_2 \qquad\qquad CH_3—\underset{\underset{CH_3}{|}}{C}=CH_2$$

Propylene   Isobutylene

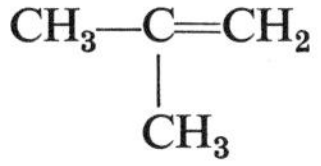

Most compounds in this series, however, are named as derivatives of the first member of the series or by the IUC system.

Naming as a derivative of ethylene. The system is that already described (Chap. 5) in application to alkanes and alcohols; however, it is necessary to specify which carbon bears a substituent in the instances where more than one substituent is present. The two carbons in ethylene are distinguished by the Greek letters α and β. A few examples will illustrate the system.

$$C_4H_9—CH=CH_2 \qquad\qquad CH_3—CH=CH—CH_3$$

n-Butylethylene α,β-Dimethylethylene

$$CH_3—\underset{\underset{C_2H_5}{|}}{C}=\underset{\underset{CH_3}{|}}{C}—CH—CH_3$$

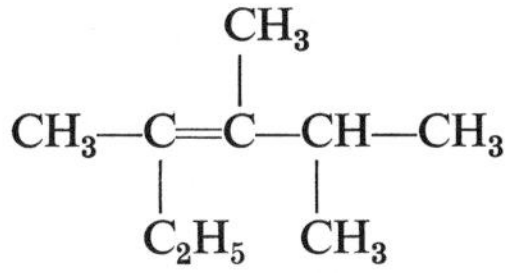

α,β-Dimethyl-α-ethyl-β-
isopropylethylene

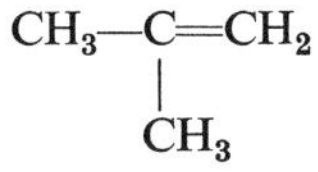

$$CH_3—\underset{\underset{CH_3}{|}}{C}=CH_2$$

α,α-Dimethylethylene

Of course the Greek letters are necessary only if more than one group is substituted on the ethylene. For a disubstituted ethylene, the prefix *sym-* (for "symmetrical") is sometimes used when the two substituents are on different carbons, *unsym-* when they are on the same carbon. By this designation, the upper right formula, above, would be *sym*-dimethylethylene and the lower right formula would be *unsym*-dimethylethylene.

As in other applications of this system, it is limited to relatively simple compounds in which the radicals may be named unless the IUC system be invoked to name more complicated radicals.

IUC nomenclature. As in other applications of the IUC system, only minor additional information is necessary: the characteristic ending is *-ene*, and the longest chain containing the functional group is used as the basis for the name. As seems reasonable, the doubly-bonded carbon with the smaller number in the chain is the one whose number is used to locate the double bond in the chain. Thus, the IUC name for *n*-butylethylene is 1-hexene. The following somewhat more complicated compounds serve as illustrations.

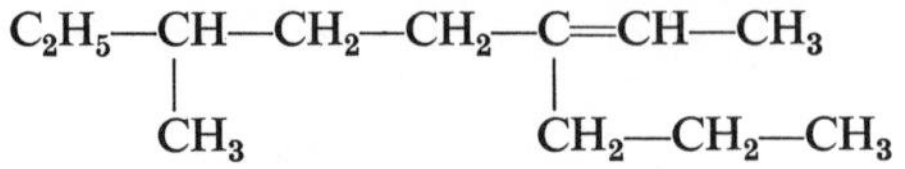

$$C_2H_5-CH-CH_2-CH_2-C=CH-CH_3$$
$$\underset{CH_3}{|} \quad \underset{CH_2-CH_2-CH_3}{|}$$
6-Methyl-3-propyl-2-octene

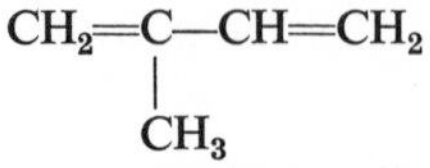

$$CH_2=C-CH=CH_2$$
$$\underset{CH_3}{|}$$
2-Methyl-1,3-butadiene

$$CH_3-CH-CH_2-C=CH_2$$
$$\underset{OH}{|} \quad \underset{CH_3}{|}$$

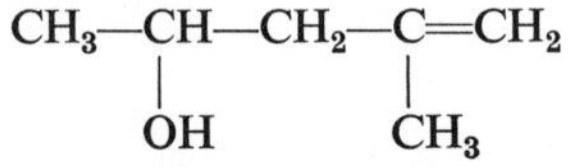

2-Methyl-4-hydroxy-1-pentene
or
2-Methyl-1-penten-4-ol

Naming of the unsaturated alcohol illustrates the two variations by which polyfunctional compounds may be named according to the IUC system.

Naming of *cis* and *trans* isomers. Although many of the illustrative formulas named above may exist as *cis* and *trans* isomers, it is more convenient to discuss the naming of geometric isomers in a separate section. In the butenes, 1-butene and 2-methyl-1-propene do not exist in geometric isomers, on account of their structure; however, geometric isomers are possible in the 2-butenes.

$$CH_3-CH_2-CH=CH_2$$

1-Butene

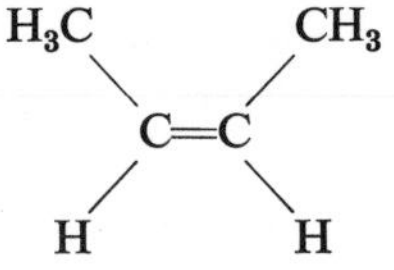

cis-2-Butene

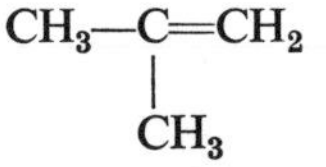

$$CH_3-C=CH_2$$
$$\underset{CH_3}{|}$$

2-Methyl-1-propene

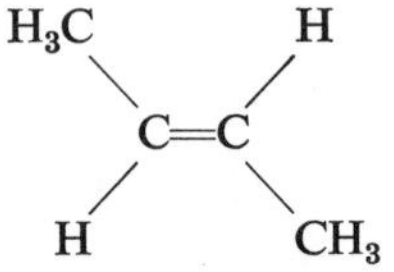

trans-2-Butene

In instances where *cis* or *trans* may refer to either of two pairs of groups, the reference is specified as applying to the components of the chain which is used as the basis of the name.

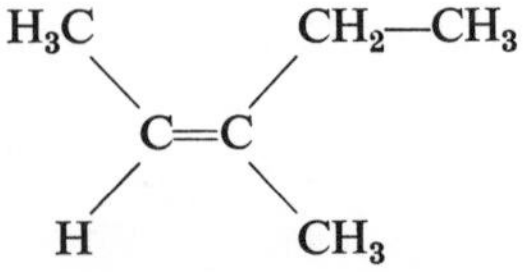

3-Methyl-*cis*-2-pentene

In the above illustration, *cis* refers to the ethyl and methyl because they are a part of the chain, pentene, which is the basis of the name (the longest chain containing the double bond). It is only in instances where this rule does not apply that *cis* refers to like groups.

It is sometimes the case that an unambiguous name may be attained only by specifying the groups to which *cis* or *trans* refers:

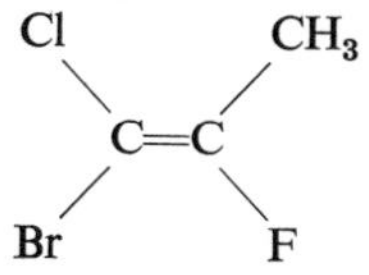

$$\underset{Br}{\overset{Cl}{\diagdown}}C=C\underset{F}{\overset{CH_3}{\diagup}}$$

1-Bromo-1-chloro-2-fluoro-1-propene
(chlorine *cis* to methyl)

Obviously, other designations are equally applicable, e.g., chlorine *trans* to fluorine.

Nomenclature in Alkynes

Alkynes are usually named as derivatives of acetylene or by the IUC system. When a substance is named as a derivative of acetylene, no distinction between the two carbon atoms in acetylene is required, for each can carry only one substituent. In order to apply the IUC system, it is necessary only to state that the characteristic ending is -*yne*. Otherwise, the system of naming is the same as that used in alkenes. A brief illustration of the naming of acetylenes seems sufficient:

$$CH_3-\underset{\underset{CH_3}{|}}{CH}-C\equiv C-CH_3$$

Methylisopropylacetylene
or
4-Methyl-2-pentyne

$$C_2H_5-\underset{\underset{CH_3}{|}}{CH}-CH=CH-CH_2-CH_2-C\equiv CH$$

7-Methyl-1-nonyne-5-ene

EXERCISES

1. In a disubstituted ethylene, one geometrical isomer may be changed into the other by heating. Why is this not possible in the case of 1,2-dimethylcyclopentane?

2. Explain why all the atoms in ethylene lie in the same plane, while the atoms in ethane do not lie in the same plane.

3. In dimethylacetylene, how many atoms may lie, at the same time (that is, for a given position of rotation of the methyl groups), in a plane which includes the axis of the *sp* bond?

4. In *sym*-dimethylethylene, how many atoms may lie, at the same time, in a plane at right angles to the pi orbital and including the sigma bond component of the double bond?

5. Draw or construct a model showing the geometry of the atoms in 1,3,5-hexatriyne.

6. Write the structural formulas and IUC names for all the structurally possible pentenes, including geometrical isomers.

7. Write a structural formula and one name for each of the isomeric 2,4-dimethyl-hexenes. Include any *cis* and *trans* isomers that occur.

8. Write one name for each of the following compounds (geometrical isomers need not be indicated).

(a) 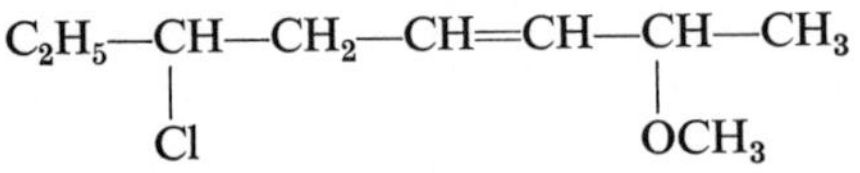 C_2H_5—CH—CH_2—CH=CH—CH—CH_3
        | |
        Cl OCH_3

(b) CH_3—CH=CH—CH_2—CH—C_3H_7
                                |
                                OH

(c) C_4H_9—CH=CH—CH—C_9H_{19}
                          |
                          CH—CH_2—CH—C_2H_5
                          | |
                          C_2H_5 Cl

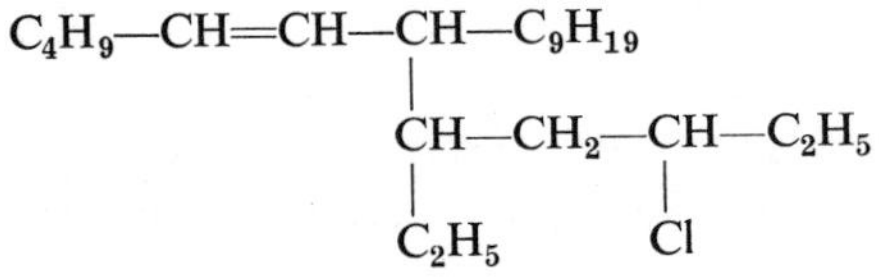

(d) 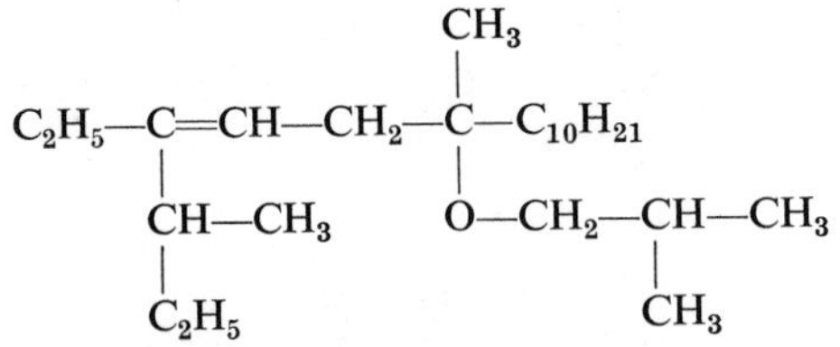
                        CH_3
                        |
C_2H_5—C=CH—CH_2—C—$C_{10}H_{21}$
     | |
    CH—CH_3 O—CH_2—CH—CH_3
    | |
    C_2H_5 CH_3

(e) 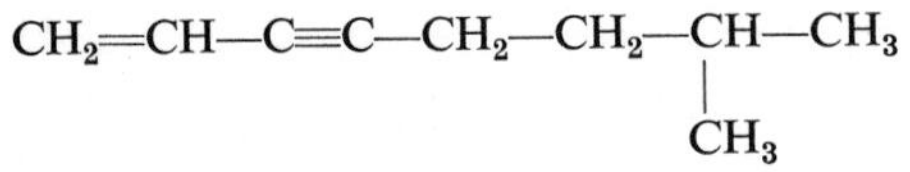 CH_2=CH—C≡C—CH_2—CH_2—CH—CH_3
                                        |
                                    CH_3

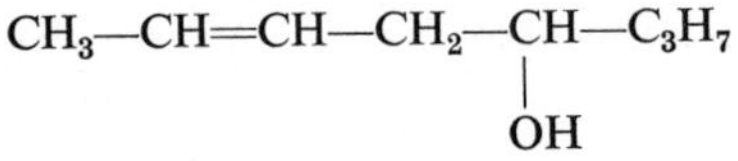

(f) 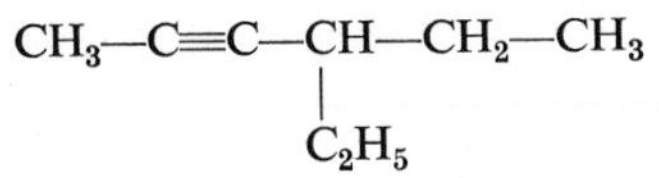 CH_3—C≡C—CH—CH_2—CH_3
                |
                C_2H_5

(g) 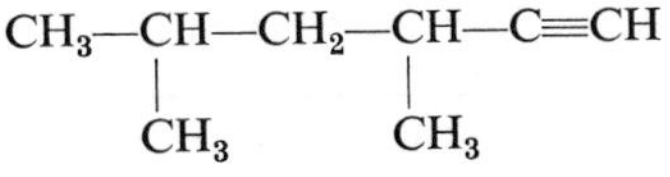 CH_3—CH—CH_2—CH—C≡CH
           | |
           CH_3 CH_3

9. Write the structural formulas for each of the following compounds.

(a) *trans*-3,4-Dimethyl-3-heptene.
(b) *cis*-3-Methyl-6-methoxy-3-octene.
(c) *cis*-4-Ethyl-4-octene-1,8-diol.

The Alkenes
Elimination and Addition
Reactions

Many chemical reagents will add to the carbon-carbon double bond, the functional group characteristic of the alkenes; therefore, this class of compounds is of considerable use in chemical synthesis. This in turn lends significance to the elimination reactions by which the alkenes are synthesized. Furthermore, a variety of alkenes occurs in plants, and many of these compounds are rather important. They include such diverse substances as rubber, from the sap of a tropical tree, and carotene, the orange pigment of carrots. A still larger number of natural products contains the double bond in addition to some other functional group; in fact, it is probably safe to say that a majority of the biologically important compounds contain one or more carbon-carbon double bonds.

The general formula for alkenes is C_nH_{2n}. Polyalkenes contain two hydrogen atoms less for each double bond, so we have C_nH_{2n-2} for dienes, C_nH_{2n-4} for trienes, etc. The general formula for a diene is the same as that for a monoacetylene (Chap. 10). The most general formula for an alkene which indicates the functional group is

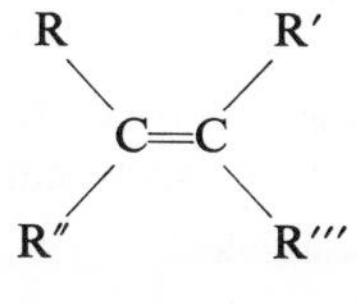

$$\begin{array}{ccc} R & & R' \\ & \diagdown \diagup & \\ & C=C & \\ & \diagup \diagdown & \\ R'' & & R''' \end{array}$$

where the R groups may be alkyl or hydrogen, and geometrical isomers occur in appropriately constituted compounds (Chap. 8). The entire class of compounds is sometimes termed ethylenes, after the common name for the first member of the series. Since nomenclature has already been discussed, we will proceed to the synthesis of alkenes.

Elimination Reactions. Synthesis of Alkenes

As the name implies, elimination reactions involve the removal of atoms or groups from adjacent carbons to yield a doubly-bonded structure. These reactions bear a strong analogy to the displacement reactions, in that there may be involved a bimolecular mechanism in which no intermediate ion is involved or a mechanism in which the slow step is formation of a carbonium ion. Furthermore, the bimolecular mechanism is similar to that of the S_N2 reaction, thus requires a good leaving group. This results in an important role for the alkyl halides in bimolecular elimination reactions.

The only alkene syntheses to be discussed at this time depend on elimination reactions; however, other syntheses are known. The important Wittig synthesis of alkenes is described in Chapter 34 as a part of the discussion of organophosphorus compounds.

E2 reactions. The term E2, elimination second order, is parallel to the designation S_N2, and the mechanism differs from that of the displacement reaction principally in that the negative group accomplishing the displacement is an electron pair associated with a carbon atom which is already attached by a sigma bond to the atom from which a group is displaced. The geometry of elimination of HBr from an alkyl halide by use of hydroxide ion may be shown graphically in a simple formulation as follows, where a curved arrow is used to designate movement of an electron pair:

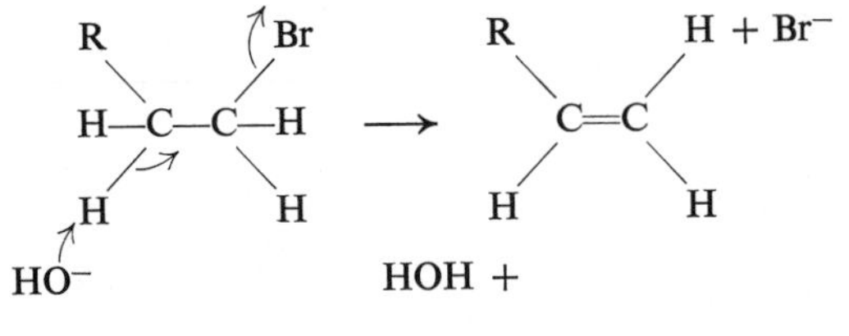

$$
\begin{array}{ccc}
\underset{\underset{HO^-}{\overset{|}{H}}}{\overset{R}{\underset{|}{H-C-C-H}}}\overset{Br}{\underset{|}{}} & \longrightarrow & \underset{\underset{H}{}}{\overset{R}{}}C=C\underset{\underset{H}{}}{\overset{H+Br^-}{}}
\end{array}
\qquad (1)
$$

$$HOH +$$

There are two especially important features of this transformation.

First, there is a *concerted transfer of electrons*, with a transition state such as shown on the left side of Eq. 1. *The process does not involve separate steps*, such as extraction of the proton by base to give water and a carbanion, with displacement of halogen by the electron pair of the carbanion. Secondly, the displacement of halogen by the electron pair must be a *backside displacement*, just as in the S_N2 reaction. This means that, in the transition state, rotation around the valence directions must be such that the hydrogen which is extracted is on the opposite side of the molecule from the bromine which leaves. One way to depict this situation is by use of a Newman projection, as follows:

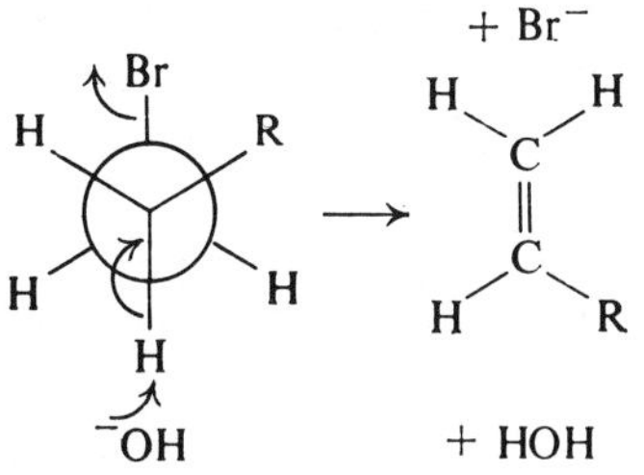

$$(2)$$

The product has been "tipped over" so that the direction of the carbon-carbon double bond is at right angles to that direction in the Newman projection. If the view "down" the double bond were retained, then the groups attached to the two carbon atoms would appear on top of each other. Remember that all the atoms attached to a doubly bonded pair of carbon atoms are in the same plane. Thus, in the transition state for the E2 elimination, as the hydrogen is abstracted, and the electron pair displaces the halogen, the two groups on each carbon swing into a common plane. This process is best understood by examining molecular models of the compounds in Eq. 2.

Stereochemistry of the E2 elimination. The geometrical relationships displayed in Eq. 2 have several interesting consequences, of which the most important, perhaps, is that **no rearrangement occurs in an E2 elimination.** This is a reasonable expectation, since there is actually no ionic intermediate; and the experimental fact is that this is true.

In case a secondary alkyl halide is subjected to E2 elimination, there are two relatively low-energy conformations whose geometry is suitable for yielding the transition state required for concerted elimination. These are illustrated in the two following Newman projections:

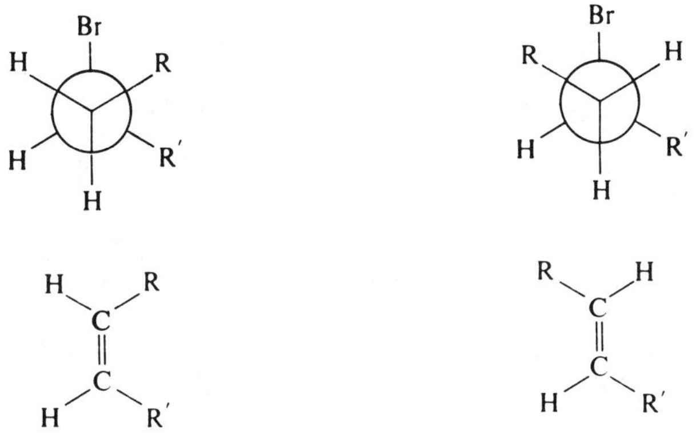

As shown in the alkene beneath each projection, the conformation on the left leads to the *cis* alkene, while that on the right leads to the *trans* alkene. A third low-energy conformation, where the R on the top carbon is on the opposite side from bromine on the lower carbon, cannot lead to elimination; a hydrogen must be opposite bromine before E2 elimination can occur. It would be judged, on the basis of steric interference, that the conformation on the right above would be of lower energy than the one on the left, for the latter has the large groups on the same side. The energy relations existing, as rotation from one conformer to the other occurs, are depicted in Fig. 1. Since the conformer on the right is of lower energy, the population of molecules in this conformation will be greater

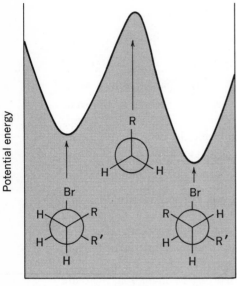

Conformation

Fig. I. Energy relations among rotational conformers in a sec-alkyl bromide. As the groups on adjacent carbons approach eclipsing each other, energy increases until at the transition state the groups on the upper carbon are directly above those on the lower carbon.

than for the higher-energy conformation. Furthermore, at the transition state for the elimination, as the geometry of the alkene is approached, the R groups will begin to pull into the same plane and thus increase interference in the case where the R groups are on the same side. In summary, the conformer yielding the *cis* isomer is in lower abundance and gives a higher-energy transition state; therefore, the dehydrobromination should give a much higher percentage of the *trans* isomer. This proves to be the case experimentally! The *trans* isomer is the dominant product in an E2 elimination, and its predominance becomes greater as the groups on the double bond become larger. This result is not only an impressive support for the correctness of the reaction mechanism; it is also useful in synthesis in instances where the *trans* isomer is desired. In the next chapter will be discussed a method for securing a *cis* alkene. Since *cis* and *trans* isomers are ordinarily separable by orthodox methods (cf. Chap. 8), a reaction which gives a predominance of one isomer is normally regarded as a satisfactory method of synthesis of that isomer.

An additional complication that must be considered in the elimination reaction is the *direction of elimination*, as arises in the following reaction:

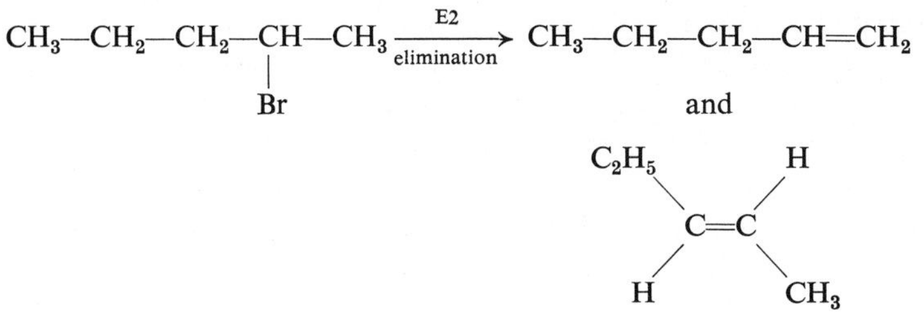

$$CH_3\!-\!CH_2\!-\!CH_2\!-\!\underset{\underset{\displaystyle Br}{|}}{CH}\!-\!CH_3 \xrightarrow[\text{elimination}]{\text{E2}} CH_3\!-\!CH_2\!-\!CH_2\!-\!CH\!=\!CH_2 \qquad (3)$$

and

$$\underset{H}{\overset{C_2H_5}{\diagdown}}C\!=\!C\underset{CH_3}{\overset{H}{\diagup}}$$

(+ some *cis* isomer)

There prove to be two major factors which control the direction of elimination:

    (a) The more substituted double bond is of lower energy, unless there are several substituents larger than methyl;

    (b) the hydrogen on a more substituted carbon is more shielded by hindrance from attack by the base.

The net result of the combination of these factors is that the more substituted double bond is predominant (lower isomer in Eq. 3) if a base of relatively small size is used. Such small bases are ^-OH, $^-OCH_3$, $^-OC_2H_5$, etc. Bases of this size generate no significant hindrance, so the determining factor is the relative stability of the alkene.

    If a base as large as *t*-butoxide is used, hindrance is sufficient to cause the

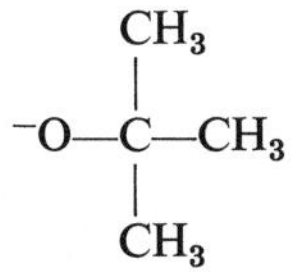

$$^-O\!-\!\underset{\underset{\displaystyle CH_3}{|}}{\overset{\overset{\displaystyle CH_3}{|}}{C}}\!-\!CH_3 \quad \text{\textit{t}-Butoxide anion}$$

less substituted alkene to be formed in larger amount.[1] It is also the case that the larger base gives a higher yield in the elimination reaction, on account of the factor to be discussed next.

Competition between elimination and displacement. It is apparent that the reagent used for securing an elimination reaction or a displacement reaction may be the same—it is a base, an electron donor. For this reason, one reaction is nearly always a side reaction when the other is desired. The ratio of the two reactions in different cases differs considerably because of two factors: (a) nucleophilicity and basicity are not the same, as discussed in Chapter 6; (b) the steric requirements of the two reactions differ greatly.

---

[1] Factors involved in these eliminations were poorly understood, and results to be expected in a given elimination could not be predicted with any reliability until 1954. In that year, Prof. H. C. Brown, of Purdue University, published the first of several papers which correlated and made understandable the two principal factors involved: alkene stability and steric requirements of the base.

In the displacement reaction, the entering group must crowd close enough to the carbon atom to form the new bond to carbon by way of a transition state in which five groups are intimately associated with the reacting carbon (cf. Fig. 6-1). In elimination, the base need only approach the hydrogen atom, which is associated with only one other atom. Perhaps it is not surprising that *t*-butoxide gives very little displacement, and a good yield in elimination, while hydroxide gives a very poor yield of elimination product and more displacement. Ethoxide gives a somewhat better yield of elimination than does hydroxide, but only the large bases ordinarily give a good yield of elimination. *It is rarely possible, therefore, to secure a good yield of the more substituted alkene by the E2 elimination reaction.* Even though displacement in the secondary position is sterically hindered and the more substituted alkene is of lower energy, displacement is usually a serious side reaction when elimination is attempted with a small base. The elimination by way of ionization, to be discussed soon, would be a suitable approach to the more substituted alkene if the process were not defeated by rearrangement in most cases.

With a tertiary halide, displacement becomes so hindered (cf. Chap. 6) that elimination is virtually the only reaction obtained even if displacement is desired. This is true, even with cyanide, for the almost complete association of hydrogen cyanide generates small amounts of base, even in an alcohol solvent:

$$R\text{---}OH + {}^-CN \rightleftharpoons RO^- + HCN \tag{4}$$

In absence of a protic (hydrogen-supplying) solvent, base formation is avoided but displacement by cyanide in a tertiary halide simply does not occur.

Bimolecular elimination in vicinal dibromides. Although dehydrohalogenation is the most important of the E2 eliminations, others are known. The other to be mentioned at this time is elimination of bromine from adjacent carbons by use of a metal, usually zinc (Eq. 5).

$$\underset{\underset{\displaystyle Br \quad Br}{\displaystyle |\quad\;\, |}}{R\text{---}CH\text{---}CH\text{---}R'} + Zn \longrightarrow RCH\text{=}CHR' + ZnBr_2 \tag{5}$$

The stereochemistry of this process is that shown in the Newman projection, with zinc acting as electron donor and one halogen acting as an electron acceptor (Lewis acid). This amphoteric nature of covalently bonded halogen

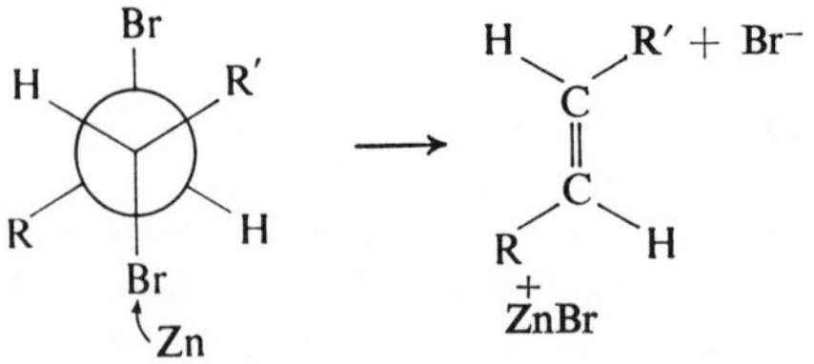

$$\tag{6}$$

is common, especially in reactions of molecular halogen, such as Br_2, to be discussed shortly.

The *trans* alkene is obtained in Eq. 6 if the indicated geometric isomer is used as reactant. Since there is a single bromine on each carbon and these atoms must be on opposite sides of the molecule in order for an E2 elimination to occur, it follows that the *trans* alkene is the only product in Eq. 6. If the reactant had been the other geometric isomer, with R' and H exchanged on the top carbon, the *cis* alkene would have resulted. Factors determining stereochemistry in the vicinal dibromide will be discussed below in the section on addition reactions.

Since the reaction shown in Eqs. 5 and 6 usually gives a good yield, and there is no hazard of rearrangement, it would be useful in synthesis if it were not for the unfortunate fact that essentially the only source of the vicinal dibromides is addition of halogen to the alkene (cf. Eq. 12). Thus, we have another illustration of a reaction giving good results, but of little use in synthesis. About the only use of the dibromide elimination is regeneration of an alkene after bromine has been added to the double bond, either to protect this group from reaction with some other reagent or to make a derivative by means of which the alkene may be purified. For example, a liquid alkene may give a solid dibromide which can be purified by crystallization. As will be discussed below, the geometry of addition of bromine to an alkene is *trans*; therefore elimination of bromine as in Eq. 6 gives back the original alkene.

E1 elimination. If an alcohol is treated with an acid whose anion is a poor nucleophile, displacement by this anion occurs very slowly or not at all. If excess of the alcohol is used, and it is a primary alcohol, the alcohol may accomplish displacement of water from the oxonium salt (cf. Eq. 6-19) at rather high temperature. If, however, excess of acid is used, or if the alcohol is secondary (especially, if it is tertiary), dissociation to the carbonium ion becomes the most rapid reaction (Eq. 7). As discussed in Chapter 6, this reaction is

$$CH_3-\overset{+}{\underset{\underset{CH_3}{|}}{CH}}-\overset{+}{OH_2}\quad {}^-OSO_2OH \rightleftharpoons CH_3-\underset{\underset{CH_3}{|}}{CH^+} + HOH + {}^-OSO_2OH \qquad (7)$$

encouraged by the greater stability of the secondary and tertiary carbonium ions. One reaction that the carbonium ion can give (reversibly) is loss of a proton from an adjacent carbon to give the alkene (Eq. 8). Competing reactions

$$\underset{\underset{H}{|}\ \underset{CH_3}{|}}{\overset{\overset{H}{|}}{H-C}-CH^+} \rightleftharpoons CH_2{=}\underset{\underset{CH_3}{|}}{CH} + H^+ \qquad (8)$$

of the carbonium ion would be reaction with water (reversal of Eq. 7), reaction with the alcohol to give the oxonium ion of the ether, and reaction with the acid sulfate anion to give the alkyl hydrogen sulfate. Even with formation of a monosubstituted alkene, as in Eq. 8, the loss of the proton is a prominent reaction route; however, it becomes the principal reaction route when a more highly substituted (hence, more stable) alkene may be formed. Thus, the reaction shown in Eq. 9 occurs readily and that in Eq. 10 still more so.

$$
\begin{array}{c}
CH_3-CH-CH_2-CH_3 \xrightarrow{H_2SO_4} CH_2\!=\!CH-CH_2-CH_3 \text{ (less)} \\
\underset{OH}{|} \qquad\qquad\qquad \text{and} \\
CH_3-CH\!=\!CH-CH_3 \text{ (more)}
\end{array}
\qquad + HOH \qquad (9)
$$

$$
\begin{array}{c}
\underset{CH_3}{\overset{CH_3}{|}}\\
CH_3-CH_2-C-OH \xrightarrow{H_2SO_4}
\end{array}
$$

$$
\begin{array}{c}
\underset{CH_3}{\overset{CH_2}{\|}}\\
CH_3-CH_2-C \quad \text{(less)}
\end{array}
$$

and   + HOH   (10)

$$
CH_3-CH\!=\!C\!\!\begin{array}{c} {}^{CH_3}\\ {}_{CH_3}\end{array} \quad \text{(more)}
$$

In the E1 elimination, formation of the more stable alkene will proceed *via* a transition state of lower activation energy, hence this isomer is expected in larger amount.

A major difficulty with alkene formation *via* the E1 route is that carbonium ions rearrange if there is available for the charge an adjacent position of equal or lower energy. Thus, the synthesis is limited largely to tertiary alcohols and secondary alcohols where all secondary positions are equivalent, as in Eq. 9 or in conversion of cyclohexanol to cyclohexene. In tertiary alcohols, there is rarely any liability of rearrangement; however, there is the complication of elimination in more than one direction, as in Eq. 10. Relatively high temperatures are required to dehydrate a primary alcohol, on account of the high energy of the carbonium ion; for the same reason, the ion rearranges as soon as formed.

$$
CH_3-CH_2-CH_2-CH_2-OH \xrightarrow[H_2SO_4]{\Delta}
$$

$$
\underset{\text{(less)}}{CH_3-CH_2-CH\!=\!CH_2} + \underset{\text{(more)}}{CH_3-CH\!=\!CH-CH_3} + HOH \quad (11)
$$

Thus, results are of the sort shown in Eq. 11. The resultant compounds in Eqs. 9 and 11 may be noted as the same—logically so on account of the rapidity of rearrangement of the carbonium ion.

Addition Reactions

Numerous reagents add readily to the double bond in alkenes, and side reactions tend to be minimal. Many of the products are best obtained by this reaction pathway, so the addition reactions of alkenes are of considerable use in synthesis. Addition of symmetrical reagents (halogen and hydrogen) will be discussed first since some features of these reactions are more simple than is the case with unsymmetrical reagents (such as halogen acid).

Halogen addition. Addition of halogen to alkenes actually applies satisfactorily to bromine and chlorine only. Energy relations are such that the vicinal di-iodide forms readily at room temperature or below, but on mild heating it is unstable with respect to the alkene and halogen molecules. Addition of fluorine is so violent that it is usually difficult to control. A representative reaction is addition of bromine to 1-pentene (Eq. 12), which occurs in nearly

$$C_3H_7-CH=CH_2 + Br_2 \longrightarrow C_3H_7-CH-CH_2-Br \qquad (12)$$
$$| $$
$$Br$$

$$\longrightarrow C_3H_7-CH\text{------}CH_2 + Br^- \longrightarrow$$
$$+$$
$$Br$$

Bromonium ion

quantitative yield. The reaction pathway *via* the bromonium ion has been well established.[2] The bromine molecule attacks the π-orbital system of the alkene on one side and gives the intermediate where the halogen is about equally associated with the two carbon atoms. The charge may be regarded as distributed among the three atoms that are closely associated. This charge results from cleavage of the bromine molecule so as to leave an electron pair with the bromide ion displaced from Br—Br by the alkene. The first step in this reaction may be likened to a simple displacement reaction, wherein the alkene acts as a nucleophile which displaces halide ion from the halogen molecule. Since the alkene was neutral, the product after displacement is charged. This intermediate cation retains its geometry long enough to allow attack by a bromide ion (not necessarily the same one displaced by this alkene molecule) on the opposite side from the bromine in the bromonium ion. The bromine in the bromonium ion becomes attached to the other carbon than that attacked by the bromide ion, and the geometry of the molecule is maintained in the second step. This results in a *trans* addition of the halogen to the double bond. Thus, addition to *cis* and *trans* alkenes gives different products. Newman projections of bromine addition products from the *cis* and *trans* 2-pentenes are shown on the next page. Models of these molecules will show clearly that the two have different relationships of the groups, regardless of the position of rotation about valence directions. These two substances are, then, geometric isomers. The positions shown in the projections are convenient for recognition of the difference between the isomers. The top projections are the positions in which the groups would be

[2] The mechanism of halogen addition to alkenes and the intermediacy of the halonium ion were established by investigations published by Professor Saul Winstein of the University of California, Los Angeles. Professor Winstein has been quite prominent in investigations concerned with the mechanisms of organic reactions.

immediately after bromine addition—with the bromine atoms on opposite sides. If the upper carbon is rotated until the bromine atoms are above each other (bottom projections) it may be noted that in the left-hand formula the other

Bromine addition to
cis-2-pentene

Bromine addition to
trans-2-pentene

like groups are not above each other, nor are the components of the alkane chain. In contrast, all pairs of like groups are above each other in the formula on the right. This demonstrates the fact that these molecules are indeed different substances. When the like groups on adjacent carbons may be aligned, as in the formula on the right, this is the *erythro* isomer. The other isomer, in which the substituents cannot be paired above each other, is the *threo* isomer.[3] Thus, addition of bromine to *cis*-2-pentene gives *threo*-2,3-dibromopentane, while addition to the *trans* isomer gives *erythro*-2,3-dibromopentane.

In recapitulation of an earlier discussion, it should be noted that if bromine is eliminated in the E2 manner from *threo*-2,3-dibromopentane, there results *cis*-2-pentene. Similarly, the *erythro* isomer gives *trans*-2-pentene. Thus, addition of halogen to an alkene, followed by elimination of halogen with zinc, gives back the starting alkene.

Hydrogen addition. Addition of molecular hydrogen, H—H, to an alkene requires breaking of the very strong hydrogen-hydrogen bond, and this does not happen under ordinary reaction conditions. This transformation does occur, however, when the organic compound and the molecular hydrogen are adsorbed on a surface adapted for such an adsorption. The nature of surface energies is not understood as well as many aspects of physics; however, it is observed experimentally that the energies involved in surface adsorption are able to weaken covalent bonds to the extent that hydrogen molecules assume a

---

[3] This difference in geometry is that of *cis* and *trans* isomers in a ring, but the lack of rotation about the bonds joining the atoms in the ring makes the situation much more easily recognized in a ring. As a memory aid, in keeping clear on *threo* and *erythro*, it is convenient to note that in the *threo* configuration (word begins with *t*) in the conformation shown in the Newman projections above, all but one pair of like groups must be on opposite sides. In the *trans* (word begins with *t*) isomer in ring compounds, like groups are on opposite sides.

reactivity similar to that of hydrogen atoms. A substance able to adsorb hydrogen in such manner as to promote this reactivity is called a **hydrogenation catalyst,** and these substances are nearly always metals or metallic oxides. The catalyst must be prepared in a way that produces a physical state possessing a very large surface, in addition to the right kind of surface for the desired adsorptions. Many suitable catalysts have been discovered, largely by patient, empirical experimentation. Furthermore, a great deal has been learned, again largely by empirical experimentation, as to which functional groups are reduced by hydrogen in presence of a given catalyst. The alkene group is usually reduced in presence of a platinum or palladium catalyst at room temperature and with a low ($<$ 100 lbs. per sq. in.) pressure of hydrogen. Such hydrogenations are usually called low pressure hydrogenations. At high pressure (usually $>$1000 lbs. per sq. in.), frequently at temperatures above 100°, alkenes may be reduced with less expensive catalysts, notably nickel or the mixture of cupric and chromium oxides known as copper chromite catalyst (CuO, Cr_2O_3, or $CuCr_2O_4$).

Choice of catalyst for hydrogenation of an alkene is usually of no great importance in instances where no other reducible groups are present in the molecule, hence, a selective reduction is not necessary. For example, hydrogenation of 2-pentene might be written in either of the ways shown in Eq. 13.

$$C_2H_5\text{---}CH\text{=}CH\text{---}CH_3 + H_2 \xrightarrow{\text{Pt}} C_2H_5\text{---}CH_2\text{---}CH_2\text{---}CH_3 \quad (13)$$

$$\text{or}$$

$$\xrightarrow[\text{high pressure}]{\text{Ni, 100°}}$$

Only in very rare circumstances can the alkene linkage be reduced by use of chemical reagents such as sodium and alcohol or a metal and acid. It is only by adsorption of the organic compound and hydrogen gas on a catalyst that reduction of the double bond occurs. This process is known as catalytic hydrogenation, and it is a very different process than chemical reduction.

The **geometry of catalytic hydrogenation** is not of importance in most open-chain compounds, but it is frequently of great importance in cyclic compounds, especially if synthesis of a natural product is desired. In view of the fact that the process is an adsorption, it might be expected that the hydrogen would be added predominantly in a *cis* manner on the side of the double bond next to the surface on which adsorption occurs. This proves to be the case, especially with a platinum catalyst and at low temperature (room temperature) where the molecules are subject to less vigorous vibrational motions. It is common for as much as 90% of the hydrogenation to occur in a *cis* manner, uncommon for as little as two-thirds of the addition to be *cis*. Furthermore, the hydrogen becomes attached to the side opposite to any groups larger than hydrogen on the ring. Illustrations are hydrogenation of 1,2- and 2,3-dimethylcyclohexenes (Eqs. 14 and 15). The bulky groups go away from the catalyst whether this occurs on adsorption (alkyl not at double bond) or as addition of hydrogen occurs (alkyl at double bond).

$$(14)$$

$$(15)$$

Addition of halogen acid, an unsymmetrical reagent. If an unsymmetrical reagent adds to a symmetrical alkene, only one product can result in absence of rearrangement; however, addition to an unsymmetrical alkene can give two products, depending on the orientation of the addition. In actuality, the addition occurs almost entirely with a single orientation if one doubly-bonded carbon atom bears more hydrogen atoms than the other. **The more positive part of the reagent adds to the carbon already having the most hydrogen atoms.** This behavior, known as **Markownikoff's Rule**, is illustrated in Eq. 16.

$$C_2H_5—CH_2—CH=CH_2 + HBr \xrightarrow[\text{solvent}]{\text{non-aqueous}} C_2H_5—CH_2—CH—CH_3 \quad (16)$$
$$\underset{\text{Br}}{|}$$

(almost exclusively)

Although Markownikoff's Rule was established empirically long before any knowledge of the mechanisms of organic reactions, this direction seems reasonable on the basis of what is now known about the mechanism of this type of addition reaction.

In all types of addition reactions to alkenes, the addition is led by the positive group, i.e., the positive end of the reagent adds first. Thus, if the proton in hydrogen bromide adds to the 1-carbon in 1-pentene (Eq. 16), the intermediate would be a secondary carbonium ion, whereas addition to the 2-carbon would give the primary carbonium ion. As already discussed (Chap. 6), the secondary carbonium ion has a considerably lower energy than the primary ion, so the addition should favor the lower-energy secondary ion, and this leads to 2-bromopentane. If the carbonium ion is an intermediate in this addition reaction, carbonium ion rearrangement would be expected; however, there proves to be no 3-bromopentane formed in the reaction shown in Eq. 16, under the anhydrous conditions used for the reaction.[4] On the other hand, in case of severe hindrance, a significant amount of rearrangement does occur. Such an instance

---

[4] If conditions leading to ionization of acids are used, especially water-containing solvents, there occurs addition of a proton to the alkene to give a free carbonium ion, the reversible reaction shown in Eq. 8. This species rearranges, as usual, if such rearrangement leads to ions of equal or lower energy. This addition of a previously generated proton to an alkene is a different process than that shown in Eq. 16 or Eq. 18, where the hydrogen is abstracted from the halogen acid by virtue of the alkene acting as a nucleophilic agent.

is outlined in Eq. 17. In case hydrogen iodide is used, where the anion is the more highly nucleophilic iodide ion, the rearranged product drops to about 10%. The

$$
\underset{\underset{CH_3}{|}}{\overset{\overset{CH_3}{|}}{CH_3-C-CH=CH_2}} + HCl \longrightarrow \underset{\underset{CH_3\ \ Cl}{|\ \ \ |}}{\overset{\overset{CH_3}{|}}{CH_3-C-CH-CH_3}} \quad \text{and} \quad \underset{\underset{Cl\ \ CH_3}{|\ \ \ |}}{\overset{\overset{CH_3}{|}}{CH_3-C-CH-CH_3}}
$$

$$\text{(about one-third)} \qquad\qquad \text{(about two-thirds)}$$

$$(17)$$

details of this mechanism have not been established with certainty, but these observations and others are best accommodated by proposing that an **ion pair** is an intermediate. According to this proposal, as the proton adds to carbon, the accompanying halogen must be immediately adjacent to the other carbon, as indicated in Eq. 18. In the ion pair, the anion is immediately at its point of

$$
\underset{Br-H}{C_3H_7-CH=CH_2} \longrightarrow \underset{Br^-\ \ H}{\overset{+}{C_3H_7CH-CH_2}} \longrightarrow \underset{Br}{C_3H_7-CH-CH_3} \qquad (18)
$$

attack on the carbonium ion, so it becomes attached so quickly that the carbonium ion has no opportunity to rearrange, even with hardly any activation energy for the rearrangement. The process is visualized as almost a simultaneous addition of the two fragments, *unless* serious hindrance prevents this rapid follow-up attack of the anion. In this latter case, rearrangement can occur in part (Eq. 17), but a more nucleophilic anion reduces the amount of rearrangement. A critical test of the above-cited mechanism concerns whether addition is *cis* (rather than *trans* as for bromine addition), and this is the case in some well-documented instances. In other cases, however, the addition appears to be *trans*. In any case, rearrangement does not occur in addition to alkenes unless there is rather severe hindrance (at least two adjacent methyl groups).

In case the unsymmetrical alkene has two equally substituted carbon atoms, then the governing principle of energy difference between carbonium ions can no longer distinguish between the two possibilities, and about equal amounts of two products result (Eq. 19), so the reaction is unlikely to be of synthetic utility. Isomeric secondary alkyl halides, such as shown in Eq. 19,

$$
C_2H_5-CH=CH-CH_3 + HBr \longrightarrow
$$

$$
\underset{Br}{C_2H_5-CH-CH_2-CH_3} \quad \text{and} \quad \underset{Br}{C_2H_5-CH_2-CH-CH_3} \quad (19)
$$

are remarkably difficult to separate, even by such advanced techniques as gas phase chromatography.

If the addition of hydrogen bromide to an alkene is carried out under conditions such that radicals are intermediates in the reaction, the direction of addition defined by Markownikoff's Rule may be reversed. This process will be discussed in connection with the treatment of radical reactions (Chap. 11).

Addition of other unsymmetrical reagents to alkenes. Among the reagents which add to the alkene linkage are hypochlorous acid, HOCl, and sulfuric acid. In the former case, halogen proves to be the positive fragment (Eq. 20). In the case of sulfuric acid, the adduct is the same alkyl hydrogen

$$C_2H_5-CH{=}CH_2 + HOCl \longrightarrow C_2H_5-\underset{\underset{\displaystyle OH}{|}}{CH}-CH_2-Cl \qquad (20)$$

sulfate (Eq. 21) that results from reaction of an alcohol with sulfuric acid (cf.

$$C_2H_5-CH{=}CH_2 + H_2SO_4 \longrightarrow C_2H_5-\underset{\underset{\displaystyle OSO_2OH}{|}}{CH}-CH_3 \qquad (21)$$

Chap. 6, footnote 6), so the product may be hydrolyzed in presence of a large excess of water (Eq. 22) to displace the equilibrium forward. This two-step

$$C_2H_5-\underset{\underset{\displaystyle OSO_2OH}{|}}{CH}-CH_3 + HOH \underset{}{\overset{H^+}{\rightleftarrows}} C_2H_5-\underset{\underset{\displaystyle OH}{|}}{CH}-CH_3 + H_2SO_4 \qquad (22)$$

process[5] gives a net conversion of a 1-alkene to a 2-alkanol, and is of synthetic interest for accomplishing this type of conversion. If the process is applied to ethylene, ethyl alcohol is the product, and a small commercial production of ethyl alcohol is based on this process. However, the principal source of ethyl alcohol continues to be the fermentation process (Chap. 4).

Oxidation of Alkenes

The net conversion resulting from an oxidation is either removal of electrons or addition of oxygen at a region of high electron density; however, the mechanisms of such reactions are rather diverse, and several steps are nearly always involved. The intermediates may be of the polar type, the type of intermediates that have been discussed so far, or they may be radical intermediates,

---

[5] If ethylene is treated with moderately concentrated aqueous sulfuric acid, the over-all conversion of the alkene to alcohol can be accomplished in one operation. Under these conditions, where there is some ionization of the sulfuric acid, it is probable that a major reaction pathway is formation of the carbonium ion, followed by reaction thereof with water:

$$CH_2{=}CH_2 + H^+ \longrightarrow CH_3-CH_2^+ \overset{HOH}{\longrightarrow} CH_3-CH_2-OH + H^+$$

In instances where this reaction pathway is followed, there will occur rearrangement of the carbonium ion if an equal or lower-energy ion can be formed. Thus, conversion to the 2-alkanols of 1-alkenes with more than four carbon atoms would result in contamination with isomeric secondary alcohols. Rearrangement could be avoided (except in highly hindered structures) by use of the two-step process in Eqs. 21 and 22.

the types to be discussed in Chapter 11. In spite of considerable investigation of the mechanisms of oxidation reactions, the details are often poorly understood, and they are always rather complex. For these reasons, there has been relatively little systematic correlation of oxidation reactions, and the mechanisms are not studied to advantage except in advanced courses. Nevertheless, oxidations are of tremendous significance in synthetic chemistry, and much is known about conversions that may be accomplished. Two of the more useful oxidations of alkenes will be described. In general, acidic oxidizing agents should be avoided, for rearrangement of the alkenes is likely to occur prior to oxidation.

Potassium permanganate. This useful reagent may be controlled so as to give either of two stages of oxidation, as illustrated[6] in Eqs. 23 and 24.

$$R\text{---}CH\text{=}CH\text{---}R' + \underset{(KMnO_4, \ ^-OH)}{[O]} + HOH \xrightarrow[\substack{or \\ below}]{25°} R\text{---}\underset{OH}{\underset{|}{CH}}\text{---}\underset{OH}{\underset{|}{CH}}\text{---}R' \quad (23)$$

(a vicinal diol)

$$R\text{---}\underset{OH}{\underset{|}{CH}}\text{---}\underset{OH}{\underset{|}{CH}}\text{---}R' + \underset{(KMnO_4, \ ^-OH)}{3[O]} \xrightarrow{\Delta} R\text{---}\overset{O}{\overset{\|}{C}}\diagdown_{OH} + R'\text{---}\overset{O}{\overset{\|}{C}}\diagdown_{OH} + HOH \quad (24)$$

(organic acids)

These processes are useful for synthesis of both types of compounds indicated, provided the alkene is more easily available than the acid. In practice, this is usually true only in instances where the alkene is a natural product that is relatively cheap. In other cases, the alkene is more likely to be made from the acid. The organic acids will be discussed in Chapters 13 and 14.

Ozone. This valuable reagent has long been used to great advantage for oxidation of alkenes on a small laboratory scale. Since 1948, there have become available machines for making ozone ("ozinators") from oxygen on a large laboratory scale or even on a tons-per-day industrial scale.[7] The explosive *ozonide* formed as the initial product of ozone oxidation is dangerous, but the

---

[6] Since the balancing of oxidation-reduction equations seems more appropriately studied in detail in connection with laboratory work in organic chemistry, oxygen or hydrogen atoms in brackets will be used for balancing such equations in this book. The reagent used for accomplishing the oxidation or reduction will be specified beneath the oxygen or hydrogen atoms. An equation of this type may be regarded as a half reaction. The other half reaction applies to the oxidizing or reducing reagent, and the two half reactions may be very conveniently added to give the net balanced equation. Application of this system for balancing oxidation-reduction equations is described by Cason and Rapoport, *Laboratory Text in Organic Chemistry*, Prentice-Hall, Inc., New York (1962).

[7] Cf. "Tonnage Ozone for Chemical Processing," by V. Hann, *Chemical Industries*, September, 1950.

hazard is reduced or eliminated by decomposing the ozonide at about the rate at which it is formed. Typical oxidations with ozone are shown in Eqs. 25

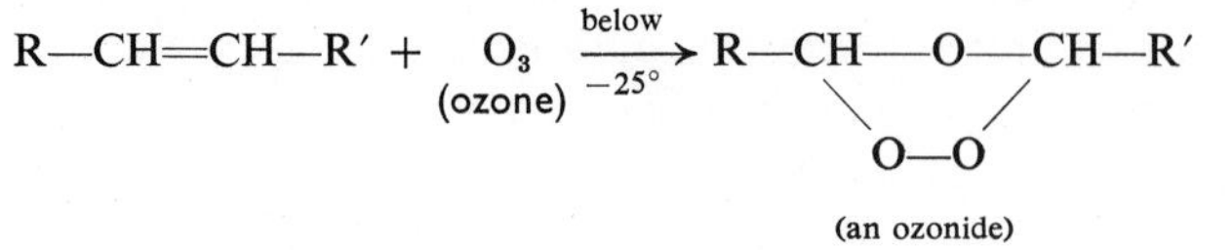

$$R—CH=CH—R' + O_3 \;(ozone) \xrightarrow[-25°]{below} R—CH \underset{O—O}{\overset{O}{\diagdown \diagup}} CH—R' \qquad (25)$$

(an ozonide)

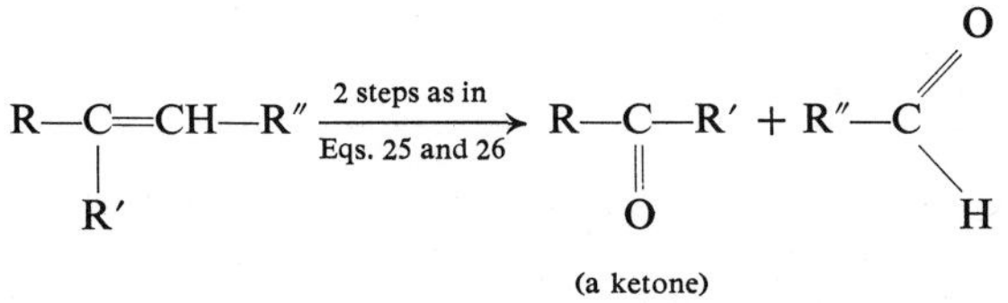

$$R—CH \underset{O—O}{\overset{O}{\diagdown \diagup}} CH—R' + HOH \longrightarrow R—\overset{O}{\overset{\diagup}{C}}\diagdown_H + R'—\overset{O}{\overset{\diagup}{C}}\diagdown_H + H_2O_2 \qquad (26)$$

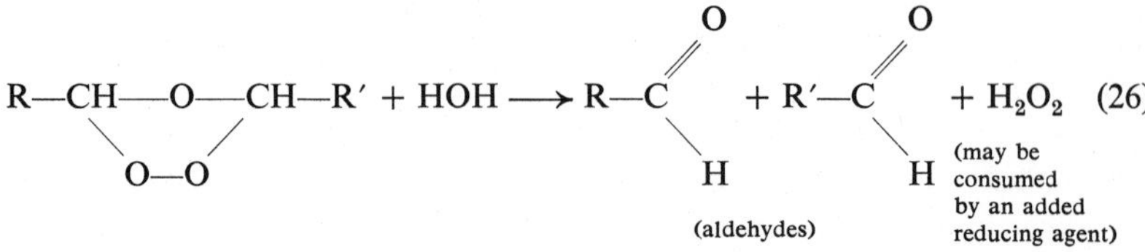

(aldehydes)   (may be consumed by an added reducing agent)

$$R—\underset{R'}{\overset{|}{C}}=CH—R'' \xrightarrow[\text{Eqs. 25 and 26}]{\text{2 steps as in}} R—\underset{O}{\overset{||}{C}}—R' + R''—\overset{O}{\overset{\diagup}{C}}\diagdown_H \qquad (27)$$

(a ketone)

through 27. Aldehydes and ketones are very useful and important classes of organic compounds which will be discussed in subsequent chapters.

Location of double bonds. Since a large number of natural products contain double bonds, and since migration of the double bond sometimes occurs during synthesis of alkenes (cf. dehydration of alcohols), the location of a double bond in a molecule is often desirable. This is nearly always accomplished by oxidation of the alkene and identification of the products of oxidation. Oxidation with ozone or permanganate is regarded as the most reliable method for structure determination. The procedure may be illustrated with a simple case such as distinction between 2-hexene and 3-hexene.

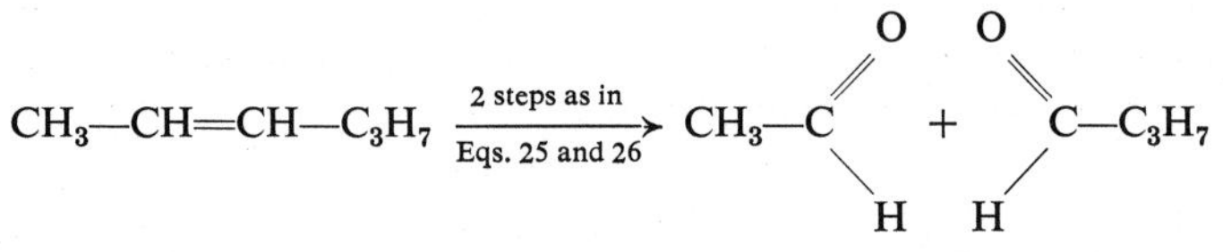

$$CH_3—CH=CH—C_3H_7 \xrightarrow[\text{Eqs. 25 and 26}]{\text{2 steps as in}} CH_3—\overset{O}{\overset{\diagup}{C}}\diagdown_H + \overset{O}{\overset{\diagup}{C}}\diagdown_H C_3H_7 \qquad (28)$$

$$C_2H_5—CH=CH—C_2H_5 \xrightarrow[\text{Eqs. 25 and 26}]{\text{2 steps as in}} 2C_2H_5—\overset{O}{\overset{\diagup}{C}}\diagdown_H \qquad (29)$$

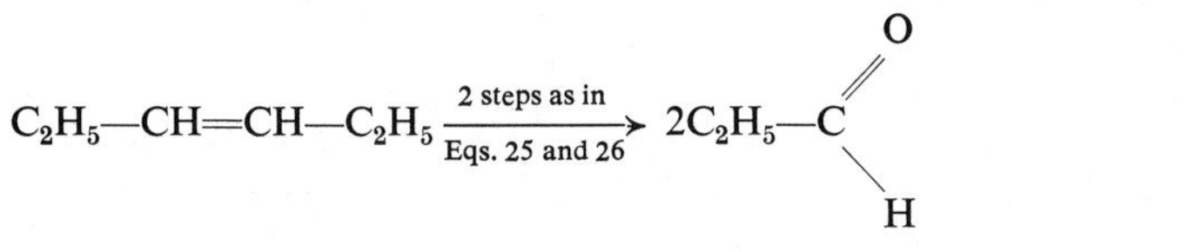

From Eqs. 28 and 29, it may be noted that if the double bond is in the 2-position, two aldehydes will result from the oxidation, one with two carbons and one with four carbons. If the double bond is in the 3-position, only one aldehyde (with three carbons) will result. In more complicated molecules, additional investigation is often necessary in order to identify the products of oxidation, but the structural problem is always simplified by breaking of the large molecule into two smaller ones. Such a breaking down of molecules into smaller ones is known as **degradation**, whereas building up of smaller molecules into larger ones is known as synthesis.

It is also possible, in many cases, to locate a double bond by the use of such physical methods as discussed in Chapter 2, especially nuclear magnetic resonance (NMR). Since the frequency at which resonance occurs depends on the environment of the hydrogens, hydrogens in a methyl immediately adjacent to a double bond are shifted somewhat from the position of those in a methyl group attached to a methylene. Thus, 2-hexene, with the methyl group attached to the doubly-bonded carbon, may be distinguished from 3-hexene, in which only methylene groups are adjacent to the double bond, not only by frequency of the resonance but also by the difference in spin-spin coupling.

Multistep Syntheses

We have now studied the important types of **polar reactions,** sometimes called ionic reactions although there is frequently no free existence of an organic ion. These reactions are the displacement reactions occurring with functional groups on saturated carbon atoms, the elimination reactions by which alkenes are synthesized, and the addition reactions in which various reagents are added to the double bond. The addition reactions are also quite important in compounds containing a polar double bond, that is, a double bond between carbon and oxygen or carbon and nitrogen. These reactions will be studied in subsequent chapters, but there are already available to us a sufficient number of reactions to allow synthesis of many types of compounds.

The planning of syntheses involving several steps can become a rather fascinating type of puzzle-working, in which success is highly dependent on use of the right system for solving the puzzles. As an illustration of the proper method of attack on such problems, we may consider a conversion such as the following:

$$CH_3—CH_2—CH_2OH \longrightarrow CH_3—CH—CH_3 \qquad (30)$$
$$|$$
$$Br$$

In considering the solution to such a synthetic problem, one should always *work backward;* this practice should always be followed by both the experienced research chemist and the most inexperienced tyro. This means that for the problem presented in Eq. 30, the first consideration is of methods for making the product isopropyl bromide, without any regard for a starting material that may be specified in the statement of the problem. Isopropyl bromide is an alkyl bromide, and we have discussed only two methods of making alkyl bromides: (a) conversion of an alcohol to a bromide, Chapter 6; (b) addition of hydrogen bromide to an alkene, as described in the present chapter. Thus we have completed step one in the process of working backward; we have discovered two compounds, isopropyl alcohol and propylene, from which the desired product can be made.

$$CH_3\!-\!CH\!-\!CH_3 \qquad\qquad CH_3\!-\!CH\!=\!CH_2$$
$$\qquad\quad |$$
$$\qquad\;OH$$

A similar procedure is pursued for each of these compounds until we eventually arrive at the specified starting material or wind up in a "blind alley." Sometimes, only one possible route to the starting material develops; in other instances, such as the present one, more than one route will prove productive. Let us first explore the route proceeding backward through isopropyl alcohol, route (a) just mentioned.

Examination of material discussed by us thus far reveals that only one method for making secondary alcohols has been discussed. This is the process described in Eqs. 21 and 22, which is hydrolysis of an alkyl hydrogen sulfate prepared in turn from addition of sulfuric acid to an alkene. In the present instance, the required alkene is propylene, which may be obtained by dehydration of n-propyl alcohol, so we have arrived at the starting material specified in Eq. 30.

If we now return to route (b) mentioned above, we note that the required material is the same alkene, propylene, just encountered as an intermediate in route (a); so we have also arrived at the specified starting material by this alternative route. Furthermore, we would conclude that route (b) is shortest and probably to be preferred. We would outline the synthesis as follows:

$$CH_3\!-\!CH_2\!-\!CH_2OH \xrightarrow[H_2SO_4]{\Delta} CH_3\!-\!CH\!=\!CH_2 \xrightarrow{HBr} CH_3\!-\!CH\!-\!CH_3 \qquad (31)$$
$$\qquad\qquad\qquad\qquad\qquad\qquad\qquad\qquad\qquad\qquad\qquad\quad |$$
$$\qquad\qquad\qquad\qquad\qquad\qquad\qquad\qquad\qquad\qquad\quad\; Br$$

The outlining of multistep syntheses is ordinarily presented as in Eq. 31; that is, the equations are not balanced but there are specified all conditions and reagents necessary to make the reactions proceed properly. It should be noted that the dehydration with sulfuric acid is acceptable only because the secondary carbonium ion formed by rearrangement gives the same alkene as results from the primary carbonium ion. If a higher alcohol were being used, it would be necessary to convert the alcohol to the 1-bromoalkane, then dehydrohalogenate the alkyl bromide in order to obtain the 1-alkene without rearrangement.[8]

Route (a) for accomplishing the conversion discussed above would be written as presented in Eq. 32. Note that after one line is completed the sequence is continued on the next line, as is customary in other types of writing. Long

---

[8] There are known other methods for accomplishing the conversion of an alcohol to an alkene without rearrangement; however, the route *via* the bromide, which we have studied, is a good one.

winding arrows pointing to the beginning of the next line are not only unnecessary but undesirable. It is even more undesirable to have the synthetic
sequence snaking around the page in various erratic patterns.

$$CH_3-CH_2-CH_2-OH \xrightarrow[H_2SO_4]{\Delta} CH_3-CH=CH_2 \xrightarrow{H_2SO_4} CH_3-\underset{\underset{OSO_2OH}{|}}{CH}-CH_3 \xrightarrow[H_2O]{H^+}$$

$$CH_3-\underset{\underset{OH}{|}}{CH}-CH_3 \xrightarrow{HBr} CH_3-\underset{\underset{Br}{|}}{CH}-CH_3 \tag{32}$$

It should be apparent, from this illustrative synthetic problem, that
solution of such problems is *possible only if one is familiar with the chemical
conversions that can be accomplished.* The acquiring of this knowledge is
greatly facilitated by a study of the reactions according to type and mechanism.
In particular, knowledge of the mechanistic principles keeps one out of traps,
such as failure of the reaction to occur with the type of compound being used,
or rearrangement to an undesired structure. The solution of each individual
synthetic problem is a specific puzzle, but it can be unravelled successfully if one
knows the conversions that can be applied. If the chemical conversions are not
known, a solution of a synthetic problem is hopeless.

The synthetic problems included in the exercises at the end of this chapter
may be solved by use of reactions discussed thus far in the book, but the required
reactions are not confined to the present chapter. Such will be the case for all
synthetic problems subsequently presented. Solution of such problems gives
practice in applying the methods that are useful, also gives a frequent review of
the chemical reactions that have been studied. Synthesis is a major concern of
many organic chemists, perhaps a majority of them. When a chemist goes into
the laboratory to carry out syntheses, he invariably refers to the specific original
literature in order to learn the details of the exact procedures found best by
other workers. Sometimes, he finds it necessary to learn by his own experiments
what procedures are best. For planning the synthetic route, however, he must
carry a considerable body of knowledge concerning what chemical conversions
man has been able to accomplish, and the types of structures on which they are
successful. Only a fraction of such known conversions can be presented in this
book, of necessity, but there will be presented a sufficient number of the more
important conversions to allow realistic practice in the fascinating art of
organic syntheses.

EXERCISES

1. Using Newman projections to show geometry, outline the following sequence:

(a) reaction of *trans*-3-heptene with bromine to give *erythro*-3,4-dibromoheptane,
(b) debromination of this product.

2. In the addition of HBr to 1-pentene, why would there not be expected an intermediate species in which the proton is about equally associated with two carbons (as in the bromonium ion)?

3. If A is the more positive group in the reagent A—B, what products would you expect from addition of A—B to 3,3-diethyl-1-octene? Name the products, using nomenclature such as 1-A-2-B-3,3-diethyloctane.

4. If the following alcohols were heated with sulfuric acid, what alkenes would you expect? Name these alkenes.

$$\text{(a) } CH_3\text{—}CH\text{—}CH\text{—}CH_3 \quad \overset{C_2H_5}{\underset{OH}{|}}$$

(a) C_3H_7—CH—CH—CH$_3$ with C_2H_5 above the first CH and OH below the second CH

(b) C_2H_5—C—CH$_2$—OH with CH$_3$ above and CH$_3$ below the central C

(c) (What cyclopentane derivative would be formed?) — cyclohexane with CH$_3$, CH$_3$, and OH substituents

5. A compound of unknown structure was found to react with bromine, and no hydrogen bromide was evolved during the reaction. When this same compound was oxidized with warm permanganate solution, there were formed two acids. One of these acids contained two carbon atoms, and the other contained four carbon atoms. From this evidence, it was concluded that the original compound must have one of two structures, although each of these structures might exist as either of two geometric isomers. Write the formulas for these four compounds.

The four-carbon acid obtained from the above oxidation was examined by nuclear magnetic resonance. In addition to the hydrogen in the carboxyl group, there were found to be present two kinds of hydrogen, six of one kind and one of the other. Which of the formulas you have written are eliminated by this information as possible structures for the compound under investigation?

6. If it be assumed that 1- and 2-hexenes, as well as *cis* and *trans* 2-hexenes can be separated, outline a synthetic sequence by which 1-hexanol may be converted to *erythro*-2,3-dibromohexane. In this conversion, there should not be used processes that lead to rearrangement, and when hexenes are synthesized conditions should be specified that will favor the isomer desired for the remaining steps in the synthesis.

7. Outline by chemical equations, not necessarily balanced but with all conditions and reagents specified, routes by which the following conversions can be accomplished.

(a) CH_3—CH_2—CH_2—CH_2—OH $\longrightarrow$ CH_3—CH_2—CH—CH$_3$ with OCH$_3$ below the CH

(b) CH_3—CH—CH$_3$ $\longrightarrow$ CH_3—CH—CH_2—OH, with OH below the first CH on the left and OH below the CH on the right

(c) cyclohexane with OH substituent $\longrightarrow$ cyclohexane with Br and Br substituents

The Alkynes

In contrast with the alkenes, the alkynes rarely occur in nature,[1] and the triple bond appears to be of essentially no significance in the metabolism of either plants or animals. Furthermore, all alkynes except acetylene, the first member of the series, are relatively expensive to synthesize, so the importance of this homologous series is insignificant in comparison with the alkenes.

There has been very little direct investigation of the elimination reaction by which alkynes are formed or of the addition reactions to the triple bond. This should be ascribed, presumably, to the considerable difficulties associated

---

[1] One of the few naturally occurring compounds containing the triple bond is the substance mycomycin, which has antibiotic properties. An **antibiotic** is a substance produced by a living organism which tends to kill or inhibit the growth of other organisms. Some antibiotics, such as penicillin and streptomycin, are important in medical therapy, for they are much more damaging to microorganisms than to mammals. Mycomycin has the following rather remarkable structure:

$$HC \equiv C - C \equiv C - CH = C = CH - CH = CH - CH = CH - CH_2 - C \underset{OH}{\overset{O}{<}}$$

Reference: W. D. Celmer and I. A. Solomons, *J. Am. Chem. Soc.*, **75**, 1372 (1953).

with efforts to do quantitative work with the rather unstable alkynes. It is commonly assumed, however, that these reactions occur by mechanisms similar to those which have been rather carefully investigated in the alkene series. There is some indirect or qualitative evidence which supports this assumption; for example, the bromoalkene on the left below gives dehydrohalogenation much more rapidly than that on the right. This is consistent with the view that the

$$\begin{array}{ccc} Br & & CH_3 \\ \diagdown & & \diagup \\ & C{=}C & \\ \diagup & & \diagdown \\ H & & H \end{array} \qquad\qquad \begin{array}{ccc} Br & & H \\ \diagdown & & \diagup \\ & C{=}C & \\ \diagup & & \diagdown \\ H & & CH_3 \end{array}$$

normal mechanism for the E2 elimination is a concerted reaction requiring the hydrogen and halogen to be on opposite sides of the molecule. In the isomer on the right, whose geometry does not allow the concerted reaction, the carbanion would be expected as an intermediate, and this would give a higher-energy transition state than in the isomer which has hydrogen *trans* to bromine so that a concerted mechanism is applicable.

Synthesis of Alkynes

Acetylene, synthesized by the specific method described in Eq. 3, is the only alkyne produced on a significant scale commercially; however, 1-alkynes may be prepared satisfactorily by dehydrohalogenation of a 1,2-dibromo-alkane (Eq. 1). The over-all reaction shown in Eq. 1 proceeds in two steps, and

$$R{-}CH{-}CH_2{-}Br + 2^-OH \longrightarrow R{-}C{\equiv}CH + 2HOH + 2Br^- \qquad (1)$$
$$\mid$$
$$Br$$

the second step is considerably slower than the first. It is possible, therefore, to isolate a useful yield of the intermediate bromoalkene, but this is only rarely of interest. In the formula shown in Eq. 1, the intermediate would be a mixture of the 1-bromoalkene and the 2-bromoalkene.

The synthesis of acetylenes from vicinal 1,2-dibromoalkanes is useful only for 1-alkynes, for the strong alkali and heat required for the dehydrohalogenation will *isomerize the triple bond*. With a base strong enough to give the salt of the 1-alkyne (cf. Eq. 16), this salt (the 1-acetylide) is the principal product of the isomerization. With a weaker base, such as potassium hydroxide, there is less isomerization, but there is some equilibration to a mixture of alkynes, with the 2-alkyne present in the larger amount. Pure samples of alkynes with the triple bond at an "interior" position are normally synthesized from a 1-alkyne (cf. Eq. 18).

Specific synthesis for acetylene. The process shown in Eqs. 2 and 3 is applicable only to synthesis of acetylene, the first member of the alkyne series.

It is mentioned because of the importance of acetylene[2] as an intermediate for conversion of coal and limestone to a variety of organic compounds. Among the addition reactions of acetylene discussed below, the conversion to acetaldehyde (Eq. 8) is of particular interest for further synthesis, for acetaldehyde

$$3C + CaO \xrightarrow{\text{about } 2000°} CaC_2 + CO \qquad (2)$$
$$\text{(coke)} \quad \text{(from limestone)}$$

$$CaC_2 + 2HOH \longrightarrow HC\equiv CH + Ca(OH)_2 \qquad (3)$$

may be oxidized to acetic acid (cf. Chaps. 13 and 14 for synthetic importance of acids) or reduced to ethyl alcohol (synthetic importance of alcohols already discussed).

Addition Reactions of Alkynes

As is the case with alkenes, addition reactions are the most important reactions of alkynes. In contrast with alkenes, the alkynes give two different types of addition reactions. One type almost surely involves attack of the multiple bond as a nucleophilic reagent, and thus results in initial addition of the positive part of the addendum to the triple bond. This type of reaction is often called electrophilic attack on the multiple bond. The other type of alkyne addition may involve initial attack of a negative species on the triple bond. In both types of reaction, the direction of addition of an unsymmetrical reagent is that predicted by application of Markownikoff's rule.

Electrophilic addition to the triple bond. Halogen and halogen acid appear to add to the triple bond by a mechanism similar to addition to the double bond. Addition of hydrogen bromide may be represented as in Eq. 4. The radical name **vinyl** should be noted.

Since halogen is a powerful electron-attracting group,[3] its presence on the double bond in vinyl halide reduces the electron density in the double bond to the

$$HC\equiv CH + HBr \longrightarrow BrCH=CH_2 \xrightarrow{\text{HBr}} BrCH-CH_3 \qquad (4)$$
$$\text{Vinyl bromide} \qquad \qquad \overset{|}{Br}$$
$$\text{1,1-Dibromoethane}$$

---

[2] During World War II, Germany was rather short of petroleum, which was the principal ultimate source (via 1,3-butadiene) of synthetic rubber in the United States. Intensive investigation of the chemistry of acetylene in Germany resulted in many interesting developments which led to the synthesis of raw materials for synthetic rubber and other things. An interesting account of these developments has been written by M. H. Bigelow: "Reppe's Acetylene Chemistry," *Chem. Eng. News*, **25**, 1038–1042 (1947).

[3] Evidence of the electrostatic attraction of electrons by halogen is frequently encountered, and will be mentioned as a prominent factor in many organic reactions. This is, of course, responsible for the fact that halogen is such a good leaving group in displacement reactions. This stability of the halide ion is also manifested by the ionization of halogen acids in water solution. Another good leaving group which has a similarly deactivating effect on the double bond is the sulfonate anion, $^-OSO_2OH$.

extent that the second step in Eq. 4 becomes slower than the first step. This follows logically if, indeed, the electrons in the double bond exert a nucleophilic attack on the reagent being added (cf. Chap. 9). Thus, a useful yield of vinyl bromide may be isolated by addition of a mole of hydrogen bromide to acetylene.

Although the first step in Eq. 4 is faster than the second, it should not be concluded that alkynes give a faster addition reaction than alkenes. *The reverse is true*; that is, 1-propene will add hydrogen bromide or bromine at a faster rate than will 1-propyne. In other words, an alkene is more highly nucleophilic than an *analogous* alkyne. The reversal of the normal situation in the sequence in Eq. 4 is caused by the powerful electron-attracting influence of halogen.

Nucleophilic addition to the triple bond. Several types of addition to the triple bond occur only if the reaction is catalyzed by a Lewis acid, more specifically, heavy metal salts of the type known to form "complexes" with multiple bonds. These complexes are believed to result from donation of electrons by the multiple bond to the electron-accepting metal. Since these electrons are in the π-bond, the complex is frequently called a π-complex. The reaction of mercuric sulfate with acetylene may be represented as in Eq. 5,

$$HC\equiv CH + HgSO_4 \longrightarrow HC\equiv CH \qquad (5)$$
$$\downarrow$$
$$HgSO_4$$

where the arrow indicates electron transfer in the direction of the arrow. The situation is similar to that in the coordinate covalence (Chap. 3); therefore, there is a decrease in electron density (generation of at least a partial plus charge) in the multiple bond. Thus, attack of a negative group on the multiple bond would be facilitated. Since this seems to be the most logical explanation of the Lewis acid catalysis, it is believed that this type of addition is led by the negative group.[4] Important synthetic reactions that depend on this type of addition are those shown in Eqs. 6 through 8. The first two reactions give compounds of considerable importance for forming polymers by way of free radical reactions (Chap. 11), while the importance of acetaldehyde has been mentioned earlier in this chapter.

Although it is assumed that vinyl hydrogen sulfate is an intermediate in Eq. 8, as shown, it is not an isolated product. Under the conditions of the reaction, it would be hydrolyzed to vinyl alcohol, which is more stable in the form of acetaldehyde. Acetaldehyde and vinyl alcohol differ from each other by the positions of a double bond and a hydrogen atom. In the case of such isomers, the one containing the carbon-oxygen double bond is so much more

---

[4] Since the first step in these processes is actually an electrophilic addition (as in Eq. 5), reactions such as shown in Eqs. 6 through 8 are sometimes classified with the previously-discussed electrophilic additions to alkynes. In contrast, the initial step in the reaction shown in Eq. 10 is nucleophilic.

stable[5] in most structures that mere traces of the alcohol are present, so equilibrium is not shown in Eq. 8. If the reverse arrow were only a dot, the forward arrow would need to be several feet long.

$$HC\equiv CH + HCN \xrightarrow{\text{CuCl}} CH_2=CH-CN \qquad (6)$$

Acrylonitrile

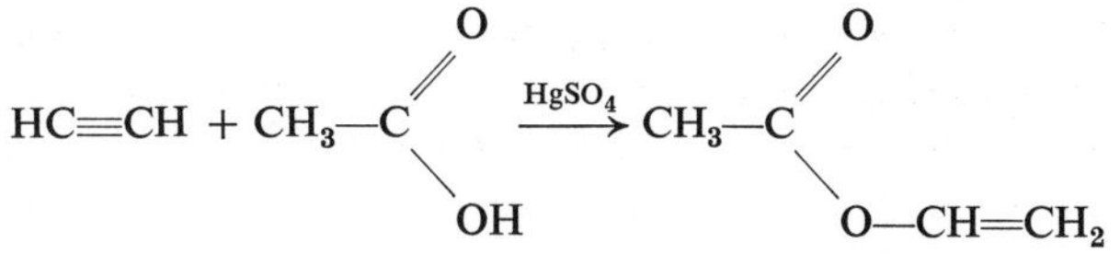

$$HC\equiv CH + CH_3-C\overset{O}{\diagdown}_{OH} \xrightarrow{\text{HgSO}_4} CH_3-C\overset{O}{\diagdown}_{O-CH=CH_2} \qquad (7)$$

Vinyl acetate

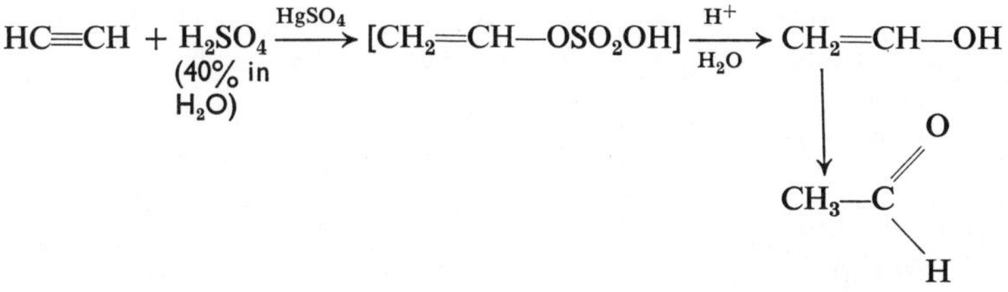

$$HC\equiv CH + H_2SO_4 \xrightarrow{\text{HgSO}_4} [CH_2=CH-OSO_2OH] \xrightarrow[H_2O]{H^+} CH_2=CH-OH \qquad (8)$$
(40% in
H_2O)

$$CH_3-C\overset{O}{\diagdown}_{H}$$

Acetaldehyde

Hydration of the triple bond is occasionally applied to a higher 1-alkyne (Eq. 9). In accord with Markownikoff's rule, addition of oxygen is to the 2-carbon. Utility of this synthesis is severely limited because other routes to ketones are more convenient than synthesis of an acetylene.

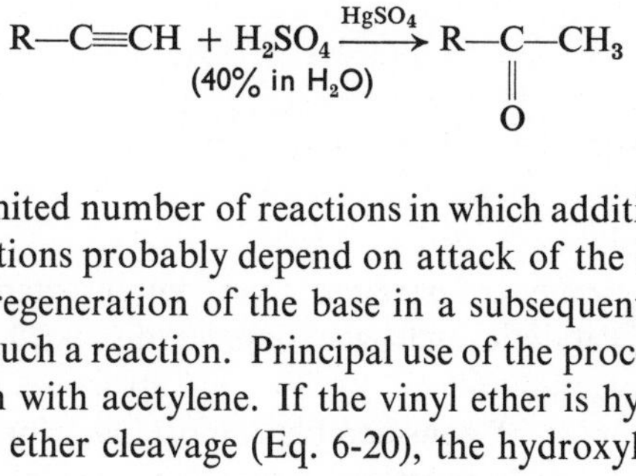

$$R-C\equiv CH + H_2SO_4 \xrightarrow{\text{HgSO}_4} R-\underset{\underset{O}{\|}}{C}-CH_3 \qquad (9)$$
(40% in H_2O)

There are a limited number of reactions in which addition is catalyzed by a base, and these reactions probably depend on attack of the base on the double bond, followed by regeneration of the base in a subsequent step. Addition of alcohols (Eq. 10) is such a reaction. Principal use of the process shown in Eq. 10 has been in reaction with acetylene. If the vinyl ether is hydrolyzed with acid catalysis, in a usual ether cleavage (Eq. 6-20), the hydroxyl group in the vinyl

$$HC\equiv CH + CH_3-OH \xrightarrow{\text{CH}_3\text{O}^-} CH_3O-CH=CH_2$$

Methyl vinyl ether

$$\Big\downarrow {}^-\text{OCH}_3 \qquad (10)$$

$$CH_3O-CH=CH^- \xrightarrow{\text{CH}_3\text{OH}} CH_3O-CH=CH_2 + CH_3O^-$$

---

[5] It is only in cases where the carbon-carbon double bond is part of a more extensive double bond system stabilized by resonance, as discussed in Chapter 12, that the isomer containing hydroxyl is the more stable one.

alcohol is not displaced by halogen, for displacement reactions are extremely slow in the case of groups attached to a double bond (for discussion of this phenomenon, cf. Chap. 12). It follows that an aldehyde is the product of the

$$CH_3-O-CH=CH_2 + HBr \longrightarrow CH_3-Br + CH_3-C\overset{\displaystyle O}{\underset{\displaystyle H}{\diagdown}} \qquad (11)$$

hydrolytic reaction (Eq. 11), and this is an alternate way of converting acetylene to acetaldehyde.

Hydrogenation of acetylenes. The catalytic addition of hydrogen to the triple bond occurs in two stages, to give the alkene as an intermediate (Eq. 12), and it has been possible to discover catalysts such that the alkene is

$$R-C{\equiv}C-R' + H_2 \xrightarrow[\text{catalyst}]{\text{Pt}} R-CH{=}CH-R' \xrightarrow[\text{H}_2]{\text{Pt}} R-CH_2-CH_2-R' \quad (12)$$

hydrogenated considerably more slowly than the alkyne. Since hydrogenation involves adsorption of the reactants, any predictions of relative reaction rates, such as used in connection with the ionic reactions discussed above, do not apply. Since the only useful applications of alkyne hydrogenation are for production of the alkene, considerable empirical experimentation has been directed towards discovery of catalysts giving a much higher rate of hydrogenation for alkynes than for alkenes. Since the specific conditions are of importance only at the time one is carrying out the experimental work, it is appropriate to write the reaction as in Eq. 13. It should be noted that the *cis* isomer is obtained in this

$$R-C{\equiv}C-R' + H_2 \xrightarrow[\text{catalyst}]{\text{special}} \overset{\displaystyle R \qquad R'}{\underset{\displaystyle H \qquad H}{C=C}} \qquad (13)$$

reaction. The *trans* isomer is formed to a very minor extent. This is consistent with the theory of catalytic hydrogenation, as discussed in connection with hydrogenation of alkenes (Chap. 9). The *cis* structure in the alkene from alkyne hydrogenation is of considerable importance, for most naturally oc-curring alkenes have the *cis* geometry, and alkene synthesis by E2 elimination reactions (Chap. 9) gives predominantly the *trans* isomer. It is probably safe to say that fully half the syntheses of alkynes in chemical research are for the purpose of supplying intermediates for hydrogenation to *cis* alkenes.

Metallic Derivatives of l-Alkynes

As discussed in Chapter 6, hydrogen atoms attached to oxygen or nitrogen are "active," that is, slightly acidic. The same is also true of the hydrogen attached to the triply-bonded carbon. Such a hydrogen is less acidic than hydrogen in water; however, reaction with metals can be secured under appropriate conditions. Indeed, calcium carbide (cf. Eq. 2) is the calcium salt of acetylene, presumably a linear polymer, $-C\equiv C-Ca-C\equiv C-Ca-$ etc. Since water is a stronger acid than acetylene, reaction of calcium carbide with water yields acetylene and calcium hydroxide (Eq. 3).

Cuprous and silver acetylides are so insoluble in water that they will precipitate from aqueous solution, and the acetylene is regenerated only in presence of a strong acid. The salts are ordinarily formed from ammonium complexes of the cations, as in Eq. 14. The cuprous and silver acetylides are

$$R-C\equiv CH + Cu^+ \xrightarrow[\text{solution}]{NH_3} R-C\equiv C-Cu + NH_4^+ \qquad (14)$$
$$\text{(ppt.)}$$

relatively stable when pure, but the products formed directly in the reaction mixtures are contaminated with impurities which render them very sensitive to explosion; so these materials should be regarded as *quite dangerous when dry*.

The reaction shown in Eq. 14 is of use as a *diagnostic test* for 1-alkynes as well as a *method of separation* of 1-alkynes from other alkynes. In case of the latter application, the precipitated salt of the 1-alkyne is treated with strong acid (Eq. 15) to regenerate the alkyne. It may be noted that strong acid is used

$$R-C\equiv C-Cu + H^+ \rightleftharpoons R-C\equiv C-H + Cu^+ \qquad (15)$$

in Eq. 15 to reverse the direction of the reaction in Eq. 14.

Alkali metal acetylides. Sodium and potassium acetylides may be prepared by use of the extremely strong bases, sodium or potassium amides, in liquid ammonia solution[6] (Eq. 16). These metallic salts give sufficient ionization,

$$C_3H_7-C\equiv C-H + NaNH_2 \xrightarrow[\substack{NH_3 \\ \text{solvent}}]{\text{liquid}} C_3H_7-C\equiv C-Na + NH_3 \qquad (16)$$

especially in ammonia solution, to allow a displacement reaction by the acetylide ion. Since the acetylide ion is not highly nucleophilic, a relatively unhindered alkyl halide must be employed, preferably a primary halide (Eq. 18).

$$C_3H_7-C\equiv C-Na + C_2H_5-Br \longrightarrow C_3H_7-C\equiv C-C_2H_5 + NaBr \qquad (18)$$
$$\text{3-Heptyne}$$

---

[6] Liquid ammonia acts as a protic solvent, in manner somewhat analogous to water or an alcohol, and is extremely useful for certain organic reactions, especially those requiring a strong base. Since ammonia is such a weak acid, the metallic salts obtained from it (Eq. 17) are very strong bases. It is customary to prepare the sodium amide in ammonia solution, then

$$2NH_3 + 2Na \longrightarrow 2NaNH_2 + H_2 \qquad (17)$$

proceed with its use in the same solution, as in Eq. 16. Further reaction, such as Eq. 18, may be carried out in the same solution.

The process shown in Eq. 18 is probably the most widely used method of obtaining "inner" alkynes. It is much less satisfactory with secondary halides, but gives a sufficient yield to be useful.

It should be mentioned that the monosodium acetylide of acetylene may be obtained, so it is useful as a starting material for synthesis of 1-alkynes (Eq. 19), an alternate synthesis to that depending on dehydrohalogenation.

$$HC\equiv CH + NaNH_2 \xrightarrow[\text{solution}]{NH_3} HC\equiv C-Na + NH_3$$
$$\downarrow \scriptstyle{C_4H_9-Br}$$
$$C_4H_9-C\equiv CH + NaBr \tag{19}$$

Acetylenic Grignard reagents. Since the Grignard reagent reacts with active hydrogens, the acetylenic Grignard reagent may be easily formed (Eq. 20) from another Grignard reagent. Ordinarily, a Grignard reagent from a

$$R-C\equiv C-H + CH_3-MgBr \xrightarrow[\text{solvent}]{\text{ether}} R-C\equiv C-MgBr + CH_4 \tag{20}$$

Methylmagnesium bromide $\qquad\qquad$ (a gas, hence easily removed)

cheap alkyl bromide is used. This reagent is quite useful, for it gives the usual reactions of other compounds in which there is the carbon-magnesium bond. The importance of the Grignard reagents will be developed in the chapters on acid derivatives and on aldehydes and ketones. It should be emphasized that the carbon-magnesium bond does not ionize, so the *Grignard reagent does not give a displacement reaction of the sort shown in Eqs*. 18 *and* 19. In making a Grignard reagent from an alkyl halide there is some "coupling product" (Eq. 21), but this

$$2C_2H_5-Br + Mg \longrightarrow C_2H_5-C_2H_5 + MgBr_2 \tag{21}$$

is formed by a different mechanism. An already-formed Grignard reagent reacts with an alkyl bromide at an infinitesimally slow rate, and gives a practical rate of reaction only with unusually reactive halides.

Until after 1950, it had proved impossible to form a mono-Grignard reagent from acetylene; however, it has now been found that if a special ether, tetrahydrofuran,[7] is used as solvent it is possible to obtain the mono-Grignard reagent of acetylene (Eq. 22).

$$HC\equiv CH + C_2H_5-MgBr \xrightarrow[\text{solvent}]{\text{tetrahydrofuran}} HC\equiv C-MgBr + C_2H_6 \tag{22}$$

Other Reactions of Acetylenes

Acetylenes polymerize, presumably by way of radical formation, so readily that they are rather difficult to isolate without significant decomposition, and

---

[7] Tetrahydrofuran is a heterocyclic compound of formula shown at right. It is commercially available and has a convenient boiling point (66°) for use as a solvent.

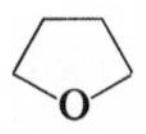

usually form tars relatively rapidly on storage. This is the principal disadvantage of their utilization as intermediates in chemical reactions.

Oxidation of the triple bond leads to carboxylic acids, but the process is of no synthetic significance, for there are many better ways of making carboxylic acids (Chap. 13). Oxidation (Eq. 23) has been used to locate the triple bond in compounds where its position is not known.

$$R-C\equiv C-R' + 3[O] + HOH \longrightarrow R-C\underset{OH}{\overset{O}{\diagup}} + R'-C\underset{OH}{\overset{O}{\diagup}} \tag{23}$$

EXERCISES

1. Write formulas for the final products that would be obtained if the following sequence were carried out: 2-decanol was converted to the corresponding bromide with hydrogen bromide; the resultant 2-bromodecane was dehydrohalogenated to yield a mixture of alkenes; the mixture of alkenes was treated with bromine; the mixture of dibromides was converted to alkynes by treatment with potassium hydroxide.

Outline by means of balanced equations a process for separating the mixture of alkynes obtained by the above sequence.

2. Outline by equations practical sequences of reactions by which acetylene may be converted to each of the following compounds. So long as continuity is maintained, any desired reagents may be used to accomplish the conversions. Of course some of the desired products may serve as intermediates for forming others.

(a) $Br-CH_2-\underset{\underset{Br}{|}}{CH}-O-C_2H_5$

(b) $CH_3-(CH_2)_4-C\equiv C-C_2H_5$

(c) $C_2H_5-\underset{\underset{Br}{|}}{\overset{\overset{Br}{|}}{C}}-CH_3$

(d) $C_2H_5-\underset{\overset{\|}{O}}{C}-CH_3$

(e) $CH_3-(CH_2)_4-\underset{\underset{OH}{|}}{CH}-\underset{\underset{OH}{|}}{CH}-CH_3$

(f) $CH_3-(CH_2)_4-\underset{\underset{Cl}{|}}{\overset{\overset{Br}{|}}{C}}-CH_2$

3. Explain the basis on which you would classify acetylene or ethylene as the stronger Lewis base. How would bromoethylene compare with ethylene?

4. On the basis of electrostatic effects, explain why the 1,1-dibromoethane is the product in Eq. 4, rather than the 1,2-dibromoethane.

Chapter

11

Free Radical Reactions

The overwhelming majority of organic reactions proceed by pathways involving ionic or polar intermediates, and these are the types of reactions which have been discussed thus far. The first and second order displacement reactions, the first and second order elimination reactions, and the addition reactions are the more important broad categories of polar reactions. These reactions involve intermediates or transition states which are highly polar or actually bear full electric charges. A smaller number of reactions proceed by way of intermediates which are neutral, but certain of these reactions are very important, especially in the manufacture of polymers. An atom is such a neutral intermediate, as is an organic radical which has only one electron in one orbital. Electronic formulas for the bromine atom and the methyl radical are the following:

$$\begin{array}{c} \cdot\cdot \\ :Br\,. \\ \cdot\cdot \end{array} \qquad\qquad \begin{array}{c} \;\;H \\ \;\;\cdot\cdot \\ H:C\,. \\ \;\;\cdot\cdot \\ \;\;H \end{array}$$

A radical which is free to move about in a solution or gas, even for extremely brief periods of time, is termed a free radical. Except in very unusual structures, the free radical is such a high energy (unstable) species that it will react with nearly anything with which it collides. The lifetime of a radical is usually very short, therefore, and the maximum concentration reached during most reactions is quite small.

Generation of Radicals

One method by which radicals may be generated is **oxidation**, usually of an anion. Since the basic process involved in oxidation is removal of electrons, a one-electron oxidation of an anion gives the neutral radical. Such intermediates are involved in the complicated mechanisms of certain oxidation reactions, especially gas phase oxidations with oxygen. Another, less complicated process involves electrolytic oxidation of an anion. An illustration of this type of reaction will be discussed below.

The most widely used method for generation of radicals is simple **heating** of a substance until a finite fraction of the molecule is at an energy sufficiently high to permit bond dissociation. Such a dissociation nearly always gives two radicals, rather than a pair of ions, and thus differs sharply from the dissociation occurring on ionization in solution. Such a dissociation to give two neutral radicals is termed **homolytic** dissociation. At the moment at which bond dissociation occurs the molecule must be at a sufficiently high energy above average energy to equal or exceed the bond energy of the bond that dissociates.[1] The lower the dissociation energy, the lower is the temperature required for effecting the dissociation. In general, dissociation energies are relatively low for bonds between two like atoms. For example, the Br—Br and O—O dissociation energies are 50 kcal. per mole or less, in contrast to the C—H dissociation energy of about 100 kcal. and the C—Br value of about 70 kcal. For generation of radicals to initiate radical chain reactions (see below), substances containing the O—O bond are most commonly used. Di-*t*-butyl peroxide, *t*-Bu—O—O—*t*-Bu, dissociates at temperatures of about 130°, while diacetyl peroxide, Ac—O—O—Ac[2], dissociates at temperatures below 100°. The latter is quite dangerous when dry, because it will readily detonate from shock, but is relatively safe in solution.

A third method of generating radicals is by **irradiation** with a wavelength which is absorbed by the molecule in question. For example, visible light is absorbed by molecular bromine, and the energy so absorbed exceeds the dissociation energy, so bromine atoms are formed (Eq. 1).

$$\text{Br—Br} \xrightarrow[\text{light}]{\text{visible}} 2\text{Br·} \tag{1}$$

---

[1] Bond energies, as determined by heats of combustion, frequently differ somewhat from dissociation energies. This is probably due to the fact that the radical formed immediately after the dissociation is not at the average energy for such a radical. Also, either bond energies or dissociation energies for specified bonds (such as C—C or C—H) vary significantly depending on the structure of the remainder of the molecule. Nevertheless, average values for dissociation energies of various bonds have been compiled, and they are useful for reference in determining the type of bond most useful for generation of radicals.

[2] In writing of formulas, it is common practice to designate the acetyl group, CH_3—C—, by Ac.
$$\overset{\|}{\underset{O}{}}$$

Many molecules absorb radiation in the ultraviolet region and give radicals which may react either with another part of the same molecule or with another molecule also included in the solution. The irradiation of milk to convert certain compounds present to vitamin D has been known for many years, but since 1950 the study of **photochemical** reactions has been greatly intensified, and a significant number of useful syntheses have been developed. These syntheses depend on the further conversion products of radicals generated by absorption of radiation of an appropriate wavelength.

Types of Reactions Given by Radicals

Radicals give types of reactions which have no counterpart in polar reactions, so the more important radical reactions will be illustrated with examples which are either of synthetic utility or of importance as side reactions in processes of synthetic usefulness.

Coupling

The joining of two radicals (Eq. 2) to form a covalent bond comprised of

$$R\cdot + R\cdot \longrightarrow R\text{---}R \tag{2}$$

one electron from each radical, is a highly exothermic reaction which is likely to occur whenever two radicals collide; however, there are very few processes in which coupling is the main reaction. Radicals are so reactive that they give some type of reaction with nearly any molecule with which they collide, hence the concentration usually remains too low to permit frequent collisions between two radicals.

One synthetic process (perhaps the only useful one) that depends on radical coupling is the **Kolbe electrolysis**, in which the anion of an acid is oxidized electrolytically (Eq. 3). The acetoxy radical rapidly fragments in the

$$
\underset{\substack{\|\\O}}{R\text{---}C\text{---}O^-} \xrightarrow[\substack{\text{oxidation}\\\text{at anode}}]{\text{electrolytic}} \underset{\substack{\|\\O}}{R\text{---}C\text{---}O\cdot} + e \tag{3}
$$
$$\longrightarrow R\cdot + CO_2$$

manner shown (cf. fragmentation of radicals below). The reaction is run at a high current density so that a sufficiently high concentration of radicals builds up, in the region of the anode or possibly directly at the surface of the anode, so that the coupling reaction occurs in rather high yield if the radical is primary. Secondary radicals couple much less readily than primary ones, probably due to steric factors, so if R is secondary the yield of coupling product is poor, usually less than 30%. As might be expected, the tertiary radical gives no coupling product.

In a radical which couples or gives some other desired reaction relatively slowly, side reactions may occur with the solvent, but there are also known two additional reactions involving the radical which are of little synthetic significance except as side reactions in processes where other reactions are desired. These reactions will be discussed next.

Oxidation

Removal of one electron from a radical gives a carbonium ion, and this is a side reaction in the Kolbe electrolysis (Eq. 4). The carbonium ion is also a

$$R\cdot \xrightarrow[\text{oxidation}]{\text{electrolytic}} R^+ + e \qquad (4)$$

highly reactive species, as previously discussed (Chap. 6), so it rapidly gives some further reaction such as loss of a proton to give an alkene.

Disproportionation

Conversion of a pair of radicals to an alkene and alkane (Eq. 5) is a reaction whose mechanism is poorly understood. The shift of a hydrogen from

$$2R\text{—}CH_2\text{—}CH_2\cdot \longrightarrow R\text{—}CH_2\text{—}CH_3 + R\text{—}CH\text{=}CH_2 \qquad (5)$$

one radical to the other probably occurs in more than one step. This is a side reaction in most syntheses involving radicals.

Fragmentation of Radicals

The fragmentation of radicals occurs (with one exception noted below) so as to give a cleavage between atoms two and three (the atom bearing the lone electron is numbered one). In the case of oxygen radicals, this cleavage occurs readily, sometimes as low as room temperature. The cleavage shown in Eq. 3 is such a process which occurs near room temperature. The electron transfers involved may be shown as in Eq. 6. Just as a double-barbed arrow is frequently

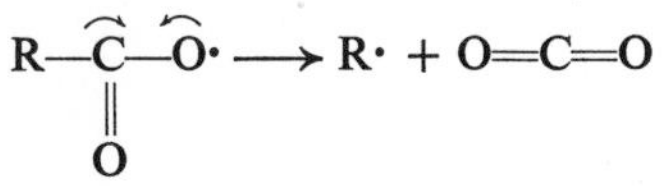

$$R\overset{\frown}{—}\overset{\frown}{C}\text{—}O\cdot \longrightarrow R\cdot + O\text{=}C\text{=}O \qquad (6)$$
$$\underset{O}{\overset{\|}{}}$$

used to indicate movement of an electron pair (e.g., cf. Eq. 6-24), the single-barbed arrow is used to indicate movement of one electron.

The usual pattern of radical fragmentation is not followed in instances where the lone electron is on a carbonyl carbon. In such structures, cleavage occurs between atoms one and two (Eq. 7). This altered pattern of cleavage

$$R\!-\!\underset{\underset{O}{\|}}{C}\!\cdot \longrightarrow R\!\cdot + CO \tag{7}$$

probably depends on elimination of the relatively stable carbon monoxide molecule (cf. Chap. 13, footnote 4).

Abstraction

A moderately important radical reaction, so far as concerns organic synthesis, is the abstraction of an atom from another molecule. A typical reaction of this sort is abstraction of hydrogen from an alkane, as shown in Eq. 8. This sort of reaction has sometimes been called a displacement reaction

$$CH_3\!-\!CH_3 + Br\!\cdot \longrightarrow \underset{\substack{\text{Ethyl}\\\text{radical}}}{CH_3\!-\!CH_2\!\cdot} + H\!-\!Br \tag{8}$$

of a radical, but this nomenclature is likely to be quite misleading. The process shown in Eq. 8 bears no resemblance to the polar reaction known as displacement, unless one regards the rest of the molecule as displaced from the hydrogen. It seems much more descriptive to say that the radical abstracted a hydrogen from the molecule.

The rate of a reaction of the kind shown in Eq. 8 will depend in part on the energy gain in forming the new molecule on the right; therefore, the nature of the radical as well as the nature of the atom abstracted are important. The bond energy of the bond broken might be assumed to be a very significant factor in determining which atom is abstracted; however, this proves to be less important than the amount the atom is shielded from attack. Electron shielding as well as steric protection prove important. The former factor is probably important, in spite of the net neutrality of the radical, because it has a lone electron that is unpaired. Illustrative of these factors, hydrogen is abstracted in Eq. 8; a carbon is not attacked, in spite of the fact that the dissociation energy of C—H is about 100 kcal. and that of C—C is only about 85 kcal. Further, hydrogen is abstracted from a bromoalkane rather than bromine, in spite of the fact that the C—Br dissociation energy is about 65 kcal.

Several important factors in abstraction are illustrated by Eq. 9. Although there are nine primary hydrogen atoms in isobutane and only one tertiary

$$\underset{\substack{|\\CH_3}}{\overset{\substack{H\\|}}{CH_3\!-\!C\!-\!CH_3}} + Br\!\cdot \longrightarrow \underset{\substack{|\\CH_3\\ \text{(predominantly)}}}{\overset{\substack{CH_3\\|}}{CH\!-\!C\!\cdot}} + H\!-\!Br \tag{9}$$

hydrogen atom, the principal radical formed is the tertiary radical, not the primary isobutyl radical. This is because of the lower dissociation energy of the tertiary hydrogen, combined with the fact that the energy gain in forming hydrogen bromide is such that the activation energy for the conversion is moderately large. If the chlorine atom is used, the activation energy is much lower, so the differentiation between primary and tertiary nearly vanishes. Whenever discrimination between primary, secondary, and tertiary hydrogens is desired, bromine should be used in preference to chlorine. This is of significance in a few useful syntheses involving halogenation of alkanes, a reaction discussed below.

Chain reactions. Halogenation of alkanes. In a process such as shown in Eqs. 8 and 9, the radical formed would be expected to rapidly react further. This is the case, and proper reactants can result in a self-sustaining cycle which does not consume radicals. Such a chain reaction is responsible for the halogenation of alkanes, for which the net reaction is shown in Eq. 10.

$$CH_4 + Br_2 \xrightarrow{\text{light}} CH_3{-}Br + HBr \tag{10}$$

The process involves the **initiating step** by which radicals are generated, the homolytic dissociation of bromine as shown in Eq. 1, followed by the **chain-propagating** steps shown in Eqs. 11 and 12. It will be noted that the radical

$$CH_4 + Br\cdot \longrightarrow \cdot CH_3 + HBr \tag{11}$$

$$\cdot CH_3 + Br_2 \longrightarrow CH_3{-}Br + Br\cdot \tag{12}$$

generated in the first step enters the second step which generates the radical required in the first step. The over-all process consumes only methane and molecular bromine, as shown in Eq. 10. Theoretically, one bromine atom could cause bromination of an indefinite amount of methane, according to Eqs. 11 and 12; however, there is some dissipation of atoms by **chain-terminating reactions**, such as coupling of two methyl radicals to give ethane. As mentioned in an earlier paragraph, this reaction occurs rarely on account of the low concentration of radicals. For radicals larger than methyl, disproportionation (Eq. 5) is another chain-terminating step.

It should be mentioned that chain reactions succeed only when energy relations are such as to favor the combination of reactions. For example, in the process just described, it is important that bromine is extracted from molecular bromine more readily than from methyl bromide, and that the extraction of bromine from molecular bromine is favored over extraction of hydrogen from methane by the methyl radical. These considerations lead to the most serious side reaction in the process just discussed, if one is trying to make methyl bromide. *Hydrogen is abstracted from methyl bromide at least as easily as from methane.* This means that reactions 13 through 15 are proceeding concurrently with reaction 10. The ratio of bromine to methane will affect the ratio of the four organic products of these reactions, but one product cannot be formed to the exclusion of the others. For these reasons, halogenation of alkanes is of

$$CH_3\text{—}Br + Br_2 \longrightarrow CH_2Br_2 + HBr \qquad (13)$$
Methylene dibromide

$$CH_2Br_2 + Br_2 \longrightarrow CHBr_3 + HBr \qquad (14)$$
Bromoform

$$CHBr_3 + Br_2 \longrightarrow CBr_4 + HBr \qquad (15)$$
Carbon
tetrabromide

limited usefulness. Since halogenation is, nevertheless, the most important reaction of alkanes, except combustion, it follows that the chief use of alkanes is for fuel.

In practice, the only product in Eqs. 10 and 13 through 15 that is manufactured by halogenation is carbon tetrabromide. The others are best made in different ways that are more subject to control. For example, methyl bromide is made from methanol, as discussed earlier. On account of its expense, carbon tetrabromide is of limited usefulness; however, carbon tetrachloride, prepared by chlorination of methane, is a widely useful solvent.[3] A few higher alkanes are chlorinated commercially to give mixtures of chloroalkanes of use as solvents.

Addition

The addition of a radical to an unsaturated linkage is no doubt the most important reaction of radicals. In addition to providing several syntheses of relatively low molecular weight compounds (such compounds as discussed thus far), this reaction is the basis for a substantial number of the polymerizations used to produce plastics and elastomers (synthetic rubber and related compounds).

Polymerization. Exposure of an alkene to a source of radicals will initiate chain reactions which result in polymerization. A wide variety of radicals will initiate the process, but peroxides that are easily dissociated by heat are common initiators. For polymerization of ethylene, di-*t*-butyl peroxide

---

[3] In common with virtually all halogenated alkanes, carbon tetrachloride is dangerously toxic when inhaled in significant quantities. Furthermore, damage is to the liver, which is not repaired in time; so the toxic effect is cumulative. Since carbon tetrachloride is a widely used "dry cleaner" or "spot remover," caution should be exercised that ventilation is adequate when a "non-flammable" spot remover is used. Cleaners labeled "Flammable" are usually mixtures of alkanes, low-boiling fractions from petroleum distillation. In a dry cleaner, one must accept either flammability or toxicity—protection against the former is easier.

may serve as initiator (Eqs. 16 and 17). The chain continues by reaction of

$$(CH_3)_3C\!-\!O\!-\!O\!-\!C(CH_3)_3 \xrightarrow{\Delta} 2(CH_3)_3CO\cdot \tag{16}$$

$$(CH_3)_3CO\cdot + CH_2\!=\!CH_2 \longrightarrow (CH_3)_3CO\!-\!CH_2\!-\!CH_2\cdot \tag{17}$$

additional molecules of ethylene:

$$(CH_3)_3C\!-\!O\!-\!CH_2\!-\!CH_2\cdot \quad CH_2\!=\!CH_2 \ \ CH_2\!=\!CH_2 \ \ CH_2\!=\!CH_2 \ \text{etc.}$$

Of course the sequence shown above occurs stepwise—the initial radical adds to ethylene, the resultant radical adds to another ethylene, and so on until the chain is terminated by a chain-terminating reaction or because the polymer becomes so insoluble that any further reaction would be a heterogeneous process. The usual chain-terminating steps apply, such as disproportionation, hydrogen abstraction, or coupling. Many factors control the average chain length of the polymer, as well as its exact physical properties, including the nature of the initiator, the temperature, solvent, etc. These factors have been intensively investigated, for polyethylene is manufactured in truly enormous quantities. Numerous patents have been filed to cover specific details of this technology.

Direction of radical addition. In case a 1-alkene of higher molecular weight than ethylene is used in polymerization (or other radical addition reactions), addition proves to prefer the 1-carbon by a very large margin. This results from the fact that the order of radical stability is the same as that of carbonium ion stability, as follows: tertiary > secondary > primary. The difference in energy between the types of radicals is not so great as in the case of carbonium ions; however, it is large enough to cause a highly directed reaction. Polymerization of propylene occurs then, as shown in Eqs. 18 and 19, where I·

$$I\cdot + CH_3\!-\!CH\!=\!CH_2 \longrightarrow \underset{\underset{CH_2I}{|}}{CH_3\!-\!CH\cdot} \tag{18}$$

$$\underset{\underset{CH_2I}{|}}{CH_3\!-\!CH\cdot} + CH_3\!-\!CH\!=\!CH_2 \longrightarrow \underset{\underset{CH_2I}{|}}{CH_3\!-\!CH}\!-\!CH_2\!-\!\underset{\underset{CH_3}{|}}{CH\cdot} \tag{19}$$

is the radical generated by an initiator. It may be noted that addition to the end-carbon results in the secondary radical, and this in turn gives a branched chain in the polymer. For this reason, polypropylene has different properties than polyethylene, especially as regards an increased stiffness; so this more expensive polymer is being manufactured in increasingly larger amounts.

The clear plastic known by the trade names of Plexiglas or Lucite is a polymer of the substituted alkene, methyl methacrylate, while polymers of acrylonitrile are useful as filaments which can be spun into fibers. Common trade names for the latter are Orlon and Acrilan.

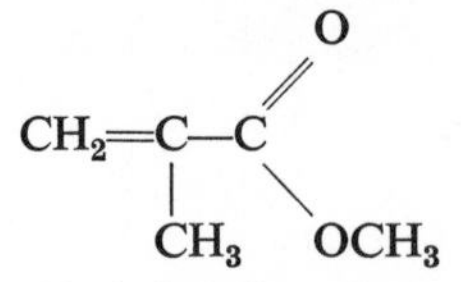

$$CH_2=C-C \underset{CH_3 \quad OCH_3}{\overset{O}{\diagup}}$$

Methyl methacrylate

$$CH_2=CH-CN$$

Acrylonitrile

One of the most remarkable polymers is that of tetrafluoroethylene, $CF_2=CF_2$, which is marketed under the trade name, Teflon. This polymer has a soft, tough, greasy consistency which makes it useful in bearings, but its most remarkable properties are its resistance to attack by chemical reagents and high temperature. At 500°, it decomposes slowly while glowing red.

Elastomeric material, suitable for use as rubber, is frequently made from a di-unsaturated monomer[4] in which the double bonds are **conjugated**. Such a compound has one single bond between the two double bonds, so can give an unsaturated polymer by way of a 1,4-*addition reaction*, as illustrated in Eqs. 20

$$I\cdot + \quad CH_2=CH-CH=CH_2 \longrightarrow I-CH_2-CH=CH-CH_2\cdot \qquad (20)$$

1,3-Butadiene

$$I-CH_2-CH=CH-CH_2\cdot + CH_2=CH-CH=CH_2 \longrightarrow$$
$$I-CH_2-CH=CH-CH_2-CH_2-CH=CH-CH_2\cdot \overset{etc.}{\longrightarrow} \quad (21)$$

and 21. Synthetic elastomers are frequently **co-polymers** formed by polymerizing a mixture of butadiene and a mono-unsaturated compound. This gives a wider spacing between the double bonds in the polymer. The stretchability of elastomers, as well as other important properties, depend on the geometric isomerism at the double bonds, and this has been the subject of much study. *Natural rubber* consists of a polymerized chain of units of isoprene, with a specific geometry in the polymerization. Indeed, a host of other natural products

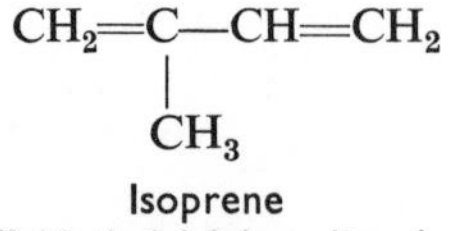

$$CH_2=C-CH=CH_2 \atop CH_3$$

Isoprene
(2-Methyl-1,3-butadiene)

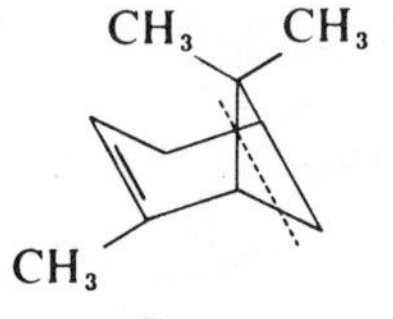

α-Pinene

are formed from isoprene units joined in various sequences in rings or chains. A bicyclic substance of this sort is α-pinene, the chief constituent of turpentine.

---

[4] The term, monomer, is used in describing the low molecular weight molecule used in the reaction which generates the polymer.

If the α-pinene formula is inspected carefully, it may be noted that one isoprene unit is on the right-hand side of the dotted line and the other is on the left. The isoprenoid structure occurs in so many natural products that application of the so-called "isoprene rule" has been of great help in elucidating many structures.

Monomeric radical additions. If an alkene and an initiator are accompanied by a molecule containing an atom which is abstracted more rapidly than the radical addition reaction occurs, a chain reaction ensues which results in addition to the alkene. Such a process is addition of chloroform to a 1-alkene (Eqs. 22 through 24). It may be noted that Eqs. 23 and 24 constitute

$$I\cdot + H-CCl_3 \longrightarrow I-H + \cdot CCl_3 \tag{22}$$

$$R-CH=CH_2 + \cdot CCl_3 \longrightarrow R-\underset{\cdot}{C}H-CH_2-CCl_3 \tag{23}$$

$$R-\underset{\cdot}{C}H-CH_2-CCl_3 + H-CCl_3 \longrightarrow R-CH_2-CH_2-CCl_3 + \cdot CCl_3 \tag{24}$$

the chain reaction, which will sustain itself until a chain-terminating reaction occurs.

The **peroxide-catalyzed addition of hydrogen bromide** to 1-alkenes is of occasional synthetic utility, and of great interest in connection with the development of understanding of the mechanisms of addition reactions to alkenes. A peroxide will abstract hydrogen from hydrogen bromide (Eq. 25) and thereby initiate a chain reaction (Eqs. 26 and 27) which results in addition of hydrogen

$$R-O\cdot + HBr \longrightarrow R-O-H + Br\cdot \tag{25}$$

$$R-CH=CH_2 + Br\cdot \longrightarrow R-\underset{\cdot}{C}H-CH_2-Br \tag{26}$$

$$R-\underset{\cdot}{C}H-CH_2-Br + H-Br \longrightarrow R-CH_2-CH_2-Br + Br\cdot \tag{27}$$

bromide to the multiple bond in the opposite sense to that predicted by the Markownikoff rule. This results from the bromine atom attacking in such a position as to give the more stable secondary radical as intermediate.

It should be emphasized that *hydrogen bromide is the only halogen acid which gives the peroxide effect.* Hydrogen chloride fails to give the radical reaction because the hydrogen-chlorine bond is of too high energy to permit an abstraction such as shown in Eq. 25. Hydrogen iodide fails for a different reason—the carbon-iodine bond is not of sufficient energy to promote the reaction analogous to Eq. 26. In the bromine-containing compounds, bond energies are balanced so that the necessary reactions are favored.

Since alkenes are sometimes oxidized by oxygen in air to give a peroxide, which dissociates readily to give a low concentration of radicals, old samples of alkene will frequently give anti-Markownikoff addition of hydrogen bromide, without addition of a peroxide. Freshly distilled alkene will give Markownikoff addition, however. This situation was quite confusing to chemists seeking to predict the direction of addition to alkenes until the early nineteen-thirties, when the pioneering studies of M. S. Kharasch[5] on radical reactions revealed the true situation.

Rearrangement of Free Radicals

It should be emphasized at the outset that a free radical is not at all prone to rearrange, in comparison to a carbonium ion, and this is a great virtue of the radical reactions. Even the neopentyl radical has not been observed to rearrange.

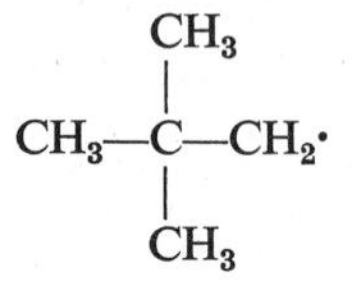

$$
\begin{array}{c}
CH_3 \\
| \\
CH_3\!-\!C\!-\!CH_2\!\cdot \\
| \\
CH_3
\end{array}
$$

Neopentyl radical

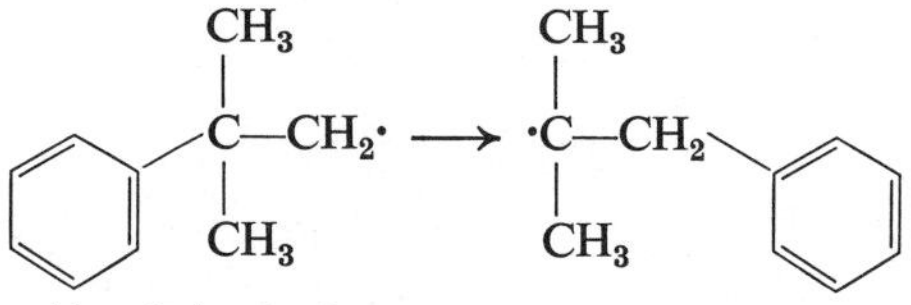

$$
\begin{array}{ccc}
CH_3 & & CH_3 \\
| & & | \\
C6H5\!-\!C\!-\!CH_2\!\cdot & \longrightarrow & \cdot C\!-\!CH_2\!-\!C6H5 \\
| & & | \\
CH_3 & & CH_3
\end{array} \tag{28}
$$

Neophyl radical

Only when there is introduced a group especially prone to rearrange, as in the neophyl radical, has rearrangement been observed. The special properties of the phenyl group will be discussed in the next chapter. Even in this case, there is a significant activation energy to the reaction, so that rearrangement frequently does not compete successfully with other radical reactions unless dilute solutions are used for the reaction. The more dilute the solution the longer the radical exists before encountering another species with which to react. Since the rearrangement does not require encountering another species, dilution favors rearrangement. The bromination shown in Eq. 29 has been accomplished without rearrangement.

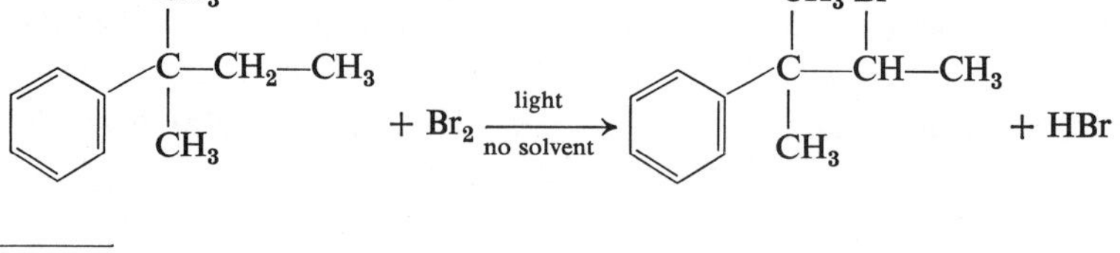

$$
\begin{array}{c}
CH_3 \\
| \\
C6H5\!-\!C\!-\!CH_2\!-\!CH_3 \\
| \\
CH_3
\end{array}
+ Br_2 \xrightarrow[\text{no solvent}]{\text{light}}
\begin{array}{c}
CH_3\ Br \\
|\quad | \\
C6H5\!-\!C\!-\!CH\!-\!CH_3 \\
| \\
CH_3
\end{array}
+ HBr \tag{29}
$$

---

[5] Professor M. S. Kharasch, who died in 1957 while on a scientific mission in Europe, spent the most productive part of his career at the University of Chicago. Virtually all the development of the chemistry of free radicals has been due to Kharasch and his students, notably Prof. Cheves Walling, Columbia University, Dr. Frank Mayo, Stanford Research Institute, and Prof. W. H. Urry, University of Chicago.

EXERCISES

1. (a) Write equations for the steps involved in addition of hydrogen bromide to 2-methyl-2-butene with careful exclusion of peroxides, then with addition of a peroxide. (b) Write equations for the similar reaction of hydrogen chloride.

2. Methyl mercaptan, CH_3—SH, the foul-smelling sulfur analog of methyl alcohol, gives ready abstraction by radicals of the hydrogen on sulfur. The resultant sulfur radical adds readily to double bonds. Write equations for the reactions occurring if a mixture of 1-hexene and methyl mercaptan is treated with a small amount of diacetyl peroxide.

3. Outline a sequence of reactions by which ethylene may be converted to the following compounds. Name these compounds.

(a) 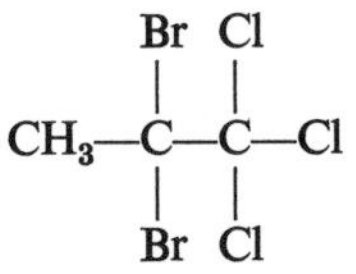
$$CH_3\underset{\underset{\displaystyle Br}{|}}{\overset{\overset{\displaystyle Br}{|}}{C}}\underset{\underset{\displaystyle Cl}{|}}{\overset{\overset{\displaystyle Cl}{|}}{C}}Cl$$

(b) $CH_3CH{=}CCl_2$

4. If the acid anion shown below were subjected to Kolbe electrolysis in methyl alcohol solution, by-products expected would include the ether shown on the right below. Write equations showing formation of the normal coupling product from the electrolysis, as well as three by-products, including the ether shown below.

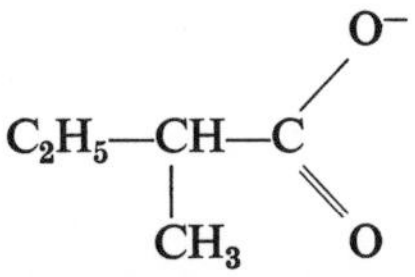

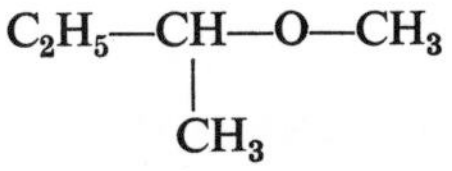

$$C_2H_5\underset{\underset{\displaystyle CH_3}{|}}{CH}\overset{\overset{\displaystyle O^-}{\diagup}}{\underset{\displaystyle\diagdown O}{C}}$$

$$C_2H_5\underset{\underset{\displaystyle CH_3}{|}}{CH}{-}O{-}CH_3$$

5. Write equations showing how a pure sample of 2-bromopentane may be synthesized from 1-pentanol and obtained free of 1- and 3-bromopentanes. (Note: 1- and 2-bromopentanes may be separated by fractional distillation; 2- and 3-bromopentanes cannot be thus separated.)

6. Let us suppose that 1,3-butadiene and 1-hexene are co-polymerized with a peroxide catalyst. Write a sequence in the polymer chain consisting of the units in order: hexene-butadiene-hexene-hexene-butadiene.

7. When di-*t*-butyl peroxide is used to catalyze free radical reactions, there is usually formed a little acetone, $CH_3\underset{\underset{\displaystyle O}{\|}}{C}CH_3$. Write the equations leading to this product.

Stabilization of Organic Molecules by Electron Delocalization

It has long been recognized that many unsaturated structures in organic molecules or ions have lower energies than would normally be predicted. In some instances, this lowering of energy is quite large, 30 kcal. or more per mole. During the nineteen-thirties, there was developed a rather extensive application of the theory that this lowering of energy should be ascribed to the occurrence of molecular orbitals large enough to encompass more than two atoms. Just as a lowering of energy results from formation of molecular orbitals wherein electrons may be associated with two positive nuclei, a further lowering of energy should result if association of an electron pair with more than two nuclei becomes possible by virtue of larger molecular orbitals. Thus, the electrons in question are no longer localized around two atoms, but have become **delocalized**, associated with more than two atoms. In the early discussions of this phenomenon, it was termed **resonance**, and this term has continued in general usage, in spite of the fact that there is possible some confusion with other applications of this term to wholly unrelated physical phenomena.

The basic theory of resonance has been so successful in correlating many phenomena that it has become an integral part of an understanding of the behavior of organic molecules. The present chapter will include consideration of a number of examples sufficient to serve as a basis for development of this theory. Numerous additional manifestations of **resonance stabilization** (energy-lowering by electron delocalization) will be encountered in later chapters.

Basis for the Acidity of Carboxylic Acids

In suitable solvents of high dielectric constant, notably water, a carboxylic acid is ionized to the extent of a few per cent, as shown[1] in Eq. 1. Thus, the

$$
\begin{array}{ccc}
 & O & O \\
 & \parallel & \parallel \\
R-C & \rightleftarrows R-C & + H^+ \\
 & \diagdown & \diagdown \\
 & OH & O^-
\end{array}
\tag{1}
$$

molecule ionizes in water to furnish hydrogen ion and is an acid in the classical sense. Since the proton is an electron acceptor, the carboxylic acids are also acids in the Lewis sense. In contrast, a substance such as ethyl alcohol, which also has hydrogen bonded to oxygen, does not ionize to a significant extent. Alcohol does have some acidity, it will react with metallic sodium to give the alkoxide ion; however, it is less acidic than water, so the actual ionization of ethyl alcohol (Eq. 2) is negligible. Since the proton is a product in both Eq. 1

$$
C_2H_5-OH\,[\rightleftarrows C_2H_5O^- + H^+]
\tag{2}
$$

and Eq. 2, the very large difference in position of equilibrium in the two cases must be ascribed to the energy differences between the associated species and the anions. It may be recalled that the position of equilibrium depends on the energy difference between the species on the two sides of the equation. Thus, the *anion in Eq. 1 must be of considerably lower energy in relation to the associated species than is the case in Eq. 2.*

In order to understand the possibility for delocalization of electrons in the carboxylate anion, we may consider the electronic structure of this ion in some detail. As it is written in Eq. 1 the charge is placed on the lower oxygen and the upper oxygen is doubly bonded to carbon. This structure results from

---

[1] A very important factor in displacing equilibrium forward in any ionization is solvation of the ions; hence the position of an equilibrium such as shown in Eq. 1 varies greatly in different solvents. In general, good ionizing solvents have a high dielectric constant, but power to solvate ions also depends on other factors. In water, which is an excellent ionizing solvent, a large percentage of the protons are combined with water to give hydronium ions (previously mentioned in Eq. 3-2) so that the following equation, which is an acid-base reaction, depicts the principal products resulting from "ionization" of an acid in water:

$$
\begin{array}{ccccc}
 & O & & O & & \\
 & \parallel & & \parallel & & \overset{+}{} \\
R-C & + H-O-H & \rightleftarrows R-C & + H-O-H \\
 & \diagdown & & \diagdown & & \mid \\
 & OH & & O^- & & H
\end{array}
$$

According to this equation, the carboxylic acid acts as a Lewis acid in the sense that the hydrogen accepts an electron pair as it departs from carboxyl.

removal of the proton from the lower oxygen in the carboxylic acid. Obviously, we may consider rotation of the molecule in space (turn the paper upside down, for example) and place the charged oxygen up. Regardless of how the molecule is orientated in space, however, the fact remains that one oxygen is designated as carrying a single bond and a charge, the other a double bond. By the transfer of electrons indicated below, however, the charge is shifted from one oxygen to the other:

$$\begin{array}{cc}
\overset{\cdot\cdot}{\underset{\cdot\cdot}{:O}}\!\!\curvearrowright & \overset{\cdot\cdot}{\underset{\cdot\cdot}{:O:}}^{-} \\
\overset{\cdot\cdot}{\underset{\cdot\cdot}{R:C:O:}}^{-} & \overset{\cdot\cdot}{\underset{\cdot\cdot}{R:C::O:}} \\
\end{array}$$

So far as chemical reactions and chemical structure are concerned, the two formulas above are identical, for the positions of atoms relative to each other are the same; in fact, *the only difference between the formulas as written is in the position of electrons.*

If we consider the nature of a double bond in terms of the molecular orbital theory of valence, we will remember (Chap. 8) that the "second" bond in a double bond is a π-bond consisting of the overlapping orbitals of the p electrons on adjacent atoms. Thus, the π-bonds corresponding to the positions of the

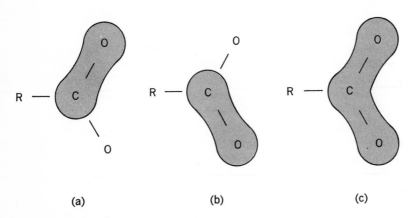

Fig. 1. The carboxylate anion. In (a) and (b) are shown cross sections of π-orbitals for bonding to one or the other of the oxygen atoms. In (c) is shown the true nature of this resonance-stabilized anion, which contains the three-atom π-orbital. Concerning charge distribution in this anion, refer to footnote 2, p. 157.

double bonds in the two forms for the carboxylate anion are those indicated in Fig. 1, (a) and (b). This is merely a pictorial representation of the fact that the carbon may form a π-bond with either of the oxygens. If, on the other hand, we consider a larger π-orbital (or two expanded, overlapping orbitals) extending from oxygen to oxygen by way of the carbon and accommodating four electrons, the situation would be that represented in Fig. 1(c). If we remember that a lowering of energy results when electrons occupy an orbital encompassing two positive nuclei, it follows logically that an orbital encompassing three positive nuclei would result in a still greater lowering of energy and would therefore be favored over the orbital encompassing only two nuclei.[2] Furthermore, there would be a lowering of energy for the carboxylate anion below the value it would have if there were no delocalization of electrons. Thus, the equilibrium in the dissociation is displaced forward.

There are many different structures known in organic molecules which dissociate in solution to give protons. With one common exception, the sulfonic acids, acidity is attributable to resonance stabilization of the anion formed on ionization; so the phenomenon here described for carboxylic acids is a general one of considerable importance.

Resonance forms. The writing of a species such as the carboxylate anion with delocalized electrons is a bit awkward since use of the classical methods of writing formulas requires putting the charge and double bond partly in two positions. This is sometimes effected as shown on the left, below;

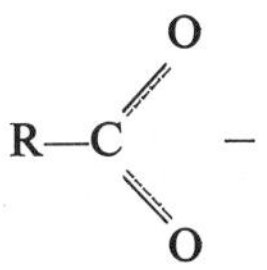

Carboxylate anion
showing delocalized charge

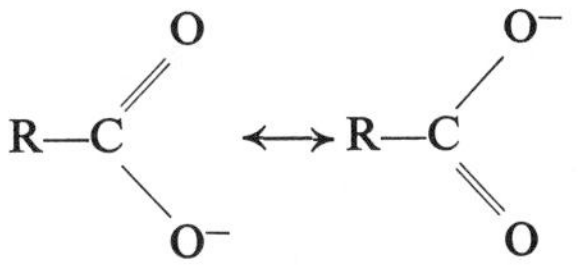

Resonance forms of the
carboxylate anion

however, this type of formulation lacks several useful features[2] inherent in writing the two classical formulas showing the charge and π-bond localized. Such formulas are known as **resonance forms**, and they are actually a representation of the limiting positions in which the electrons may be. The electrons are regarded as actually in these limiting positions sometimes, but at other times they are located in various other positions within the enlarged orbital. These resonance forms are quite useful in discussion of reaction mechanisms (see below) and in predicting the site of reaction that will give a stable molecule.[2]

---

[2] The limiting assumptions and mathematical calculations on which molecular orbital theory is based do, indeed, indicate that such a three-atom orbital (or two orbitals occupying the same space) should be favored because of its lower energy. Further, four electrons should be accommodated in such an orbital. Since this enlarged orbital contains the electron pair giving a charge to the carboxylate anion, this charge is most accurately regarded as distributed over the three atoms involved in the large orbital represented in Fig. 1(c). It should be noted, however, that a stable compound would not result if this electron pair should be utilized by carbon to form a covalent bond with some positive group, for this would leave the two oxygens with one electron pair for each in a sigma bond and one more electron pair between them. This "extra" electron pair can be utilized effectively by one of the oxygens to form a bond, however, as in Eq. 1, for all valences become satisfied by formation of a π-bond between carbon and the other oxygen. This illustrates one very useful feature of writing the so-called resonance forms, discussed in this chapter, wherein the bonds are localized. It should be remembered, however, that the true electronic condition of a resonance hybrid is that shown in Fig. 1(c), wherein the electrons are delocalized.

Nevertheless, it should be recognized that resonance forms are a useful symbolism, not a representation of an actual molecule. The carboxylate anion is a single species whose properties may be regarded as resulting from hybridization of the properties of the resonance forms, hence the term **resonance hybrid** is frequently applied to a species in which delocalization of electrons occurs. In order to clearly designate formulas as resonance forms, a *single double-headed arrow* is placed between such formulas. In case there are more than two resonance forms, as is frequently the case, the formulas are written in line with single double-headed arrows between them, thus:

$$A \longleftrightarrow B \longleftrightarrow C \longleftrightarrow D$$

It is important to realize that the double-headed arrow indicates resonance forms, *not* equilibrium between the two formulas. Equilibrium between different molecules is indicated by two parallel arrows pointing in opposite directions. The resonance hybrid is only one substance, and the double-headed arrow indicates this.

Consequences of Resonance Stabilization

A prime consequence of electron delocalization is a lowering of energy, and this is always evident in the characteristics of a resonance hybrid. For example, the carboxylate anion has a sufficiently lowered energy to induce significant ionization in a carboxylic acid. In contrast, in an alcohol which has no π-bond, hence no opportunity for electron delocalization of the type being discussed, ionization does not occur. The magnitude of this lowering of energy resulting from electron delocalization can be measured, and it is known as the **resonance energy** of the molecule. One method of measuring this energy will be discussed later in this chapter in connection with the resonance stabilization of benzene. If it were possible to measure the energy change required for a molecule to pass from a condition in which the electrons are localized (e.g., as in a resonance form) to the condition that actually exists where the electrons are delocalized, the heat *evolved* in this change by a mole of the molecules would be the resonance energy. Thus, the *resonance energy is the energy the molecule does not have* on account of the occurrence of the delocalization phenomenon. There is no problem about where this energy goes; the molecule simply never has it. Although this type of designation may seem a bit unexpected, it may be likened to the usage in designating bond energy. Bond energy is the energy the molecule does not have because of the bond formation; therefore, a molecule containing high-energy bonds is a particularly stable molecule.

The description of the delocalization phenomenon predicts that the *bonds between carbon and the two oxygens in the carboxylate anion are the same kind of bond, a hybrid between a double and single bond.* The species should have the properties resulting from a hybridization of the resonance forms. There is considerable experimental evidence supporting the reality of this view, but one of the easiest to recognize concerns bond lengths. As described in Chapter 3, the various types of bonds have characteristic lengths (distances between the centers of the atoms). The bond length for the carbon-oxygen single bond is 1.51 Å. (cf. Table 3-2), while the carbon-oxygen double bond, as in an aldehyde,

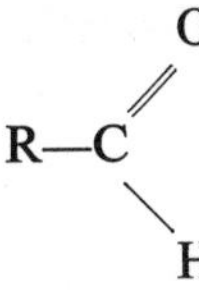

$$R—C\overset{\displaystyle O}{\underset{\displaystyle H}{\big/}}$$

, is shorter, 1.21 Å. Measurement of the interatomic distances in the

carboxylate anion by x-ray diffraction verifies the predictions stated above, in two senses: (a) each oxygen is the *same* distance from the carbon, (b) this distance is 1.27 Å., thus *between* the bond lengths for the double and single bonds.[3]

Sluggishness of Vinyl Halides in the Displacement Reaction

When a halogen atom is attached to a doubly-bonded carbon as in vinyl bromide, CH_2=CH—Br, the halogen proves unusually sluggish in the displacement reaction. On first consideration, this seems quite unexpected, for the double bond means less substituents on the carbon bearing halogen, hence one might assume that approach of the entering group should be facilitated. More than one factor probably contributes to the inertness of vinyl halides; however, there is good evidence indicating a significant electron delocalization in such structures. This delocalization, which lowers electron density on halogen and thus decreases its tendency to leave as a negative ion, may be easily visualized by considering a resonance form of the molecule:[4]

$$CH_2\!=\!CH\!-\!\overset{..}{\underset{..}{Br}}: \;\longleftrightarrow\; {}^{-}CH_2\!-\!CH::\overset{..}{\underset{..}{Br}}:^{+}$$

Since the resonance form on the right bears a plus charge on halogen, and since the character of the molecule is that of a hybrid of the resonance forms, the prediction is that the electron density on halogen is reduced by the adjacent double bond. Since the halide leaves as a negative ion in a displacement reaction, this lowering of electron density on the halogen should reduce the rate of the displacement. As mentioned above, this is the experimental fact, so application of resonance theory leads to deduction of the correct behavior.

---

[3] There is nothing in the theory, or in experimental observation, that indicates the bond distance in a resonance hybrid should be located midway between the two components. The prediction requires only that the hybrid distance must lie somewhere between the distances for the two types hybridized.

[4] Since resonance forms must differ from each other only in the positions of electrons, not in the positions of any atoms, those formulas qualify as resonance forms which can be changed into each other by movement of electrons only, as all valences remain satisfied. In the form for vinyl bromide shown on the left, curved arrows are used to indicate the transfer of electrons which results in the form shown on the right.

After a further study of examples of resonance stabilization, there will be considered factors which may be used to gain a qualitative estimate of the magnitude of resonance energy in a molecule, by examination of the resonance forms that may be written.

Abnormally High Reactivity of the Allylic System

An allylic radical bears a double bond one carbon removed from the point of attachment of the radical, thus: $CH_2=CH-CH_2-$. This interposition of the methylene between the double bond and the point of attachment of a functional group causes a dramatic change in the level of reactivity just described for a vinyl system. The allylic compounds are highly reactive, especially prone to give a carbonium ion as intermediate in displacement reactions. In conversion of crotyl alcohol (2-buten-1-ol) to the bromide, isomers are obtained as shown in Eq. 3. Isomers differing in this manner in the positions of a double bond and

$$CH_3-CH=CH-CH_2-OH + HBr \longrightarrow CH_3-CH=CH-CH_2-Br$$

Crotyl alcohol   and   + HOH   (3)

$$CH_3-CH-CH=CH_2$$
$$\quad\quad |$$
$$\quad\quad Br$$

functional group are known as **allylic isomers**. These isomers result because the crotyl alcohol is unusually prone to dissociate to give a carbonium ion, in marked contrast to saturated primary alcohols. Resonance stabilization of the carbonium ion is not only responsible for the predisposition towards its formation but also the formation of allylic isomers as products. Dissociation of the oxonium salt is shown in Eq. 4. The resonance stabilization responsible for

$$CH_3-CH=CH-CH_2\overset{+}{O}H_2 \longrightarrow CH_3-CH=CH-CH_2{}^+ \longleftrightarrow CH_3-\overset{+}{C}H-CH=CH_2$$
$$+ HOH \quad\quad (4)$$

lowering the energy of the allylic carbonium ion can be predicted from the fact that resonance forms may be written. Further, inspection of the resonance forms makes clear that the two isomers obtained must have halogen attached at the 1-position or the 3-position, *not* at the 2-position. Distribution of the electrons into the bonds required for a stable molecule cannot result if the entering group becomes attached at the 2-position; the group must become attached at the site of a plus charge in the resonance forms.

Terminal Addition to Conjugated Unsaturated Systems

In conjugated unsaturated systems, an addition may occur to a single double bond (1,2-addition) or it may occur at the ends of the conjugated system.

$$CH_2=CH-CH=CH_2 + Cl_2 \longrightarrow CH_2-CH-CH=CH_2$$
$$\quad\quad\quad\quad |\quad\ |$$
$$\quad\quad\quad\quad Cl\ \ Cl$$

and   (5)

$$CH_2-CH=CH-CH_2$$
$$|\quad\quad\quad\quad\quad |$$
$$Cl\quad\quad\quad\quad\quad Cl$$

The latter type of addition frequently predominates, as in the addition of chlorine to 1,3-butadiene (Eq. 5). In this type of addition, an intermediate resonance-stabilized ion is not easily formulated, if the chloronium ion (Chap. 9) is assumed to be an intermediate. A reasonable transition state for the second stage of the reaction would be the following:

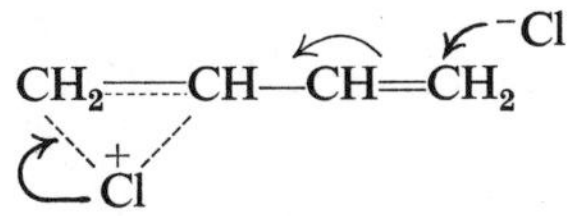

$$CH_2\text{------}CH\text{---}CH\text{===}CH_2 \quad \begin{array}{c} {}^-Cl \end{array}$$

In the addition of an unsymmetrical reagent such as HCl, however, the ion formed after proton addition is the *allylic carbonium ion*; therefore addition could occur at either the adjacent position or the terminal position, just as when such a carbonium ion is formed by another mechanism, for example, that in Eq. 4. It is of interest that 1,4-addition can occur in the ion pair in a nearly concerted reaction (cf. Chap. 9) by way of the conformation for this ion pair shown below:

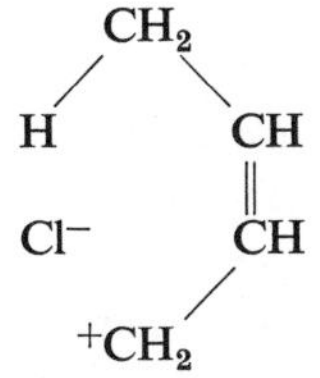

$$
\begin{array}{ccc}
 & CH_2 & \\
H & & CH \\
 & & \| \\
Cl^- & & CH \\
 & {}^+CH_2 &
\end{array}
$$

This type of transition state has the geometrically favored six-membered ring. Further, it should be remembered that a resonance hybrid has any site available for reaction as soon as the ion is formed. There is no time factor involved while a rearrangement occurs, as is the case in carbonium ion rearrangements. A resonance-stabilized ion is a single species; and the allylic carbonium ion can react at either of two sites.

The Structure of Benzene

Benzene[5] is the parent compound of the series known as "aromatic" compounds. Although the origin of the term may have been involved with

---

[5] The earliest name applied to this substance was *benzin*, but this name has never been applied extensively in the chemical literature; in fact, *benzine* is the name applied in the chemical industry to low-boiling fractions of alkanes obtained from petroleum. Such petroleum fractions are usually called *petroleum ether* or *ligroin* by research chemists, and these names are highly recommended in order to avoid confusion arising from use of a term pronounced in the same way as benzene. It should also be mentioned that in the German literature of the nineteenth century the name, *benzol*, was used instead of benzene, and benzol has continued in common use in the German literature, also in industrial usage in the United States, unfortunately. Benzene has been adopted in IUC nomenclature and is used in most countries by research chemists. Its use is recommended in order to avoid confusion arising from the ending -*ol*, which is normally applied as the characteristic suffix for hydroxy compounds such as alcohols (review IUC nomenclature in Chap. 5).

odor, present application of it has nothing to do with odor. *Aromatic compounds are those stabilized by electron delocalization in a cyclic conjugated system.* The magnitude of the resonance energy in aromatic systems is such that the addition reactions characteristic of unsaturated compounds fail to occur under normal conditions, and a sequence resulting in substitution occurs instead. This has such a profound effect on the types of reactions which are important in aromatic systems that the nature of resonance stabilization in aromatic systems will be included in the present chapter. Applications of the aromatic reactions in synthesis will be studied in subsequent chapters.

Historical development of the benzene structure. By the middle of the nineteenth century, it had been established that benzene, obtained from several sources including the tar distilling from coal heated in absence of air, has the molecular formula C_6H_6. It was further recognized that the structure of this substance must be quite different from that of the alkanes, alkenes, or alkynes, for benzene is rather stable to oxidation, in spite of having eight hydrogens fewer than required for the alkane, $C_6H_{14}(C_nH_{2n+2})$. The hydrogen ratio indicates double bonds in benzene, yet the substance gives none of the characteristic addition reactions of alkenes under mild conditions (cf. Chap. 9). Numerous structures were suggested for benzene, but it eventually became established that the structure proposed by Kekulé in 1865 was the only one consistent with the experimental observations. Kekulé's structure contained alternate double bonds in a six-membered ring, thus:

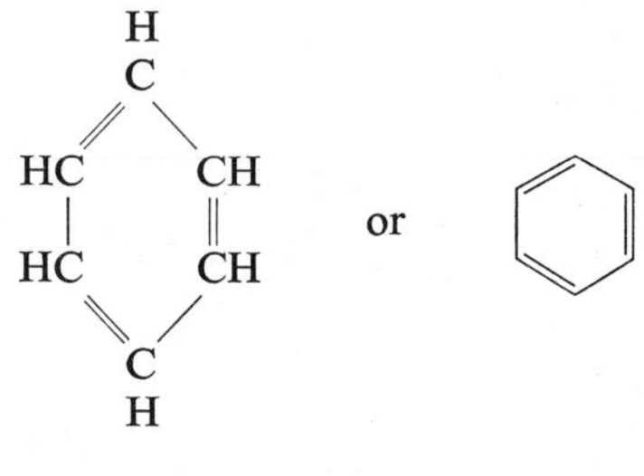

Important features of this structure are that all the hydrogens are equivalent, but if two hydrogens are substituted there are three possible arrangements of the substituted groups, as follows:

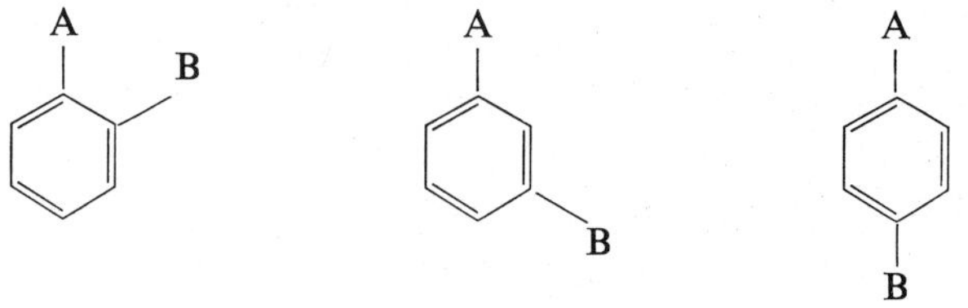

It had been established experimentally that substitution of one hydrogen can lead to only a single compound, but that substitution of two hydrogens can lead to three different compounds.

An objection which was raised to Kekulé's formula concerned a benzene substituted with groups on adjacent carbons, as in (a) and (b) below:

(a)   (b)

Formula (a) has a double bond between the substituents, while formula (b) does not; yet all efforts to isolate such isomers failed. Kekulé met this objection to his benzene formula by postulating that the double bonds are shifting rapidly back and forth, even at low temperature. Thus, only one substance could be isolated, the equilibrium mixture of the two structures. This interpretation was favorably received and Kekulé's formulation for benzene became generally accepted in spite of the fact that it could not explain the failure of benzene to add reagents in the normal manner of alkenes.

The modern concept of electron delocalization may be regarded super-ficially as differing only slightly from Kekulé's proposal of rapid equilibrium; however, there are actually some very important differences in the modern concept. First of all, benzene is a single substance with electron delocalization, not an equilibrium mixture; hence, isolation of isomers such as (a) and (b) under any circumstances whatever is impossible; these formulas are resonance forms. Secondly, the magnitude of the resonance energy (see below) involved in this type of electron delocalization is sufficient to effectively prohibit normal addition reactions at the double bonds.

Electron delocalization in benzene. Inspection of formulas (a) and (b) above indicates that the resonance hybrid of these structures would involve a π-orbital (actually a set of three overlapping π-orbitals) encompassing all six atoms in the ring. These orbitals would be two volumes, shaped somewhat like a doughnut, one on each side of the flat benzene ring. Such a structure, with indication of the π-orbitals, is illustrated in Fig. 2. The six π-electrons (equiv-alent to three double bonds) may be at any positions in the π-orbitals at a given moment, and will have moved on to other positions a moment later. It would be assumed that the energy-lowering resulting from such a large orbital would be substantial, and this proves to be the case, as discussed below.

One consequence of electron delocalization in benzene would be the occurrence of only one type of bond in the ring, the hybrid of the double and single bond. Thus, all the carbon-carbon distances should be the same. The experimental data give striking support to this prediction:

> carbon-carbon single bond distance: 1.54 Å.
> carbon-carbon double bond distance: 1.34 Å.
> carbon-carbon distance in benzene: 1.39 Å.

It may be noted that the benzene bond distance is indeed between the distances for the double and single bonds.

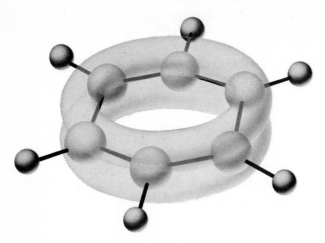

Fig. 2. π-Orbitals in the benzene molecule.

The resonance energy of benzene. Perhaps the reality of resonance stabilization may be best illustrated by a consideration of one method by which the resonance energy of benzene has been measured quantitatively. A study of the heat evolved in hydrogenation of unsaturated compounds is a direct method for determining the relative energy content of the unsaturated compounds hydrogenated. As discussed in Chapter 9, the stability of an alkene increases (energy becomes lower) as the number of substituents on the double bond increases. The bond energy of the π-bond is relatively constant, however, for compounds having the same number of substituents on the double bond and the same cis-trans isomerism. For example, the following has been observed:

$$
\begin{array}{ccc}
\text{CH}_3 & & \text{CH}_3 \\
\quad\diagdown & & \quad\diagdown \\
\text{CH} & & \text{CH}_2 \\
\parallel \quad + \text{H}_2 \xrightarrow[\text{catalyst}]{\text{Pt}} & & \mid \quad + \quad \begin{array}{l}\text{evolution of}\\ 28 \text{ kcal. of}\\ \text{heat per mole}\end{array} \\
\text{CH} & & \text{CH}_2 \\
\quad\diagup & & \quad\diagup \\
\text{CH}_3 & & \text{CH}_3
\end{array} \qquad (6)
$$

$$
\bigcirc\!\!\parallel + \text{H}_2 \xrightarrow[\text{catalyst}]{\text{Pt}} \bigcirc + \quad \begin{array}{l}\text{evolution of}\\ 28.6 \text{ kcal. of}\\ \text{heat per mole}\end{array} \qquad (7)
$$

Cyclohexene · · · · · · · · · · Cyclohexane

When heat is evolved, this constitutes loss of energy by the molecules, so the heat of reaction per mole, ΔH, for Eq. 6 is -28 kcal. Since very little entropy change (extent of disorder) should be involved in the transformation in Eqs. 6 and 7, the heat evolved should be very close to the free energy change (total true energy change) in the processes. There has, therefore, been a rather large decrease in energy in hydrogenation of 2-butene, so the reaction proceeds readily. The energy drop in hydrogenation of cyclohexene is only slightly different from that recorded in the 2-butene hydrogenation, in spite of the rather different type of structure.

If a cyclohexadiene, containing two double bonds, is hydrogenated, a drop in energy about twice that observed for the reaction in Eq. 7 would be predicted. This is the observation if 1,4-cyclohexadiene is hydrogenated; however, hydrogenation of 1,3-cyclohexadiene, containing conjugated double bonds, has yielded the following experimental results:

$$\text{(structure)} + 2H_2 \xrightarrow[\text{catalyst}]{\text{Pt}} \text{(structure)} \qquad \begin{array}{l} \text{observed } \Delta H, \ -55.4 \text{ kcal.} \\ \text{predicted } \Delta H, \ -57.2 \text{ kcal.} \\ \qquad\qquad (2 \times 28.6) \end{array} \qquad (8)$$

Thus the heat evolved in the hydrogenation in Eq. 8 is slightly, but significantly lower than the simple prediction; that is, the energy of the 1,3-cyclohexadiene is lower than predicted for two double bonds. This may reasonably be ascribed to resonance stabilization in the conjugated diene, and this is qualitatively indicated by examination of resonance forms[6] which may be written for the conjugated diene:

These limiting forms quickly indicate the possibility for electron delocalization in the conjugated diene, so the bond between the double bonds should have some double bond character. Physical measurement of the positions of the atoms in 1,3-butadiene has shown that the central bond (between the double bonds) is shorter than the normal bond length of the carbon-carbon single bond, although by a small factor. The amount of resonance stabilization in the conjugated diene should be small. One of the principles determining the magnitude of resonance energy to be expected is that resonance forms depending on charge separation do not make a large contribution to resonance stabilization (cf. summary at end of chapter).

---

[6] Resonance forms (or formulas bearing a formal resemblance to resonance forms) may be written for any alkene, by utilization of charge separation. Thus, such forms may be written for cyclohexene (left side of row) or 1,3-cyclohexadiene:

etc.

These forms, however, involve only two carbon atoms, hence there is indicated no delocalization of electrons beyond that occurring in a normal two-atom bond. *Resonance stabilization*, as normally considered by the organic chemist, *is that lowering of energy resulting from delocalization of electrons into orbitals encompassing more than two atomic nuclei.* Thus, resonance forms that may be written for a conjugated diene indicate that some resonance stabilization should be expected, while those that may be written for a non-conjugated diene do not indicate resonance stabilization.

Resonance forms involving only two atoms and depending on charge separation are frequently written in connection with consideration of reaction mechanisms; however, this is merely a convenient symbolism for indicating polarity of double bonds.

Hydrogenation of benzene proves much more difficult than is the case for the alkenes thus far discussed, and this immediately suggests a significant difference in the unsaturation in benzene. Under severe conditions, however, the hydrogenation can be accomplished, and the experimental results are as follows:

$$+ \; H_2 \xrightarrow[\text{high temperature}]{\substack{\text{Ni catalyst} \\ \text{high pressure}}}$$

observed ΔH, -49.8 kcal.
predicted ΔH, -85.8 kcal.   (9)
(ignoring resonance
stabilization)

The above data show clearly that the **resonance energy of benzene** is 36 kcal. per mole ($85.8 - 49.8$), for this is the amount that the energy of benzene is below what it would be if there were no electron delocalization. This is the amount of energy that benzene does not have on account of resonance stabilization.

As a final illustrative point, it may be mentioned that cycloheptatriene, with three conjugated double bonds, has only a small resonance energy, for

Cycloheptatriene

electron delocalization can be accomplished only by virtue of the forms with separation of charge. As noted above, such delocalization results in a relatively small energy gain. Particularly large energy gains result from limiting forms which are structurally identical and not dependent on charge separation. Such forms occur in the carboxylate anion[7] and in benzene.

Energy relationships in benzene and its hydrogenation products. By subtraction of appropriate values for ΔH given in the equations cited above, the energy differences assembled in Fig. 3 may be determined. The data in this chart make clear the fact that the resonance energy of benzene is so large that benzene has a lower energy than 1,3-cyclohexadiene. It follows that addition of one mole of hydrogen (or some other reagent) to benzene results in an *increase* in energy. Addition of a second and a third mole of hydrogen results in an energy drop, as usual in addition reactions to alkenes; however, these energetically favored reactions can occur only *after* the energetically unfavored initial addition occurs. This makes clear the reason why benzene does not give the facile addition reactions characteristic of alkenes.

Chemical reactions of benzene. Since addition of the first mole of a reagent to benzene requires an increase in energy, the drastic conditions necessary to accomplish this initial addition give an extremely rapid reaction with

---

[7] Distinction should be drawn between a charged species, such as the carboxylate anion, and a species whose charges result from charge separation, i.e., movement of an electron pair so as to generate one positive charge and one negative charge.

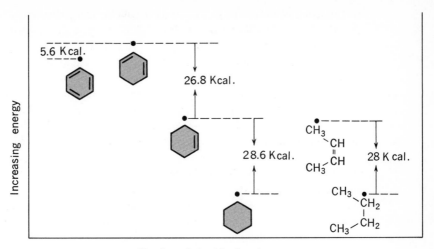

Fig. 3. Energy relationships in benzene and its hydrogenation products.

the normal unsaturated linkages remaining after the resonance stabilized system of double bonds is broken by the first addition. Thus, hydrogenation of benzene gives no cyclohexadiene or cyclohexene, only cyclohexane.

Addition of other reagents to benzene is subject to the same limitations as is hydrogenation. The addition of chlorine to benzene and other alkenes is illustrated in Eqs. 10 through 12.

$$CH_3-CH=CH-CH_3 + Cl_2 \xrightarrow[\text{room temperature}]{\text{rapid at}} CH_3-\underset{\underset{Cl}{|}}{CH}-\underset{\underset{Cl}{|}}{CH}-CH_3 \qquad (10)$$

$$\text{\raisebox{0pt}{⬡}} + 2Cl_2 \xrightarrow[\text{two steps}]{\text{rapid at room temperature}} \qquad (11)$$

$$+ Cl_2 \longrightarrow \text{some dichloro compound isolable}$$

$$\text{⬡} + 3Cl_2 \xrightarrow[\text{room temperature}]{\text{no reaction at}}$$

$$\xrightarrow[\text{high pressure}]{\text{high temperature}} \qquad (12)$$

In the reaction shown in Eq. 12, only hexachlorocyclohexane[8] is isolable from the reaction. If less than three moles of chlorine are used, benzene is recovered, while no di- or tetra-chloro compounds are isolated.

In the normal addition reactions to alkenes, e.g., chlorine as cited above, the electrons in the double bond must make a nucleophilic attack on the reagent to displace a negative ion. The addition reaction is completed in a second step involving reaction of the cation generated from the alkene and the displaced anion. On account of the great energy increase in the initial addition to benzene, high temperature is required to give an appreciable rate of reaction (appreciable fraction of the molecules at an energy high enough to reach the transition state). If, on the other hand, the electrophilic reagent consists of a positive ion generated in some way, attack of this species on benzene gives a lower energy transition state. This is a logical consequence since a positive ion should be a much stronger electrophile than a species from which a negative ion must be displaced before the new bond can be formed. Such a positive ion may be formed in several ways, of which one is attack on bromine by the Lewis acid, ferric bromide (Eq. 13).

$$Br—Br + FeBr_3 \longrightarrow {}^-FeBr_4 + Br^+ \tag{13}$$

Although bromine does not react with benzene unless at very high temperature, under pressure, addition of ferric bromide causes reaction to occur under mild conditions, on account of generation of the positive bromine species. Addition of such a positive species to benzene (Eq. 14) gives an intermediate of the same

$$\tag{14}$$

type that results from normal addition reactions to an alkene; however, *the addition is not completed* by addition of a negative fragment at the site of the plus charge in the transition state, for this would give a higher energy species than benzene, as discussed above. Instead, a proton is lost[9] from carbon to give a resonance-stabilized benzene derivative (Eq. 14). Thus, the *over-all result of the reaction is substitution* of a bromine in the benzene ring. Although the

---

[8] Hexachlorocyclohexane has found much use as an insecticide. Several geometrical isomers are possible in this compound, depending on which chlorine atoms are *cis* to each other. One of the geometrical isomers is far more effective as an insecticide, and another one has a rather disagreeable odor; so the insecticidal isomer is commercially separated and marketed under the name *Lindane*. It is of interest that although Lindane is a very effective insecticide it stimulates the growth of mites; therefore a miticide must be included in Lindane sprays.

[9] Ferric bromide is regenerated by Eq. 15, so the reaction consumes only bromine and

$$H^+ + {}^-FeBr_4 \longrightarrow FeBr_3 + HBr \tag{15}$$

benzene. A catalytic amount of ferric bromide suffices.

reaction is initiated by attack of a positive species on a double bond, as usual in alkene addition reactions, the addition cannot be completed on account of the energetically unfavorable reaction product that would result. There is available a lower-energy product, reached by loss of a proton. This product has an energy sufficiently lower than benzene to make the final step of this process non-reversible.

Substitution reactions in benzene, analogous to the bromine substitution shown in Eq. 14, are the most important reactions of benzene and alkylbenzenes. Other derivatives are made from the functional groups that may be substituted. These reactions will be discussed in subsequent chapters devoted to aromatic compounds.

Estimation of Resonance Energy from Resonance Forms

Since resonance forms indicate the limiting positions in which electrons may be, one method of calculation of resonance energy employs a summation of the contributions of all the resonance forms. Estimates of resonance stabilization, especially on a comparative basis between different structures, may be reached by employing a set of principles which set forth the contribution to the total resonance energy of various types of resonance forms. A description of the more important of these principles will be included in summary of this chapter.

1. The largest contributions to the resonance energy are made by low-energy forms which are also of equal or nearly equal energy. Especially effective in this category are structurally identical forms such as the two forms for the carboxylate anion and the two forms showing alternate positions for the double bonds in benzene.

2. In absence of other overriding factors, the larger the multi-atom orbital the greater the resonance stabilization. The large size of the π-orbitals is a factor in the rather large resonance energy of benzene.

3. The resonance stabilization is also larger in the molecule for which more resonance forms may be written (excepting those of exceptionally high energy). This often accompanies the larger orbital. For example, more forms may be written for 1,3,5-heptatriene than for 1,3,6-heptatriene.

4. The higher the energy of a resonance form the less its contribution to the character of the resonance hybrid and to the resonance stabilization. For example, the resonance form shown on the left below for an α,β-unsaturated ketone is much more significant than that on the right.

$$\underset{+}{R-CH-}CH=\underset{\substack{| \\ O_-}}{C}-R \qquad \underset{-}{R-CH-}CH=\underset{\substack{| \\ O_+}}{C}-R$$

Oxygen is more prone to attract electrons and assume a negative charge than is carbon, thus the polarity of the resonance form on the right is contrary to the inherent polarity of the atoms involved. The form on the right is of sufficiently high energy to be insignificant, so it is ordinarily not considered as a resonance form.

5. Forms which depend on charge separation are of higher energy than similar forms which do not depend on charge separation. Several forms depending on charge separation have been discussed in this chapter, including the forms above for an α,β-unsaturated ketone.

These are the more important principles needed in order to make an estimate of the significance of a resonance form in contributing to the resonance stabilization and to the character of the resonance hybrid.

EXERCISES

1. Predict the heat of hydrogenation that would be observed in hydrogenation of 2,5-heptadiene and of 2,4-heptadiene. Explain how the figures were deduced.

2. There is much discussion in this chapter concerning the π-electrons in benzene. What type of bonds are the remaining bonds on the carbon atoms in benzene?

3. Construct a model of benzene and measure the distance from carbon-1 to carbon-4. Do the same for cyclohexane in the chair form. Note the relative size of the rings, as well as the thickness.

4. Write resonance forms showing electron delocalization in 1,3-pentadiene.

5. Suppose that a hydride ion, $H:^-$, were removed from the methylene group in cycloheptatriene. What resonance forms can be written for the resultant cyclo-heptatrienyl cation? Would you predict that cycloheptatriene is somewhat basic?

6. Why is it not possible to avoid the high-energy hump at cyclohexadiene by going directly from benzene to cyclohexene?

7. Write four of the geometrical isomers of hexachlorocyclohexane, using conformational formulas for the more stable forms.

8. From data included in this chapter, calculate the energy differences shown in Fig. 3.

9. Write the equation showing the products that would be obtained if 3-methyl-2-penten-1-ol were treated with hydrogen bromide.

10. Predict which reaction would be faster: displacement of bromide by methoxide ion in bromocyclohexane, or in bromobenzene. Explain how your conclusion was reached.

Chapter

13

The Carboxylic Acids
Reactions at Polar
Multiple Bonds

The carboxylic acids are a very important class of compounds, not only in the synthetic chemical industry but also in biological processes. Many compounds of fundamental biological significance are carboxylic acids or their derivatives; these include the fats and proteins, two of the three classes of foodstuffs. Chemical conversions of carboxylic acids and their derivatives are integral parts of the life processes of plants, animals, and microorganisms. Essential aspects of the basic chemistry of carboxylic acids will be described in the present chapter, and their more important derivatives[1] are the subject of the following chapter.

The characteristic functional group of the carboxylic acids is the carboxyl

group, $-C\overset{O}{\underset{OH}{\diagup}}$, as has been mentioned in earlier chapters. For the saturated

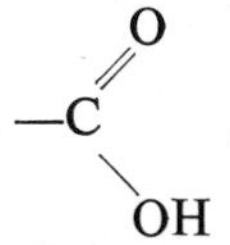

carboxylic acids (containing no carbon-carbon multiple bonds), the *general*

---

[1] Although the term, derivative, is widely used in discussions of organic chemistry, it is defined somewhat vaguely as a compound obtained relatively easily and directly from a parent compound. Usually, it is also the case that the parent compound may be reformed, if desired, from the derivative by a relatively direct process.

formula is $C_nH_{2n}O_2$, or $C_nH_{2n+1}CO_2H$. They may be regarded as consisting of an alkyl group attached to a carboxyl group.

Properties and Trivial Names

Since acids are readily separated from other compounds by procedures to be discussed shortly, and since they occur widely in nature, many of them were separated in the early days of chemistry and given "common" names. These "common" or "trivial" names have become so firmly entrenched in chemical nomenclature and are applied to so many of the derivatives of the acids that learning these names is essential. The acids occurring in nature nearly always have straight chains, and among those having more than five carbon atoms only the acids with an *even number* of carbons are common in nature. Thus, the common names which should be learned are those included in Table 1.

Table I. Trivial Names of Important Carboxylic Acids

Acid	Formula	Boiling point	Melting point
Formic	$H—CO_2H$	101°	
Acetic	$CH_3—CO_2H$	118°	
Propionic	$CH_3—CH_2—CO_2H$	141°	
Butyric	$CH_3—(CH_2)_2—CO_2H$	164°	
Valeric	$CH_3—(CH_2)_3—CO_2H$	187°	
Caproic	$CH_3—(CH_2)_4—CO_2H$	205°	
Caprylic	$CH_3—(CH_2)_6—CO_2H$	239°	16°
Capric	$CH_3—(CH_2)_8—CO_2H$	269°	31°
Lauric	$CH_3—(CH_2)_{10}—CO_2H$		43°
Myristic	$CH_3—(CH_2)_{12}—CO_2H$		54°
Palmitic	$CH_3—(CH_2)_{14}—CO_2H$		63°
Stearic	$CH_3—(CH_2)_{16}—CO_2H$		70°

The boiling points and melting points of the acids in Table 1 are included to give an idea of the properties of these compounds, and to illustrate again the way in which properties vary in a regular manner in a homologous series. Most of these names are based in some way on the plant or animal from which the respective acids were first isolated. For example, the names for the C_6, C_8, and C_{10} acids are derived from the Latin word, *caper*, meaning goat. These acids are responsible for the notorious odor of goats. The name, valeric, is one of those not based on the original source of the acid, but is derived from a Latin word meaning "to be strong." The thing which is strong about valeric acid is the odor; it is the most disagreeable of the carboxylic acids, although all of them with sufficient vapor pressure (those below C_{10}) have a rather unpleasant odor. Butyric acid is a constituent of perspiration, and acetic acid is the principal organic component of vinegar.

It is of interest that the odd-carbon normal acids form a series with steadily increasing melting points, but *lying below* the melting points of the even-carbon acids. This is illustrated by the following tabulation:

Acid	Melting point
Hendecanoic (C_{11})	30°
Tridecanoic (C_{13})	41°
Pentadecanoic (C_{15})	52°
Heptadecanoic (C_{17})	62°
Nonadecanoic (C_{19})	69°

In each instance, the odd-carbon acid melts just below the even-carbon acid with one less carbon (compare in Table 1). If melting points of the entire series of odd- and even-carbon acids are plotted on a single chart, there results a regular rise and fall of melting point; hence, an "alternation" of melting points in the carboxylic acid series is sometimes mentioned. This alternation results from the fact that the "chains" of fatty acids lie parallel to each other in the crystal lattice, but the "chain" is actually a zig-zag on account of the 109° angle between the carbon-carbon bonds. This means that the terminal carbon is always on the opposite side from carboxyl in the even-carbon acids and on the same side in odd-carbon acids, thus:

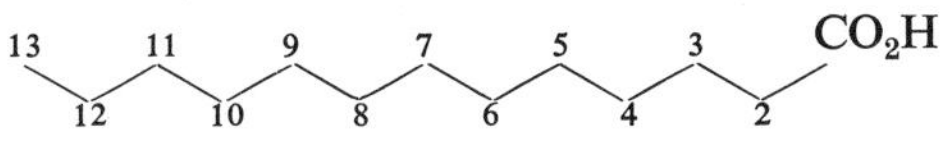

Systematic Nomenclature

The systems of nomenclature previously described may be readily applied to the carboxylic acids. One additional system of nomenclature is also used; the description of this will complete our coverage of the ways in which organic compounds are named. This is a good time at which to review thoroughly all the principles of nomenclature presented in earlier chapters.

IUC nomenclature. The characteristic ending for carboxylic acids is *-oic acid*; this is used to replace the *e* at the end of the alkane names. The longest chain *containing the carboxyl group* is used as the basis of the name even if this is not the longest chain of carbons in the molecule. The carboxyl must be at the end of the chain (three valences of carbon are occupied in this functional group), hence the carbon in this group is always the number one carbon, and numbering it is superfluous. With the addition of these specific points, naming of carboxylic acids follows the usual principles of IUC nomenclature.

In polyfunctional compounds, sometimes in di- or tricarboxylic acids, it may be convenient to name the carboxyl group as a *substituent*, in which case it is called *carboxy*.

As in other classes of compounds, it is not entirely correct to name the carboxyl group as a substituent unless some other functional group serves as the basis for the name, **except** in instances where a modified nomenclature becomes necessary in carboxylic acids. In certain structures, especially cyclic structures, application of the normally applied IUC system becomes awkward or impossible. Illustrations follow:

Cyclopentanecarboxylic
acid

trans-2-Methylcyclo-
hexanecarboxylic acid

It will be noted that the system used in these illustrations *adds -carboxylic acid to the hydrocarbon name*. This is basically a modified system of naming the carboxyl group as a substituent, for the *carbon in carboxyl is not included in the hydrocarbon* which serves as the basis for the name. Thus, cyclopentanecarboxylic acid has a total of six carbons, whereas pentanoic acid has a total of five carbons. This difference should be noted carefully.

The system of nomenclature just described is occasionally used for open-chain compounds, but it is not recommended, for it tends to be rather confusing on account of the total number of carbons being more than indicated in the hydrocarbon name. For example, hexane-1,6-dicarboxylic acid has eight carbons; a better name is octanedioic acid (unnecessary to specify the location of the carboxyls, for they must be at the ends of the chain). The need for this system of naming arises in the cyclic compounds—cyclopentanoic acid is an incorrect name; cyclopentanecarboxylic acid has six carbons.

Naming as a derivative of a simple member of the series. The principles involved here are the same as in the carbinol system for naming alcohols. Acetic acid, the second member of the series, is used as the basis of the name. Formic acid has no carbon capable of carrying substituents since it has no alkyl group attached to the functional group.

Systematic nomenclature based on trivial basic names. This system differs only slightly from the IUC system and may be regarded as the ancestor of the IUC system; however, there are certain important differences in this system:

(a) The basic common names of the acids listed in Table 1 are used rather than the IUC basic names.

(b) Substituents are located, not by numbers, but by Greek letters. The carbon adjacent to the carboxyl (No. 2 by IUC numbering) is the α-carbon and the others in the chain are lettered in the order of the letters in the Greek alphabet.

This system is rather widely used for naming compounds having substituents near carboxyl, and it has the virtue that the name immediately specifies whether the substituent is adjacent to carboxyl, one carbon removed, etc. If the substituent is more than four or five carbons removed from carboxyl this system becomes quite inferior to the IUC system and is not recommended.

It becomes necessary to number the letters of the Greek alphabet before the substituent can be located. For this reason, it seems worth while to learn only the first five letters of the Greek alphabet: α (alpha), β (beta), γ (gamma), δ (delta), ϵ (epsilon).

Two important features of this last-mentioned system of nomenclature should be emphasized. First, *the α-carbon is not the No. 1 carbon*, but the No. 2 carbon. Secondly, if the IUC basic name is used, numbers must be used; if the trivial basic name is used, Greek letters must be used.

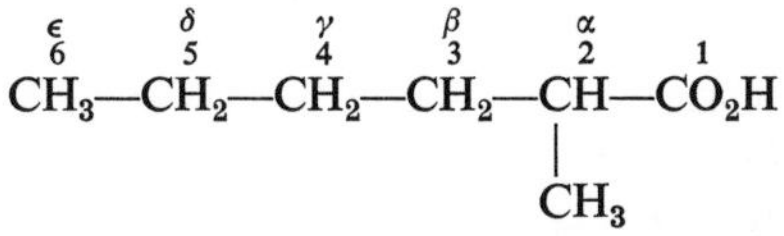

$$\overset{\overset{\epsilon}{6}}{CH_3}-\overset{\overset{\delta}{5}}{CH_2}-\overset{\overset{\gamma}{4}}{CH_2}-\overset{\overset{\beta}{3}}{CH_2}-\overset{\overset{\alpha}{2}}{CH}-\overset{\overset{}{1}}{CO_2H}$$
$$\mid$$
$$CH_3$$

correct: 2-Methylhexanoic acid   **incorrect:** 2-Methylcaproic acid
or   or
α-Methylcaproic acid α-Methylhexanoic acid

Mixing these systems is incorrect in the same manner as describing an object as weighing two pounds and three grams.

The **three systems of naming acids** may be illustrated with two examples.

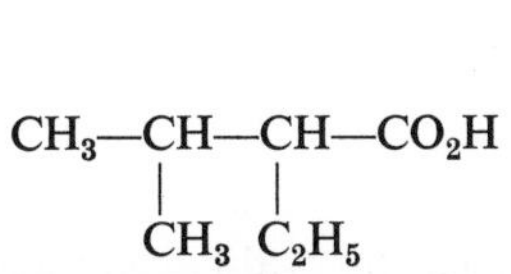

$$CH_3-CH-CH-CO_2H$$
$$\mid \quad \mid$$
$$CH_3 \ C_2H_5$$

2-Ethyl-3-methylbutanoic acid
Ethylisopropylacetic acid
α-Ethyl-β-methylbutyric acid

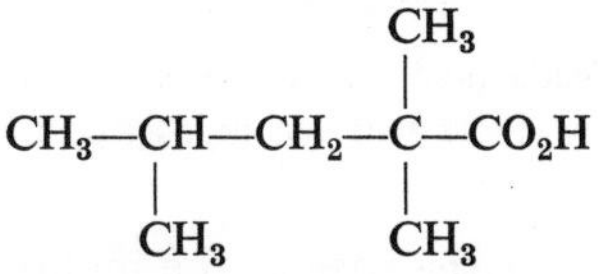

$$CH_3-CH-CH_2-\overset{\overset{CH_3}{\mid}}{C}-CO_2H$$
$$\mid \qquad\qquad \mid$$
$$CH_3 \qquad\quad CH_3$$

2,2,4-Trimethylpentanoic acid
Isobutyldimethylacetic acid
α,α,γ-Trimethylvaleric acid

Highly substituted and polyfunctional acids are usually named most effectively by the IUC system.

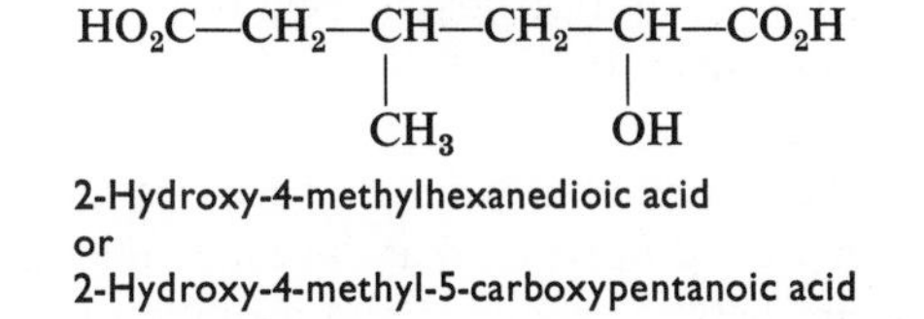

$$CH_3-CH-CH=C-CH-CH_2-CH-CO_2H$$
$$\mid \qquad \mid \quad \mid \qquad\quad \mid$$
$$Cl \quad\; H_3C \ \ CH-CH_3 \ \ OH$$
$$\mid$$
$$CH_3$$

7-Chloro-2-hydroxy-5-methyl-
4-isopropyl-5-octenoic acid

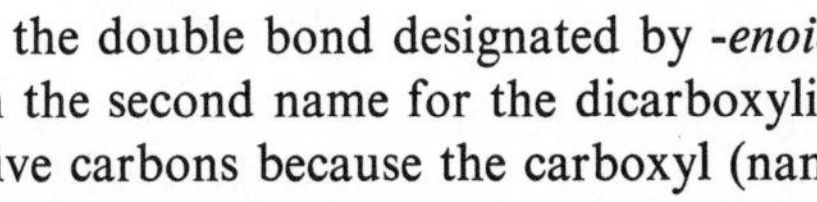

$$HO_2C-CH_2-CH-CH_2-CH-CO_2H$$
$$\mid \qquad\qquad \mid$$
$$CH_3 \qquad\quad OH$$

2-Hydroxy-4-methylhexanedioic acid
or
2-Hydroxy-4-methyl-5-carboxypentanoic acid

In the name for the unsaturated acid, note that the number preceding *octenoic* refers to location of the double bond designated by *-enoic* (the saturated acid would be *-anoic*). In the second name for the dicarboxylic acid, note that the basic chain is only five carbons because the carboxyl (named as a substituent) contains one of the carbons included in the chain in the first name.

Dicarboxylic acids. The naming of dicarboxylic acids may be readily accomplished by use of the IUC system, as has been illustrated; however, trivial names for these acids with ten or less carbons have become rather firmly entrenched. Above ten carbons, IUC names are always used; below ten carbons, IUC names are rarely used. For this reason, the names in Table 2 should be learned.

Table 2. Trivial Names of Dicarboxylic Acids

Acid	Formula	Melting point
Oxalic	$HO_2C—CO_2H$	101.5°*
Malonic	$HO_2C—CH_2—CO_2H$	135°**
Succinic	$HO_2C—(CH_2)_2—CO_2H$	190°
Glutaric	$HO_2C—(CH_2)_3—CO_2H$	98°
Adipic	$HO_2C—(CH_2)_4—CO_2H$	152°
Pimelic	$HO_2C—(CH_2)_5—CO_2H$	106°
Suberic	$HO_2C—(CH_2)_6—CO_2H$	141.5°
Azelaic	$HO_2C—(CH_2)_7—CO_2H$	106.5°
Sebacic	$HO_2C—(CH_2)_8—CO_2H$	134.5°

* Oxalic acid crystallizes as a dihydrate.
** Malonic acid decomposes on melting (loses CO_2 readily).

As was the case in the monocarboxylic acids, the odd-carbon acids have considerably lower melting points than do the even-carbon acids. In the dicarboxylic acids, however, melting point goes down with increasing molecular weight in the even-carbon acids, and remains almost constant for the odd-carbon acids (above malonic acid, which has two carboxyls attached to one carbon). This reflects the prominent effect of the carboxyl group in raising the melting point.

Malonic, succinic, glutaric, and adipic acids are especially important and useful compounds, and they will be mentioned in subsequent chapters.

Hydrogen Bonding

If the molecular weight of a carboxylic acid is determined there is always obtained a value higher than that calculated from the molecular formula. The value varies, for different acids, from 25% to 100% too high for the molecular formula. There is reliable evidence, based on measurement of dipole moments and other physical properties, that this high molecular weight is due to a reversible equilibrium between the acid and a dimer of the structure shown in Eq. 1.

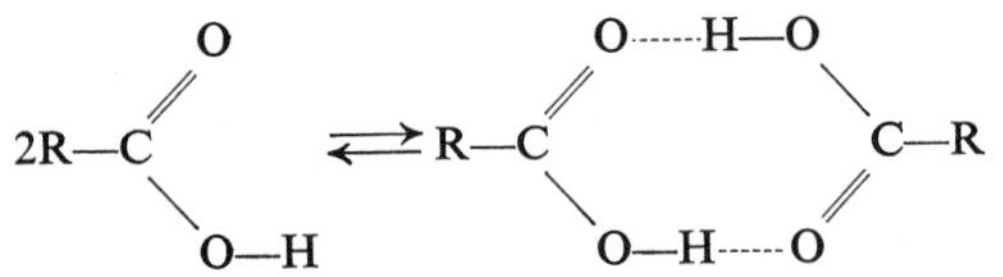

$$2R—C \overset{O}{\underset{O—H}{\big\langle}} \quad \rightleftarrows \quad R—C \overset{O\text{-----}H—O}{\underset{O—H\text{-----}O}{\big\langle}} C—R \tag{1}$$

The position of this equilibrium determines the exact molecular weight that will be observed. For formic acid, the equilibrium lies so far to the right that the molecular weight is almost twice that of the monomeric species shown on the left.

In the dimer shown in Eq. 1, the two molecules are held together by an electrostatic type of valence force resulting from the polarity of the hydrogen-oxygen bond. Hydrogen is such a strongly positive atom that when it is attached to a highly negative atom such as oxygen or nitrogen the combination is sufficiently polarized to have the electrical properties of a magnet. The positive end of this magnet of molecular dimensions, known as a **dipole,** is attracted sufficiently strongly by an oxygen atom to hold molecules together, temporarily at least. This type of force is much weaker than a covalence, but is of the order of magnitude of many orthodox electrovalences. As roughly indicated in Eq. 1, the hydrogen is closer to the oxygen to which it is covalently bonded than to the one to which it is attracted electrostatically. This type of secondary valence force is known as a **hydrogen bond,** and is usually indicated by a dotted line. It imparts certain easily observable properties to molecules in which it occurs. A particularly significant effect is a considerable raising of the boiling point. This may be regarded as resulting from a raising of the molecular weight, which is known to raise the boiling point. In most cases (but not formic acid) the vapor of the acid is monomeric, so the process of vaporization involves not only escaping from the liquid surface but also pulling the hydrogen-bonded molecules apart. Thus, the heat of vaporization, as well as the boiling point, is abnormally high. The unusually high boiling points of carboxylic acids may be illustrated by comparing the boiling point of acetic acid (molecular weight 60) with that of butane (molecular weight 58). Whereas acetic acid boils at 118°, n-butane boils at 0°; therefore, an increase in boiling point of about 118° may be attributed to hydrogen bonding in acetic acid.

Infrared spectra of carboxylic acids. The most prominent features of the infrared spectrum of a carboxylic acid (cf. Fig. 1) reflect the hydrogen bonding which is so characteristic of this functional group. The absorption due to hydroxyl is broadened and shifted to a sufficiently long wavelength that the hydroxyl band is merged into the C—H band. This gives a rather diffuse edge to the C—H absorption in the region between 3.1 and 3.3 μ. The characteristic appearance of the absorption by hydroxyl in carboxylic acids is best appreciated by comparing this region of the spectrum with that in a carboxylic acid ester (Fig. 2). Since the ester has $-\overset{\displaystyle O}{\underset{\displaystyle OH}{C}}$ replaced with $-\overset{\displaystyle O}{\underset{\displaystyle OCH_3}{C}}$ the hydrogen-bonded hydroxyl is no longer present. The infrared spectrum clearly reflects this change in structure. The edge of the C—H absorption is very sharp at about 3.35 μ in the ester.

Carbonyl absorption in acids and derivatives, as well as aldehydes and ketones, nearly always occurs in the region between 5.5 and 6.1 μ, and

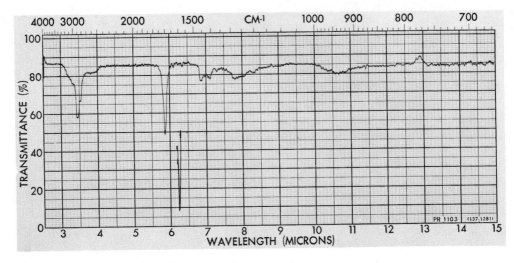

Fig. I. Infrared spectrum of 5-methylhendecanoic acid,

The absorption was determined on a thin film of the liquid placed between sodium chloride plates. The calibration line (6.24 μ) is very near its true location.

hydrogen bonding with the carbonyl oxygen tends to shift the absorption to longer wavelengths. It will be noted that in the ester (Fig. 2) the strong carbonyl absorption is at 5.75 μ, whereas in the acid (Fig. 1) the carbonyl absorbs at 5.85 μ.

Both the carboxyl and ester groups have characteristic absorption at longer wavelengths than 6 μ. In Fig. 1, for example, the relatively weak bands on either side of 7 μ, the broad band with a shoulder near 8 μ, and the very broad band centered at about 10.7 μ are due to absorptions by the carboxyl group. Shifts in these bands are sometimes diagnostic in structures with substituents near carboxyl. In such cases, where the longer wavelength bands become of interest, a thicker film (or solution) may be used in order to define these bands more clearly, in which case the carboxyl and C—H bands will be off-scale (essentially all the radiation in those regions absorbed).

Hydrogen bonding in other molecules. Hydrogen bonding is especially strong in carboxylic acids because it may occur twice between a single pair of molecules, as shown in Eq. 1. A single hydrogen bond may occur, however, between any molecules containing a hydroxyl group, and several

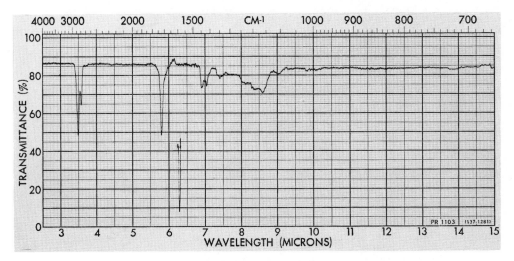

Fig. 2. Infrared spectrum of methyl dodecanoate,

$$CH_3—(CH_2)_{10}—C\overset{\displaystyle O}{\underset{\displaystyle OCH_3}{\Big\backslash}}$$

This spectrum was determined on a thin film. The calibration line shows that about 0.08 μ should be subtracted from the wavelength values shown in the tracing.

molecules may be held loosely in a chain. Since such bonds are rather weak, chains of various lengths would be expected to be constantly forming and dissociating. For an alcohol, association may occur as follows:

If alcohols do hydrogen bond in this manner, it would be expected that their boiling points would be higher than those of molecules of similar molecular weights which are not capable of hydrogen bonding. Such is the case, for *n*-propyl alcohol (molecular weight 60) boils at 98°, almost as high as acetic acid and far above *n*-butane. Furthermore, the infrared spectrum of ethyl alcohol (cf. Fig. 2-1) in solution shows absorption at about 3 μ for the associated species, and at about 2.8 μ for the unassociated alcohol. In the 0.1 molar solution whose spectrum is shown in Fig. 2-1, most of the alcohol is associated. In more dilute solution, there is less hydrogen bonding, so the absorption at 2.8 μ becomes more intense.

Since water has two hydrogens on oxygen, it may hydrogen bond in two directions:

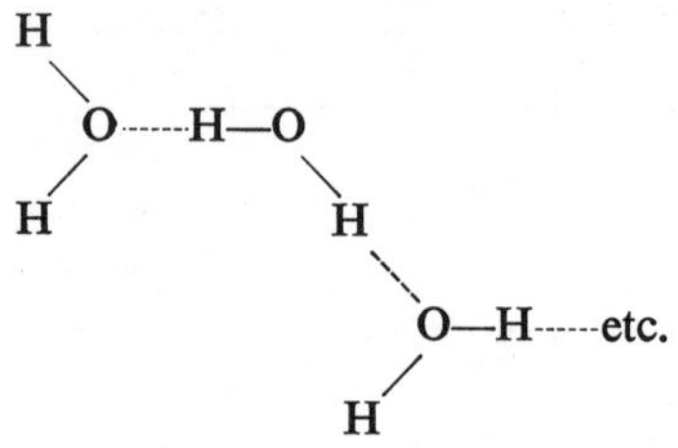

$$
\begin{array}{c}
H \\
\quad \backslash \\
\quad O \text{-----} H \text{---} O \\
\quad / \qquad\qquad \backslash \\
H \qquad\qquad H \\
\qquad\qquad\qquad \backslash \\
\qquad\qquad\qquad O \text{---} H \text{-----etc.} \\
\qquad\qquad / \\
\qquad\qquad H
\end{array}
$$

This makes rational the remarkable fact that water, of molecular weight 18, boils at 100°. Thus, if it were not for the phenomenon of hydrogen bonding, water would be a gas at ordinary temperatures, and the world as we know it could not exist.

Differentiation between hydrogen bonding and resonance stabilization. Hydrogen bonding is a different phenomenon than electron delocalization,[2] in that molecular orbitals encompassing more than two atoms are not involved in hydrogen bonding. In the oxygen-hydrogen covalence the bond is polarized by a shift of the electron density more in favor of oxygen than hydrogen, but the orbital still involves only the two atoms. The hydrogen which is covalently bonded to oxygen is closer to that oxygen than to the oxygen to which it is electrostatically attracted. If electron delocalization were involved, the hydrogen would be the same distance from the two oxygens. Furthermore, the direction of maximum electrostatic attraction by the polar oxygen-hydrogen bond is in a line with the direction of that bond, as indicated by the geometry shown in Eq. 1. If the geometry of the molecule in which hydrogen bonding occurs prevents the hydrogen bond from being linear, then the strength of the bond is weakened proportionately to the amount the bond is "bent." In the case of resonance stabilization, there is no requirement that the bond directions be linear; in fact, this is rarely the case (cf. carboxylate anion, allylic carbonium ion, benzene delocalization, etc.).

Acid Strength of Carboxylic Acids

The aliphatic carboxylic acids, except for formic acid, are of similar acid strength, i.e., have similar dissociation constants. Acetic acid, whose dissociation

---

[2] Electron delocalization, resulting in resonance stabilization, can result in the effective bonding of hydrogen to two atoms, and will be discussed later in connection with chelation. This is a different structural feature than hydrogen bonding, however.

constant, K, is 1.86×10^{-5} (pK_a 4.76),[3] is ionized in dilute solution (1 molar) to the extent of about 2.5%. For comparison, pK_a values reported for propionic acid and caprylic acid, respectively, are 4.88 and 4.85. Formic acid, the first member of the series, is appreciably stronger, pK_a 3.77.

The ionization of an acid involves the hydrogen leaving without an electron, so it would seem reasonable to propose that an electrostatic effect in the molecule which tends to withdraw electrons from carboxyl would encourage the proton to leave as a cation. Since a group substituted in the α-position cannot engage in resonance interaction with the carboxyl (verified by an attempt to write resonance forms involving delocalization between carboxyl and an α-substituent), any effect on the ionization constant of the acid must be ascribed to an electrostatic effect (inductive effect). In practice, measurement of ionization constants of α-substituted acids has proved a very useful method for determining the direction and magnitude of inductive effects of groups or atoms. The following acids have the pK_a values shown beneath the respective formulas:

$$Cl-CH_2-CO_2H \qquad Cl_2CH-CO_2H \qquad Cl_3C-CO_2H$$
$$pK_a \quad 2.81 \qquad\qquad 1.29 \qquad\qquad\quad 0.08$$

$$HO-CH_2-CO_2H \qquad (CH_3)_3C-CO_2H$$
$$3.83 \qquad\qquad\quad 5.02$$

Thus, halogen is a powerful electron-attracting group, as has been previously discussed; in fact, trichloroacetic acid is about 90% ionized in solution. Hydroxyl is also an electron-attracting group, although not so powerful as halogen. The pK_a of trimethylacetic acid, very slightly higher than that for propionic acid, suggests that methyl (or any other alkyl) is an extremely weak electron-donating group (the basis of comparison is always hydrogen). Other evidence is in agreement that methyl is an electron-donating group but not very strongly so. The minor decrease in dissociation of α-alkyl acids may be caused largely by steric interference of the α-substitutent with solvation of the anion.

Properties of the Salts of Carboxylic Acids

Although alcohols do not dissociate in solution, as has been developed in Chapter 12, a sodium alkoxide, NaOR, does dissociate in solution to give

---

[3] For many purposes, the pK_a (acidic pK) of an acid is more convenient than the dissociation constant. The pK_a is defined as $\log 1/K_a$, thus is a parallel expression to pH, which is $\log(1/[H^+])$, i.e., the logarithm of the reciprocal of the hydrogen ion concentration. Of course the pK_a becomes smaller as the K_a becomes larger. A particularly convenient relationship exists when the pH of a solution is equal to the pK_a of an acid. At this pH, one-half the acid is present in solution as the anion and half as the associated acid. This relationship may be easily demonstrated as follows:

since $\qquad K_a = \dfrac{[H^+][A^-]}{[HA]}$, then $pK_a = \log(1/K_a) = \log \dfrac{[HA]}{[H^+][A^-]}$.

It follows that when $[HA] = [A^-]$, $pK_a = \log(1/[H^+]) = pH$.

sodium ions, Na^+, and alkoxide ions, RO^-. This phenomenon is ascribed to the electrostatic type bonds formed by alkali metals and the stability of the ions of alkali metals. It may be readily deduced that this dissociation is properly ascribed to the metal involved, for other alkoxides such as aluminum alkoxides are not dissociated in solution. Similarly, alkali salts of carboxylic acids are highly dissociated in water solution, in contrast with the small ionization just described for the carboxylic acids.

The presence of the single ionic bond in alkali salts of carboxylic acids imparts to them many of the properties associated with electrovalent compounds. A relatively high molecular weight (more than a dozen carbon atoms) is required to significantly obscure the character of the electrovalence. Thus, the alkali salts of carboxylic acids are relatively soluble in water, usually insoluble in organic solvents such as benzene and ether, and non-volatile. **These properties of salts can be turned to great use for the separation of acids from non-acidic substances.** For this purpose, the acid is converted to its salt by neutralization with sodium or potassium hydroxide, and the salt is dissolved in water. Other organic compounds are then separated from the water solution of the salt, either by filtration of solids or extraction of liquids with an organic solvent. The aqueous solution of the salt is then made acidic with a strong inorganic acid such as hydrochloric acid, and this liberates the weak organic acid from its salt according to Eq. 2.

$$R-CO_2^-Na^+ + H^+ \rightleftharpoons R-CO_2^-H^+ + Na^+$$
$$\downarrow\uparrow \qquad (2)$$
$$R-CO_2H$$

Since carboxylic acids are weak acids, they are only slightly ionized; hence the upper equilibrium is displaced to the right by removal of most of the carboxylate anions as undissociated acid. Furthermore, unless the organic acid is of rather low molecular weight (less than C_5) it is sparingly soluble or nearly insoluble in water. In this instance, the equilibrium is displaced completely to the right by removal of all the carboxylate anions as insoluble undissociated acid. Thus the acid is easily recovered from the salt after all non-acidic material has been removed from the salt. This easy separation of acids was responsible for the isolation of many of them in the very early days of chemistry, as mentioned near the beginning of this chapter.

Synthesis of Carboxylic Acids

Several specific carboxylic acids are produced on a very large scale commercially by processes which are not of general use for preparing various carboxylic acids, but apply only to the specific compounds. As usual, we will devote most of our attention to methods of general utility, but the industrial methods may be illustrated by the syntheses of formic acid from carbon monoxide[4] and acetic acid from acetaldehyde, as in Eqs. 3 and 4. The process shown in Eq. 4 would be suitable for preparation of other acids were it not for the circumstance that other acids are cheaper than the corresponding aldehyde.

$$CO + NaOH \xrightarrow[\text{pressure}]{200°} HCO_2Na \xrightarrow{H^+} HCO_2H + Na^+ \qquad (3)$$

$$\underset{\text{Sodium}}{\underset{\text{formate}}{}}$$

$$CH_3-\overset{\displaystyle O}{\overset{\|}{C}}\diagdown_H + O_2 \xrightarrow[\text{(air)}]{\text{catalyst}} CH_3-\overset{\displaystyle O}{\overset{\|}{C}}\diagdown_{OH} \qquad (4)$$

Acetaldehyde is unique in that it is available from acetylene (cf. Eq. 10-8). Thus the ultimate industrial source of acetic acid is coal and limestone.

Four general methods of preparing carboxylic acids will suffice to illustrate the methods which are available for synthesis of acids of a variety of structures.

Methods dependent on oxidation: (1) ALCOHOLS. Although direct oxidative attack on alkanes is a process requiring rather drastic conditions, oxidative attack on a carbon atom attached to an oxygen atom is relatively easy.[5] Oxidation of a primary alcohol eventually leads to an acid (Eq. 5).

$$R-CH_2-OH + \underset{\substack{(HNO_3)\\ \text{or}\\ (Na_2Cr_2O_7 + H_2SO_4)}}{[O]} \longrightarrow R-\overset{\displaystyle O}{\overset{\|}{C}}\diagdown_H \xrightarrow{[O]} R-\overset{\displaystyle O}{\overset{\|}{C}}\diagdown_{OH} \qquad (5)$$

$$+ HOH$$

Although the aldehyde is an intermediate in the oxidation shown in Eq. 5, this is not a satisfactory method of preparing aldehydes, because the aldehyde

---

[4] Carbon monoxide is a very interesting molecule, structurally, for all four valences of carbon must be occupied by oxygen if carbon is to be tetravalent. The evidence is good that the structure is fundamentally that of an onium salt of oxygen (cf. Chap. 3). This means that there are three covalences and one electrovalence between oxygen and carbon, so carbon is in the uncommon condition of bearing a formal negative charge. Electronic and line formulas for carbon monoxide follow:

$$^-:C:::O:^+ \qquad\qquad\qquad C\overset{\text{---}}{\equiv}O$$

[5] Initial action of the oxidizing agent, in solution under acidic conditions, usually involves attack of a positive species on oxygen, with elimination of hydrogen from carbon occurring as a subsequent step. As mentioned previously, oxidations nearly always involve a sequence of several steps. A clear and interesting analysis of the mechanism of chemical oxidation in acid solution has been presented by L. S. Levitt, *J. Org. Chem.*, **20**, 1297 (1955).

is oxidized at least as easily as the alcohol. It follows that a satisfactory yield of aldehyde will not accumulate[6] in the reaction mixture.

Breaking of a carbon-carbon bond by oxidation is more difficult than breaking a carbon-hydrogen bond; so usual methods of oxidation of a secondary alcohol lead to a ketone as final product (Eq. 7). This is a good synthesis of

$$\begin{array}{ccc} \text{R—CH—R′} + & [O] & \longrightarrow \text{R—C—R′} + \text{HOH} \\ | & \text{(dichromate)} & \parallel \\ \text{OH} & & \text{O} \end{array} \qquad (7)$$

ketones (Chap. 15), but rather drastic conditions are required to break the carbon-carbon chain and yield acids. Furthermore, unless the groups R and R′ are the same, two acids will result from cleavage on either side of the carbon bearing oxygen; consequently, oxidation of secondary alcohols is rarely applied to synthesis of acids.

As would be expected, from the comments above, a tertiary alcohol is not oxidized under mild conditions (Eq. 8). It follows from the descriptions of

$$\begin{array}{ccc} \text{R} & & \\ | & & \\ \text{R—C—OH} + & [O] & \longrightarrow \text{no reaction under mild conditions} \\ | & \text{(dichromate)} & \\ \text{R} & & \end{array} \qquad (8)$$

alcohol oxidations that *this reaction may be used to distinguish between primary, secondary, and tertiary alcohols.* If mild oxidation gives an acidic substance, the alcohol is primary; if a neutral substance results, the alcohol is secondary, if no oxidation occurs, the alcohol is tertiary.

(2) ALKENES. Although it is relatively uncommon that an alkene is synthesized for the purpose of oxidizing it to yield acids, this is done in certain rather important cases. For example, the dibasic acid, adipic acid, from which Nylon is made (cf. Chap. 14), may be prepared by oxidation of cyclohexene, as

---

[6] Since aldehydes have a lower boiling point than alcohols or acids, the oxidative process has been recommended for synthesis of aldehydes under conditions of temperature and pressure such that the aldehyde boils out of the mixture as rapidly as formed. Even under these conditions, however, the process is always inferior to methods such as those discussed in Chapter 15 for synthesis of aldehydes. A major difficulty is that the oxidative process occurs in large measure by a pathway more complicated than that shown in Eq. 5. As the aldehyde is formed it reacts with the alcohol to establish equilibrium with a type of compound known as the hemi-acetal (cf. Chap. 15), and this is oxidized to the ester of the acid (Eq. 6). Hydrolysis of

$$\begin{array}{ccc} \text{OH} & & \text{O} \\ / & & \parallel \\ \text{R—CH} & + [O] \longrightarrow \text{R—C} & + \text{HOH} \\ \backslash & & \diagdown \\ \text{O—CH}_2\text{—R} & & \text{O—CH}_2\text{—R} \end{array} \qquad (6)$$

the ester by water in the aqueous oxidizing medium (cf. Chap. 14) yields the acid and the alcohol, which is then available for further oxidation.

shown in Eq. 9 (for stepwise oxidation of alkenes, cf. Eqs. 9-23 and 9-24).

$$\text{(cyclohexene)} + \underset{\text{(KMnO}_4)}{4[O]} \longrightarrow \text{(ring)}\underset{\text{CO}_2\text{H}}{\overset{\text{CO}_2\text{H}}{<}} \quad \text{or } HO_2C—(CH_2)_4—CO_2H \qquad (9)$$

Adipic acid

A much more common application of alkene oxidation involves utilization of the rather significant number of alkenes which occur in nature. The unsaturated acids have been especially useful for oxidation to dibasic acids. This process is illustrated by oxidation of the naturally abundant oleic acid (cf. Chap. 14), as in Eq. 10. Chemical oxidation, as shown in Eqs. 9 and 10,

$$CH_3—(CH_2)_7—CH{=}CH—(CH_2)_7—CO_2H + \underset{(KMnO_4)}{4[O]} \longrightarrow CH_3—(CH_2)_7—CO_2H$$
$$+ \qquad (10)$$
$$HO_2C—(CH_2)_7—CO_2H$$

Azelaic acid

is the preferred laboratory procedure, but these conversions are carried out on an industrial scale by cheaper processes such as catalytic oxidation with air.

Methods dependent on addition to polar multiple bonds. The starting material for the two methods discussed in this category is an alkyl halide. In the first method, the alkyl halide is initially converted to an alkyl cyanide (more commonly known as a nitrile; cf. Chap. 14) by the simple displacement reaction (cf. Eq. 6-1), while the initial conversion in the second method is to the Grignard reagent (cf. Eq. 6-25). Since the mechanisms of additions to polar multiple bonds are somewhat different from those involved in additions to carbon-carbon multiple bonds (Chap. 9), these mechanisms will be considered in the present section. Differences from and similarities to the addition reactions discussed in Chapter 9 should be noted.

(1) CYANIDE PROCESS. The hydrolysis of a nitrile, for which the net reactions are given in Eq. 11, is a two-step process which illustrates two types of addition

$$R—C{\equiv}N + HOH \xrightarrow[\text{H}^+ \text{ or } ^-\text{OH}]{\text{catalysis by}} R—C\overset{\displaystyle O}{\underset{NH_2}{<}} \xrightarrow{HOH} R—C\overset{\displaystyle O}{\underset{ONH_4}{<}} \qquad (11)$$

(an amide)

to a polar multiple bond. Addition to a polar multiple bond is led by attack of a negative fragment on the positive end of the multiple bond except in instances where a proton or organometallic compound is one of the reagents. In the latter case, initial attack by the strongly positive species is at the negative end of the multiple bond.

Water is not sufficiently nucleophilic to attack the nitrile grouping at an appreciable rate; however, when the nitrile grouping is polarized by initial attack of a proton (Eq. 12), water adds at a reasonable rate. After loss of a

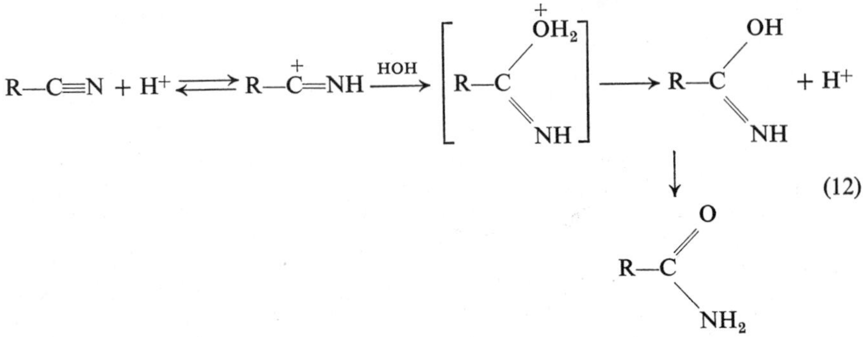

$$R-C\equiv N + H^+ \rightleftarrows R-\overset{+}{C}=NH \xrightarrow{\text{HOH}} \left[R-C\overset{\overset{+}{O}H_2}{\underset{NH}{\diagdown}} \right] \longrightarrow R-C\overset{OH}{\underset{NH}{\diagdown}} + H^+$$

$$R-C\overset{O}{\underset{NH_2}{\diagdown}}$$

(12)

proton,[7] rearrangement to the more stable carbonyl form of the amide occurs. The sequence in Eq. 12 illustrates the mechanism of catalysis by acid. In case alkali is used as catalyst, this highly nucleophilic species readily attacks the nitrile (Eq. 13). The resultant anion abstracts a proton from water (or other protic solvent that may be present) to complete the addition and give the amide. In both Eq. 12 and Eq. 13, it may be noted that the catalyst is regenerated. In

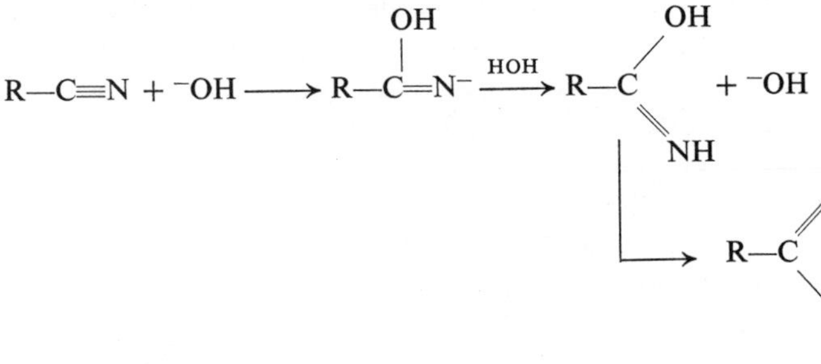

$$R-C\equiv N + {}^-OH \longrightarrow R-\overset{OH}{\underset{}{C}}=N^- \xrightarrow{\text{HOH}} R-C\overset{OH}{\underset{NH}{\diagdown}} + {}^-OH$$

(13)

$$R-C\overset{O}{\underset{NH_2}{\diagdown}}$$

most reactions of the polar multiple bonds, either acid or alkali will function as catalyst, by attacking the negative or positive ends of the double bond respectively. Of course, if some base other than hydroxyl ion is used in a reaction such as shown in Eq. 13 another product will be obtained rather than the amide. Such reactions will be discussed in Chapter 14.

The second step in Eq. 11 involves the *mechanism of an addition reaction, but the structures are such that the addition is not completed.* When the amide

---

[7] The isomer with the carbonyl group, rather than the one with hydroxyl on a double-bonded carbon, is ordinarily much the more stable. Thus, an amide is ordinarily written as in the lower formula in Eq. 12 (cf. Chap. 10, footnote 4, regarding the similar situation in aldehydes).

When a highly unstable, therefore transitory, intermediate is involved in a reaction, this formula is often put in brackets, as in Eq. 12. The existence of such structures is frequently difficult to actually establish.

reacts with a nucleophile (Eq. 14), there results an intermediate which gives a lower-energy molecule by losing one of the negative groups on carbon rather than by completing the addition by adding a proton to oxygen. This course

$$
R-\overset{\displaystyle O}{\underset{\displaystyle NH_2}{C}} + {}^-OH \rightleftarrows R-\overset{\displaystyle O^-}{\underset{\displaystyle OH}{C}}-NH_2 \rightleftarrows R-\overset{\displaystyle O}{\underset{\displaystyle OH}{C}} + {}^-NH_2 \tag{14}
$$

$$\downarrow \text{base} \qquad \downarrow \text{HOH}$$

$$\text{anion} \qquad NH_3 + {}^-OH$$

of the reaction results because a species with three negative groups on carbon is of such high energy that in most cases a more stable molecule results from losing one negative group. If ^-OH is lost, this reverses the initial addition; if $^-NH_2$ is lost the acid is the product, so hydrolysis has occurred. The highly basic $^-NH_2$ abstracts a proton from a protic solvent (or the acid), while the acid is converted to its anion by one of the bases present. This latter step draws the hydrolysis to completion in a forward direction when basic catalysis is used. Equation 11 is written with the ammonium salt of the acid, since this balances the equation with the reagents shown. In Eq. 14, the acid anion would be balanced in part by the ammonium ion and in part by the cation of the base used for catalysis.

With acid catalysis of the amide hydrolysis, there would result, initially, species where addition is completed (Eq. 15, or by routes involving slightly different transitory intermediates). The unstable intermediate or intermediates

$$
R-\overset{\displaystyle OH}{\underset{\displaystyle +}{C}}-NH_2 + HOH \rightleftarrows \left[R-\overset{\displaystyle OH}{\underset{\displaystyle \overset{\displaystyle OH_2}{+}}{C}}-NH_2\right] \rightleftarrows \left[R-\overset{\displaystyle OH}{\underset{\displaystyle OH}{C}}-NH_2\right] + H^+
$$

$$
\overset{+}{NH_4}
$$

$$
\uparrow H^+ \tag{15}
$$

$$
\longrightarrow R-\overset{\displaystyle O}{\underset{\displaystyle OH}{C}} + NH_3
$$

would rapidly lose a proton and $^-NH_2$ to give the product in which addition has not been completed. In this instance, the reaction is drawn to completion by removal of ammonia as ammonium ion, from reaction with the acid catalyst.

In recapitulation, it should be noted that when a negative group is attached to carbonyl, as is the case in acids and their derivatives, attack by a nucleophilic agent gives a net replacement of the negative group. However, the mechanism of this reaction is that of addition—an addition not completed because a lower-energy reaction path is available. The situation is rather analogous to that in aromatic compounds (Chap. 12) where, after the initial addition, a proton is lost in order to restore the resonance stabilized system. The principal difference in the case of aromatic compounds is that the attacking group is positive, whereas the group attacking the carbonyl carbon is negative.

(2) UTILIZATION OF GRIGNARD REAGENTS. The most useful reactions of Grignard reagents (prepared as described in Eq. 6-25) are additions to polar multiple bonds. Such an addition to carbon dioxide gives the magnesium salt of an acid,[8] as shown in Eq. 16. The carboxylic acid is freed from its salt by

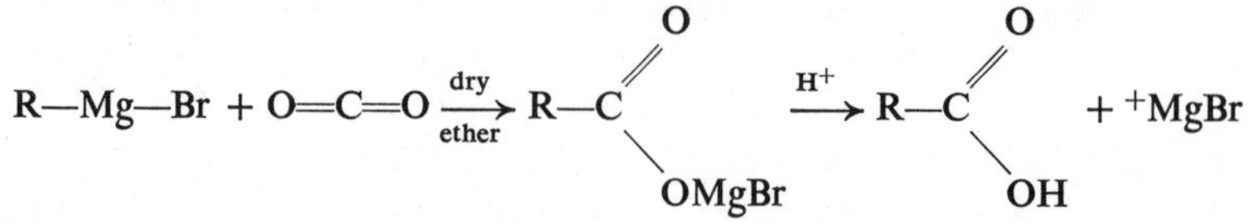

$$R\!-\!Mg\!-\!Br + O\!\!=\!\!C\!\!=\!\!O \xrightarrow[\text{ether}]{\text{dry}} R\!-\!\overset{\displaystyle O}{\underset{\displaystyle OMgBr}{C}} \xrightarrow{\text{H}^+} R\!-\!\overset{\displaystyle O}{\underset{\displaystyle OH}{C}} + \,^+MgBr \quad (16)$$

addition of a strong acid after completion of the Grignard reaction, which must be carried out in dry ether. The Grignard reagent might be expected to add to the polar multiple bond in the salt of the acid, for this reagent does add to the carbonyl group in other acid derivatives (cf. Chap. 14). In practice, this rarely occurs, no doubt because the magnesium salt of the acid is nearly always very insoluble in ether. Any reaction with the insoluble salt would necessarily be slow.

The mechanism of reaction of a Grignard reagent with a polar multiple bond has been the subject of much study and is a more complicated process than suggested in Eq. 16. The Grignard reagent in solution is a mixture of several species, the most important of which is probably the dimer shown below, held together by coordination of the halogen with the metal.

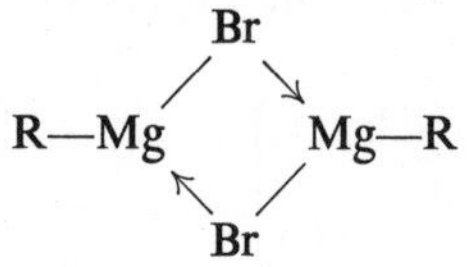

$$\begin{array}{ccc} & \text{Br} & \\ & \diagup \searrow & \\ R\!-\!Mg & & Mg\!-\!R \\ & \nwarrow \diagup & \\ & \text{Br} & \end{array}$$

There is considerable evidence that in the transition state the dimer (containing only one halogen-metal coordination) is involved, and one magnesium is

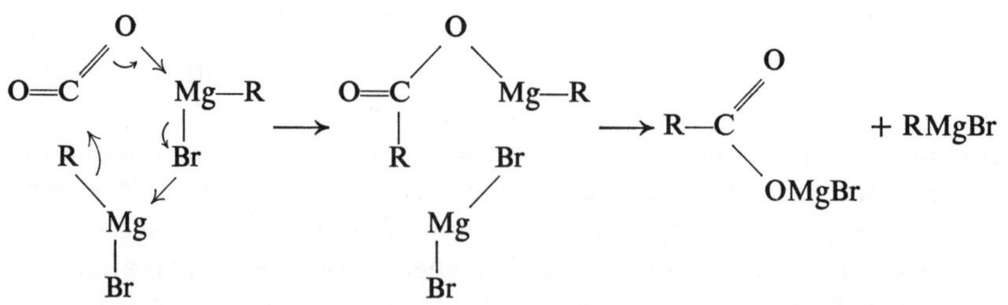

$$\begin{array}{ccc} \overset{\displaystyle O}{\underset{\displaystyle R}{O\!\!=\!\!C}} \overset{}{\underset{\displaystyle Br}{Mg\!-\!R}} & \longrightarrow & \overset{\displaystyle O}{\underset{\displaystyle R}{O\!\!=\!\!C}} \overset{}{\underset{\displaystyle Br}{Mg\!-\!R}} \longrightarrow R\!-\!\overset{\displaystyle O}{\underset{\displaystyle OMgBr}{C}} + RMgBr \quad (17) \\ \underset{\displaystyle Br}{Mg} & & \underset{\displaystyle Br}{Mg} \end{array}$$

---

[8] As a convenience in balancing Eq. 16, the product of the Grignard reaction is written as the mixed salt, magnesium carboxylate and bromide. Actually, this is probably the chief product of the reaction since the magnesium salt would not be ionized in the dry ether solution. This mixed salt is equivalent to half a mole of magnesium carboxylate and half a mole of magnesium bromide.

coordinated with the negative end of the multiple bond. The transition state shown in Eq. 17, in the conformation shown, would give the products if the exchange with magnesium bromide (second step) can occur. There is much evidence that such an exchange does occur.

Summary of methods for synthesis of carboxylic acids. The methods depending on oxidation are sometimes of use, but not applicable to the wide variety of compounds that may be made from alkyl halides *via* the nitrile or Grignard reagent. Principal use of the alkene oxidation is with naturally occurring alkenes, and a similar situation frequently applies to the alcohol oxidation. It is more common to synthesize an alcohol from the corresponding acid (cf. Chap. 14) than vice versa. Primary alcohols may be made by hydrolysis of the alkyl halide, but this route to the acid would not be profitable, since the alkyl halide may be converted to the acid more efficiently by the methods just discussed. Thus, the importance of alkyl halides in organic synthesis is again illustrated in the synthesis of carboxylic acids.

Chemical Reactions of Carboxylic Acids

A characteristic reaction of all acids is salt formation, as discussed earlier in this chapter; however, the other reactions of the carboxyl group involve nucleophilic attack on the carbonyl group followed, not by completion of the addition reaction, but by loss of hydroxyl. This is also the reaction given by the acid derivatives, as described for amide hydrolysis (Eqs. 11, 14, and 15). Since such reactions are reversible, and the product depends on the negative group lost from the carbonyl, the direction of reaction (or direction of displacement of the equilibrium) depends on the relative stabilities of the compounds involved. The acid has a lower energy than most of the derivatives, partly on account of hydrogen bonding in the carboxyl group, so the conversion of an acid to the derivatives usually proceeds by an indirect route. The ester may be formed directly in an equilibrium which is usually displaced slightly in favor of the ester, but other acid derivatives are usually formed from the acid chloride, $R-C\overset{O}{\underset{Cl}{}}$.

The latter is obtainable from the acid with reagents which reach the high-energy acid chloride in a multistep process. Thus, the most important reaction of acids for synthetic purposes is conversion to the acid chloride.

Formation of acid chlorides. Although acid bromides and iodides are known compounds, they are rarely used and are of no significance in comparison with the acid chlorides, or acyl chlorides (the acyl group is $R-C\overset{O}{\underset{}{}}$).

The chloride is virtually always used as the intermediate for formation of other acid derivatives. Several reagents will give very high-yield conversions (usually

90–100%) of acids to the acid chlorides, but the reagents most commonly employed are phosphorus trichloride (Eq. 18), phosphorus pentachloride (Eq. 19) and thionyl chloride (Eq. 20). For some structures, the yield in Eq. 18

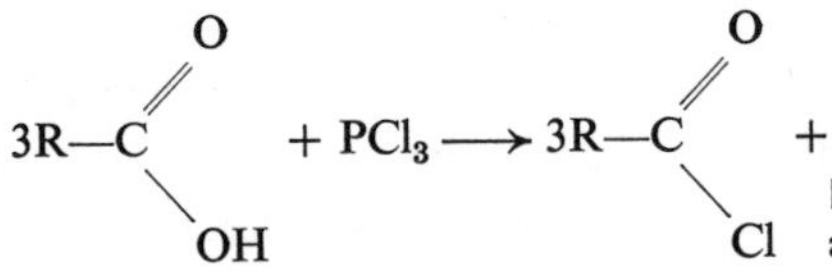

$$3R-\overset{\displaystyle O}{\underset{\displaystyle OH}{C}} + PCl_3 \longrightarrow 3R-\overset{\displaystyle O}{\underset{\displaystyle Cl}{C}} + H_3PO_3 \qquad (18)$$
Phosphonic acid

$$R-\overset{\displaystyle O}{\underset{\displaystyle OH}{C}} + PCl_5 \longrightarrow R-\overset{\displaystyle O}{\underset{\displaystyle Cl}{C}} + POCl_3 + HCl \qquad (19)$$
Phosphorus oxychloride

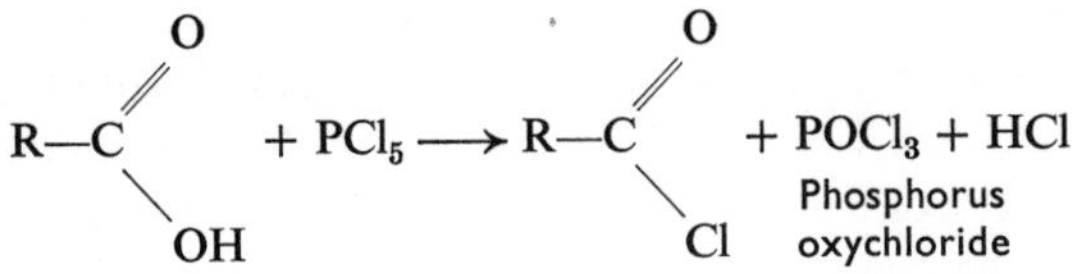

$$R-\overset{\displaystyle O}{\underset{\displaystyle OH}{C}} + SOCl_2 \longrightarrow R-\overset{\displaystyle O}{\underset{\displaystyle Cl}{C}} + SO_2 + HCl \qquad (20)$$

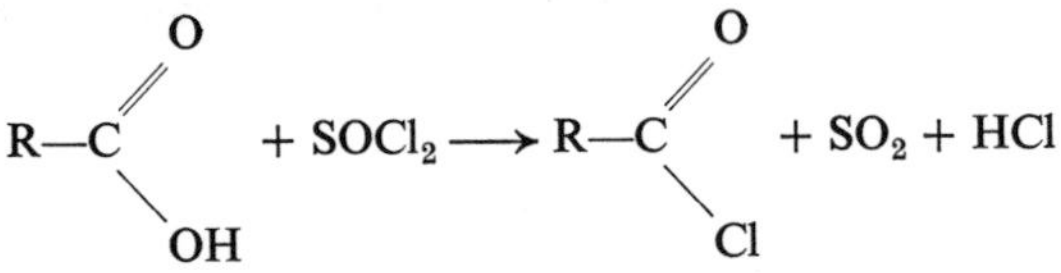

is less than in the other two processes, but this procedure has the advantage that no hydrogen chloride is evolved. In structures containing a carbon-carbon double bond, use of phosphorus trichloride eliminates the hazard of attack on the double bond by hydrogen chloride.

The mechanism of the reaction of phosphorus pentachloride with acids is not well understood; however, the reaction pathway of the other two reagents is rather well defined. In both cases, the conversion to the high-energy acid chloride is accomplished by developing a leaving group that is such a poor nucleophile that attack on the carbonyl in the acid chloride does not occur. The reaction route for phosphorus trichloride (Eq. 21) is illustrative. The first

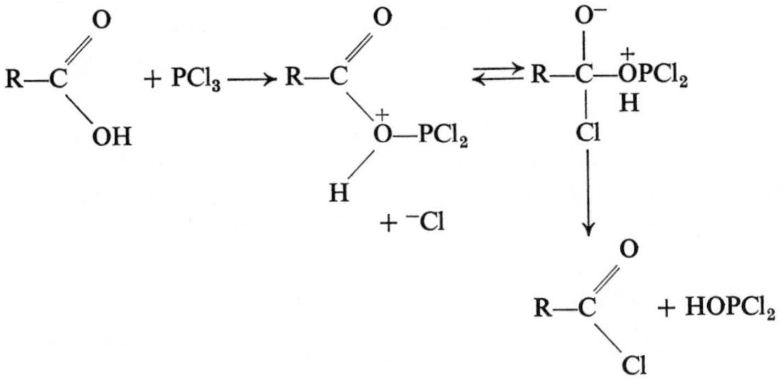

$$R-\overset{\displaystyle O}{\underset{\displaystyle OH}{C}} + PCl_3 \longrightarrow R-\overset{\displaystyle O}{\underset{\displaystyle \overset{+}{O}-PCl_2}{C}} \rightleftarrows R-\overset{\displaystyle O^-}{\underset{\displaystyle Cl}{\overset{\displaystyle |}{\underset{\displaystyle |}{C}}}}-\overset{+}{O}PCl_2 \qquad (21)$$

$$+ {}^-Cl$$

$$\downarrow$$

$$R-\overset{\displaystyle O}{\underset{\displaystyle Cl}{C}} + HOPCl_2$$

step depends on displacement of chlorine from phosphorus by the acid, a step that occurs easily even with such a poor nucleophile. This initial step supplies chloride ion for attack on carbonyl in the second step. Equation 21 is written for displacement of a single chloride, since this illustrates the mechanism; however, the other chlorides are similarly displaced so that the final product is phosphonic acid, which is a very poor nucleophile, partly because its structure is not $P(OH)_3$ as would be expected, but is $HPO(OH)_2$ (cf. Chap. 6, footnote 5). Presumably the intermediates, such as $HOPCl_2$, also have the phosphonic acid structure.

In the case of thionyl chloride, a similar intermediate is involved: RO—S—Cl. The final product in this case, sulfur dioxide, is not a nucleophile
$\downarrow$
O

and is also a gas which tends to escape from the reaction mixture.

Esterification. Alcohols react with acids according to the same mechanism outlined for hydrolysis of an amide so that an equilibrium between the acid and ester is established (Eq. 22). In esterification, however, only acid

$$
\underset{\substack{\\ \text{OH}}}{\overset{\overset{\displaystyle O}{\parallel}}{R-C}} \ + \ R'-OH \ \underset{}{\overset{H^+}{\rightleftarrows}} \ \underset{\substack{\\ \text{O}-R'}}{\overset{\overset{\displaystyle O}{\parallel}}{R-C}} \ + \ HOH \tag{22}
$$

catalysis is satisfactory. A base converts the acid to its anion, which is a resonance hybrid whose negative charge is partly delocalized to the carboxyl carbon. Thus, the positive character of this carbon is destroyed and it is no longer attractive to nucleophiles.

The equilibrium constant in Eq. 22 is usually between 1 and 2, so a good yield of ester can be obtained only if the equilibrium is displaced in some way, usually by the law of mass action. One method of accomplishing displacement of the equilibrium is by removal of water, either with a drying agent or by addition of a compound such as benzene which gives a minimum-boiling azeotrope with water and allows removal of the water by azeotropic distillation. In nearly all cases, direct esterification is employed only when a cheap alcohol, such as methanol or ethanol, is used. If fifteen to twenty equivalents of alcohol are used, ester yields based on acid are excellent. If both acid and alcohol are expensive, it is common to make the ester by another route, such as *via* the acid chloride (Chap. 14).

Reduction of acids. The reduction of carboxylic acids is a difficult reaction, and there has never been developed a satisfactory method of reducing the acid directly to the corresponding aldehyde.[9] Direct reduction to an alcohol

---

[9] There are numerous methods for converting various acid derivatives to aldehydes, so the acid is a major source of aldehydes by an indirect route. One such route, the Rosenmund reduction of acid chlorides, is discussed in Chapter 14.

can be accomplished in moderate yield (Eq. 23, not balanced; at least two

$$R-C\underset{OH}{\overset{O}{\big\langle}} + LiAlH_4 \longrightarrow Li_2O + H_2 + (R-CH_2O)_3Al \xrightarrow{\text{HOH}}$$

$$R-CH_2OH + Al(OH)_3 \quad (23)$$

multistep reaction mechanisms are operative) by use of a specific and rather expensive reagent, lithium aluminum hydride; however, the yield is much better if the ester is employed instead of the acid. Cheaper methods of reducing esters are discussed in Chapter 14.

The principal difficulty in reducing acids no doubt arises from the stabilization introduced by dimerization. Hydrogen bonding of the carbonyl group lowers its reactivity to attack by reducing agents. In the case of alkaline reducing agents, the resonance-stabilized carboxylate anion would be the species present, so the double bond character of the carbonyl is greatly reduced by electron delocalization.

High Reactivity of Acids and Acid Derivatives

When a given group, such as hydroxyl, halogen or alkoxy (—OR), is attached to an acyl group it is much more easily replaced ("more reactive") than when it is attached to an alkyl group. For example, the process shown in Eq. 22 goes at a tremendously higher rate in both directions than is the case for the corresponding reactions involving an alcohol instead of an acid. The equilibrium in Eq. 22 is reached in about a minute at 100°, if no significant steric hindrance is present. In contrast, reaction of two alcohols to form an ether, with acid catalysis, proceeds at an insignificant rate at 100°, goes moderately rapidly above 130° (cf. Eq. 6-19). The reverse reaction, cleavage of ethers, does not occur in boiling concentrated hydrochloric acid, but requires hydriodic acid which supplies the more nucleophilic iodide ion (cf. Eq. 6-20). In similar fashion, all the acid derivatives discussed in Chapter 14 show a greatly increased reactivity in comparison with the alkyl derivatives.

The high reactivity of acid derivatives stems largely from two factors. One of these is the relatively positive nature of the carbonyl carbon, caused by the electron-attracting nature of oxygen. This polarization of the carbonyl group is frequently indicated by writing resonance forms:

$$R-\underset{O}{\overset{|}{C}}-R' \quad \longleftrightarrow \quad R-\overset{+}{\underset{O^-}{\overset{|}{C}}}-R'$$

The electron attraction by oxygen makes the carbonyl carbon more positive than is the case in an alkyl carbon, hence the rate of attack of a nucleophile is greater.

A second consideration, probably more important than the first, is the steric factor. In the transition state in a displacement reaction (cf. Chap. 6, Fig. 1), there are *five* groups intimately associated with the reacting carbon. In contrast, in the attack on an acid derivative (as in Eq. 14 or 15), there are never more than *four* groups around the reacting carbon. In view of the abundant evidence (cf. Chap. 6) to the effect that atoms occupy space and steric considerations have a profound effect on the course of reactions; the steric requirements of the additional group in displacement reactions should be a major factor in the high reactivity of acid derivatives. The activation energy should be higher for the more crowded transition state, and this would result in a lower rate of reaction.

An illustration of the importance of the steric factor is encountered in connection with the relative rates of the two-step hydrolysis of a nitrile to an acid anion (Eq. 11). In the first step, yielding an amide, there are only *three* groups around the reacting carbon (cf. Eqs. 12 and 13), whereas in the second step there are *four* groups as just discussed. In molecules having no significant steric hindrance (substitution of bulky groups alpha or beta to the functional group), the rates of the two steps in Eq. 11 prove to be approximately the same. If, however, *steric hindrance is introduced, the second step is slowed up much more than the first*. In instances of severe hindrance, the second step becomes slower than the first by a factor of *at least one million*. As one chemist put it, everybody knows that it is harder to raise an umbrella in a crowd. In the displacement reaction, the umbrella must turn inside out.

EXERCISES

1. Give one additional name for each of the following acids.

(a) Stearic acid.
(b) Myristic acid.
(c) Isovaleric acid.
(d) *sec*-Butylacetic acid.
(e) Ethylisopropyl-*n*-butylacetic acid.
(f) α-Chloro-α-methyl-γ,δ-diethylcaprylic acid.
(g) Dimethylvinylacetic acid.
(h) β-Isopropoxy-α,γ-dimethylcapric acid.

(i) γ-Hydroxylauric acid.
(j) α-Cyano-β-methylisocaproic acid.
(k) β-Methyl-δ-carboxyvaleric acid.
(l) 1,9-Nonanedioic acid.

2. Indicate which of the following pairs of formulas are resonance forms and which are isomers.

(a) 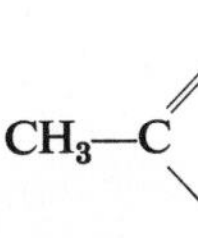 $CH_3-C\overset{O}{\underset{H}{\diagdown}}$ and $CH_2=C\overset{OH}{\underset{H}{\diagdown}}$

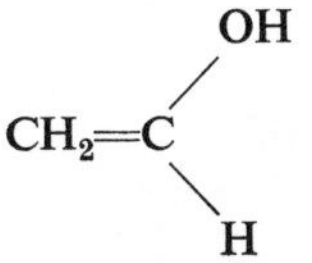

(b) 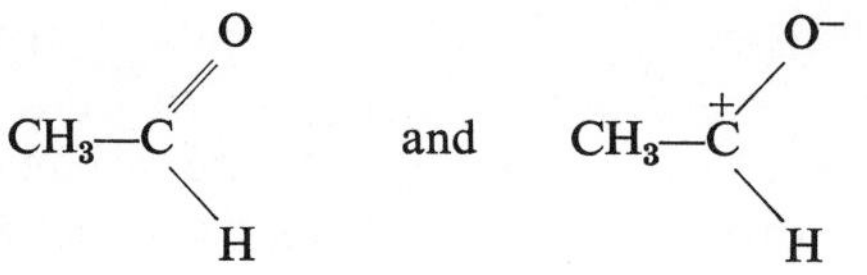 $CH_3-\overset{\displaystyle O}{\underset{\displaystyle H}{C}}$ and $CH_3-\overset{\displaystyle O^-}{\underset{\displaystyle H}{\overset{+}{C}}}$

(c) $CH_3-\overset{\displaystyle O}{\underset{\displaystyle O^-}{C}}$ and $CH_3-\overset{\displaystyle O^-}{\underset{\displaystyle O}{C}}$

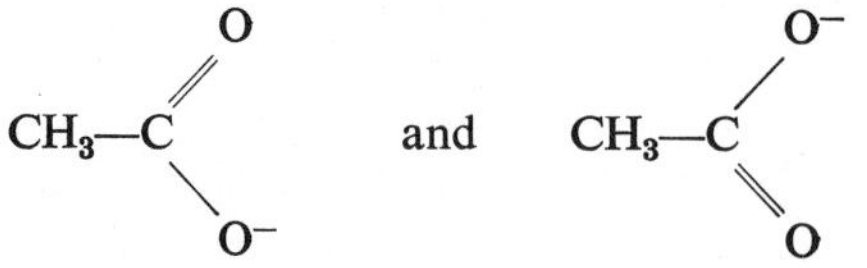

(d) 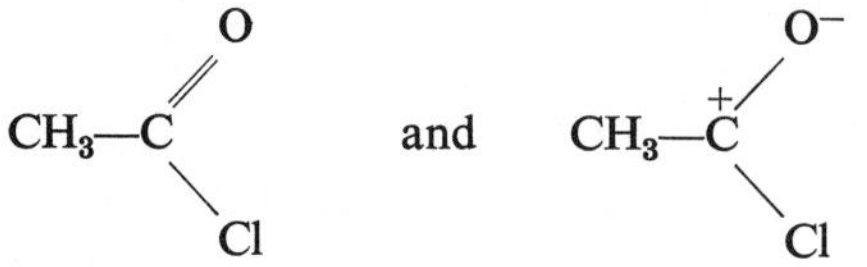 $CH_3-\overset{\displaystyle O}{\underset{\displaystyle Cl}{C}}$ and $CH_3-\overset{\displaystyle O^-}{\underset{\displaystyle Cl}{\overset{+}{C}}}$

(e) 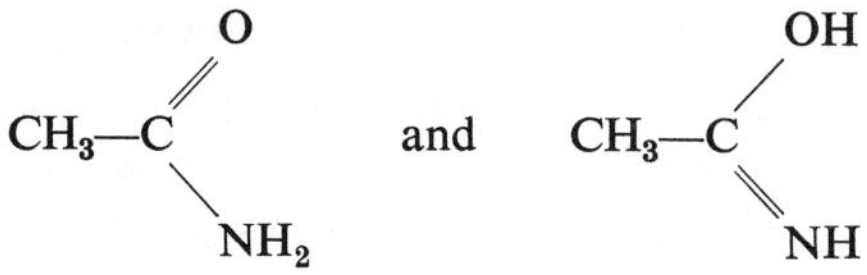 $CH_3-\overset{\displaystyle O}{\underset{\displaystyle NH_2}{C}}$ and $CH_3-\overset{\displaystyle OH}{\underset{\displaystyle NH}{C}}$

3. What is the angle between the valence directions to carbon in carbon dioxide? Explain the basis for your conclusion.

4. Ethyl alcohol boils at about 78°, and ethyl bromide boils at about 39°. Explain why ethyl bromide, which has the higher molecular weight, boils considerably lower than ethyl alcohol.

5. Write electronic formulas for the following substances.

(a) Carbon dioxide.
(b) Carbon monoxide.
(c) Formic acid (dimeric form).
(d) Formate anion (resonance forms).

6. Outline by equations, not necessarily balanced but with all necessary conditions and reagents indicated, practical methods for accomplishing each of the following conversions. Any desired reagents may be used for effecting the conversions.

(a) 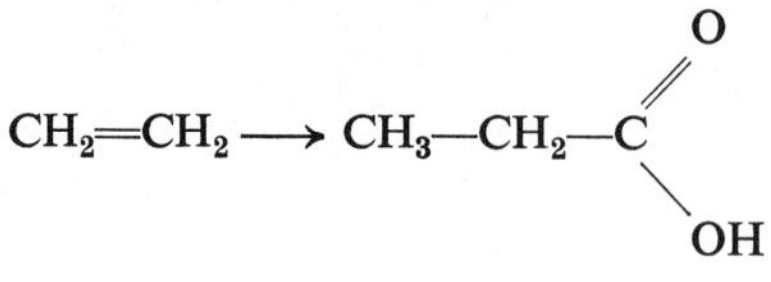 $CH_2{=}CH_2 \longrightarrow CH_3-CH_2-\overset{\displaystyle O}{\underset{\displaystyle OH}{C}}$

(b) $CH_3-CH_2-CH_2-CH_2OH \longrightarrow CH_3-CH_2-\underset{\displaystyle CH_3}{CH}-\overset{\displaystyle O}{\underset{\displaystyle OH}{C}}$

(c) $CH_2{=}CH_2 \longrightarrow \underset{\displaystyle HO}{\overset{\displaystyle O}{C}}-CH_2-CH_2-\overset{\displaystyle O}{\underset{\displaystyle OH}{C}}$

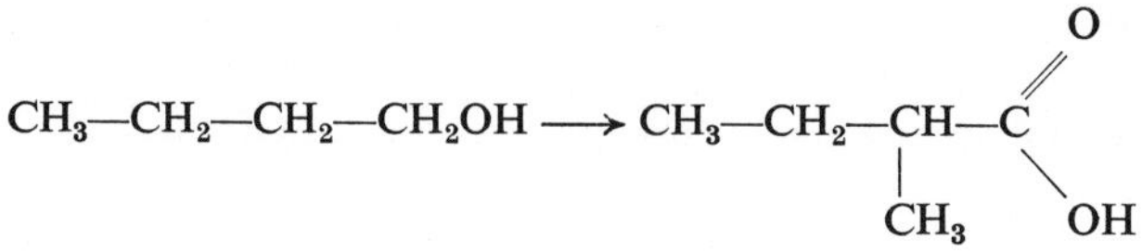

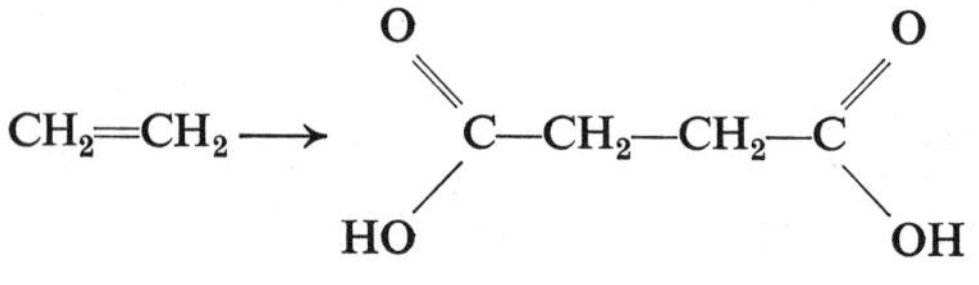

(d) 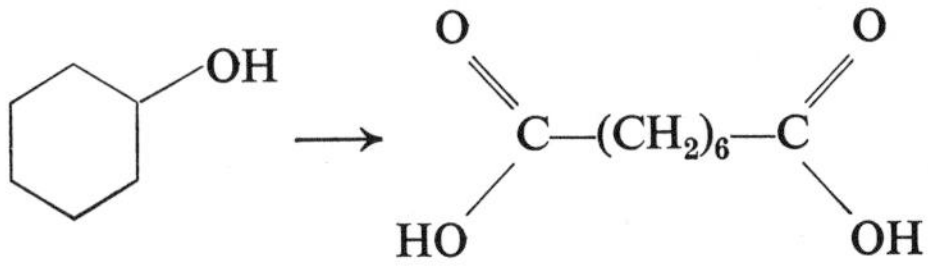 ![cyclohexanol with OH] $\longrightarrow$ $\underset{HO}{\overset{O}{\underset{}{\parallel}}}C-(CH_2)_6-\underset{OH}{\overset{O}{\underset{}{\parallel}}}C$ (*via* adipic acid)

(e) Coal and limestone $\longrightarrow$ $CH_3-\underset{OH}{\overset{O}{\underset{}{\parallel}}}C$

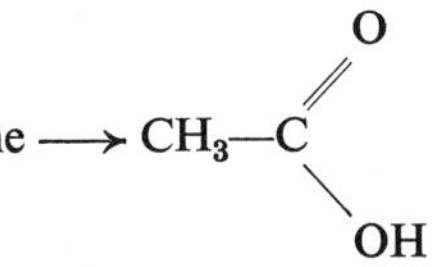

(f) 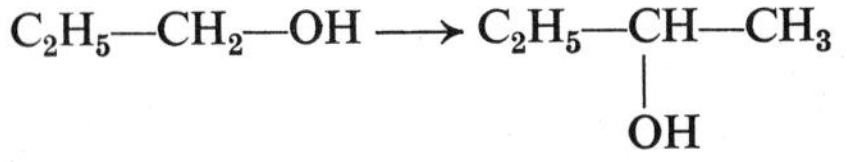 $C_2H_5-CH_2-OH \longrightarrow C_2H_5-\underset{\underset{OH}{|}}{CH}-CH_3$

(g) 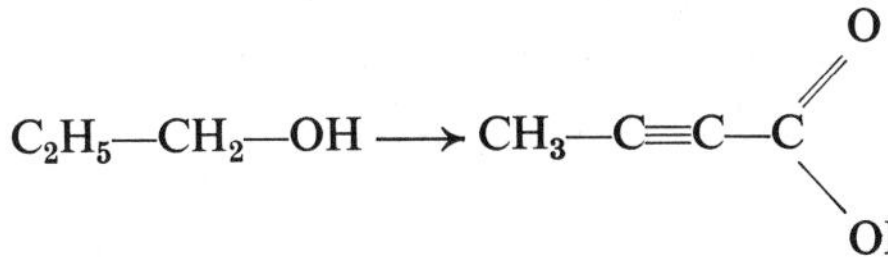 $C_2H_5-CH_2-OH \longrightarrow CH_3-C{\equiv}C-\underset{OH}{\overset{O}{\underset{}{\parallel}}}C$

(h) 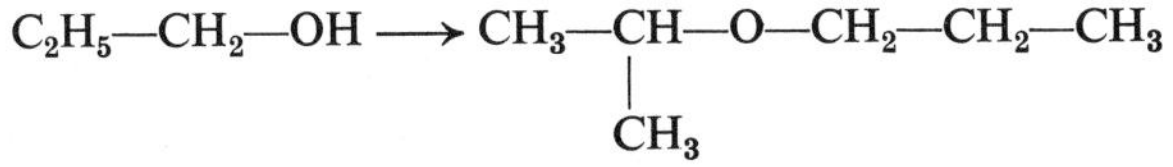 $C_2H_5-CH_2-OH \longrightarrow CH_3-\underset{\underset{CH_3}{|}}{CH}-O-CH_2-CH_2-CH_3$

7. Name, by the IUC system, all the end-products of the syntheses which are indicated in Exercise 6.

8. For the acid-catalyzed esterification of butyric acid with ethanol, indicate the reaction pathway and show the intermediates involved.

9. Arrange the following groups in the order of their electron-withdrawing capacity: OH, Br, CO_2H, C_2H_5. Explain how the order was determined. (Note: The pK_a for the first ionization of malonic acid is 2.80.)

14

Derivatives of Carboxylic Acids

In the functional derivatives of carboxylic acids, the hydroxyl is replaced by another group, except in nitriles where carboxyl is replaced. This modification eliminates both the hydrogen bonding and acidity which are characteristic of the acids, thus gives compounds of rather different physical and chemical properties. The derivatives of the acids are actually of considerably greater importance than the acids themselves, in both chemical industry and biochemical processes.

Nomenclature

The acid derivatives may be named by any of the systems used for naming acids. In each instance, the only modification in the acid name is substitution of the ending characteristic of the derivative. The characteristic endings for the derivatives are best illustrated by examples such as those assembled on the next page.

$CH_3-(CH_2)_3-CO_2H$ Valeric acid   Pentanoic acid

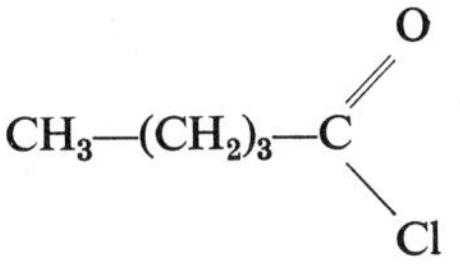

$$CH_3-(CH_2)_3-C\overset{O}{\underset{Cl}{\big\langle}}$$ Valeryl chloride   Pentanoyl chloride

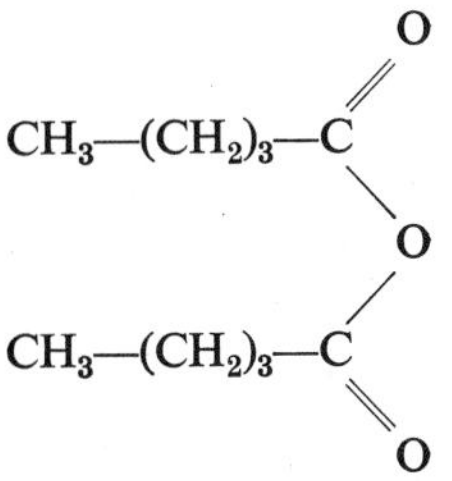

$$CH_3-(CH_2)_3-C\overset{O}{\underset{O}{\big\langle}}$$
$$CH_3-(CH_2)_3-C\overset{}{\underset{O}{\big\langle}}$$ Valeric anhydride   Pentanoic anhydride

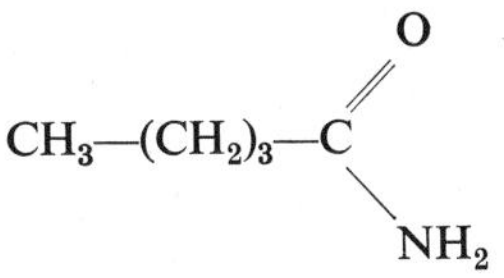

$$CH_3-(CH_2)_3-C\overset{O}{\underset{NH_2}{\big\langle}}$$ Valeramide   Pentanamide

$CH_3-(CH_2)_3-C\equiv N$ Valeronitrile   Pentanenitrile

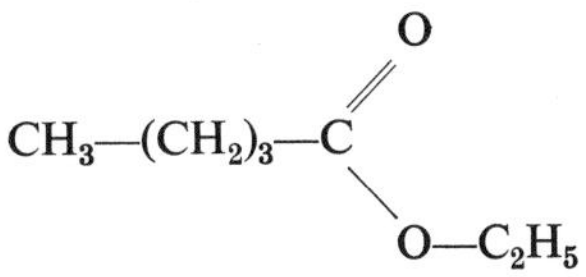

$$CH_3-(CH_2)_3-C\overset{O}{\underset{O-C_2H_5}{\big\langle}}$$ Ethyl valerate   Ethyl pentanoate

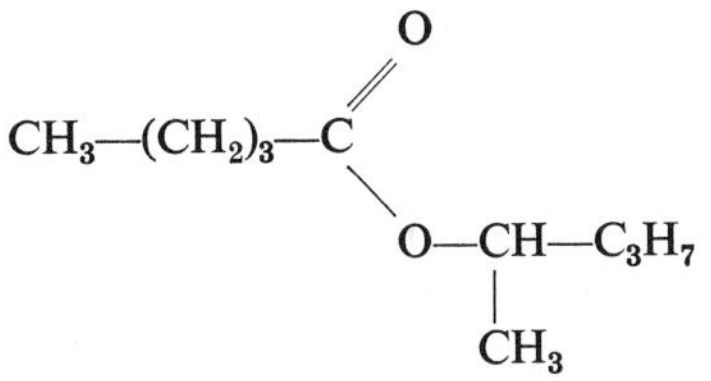

$$CH_3-(CH_2)_3-C\overset{O}{\underset{O-CH-C_3H_7 \atop CH_3}{\big\langle}}$$ 1-Methylbutyl pentanoate

For acid chlorides and anhydrides, as well as esters, the characteristic endings for the names are derived in the same way for the system based on trivial acid names and for the IUC system; however, this is not the case for amides and nitriles. To name amides in the former system, the acid name is altered by replacing *-ic acid* with *-amide*, whereas in the IUC system *-oic acid* is replaced with *-amide*. For naming nitriles by the system based on trivial names, the acid name is altered by replacing *-ic acid* with *-onitrile*. In the IUC system, nitriles are named by adding *-nitrile* to the basic alkane name. In naming of esters, it should be noted that the radical on oxygen (arising from the alcohol from which the ester could be made) is named according to the usual system for naming radicals (cf. Chap. 5), and this name is a separate word. As usual, all but rather simple radicals must be named by the IUC system.

Since acetic acid is a trivial name, the naming of derivatives as those of a substituted acetic acid follows directly the system based on trivial names. For example, derivatives of methylethylacetic acid would be methylethylacetyl chloride, methylethylacetonitrile, and ethyl methylethylacetate.

One additional item is necessary for the complete description of the naming of amides. If alkyl is substituted for a hydrogen in the $-NH_2$ group, this is denoted by placing N- (note capital letter) before the name of the alkyl group so substituted. This device is applied in all systems of nomenclature, and may be illustrated in the IUC system:

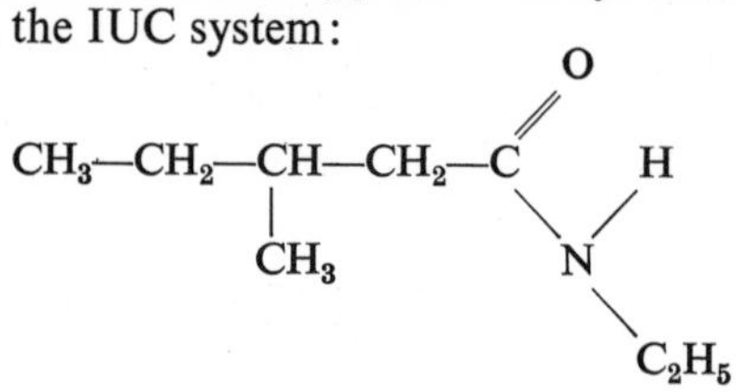

$$CH_3-CH_2-CH-CH_2-C \overset{O}{\big\Vert} \quad \begin{matrix} H \\ N \\ C_2H_5 \end{matrix}$$

with CH_3 below the CH.

N-Ethyl-3-methylpentanamide

If both hydrogens on nitrogen are substituted, N must be repeated, e.g., N,N-dimethyl- or N-ethyl-N-propyl-.

Whenever a rather complicated acid derivative is to be named, it is wise to first name the acid, then modify this name in the same way that one would a simple acid name. For example, in the structure below, one would first name the corresponding acid, then change the ending, *-enoic acid*, to *-enamide*.

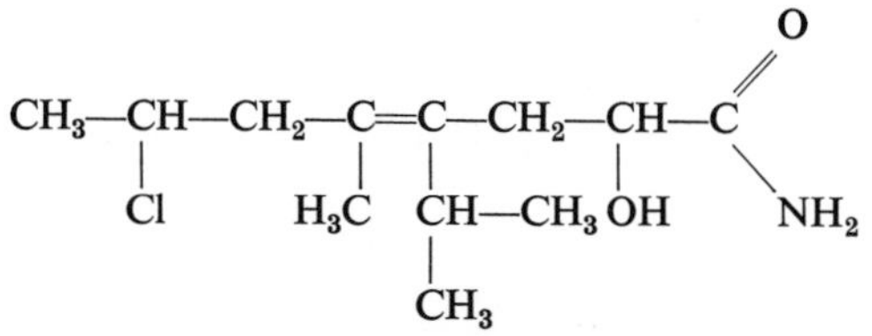

$$CH_3-CH-CH_2-C=C-CH_2-CH-C \overset{O}{\big\Vert}$$

with substituents Cl, H₃C, CH—CH₃ (CH₃), OH, NH₂

7-Chloro-2-hydroxy-5-methyl-
4-isopropyl-4-octenamide

Naming of functional groups as substituents. The only functional groups here discussed that are commonly named as substituents are the nitrile and ester groups. As a substituent, the nitrile group is termed **cyano,** while the ester group is named **alkoxycarbonyl** (methoxycarbonyl, *t*-butoxycarbonyl, 1-methylpropoxycarbonyl, etc.). The following are illustrative:

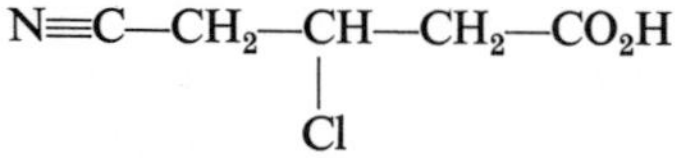

$$N\equiv C-CH_2-CH-CH_2-CO_2H$$

with Cl below the CH

3-Chloro-4-cyanobutanoic acid

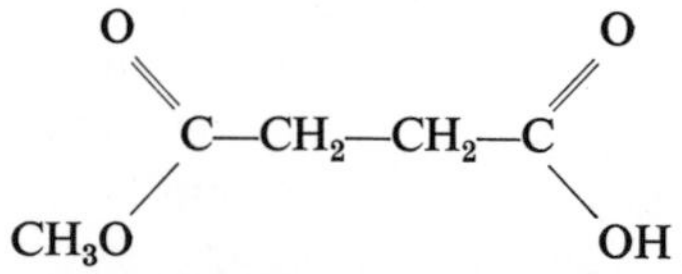

$$CH_3O \overset{O}{\diagup} C-CH_2-CH_2-C \overset{O}{\diagdown} OH$$

Methyl hydrogen succinate
or
β-Methoxycarbonylpropionic acid

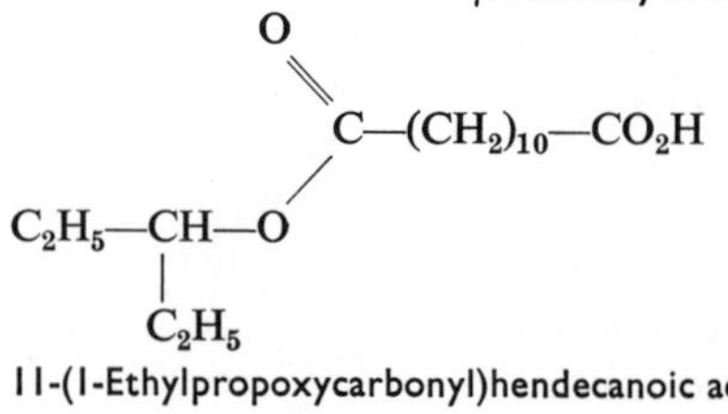

$$C_2H_5-CH-O \overset{O}{\diagup} C-(CH_2)_{10}-CO_2H$$

with C_2H_5 below the CH

11-(1-Ethylpropoxycarbonyl)hendecanoic acid

Infrared Spectra of Carboxylic Acid Derivatives

As stated in the preceding chapter, the derivatives of carboxylic acids show carbonyl absorption in the region between 5.5 and 6.1 μ. Other structural features in the molecule cause small shifts in the carbonyl absorption, and these are sometimes of considerable diagnostic value. For example, an ester ordinarily absorbs at about 5.75 μ (cf. Fig. 13-2), but if there is a double bond in the position alpha-beta to the ester group (i.e., conjugated with the ester group) the infrared absorption of the carbonyl is shifted to somewhat longer wavelength, usually to a position above 5.8 μ (the region where ketones absorb, cf. Chap. 15).

The acid derivative absorbing at longest wavelength is the amide, whose absorption is near 6.1 μ, while the carbonyl group with the shortest wavelength absorption is the acid chloride, at 5.55 to 5.6 μ. The nitrile group is usually classified as an acid derivative, but it does not contain a carbonyl. The nitrile exhibits a rather weak absorption band near 4.5 μ, and it is the only common functional group with absorption near this region. Numerous synthetic compounds containing deuterium have been made, and these show absorption not far removed from the nitrile, on account of the carbon-deuterium bond.

Acid anhydrides show a rather surprising feature in infrared absorption, in that they normally exhibit *two* carbonyl bonds, even when the structure is quite symmetrical. Ordinarily, two of the same functional group in the same environment absorb at the same wavelength. For example, a dibasic acid such as sebacic acid gives the same absorption as a monocarboxylic acid, except that the absorption is more intense. The two bands in anhydrides (usually found between 5.55 and 5.95 μ) are ascribed to absorptions by vibrations of the two carbonyl groups which are either in phase with each other or out of phase. This type of absorption can occur when groups are so close together that the vibrations of the two become interdependent.

Acid Chlorides and Anhydrides

The acid chlorides and anhydrides give the same reactions with nucleophiles, but chloride is a better leaving group than acyloxy, $R-C\begin{smallmatrix} O^- \\ \\ O \end{smallmatrix}$, so the acid chlorides give considerably higher rates of reaction. Indeed, the **acid anhydrides are usually synthesized** by a characteristic reaction of acid chlorides, attack of a nucleophile on the carbonyl. This is the type of reaction discussed for acids and derivatives in the preceding chapter. Thus, an acid chloride and salt of an acid (furnishing the anion) yield an anhydride (Eq. 1). Since anhydrides, except for acetic anhydride, are synthesized from the acid chlorides, the anhydrides are considerably more expensive. As mentioned above, the two types of compounds give the same products, and the acid chlorides are more reactive, so acid anhydrides are used in synthesis only in special structures.

$$
\underset{\substack{\\ \text{Cl}}}{\overset{\overset{\displaystyle O}{\parallel}}{R-C}} + \underset{\substack{\\ \text{ONa}}}{\overset{\overset{\displaystyle O}{\parallel}}{R-C}} \; \rightleftharpoons \; \left[\underset{\substack{O-C-R\\ \parallel\\ O}}{\overset{\overset{\displaystyle O^-}{|}}{R-C-Cl}} \right] \; \longrightarrow \; \begin{array}{c} R-C \\ \diagdown \\ O \\ \diagup \\ R-C \end{array} + \text{NaCl} \quad (1)
$$

The most commonly used anhydrides are the cyclic ones, which may be formed from succinic or glutaric acids simply by heating (Eq. 2). Normally, the cyclic anhydride forms only when the ring contains five or six atoms, for

$$
\begin{array}{c} \text{CH}_2-\text{CO}_2\text{H} \\ \diagup \\ \text{H}_2\text{C} \\ \diagdown \\ \text{CH}_2-\text{CO}_2\text{H} \end{array} \; \xrightarrow{\Delta} \; \text{(cyclic anhydride)} + \text{HOH} \quad (2)
$$

Glutaric acid   Glutaric anhydride

these rings are the sizes formed without strain of the valence angles (cf. Chap. 7). The cyclic anhydrides are of interest because of the polyfunctional products of their reactions (see below).

Acid chlorides are synthesized from the acids by use of one of the reagents discussed in the preceding chapter.

Reactions of Acid Chlorides and Anhydrides

Reaction with nucleophiles. As has been mentioned in the preceding chapter, the acid chlorides are of importance as intermediates for synthesis of other acid derivatives, on account of the higher energy of the acid chlorides. A typical reaction is that shown in Eq. 1 for synthesis of anhydrides. Other nucleophiles also attack the carbonyl, to give high yields of reaction products. Important synthetic reactions are shown in Eqs. 3 through 5. Since the reaction in Eq. 6 is also rapid and exothermic, it follows that acid chlorides must be prepared under strictly anhydrous conditions, stored with protection from atmospheric moisture, and utilized in synthesis with dry reagents and solvents. Naturally, acid chlorides are never isolated from living organisms.

$$
\underset{\substack{\\ \text{Cl}}}{\overset{\overset{\displaystyle O}{\parallel}}{R-C}} + \text{H}-\text{OR}' \longrightarrow \underset{\substack{\\ \text{OR}'}}{\overset{\overset{\displaystyle O}{\parallel}}{R-C}} + \text{HCl} \quad (3)
$$

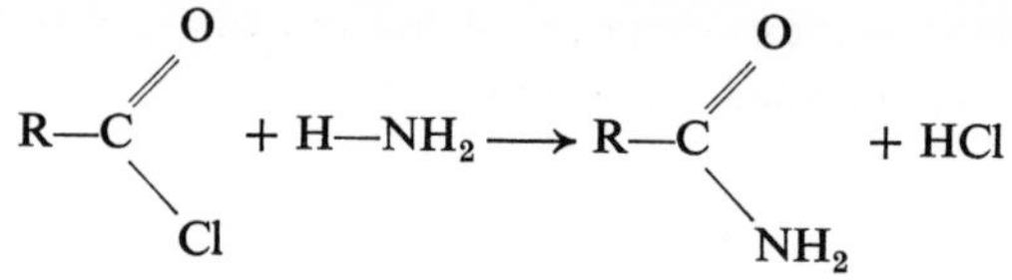

$$R-\overset{\displaystyle O}{\underset{\displaystyle Cl}{C}} + H-NH_2 \longrightarrow R-\overset{\displaystyle O}{\underset{\displaystyle NH_2}{C}} + HCl \tag{4}$$

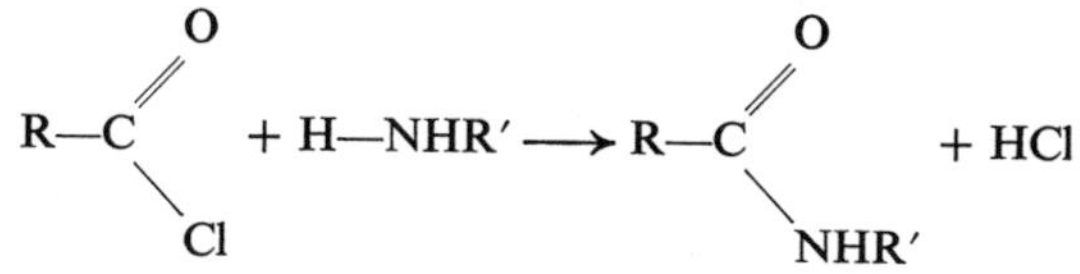

$$R-\overset{\displaystyle O}{\underset{\displaystyle Cl}{C}} + H-NHR' \longrightarrow R-\overset{\displaystyle O}{\underset{\displaystyle NHR'}{C}} + HCl \tag{5}$$

$$R-\overset{\displaystyle O}{\underset{\displaystyle Cl}{C}} + H-OH \longrightarrow R-\overset{\displaystyle O}{\underset{\displaystyle OH}{C}} + HCl \tag{6}$$

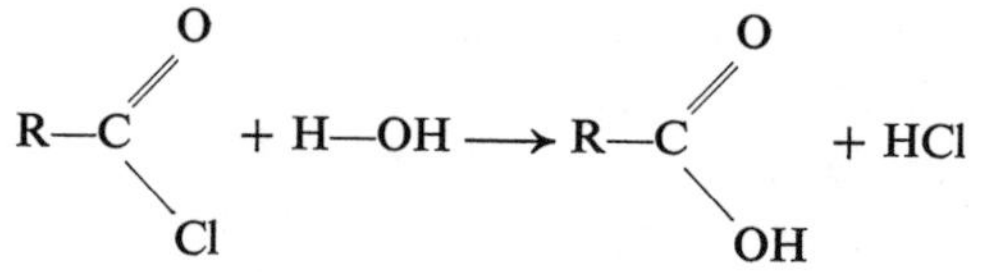

It is also clear, from Eq. 6, that acids cannot be converted to acid chlorides by use of halogen acid. This should be noted as in marked contrast to the situation in the alcohol series, where an equilibrium is established between alcohol and alkyl chloride.

As has been mentioned, the acid anhydride could be substituted for the acid chloride in Eqs. 3 through 6; however, acetic anhydride is the only anhydride which is not considerably more expensive than the corresponding acid chloride. The cyclic anhydrides are of interest, however, for they yield difunctional compounds of considerable utility in synthesis. Illustrative reactions are shown in Eqs. 7 and 8. The half esters are especially useful, for they may be

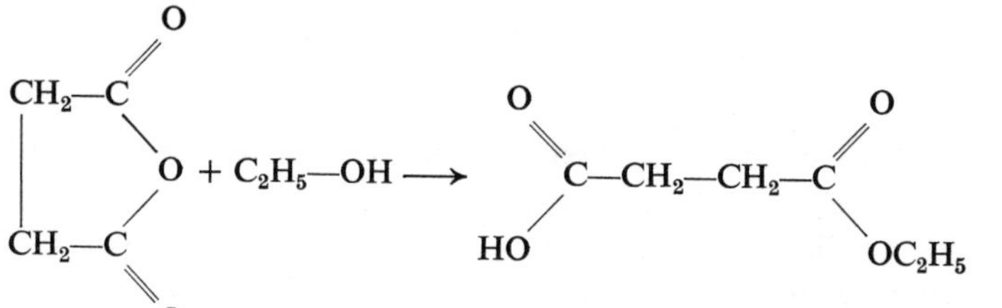

$$\begin{array}{c} CH_2-\overset{\displaystyle O}{C} \\ | \qquad\;\; O + C_2H_5-OH \longrightarrow \\ CH_2-\overset{}{C} \\ \overset{\displaystyle \|}{O} \end{array} \qquad HO-\overset{\displaystyle O}{C}-CH_2-CH_2-\overset{\displaystyle O}{C}-OC_2H_5 \tag{7}$$

Ethyl hydrogen succinate

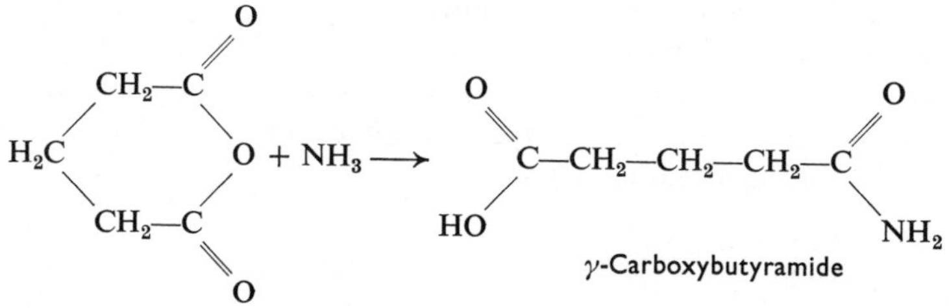

$$\begin{array}{c} CH_2-\overset{\displaystyle O}{C} \\ H_2C \qquad\;\; O + NH_3 \longrightarrow \\ CH_2-\overset{}{C} \\ \overset{\displaystyle \|}{O} \end{array} \qquad HO-\overset{\displaystyle O}{C}-CH_2-CH_2-CH_2-\overset{\displaystyle O}{C}-NH_2 \tag{8}$$

γ-Carboxybutyramide

converted to the ester acid chlorides by use of the usual reagents for synthesis of acid chlorides (cf. Chap. 13). In turn, the ester acid chloride may be used in any of the reactions given by acid chlorides. The acid chloride will react much more rapidly than the ester group. For example, a reaction such as shown in Eq. 9 may be accomplished.

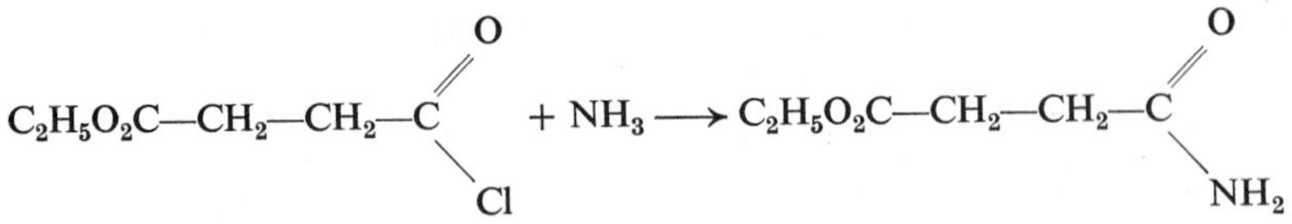

$$C_2H_5O_2C-CH_2-CH_2-\overset{\displaystyle O}{\underset{\displaystyle Cl}{C}} + NH_3 \longrightarrow C_2H_5O_2C-CH_2-CH_2-\overset{\displaystyle O}{\underset{\displaystyle NH_2}{C}} \qquad (9)$$

β-Ethoxycarbonylpropionamide

Reaction with Grignard reagents. As discussed in Chapter 13, the Grignard reagent will add to nearly all polar multiple bonds, by way of initial attack of the metal on the negative end of the polar bond. The acid derivatives are no exception to this generality, and all of them react with the Grignard reagent. As usual, however, when negative groups accumulate on the single carbon, a simple molecule is lost to yield a more stable structure. In the product of the Grignard reaction, this results in a ketone, as illustrated in Eq. 10 for reaction of butyryl chloride with ethylmagnesium bromide. As rapidly as addition

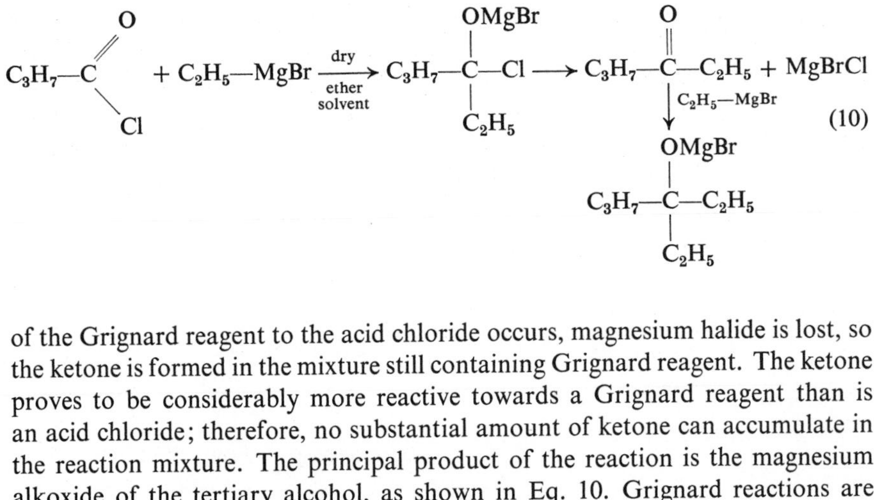

$$C_3H_7-\overset{\displaystyle O}{\underset{\displaystyle Cl}{C}} + C_2H_5-MgBr \xrightarrow[\text{ether}~\text{solvent}]{\text{dry}} C_3H_7-\overset{\displaystyle OMgBr}{\underset{\displaystyle C_2H_5}{C}}-Cl \longrightarrow C_3H_7-\overset{\displaystyle O}{\underset{}{\overset{\|}{C}}}-C_2H_5 + MgBrCl$$

$$\downarrow C_2H_5-MgBr \qquad (10)$$

$$C_3H_7-\overset{\displaystyle OMgBr}{\underset{\displaystyle C_2H_5}{C}}-C_2H_5$$

of the Grignard reagent to the acid chloride occurs, magnesium halide is lost, so the ketone is formed in the mixture still containing Grignard reagent. The ketone proves to be considerably more reactive towards a Grignard reagent than is an acid chloride; therefore, no substantial amount of ketone can accumulate in the reaction mixture. The principal product of the reaction is the magnesium alkoxide of the tertiary alcohol, as shown in Eq. 10. Grignard reactions are always worked up by addition of water to free the product from its magnesium salt, and acid is also added to convert the insoluble, foamy magnesium hydroxide to a soluble salt (Eq. 11). Regeneration of water in Eq. 11 results from neutralization of the magnesium hydroxide.

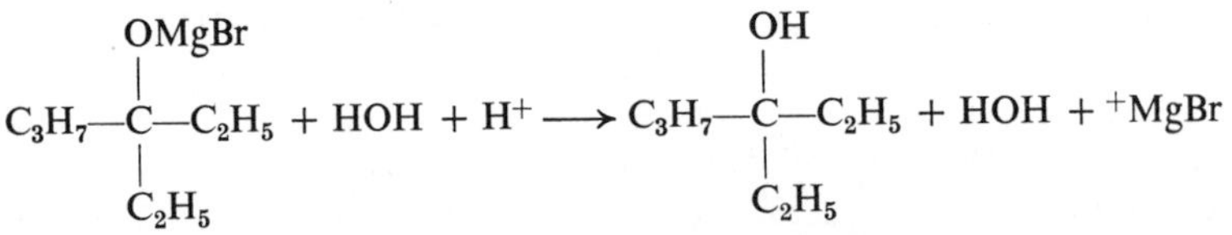

$$C_3H_7-\overset{\displaystyle OMgBr}{\underset{\displaystyle C_2H_5}{C}}-C_2H_5 + HOH + H^+ \longrightarrow C_3H_7-\overset{\displaystyle OH}{\underset{\displaystyle C_2H_5}{C}}-C_2H_5 + HOH + {}^+MgBr \quad (11)$$

3-Ethyl-3-hexanol

It may be noted that the end result of reaction of a Grignard reagent with an acid chloride is formation of a tertiary alcohol in which *two groups on the carbinol carbon are the same* (the group furnished by the Grignard reagent). This is a satisfactory synthesis of such tertiary alcohols; however, side reactions are usually more serious than when an ester is used (cf. Eq. 26), so the acid chloride is rarely utilized for conversion to an alcohol.

The acid chloride is frequently used for synthesis of a ketone, in spite of the fact that the straightforward procedure, as described in Eq. 10, is of no value at all for ketone synthesis. As the result of an accidental observation,[1] and a follow-up of careful experimentation, it has been established that, at low temperature, a catalytic amount of anhydrous ferric chloride (3–5% of a mole equivalent) has a remarkable effect in giving ketone as the chief product of a Grignard reaction with an acid chloride. Under the conditions displayed in Eq. 12, the yield of

$$C_3H_7-\overset{\displaystyle O}{\underset{\displaystyle Cl}{\overset{\diagup}{C}}} + C_2H_5-MgBr \xrightarrow[FeCl_3]{-65°} C_3H_7-\overset{\displaystyle O}{\overset{\|}{C}}-C_2H_5 + MgBrCl \qquad (12)$$

ketone is rather good, in some cases as high as 80%. Although it might be assumed at first consideration, that the ferric chloride must be inhibiting the reaction of the Grignard reagent with the ketone, it proves difficult to formulate any reasonable mechanism for such an effect. On the other hand, the result can also be achieved if the ferric chloride greatly favors the reaction with acid chloride, and this proves to be the case. At −65°, the Grignard reaction with any of the carbonyl groups is extremely sluggish, but addition of ferric chloride gives a rapid reaction with the acid chloride. It seems apparent that this must be a different type of reaction than the normal addition to carbonyl. The best evidence is that the Lewis acid is pulling out the halogen as the alkyl from the Grignard reagent is displacing it. This is similar to the concerted displacement reaction at a saturated carbon. A cyclic transition state has been proposed for this reaction (Eq. 13), differing from that normally proposed for the Grignard reaction in that the ferric chloride is coordinated with halogen, not oxygen.

---

[1] Prior to World War II, an interesting observation was made by Prof. F. W. Whitmore and his students who were carrying out large-scale Grignard reactions at Pennsylvania State College in connection with making branched-chain hydrocarbons. This work, incidentally, led to the discovery that it is the highly branched alkanes which give less knock at high compression in a gasoline engine. It was noted that when a Grignard reaction with an acid chloride was carried out in a copper reaction vessel a surprisingly large amount of ketone was found in the reaction product. Follow-up of this unexpected result after the war, at Penn State and elsewhere, revealed first that cuprous chloride is an effective catalyst for promoting ketone in the product. Later investigation of other Lewis acids revealed that the best catalyst is ferric chloride, which is well-known to complex halogen in preference to oxygen.

This important difference explains the discrimination in favor of the acid chloride.

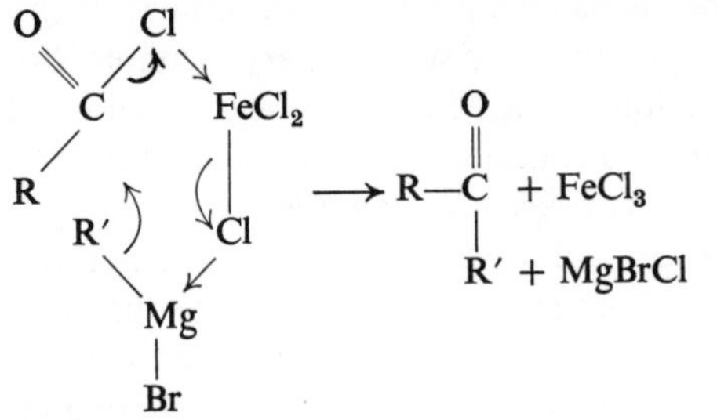

$$R-\overset{O}{\underset{\underset{Cl}{R'}}{\overset{\|}{C}}} \quad \xrightarrow{\text{FeCl}_2} \quad R-\overset{O}{\underset{R' + \text{MgBrCl}}{\overset{\|}{C}}} + \text{FeCl}_3 \qquad (13)$$

The ferric chloride-catalyzed Grignard reaction at low temperature is a useful synthesis of ketones, and it may be applied to ester acid chlorides (see above) to yield polyfunctional compounds. Other devices, depending on similar mechanisms of reaction, have been used effectively, but the ferric chloride-catalyzed reaction is sufficient for present consideration.

Amides

Amides are of great importance in biological processes, principally on account of the occurrence of the amide linkage as the principal structure in proteins, the substance from which animal tissue is built. These important compounds will be the subject of a later chapter. Polymeric amides of structure only slightly different from the protein structures have been synthesized from di-amines and di-acids or their derivatives. For example, a polymer may be constructed from the reaction shown in Eq. 14. Polymers of this structure have

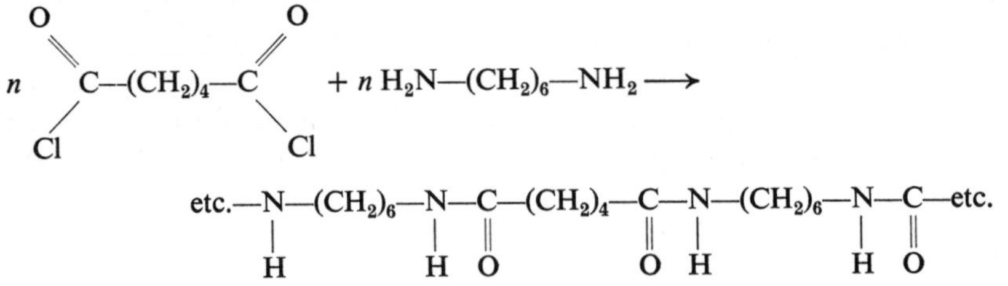

$$n \quad \overset{O}{\underset{Cl}{\overset{\|}{C}}}-(CH_2)_4-\overset{O}{\underset{Cl}{\overset{\|}{C}}} \quad + \, n \, H_2N-(CH_2)_6-NH_2 \longrightarrow$$

$$\text{etc.} - \overset{}{\underset{H}{N}} - (CH_2)_6 - \overset{}{\underset{H}{N}} - \overset{}{\underset{O}{C}} - (CH_2)_4 - \overset{}{\underset{O}{C}} - \overset{}{\underset{H}{N}} - (CH_2)_6 - \overset{}{\underset{H}{N}} - \overset{}{\underset{O}{C}} - \text{etc.} \quad (14)$$

been especially successful for making fibers suitable for spinning into thread, marketed under the familiar trade name *Nylon*. The most widely used Nylon has six carbons between the nitrogens and four between the carbonyls (the structure in Eq. 10), and is known as 6-4 Nylon. It should be noted that this type of polymer is not the product of a free radical chain reaction (Chap. 11), but results from simple repetition of a normal reaction of the polar type. The only requirement is polyfunctional compounds.

Numerous low molecular weight amides are also of importance in nature, one of these being urea, $H_2N-C-NH_2$, the diamide of carbonic acid,[2] which
$$\parallel$$
$$O$$

has been mentioned in Chapter 1 as an end product of metabolism in animals.

Synthesis of Amides

From acid chlorides. The process illustrated in Eqs. 4 and 5 is usually the highest-yield method for obtaining amides, and is the method by which N-substituted amides are nearly always made.

From nitriles. The hydrolysis of nitriles to amides has been described in some detail in the preceding chapter (Eq. 13-12); however, this method is of essentially no value for synthesis of amides. As mentioned in the preceding chapter, the second step of the hydrolysis, amide to acid anion, proceeds about as rapidly as does the first step, so a useful yield of amide can be accumulated only if the functional group is highly hindered.

If there is no other structural feature in the molecule sensitive to hot sulfuric acid, the amide can be obtained in high yield from the nitrile by way of sulfuric acid addition (Eq. 15). As in addition of sulfuric acid to alkynes, only

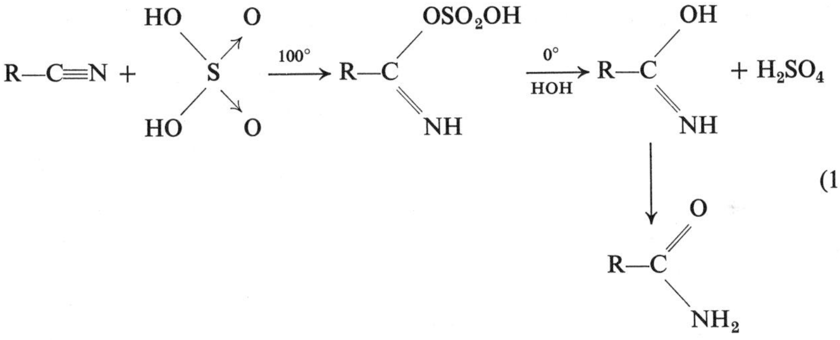

$$(15)$$

one addition takes place. The proton attacks the negative end of the triple bond in the nitrile, as would be expected. This type of ester of sulfuric acid,

---

[2] Urea is much more stable than the parent carbonic acid, which tends to dissociate into water and carbon dioxide. The di-acid chloride of carbonic acid is also a stable compound, and has the common name *phosgene*. Phosgene is surprisingly stable to hydrolysis, for an acid chloride; in fact, it survives in the fluids of an animal adequately long to function as an extremely toxic compound. It has been used as a war gas. Phosgene is especially dangerous, for it has a rather mild odor, and a man who has inhaled a lethal dose feels entirely healthy—for a little while.

In general, the properties of one-carbon compounds tend to be rather anomalous, not at all characteristic of the higher members of the series. Formic acid is a stable compound, as is formamide, but formyl chloride is so unstable that attempts to prepare it lead to carbon monoxide and hydrogen chloride. This relative stability of acid and acid chloride is, then, opposite in formic and carbonic acids.

which is actually a mixed anhydride, hydrolyzes so readily that cold water converts the adduct to the amide.

From ammonium salts. Heating the ammonium salt of an acid yields the amide, and this cheap method is that commonly used industrially. It is probable that the actual reactants are the acid and ammonia, formed by dissociation of the salt of the weak acid and the weak base. The amide would result, as in Eq. 16, by a sequence entirely analogous to esterification (Eq. 13-22).

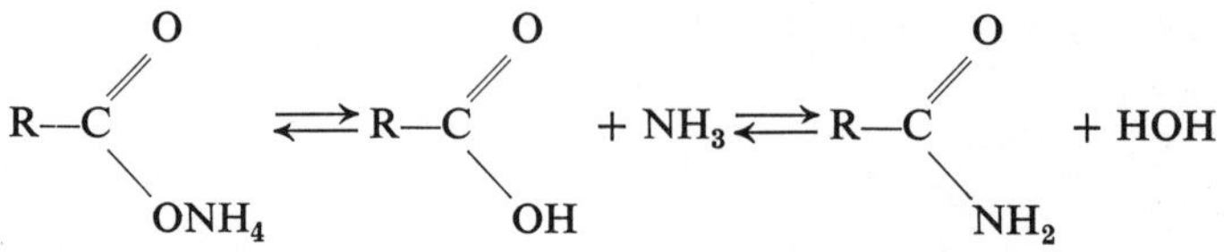

$$
R-C\overset{O}{\underset{ONH_4}{\Big\backslash\!\!/}} \rightleftarrows R-C\overset{O}{\underset{OH}{\Big\backslash\!\!/}} + NH_3 \rightleftarrows R-C\overset{O}{\underset{NH_2}{\Big\backslash\!\!/}} + HOH \qquad (16)
$$

Thus, attack of ammonia on the carbonyl would be followed by loss of a proton from nitrogen and hydroxyl from carbon, to give the amide. It is common practice to heat the mixture under pressure to avoid loss of ammonia. Urea may be obtained by heating ammonium carbonate under pressure (Eq. 17), and

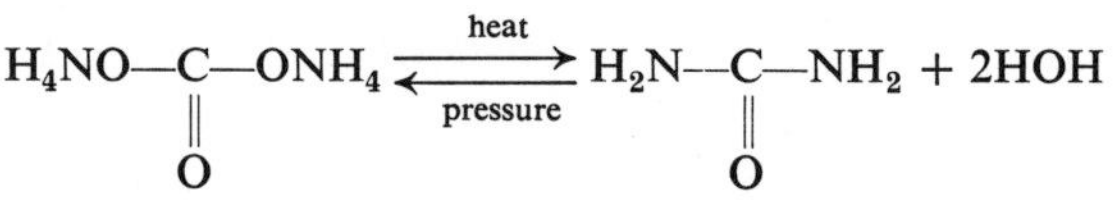

$$
H_4NO-\underset{O}{\overset{\|}{C}}-ONH_4 \underset{\text{pressure}}{\overset{\text{heat}}{\rightleftarrows}} H_2N-\underset{O}{\overset{\|}{C}}-NH_2 + 2HOH \qquad (17)
$$

is prepared industrially in large amounts by this process.

From esters. Esters will react with ammonia or amines, as will the other acid derivatives (cf. Eq. 24); however, the equilibrium between ester and amide is usually difficult to displace sufficiently towards the amide to make the conversion of synthetic interest. Synthesis from acid chlorides is much more useful.

Reactions of Amides

Although amides give the usual reactions with nucleophilic reagents, as do the other acid derivatives, the amide is the most stable of the acid derivatives, and is rarely used for conversion to the other derivatives, except for the nitrile.

Hydrolysis. The amide may be hydrolyzed to the acid, as has been described in detail (Eqs. 13-14 and 13-15), but the rate of reaction is much lower than that of other acid derivatives. The rate of base-catalyzed hydrolysis of esters, for example, is at least a million times faster than that of amides. The most frequent reason for hydrolysis of amides is as a part of the synthesis of acids *via* the cyanide.

Dehydration. Although dehydration of an amide to form a nitrile is formally the reverse of the hydrolytic reaction, that is not actually the situation. This process differs, therefore, from the conversion of an ammonium salt to an amide, which probably proceeds by way of the same transition state as does hydrolysis of the amide in base. Reversal of the nitrile hydrolysis does not actually occur, for dehydration of an amide requires a powerful dehydrating agent. The dehydration probably proceeds by way of formation of an oxonium salt of the isomeric form of the amide having hydroxyl on carbon (upper formula in Eq. 15), and dissociation of this by heat. A typical process is that shown in Eq. 18.

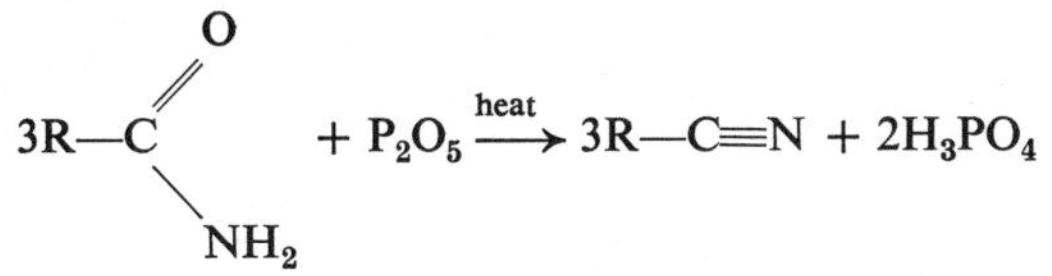

$$3R-\overset{O}{\underset{NH_2}{C}} + P_2O_5 \xrightarrow{\text{heat}} 3R-C{\equiv}N + 2H_3PO_4 \qquad (18)$$

Nitriles

Synthesis of Nitriles

The principal methods for synthesis of nitriles have already been discussed. One is displacement of halogen in an alkyl halide with cyanide ion (Eq. 6-1), and the other is dehydration of amides, Eq. 18 just presented. The first method is nearly always used for primary alkyl cyanides, but this displacement is poor with secondary halides, and fails with tertiary halides (cf. Chap. 6). Thus, the secondary alkyl cyanides are frequently made *via* the acid, and the tertiary alkyl cyanides (trialkylacetonitriles) are nearly always made in this way.

Reactions of Nitriles

Alcoholysis. Hydrolysis of nitriles has already been discussed repeatedly. Reaction with alcohol occurs similarly (Eq. 19) but with acid catalysis the salt of the imino ester is formed. An imino ester is a much weaker base than ammonia, so some free base would be in equilibrium with the salt. Imino esters are so very reactive that isolation of this product from the reaction in Eq. 19

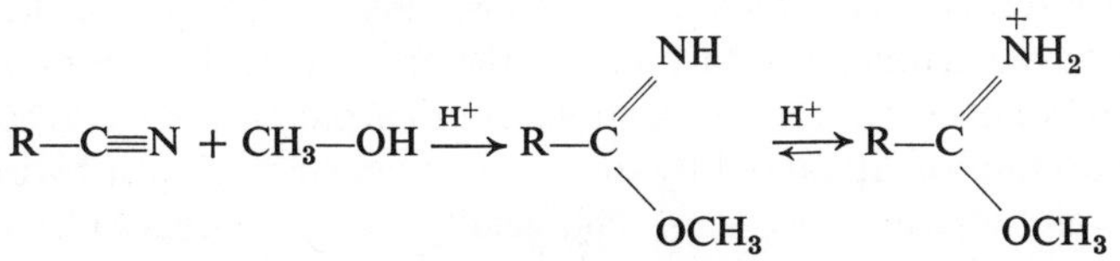

$$R-C{\equiv}N + CH_3-OH \xrightarrow{H^+} R-\overset{NH}{\underset{OCH_3}{C}} \underset{\text{(an imino ester)}}{\overset{H^+}{\rightleftarrows}} R-\overset{\overset{+}{N}H_2}{\underset{OCH_3}{C}} \qquad (19)$$

can be accomplished only if the process is carried out under rigorously anhydrous conditions. With anything less than extreme precautions, enough water will be present in the alcohol to give hydrolysis as in Eq. 20. Thus, the usual product of alcoholysis of a nitrile is the ester of the alcohol.

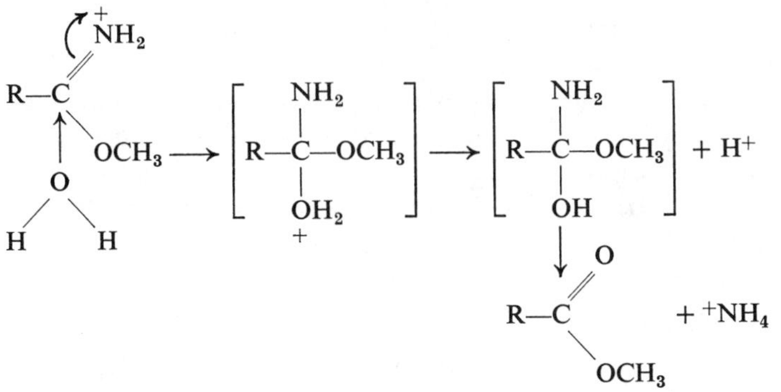

$$
R-C\underset{\substack{\uparrow\\O\\H\quad H}}{\overset{\overset{+}{N}H_2}{\underset{}{\diagdown}}}OCH_3 \longrightarrow \left[R-\underset{\substack{|\\\overset{+}{O}H_2}}{\overset{\overset{NH_2}{|}}{C}}-OCH_3 \right] \longrightarrow \left[R-\underset{\substack{|\\OH}}{\overset{\overset{NH_2}{|}}{C}}-OCH_3 \right] + H^+ \qquad (20)
$$

$$
R-C\underset{OCH_3}{\overset{O}{\diagup}} + {}^+NH_4
$$

Reaction with Grignard reagents. The Grignard reagent adds to the polar nitrile group in an expected manner, and the addition product is stable in this case. In contrast with the other acid derivatives (cf. Eq. 10), there is only a single negative group on carbon in the nitrile addition product, hence its stability. The reaction is illustrated in Eq. 21. When the reaction is worked

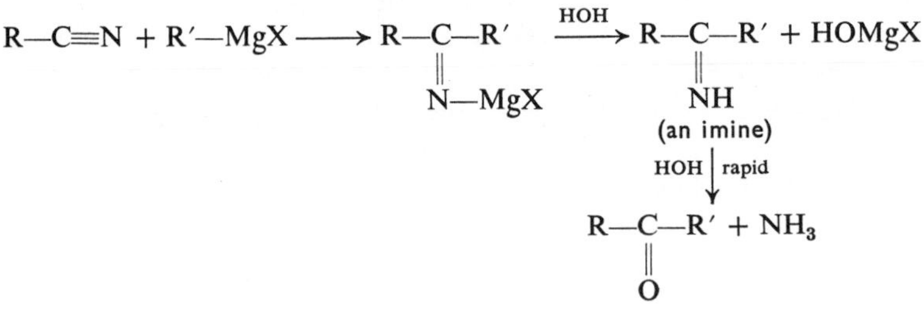

$$
R-C\equiv N + R'-MgX \longrightarrow R-\underset{\substack{||\\N-MgX}}{C}-R' \xrightarrow{\text{HOH}} R-\underset{\substack{||\\NH\\\text{(an imine)}}}{C}-R' + HOMgX \qquad (21)
$$

$$
\text{HOH} \downarrow \text{rapid}
$$

$$
R-\underset{\substack{||\\O}}{C}-R' + NH_3
$$

up by addition of water, the imine is hydrolyzed rapidly at room temperature unless the molecule is severely hindered. This is especially the case when acid is used in the work-up in order to neutralize the magnesium hydroxide. Hydrolysis of the weakly basic imine is catalyzed by acid as is the case in reactions of acid derivatives.

Since the ketone is not obtained in the Grignard reaction with a nitrile until after water is added, there is no opportunity for reaction of the Grignard reagent with the ketone. For this reason, the process shown in Eq. 21 is a good synthesis of ketones, with one exception. *Acetonitrile fails in this reaction.* This failure of acetonitrile is caused by the relatively great acidity of hydrogens in a methyl group adjacent to cyano. The acidity of hydrogens alpha to a polar multiple bond will be discussed in some detail in the next chapter.

Discussion of the **reduction** of nitriles or amides, to give amines, will be deferred until the chapter in which the chemistry of amines is developed in some detail.

Esters

Esters occur very widely in nature, in both plants and animals. In contrast to the acids, the esters have pleasant odors. Many of the fragrances found in fruits and flowers are esters, and they are sometimes used in perfumes; however, a disadvantage of esters in perfumes is that hydrolysis (catalyzed by the acids in perspiration, for example) yields foul-smelling acids. The natural fats, one of the three major classes of foodstuffs, are higher molecular weight esters, so they will be discussed in this chapter.

Since esters have many commercial uses, and also give chemical reactions of utility in organic synthesis, they are important articles of commerce. Many of them are powerful solvents for a variety of compounds and are used in such products as enamel and lacquer. It seems safe to state that the esters are the most important class of compounds among the simple derivatives of carboxylic acids.

Synthesis of Esters

The principal methods for synthesis of esters have already been discussed: **direct esterification** (Eq. 13-22), **from acid chlorides** (Eq. 3), and **from alcoholysis of nitriles** (Eqs. 19 and 20). In recapitulation, it should be noted that the second method, using an acid chloride, is the principal method for securing a high yield based on alcohol. In alcoholysis of either an acid or a nitrile, an *excellent yield on the basis of acid* may be obtained by use of an excess of alcohol.

It will be recalled that direct esterification of carboxylic acids is a very slow reaction unless it is catalyzed by a strong acid; furthermore, conversion of a carboxylic acid to the acid chloride involves strongly acidic reagents. In some structures, decomposition or rearrangement will result from exposure to strong acid, so the usual methods of securing esters are of no value. In such cases, the ester may be formed by displacement of a reactive halide, as in methyl iodide, by the anion of the acid; however, this reaction is handicapped by the fact that the carboxylate anion is a relatively poor nucleophile, and carboxylic acids are ionized to a small extent. If the ion concentration is increased by use of a base, to form the highly ionized salt of the acid, the base is likely to compete successfully in attacking the methyl iodide. This difficulty has been circumvented in several ways, but the most effective is probably the use of a base that is so hindered sterically that its rate of attack on the alkyl halide is slow. Steric requirements of combination with a proton are so small that this reaction is essentially unaffected by the hindrance. A base that has been used quite successfully is dicyclohexylethylamine, called DICE. A typical process is shown in Eq. 22. This is actually a very easy way to obtain esters in high yield; however, in instances where acid can be tolerated, the more traditional esterification has been most often used, thus far.

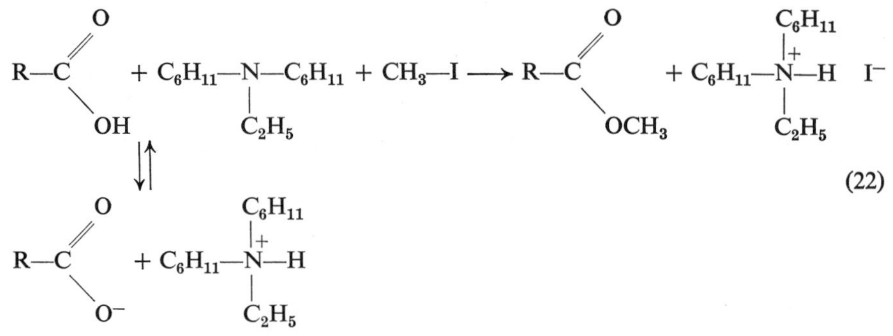

$$
\begin{array}{c}
\text{O} \\
\parallel \\
\text{R—C} \\
\diagdown \\
\text{OH}
\end{array}
+ \text{C}_6\text{H}_{11}\text{—N—C}_6\text{H}_{11} + \text{CH}_3\text{—I} \longrightarrow
\begin{array}{c}
\text{O} \\
\parallel \\
\text{R—C} \\
\diagdown \\
\text{OCH}_3
\end{array}
+ \text{C}_6\text{H}_{11}\text{—N—H} \quad \text{I}^-
\tag{22}
$$

$$
\begin{array}{c}
\text{O} \\
\parallel \\
\text{R—C} \\
\diagdown \\
\text{O}^-
\end{array}
+ \text{C}_6\text{H}_{11}\text{—N—H}
$$

Reactions of Esters

With nucleophiles. The esters give the usual reactions with nucleophiles, as discussed for the other derivatives. **Hydrolysis** is actually the reverse of the esterification reaction, and may be carried out with acid catalysis and use of a large excess of water. It is usually more convenient, however, to use basic catalysis of the hydrolysis, for this yields the anion of the acid which does not react with an alcohol, so the reaction becomes non-reversible (Eq. 23). Since

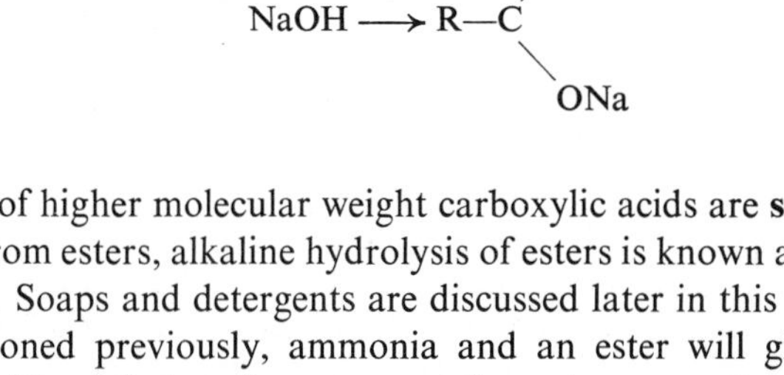

$$
\begin{array}{c}
\text{O} \\
\parallel \\
\text{R—C} \\
\diagdown \\
\text{OCH}_3
\end{array}
+ {}^-\text{OH} \longrightarrow
\begin{array}{c}
\text{O} \\
\parallel \\
\text{R—C} \\
\diagdown \\
\text{O}^-
\end{array}
+ \text{CH}_3\text{OH}
\tag{23}
$$

$$
\text{or}
$$

$$
\text{NaOH} \longrightarrow
\begin{array}{c}
\text{O} \\
\parallel \\
\text{R—C} \\
\diagdown \\
\text{ONa}
\end{array}
$$

the alkali salts of higher molecular weight carboxylic acids are **soaps,** which are usually made from esters, alkaline hydrolysis of esters is known as **saponification** (soap-making). Soaps and detergents are discussed later in this chapter.

As mentioned previously, ammonia and an ester will give equilibrium with an amide (Eq. 24), but there are usually serious experimental difficulties

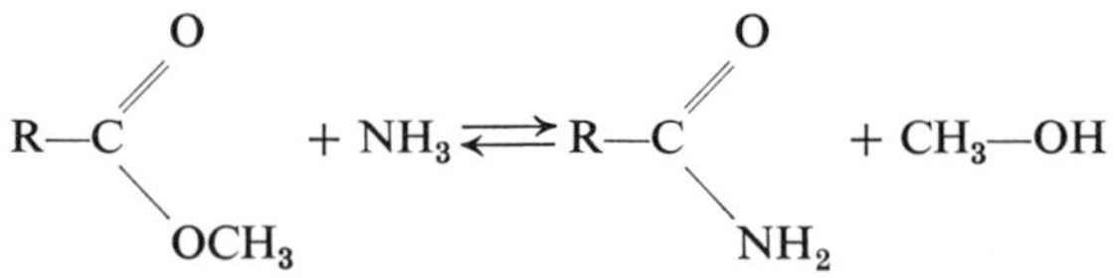

$$
\begin{array}{c}
\text{O} \\
\parallel \\
\text{R—C} \\
\diagdown \\
\text{OCH}_3
\end{array}
+ \text{NH}_3 \rightleftharpoons
\begin{array}{c}
\text{O} \\
\parallel \\
\text{R—C} \\
\diagdown \\
\text{NH}_2
\end{array}
+ \text{CH}_3\text{—OH}
\tag{24}
$$

involved in displacing this equilibrium forward so as to make the reaction a useful synthesis of amides.

As might be expected, an ester and an alcohol will give equilibrium with another ester and alcohol (Eq. 25). This process, commonly known as **trans-**

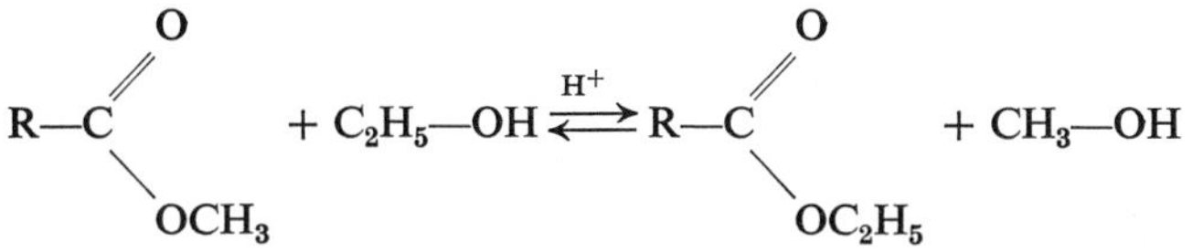

$$R-C\overset{\displaystyle O}{\underset{\displaystyle OCH_3}{\diagup}} + C_2H_5-OH \underset{}{\overset{H^+}{\rightleftarrows}} R-C\overset{\displaystyle O}{\underset{\displaystyle OC_2H_5}{\diagup}} + CH_3-OH \qquad (25)$$

esterification, has some use for conversion of one ester to another by use of an excess of an alcohol.

With Grignard reagents. The Grignard reaction with esters follows the same course as that with acid chlorides, except that there is known no device for securing the ketone as a major product. This reaction (Eq. 26) is,

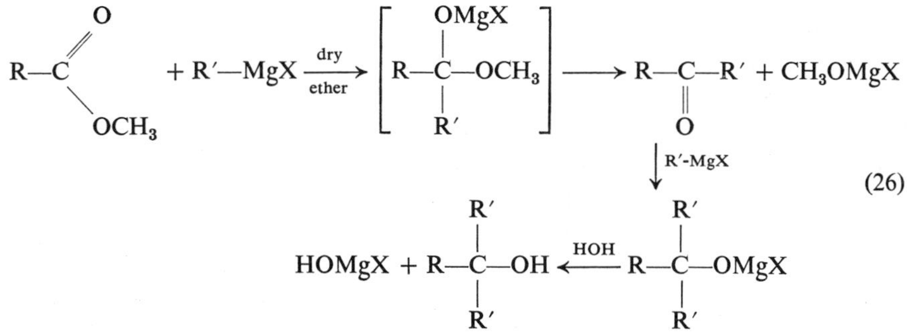

$$R-C\overset{\displaystyle O}{\underset{\displaystyle OCH_3}{\diagup}} + R'-MgX \xrightarrow[\text{ether}]{\text{dry}} \left[R-\underset{R'}{\overset{OMgX}{\underset{|}{\overset{|}{C}}}}-OCH_3 \right] \longrightarrow R-\underset{\displaystyle O}{\overset{\displaystyle |}{C}}-R' + CH_3OMgX$$

$$\Big\downarrow R'\text{-MgX} \qquad (26)$$

$$HOMgX + R-\underset{R'}{\overset{R'}{\underset{|}{\overset{|}{C}}}}-OH \xleftarrow{HOH} R-\underset{R'}{\overset{R'}{\underset{|}{\overset{|}{C}}}}-OMgX$$

however, the preferred method for synthesis of tertiary alcohols containing two of one group on the carbinol carbon.

Reduction. As mentioned in the preceding chapter, the best method of converting an acid to the corresponding alcohol usually involves proceeding through the ester. Esters are normally obtained from acids in nearly quantitative yields, and yields in the reduction with lithium aluminum hydride (Eq. 27) are

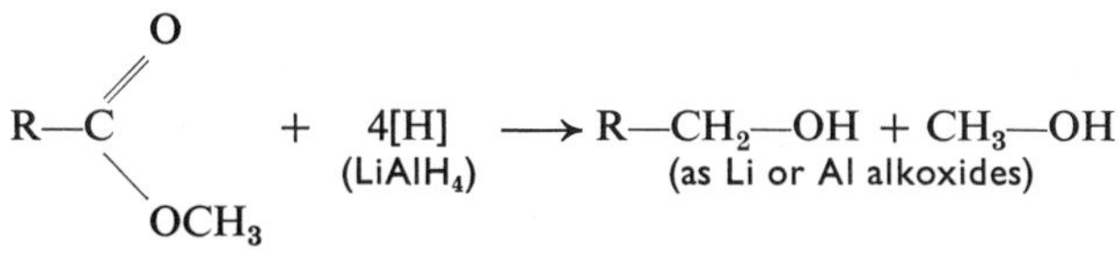

$$R-C\overset{\displaystyle O}{\underset{\displaystyle OCH_3}{\diagup}} + \underset{\text{(LiAlH}_4)}{4[H]} \longrightarrow R-CH_2-OH + \underset{\text{(as Li or Al alkoxides)}}{CH_3-OH} \qquad (27)$$

considerably higher with esters than with acids. In addition, esters may be reduced either chemically (Eq. 28) or catalytically (Eq. 29) by high-yield processes which do not apply at all to acids. The mixture of copper and chromium oxides, indicated as one of the useful catalysts for the hydrogenation shown in Eq. 29, is known as **copper chromite,** and it has been found to be a very useful catalyst for many hydrogenations.[3] A low molecular weight alcohol is always used for esterification when reduction is anticipated, for this avoids difficulty

$$R-C \overset{O}{\underset{OC_2H_5}{\diagdown}} \quad + \quad 4[H] \underset{(Na \, + \, C_2H_5OH)}{\longrightarrow} R-CH_2-OH + C_2H_5-OH \quad (28)$$

$$R-C \overset{O}{\underset{OC_2H_5}{\diagdown}} \quad + \, 2H_2 \xrightarrow[\substack{or \\ CuCr_2O_4 \\ \Delta, \, high \, pressure}]{nickel} R-CH_2-OH + C_2H_5-OH \quad (29)$$

with separation of this alcohol from the alcohol desired from the reduction. In the case of hydrogenation, it is important not to use methanol, however, for this alcohol is sufficiently acidic to interfere with the function of the catalyst.

Esters of Inorganic Acids

If an ester may be defined as the covalently-bonded product of the reaction of an alcohol with an acid, then the alkyl halides may be properly regarded as esters of inorganic acids. It has been pointed out, however, that the displacement reaction of alkyl halides is rather different from the attack of a nucleophile on the carbonyl of the ester of a carboxylic acid. In other inorganic esters, notably the esters of sulfuric acid, the reactions given with nucleophiles are the displacement reaction characteristic of alkyl halides. For example, dimethyl sulfate may be used instead of methyl iodide in a reaction such as the ester synthesis shown in Eq. 22. In fact, *dimethyl sulfate is more reactive than methyl iodide in a displacement*, and is a better and cheaper reagent than methyl iodide for forming esters. The only objection to dimethyl sulfate is its rather high toxicity. On account of its greater reactivity, dimethyl sulfate is very commonly used for making methyl ethers, as in Eq. 30.

$$R-OH + Na \longrightarrow R-O^-Na^+ \xrightarrow[\substack{CH_3O \diagup S \diagdown O \\ CH_3O \diagup \diagdown O}]{} R-O-CH_3 + {}^-OSO_2OCH_3 \quad (30)$$

Nitrate esters. The esters of nitric acid are formed by a normal type of acid-catalyzed esterification reaction. The lower molecular weight nitrate esters have the high ratio of oxygen and nitrogen in them which renders them

---

[3] The development and applications of the copper chromite catalyst were pioneered largely by the late Professor Homer Adkins of the University of Wisconsin and two of his students, W. A. Lazier and Karl A. Folkers. Much of the work carried out in the Wisconsin laboratories and the manipulation of high-pressure equipment are described with clarity in Professor Adkin's book, *Reactions of Hydrogen with Organic Compounds over Copper-Chromium Oxide and Nickel Catalysts*, The University of Wisconsin Press, 1937.

potentially **explosives.** Such compounds as ethyl nitrate, $C_2H_5-ONO_2$, are quite sensitive to shock and very dangerous to handle. The most widely used explosive of the nitrate ester type is glyceryl trinitrate[4] (nitroglycerin), formed by esterification of glycerol (Eq. 31).

$$
\begin{array}{ll}
CH_2-OH & CH_2-O-NO_2 \\
| & | \\
CH-OH + 3HNO_3 \xrightleftharpoons[]{H_2SO_4} & CH-O-NO_2 + 3H_2O \qquad (31) \\
| & | \\
CH_2-OH & CH_2-O-NO_2 \\
& \text{Nitroglycerin}
\end{array}
$$

Fats, Oils, and Waxes

The fats, oils, and waxes, all of which are high molecular weight esters, are frequently termed **lipids.** The naturally occurring **waxes** may contain free acids and alcohols, as well as higher molecular weight alkanes; however, the most characteristic components of the waxes are esters of higher molecular weight monocarboxylic acids and monohydroxy alcohols. The waxes are quite widespread in nature[5] and are produced by animals, plants, and insects. The alcohols and acids found in them are usually in the molecular weight range of twenty to forty carbon atoms, and compounds containing more than thirty carbon atoms are not uncommon. Usually, these compounds have normal (unbranched) chains of carbon atoms. A major use of waxes is for the inert, glossy, protective

---

[4] Although the oily nitroglycerin is very sensitive to shock, methods for its manufacture have been so highly developed that accidents have become rare. As an industrial explosive, it is ordinarily marketed as dynamite. In this product, the nitroglycerin is absorbed on some soft porous material such as sawdust. Nitroglycerin is also a component of double-base powder; the other component is nitrocellulose, the nitrate ester of the carbohydrate, cellulose.

In World War II, the solid nitrate ester pentaerythritol tetranitrate (PETN) was successfully used in grenades, especially the antitank grenades containing a shaped charge capable of blasting a hole through an inch or more of armor plate.

$$
\begin{array}{c}
ONO_2 \\
| \\
CH_2 \\
| \\
O_2NO-CH_2-C-CH_2-ONO_2 \qquad PETN \\
| \\
CH_2 \\
| \\
ONO_2
\end{array}
$$

[5] The great variety of waxes occurring in nature and the multiplicity of acids and alcohols found in them is somewhat astonishing. It seems odd that the various organisms should make such a variety of compounds. The composition of many of the waxes has been determined only in part or not at all. An interesting and easily understandable survey of what is known about naturally occurring waxes may be found in Professor Harry J. Deuel's book, *The Lipids, Their Chemistry and Biochemistry*, Vol. 1, Interscience Publishers, 1951.

coating which they will form over wood, metal, or paint; however, there are other significant uses. Carnauba wax, from a Brazilian palm tree, shears cleanly under mild pressure, hence finds wide use in carbon paper and Mimeograph stencils.

So far as chemical composition is concerned, beeswax may be regarded as typical, in that it is a mixture of many components. The constituent present in largest amount is triacontyl hexadecanoate; however, this constitutes only 33% of the wax.

$$C_{15}H_{31}-\overset{\displaystyle O}{\underset{\displaystyle \parallel}{C}}-O-C_{30}H_{61}$$

The **fats** and **fatty oils** have the same type of chemical structure; they are *triglycerides*, that is, tri-esters of glycerol and higher molecular weight carboxylic acids. Those which are solids at room temperature are commonly called fats, while those which are liquids at room temperature are termed oils or fatty oils. Since the principal constituents of these substances, by weight, are the higher molecular weight acids, such acids are usually called **fatty acids.** Although there seems to be no clear agreement on the subject, the term fatty acid is most commonly applied to those acids having eight or more carbons. The liquid fats, or oils, may have a low melting point because of the occurrence in them of either low molecular weight or unsaturated acids, but the occurrence of unsaturated acids is more common. One of the few oils containing sufficient low molecular weight acids to cause the low melting point is palm oil.

Essentially all fats and oils contain several fatty acids, and these are distributed more or less at random in the various glyceride molecules. There result mixtures of many triglycerides; for example, only three fatty acids may form numerous triglycerides. In the following formula, each of the three alkyls might be attached to the respective carbonyl groups as shown, or the arrangement might be that in any of the subsequent rows of R groups. From

$$
\begin{array}{c}
\qquad\qquad\quad \overset{\displaystyle O}{\underset{\displaystyle \parallel}{}} \\
CH_2-O-C-R \quad R \quad R' \quad R'' \quad R \quad R \quad R' \\[4pt]
\qquad\qquad\quad \overset{\displaystyle O}{\underset{\displaystyle \parallel}{}} \\
CH-O-C-R' \quad R \quad R' \quad R'' \quad R' \quad R \quad R \qquad \text{etc.} \\[4pt]
\qquad\qquad\quad \overset{\displaystyle O}{\underset{\displaystyle \parallel}{}} \\
CH_2-O-C-R'' \quad R \quad R' \quad R'' \quad R \quad R' \quad R'
\end{array}
$$

this consideration, it follows that the isolation from a natural fat of a pure triglyceride is essentially impossible. This is no great disadvantage, for the principal consumption of the fats is as foodstuff. When pure triglycerides are desired for biological studies of nutrition or metabolism, they are always synthesized. Triglycerides containing only one fatty acid are easily synthesized by standard methods of ester synthesis, and acid chlorides are frequently used,

$$
\begin{array}{c}
\text{CH}_2\text{—OH} \\
| \\
\text{CH—OH} + 3\text{R—C} \\
| \\
\text{CH}_2\text{—OH}
\end{array}
\quad
\begin{array}{c}
\text{O} \\
\diagup \\
\diagdown \\
\text{Cl}
\end{array}
\longrightarrow
\begin{array}{c}
\text{O} \\
\| \\
\text{R—C—O—CH}_2 \quad \text{O} \\
\qquad\qquad\quad | \quad\; \| \\
\text{O} \qquad \text{CH—O—C—R} + 3\text{HCl} \\
\| \qquad\; | \\
\text{R—C—O—CH}_2
\end{array}
\qquad (32)
$$

as in Eq. 32. The synthesis of pure glycerides containing two or three different acyl groups is possible, but is a much more difficult and laborious process.

Commercial Utilization of Fats and Oils

In addition to the use of fats and oils as foodstuffs, they are also used extensively in paints, for manufacture of detergents, and as a source of fatty acids for chemical syntheses.

Fatty acids. In contrast with the waxes, the fats rarely contain acids with more than eighteen carbons, although certain fish oils contain highly unsaturated acids with twenty to twenty-six carbon atoms. Further, acids with fewer than sixteen carbons are moderately rare, although the abundant palm oil contains considerable quantities of capric, lauric, and myristic acids; and creamery butter also contains a variety of fatty acids. Branched-chain acids occur rather widely in bacteria, and some of them have important physiological properties.

The fatty acids from plants and animals, then, consist largely of those containing sixteen or eighteen carbons. The normal saturated acids, palmitic (hexadecanoic) and stearic (octadecanoic) acids are abundant. Also abundant are the four unsaturated acids whose formulas are shown. Each of these except palmitoleic acid contains eighteen carbons. It seems of particular interest that

$$\text{CH}_3\text{—(CH}_2)_5\text{—CH}\!=\!\text{CH—(CH}_2)_7\text{—CO}_2\text{H}$$
Palmitoleic acid

$$\text{CH}_3\text{—(CH}_2)_7\text{—CH}\!=\!\text{CH—(CH}_2)_7\text{—CO}_2\text{H}$$
Oleic acid

$$\text{CH}_3\text{—(CH}_2)_4\text{—CH}\!=\!\text{CH—CH}_2\text{—CH}\!=\!\text{CH—(CH}_2)_7\text{—CO}_2\text{H}$$
Linoleic acid

$$\text{CH}_3\text{—CH}_2\text{—CH}\!=\!\text{CH—CH}_2\text{—CH}\!=\!\text{CH—CH}_2\text{—CH}\!=\!\text{CH—(CH}_2)_7\text{—CO}_2\text{H}$$
Linolenic acid

all these acids have the same number of carbons between the carboxyl and the first double bond. Also, the double bonds in the polyunsaturated acids are not conjugated, but are separated by a single methylene group in both instances.

In view of the above-mentioned composition of natural fats, it follows that hydrogenation of the mixed fatty acids from natural fats leads to a mixture of normal saturated acids differing from each other by two carbon atoms. Such a mixture may be separated readily in industrial distillation equipment, and the even-carbon acids so obtained constitute the principal ultimate source of the various higher molecular weight, even-carbon compounds, for the acids may be converted directly or indirectly to nearly all the various classes of compounds. Separation of the unsaturated acids in a pure state is relatively difficult, and except for oleic acid, they are expensive laboratory chemicals.

Edible fats. Fatty oils containing unsaturated acids are entirely satisfactory foodstuffs, in fact, linoleic acid has been found to be a dietary component necessary for normal growth and health. In many countries, the oils are used for cooking, but in the United States initial use of the solid hog lard and creamery butter has led to a strong prejudice that a cooking fat should be solid. Since the most abundant and cheapest fatty foodstuffs are the oils, such as corn oil, cottonseed oil, and soybean oil, a considerable industry has become devoted to catalytic hydrogenation of these oils. By thus converting the unsaturated acyl groups to saturated ones, the fats are thereby rendered solid and therefore aesthetically acceptable as food. Cooking fats are marketed under such names as Snowdrift (hydrogenated cottonseed oil) and Crisco (hydrogenated corn oil), while the vegetable fats prepared for table use are known as margarine or oleomargarine. Since solid vegetable fats can be produced at a considerably lower cost than can butter, the use of margarine has rapidly increased.

There has accumulated considerable evidence that the prejudice in the United States in favor of solid cooking fats is quite unfortunate, indeed, unhealthy. The principal cause of death in recent years has been atherosclerotic diseases, which have caused three or four times as many deaths as all varieties of cancer. These diseases, of which paralytic strokes and coronary thrombosis are the principal killers, are caused by blocking of a critical artery with a blood clot. The clot lodges at a point where a tough mass of tissue has developed and formed a partial constriction of the artery. Extensive statistical studies, including groups of the same race eating different diets, have shown a significant correlation between solid fat in the diet and the atherosclerotic diseases. The damaging effect of the solid fats is believed to arise because they do not have a high percentage of linoleic acid (as do "polyunsaturated fats"). Since the studies are largely statistical, conceivably there might actually be something unknown but which travels with the solid fats, not with the liquid fats ("polyunsaturated fats"); however, the fact remains that the statistical studies are a strong recommendation against solid fats in the diet. For these reasons, corn oil and safflower oil, high in linoleic acid, have been introduced into the United States market in increasingly larger quantities. There have also been developed emulsifying agents which allow production of margarine from the unsaturated oils, which will remain "reasonably solid" at normal room temperatures.

Drying oils. Highly unsaturated acids, such as linolenic acid, undergo a moderately rapid oxidative polymerization when exposed to oxygen. Although the exact structure of these polymers may not be regarded as known with complete certainty, the polymers contain oxygen and it seems probable that the polymerization is induced by attack of oxygen on the carbon between the double bonds. When highly unsaturated oils, such as linseed oil (from flax seed) or tung oil (from the Asiatic tung nut) are spread in a thin film so that there is a large surface exposed to air, the polymerization is completed in a few days. The resultant film is glossy, very tough, and inert, thus valuable as a protective coating. **Paints** for external use have long consisted largely of such drying oils in which are dispersed finely divided pigments. Considerable research has led to discovery of various oxygen-containing compounds which speed up the drying process. It may also be mentioned that modern paints frequently contain polyesters of such alcohols as pentaerythritol (cf. footnote 4), but such items of industrial technology will not be discussed further at this time.

Detergents. A detergent may be defined, in the broadest sense, as a substance which can emulsify, and thus disperse in water, various water-insoluble substances such as dirt and grease. Since cleanliness is highly prized by man, the industrial significance of detergents may be properly described as enormous. Although the physics of the process by which detergents are able to emulsify and disperse has been studied intensively, it may not be said that it is entirely understood. It has been long known, however, that all effective detergents are molecules containing a large alkane portion (oil soluble) and one or more polar, water-soluble groups. This leads to the situation where one part of the molecule is dissolved in the grease or oil and the other is soluble in water; so an emulsion is formed, and solid particles of dirt will become dispersed in the emulsion.

The traditional cleansing agent has been **soap,** alkali salts of the higher fatty acids. These materials have the required structure in that the salt grouping, containing the ionizable electrovalence, is attached to a large alkane chain. Soaps are very easily made by saponification of the natural fats or oils, as shown in Eq. 33. In natural fats, of course, the R groups are usually different and so

$$
\begin{array}{l}
CH_2-O_2CR \\
| \\
CH-O_2CR + 3NaOH \longrightarrow CHOH + RCO_2Na \qquad (33) \\
| \\
CH_2-O_2CR
\end{array}
\qquad
\begin{array}{l}
CH_2OH \\
| \\
CHOH \\
| \\
CH_2OH
\end{array}
$$

the salts of various fatty acids result. This mixture of alkali salts is marketed as soap. The glycerol is separated, and the soap industry is a major source of the industrially important glycerol; however, the demand for glycerol has become so great that an industrial synthesis from propene has been developed.

Salts of heavier metals, notably iron and calcium, are not soluble in water, and are therefore of no value as soaps. It follows that water containing soluble inorganic salts of such metals will precipitate the soap as the insoluble iron or calcium salts. Such water is known as *hard water*. Since most commercial water supplies contain some "hardness," much of the soap is wasted by precipitation. Since the alkyl hydrogen sulfates (half esters of sulfuric acid) give water-soluble calcium and iron salts, they offer many advantages, and the use of such cleansing agents has rapidly increased since their introduction in the nineteen-thirties. Such substances are usually called **detergents** and are distinguished from soaps, although soaps may really be regarded as one type of detergent. The higher cost of detergents is well compensated by their effectiveness in hard water.

Detergents were first synthesized from natural fats by application of reactions already discussed. The sequence[6] is shown in Eq. 34. Detergents

$$
\begin{array}{l}
CH_2{-}O_2CR \\
| \\
CH{-}O_2CR + 6H_2 \xrightarrow[\text{high pressure, 250°}]{\text{catalyst}} \\
| \\
CH_2{-}O_2CR
\end{array}
\quad
\begin{array}{l}
CH_2OH \\
| \\
CHOH + 3R{-}CH_2{-}OH \xrightarrow{3H_2SO_4} \\
| \\
CH_2OH
\end{array}
\tag{34}
$$

$$
3R{-}CH_2{-}OSO_2OH \xrightarrow{3NaOH} 3R{-}CH_2{-}OSO_2ONa + 3H_2O
$$

prepared in this way contain the straight alkyl chains in the natural fats, and they are metabolized by bacteria in septic tanks or sewage treatment plants. Thus, the detergent is destroyed and does not appear in the sewage outflow to streams. Such detergents are known as "bio-degradable."

When detergents became so widely used, cheaper methods for synthesis were developed, of which the most prominent consisted of building up the necessary alkane chain by acid-catalyzed polymerization of propylene, abundant from cracking gases in petroleum refining. Since the proton adds to give the secondary carbonium ion, a sequence as shown in Eq. 35 develops. The polymerization chain is terminated if a proton is lost from a carbonium ion to give

$$
CH_3{-}CH{=}CH_2 + H^+ \longrightarrow CH_3{-}\underset{\underset{CH_3}{|}}{CH^+} \xrightarrow{CH_3{-}CH{=}CH_2} CH_3{-}\underset{\underset{CH_3}{|}}{CH}{-}CH_2{-}\underset{\underset{CH_3}{|}}{CH^+}
$$

$$
\Big\downarrow \text{etc.}
\tag{35}
$$

an alkene. The mixture of polymeric alkenes in the C_{11} to C_{15} range was converted to a compound with the necessary sulfonic acid grouping, and the salts

---

[6] This reduction may also be carried out with sodium (Eq. 28), and the industrial application of this method is a rather spectacular process involving addition of molten sodium from a four-inch pipe. The use of the chemical reduction is practical in this instance because the resultant sodium hydroxide may be utilized in the final step to form the required salt, or used to form soap in the orthodox manner (Eq. 33).

The chemical industry devoted to production of edible fats, detergents, and paints has become so large that chemists engaged in studying fats have formed the American Oil Chemists Society, which sponsors the publication of the internationally circulated chemical journal known as the *Journal of the American Oil Chemists Society.*

thereof sold as detergents. Such detergents make especially good cleansing agents; however, the bacteria are baffled by the branched chain and do not decompose these detergents in sewage. Such detergents have become known as "hard" detergents. By the time that the entire Mississippi River had become sudsy, processes were developed for cheaply making a straight-chain material from petroleum products, so that bio-degradable detergents might be made at a competitive price. Elimination of hard detergents from the market was pursued so vigorously that the process was near completion by 1965.

EXERCISES

1. Give two names for each of the following acids, and in each case give the corresponding names for five derivatives of each acid (including only one ester among the five derivatives).

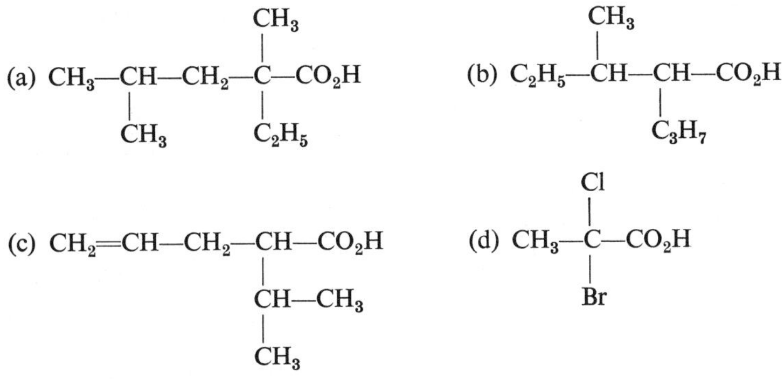

(a) $CH_3-\underset{\underset{CH_3}{|}}{CH}-CH_2-\underset{\underset{C_2H_5}{|}}{\overset{\overset{CH_3}{|}}{C}}-CO_2H$

(b) $C_2H_5-\underset{\underset{C_3H_7}{|}}{CH}-\underset{\underset{}{}}{\overset{\overset{CH_3}{|}}{CH}}-CO_2H$

(c) $CH_2{=}CH-CH_2-\underset{\underset{\underset{\underset{CH_3}{|}}{CH-CH_3}}{|}}{CH}-CO_2H$

(d) $CH_3-\underset{\underset{Br}{|}}{\overset{\overset{Cl}{|}}{C}}-CO_2H$

2. Give one name for each of the following compounds.

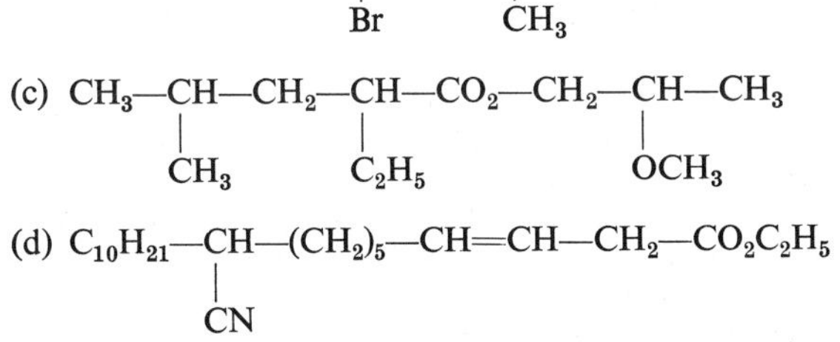

(a) $CH_3-\underset{\underset{OC_2H_5}{|}}{CH}-\underset{\underset{}{}}{\overset{\overset{CO_2C_2H_5}{|}}{CH}}-CH_2-CH_2-CO_2CH_3$

(b) $CH_3-CH_2-CH{=}\underset{\underset{Br}{|}}{C}-CO_2-\underset{\underset{CH_3}{|}}{CH}-CH_3$

(c) $CH_3-\underset{\underset{CH_3}{|}}{CH}-CH_2-\underset{\underset{C_2H_5}{|}}{CH}-CO_2-CH_2-\underset{\underset{OCH_3}{|}}{CH}-CH_3$

(d) $C_{10}H_{21}-\underset{\underset{CN}{|}}{CH}-(CH_2)_5-CH{=}CH-CH_2-CO_2C_2H_5$

3. (a) For saponification of an ester, as in Eq. 23, write equations showing intermediates in the reaction, as well as the transition state for attack of base on the ester.

(b) For the trans-esterification shown in Eq. 25, outline the reaction pathway, and show the intermediates involved.

(c) Why is an acid anion less attractive to nucleophiles than is an acid?

4. At sufficiently high temperature, chlorine dissociates into chlorine atoms, and under these conditions reacts with propene to give allyl chloride, $CH_2=CH-CH_2-Cl$. Write the equations for this reaction. Suggest a sequence of reactions suitable for converting allyl chloride to glycerol.

5. Outline by equations, not necessarily balanced but with all conditions and reagents indicated, practical methods for conversion of ethyl alcohol to each of the following compounds. All organic compounds used in the syntheses, except solvents for reactions, must be prepared from ethyl alcohol. Remember the suggestions in Chapter 9 concerning the solving of synthetic problems, especially the device of working backwards from the compound to be synthesized.

(a) Ethyl propionate

(b) 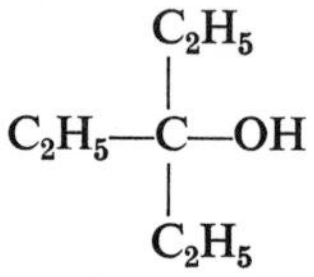 $C_2H_5-\underset{\underset{\displaystyle C_2H_5}{|}}{\overset{\overset{\displaystyle C_2H_5}{|}}{C}}-OH$

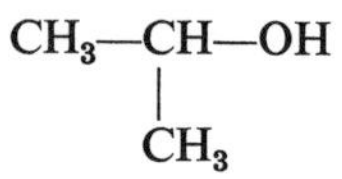

(c) $CH_3-\underset{\underset{\displaystyle CH_3}{|}}{CH}-OH$

(d) 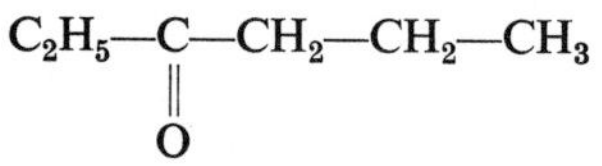 $C_2H_5-\underset{\underset{\displaystyle O}{\|}}{C}-CH_2-CH_2-CH_3$

(e) 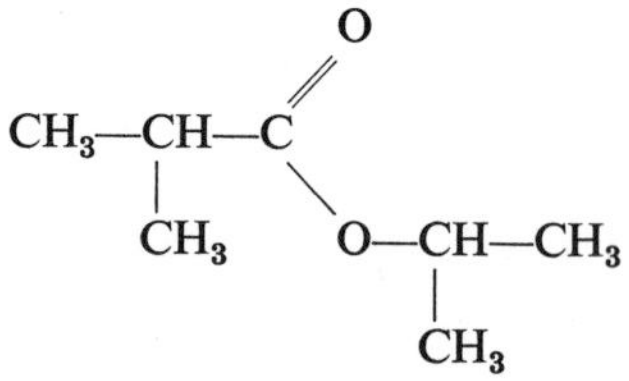 $CH_3-\underset{\underset{\displaystyle CH_3}{|}}{CH}-\overset{\overset{\displaystyle O}{\|}}{C}\diagdown_{O-\underset{\underset{\displaystyle CH_3}{|}}{CH}-CH_3}$

(f) $HO_2C-CH_2-CH_2-CO_2H$

(g) 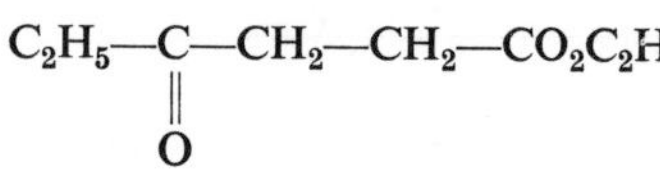 $C_2H_5-\underset{\underset{\displaystyle O}{\|}}{C}-CH_2-CH_2-CO_2C_2H_5$

(h) $HO_2C-(CH_2)_4-CO_2H'$

(i) $CH_3-CH_2-CH_2-OSO_2ONa$

(j) Nitroglycerin (cf. Exercise 4)

(k) 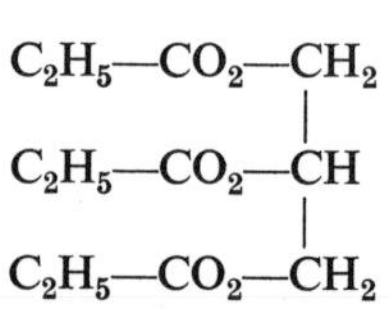 $C_2H_5-CO_2-CH_2$
$C_2H_5-CO_2-\overset{|}{C}H$
$C_2H_5-CO_2-CH_2$

6. Give one name for each of the compounds whose formulas are shown in Exercise 5, except for the compounds in (d), (g), and (i).

7. Outline by equations a method for conversion of oleic acid to the following aldehydo acid.

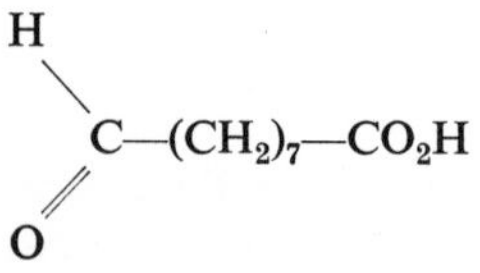

$\underset{\underset{\displaystyle O}{\diagup\!\!\diagup}}{\overset{\overset{\displaystyle H}{\diagdown}}{C}}-(CH_2)_7-CO_2H$

8. Show by equations how palmitic acid may be used as the starting material for synthesis of each of the following compounds.

(a) Hexadecanenitrile.

(b) Hexadecyl alcohol.

(c) Heptadecanoic acid.

(d) 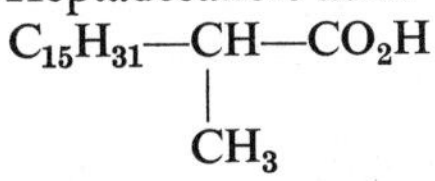 $C_{15}H_{31}$—CH—CO_2H
　　　　　|
　　　　CH_3

(e) Pentadecanoic acid.

(f) 1-Hexadecyne.

(g) Heptadecyl methyl ether.

(h) 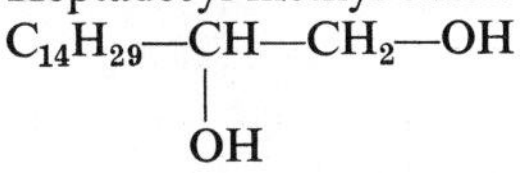 $C_{14}H_{29}$—CH—CH_2—OH
　　　　　|
　　　　 OH

9. Indicate practical methods, subject to the usual conditions, for accomplishing each of the following conversions. So long as continuity is maintained, any desired organic or inorganic reagents may be used.

(a) 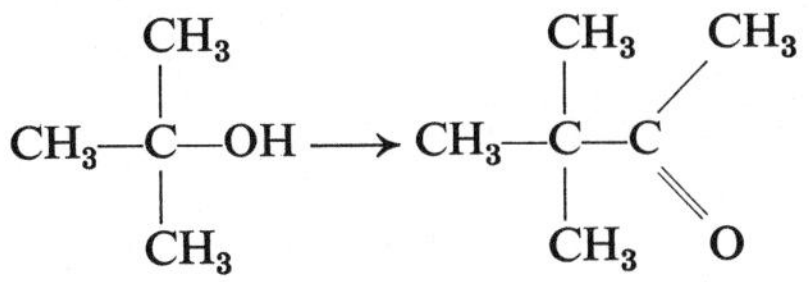
$$CH_3\text{—}\underset{\underset{CH_3}{|}}{\overset{\overset{CH_3}{|}}{C}}\text{—OH} \longrightarrow CH_3\text{—}\underset{\underset{CH_3}{|}}{\overset{\overset{CH_3}{|}}{C}}\text{—}\underset{O}{\overset{CH_3}{C}}$$

(b) 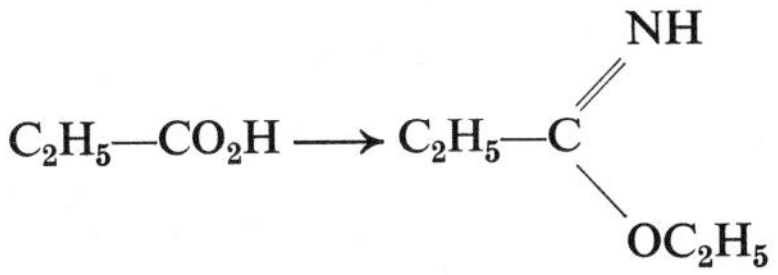
$$C_2H_5\text{—}CO_2H \longrightarrow C_2H_5\text{—}\overset{\overset{NH}{\|}}{\underset{OC_2H_5}{C}}$$

10. Most classes of compounds having oxygen in a functional group have analogs (analogous compounds) in which sulfur occurs instead of oxygen. For example, mercaptans are the sulfur analogs of alcohols. If *n*-butyl mercaptan (responsible for the odor of skunks) is an available compound, suggest a synthesis of butyl thioacetate:

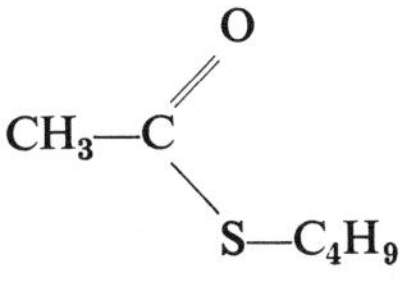

$$CH_3\text{—}\overset{\overset{O}{\|}}{\underset{S\text{—}C_4H_9}{C}}$$

Aldehydes and Ketones

The functional group characteristic of both aldehydes and ketones is the carbonyl group. The two classes of compounds differ only with respect to the

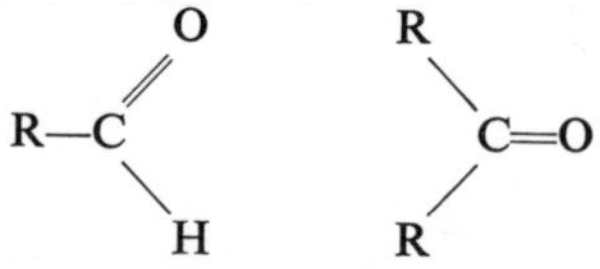

$$R-C \overset{\displaystyle O}{\underset{\displaystyle H}{\Big\langle}} \qquad \overset{\displaystyle R}{\underset{\displaystyle R}{\diagdown}} C{=}O$$

An aldehyde · · · · A ketone

number of carbon atoms attached to the functional group (the same difference as that between primary and secondary alcohols); therefore, the reactions of the compounds are quite similar, and it is convenient to consider the two classes together. It is rarely that the two classes differ in basic type of reaction that occurs. In general, the reactions with an aldehyde proceed at a considerably higher rate than with ketones. The major factor in this difference is probably a steric effect, although hydrogen induces a somewhat reduced electron density on the carbonyl carbon and thus increases the electrophilicity of this group.

The aldehydes and ketones occur widely in nature,[1] and carbonyl compounds are important in biological processes. Of particular significance is the carbonyl group present in sugars and other carbohydrates (cf. Chaps. 23 and 24). Another important group of naturally occurring ketones is that of the hormones containing the complex structure characteristic of compounds known as sterols. This structural type may be illustrated by the male sex hormone, testosterone.

Testosterone

The intensively investigated hormone, cortisone, is also of this structural type.

Certain of the simple ketones, especially acetone, $CH_3-\overset{\overset{\displaystyle O}{\|}}{C}-CH_3$, are good solvents for many organic compounds and are widely used for that purpose. A final major significance of aldehydes and ketones is their use as intermediates in chemical syntheses. The polar carbonyl group is readily attacked by numerous nucleophiles; in fact, the diversity of useful reactions is as great as that of the acid derivatives, discussed in the preceding chapter. Since the aldehydes and ketones do not have a good leaving group attached to carbonyl, *most of the reactions are completed additions*. In relatively few instances does the addition result in an unstable structure with two negative groups on a single carbon. Since the aldehydes and ketones do not contain hydroxyl or other groups capable of hydrogen bonding (cf. Chap. 13), boiling points in this series are relatively low. For example, acetaldehyde, CH_3-CHO, boils at 21°, whereas

---

[1] Some of the naturally occurring ketones have interesting structures. Among these is camphor, the bicyclic ketone mentioned in Chapter 7. Also of interest are muscone and irone, of importance in the perfume industry.

Muscone   Irone

Muscone occurs in a gland in the male musk deer of central Asia. Although it has a rather unpleasant odor when in high concentration, in great dilution it becomes a highly valued constituent of perfumes. The most interesting feature of the muscone structure is the very large ring of carbon atoms. Irone is responsible for the odor of violets, but is also present in the rhizomes of iris, from which it is more easily isolated. Chemists studied the structure of irone for some fifty years before the structure was finally established. The climax of this work is reported in a paper by Ruzicka, Seidel, Schinz, and Pfeiffer, *Helv. Chim. Acta.*, **30**, 1807 (1947). A major difficulty in studying the irone stucture is the ease with which the double bond to the methylene group migrates into the ring.

ethyl alcohol boils at 78° and acetic acid boils at 118°. Similarly, acetone boils at 56°, while isopropyl alcohol boils at 82°. Aldehydes and ketones with less than about fifteen carbon atoms are rarely solids at room temperature. A notable exception is the compact structure in the C_{10} ketone, camphor, of melting point 179°.

Nomenclature

Very few simple aldehydes and ketones have trivial names; in fact, the only common one is acetone. Many of the more complex naturally occurring ketones, such as those just mentioned, do have trivial names.

IUC nomenclature. The characteristic ending (suffix) for aldehydes is -al, and that for ketones is -one. It is apparent that care must be exercised to distinguish between -ol (an alcohol) and -al (an aldehyde). The position of the keto group is located on the chain by a number in the usual fashion, but this is unnecessary for the aldehyde group, which must be on the end of the chain—otherwise, it is a ketone. It is important to note, as in the following illustrations, that the carbon in the functional group is a part of the chain used as the basis for the name.

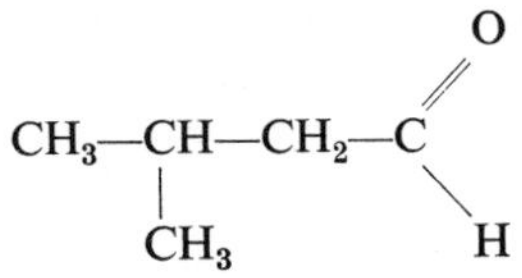

$$CH_3-CH-CH_2-C\diagdown^{O}_{H}$$

$$CH_3$$

3-Methylbutanal

$$CH_3-CH-C-CH_2-CH_3$$

$$CH_3$$

$$O$$

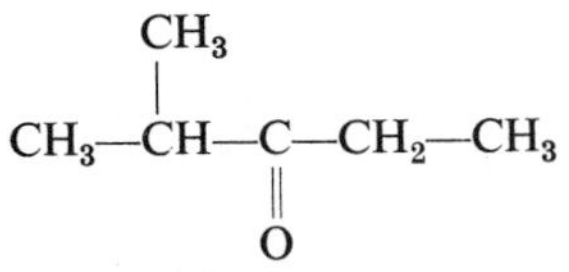

2-Methyl-3-pentanone

Other systems of naming aldehydes are based directly on the systems used for naming acids (cf. Chap. 13). The only difference is that the names end in -aldehyde rather than -ic acid. A few examples follow:

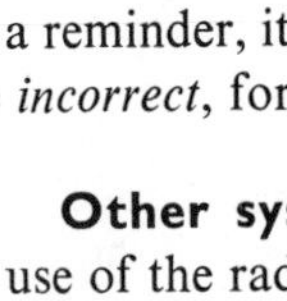

$$CH_3-C\diagdown^{O}_{H}$$

Acetaldehyde

$$CH_3-CH-CH_2-C\diagdown^{O}_{H}$$

$$CH_3$$

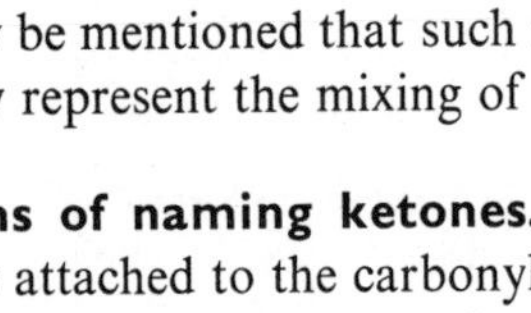

Isopropylacetaldehyde
β-Methylbutyraldehyde

$$CH_3-CH_2-CH-C\diagdown^{O}_{H}$$

$$CH_3$$

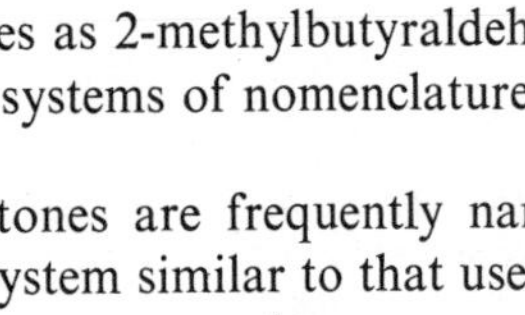

Methylethylacetaldehyde
α-Methylbutyraldehyde

As a reminder, it may be mentioned that such names as 2-methylbutyraldehyde are *incorrect*, for they represent the mixing of two systems of nomenclature.

Other systems of naming ketones. Ketones are frequently named by use of the radicals attached to the carbonyl, a system similar to that used in naming ethers. In this case, the name consists of separate words.

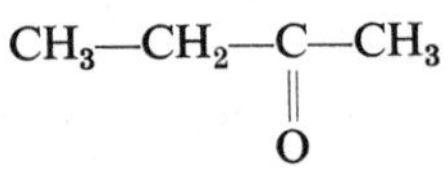

$$CH_3-CH_2-C-CH_3$$

$$O$$

Methyl ethyl ketone

$$CH_3-CH-CH_2-C-CH_3$$

$$CH_3$$

$$O$$

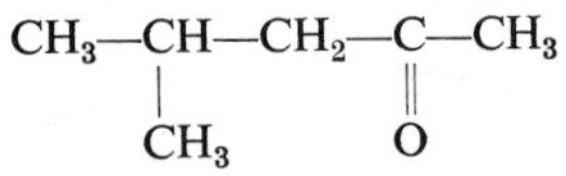

Methyl isobutyl ketone

Ketones may be named as derivatives of acetone, the simplest member of the series, but this system is relatively uncommon. By this system, methyl isobutyl ketone would be named as isopropylacetone (note the single word).

Carbonyl groups as substituents. When some other functional group is the primary basis of a name in the IUC system, the aldehydo group is termed *formyl*, and the keto group is termed *oxo*. Each is located by number in the chain as usual, but the carbon in the formyl group is not included as a part of the chain used as the basis of the name. *Keto* is often used in names not following the IUC system. Examples may be used to clarify these usages.

$$CH_3-C-CH_2-CH_2-CO_2H \qquad\qquad C-CH_2-CH_2-CO_2C_2H_5$$

γ-Ketovaleric acid
4-Oxopentanoic acid

Ethyl β-formylpropionate
Ethyl 3-formylpropanoate

$$C_2H_5-C-(CH_2)_5C$$

7-Oxononanal

Word division in nomenclature. It will have been noted that some names for organic compounds are written as one word (isopropylacetaldehyde), whereas others are written as separate words (methyl ethyl ketone). In general, the usage which applies may be predicted from the following principle: if the radicals which are named in the compound may be regarded as replacing hydrogens in the compound whose name serves as the basic root of the name, then the entire name is written as one word; otherwise, the radical names are separate words. For illustration, note that in isopropylacetaldehyde or methyl-ethylacetaldehyde, acetaldehyde is the basic root of the name and is also the name of a compound. On the other hand, "ketone" is not the name of a compound (but rather the name of a class of compounds); therefore we write methyl ethyl ketone. Similarly, "ether" is not the name of a compound, so we write diethyl ether, or methyl *n*-butyl ether. Since the basic hydrocarbon is the root of most names in the IUC system, these names are written as one word. Only when the characteristic ending, as in acids, involves a separate word do we have more than one word in IUC names.

Synthesis of Aldehydes

From alcohols. As has been discussed in Chapter 13, usual methods for oxidizing primary alcohols (cf. Eq. 13-5) constitute a worthless method for making aldehydes; however, the special type of oxidation known as **catalytic**

dehydrogenation (Eq. 1) is usually a good method for synthesis of aldehydes. This process does not involve oxidizing conditions in the ordinary sense. It is actually the reverse of hydrogenation, and no doubt proceeds by way of adsorption on the surface of the catalyst. The reaction is driven in the desired

$$R{-}CH_2{-}OH \xrightarrow[300°]{\text{Cu catalyst}} R{-}\overset{\displaystyle O}{\underset{\displaystyle H}{C}} + H_2 \qquad (1)$$

direction by allowing the hydrogen to escape, in contrast with hydrogenation where hydrogen pressure is used. Catalytic dehydrogenation is usually carried out by passing the alcohol vapor through a hot tube containing the catalyst. Such tube processes are highly regarded for industrial syntheses, for they are continuous. Such continuous processes have obvious advantages over batch processes.

Rosenmund reduction of acid chlorides. Nearly all the laboratory processes for preparation of aldehydes utilize an acid derivative as starting material. There are at least ten relatively good methods for accomplishing this conversion; however, our present interests will be served adequately by consideration of one of the better methods. The catalytic reduction of acid chlorides, discovered by the German chemist, Karl W. Rosenmund, is probably the most widely applicable and satisfactory conversion of an acid derivative to an aldehyde. The rather specific conditions required for the process are displayed in Eq. 2. An interesting and necessary feature of this reduction is the use of

$$R{-}\overset{\displaystyle O}{\underset{\displaystyle Cl}{C}} + H_2 \xrightarrow[\substack{\text{selective poison}\\ \text{boiling xylene solvent}}]{\text{Pd(BaSO}_4\text{) catalyst}} R{-}\overset{\displaystyle O}{\underset{\displaystyle H}{C}} + HCl \qquad (2)$$

Rosenmund's "selective poison,"[2] which poisons the catalyst so that it does not promote reduction of the aldehyde, but leaves the catalyst with the active sites of adsorption necessary for reduction of the acid chloride. A selectively poisoned catalyst has been used in certain other instances, but the Rosenmund reduction is the only such method that has proved to be reliably reproducible and applicable to a wide variety of compounds. The expression $Pd(BaSO_4)$ means

---

[2] The literature concerning the use of a "poison" in the Rosenmund reduction is interesting and somewhat confusing. In Rosenmund's original paper [*Ber.*, **51**, 585 (1918)], no mention was made of a poison, and it seems likely that he succeeded because sulfur compounds in the xylene used as solvent acted as appropriate catalyst poisons. In a later paper with Zetzsche [*Ber.*, **54**, 436 (1921)], Rosenmund reported the necessity of a poison and explored various compounds for use as such. A typical procedure for the Rosenmund reduction may be found in *Organic Synthesis*, **21**, 84 (1941). In recent years, other selective poisons have been used, some of which appear to be about as satisfactory as Rosenmund's poison.

that the palladium catalyst is dispersed on the surface of finely divided barium sulfate. This type of designation is frequently used to indicate the "support" which is added to accomplish dispersion of the catalyst.

Synthesis of Ketones

As is the case with other classes of compounds having a functional group within a chain, ketones may be either symmetrical, $R—C—R$, or unsym-

$$\underset{O}{\overset{\|}{}}$$

metrical, $R—C—R'$. The most versatile methods of synthesis allow preparation

$$\underset{O}{\overset{\|}{}}$$

of unsymmetrical ketones, and except for the first method, these are the types discussed below.

Heating of acids. Symmetrical ketones may be prepared in a tube process, which sometimes employs metallic oxide catalysts (Eqs. 3 and 4). If

$$2R—C\overset{\displaystyle O}{\underset{\displaystyle OH}{<}} \xrightarrow[\text{catalyst, heat}]{\text{metallic oxide}} R—\underset{O}{\overset{\|}{C}}—R + HOH + CO_2 \qquad (3)$$

$$\begin{matrix} CH_2—CH_2—CO_2H \\ | \\ CH_2—CH_2—CO_2H \end{matrix} \xrightarrow{\text{heat}} \bigcirc\!\!=O + HOH + CO_2 \qquad (4)$$

two different acids are heated together, in an effort to secure an unsymmetrical ketone, there will result three ketones: $R—C—R$, $R'—C—R'$ and $R—C—R'$.

$$\underset{O}{\overset{\|}{}} \qquad \underset{O}{\overset{\|}{}} \qquad \underset{O}{\overset{\|}{}}$$

Thus, the method is satisfactory only for symmetrical ketones. An important application of the method is synthesis of cyclic ketones with five- or six-atom rings. For a seven-atom ring, the method is very poor, and for other ring sizes it is of no synthetic value at all.

It has been mentioned frequently in books that the synthesis of ketones is more successful if a salt of the acid is used instead of the acid. Actually, there is no evidence in the literature that this is correct. Heating of salts usually gives little, if any, ketone. The heating of the barium salt of a dibasic acid gives a moderately good yield of cyclic ketone, but use of the free acid is probably better. The mechanism of this ketone synthesis no doubt involves an initial step similar to the aldol condensation, discussed later in this chapter. This gives a β-keto acid which decarboxylates readily. The special utility of β-keto acids and esters in synthesis will be discussed in a later chapter.

Oxidation of secondary alcohols. This process has already been discussed in Chapter 13 (Eq. 13-7), in connection with the general discussion of alcohol oxidation. This oxidation goes in good yield, and its utility in ketone synthesis is limited only by the types of secondary alcohols that may be obtained. An excellent source of such alcohols is reaction of a Grignard reagent with an aldehyde (Eq. 27). Many secondary methyl carbinols are obtainable from 1-alkenes, via hydration with sulfuric acid (Eqs. 9-21 and 9-22).

Grignard reactions with nitriles or acid chlorides. These syntheses have been discussed already, in connection with the reactions of acid derivatives (Eqs. 14-21 and 14-12). They are excellent syntheses of ketones, except that acetonitrile fails (cf. Chap. 14). These are also highly diversified syntheses on account of the availability of a variety of acids. In addition, the Grignard reagent may be prepared from virtually all types of organic halides, including tertiary alkyl halides. Furthermore, polyfunctional compounds, such as keto esters, may be prepared by use of appropriate starting materials. The keto ester is obtained from the acid chloride of a half ester (an ester acid chloride). The only exception to this synthetic method is the β-keto ester, whose alpha hydrogens are quite acidic and give rise to the special properties of these compounds, which will be studied later.

Reactions of Aldehydes and Ketones

Nearly all the reactions of aldehydes and ketones, which are numerous and important, involve additions to the polar double bond. As mentioned at the beginning of the chapter, these compounds are of considerable importance as starting materials for synthesis of many other compounds. Furthermore, the wide occurrence of the carbonyl compounds in nature makes their characterization and isolation of much interest. Thus, one group of reactions will be considered separately, on account of their utility in isolation and identification of the carbonyl compounds.

Reactions Useful Chiefly for Test Purposes or Identification

Test reactions are those used to reveal the presence of a particular structural feature or functional group in a molecule. For the greatest utility, such a reaction should occur relatively rapidly, and the occurrence of the reaction should be accompanied by some easily observable phenomenon such as color formation or separation of a precipitate.

The organic chemist does not depend on chemical reactions alone, at the present time, in order to detect the presence of structural features; in fact, the use of physical methods is frequently more reliable and faster than use of chemical methods. **Infrared absorption is especially useful in detecting the presence of a carbonyl group,** for absorption occurs in a region where there is little interference from other functional groups. Neighboring structural features have some influence in causing shifts of the exact positions of absorption, but the following give the approximate median positions for the several types of carbonyl groups: acid chloride, 5.60 μ; ester, 5.75 μ; aldehyde or ketone, 5.83 μ; acid, 5.90 μ; amide, 6.10 μ. Considerable information has been accumulated as to the effects of neighboring groups in shifting the positions of absorption. For example, an α,β-unsaturated ester will absorb at longer wavelength, usually in the ketone region above 5.80 μ. A cyclopentanone will, on the other hand, absorb at a shorter wavelength than acyclic ketones, at about 5.75 μ, the region of absorption of most esters. Thus, chemical tests are still needed to reinforce and supplement the physical measurements.

Identification of a compound is often accomplished, in part, by a study of its melting point. Even compounds exhibiting the same melting point usually melt at a lower temperature when mixed together (the "mixed melting point test"). On the other hand, two liquids of the same boiling point will show no change on mixing. For this reason, identification of a liquid is usually facilitated by converting it by a known process, preferably in high yield, to a *solid derivative*. Since aldehydes and ketones are prone to be low-melting the conversion of them to solid derivatives is a process of some interest.

Formation of solid derivatives. The introduction of negative groups on the carbonyl carbon involves reactions which do result in loss of a group (the hydroxyl formed from the carbonyl) to give a more stable product. This loss occurs after the addition is completed, however. The most common solid derivatives of the aldehydes and ketones are the oximes (Eq. 5), semicarbazones (Eq. 6), and phenylhydrazones (Eq. 7). In all these reactions, there is an intermediate of the type shown in Eq. 5; in fact, it will be noted that these reactions

$$R\text{---}\underset{\underset{O}{\|}}{C}\text{---}R' \; + \quad \underset{\underset{H}{\diagup}}{\overset{H}{\diagdown}}N\text{---}OH \longrightarrow \left[R\text{---}\underset{\underset{N}{\underset{H\;\;\;\;OH}{\diagdown}}}{\overset{OH}{\underset{|}{C}}}\text{---}R' \right] \longrightarrow R\text{---}\underset{\underset{N}{\|}\;\underset{OH}{\diagdown}}{C}\text{---}R' \; + \; HOH \quad (5)$$

R and R' may   Hydroxylamine   An oxime
be hydrogen
or alkyl

$$R\text{---}\underset{\underset{O}{\|}}{C}\text{---}R' \; + \quad \underset{\underset{H}{\diagup}}{\overset{H}{\diagdown}}N\text{---}NH\text{---}\underset{\underset{O}{\|}}{C}\text{---}NH_2 \longrightarrow R\text{---}\underset{\underset{R'}{|}}{C}\text{=}N\text{---}\underset{\overset{H}{\diagup}}{N}\underset{\underset{O}{\|}}{\diagdown}\underset{C\text{---}NH_2}{} \; + \; HOH \quad (6)$$

Semicarbazide   A semicarbazone

$$R\text{---}\underset{\underset{O}{\|}}{C}\text{---}R' \; + \quad \text{(phenyl)}NH\text{---}N\underset{\overset{H}{\diagup}}{\diagdown}_H \longrightarrow R\text{---}\underset{\underset{R'}{|}}{C}\text{=}N\text{---}N\underset{\overset{H}{\diagup}}{\diagdown}\text{(phenyl)} \; + \; HOH \quad (7)$$

Phenylhydrazine   A phenylhydrazone

are identical except for the nature of the group to which —NH$_2$ is attached. These reactions are examples of the reaction of a carbonyl group with an amine. The same reaction occurs with simple amines in which nitrogen is attached to carbon, as in C$_2$H$_5$—NH$_2$. In some cases in which the phenylhydrazone is a liquid, a solid may be obtained by substitution of appropriate groups in the benzene ring (the radical from benzene is called phenyl).

Since these derivatives are of such widespread use, the structures corresponding to the names should be remembered.

Tests for aldehydes dependent on oxidation. The reactions just mentioned do not distinguish between aldehydes and ketones, and it is often difficult to make this distinction reliably by use of the infrared absorption. As has been mentioned earlier, however, only vigorous oxidation will break the carbon chain and thus oxidize a ketone. Thus, if mild oxidation of a carbonyl compound gives an acid, this distinguishes the compound as an aldehyde. Such agents as permanganate or dichromate at room temperature will not oxidize ketones and will thus make the distinction from aldehydes; however, with these compounds it is usually necessary to isolate the product of the reaction and determine whether it is an acid. Reagents that have been used frequently for test purposes are **Fehling's solution** (Eq. 8) which contains bivalent copper in alkaline solution as a complex ion, and **Tollens' reagent** (Eq. 9) which contains

$$
\begin{array}{cc}
\overset{\displaystyle O}{\underset{\displaystyle H}{R-C}} + 2Cu^{++} + 5^-OH \longrightarrow & \overset{\displaystyle O}{\underset{\displaystyle O^-}{R-C}} + Cu_2O + 3HOH \qquad (8) \\
\text{(in Fehling's solution)} & \text{(precipitate)}
\end{array}
$$

$$
\begin{array}{cc}
\overset{\displaystyle O}{\underset{\displaystyle H}{R-C}} + 2Ag^+ + 3^-OH \longrightarrow & \overset{\displaystyle O}{\underset{\displaystyle O^-}{R-C}} + 2Ag + 2HOH \qquad (9) \\
& \text{black} \\
& \text{precipitate} \\
& \text{(or silver mirror)}
\end{array}
$$

silver in ammonia solution as a complex ion. Reaction is detected by the red precipitate in Fehling's test or the silver mirror (if the glassware is clean) in Tollens' test. Ketones are not oxidized by these reagents; however, a hydroxyl

$$
\underset{\underset{\displaystyle OH \ \ O}{|\ \ \ ||}}{R-CH-C-R} + 2Cu^{++} + 4^-OH \longrightarrow \underset{\underset{\displaystyle O \ \ O}{||\ \ ||}}{R-C-C-R} + Cu_2O + 3HOH \quad (10)
$$
$$
\text{(or } 2Ag^+\text{)}
$$

group adjacent to a keto is oxidized and gives a positive test (Eq. 10). This reaction is of importance in sugar chemistry (cf. Chap. 23).

Iodoform reaction. The presence of a methyl group attached to carbonyl (a methyl ketone) may be detected by reaction with alkaline sodium hypoiodite, as in Eq. 11. Iodoform is not only a yellow precipitate, but also of characteristic odor.

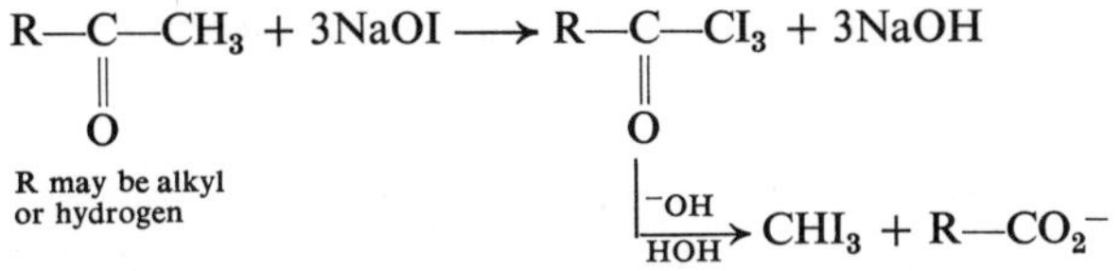

$$R—\overset{\underset{\|}{O}}{C}—CH_3 + 3NaOI \longrightarrow R—\overset{\underset{\|}{O}}{C}—CI_3 + 3NaOH$$

(11)

R may be alkyl
or hydrogen

$$\xrightarrow[\text{HOH}]{^-\text{OH}} CHI_3 + R—CO_2^-$$

The hydrolytic cleavage of a carbon-carbon bond, as in Eq. 11, is a very unusual reaction indeed. It happens in this instance because substitution of three powerful electron-attracting groups on carbon renders the group a sufficiently stable anion to be a good leaving group. The hydrolytic step occurs as in Eq. 12. Positive halogen, as in hypohalite, selectively attacks the carbon

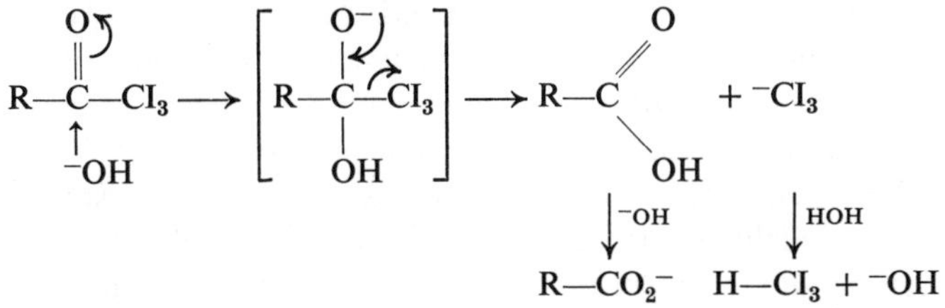

$$R—\overset{\underset{\uparrow}{\overset{\|}{O}}}{\underset{^-\text{OH}}{C}}—CI_3 \longrightarrow \left[R—\overset{\underset{\|}{\overset{O^-}{}}}{\underset{\text{OH}}{C}}—CI_3 \right] \longrightarrow R—\overset{O}{\underset{\text{OH}}{C}} + {}^-CI_3$$

(12)

$$\downarrow {}^-\text{OH} \qquad \downarrow \text{HOH}$$

$$R—CO_2^- \qquad H—CI_3 + {}^-\text{OH}$$

adjacent to carbonyl, and if there are three hydrogens to be replaced (methyl) the group becomes sufficiently good as a leaving group to give hydrolytic cleavage under mild conditions.

The mechanism of selective attack on the carbon adjacent to carbonyl involves reaction of positive halogen with the enolate form of the ketone (Eq. 13;

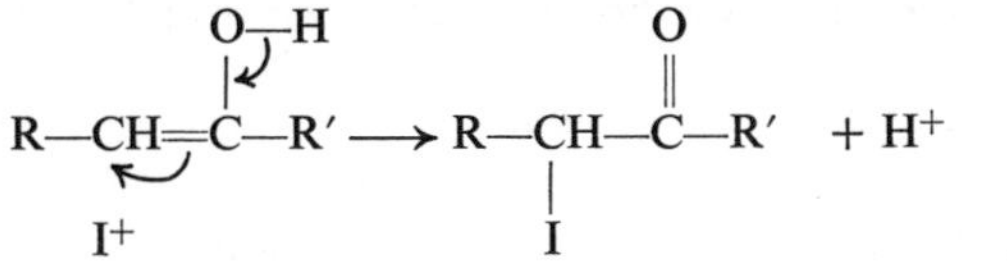

$$R—CH{=}\overset{\underset{}{\overset{O—H}{}}}{\underset{I^+}{C}}—R' \longrightarrow R—\overset{\underset{\|}{\overset{O}{}}}{\underset{I}{CH}}—\overset{}{C}—R' + H^+$$

(13)

also refer to Eq. 37). By this mechanism, it is apparent that only the α-position may be involved. This is another illustration of a reaction involving the first step of an addition, but a lower-energy product is available if a group is lost in preference to completing the addition.

In connection with use of the hypohalite oxidation as a test, it is of importance that hypohalite will oxidize a secondary alcohol to a ketone (Eq. 14).

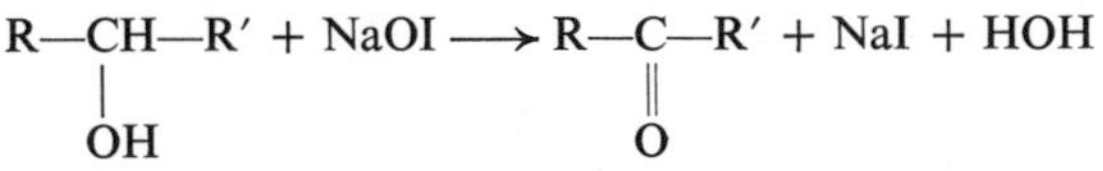

$$R—\overset{\underset{\|}{\overset{}{}}}{\underset{\text{OH}}{CH}}—R' + NaOI \longrightarrow R—\overset{\underset{\|}{\overset{O}{}}}{C}—R' + NaI + HOH$$

(14)

It follows that if one of the R groups in the carbinol is methyl, a methyl ketone results, so iodoform will be a final reaction product.

In summary, secondary methyl carbinols will give a positive iodoform test, as will methyl ketones. One primary alcohol, ethyl alcohol, and one aldehyde, acetaldehyde, will also give the iodoform test. Of course an alcohol may be distinguished from a ketone by failure of the alcohol to react with such reagents as those in Eqs. 5 through 7.

Addition of sodium bisulfite. In the pH range 4 to 6, aldehydes react with sodium bisulfite to give an adduct[3] (Eq. 15). Equilibrium in this reaction

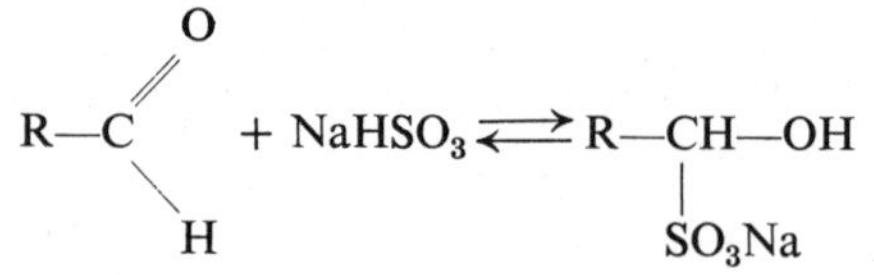

$$R-\underset{\underset{H}{|}}{\overset{\overset{O}{\parallel}}{C}} + NaHSO_3 \rightleftharpoons R-\underset{\underset{SO_3Na}{|}}{CH}-OH \tag{15}$$

may be shifted forward by use of a large excess of bisulfite. An adduct will also form with ketones of low steric requirements, principally methyl ketones and cyclic ketones. The adduct has the properties of a salt, which it is, hence is soluble in water and insoluble in organic solvents. This renders the adduct useful for purification of aldehydes, in the same manner as the salts of carboxylic acids (cf. Chap. 13). Since a solution of the adduct in water establishes equilibrium with the aldehyde (or ketone) and bisulfite, removal of bisulfite reverses the equilibrium and regenerates the aldehyde. Either acid or base rapidly destroys bisulfite, as in Eq. 16.

$$NaHSO_3 \xrightarrow{\text{HCl}} H_2SO_3 + NaCl \tag{16}$$

$$\downarrow{\scriptstyle Na_2CO_3} \qquad \qquad \updownarrow$$

$$Na_2SO_3 + NaHCO_3 \qquad H_2O + SO_2$$

Synthetically Useful Reactions of the Carbonyl Group

All the reactions in this category (except, perhaps, oxidation) consist of additions to the carbonyl group; however, some of them are not simple attack by a nucleophile, followed by completion of addition to oxygen. Reactions such as bimolecular reduction of ketones to 1,2-diols or reduction of the

---

[3] It is of interest that sulfur is attached to carbon in the bisulfite adduct. If sodium bisulfite has the structure shown on the left below, which is probable, it follows that the electron pair on sulfur makes it a nucleophilic group, which attacks the positive end of the carbonyl

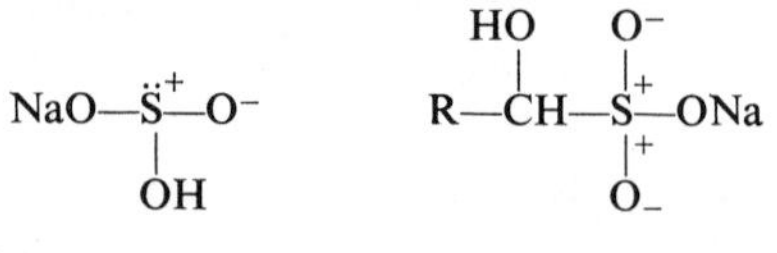

$$NaO-\underset{\underset{OH}{|}}{\overset{\cdot\cdot +}{S}}-O^- \qquad\qquad R-\underset{\underset{O_-}{\overset{\underset{|}{HO}}{|}}}{CH}-\underset{\underset{O_-}{\overset{|+}{|}}}{\overset{O^-}{\underset{|}{S}}}-ONa$$

group, in spite of the positive charge on sulfur. This attack would be accompanied by loss of a proton from —OH in bisulfite to give the structure shown on the right (after a proton is acquired from some source, perhaps water, to complete the addition to carbonyl). An alternative possibility is that the hydrogen is on sulfur in bisulfite and is displaced by the carbonyl group.

carbonyl group to methylene have rather complicated mechanisms, whose details are not understood with certainty.

Oxidation. As previously mentioned (Eqs. 8 and 9) aldehydes are readily oxidized to acids; however, the reaction is rarely of synthetic utility (cf. Eq. 46 for one of the rare applications). Conversion of the acid to the aldehyde (Eq. 2) is the most common direction for synthetic utility.

The carbon chain in ketones may be cleaved under vigorous conditions, but the process is of limited synthetic application, for four acids are formed (Eq. 17) unless the ketone is symmetrical. Even with symmetrical ketones, two acids are formed except from symmetrical cyclic ketones (Eq. 18). Oxidation of cyclohexanone is a major industrial source of the important adipic acid.

$$R-CH_2-\underset{\underset{O}{\|}}{C}-CH_2-R' + 3[O] \xrightarrow[\text{(hot HNO}_3)]{} R-CH_2-CO_2H + R'-CO_2H$$

and (17)

$$R-CO_2H + R'-CH_2CO_2H$$

Adipic acid (18)

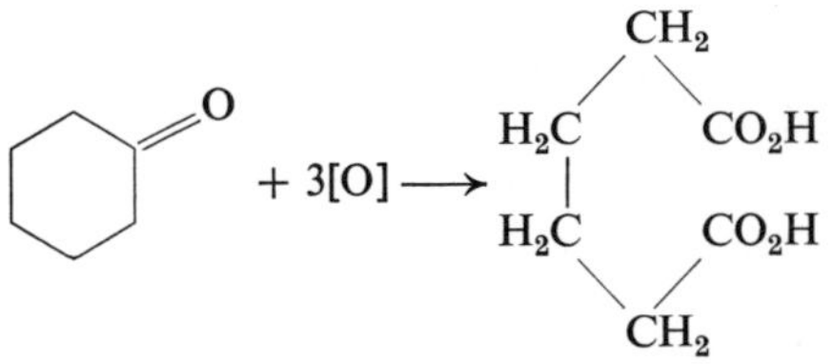

A principal application of ketone oxidation is for degradation of natural products. The acids from degradation are of lower molecular weight than the starting ketone, except in cyclic structures, and usually are easier to identify than the ketone.

Reduction. (1) ALDEHYDES. Attempts to reduce aldehydes with chemical reagents usually lead to a variety of products on account of the sensitivity of aldehydes to both acidic and basic conditions; however, catalytic hydrogenation leads to good yields of primary alcohols (Eq. 19).

$$R-\underset{\underset{H}{\diagdown}}{\overset{\overset{O}{\diagup}}{C}} + \underset{\text{(gas)}}{H_2} \xrightarrow[\text{catalyst}]{\text{Pt or Ni}} R-CH_2OH \qquad (19)$$

(2) KETONES. The reduction of a ketone to a secondary alcohol may be accomplished satisfactorily by use of catalytic hydrogenation, or with chemical reagents (Eq. 20).

$$R-\underset{\underset{O}{\|}}{C}-R' + \begin{matrix} H_2 \xrightarrow{\text{catalyst}} \\ \text{or} \\ 2[H] \xrightarrow{} \\ \text{(Sn + HCl)} \end{matrix} \quad R-\underset{\underset{OH}{|}}{CH}-R' \qquad (20)$$

(3) BIMOLECULAR REDUCTION OF KETONES. When ketones are reduced with *alkaline reagents under anhydrous conditions*, there results a dimeric reduction leading to a vicinal diol. A commonly used method for accomplishing this reduction is shown in Eq. 21. A *glycol* (di-alcohol) of the type obtained in this

$$
\text{R—C—R'} + \text{Mg} \xrightarrow[\text{catalyst}]{\text{HgCl}_2} \quad\underset{\underset{R'}{|}}{\overset{\overset{\displaystyle Mg}{\diagup \ \diagdown}}{\underset{|}{\overset{O \qquad O}{R—C—\!\!\!-\!\!\!-C—R}}}} \xrightarrow{\text{2HOH}} \text{R—}\underset{R'}{\underset{|}{\overset{HO}{\overset{|}{C}}}}\text{—}\underset{R'}{\underset{|}{\overset{OH}{\overset{|}{C}}}}\text{—R} + \text{Mg(OH)}_2
$$

$$\text{(R—C(=O)—R')} \tag{21}$$

reduction is known as a **pinacol,** and this method of reduction is a good method for obtaining symmetrical pinacols. If acetone is reduced in this manner, there results the first member of the pinacol series, which has the common name **pinacol,** and this is the origin of the name given to this type of glycol. Similarly, alkynes are sometimes called acetylenes, and alkenes may be called ethylenes.

One of the few useful reactions of pinacols is dehydration. In dehydration with sulfuric acid, some "normal" dehydration product is obtained (a diene); however, the principal product of dehydration of a pinacol is one resulting from rearrangement (Eq. 22), so the process is usually called the **pinacol rearrangement.** As is normally the case, the first step in reaction of a strong acid and

$$
\underset{\underset{CH_3}{|}}{\overset{\overset{HO}{|}}{CH_3—C}}\!\!-\!\!\underset{\underset{CH_3}{|}}{\overset{\overset{OH}{|}}{C}}\!\!-\!\!CH_3 + H^+ \longrightarrow \underset{\underset{CH_3}{|}}{\overset{\overset{HO}{|}}{CH_3—C}}\!\!-\!\!\underset{\underset{CH_3}{|}}{\overset{\overset{H}{\overset{+}{OH}}}{C}}\!\!-\!\!CH_3 \longrightarrow \underset{\underset{CH_3}{|}}{\overset{\overset{HO}{|}}{CH_3—\overset{+}{C}}}\!\!-\!\!\underset{\underset{CH_3}{|}}{\overset{\overset{CH_3}{|}}{C}}\!\!-\!\!CH_3 + HOH
$$

(a protonated ketone)

$$
\underset{\underset{CH_3}{|}}{\overset{\overset{O}{\|}}{CH_3—C}}\!\!-\!\!\underset{\underset{CH_3}{|}}{\overset{\overset{CH_3}{|}}{C}}\!\!-\!\!CH_3 + H^+ \tag{22}
$$

Pinacolone

alcohol is formation of the oxonium salt. The oxonium salt of a tertiary alcohol dissociates readily to give the carbonium ion, and this may be an intermediate in the pinacol rearrangement; however, in many instances it is probable that the migrating alkyl group displaces the water, as shown in Eq. 22. Of course the same product results, whether the alkyl displaces water or migrates to the charged carbon after water has dissociated. This product is the protonated ketone, the same species that results from treating a ketone with acid. Since the ketone is a very weak base, only in very strong acid solution is there a significant concentration of the protonated species (termed the conjugate acid of the base). Ordinarily, the pinacol rearrangement is not reversible, for the tertiary carbonium ion is a substantially higher energy species than is the conjugate acid of the ketone.

It is of interest that a good synthesis of trimethylacetic acid is application of the hypohalite oxidation to pinacolone (Eq. 23). Since there are no hydrogens

$$CH_3-\underset{\underset{\overset{|}{H_3C}}{\overset{|}{\underset{\|}{C}}}{\overset{CH_3}{|}}-C-CH_3 + 3NaOCl \longrightarrow CH_3-\underset{\underset{CH_3}{|}}{\overset{\overset{CH_3}{|}}{C}}-CO_2Na + CHCl_3 + 2NaOH \quad (23)$$

$$\downarrow H^+$$

Trimethylacetic acid

on the opposite side of carbonyl to methyl, there is no side reaction resulting from substitution of halogen on both sides of carbonyl. This structural requirement limits this synthesis of acids rather severely; in fact, the most common application of hypohalite oxidation to synthesis is in aromatic ketones. Even this type is commonly made by the hypohalite oxidation only when the aromatic group contains two or more rings (cf. chapter on naphthalene derivatives). As noted in Eq. 23, when the hypohalite oxidation is used as a synthetic method, sodium hypochlorite is commonly used. Not only is hypochlorite cheaper than hypoiodite, but the resultant chloroform is readily separated from the reaction product.

(4) REDUCTION OF CARBONYL TO METHYLENE. Although reduction of a carbonyl group nearly always yields an alcohol, as has been described in the preceding sections, certain special methods may be used to carry the reduction to methylene. This may be accomplished directly by use of hydrochloric acid and zinc amalgam (Eq. 24), the method known as **Clemmensen reduction.**

$$R-\underset{\underset{O}{\|}}{C}-R' + 4[H] \underset{[Zn(Hg) + HCl]}{\longrightarrow} R-CH_2-R' + HOH \quad (24)$$

Although conditions for this reduction seem rather simple, the specified conditions must be used; rather minor variations cause the reduction to methylene to fail. The Clemmensen method is quite satisfactory if the carbonyl is entirely unhindered; however, the reaction is surprisingly sensitive to steric hindrance. Even a single methyl group substituted adjacent to carbonyl makes the Clemmensen reduction quite sluggish, and any more hindrance causes the reaction to fail. For this reason, the two-step process known as the **Wolff-Kishner reduction** has become far more widely used than Clemmensen reduction.

Wolff-Kishner reduction is accomplished by first converting the carbonyl compound to the simple hydrazone, then heating the hydrazone with base, as outlined in Eq. 25. For many years after the discovery of this reaction, the hydrazone was prepared and isolated, then heated with sodium ethoxide in ethanol solution under pressure at about 190°. Since the late nineteen-forties, the process has been carried out in a high-boiling solvent such as diethylene glycol, $HO—CH_2—CH_2—O—CH_2—CH_2—OH$, in which the hydrazone is

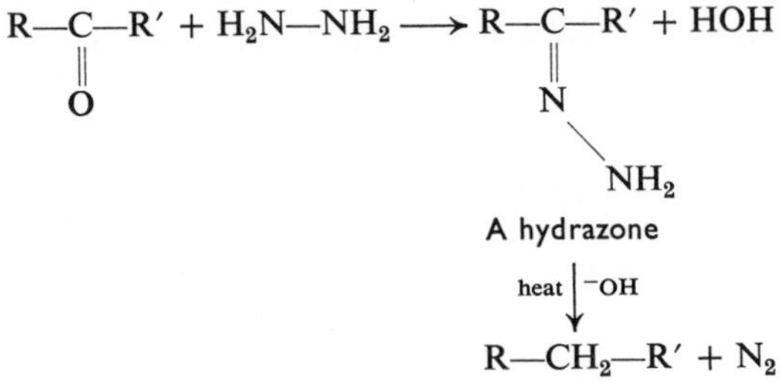

$$R—\underset{\underset{O}{\|}}{C}—R' + H_2N—NH_2 \longrightarrow R—\underset{\underset{N}{\|}}{C}—R' + HOH$$

$$\underset{NH_2}{\diagdown} \qquad (25)$$

A hydrazone

$$\text{heat} \Big| ^-OH$$

$$R—CH_2—R' + N_2$$

prepared and reduced *in situ*. This particular process was developed by the Chinese chemist, Huang-Minlon, while working at Harvard University, and is known as the Huang-Minlon modification of the Wolff-Kishner reduction.

Grignard reactions with aldehydes and ketones. The Grignard reagent adds to the carbonyl group in aldehydes and ketones in a normal manner. The adduct carries only a single negative group on carbonyl, so the magnesium alkoxide is the product of the reaction. Addition of water yields the alcohol, which is primary, secondary, or tertiary, depending on the type of carbonyl compound used (Eqs. 26 through 28). These are good syntheses for any of the

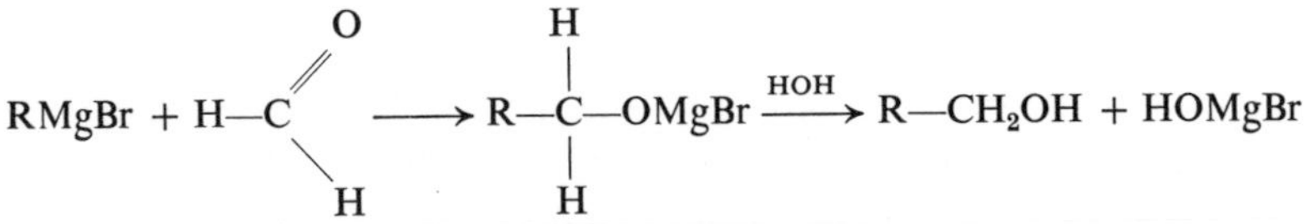

$$RMgBr + H—C\overset{\displaystyle O}{\underset{\displaystyle H}{\diagup\!\!\!\diagdown}} \longrightarrow R—\underset{\underset{H}{|}}{\overset{\overset{H}{|}}{C}}—OMgBr \xrightarrow{HOH} R—CH_2OH + HOMgBr \quad (26)$$

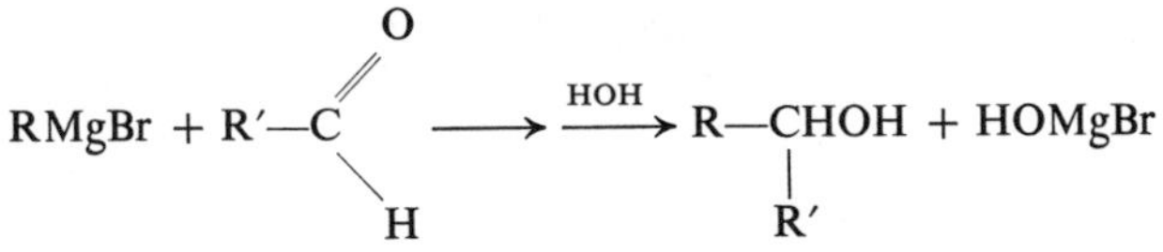

$$RMgBr + R'—C\overset{\displaystyle O}{\underset{\displaystyle H}{\diagup\!\!\!\diagdown}} \longrightarrow \xrightarrow{HOH} R—\underset{\underset{R'}{|}}{CHOH} + HOMgBr \quad (27)$$

$$RMgBr + R'—\underset{\underset{O}{\|}}{C}—R'' \longrightarrow \xrightarrow{HOH} R—\underset{\underset{R'}{|}}{\overset{\overset{R''}{|}}{C}}—OH + HOMgBr \quad (28)$$

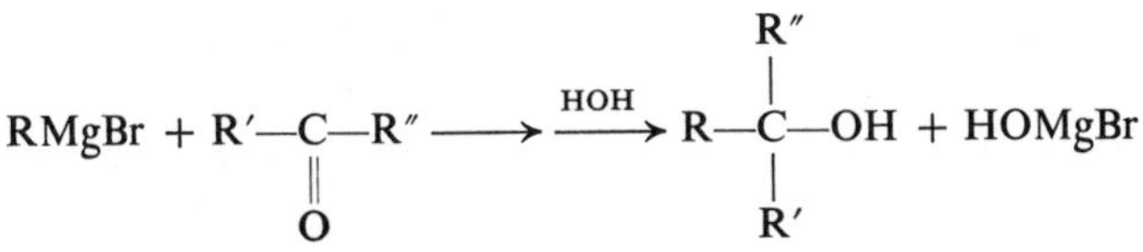

three types of alcohols. In case the ketone used for the reaction is not a symmetrical one, as in Eq. 28, the tertiary alcohol contains three different groups on the carbinol carbon. It will be recalled that synthesis of a tertiary alcohol by the Grignard reaction with an ester yields a carbinol containing two of the same group.

It should be noted that the primary alcohol synthesis (Eq. 26), utilizing formaldehyde, results in extension of the carbon chain by one carbon. In case further reactions, or chain extensions, are to be carried out, the alcohol function is a convenient one for it may be readily converted to bromide, the leaving group needed for displacement reactions.

Hydrogen cyanide addition. In spite of the extremely small ionization of hydrogen cyanide, its addition to the carbonyl group may be accomplished (Eq. 29). The α-hydroxynitrile resulting from this addition, which is called a

$$R-\overset{\displaystyle O}{\underset{\displaystyle H}{\overset{\|}{C}}} \quad + \text{ HCN} \quad \longrightarrow \quad R-\underset{\displaystyle OH}{\overset{\displaystyle |}{CH}}-C\equiv N \qquad (29)$$
$$(\text{NaCN} + \text{H}^+)$$

or
$$R-\underset{\displaystyle O}{\overset{\displaystyle \|}{C}}-R'$$

cyanohydrin, is a convenient source of α-hydroxy acids. The nitrile may be hydrolyzed in a normal fashion (Eq. 30).

$$R-\underset{\displaystyle OH}{\overset{\displaystyle |}{CH}}-CN + 2HOH \xrightarrow{\text{H}^+} R-\underset{\displaystyle OH}{\overset{\displaystyle |}{CH}}-CO_2H + {}^+NH_4 \qquad (30)$$

Acetal formation. With acid catalysis, an alcohol will attack the carbonyl in an aldehyde, as shown in Eq. 31. A large excess of alcohol is

$$R-\overset{\displaystyle O}{\underset{\displaystyle H}{\overset{\|}{C}}} + H^+ \rightleftharpoons R-\overset{\displaystyle \overset{+}{O}H}{\underset{\displaystyle H}{C}} \underset{\xleftarrow{\hspace{1cm}}}{\overset{CH_3OH}{\rightleftharpoons}} R-\underset{\displaystyle \underset{+}{CH_3OH}}{\overset{\displaystyle OH}{\underset{|}{C}}}-H \rightleftharpoons R-\underset{\displaystyle OCH_3}{\overset{\displaystyle OH}{CH}} + H^+$$

A hemi-acetal

$$(31)$$

ordinarily used to displace the equilibrium forward. Presence of the alkoxyl group on the same carbon with hydroxyl, in the hemi-acetal, renders the hydroxyl much more easily displaced than in normal alcohols. Thus, the oxonium salt of this alcohol suffers displacement of water by another mole of alcohol, so that the hemi-acetal is converted to the di-ether known as an acetal (Eq. 32).

$$R-\underset{\displaystyle OCH_3}{\overset{\displaystyle |}{CH}}-OH + H^+ \rightleftharpoons R-\underset{\displaystyle OCH_3}{\overset{\displaystyle |}{CH}}-\overset{+}{O}H_2 \underset{\xleftarrow{\hspace{1cm}}}{\overset{CH_3OH}{\rightleftharpoons}} R-\underset{\displaystyle OCH_3}{\overset{\displaystyle \overset{+}{H}OCH_3}{\underset{|}{CH}}} \rightleftharpoons R-\underset{\displaystyle OCH_3}{\overset{\displaystyle OCH_3}{CH}} + H^+$$

$$+ \text{HOH} \qquad \text{An acetal}$$

$$(32)$$

As indicated, the reactions are reversible, so this type of ether is also hydrolyzed readily with acid catalysis. The concentrated acid and long heating necessary for cleavage of ordinary ethers is not necessary. The reactions shown in Eqs.

31 and 32 are rapid in boiling methyl alcohol. The net reactions whose details are shown in Eqs. 31 and 32 may be summarized as in Eq. 33.

$$\underset{\substack{| \\ H}}{\overset{\displaystyle O}{R-C}} + CH_3-OH \underset{H^+}{\rightleftharpoons} \underset{\substack{| \\ OCH_3}}{\overset{\displaystyle OH}{R-CH}} \underset{CH_3OH, H^+}{\rightleftharpoons} \underset{\substack{| \\ OCH_3}}{\overset{\displaystyle OCH_3}{R-CH}} + HOH$$

(33)

Naming of acetals is frequently based on the common names of the aldehyde and alcohol used for formation of the acetal, as in the following examples:

$$\underset{\substack{| \\ OCH_3}}{\overset{\displaystyle OCH_3}{CH_3-CH}} \qquad\qquad \underset{\substack{| \\ OC_2H_5}}{\overset{\displaystyle OC_2H_5}{CH_3-CH_2-CH_2-CH}}$$

Dimethyl acetal
or
1,1-Dimethoxyethane

Diethyl butyral
or
1,1-Diethoxybutane

Also illustrated is the application of the IUC system to naming of acetals; it is the same system used for naming simple ethers. The names based on trivial names of the aldehydes have the advantage of describing the nature of the functional group present; however, more complicated structures must be named by the IUC system.

Ketals are formed by reaction of an alcohol with a ketone, as in Eq. 34;

$$\underset{\substack{/ \\ CH_3}}{\overset{\displaystyle CH_3}{C}}=O + 2CH_3-OH \underset{H^+}{\rightleftharpoons} \underset{\substack{/ \quad \backslash \\ CH_3 \quad OCH_3}}{\overset{\displaystyle CH_3 \quad OCH_3}{C}} + HOH$$

(34)

2,2-Dimethoxypropane

however, even with excess of alcohol, this equilibrium is not shifted forward a satisfactory amount.[4] With a 1,2-diol, however, equilibrium is forward a satisfactory amount for convenient use in synthesis (Eq. 35). This illustrates

$$\underset{\substack{/ \\ H_3C}}{\overset{\displaystyle H_3C}{C}}=O + HOCH_2-CH_2OH \underset{H^+}{\rightleftharpoons} \underset{\substack{/ \quad \backslash \\ H_3C \quad O-CH_2}}{\overset{\displaystyle H_3C \quad O-CH_2}{C}} + HOH$$

(35)

---

[4] On account of a decrease in the number of molecules in this reaction, the reactants have considerably higher entropy than do the products. As a result of this large entropy component in the free energy change in the reaction, equilibrium is actually shifted forward rapidly as the temperature is **lowered**. By operating at −25°, it has been possible to secure about 25% conversion of acetone to its dimethyl ketal (Eq. 34), and on an industrial scale the alcohol and acetone may be recovered for recycling. 2,2-Dimethoxypropane is manufactured by this process and sold at a rather low price.

the often observed phenomenon that cyclic structures have a lower energy (greater stability) than do the analogous open-chain compounds.

Utility of acetals as a protecting group depends on the fact that hydrolysis of acetals is not catalyzed by alkali. Even in the 1,1-dialkoxy type of ether, alkoxy is not displaced readily unless the oxonium salt is formed by use of acid. Thus, the aldehyde may be protected by conversion to an acetal, then reactions may be carried out on another functional group in the same molecule. As an example of this sort of procedure, let us assume that the following conversion is desired:

$$CH_3\!-\!CH\!-\!(CH_2)_4\!-\!CHO \longrightarrow CH_3\!-\!C\!-\!(CH_2)_4\!-\!CHO$$
$$\underset{OH}{|} \qquad\qquad \underset{O}{\|}$$

An attempt to carry out the oxidation directly would result in oxidation of the aldehyde to the acid; however, the desired conversion may be accomplished by first protecting the aldehyde group by converting it to the acetal. The sequence in Eq. 36 might then be used.

$$CH_3\!-\!CH\!-\!(CH_2)_4\!-\!CHO + 2CH_3OH \xrightarrow{\;H^+\;} CH_3\!-\!CH\!-\!(CH_2)_4\!-\!CH(OCH_3)_2$$
$$\underset{OH}{|} \qquad\qquad\qquad\qquad\qquad \underset{OH}{|}$$

$$\text{[O]} \;\Big|\; KMnO_4,\,{}^-OH \qquad (36)$$

$$CH_3\!-\!C\!-\!(CH_2)_4\!-\!CHO \xleftarrow[\;H^+\;]{HOH} CH_3\!-\!C\!-\!(CH_2)_4\!-\!CH(OCH_3)_2$$
$$\underset{O}{\|} \qquad\qquad\qquad\qquad \underset{O}{\|}$$

The chemistry of hemi-acetals and acetals is of much importance in connection with the structures of sugars, to be discussed in later chapters (Chaps. 23 and 24).

The aldol condensation. Acidity of carbonyl compounds. In Chapter 12, in which was discussed the basis for acidity of organic compounds, it was noted that if the dissociation of a compound gives an anion stabilized by resonance the dissociation is favored. In harmony with these considerations, the following dissociation of an aldehyde may be considered:

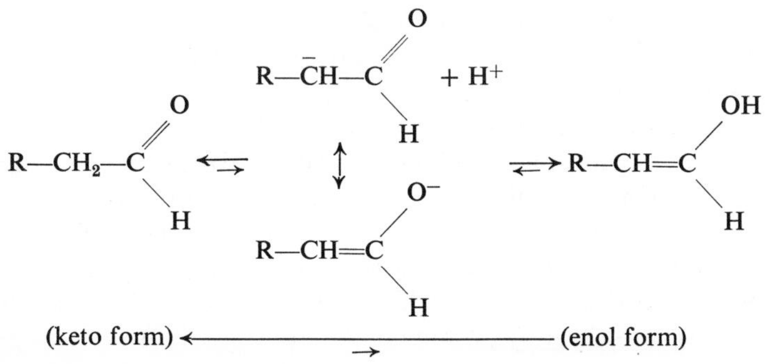

(37)

(keto form) $\longleftarrow$ _____ (enol form)

Since the anion shown in Eq. 37 is a resonance hybrid, some resonance stabilization would be expected, and some acidity for an aldehyde would be anticipated. Actually, simple aldehydes and ketones do have acidic properties, although exceedingly weak ones. They are weaker acids than water. Other carbonyl compounds to be studied in later chapters are stronger acids because they have structures giving rise to more resonance stabilization.

Another possibility which arises, if the ionization depicted in Eq. 37 is a reality, is that the hydrogen might be attached to oxygen when reassociation occurs. This gives the structure known as the **enol,** in contrast to the normal carbonyl structure known as the **keto form.** Compounds which differ from each other in the position of a hydrogen atom and of one or more double bonds are known as **tautomers;** so keto and enol forms are tautomers. In simple aldehydes, the percentage of enol form present proves to be extremely small, a tiny fraction of one per cent. Thus, the over-all equilibration via the resonance-stabilized **enolate ion,** is overwhelmingly in favor of the more stable keto form. The lower arrows in Eq. 37, indicating that the equilibrium is in favor of the keto form, do not imply that the equilibrium between the keto and enol forms is direct. Equilibrium is probably via the enolate ion.

The small percentage of enolate ion present in an aldehyde or ketone is very important in many of its reactions, for if this ion is removed in a reaction, equilibrium will tend to be re-established and thus furnish more of the ion. In absence of competing reactions, all the molecules could eventually react in the form of the ion. In practice, the concentration of enolate ion in simple aldehydes or ketones is so small that any reactions involving it are extremely slow unless the concentration of this ion is increased by addition of a base. In presence of a strong base, such as sodium hydroxide, an aldehyde would establish the following equilibrium:

$$R-CH_2-\overset{\displaystyle O}{\underset{\displaystyle H}{\overset{\|}{C}}} \ + \ \overset{+}{N}a\overset{-}{O}H \ \underset{\longrightarrow}{\overset{\longleftarrow}{}} \ R-\overset{-}{C}H-\overset{\displaystyle O}{\underset{\displaystyle H}{\overset{\|}{C}}} \ + \ Na^+ + HOH \qquad (38)$$

Since water is a considerably stronger acid than is an aldehyde, the equilibrium shown in Eq. 38 would be far to the left; nevertheless, presence of the base increases the concentration of enolate ion over that present when only the dissociation shown in Eq. 37 is contributing the ion.

Addition of alkali to an aldehyde or ketone, then, increases the concentration of enolate ion and therefore catalyzes any reaction dependent on this ion. Use of a stronger base, such as a sodium alkoxide, increases the concentration of the enolate ion still more than does hydroxide. There are many important reactions of enolate ions, including displacement of alkyl halides, and some of these will be studied in later chapters. At the present time, there will be considered the **aldol condensation,** which involves attack of the enolate ion on the carbonyl group. Thus, this reaction is catalyzed by base, although the reaction is completed by proton addition to oxygen. A reaction giving the same product as the aldol condensation occurs in acid; however, absence of the enolate ion causes this reaction to occur so slowly that it is of little synthetic importance. In the acid-catalyzed reaction, the enol attacks the protonated ketone.

A "condensation" is a reaction in which two molecules become joined by formation of a new carbon-carbon bond to make a new, larger molecule. After the initial condensation there may follow the loss of some simple molecule such as water. The over-all result of the aldol condensation is shown in Eq. 39,

$$R-CH_2-\overset{\displaystyle O}{\underset{\displaystyle H}{C}} + R-CH_2-\overset{\displaystyle O}{\underset{\displaystyle H}{C}} \xrightarrow{^-OH} R-CH_2-\underset{\underset{\displaystyle OH}{|}}{CH}-\underset{\underset{\displaystyle R}{|}}{CH}-\overset{\displaystyle O}{\underset{\displaystyle H}{C}} \qquad (39)$$

$$R-CH_2-\overset{\displaystyle O}{\underset{\displaystyle H}{C}} + {}^-OH \underset{\longrightarrow}{\longleftarrow} R-\overset{-}{\underset{\displaystyle H}{C}}H-\overset{\displaystyle O}{C} + HOH \qquad (39a)$$

$$R-CH_2-\overset{\displaystyle O^-}{\underset{\displaystyle +\ H}{C}} + R-\overset{-}{C}H-\overset{\displaystyle O}{C} \rightleftharpoons R-CH_2-\underset{\underset{\displaystyle O^-}{|}}{CH}-\underset{\underset{\displaystyle R}{|}}{CH}-\overset{\displaystyle O}{\underset{\displaystyle H}{C}} \qquad (39b)$$

$$\updownarrow$$

$$R-CH_2-\overset{\displaystyle O}{\underset{\displaystyle H}{C}}$$

$$R-CH_2-\underset{\underset{\displaystyle O^-}{|}}{CH}-\underset{\underset{\displaystyle R}{|}}{CH}-\overset{\displaystyle O}{\underset{\displaystyle H}{C}} + HOH \underset{\longrightarrow}{\longleftarrow} R-CH_2-\underset{\underset{\displaystyle OH}{|}}{CH}-\underset{\underset{\displaystyle R}{|}}{CH}-\overset{\displaystyle O}{\underset{\displaystyle H}{C}} \qquad (39c)$$

$$+ {}^-OH$$

while the mechanism is indicated in the following equations. Although the equilibrium in Eq. 39a is far to the left, the enolate ion is continually removed by occurrence of the reaction in Eq. 39b. Finally, the process is drawn further towards completion by the reaction in Eq. 39c, where the equilibrium is shifted far to the right because water is a much stronger acid than is an alcohol.

The product of reaction 39 may go to the enolate ion and react further by addition to another molecule of aldehyde. Under strenuous conditions, this process may continue until polymers are formed; however, with dilute base and limited heating a rather good yield of the mono-condensation product may be obtained. The further condensation is discouraged by the steric hindrance of the α-substituent in the mono-condensation product, for only acetaldehyde gives a mono-condensation product not having an α-substituent.

It should be noted carefully that *the aldol condensation must occur in the α-position*, for removal of a hydrogen from any other position will not give a resonance-stabilized anion. Thus, it is only the hydrogens on the α-carbon that are weakly acidic.

If the aldol condensation is carried out on a mixture of two aldehydes, four products will result (unless one aldehyde has no alpha hydrogens), for each aldehyde may condense with itself or with the other aldehyde. It follows that this type of reaction, known as a "cross condensation" is of synthetic utility only with special structures (see cross condensations below).

Ketones will engage in the aldol condensation; however, even a single ketone gives two products unless it is a symmetrical ketone, for the enolate ion may form on either α-carbon. The condensation of acetone (Eq. 40) illustrates

$$2CH_3-\underset{\underset{O}{\|}}{C}-CH_3 \underset{\xrightarrow{}}{\overset{-OH}{\longleftarrow}} CH_3-\underset{\underset{CH_3}{|}}{\overset{\overset{OH}{|}}{C}}-CH_2-\underset{\underset{O}{\|}}{C}-CH_3 \tag{40}$$

Diacetone alcohol
(4-Hydroxy-4-methyl-2-pentanone)

the useful reaction occurring with a symmetrical ketone. On account of the additional steric hindrance involved with ketones, equilibrium is not nearly so far forward as with aldehydes, so a useful yield is obtained only if the equilibrium is displaced forward in some way. One method for doing this is to heat the ketone under reflux and arrange the return flow from the condenser so that it passes over the basic catalyst. The condensation product formed is much higher boiling than the ketone so most of it remains in the boiling pot as the ketone continues to boil into the reflux condenser. Reaction may be continued until no volatile material remains to boil into the condenser.

Synthetic utility of aldol condensation products. Since the aldol products have two functional groups they are quite useful for synthesis, so a few of the applications will be mentioned. Reduction of the carbonyl leads to a 1,3-glycol (Eq. 41). Such diols may be converted to various compounds via

$$C_2H_5-\underset{\underset{C_2H_5}{|}}{\overset{\overset{OH}{|}}{CH}}-CH-CHO + H_2 \xrightarrow[\text{catalyst}]{\text{Pt}} C_2H_5-\underset{\underset{C_2H_5}{|}}{\overset{\overset{OH}{|}}{CH}}-CH-CH_2OH \tag{41}$$

the dibromide (however, review rearrangements in Chap. 6).

Dehydration of the aldol product, as illustrated in Eq. 42, gives a

$$CH_3-\overset{\overset{OH}{|}}{CH}-CH_2-CHO \xrightarrow[\text{H}^+]{\text{heat}} CH_3-CH=CH-CHO \tag{42}$$

Acetaldol   Crotonaldehyde
(2-Butenal)

particularly useful product,[5] for either of the functional groups may be reduced without significant attack on the other (Eqs. 43 and 44), both may be reduced (Eq. 45), or the aldehyde may be oxidized by use of a mild agent without attack on the double bond (Eq. 46).

$$CH_3-CH\!=\!CH-CHO + H_2 \xrightarrow[\text{catalyst}]{\text{Pd}} CH_3-CH_2-CH_2-CHO \tag{43}$$

$$CH_3-CH\!=\!CH-CHO + 2[H] \longrightarrow CH_3-CH\!=\!CH-CH_2OH \tag{44}$$
$$\text{(LiAlH}_4)\qquad\qquad\quad \text{Crotyl alcohol}$$

$$CH_3-CH\!=\!CH-CHO + 2H_2 \xrightarrow[\text{catalyst}]{\text{Pt or Ni}} CH_3-CH_2-CH_2-CH_2OH \tag{45}$$

$$CH_3-CH\!=\!CH-CHO + [O] \longrightarrow CH_3-CH\!=\!CH-CO_2H \tag{46}$$
$$\text{(Ag}_2\text{O)}\qquad\qquad\quad \text{Crotonic acid}$$

The allylic rearrangement which occurs in conversion of crotyl alcohol to the bromide has been discussed in Chapter 12. Fortunately, the primary and secondary bromides may be separated by fractional distillation, and this is the common approach to the securing of a pure allylic bromide.

In connection with the synthetic utilization of α,β-unsaturated compounds such as crotonaldehyde, it should be mentioned at this time that **conjugate addition** (terminal addition to conjugated double bonds, cf. Chap. 12) occurs in a conjugated system of this sort as well as in those consisting entirely of carbon-carbon double bonds. As a matter of fact, such reactions are far more important in the oxygen-containing systems, and several illustrations of conjugate additions to α,β-unsaturated carbonyl compounds will be discussed in subsequent chapters, especially those dealing with heterocyclic compounds.

Cannizzaro reaction. If an aldehyde has no alpha hydrogens, it follows that the aldol condensation cannot occur, for it is only the alpha hydrogens that have the weakly acidic properties necessary to yield the enolate ion. In such structures, another slower reaction, known as the Cannizzaro reaction, has the opportunity to occur in presence of alkali. Since the most important aldehydes having no alpha hydrogens are the aromatic aldehydes, the Cannizzaro reaction is illustrated (Eq. 47) with benzaldehyde, the simplest

aromatic aldehyde. It will be noted that this reaction amounts to reduction of half the aldehyde by oxidation of the other half. Thus, the yield of either

---

[5] Dehydration occurs almost entirely as shown rather than in the opposite direction to give the isomer, $CH_2\!=\!CH-CH_2-CHO$, for a double bond at the end of the chain has a substantially higher energy. Furthermore, conjugation of the double bond with that of the carbonyl also leads to a somewhat lower energy, so dehydration of higher molecular weight aldol products also gives a predominance of the α,β-unsaturated product. In branched-chain structures, however, there may be formed larger amounts of the non-conjugated isomer.

product cannot be good. The most common utility of this reaction is reduction of an aldehyde to an alcohol without reduction of other reducible groups that may be in the molecule; hence, a "cross Cannizzaro" reaction employing formaldehyde is frequently used. Since formaldehyde is much the stronger reducing agent, a rather clean-cut reaction in the direction illustrated in Eq. 48 is obtained, so the more expensive aldehyde is reduced in good yield to the alcohol. Formaldehyde is sufficiently cheap to be practical as a reducing agent.

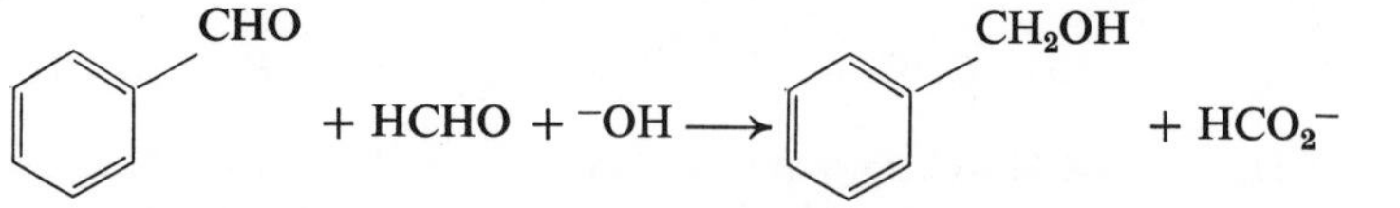

$$\text{C}_6\text{H}_5\text{CHO} + \text{HCHO} + {}^-\text{OH} \longrightarrow \text{C}_6\text{H}_5\text{CH}_2\text{OH} + \text{HCO}_2^- \qquad (48)$$

The mechanism of the Cannizzaro reaction is believed to involve a sequence of nucleophilic attacks on the carbonyl, the usual type of reaction at the carbonyl group. The final step is probably hydrogen transfer in a cyclic transition state (Eq. 49). Since the conversions involved in the aldol conden-

$$(49)$$

$$\text{R}-\text{CH}_2\text{OH} + \text{R}-\text{C}\overset{\text{O}}{\underset{\text{O}^-}{\big\langle}}$$

sation proceed at a higher rate, the Cannizzaro reaction may become prominent only in molecules having no alpha hydrogens.

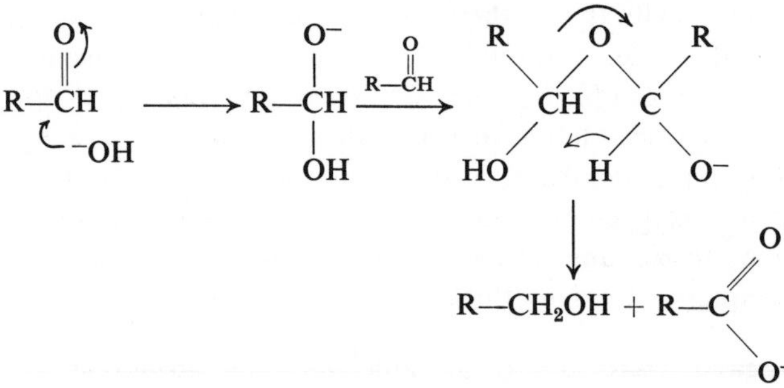

Cross aldol and Cannizzaro reactions. Perhaps the most important of the applications of the Cannizzaro reaction involve a follow reaction occurring after a cross aldol reaction with formaldehyde. Since formaldehyde has no alpha hydrogens, it can engage in an aldol condensation only if it is attacked by the enolate ion from another aldehyde or a ketone. Furthermore, the carbonyl group in formaldehyde is quite unhindered, so it is more reactive

$$\text{CH}_3-\text{CHO} + \text{H}-\text{CHO} \xrightarrow{{}^-\text{OH}} \underset{\overset{|}{\text{CH}_2\text{OH}}}{\text{CH}_2-\text{CHO}} \xrightarrow{\text{HCHO}} \underset{\overset{|}{\text{CH}_2\text{OH}}}{\text{HOCH}_2-\text{CH}-\text{CHO}}$$

$$\Big\downarrow \text{HCHO} \qquad (50)$$

$$\text{HOCH}_2-\overset{\overset{\displaystyle\text{CH}_2\text{OH}}{|}}{\underset{\underset{\displaystyle\text{CH}_2\text{OH}}{|}}{\text{C}}}-\text{CHO}$$

towards an enolate ion than is any other carbonyl group. Thus, an aldol condensation with formaldehyde and another aldehyde gives a rather clean cross reaction; in addition, subsequent reactions occur until all the alpha hydrogens in the other aldehyde have been replaced (Eq. 50). Finally, formaldehyde gives the usual type of cross Cannizzaro reaction, as a rapid follow reaction to the condensation, so that the end-product of the reaction is that shown in Eq. 51, 2,2-*bis*-(hydroxymethyl)-1,3-propanediol, known by the

$$
\underset{\underset{\text{CH}_2\text{OH}}{|}}{\overset{\overset{\text{CH}_2\text{OH}}{|}}{\text{HOCH}_2-\text{C}-\text{CHO}}} + \text{H}-\text{CHO} + \text{KOH} \longrightarrow \underset{\underset{\text{CH}_2\text{OH}}{|}}{\overset{\overset{\text{CH}_2\text{OH}}{|}}{\text{HOCH}_2-\text{C}-\text{CH}_2\text{OH}}} + \text{H}-\text{CO}_2\text{K}
$$

Pentaerythritol

(51)

common name of pentaerythritol (pronounced penta-e̽-rўth′-rĭ-tōl).[6] Since it is not practical to isolate useful quantities of any intermediates in Eqs. 50 and 51, the reaction is normally carried out with excess of formaldehyde so that a good yield of the tetra-alcohol is obtained.

It should be emphasized that the sequence of steps shown in Eq. 50 results from the low steric hindrance and high reactivity of formaldehyde. With other aldehydes, the simple condensation as shown in Eq. 39 may be secured in rather good yield. Further, the principles involved in the cross reactions should be studied with care, for they furnish an excellent vehicle for understanding the basic principles of the aldol condensation and Cannizzaro reaction.

Solution of synthetic problems involving aldol condensations and Grignard reactions with carbonyl compounds requires more sophistication than the problems previously encountered, for these reactions result in the joining of two sizeable fragments to make a larger molecule. Particular attention should be directed towards the types of structures which may be obtained and the spacing of the functional groups resulting from the aldol condensation.

Polymerization of Aldehydes

Although ketones do not polymerize under any normal conditions, many types of aldehydes polymerize so readily that this becomes a major factor in the handling and storing of these compounds. These polymerizations are studied largely for their nuisance value. There appears to be no practical use

---

[6] Higher aldehydes give tri-alcohols; for example, propionaldehyde gives CH_3-CH_2- $\text{COH}(\text{CH}_2\text{OH})_2$, 2-hydroxy-2-hydroxymethyl-1-butanol. With acetone, all six alpha hydrogens are replaced by hydroxymethyl groups. The nitrate esters of these poly-ols have received considerable investigation as high explosives (cf. Chap. 14 for PETN); however, the widest use has been for making poly-esters with dibasic acids such as $\text{HO}_2\text{C}-(\text{CH}_2)_n-\text{CO}_2\text{H}$. These highly branched polymers form tough elastic films of great use in protective coatings.

for these polymers except as a source of monomers. The ease of polymerization, and the type of polymer formed are subject to such great variation that knowledge of the subject is far from complete.

Formaldehyde polymerizes so readily that it is commercially obtainable only as a polymer or in water solution ("formalin"). If the anhydrous gas is required for a reaction (such as the Grignard reaction) it is obtained by heating one of the polymers and is passed directly into the reaction. The gas repolymerizes very rapidly when it passes out of the heated zone.

Formaldehyde forms two general types of polymers:

(a) A trimer, usually called trioxymethylene or "Trioxane"

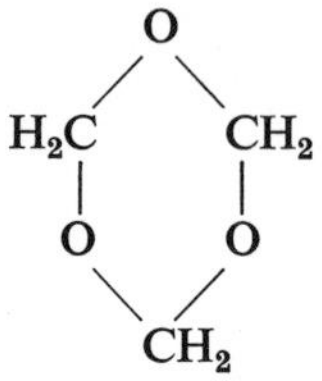

$$
\begin{array}{ccc}
 & O & \\
 & / \quad \backslash & \\
H_2C & & CH_2 \\
| & & | \\
O & & O \\
 & \backslash \quad / & \\
 & CH_2 &
\end{array}
$$

(b) Linear polymers, $(CH_2O)_n$, of various molecular weights and denoted by such names as polyoxymethylene, paraformaldehyde, and metaldehyde.

Acetaldehyde may be stored for a few days at $0°$, with careful exclusion of acid, as the monomer of boiling point $21°$. Acetaldehyde is normally marketed, however, as the trimer, **paraldehyde,** boiling point $125°$, which is a convenient source of acetaldehyde (Eq. 52).

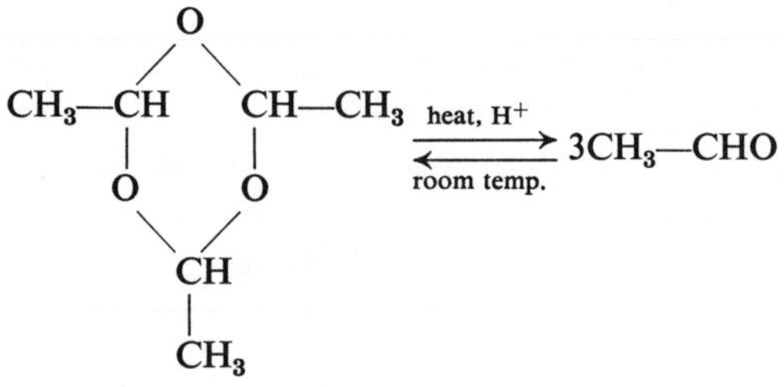

$$
\begin{array}{ccc}
 & O & \\
 & / \quad \backslash & \\
CH_3-CH & & CH-CH_3 \quad \xrightarrow[\text{room temp.}]{\text{heat, } H^+} \quad 3CH_3-CHO \qquad (52) \\
| & & | \\
O & & O \\
 & \backslash \quad / & \\
 & CH & \\
 & | & \\
 & CH_3 &
\end{array}
$$

Higher straight-chain aldehydes show a remarkable variation in their tendencies to polymerize. **Propionaldehyde,** with only one more carbon than acetaldehyde, is quite stable to storage. Samples stored under ordinary conditions for ten years or longer will contain more than 50% of the monomer. *n*-**Heptanal,** another common aldehyde, is also rather stable, but less so than propionaldehyde, and the monomer is regenerated from the polymer with great difficulty. *n*-**Hexadecanal** is a solid, melting point $34°$, but unless the melting point is taken rapidly, the partially melted material resolidifies and then melts at the melting point of the trimer. This trimer readily gives the monomer on simply heating sufficiently to distil the monomer at reduced pressure. There appears to have been presented no careful investigation of these perplexing differences in behavior.

α-**Alkyl aldehydes,** R—CH—CHO, usually polymerize slowly and may be

                                      R′

stored under ordinary conditions, but should be distilled before use.

    Trialkylacetaldehydes, RR′R″C—CHO, appear to be as stable as ketones, but rather small numbers of this type have been prepared.

EXERCISES

1. Give two names for each of the following compounds.

(a) 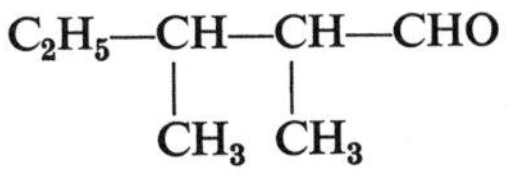 C_2H_5—CH—CH—CHO

            CH_3 CH_3

(b) 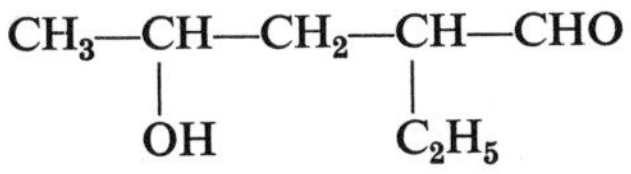 CH_3—CH—CH_2—CH—CHO

            OH C_2H_5

(c) CH_3—CH=CH—CHO

(d) 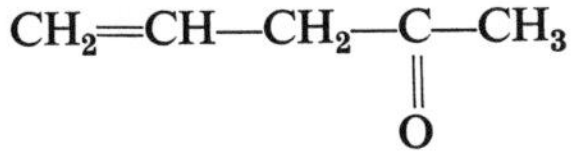 CH_2=CH—CH_2—C—CH_3

                      O

(e) 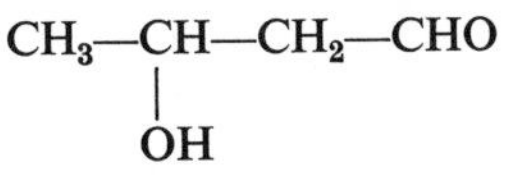 CH_3—CH—CH_2—CHO

          OH

(f) 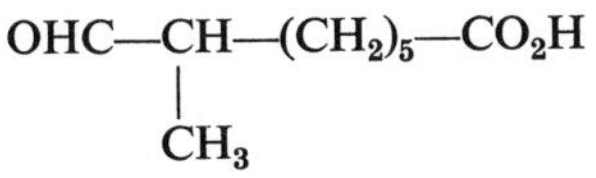 OHC—CH—$(CH_2)_5$—CO_2H

           CH_3

2. Give one name for each of the following compounds.

              OCH_3

(a) 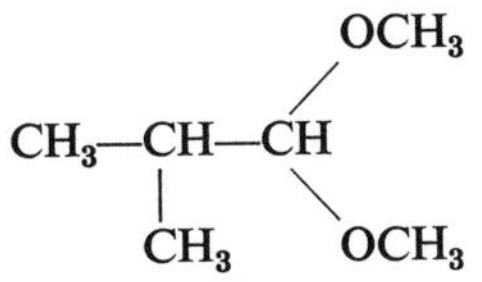 CH_3—CH—CH

         CH_3 OCH_3

(b) C_2H_5—C—CH_2—CH—$(CH_2)_4$—CH—CHO

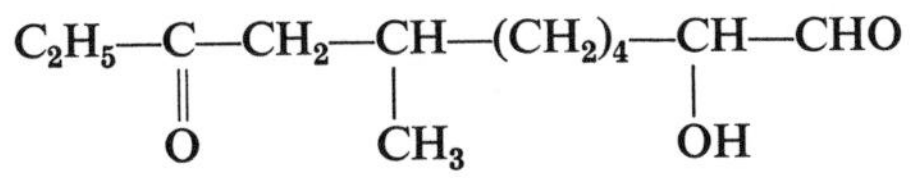

         O CH_3 OH

(c) C_2H_5—C—CH_2—CH—CH=CH—CH_2—C CH_3

         O   CH—CH_3 N

                CH_3 H

        CH_3 CH_3

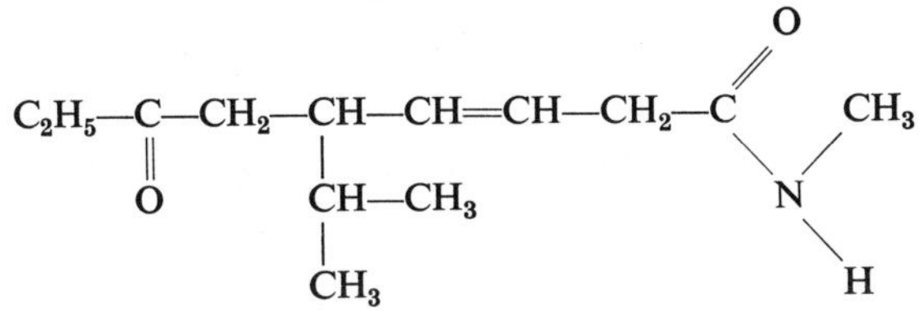

(d) 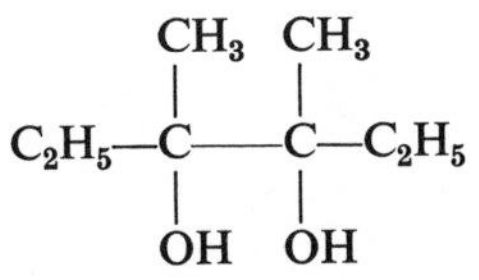 C_2H_5—C——C—C_2H_5

        OH OH

3. If you were given several test tubes, each known to contain one of the following compounds, outline by means of a flow sheet how you could identify each compound (one flow sheet per set of compounds). In each series, you have as many test tubes as compounds, and each test tube is known to contain a different compound. The identification is to be by qualitative tests, not by use of physical constants (B.P., M.P., etc.).

(a) *n*-Butyl alcohol, *n*-butyraldehyde, methyl ethyl ketone.
(b) Ethyl alcohol, *n*-propyl alcohol, isopropyl alcohol, propionaldehyde, acetone.
(c) Methyl *n*-propyl ketone, diethyl ketone, 3-hydroxy-2-butanone, butyraldehyde.
(d) *n*-Hexane, *n*-hexyl alcohol, 2-hexanol, 3-hexanol, 3-methyl-3-pentanol.
(e) Methyl *n*-propyl ketone, methyl-*n*-propylcarbinol, diethylcarbinol, valeraldehyde, diethyl ketone.

4. Outline by means of equations, not necessarily balanced but with all conditions and reagents indicated, practical methods for accomplishing each of the following conversions. So long as continuity is maintained, any desired reagents may be used.

(a) $CH_3-\underset{\underset{O}{\|}}{C}-CH_3 \longrightarrow CH_3-\underset{\underset{CH_3}{|}}{\overset{\overset{CH_3}{|}}{C}}-\underset{\underset{OH}{|}}{CH}-C_2H_5$ (*via* trimethylacetic acid, obtained by hypohalite oxidation of pinacolone)

(b) $HC\equiv CH \longrightarrow CH_3-\underset{\underset{CH_3}{|}}{C}=CH-\underset{\underset{O}{\|}}{C}-CH_3$ (*via* acetone)

(c) $CH_3-(CH_2)_3-Br \longrightarrow C_2H_5-\underset{\underset{O}{\|}}{C}-CH_3$

(d) $H-\underset{\underset{O}{\|}}{C}-CH_2-CH_2-CO_2C_2H_5 \longrightarrow H-\underset{\underset{O}{\|}}{C}-CH_2-CH_2-\underset{\underset{CH_3}{|}}{\overset{\overset{CH_3}{|}}{C}}-OH$

(e) 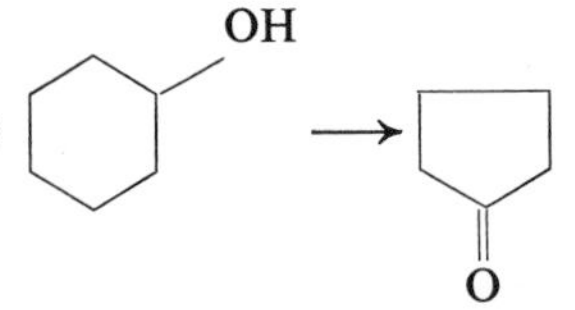 $\longrightarrow$

(f) $CH_3-CHO \longrightarrow HO_2C-\underset{\underset{CH_3}{|}}{CH}-CH_2-CH_2-CO_2H$ (*via* $HO-\underset{\underset{CH_3}{|}}{CH}-CH_2-CHO$)

(g) $CH_3-CHO \longrightarrow OHC-CH_2-\underset{\underset{CH_3}{|}}{CH}-CH_2-CH_2-CH_2-CHO$ (*via* Exercise f)

(h) $CH_3-CH_2-CHO \longleftarrow CH_3-CH_2-CH_2-\underset{\underset{CH_3}{|}}{CH}-CH_2-CO_2H$

(i) $HC\equiv CH \longrightarrow HO_2C-\underset{\underset{CH_3}{|}}{CH}-CH_2-CO_2H$

(j) $HC\equiv CH \longrightarrow$ pentaerythritol tetranitrate (PETN)

5. If you were using each of the following compounds as starting material in a synthesis where anhydrous pure reagents were required, how would you obtain each for this purpose from the material supplied commercially?

(a) Formaldehyde. (b) Acetaldehyde. (c) Acetone.
(d) Palmitaldehyde. (e) Trimethylacetaldehyde.

6. Indicate by equations, not necessarily balanced but with all conditions and reagents specified, practical methods for accomplishing each of the following conversions. All organic compounds (except solvents) must be prepared from the compounds indicated on the left (metallic cyanides and carbonates are not commonly regarded as organic compounds).

(a) Acetone
   methyl bromide

$$CH_3-\overset{\overset{\displaystyle CH_3}{|}}{\underset{\underset{\displaystyle CH_3}{|}}{C}}-\overset{\overset{\displaystyle CH_3}{|}}{\underset{\underset{\displaystyle OH}{|}}{C}}-CH_3$$

(b) Acetaldehyde $\longrightarrow C_3H_7-\underset{\underset{\displaystyle OH}{|}}{CH}-CO_2H$

7. If the pinacol reduction were carried out according to the following equation, and the reaction were worked up after adding water, what organic compounds (condensed structural formulas) would you expect as products of the main reactions?

$$C_2H_5-\overset{\overset{\displaystyle }{}}{\underset{\underset{\displaystyle O}{||}}{C}}-CH_3 + C_2H_5-\overset{\overset{\displaystyle }{}}{\underset{\underset{\displaystyle O}{||}}{C}}-C_3H_7 + Mg \longrightarrow$$

8. If the following compound were subjected to the pinacol rearrangement, what compounds (condensed structural formulas) would you expect to be formed?

$$C_2H_5-\overset{\overset{\displaystyle CH_3}{|}}{\underset{\underset{\displaystyle OH}{|}}{C}}-\overset{\overset{\displaystyle C_3H_7}{|}}{\underset{\underset{\displaystyle OH}{|}}{C}}-C_2H_5$$

9. Give one name for each of the compounds whose formulas you have written as answers to Exercises 7 and 8.

10. Write the formulas and names for all the organic compounds that would be expected if aldol condensations were carried out on the following.

(a) Equimolar amounts of propionaldehyde and *n*-butyraldehyde.
(b) Methyl ethyl ketone.
(c) Equimolar amounts of methyl *n*-propyl ketone and ethyl *n*-butyl ketone.

11. If crotonaldehyde is subjected to treatment with dilute alkali (the conditions for the aldol condensation) one of the products obtained is the following:

$$CH_3-CH{=}CH-\underset{\underset{\displaystyle OH}{|}}{CH}-CH_2-CH{=}CH-\overset{\overset{\displaystyle O}{\diagup\!\!}}{\underset{\underset{\displaystyle H}{\diagdown}}{C}}$$

Explain how the ion necessary to yield this product is resonance-stabilized.

12. Outline a conversion of acetaldehyde to the following compound:

$$CH_3—CH=CH—CH_2—CO_2H$$

Mention should be made of any unusual separations that may be necessary during the synthesis.

This conversion involves some interesting chemistry encountered in handling allylic systems. For example, if the intermediate 1-bromo-2-butene is converted to the Grignard reagent, which is in turn carbonated to yield the acid, a part of the product is the expected acid, but there is also formed a considerable amount of the isomer which probably results from the following transition state:

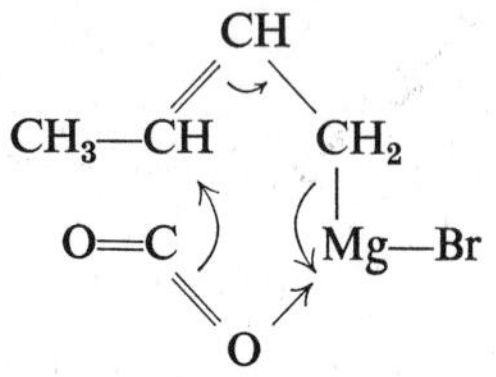

Write the structure of the product that would result from this transition state. Also review the mechanism of the Grignard reaction and the normal type of transition state (Chap. 13).

This mixture of products may be avoided by proceeding by way of the nitrile. If the nitrile is hydrolyzed with acid catalysis, double bond rearrangement is possible (review acid-catalyzed alkene rearrangement in Chap. 9); however, it proves to be quite slow in the dilute acid ordinarily used for catalysis of hydrolysis, so the desired product is obtained in a rather pure condition. If basic catalysis is used, however, there is equilibration of the nitrile with an ion (similar to an enolate ion) much more rapidly than hydrolysis of the nitrile, as follows:

$$CH_3—CH=CH—CH_2—C\equiv N + {}^-OH \rightleftharpoons CH_3—CH=CH—CH—C\equiv N + HOH$$

Write resonance structures of this ion which will explain formation of large amounts of the following α,β-unsaturated acid when base-catalyzed hydrolysis is used:

$$CH_3—CH_2—CH=CH—CO_2H$$

Substituted Acids
as Typical
Polyfunctional Compounds

In polyfunctional compounds, that is, compounds having more than one functional group, each group may give the reactions characteristic of that group when present alone in a molecule, but this is not always the case. Certain reactions of polyfunctional compounds obtained from aldol condensations have been discussed in the preceding chapter. In that discussion, it was emphasized that reagents giving a desired reaction with one functional group may also attack another functional group in some undesirable manner. Frequently it is necessary to protect one functional group (for example, cf. Eq. 15-36) while a conversion is carried out on another. It is clear, then, that successful synthetic manipulation of polyfunctional compounds requires more alertness and more thorough knowledge than is the case with monofunctional compounds.

In addition to the possibilities for the reaction of more than one group with the same reagents, there are two important additional matters which must be considered in connection with the chemistry of polyfunctional compounds:

(a) Rate of reaction (occasionally, kind of reaction) of a given functional group may be affected by a neighboring functional group.

(b) Properly spaced groups within a given molecule may react with each other; that is, intramolecular reaction may occur.

Although effects of the types just mentioned occur only when the functional groups are reasonably close to each other in the molecule, many of these reactions are quite important, and illustrative ones will be discussed in the present chapter. The substituted acids, compounds containing carboxyl in addition to some other group, include many very important types of compounds and may appropriately serve for a study of typical polyfunctional compounds. Although any other functional group may occur in the same molecule with a carboxyl group, the substituted acids considered at this time will be the halogen acids and hydroxy acids. The very important amino acids will be considered in Chapter 25.

Nomenclature

The naming of polyfunctional compounds has been discussed in connection with the nomenclature of each class of compounds. In each instance, the only specific information needed is the name of the group when it is classed as a substituent. In the naming of substituted acids, the other groups are named as substituents, and the acid is used as the basic name. Simple examples may be added as illustrations.

$$CH_3\text{—}CH\text{—}CO_2H \qquad HO\text{—}CH_2\text{—}CH_2\text{—}CH_2\text{—}CO_2H$$
$$\underset{\displaystyle Br}{|}$$

α-Bromopropionic acid   γ-Hydroxybutyric acid
2-Bromopropanoic acid   ω-Hydroxybutyric acid
                              4-Hydroxybutanoic acid

It should be noted that omega, ω, the last letter of the Greek alphabet, may be conveniently used to indicate a substituent at the opposite end of the chain from carboxyl.

Halogen Acids

Although halogen-substituted acids are very rarely found in nature, their synthesis may be accomplished in several ways, and they are very important intermediates in organic synthesis.

The presence of two functional groups renders the halogen acids relatively high-boiling and high-melting. For example, bromoacetic acid boils at 208° and melts at about 50°. The α-**halogen acids** and esters have certain very characteristic and rather unique properties. The α-halogen esters are very powerful lachrymators. A few drops of ethyl bromoacetate spilled in a laboratory is enough to drive out the occupants. The α-halogen acids are very corrosive to the skin, and cause painful burns that heal slowly. Substitution of halogen in an acid increases the acid strength (per cent dissociation in solution) very markedly. As has been discussed in Chapter 13, this effect is attributed to the powerful electron-attracting influence of halogen.

Synthesis of Halogen Acids

The methods used for synthesis of halogen acids depend on the position of halogen relative to carboxyl, so methods will be discussed separately for three different types of halogen acids.

α–Halogen acids. Although halogen does not substitute especially readily (no more so than in alkanes) in the alpha position of acids, a relatively facile substitution does occur in the acid derivatives in which the hydroxyl in the carboxyl group has been replaced. This no doubt results from the fact that hydrogen-bonding in the acid (cf. Chap. 13) gives a stable species which shifts the equilibrium in Eq. 1 far to the right so as to reduce the concentration of

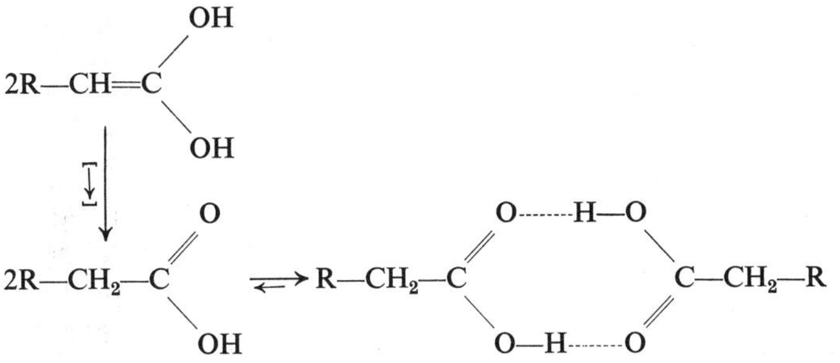

$$2R—CH{=}C\overset{\displaystyle OH}{\underset{\displaystyle OH}{}}$$

$$\downarrow$$

$$2R—CH_2—C\overset{\displaystyle O}{\underset{\displaystyle OH}{}} \quad\rightleftharpoons\quad R—CH_2—C\overset{O\text{------}H—O}{\underset{O—H\text{------}O}{}}C—CH_2—R \qquad (1)$$

enol form in an acid virtually to zero. Facile α-substitution in acid derivatives proceeds by reaction with the enol form (Eq. 2), in an uncompleted addition

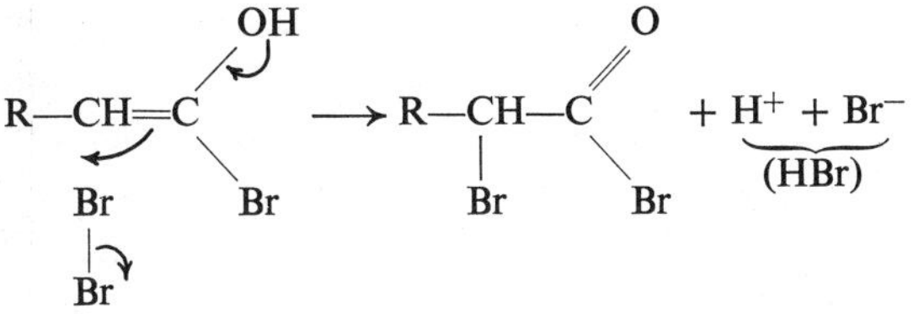

$$R—CH{=}C\overset{\displaystyle OH}{\underset{\displaystyle Br}{}} \quad\longrightarrow\quad R—CH—C\overset{\displaystyle O}{\underset{\displaystyle Br}{}} + H^+ + Br^- \qquad (2)$$
$$\underset{Br}{} \qquad\qquad\qquad \underset{Br}{} \qquad \underset{(HBr)}{}$$

reaction of the type which has been described for other carbonyl compounds (cf. Eq. 15-13). Failure of acids to give the facile α-substitution follows from the near-absence of enol form in the acid (Eq. 1).

For synthesis of the α-bromo acid, it is feasible to hydrolyze the bromo acid bromide selectively (Eq. 3), for an acid bromide is far more reactive than

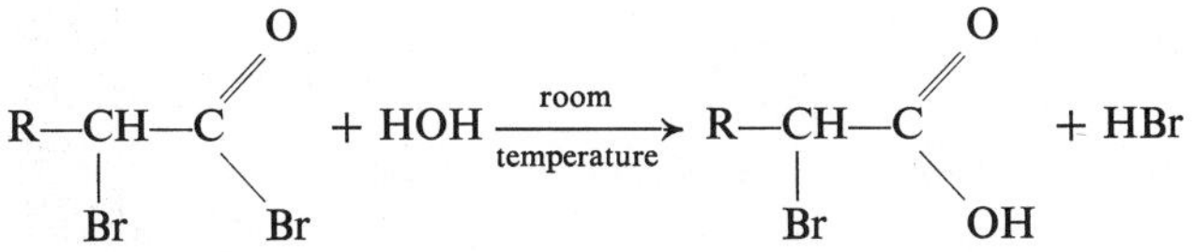

$$R—CH—C\overset{\displaystyle O}{\underset{\displaystyle Br}{}} + HOH \xrightarrow[\text{temperature}]{\text{room}} R—CH—C\overset{\displaystyle O}{\underset{\displaystyle OH}{}} + HBr \qquad (3)$$
$$\underset{Br}{}$$

an alkyl halide (cf. discussion in Chap. 13). As a matter of fact, as will be discussed further in connection with the reactions of bromo acids, halogen alpha to a carboxyl is much more reactive than normal for alkyl halides, on account of the electron-attracting influence of carboxyl. In spite of this enhanced reactivity of the α-halogen, the acid bromide is so much more reactive that the selective hydrolysis shown in Eq. 3 is clean-cut.

Although the sequence shown in Eqs. 2 and 3 results in high-yield conversion of an acid to the corresponding α-bromo acid, usually it is more convenient to accomplish this net conversion by a subterfuge known as the Hell-Volhard-Zelinsky reaction. In this process, equimolar quantities of bromine and acid are heated with a few drops of the acid chloride, or a reagent such as PBr_3 which will convert a little acid to the acid halide (cf. Eq. 13-18). *Under these conditions, all the acid is converted to bromo acid.* The catalytic effect of a little acid halide depends on the chain reaction represented in Eqs. 4 and 5. The

$$R-CH_2-COBr + Br_2 \longrightarrow R-\underset{\underset{Br}{|}}{CH}-COBr + HBr \qquad (4)$$

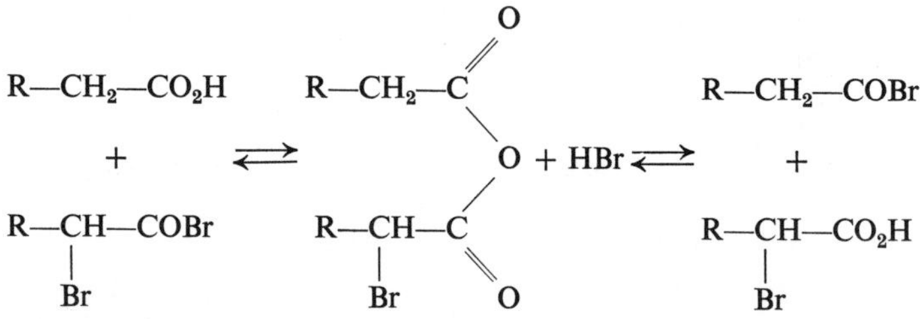

$$
\begin{array}{c}
R-CH_2-CO_2H \\
+ \\
R-\underset{\underset{Br}{|}}{CH}-COBr
\end{array}
\rightleftarrows
\begin{array}{c}
R-CH_2-C{\overset{O}{\underset{O}{\diagup\!\!\!\diagdown}}} \\
\diagdown \\
R-\underset{\underset{Br}{|}}{CH}-C{\overset{}{\underset{O}{\diagdown\!\!\!\diagup}}}
\end{array}
+ HBr \rightleftarrows
\begin{array}{c}
R-CH_2-COBr \\
+ \\
R-\underset{\underset{Br}{|}}{CH}-CO_2H
\end{array}
\qquad (5)
$$

catalytic amount of acid bromide is converted to the bromo acid bromide in normal manner (Eq. 4). The bromo acid bromide and unbrominated acid will then react to form an equilibrium with the mixed anhydride and hydrogen bromide (Eq. 5). This is the same reaction as the normal synthesis of an acid anhydride (Eq. 14-1) from an acid chloride and the anion of the acid, except that the reaction goes essentially to completion when the anion of the acid is used. It is apparent that the anhydride shown in Eq. 5 may equilibrate with either the materials from which it was initially formed or with the bromo acid and unbrominated acid bromide (right-hand equilibrium). The direction of reaction depends on which carbonyl group in the mixed anhydride is attacked by bromide ion from HBr. Since there is used an amount of bromine equivalent to the acid, as unbrominated acid bromide appears in the equilibrium in Eq. 5 it is consumed in the non-reversible process in Eq. 4. Thus, the equilibria involved in Eq. 5 are constantly drawn to the right by removal of acid bromide until all the acid has been converted to bromo acid. Only the catalytic amount of bromo acid bromide remains at the end of the reaction, and this may be recovered, if so desired, by addition of a little water.

Of course other equilibria besides that shown in Eq. 5 are active. For example, simple anhydrides from the bromo acid and the unbrominated acid would be present, and the simple anhydride $R-CH_2-CO-O-CO-CH_2-R$ would be α-brominated. This furnishes an alternate route to the mixed anhydride which equilibrates (Eq. 5) to furnish bromo acid.

β-**Halogen acids** may be conveniently made from the α,β-unsaturated acids (Eq. 6), prepared in turn from the α-halogen acids (cf. Eq. 19).

$$R—CH{=}CH—CO_2H + HBr \longrightarrow R—\underset{\underset{Br}{|}}{CH}—CH_2—CO_2H \qquad (6)$$

(or HCl or HI)

Addition of halogen occurs exclusively as shown, with no addition of halogen to the alpha carbon. This probably is because the beta carbon is rendered considerably more positive by the occurrence of a formal plus charge on two of the three charged resonance forms contributing to the character of the α,β-unsaturated acid:

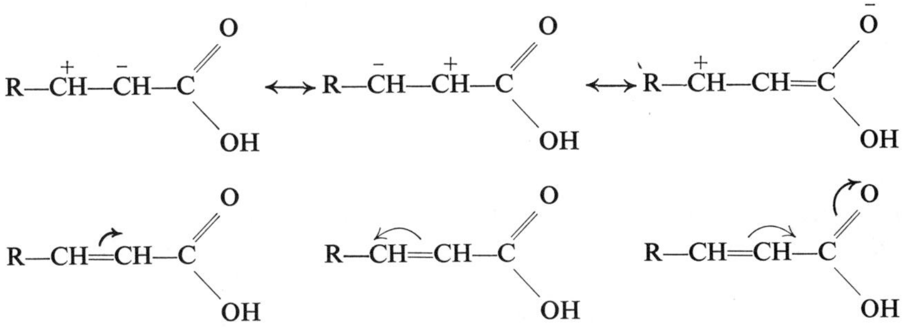

In the lower line of formulas are displayed the electron shifts leading to the resonance forms in the upper line. The steps in the addition reaction probably involve initial attack of a proton on the carbonyl group (Eq. 7), followed by

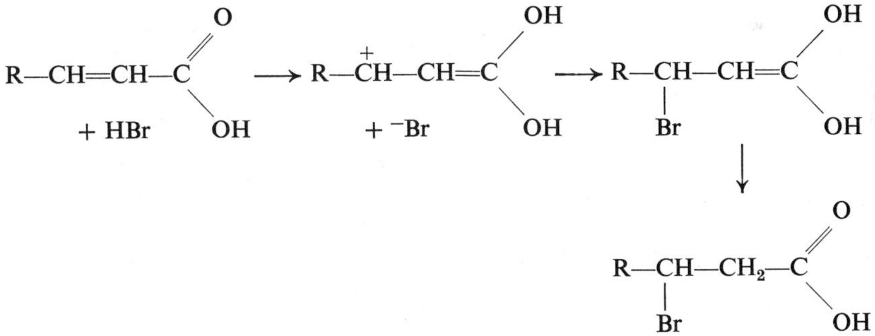

addition of halide ion in a 1,4-manner to give the enol form of the β-bromo acid, which rearranges to the more stable carbonyl form.

Other halogen acids. Numerous halogen acids are known in which halogen and carboxyl are separated by varying numbers of carbon atoms; however, general synthesis of only one other type will be discussed at this time. This type may be termed the ω-**halogen acids,** and it is selected because it is quite useful in synthesis and may be prepared from dibasic acids of the type,

$HO_2C—(CH_2)_n—CO_2H$. Such dibasic acids up to $n = 8$ are available commercially, and are therefore convenient starting materials for synthesis. The sequence leading to the ω-halogen acid is shown in Eqs. 8 through 11.

$$HO_2C—(CH_2)_n—CO_2H + C_2H_5OH \underset{H^+}{\overset{}{\rightleftarrows}} C_2H_5O_2C—(CH_2)_n—CO_2H + HOH$$

$$\text{(equivalent amount)} \quad \updownarrow C_2H_5OH \qquad (8)$$

$$C_2H_5O_2C—(CH_2)_n—CO_2C_2H_5 + HOH$$

$$C_2H_5O_2C—(CH_2)_n—CO_2H + NaOH \longrightarrow C_2H_5O_2C—(CH_2)_n—CO_2Na + HOH$$

(separated by fractional   (to pH 10) $\downarrow$ AgNO$_3$
distillation)   (9)

$$C_2H_5O_2C—(CH_2)_n—CO_2Ag + NaNO_3$$

$$\text{(precipitates)}$$

$$C_2H_5O_2C—(CH_2)_n—CO_2Ag + Br_2 \longrightarrow C_2H_5O_2C—(CH_2)_n—Br + CO_2 + AgBr$$

$$(10)$$

$$Br—(CH_2)_n—CO_2C_2H_5 + HOH \xrightarrow[\text{catalysis}]{HBr} Br—(CH_2)_n—CO_2H + C_2H_5OH \quad (11)$$

This process is very useful, indeed, for making bromo esters and bromo acids; furthermore, the reaction shown in Eq. 10 may be used for making simple alkyl halides from carboxylic acids. This latter conversion is especially useful for obtaining **odd-carbon alkyl halides,** for a carbon is lost in the reaction and the *even-carbon* higher fatty acids are the ones available in nature (cf. Chap. 13).

Although Eqs. 8 through 11 are important as representing a useful synthesis, it should also be pointed out that these equations contain many important illustrations of principles of organic syntheses using polyfunctional compounds. In Eq. 8, the desired product is the half ester which can be obtained only as an equilibrium mixture with the di-ester and di-acid. Such processes are ordinarily not recommended for practical synthesis of a single compound; however, this particular synthesis is quite practical for two reasons: the three compounds differ in boiling point by about 40°, hence are easily separated by fractional distillation; the two unwanted products are not a loss, but may be re-equilibrated to give more of the desired product in subsequent preparations. The process shown in Eq. 8 is used only with acids in which n is greater than 3, for if $n = 2$ or 3 a nearly quantitative conversion may be accomplished by proceeding through the anhydride to the half ester (cf. Eqs. 14-2 and 14-7). It should be mentioned that the preparation of half esters is a rather important topic, for they have many uses in synthesis. In one sense, they may be regarded as substituted acids.

In Eq. 9, the acid may be titrated by use of an acid-base indicator with no danger of hydrolyzing the ester group. Addition of silver nitrate then gives the desired silver salt whereas silver oxide would be precipitated in more strongly basic solution. In the hydrolysis of the bromo ester (Eq. 11), alkaline saponification would hydrolyze the halide to hydroxyl, but acid-catalyzed hydrolysis (using the same halogen in the acid as in the bromo ester) gives the desired bromo acid.

The reaction in Eq. 10 is a remarkable conversion, known as the **Huns-diecker reaction,** which usually gives a moderately good yield. Although some details of the mechanism of this reaction remain uncertain, it is known to proceed through several intermediate steps in which free radicals are involved. Essential features of the sequence are presented in Eqs. 12 through 14. This

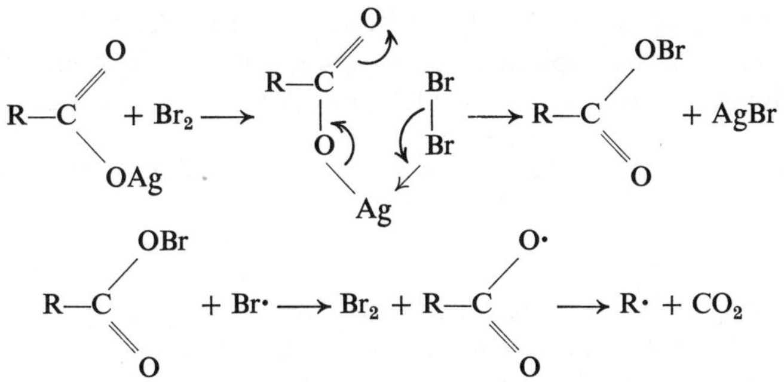

$$R-C{\overset{O}{\underset{OAg}{}}} + Br_2 \longrightarrow \quad R-C{\overset{O}{\underset{O}{}}}\;{\overset{Br}{\underset{Br}{}}} \longrightarrow R-C{\overset{OBr}{\underset{O}{}}} + AgBr \qquad (12)$$

$$R-C{\overset{OBr}{\underset{O}{}}} + Br\cdot \longrightarrow Br_2 + R-C{\overset{O\cdot}{\underset{O}{}}} \longrightarrow R\cdot + CO_2 \qquad (13)$$

$$R\cdot + Br-Br \longrightarrow R-Br + Br\cdot \qquad (14)$$

will be recognized as a chain reaction, for the bromine atoms generated in Eq. 14 are consumed in extraction of halogen from the hypobromite (Eq. 13). The most likely source of bromine atoms to serve as initiators of the chain reaction is slow dissociation of the acyl hypobromite into the acyloxy radical and bromine atom. Since the acyloxy radical rapidly cracks to alkyl as shown in Eq. 13 (and discussed in Chap. 11), the alkyl halide could result from recombination of the alkyl radical and bromine atom; however, this must be a minor source of the product, for R—R is a very minor by-product. Furthermore, the Huns-diecker reaction behaves like a chain reaction; after an induction period, it proceeds rapidly.

Reactions of Halogen Acids

If halogen is substituted in the **gamma position or more remotely** from carboxyl, the reactions are the normal ones for an alkyl halide and an acid. A sufficient number of carbons separates the two functional groups so that there is no effect of neighboring groups. When the halogen is gamma or delta to carboxyl, there is the opportunity for intramolecular reactions (cf. following discussion of hydroxy acids); however, the salt is the only acid derivative with which an alkyl halide reacts readily (cf. Eq. 14-22). The salts of gamma or

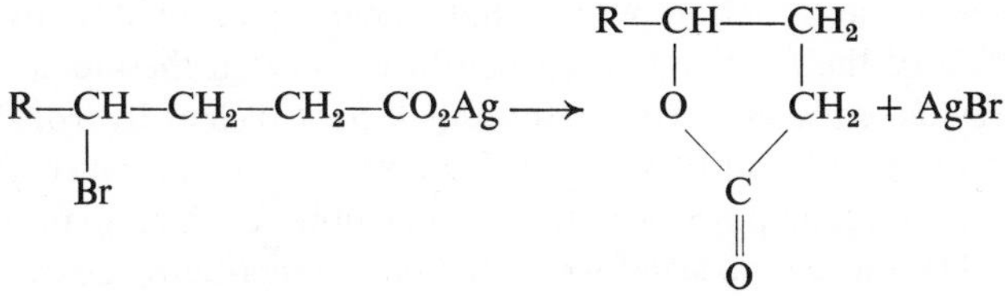

$$R-CH-CH_2-CH_2-CO_2Ag \longrightarrow \quad {\overset{R-CH{-}\!\!-{-}CH_2}{\underset{Br}{}}} \quad {\overset{}{\underset{O \quad CH_2}{}}} + AgBr \qquad (15)$$

A γ-lactone

delta halogen acids, especially the silver salts, are usually converted rapidly to the cyclic ester known as a **lactone.** Lactones are more frequently formed from hydroxy acids and are discussed in more detail under that heading in this chapter.

β-**Halogen acids** are converted to the α,β-unsaturated acids so readily that many reactions in which halogen is normally replaced cannot compete successfully with the elimination of halogen acid. For example, sodium cyanide is sufficiently basic so that replacement by cyanide fails and the principal reaction becomes elimination (Eq. 16). The elimination reaction occurs so easily because

$$R—CH—CH_2—CO_2H + NaCN \longrightarrow R—CH{=}CH—CO_2H + NaBr + HCN$$
$$\underset{Br}{|}$$

$$(16)$$

the neighboring carboxyl group, which is electron-attracting, lowers the electron density on the adjacent carbon and makes the attached hydrogens more easily removed as protons (cf. Eq. 9-1 and accompanying discussion).

α–**Halogen acids,** with the two functional groups on the same carbon, prove to be quite useful in synthesis, partly because of the ease with which they can be synthesized (Eqs. 4 and 5).

(1) DISPLACEMENT REACTIONS. The halogen in α-halogen acids gives the usual displacement reactions of alkyl halides, but the rate of reaction is considerably higher than normal. This results from the low electron density on the alpha carbon, just mentioned above, which makes this carbon much more attractive to nucleophiles. Typical displacement reactions are shown in Eqs. 17 and 18.

$$R—CH—CO_2H + {}^-OH \xrightarrow[\text{or Na}_2\text{CO}_3]{\text{dilute NaOH}} R—CH—CO_2H + Br^- \qquad (17)$$
$$\underset{Br}{|} \qquad\qquad\qquad\qquad\qquad \underset{OH}{|}$$

$$R—CH—CO_2H + NaCN \xrightarrow{\text{rapid}} R—CH—CO_2H + NaBr \qquad (18)$$
$$\underset{Br}{|} \qquad\qquad\qquad\qquad \underset{CN}{|}$$

(2) ELIMINATION REACTIONS. Elimination of halogen acid from an α-halo acid is a very useful reaction for making α,β-unsaturated acids; however, this elimination must be carried out under rather special conditions on account of the ease with which displacement of the halogen occurs. This is just the opposite of the situation with β-halo acids, and this follows logically from the effect of the relatively low electron density on the alpha carbon. An effort to carry out the elimination with a small base such as hydroxide ion leads principally to displacement of halogen; however, steric hindrance may be used to advantage to accomplish the desired reaction (cf. Chap. 6, **Competition between elimination and displacement**). If potassium t-butoxide is used as the base, the bulky t-butoxide ion is so crowded in the transition state involved in

displacement reactions (cf. Fig. 6-1) that the halogen is not displaced by this ion at a competitive rate. This allows the desired elimination to occur in good yield by attack of butoxide ion on the beta hydrogen (Eq. 19), for this does not

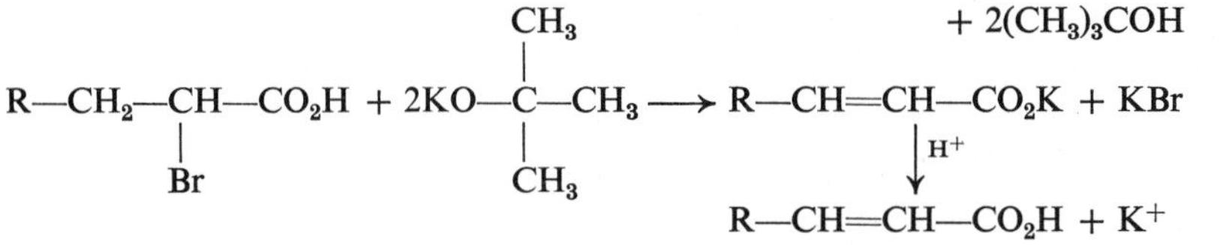

$$
\begin{array}{c}
\text{CH}_3 \qquad\qquad\qquad + 2(\text{CH}_3)_3\text{COH} \\
| \\
\text{R—CH}_2\text{—CH—CO}_2\text{H} + 2\text{KO—C—CH}_3 \longrightarrow \text{R—CH=CH—CO}_2\text{K} + \text{KBr} \\
| \qquad\qquad\qquad | \qquad\qquad\qquad\qquad\Big\downarrow {}^{\text{H}^+} \\
\text{Br} \qquad\qquad\quad \text{CH}_3 \qquad\qquad\qquad\qquad\quad\downarrow \\
\text{R—CH=CH—CO}_2\text{H} + \text{K}^+
\end{array}
\tag{19}
$$

involve crowding the butoxide ion and four other atoms around a single atom (cf. Eq. 9-2). After completion of the elimination reaction, the unsaturated acid is freed from its salt by addition of a strong inorganic acid, as shown in the equation.

(3) REFORMATSKY REACTION. One of the most useful reactions of the esters of α-halogen acids is a reaction with zinc which bears a formal resemblance to the Grignard reaction which employs magnesium. The reaction with zinc is satisfactory, however, only in the case of the α-halogenated ester. Also, the aldehyde or ketone with which reaction is desired must be included in the reaction mixture as the zinc is allowed to react with the ester. The net reaction is shown in Eq. 20.

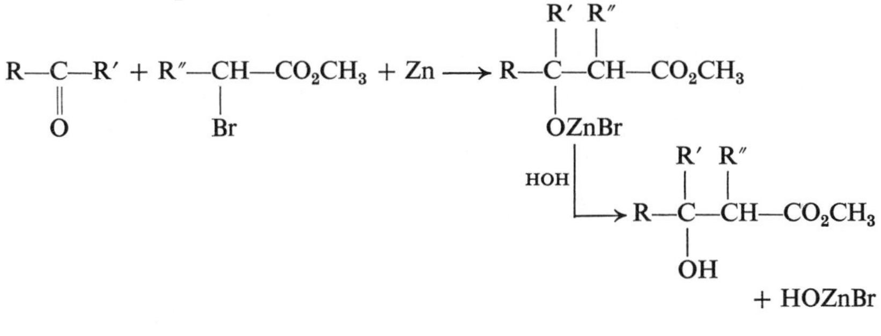

$$
\begin{array}{c}
\qquad\qquad\qquad\qquad\qquad\quad \text{R}' \ \text{R}'' \\
\qquad\qquad\qquad\qquad\qquad\quad | \ \ | \\
\text{R—C—R}' + \text{R}''\text{—CH—CO}_2\text{CH}_3 + \text{Zn} \longrightarrow \text{R—C—CH—CO}_2\text{CH}_3 \\
\ \ \| \qquad\qquad\quad | \qquad\qquad\qquad\qquad\qquad\quad | \\
\ \ \text{O} \qquad\qquad\quad \text{Br} \qquad\qquad\qquad\qquad\qquad \text{OZnBr} \\
\qquad\qquad\qquad\qquad\qquad\qquad\qquad\qquad\qquad\quad \text{R}' \ \text{R}'' \\
\qquad\qquad\qquad\qquad\qquad {}_{\text{HOH}}\Big| \qquad\qquad\qquad\quad | \ \ | \\
\qquad\qquad\qquad\qquad\qquad\qquad \big\llcorner\!\!\rightarrow \text{R—C—CH—CO}_2\text{CH}_3 \\
\qquad\qquad\qquad\qquad\qquad\qquad\qquad\qquad\qquad\quad | \\
\qquad\qquad\qquad\qquad\qquad\qquad\qquad\qquad\qquad \text{OH} \\
\qquad\qquad\qquad\qquad\qquad\qquad\qquad\qquad + \text{HOZnBr}
\end{array}
\tag{20}
$$

This reaction is quite versatile with respect to structure of starting materials. Either an aldehyde or ketone may be used, and the bromo ester may be primary, secondary or tertiary. Thus, in addition to the secondary bromo ester shown in Eq. 20, there may be used methyl bromoacetate or an α-bromo-α-alkyl ester. The methyl ester is designated arbitrarily because it is relatively cheap; other esters may be used.

The nature of the organozinc compound which is an intermediate in the first step of the reaction shown in Eq. 20 is not known with certainty, but it is probably the zinc enolate of the ester—this is consistent with the requirement of an α-halo ester. A plausible mechanism for formation of this enolate is shown in Eq. 21. Since the Reformatsky reaction is carried out in non-ionizing solvents such as benzene and ether, it is probable that the zinc enolate does not ionize to give the enolate ion. It is more probable that zinc coordinates with the carbonyl oxygen in the manner that has been discussed for the Grignard reaction (cf. Eq. 13-17). In the case of the enolate, only a single mole of organo-metallic reagent is required to give the six-atom cyclic transition state which can serve as a relatively low-energy transition state for yielding the primary product of the Reformatsky reaction (Eq. 22).

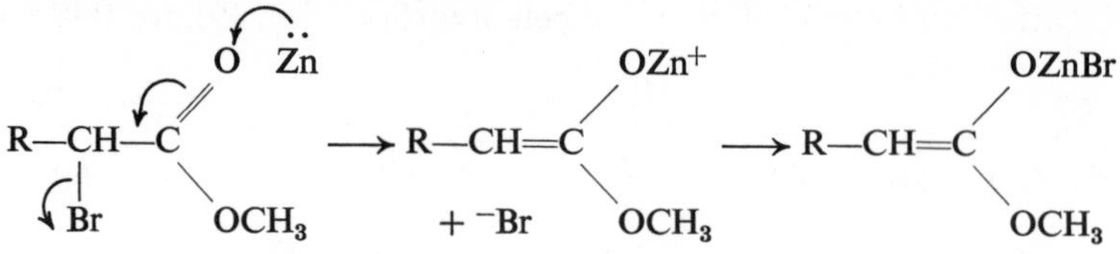

$$
\underset{\substack{| \\ Br}}{\overset{\overset{O \quad \ddot{Z}n}{\diagup}}{R-CH-C}}\diagdown_{OCH_3} \longrightarrow \underset{+ \ ^-Br}{R-CH=C}\diagdown_{OCH_3} \longrightarrow R-CH=C\diagdown_{OCH_3}^{OZnBr} \tag{21}
$$

$$
\begin{array}{c} R'-CH \quad Zn-Br \\ | \\ R-CH \quad O \\ \diagdown \quad \diagup \\ C \\ | \\ OCH_3 \end{array} \longrightarrow R'-CH-\underset{\substack{| \\ R}}{CH}-C\diagdown_{OCH_3}^{O} \tag{22}
$$

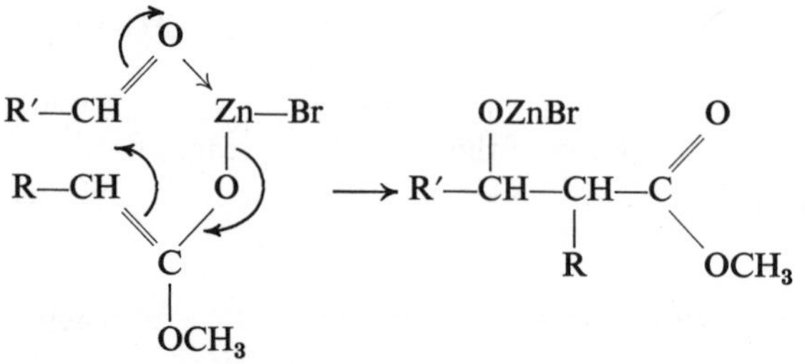

(4) UTILIZATION OF THE REFORMATSKY REACTION IN SYNTHESIS. The Reformatsky reaction is probably the best of all known methods for synthesis of β-hydroxy esters, a useful type of polyfunctional compound. The β-hydroxy ester may be converted to a β-bromo ester, in an alternate synthesis to that shown in Eq. 7 (the acid may be esterified or the ester hydrolyzed). If the hydroxyl is secondary, however, precautions must be observed to avoid rearrangement in the displacement of hydroxyl by halogen (cf. Chap. 6).

Dehydration of the β-hydroxy ester is usually not a satisfactory method for synthesis of an unsaturated acid, for a significant amount of dehydration usually occurs in the two positions shown in Eq. 23.

$$
\underset{\substack{| \\ OH}}{R-CH_2-CH-CH_2-CO_2CH_3} \xrightarrow{\text{dehydration}} R-CH=CH-CH_2-CO_2CH_3 + HOH
$$
$$
\text{and}
$$
$$
R-CH_2-CH=CH-CO_2CH_3 \tag{23}
$$
$$
\downarrow {\scriptstyle H_2, \ Pt \ catalyst}
$$
$$
R-CH_2-CH_2-CH_2-CO_2CH_3
$$

This mixture of unsaturated esters is quite useful in synthesis, however, for hydrogenation gives a single saturated ester as shown in Eq. 23. This process, then, of Reformatsky reaction, dehydration, and hydrogenation results in extending by two carbons the chain of the starting compound. By use of appropriate starting materials, branches may be introduced in the alpha or beta positions, concurrently with the chain extension.

Hydroxy Acids

The hydroxy acids occur very widely in nature, especially in fruits, and are responsible for the relatively sour taste of many fruits. A few of the more important naturally occurring hydroxy acids follow.

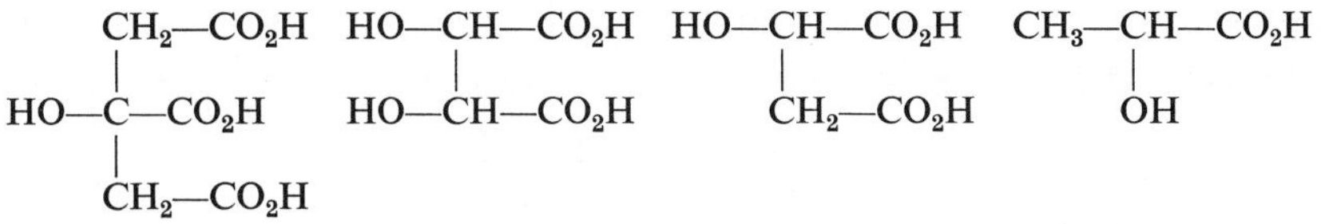

$$\begin{array}{llll}
CH_2\text{—}CO_2H & HO\text{—}CH\text{—}CO_2H & HO\text{—}CH\text{—}CO_2H & CH_3\text{—}CH\text{—}CO_2H \\
| & | & | & | \\
HO\text{—}C\text{—}CO_2H & HO\text{—}CH\text{—}CO_2H & CH_2\text{—}CO_2H & OH \\
| & & & \\
CH_2\text{—}CO_2H & & &
\end{array}$$

Citric acid	Tartaric acid	Malic acid	Lactic acid
(citrus fruits)	(grapes, wine, and grape juice)	(apples)	(sour milk, muscle metabolism)

Synthesis of Hydroxy Acids

α-**Hydroxy acids.** (1) HYDROLYSIS OF α-BROMO ACIDS (cf. Eq. 17) is more satisfactory than the usual hydrolysis of alkyl halides, on account of the slowness of the dehydrohalogenation reaction.

(2) HYDROLYSIS OF α-HYDROXYNITRILES, which has been described previously (cf. Eq. 15-30), is probably the most widely used synthesis of α-hydroxy acids.

β-**Hydroxy acids** are usually made from the corresponding esters obtained in the Reformatsky reaction (Eq. 20).

General synthesis of hydroxy acids. If the hydroxyl group is more remote from carbonyl than the beta position, reduction of a keto ester followed by saponification to the acid becomes a very useful general synthesis. Catalytic hydrogenation of the keto group without attack on the ester group, as shown in Eq. 24, is readily accomplished. The chemical reducing agent, sodium boro-

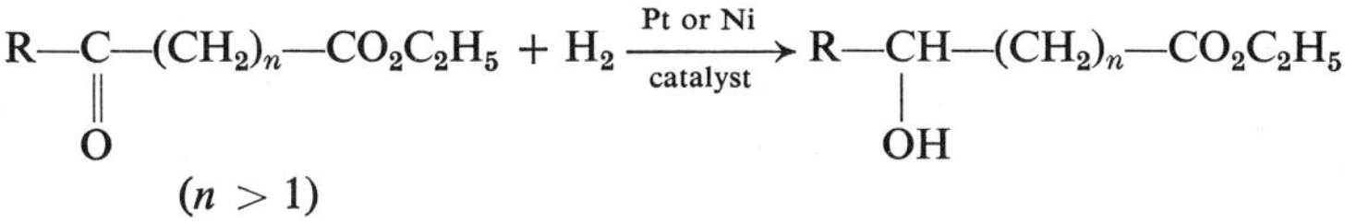

$$R\text{—}C\text{—}(CH_2)_n\text{—}CO_2C_2H_5 + H_2 \xrightarrow[\text{catalyst}]{\text{Pt or Ni}} R\text{—}CH\text{—}(CH_2)_n\text{—}CO_2C_2H_5 \quad (24)$$
$$\underset{O}{\overset{\|}{\phantom{R\text{—}C}}} \qquad\qquad\qquad\qquad \underset{OH}{\overset{|}{\phantom{R\text{—}CH}}}$$
$$(n > 1)$$

hydride, $NaBH_4$, also attacks keto selectively and leaves the ester group unaltered. A general and useful synthesis of keto esters (with keto more remote than the beta position) has been described in Chapter 14 (cf. Eq. 14-13 and related discussion).

Reactions of Hydroxy Acids

Most of the reactions of hydroxy acids are those normally expected from the functional groups present. For example, derivatives such as the following may be obtained as for the simple monofunctional compounds. An acid

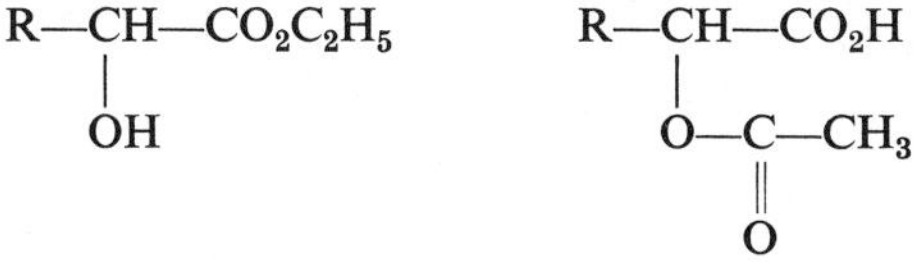

$$\begin{array}{ll}
R\text{—}CH\text{—}CO_2C_2H_5 & R\text{—}CH\text{—}CO_2H \\
| & | \\
OH & O\text{—}C\text{—}CH_3 \\
& \quad\quad\| \\
& \quad\quad O
\end{array}$$

A hydroxy ester   An acetoxy acid

chloride cannot be formed from a hydroxy acid without attack on the hydroxyl by the same reagent forming the acid chloride; however, the acetoxy acid may be converted to the acid chloride and thence to other derivatives.

Behavior of hydroxy acids on heating. If a hydroxy acid is heated, especially in the presence of a mineral acid, an ester is formed, but the type of ester depends on the number of carbons separating the two functional groups. As has been discussed in Chapter 7, the angle between the valences of carbon (and oxygen) is such that rings of five or six atoms are formed without strain of the normal valence angles. The formation of lactones (cyclic esters) from salts of gamma and delta halogen acids has already been mentioned (Eq. 15). The products formed on heating hydroxy acids, as shown in Eqs. 25 through 29, are quite consistent with the principle that rings of five or six atoms are the ones that are readily formed.

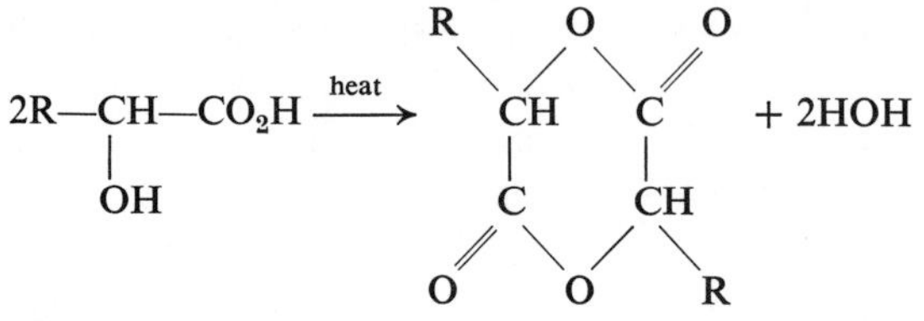

$$2R\text{—CH—CO}_2\text{H} \xrightarrow{\text{heat}} \quad + 2\text{HOH} \qquad (25)$$
$$\phantom{2R\text{—CH—}}\overset{|}{\text{OH}}$$

A lactide

$$R\text{—CH}_2\text{—CH—CH}_2\text{—CO}_2\text{H} \xrightarrow{\text{heat}} R\text{—CH=CH—CH}_2\text{—CO}_2\text{H} + \text{HOH} \quad (26)$$
$$\phantom{R\text{—CH}_2\text{—}}\overset{|}{\text{OH}} \qquad\qquad\qquad\quad \text{and} \qquad\qquad \text{and}$$
$$R\text{—CH}_2\text{—CH=CH—CO}_2\text{H} \quad \text{polyester}$$

$$R\text{—CH—CH}_2\text{—CH}_2\text{—CO}_2\text{H} \xrightarrow{\text{heat}} \qquad + \text{HOH} \qquad (27)$$
$$\phantom{R\text{—CH—}}\overset{|}{\text{OH}}$$

A γ-lactone

$$R\text{—CH—CH}_2\text{—CH}_2\text{—CH}_2\text{—CO}_2\text{H} \xrightarrow{\text{heat}} \qquad + \text{HOH} \qquad (28)$$
$$\phantom{R\text{—CH—}}\overset{|}{\text{OH}}$$

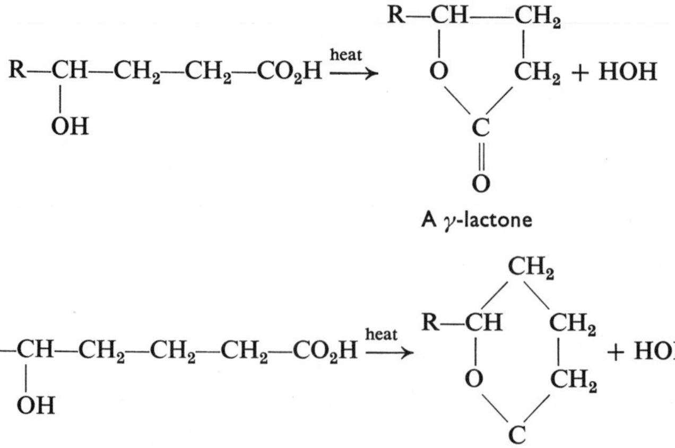

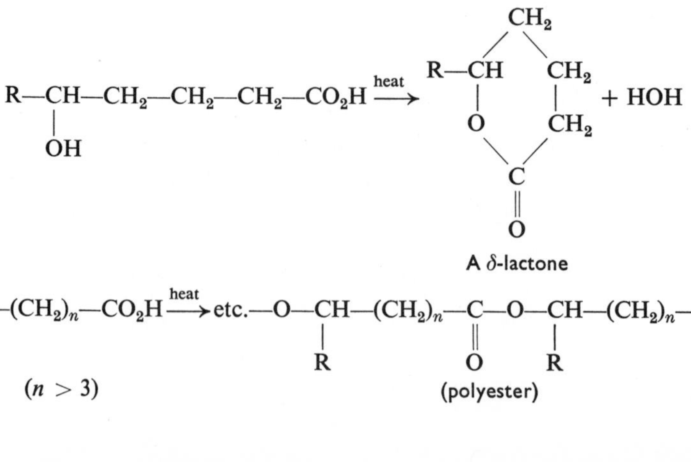

A δ-lactone

$$R\text{—CH—(CH}_2)_n\text{—CO}_2\text{H} \xrightarrow{\text{heat}} \text{etc.—O—CH—(CH}_2)_n\text{—C—O—CH—(CH}_2)_n\text{—C—etc.}$$
$$\phantom{R\text{—CH—(}}\overset{|}{\text{OH}} \qquad\qquad\qquad\qquad\quad \overset{|}{R} \qquad\quad \overset{\|}{O} \quad \overset{|}{R} \qquad\qquad \overset{\|}{O}$$
$$(n > 3) \qquad\qquad\qquad\qquad \text{(polyester)}$$
$$\qquad\qquad\qquad\qquad\qquad\qquad\qquad\qquad\qquad\qquad\qquad\qquad (29)$$

The interaction of strategically located groups within the same molecule to form cyclic structures occurs in numerous types of compounds, but the hydroxy acids well illustrate the principles involved. Additional important examples of this sort of intramolecular reaction will be described in connection with the chemistry of sugars (Chap. 23).

EXERCISES

1. Give one correct name for each of the following compounds.

(a) 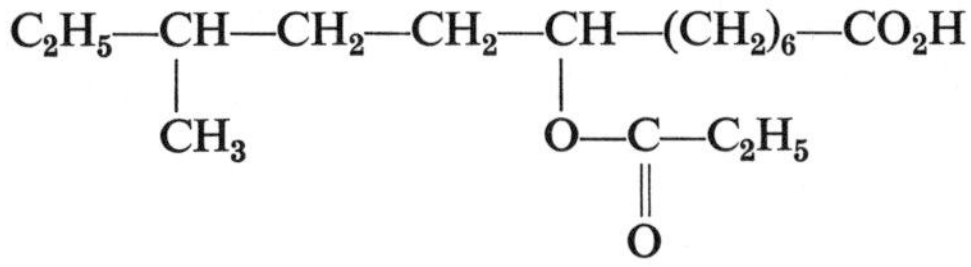 C_2H_5—CH—CH$_2$—CH$_2$—CH—(CH$_2$)$_6$—CO$_2$H
       | |
      CH$_3$ O—C—C$_2$H$_5$
                                       ‖
                                       O

(b) CH$_3$—C—CH$_2$—CH—CH$_2$—CH=CH—CO$_2$H
            ‖ |
            O   CH—CH$_3$
                         |
                        CH$_3$

(c) CH$_3$—CH—CH$_2$—CH—(CH$_2$)$_4$—C$\overset{\displaystyle O}{\diagup}$ H
         | | $\diagdown$
        OH   OH   N
                                             $\diagdown$
                                              CH$_3$

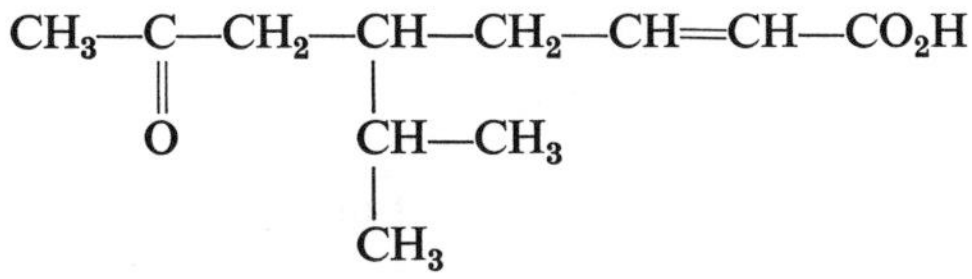

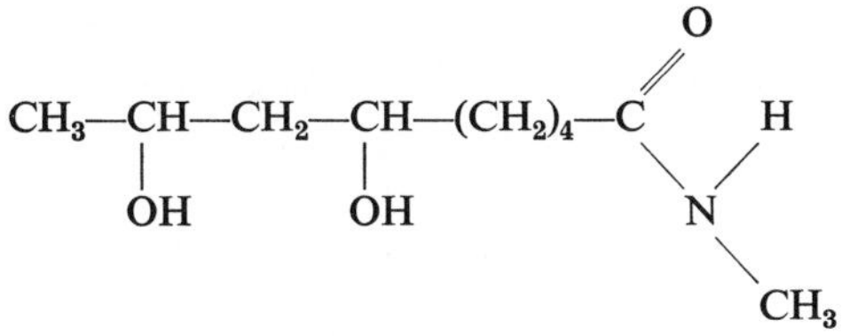

(d) 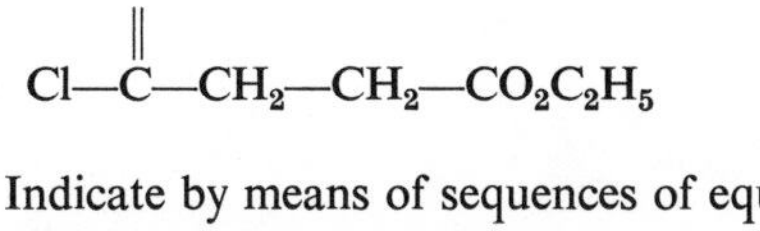 HO—CH$_2$—CH—CH$_2$—CO$_2$C$_2$H$_5$
              |
            C$_2$H$_5$

(e) 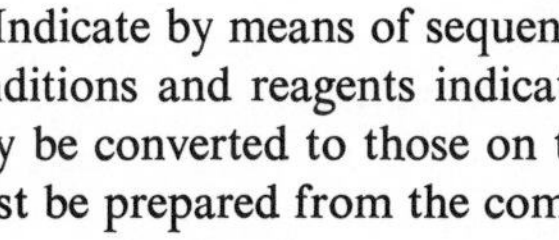 H—C—(CH$_2$)$_6$—CO$_2$C$_4$H$_9$
       ‖
       O

(f) 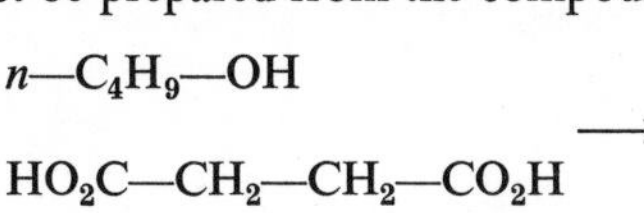 Cl—C—CH$_2$—CH$_2$—CO$_2$C$_2$H$_5$
        ‖
        O

2. Indicate by means of sequences of equations, not necessarily balanced but with all conditions and reagents indicated, how the compounds on the left in each instance may be converted to those on the right. Except for solvents, all organic compounds must be prepared from the compounds indicated as starting materials.

(a) n—C$_4$H$_9$—OH
                           $\longrightarrow n$—C$_7$H$_{15}$—CO$_2$H
     HO$_2$C—CH$_2$—CH$_2$—CO$_2$H

(b) n—C$_3$H$_7$—CO$_2$H
                           $\longrightarrow$ C$_4$H$_9$—CH=CH—CO$_2$H
     CH$_3$—CO$_2$H   (not mixed with β,γ-isomer)

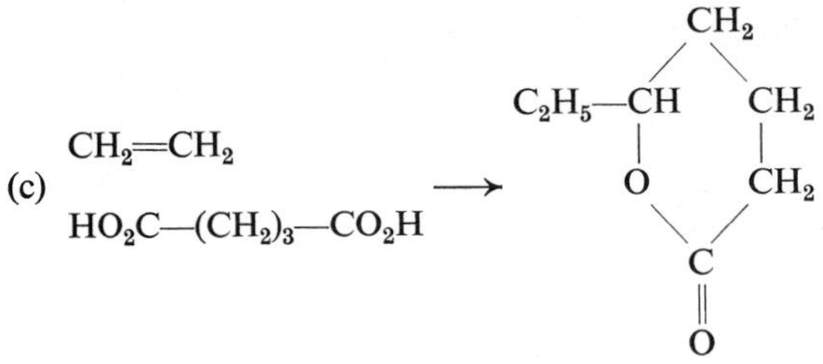

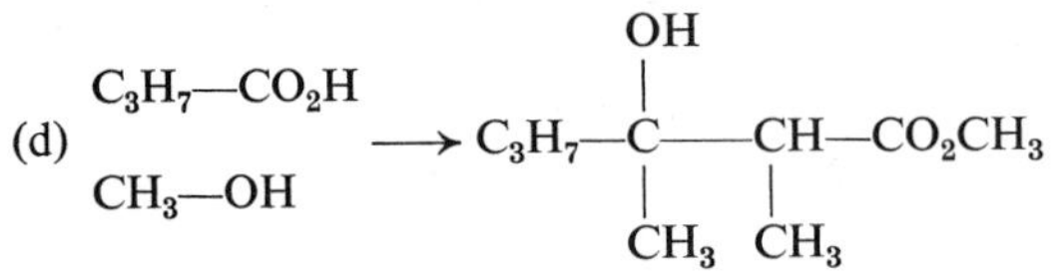

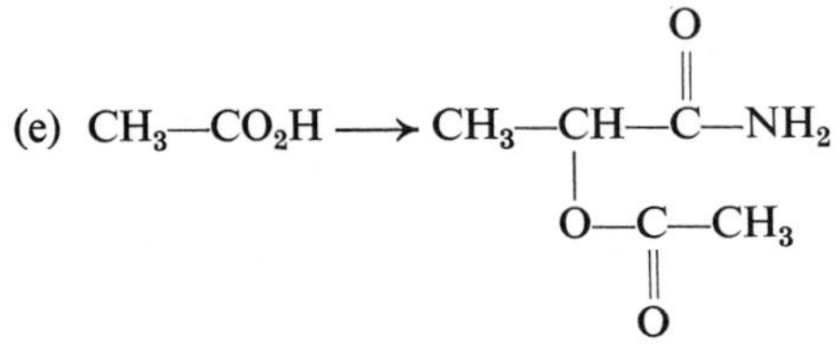

(c)

$$CH_2\!\!=\!\!CH_2$$
$$HO_2C\!-\!(CH_2)_3\!-\!CO_2H$$

$\longrightarrow$

$$
\begin{array}{c}
CH_2 \\
C_2H_5\!-\!CH \quad\ CH_2 \\
| \qquad\qquad | \\
O \qquad\ CH_2 \\
C \\
\| \\
O
\end{array}
$$

(d)

$$C_3H_7\!-\!CO_2H$$
$$CH_3\!-\!OH$$

$\longrightarrow$

$$
\begin{array}{c}
\qquad\ OH \\
\qquad\ | \\
C_3H_7\!-\!C\!-\!-\!-\!CH\!-\!CO_2CH_3 \\
| \qquad\ | \\
CH_3 \quad CH_3
\end{array}
$$

(e) $CH_3\!-\!CO_2H \longrightarrow$

$$
\begin{array}{c}
\qquad\qquad\quad O \\
\qquad\qquad\quad \| \\
CH_3\!-\!CH\!-\!C\!-\!NH_2 \\
| \\
O\!-\!C\!-\!CH_3 \\
\| \\
O
\end{array}
$$

3. Write equations for all the products that would be formed if the following reaction were carried out.

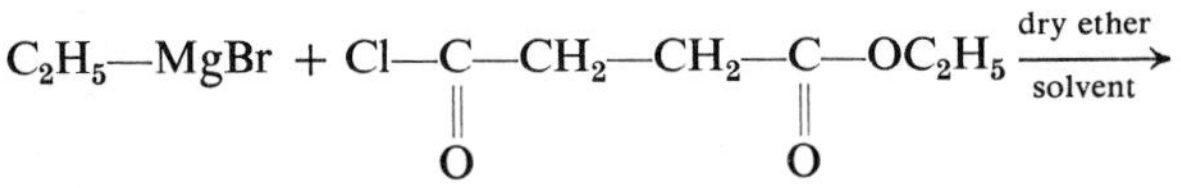

$$C_2H_5\!-\!MgBr + Cl\!-\!C\!-\!CH_2\!-\!CH_2\!-\!C\!-\!OC_2H_5 \xrightarrow[\text{solvent}]{\text{dry ether}}$$
$$\qquad\qquad\qquad\quad \| \qquad\qquad\qquad \|$$
$$\qquad\qquad\qquad\quad O \qquad\qquad\qquad O$$

4. Show how the following conversion may be accomplished in four steps.

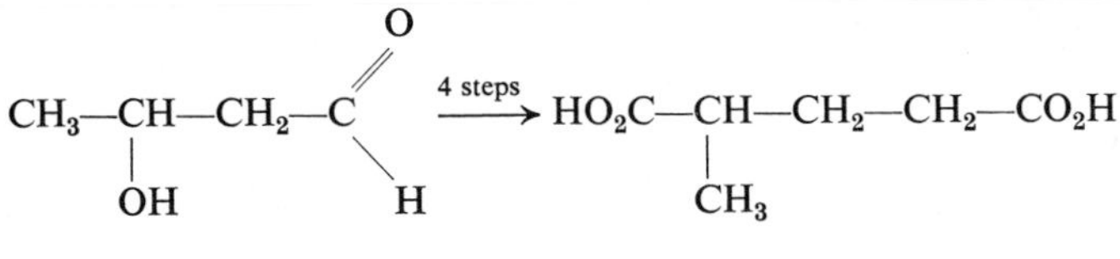

$$
\begin{array}{c}
\qquad\qquad\qquad\quad O \\
\qquad\qquad\qquad\quad \diagup\!\!\!\| \\
CH_3\!-\!CH\!-\!CH_2\!-\!C \\
| \qquad\qquad\quad \diagdown \\
OH \qquad\qquad\ H
\end{array}
\xrightarrow{\text{4 steps}}
\begin{array}{c}
HO_2C\!-\!CH\!-\!CH_2\!-\!CH_2\!-\!CO_2H \\
| \\
CH_3
\end{array}
$$

5. Give the principal organic product or products that would be formed in each of the following reactions.

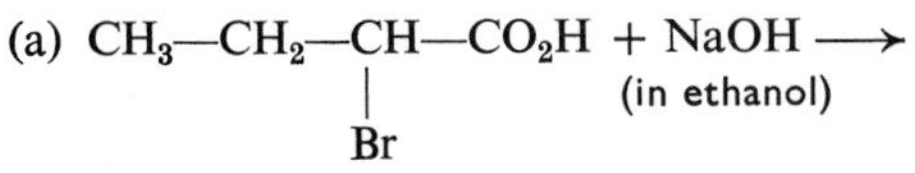

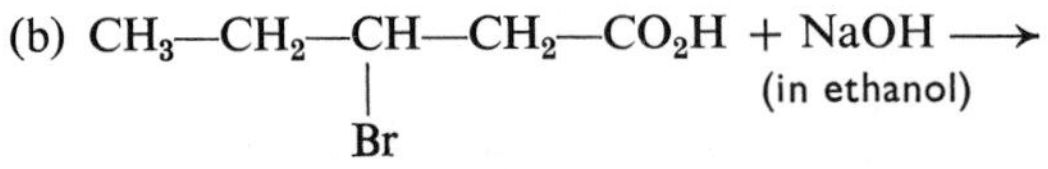

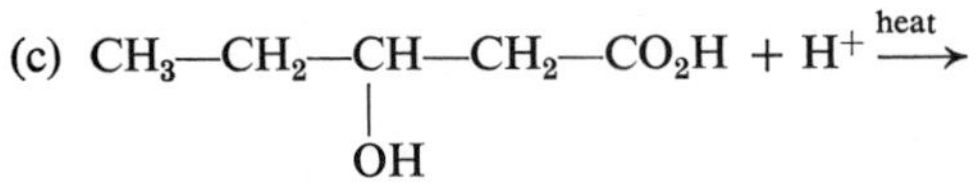

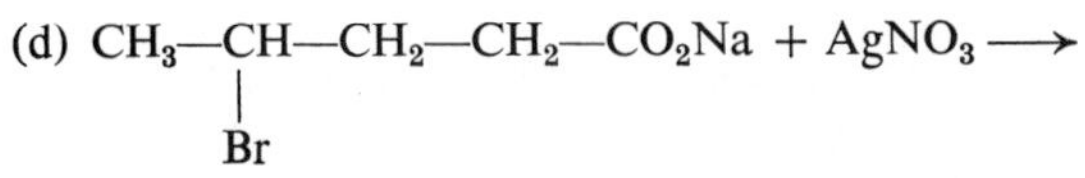

(a)
$$
\begin{array}{c}
CH_3\!-\!CH_2\!-\!CH\!-\!CO_2H + NaOH \longrightarrow \\
| \qquad\qquad\qquad \text{(in ethanol)} \\
Br
\end{array}
$$

(b)
$$
\begin{array}{c}
CH_3\!-\!CH_2\!-\!CH\!-\!CH_2\!-\!CO_2H + NaOH \longrightarrow \\
| \qquad\qquad\qquad\qquad \text{(in ethanol)} \\
Br
\end{array}
$$

(c)
$$
\begin{array}{c}
CH_3\!-\!CH_2\!-\!CH\!-\!CH_2\!-\!CO_2H + H^+ \xrightarrow{\text{heat}} \\
| \\
OH
\end{array}
$$

(d)
$$
\begin{array}{c}
CH_3\!-\!CH\!-\!CH_2\!-\!CH_2\!-\!CO_2Na + AgNO_3 \longrightarrow \\
| \\
Br
\end{array}
$$

(e) $CH_3-CH-CH_2-CO_2H + PCl_5 \longrightarrow$
$\quad\quad\quad |$
$\quad\quad\quad OH$

(f) $CH_3-CH-CH_2-CO_2CH_3 + Mg \xrightarrow[\text{ether}]{\text{dry}}$
$\quad\quad\quad |$
$\quad\quad\quad Br$

6. In the Reformatsky reaction, the aldehyde or ketone is added to the reaction mixture containing the bromo ester and zinc, rather than after formation of the organozinc compound (contrary to the usual practice in the Grignard reaction). This procedure is followed because the organozinc compound will react with the ester group of the bromo ester, although less rapidly than with an aldehyde or ketone. Write a plausible transition state for reaction of the organozinc compound with the bromo ester, also indicate the product of the reaction.

7. The Hunsdiecker reaction is usually carried out in carbon tetrachloride, for this solvent gives only a sluggish reaction with free radicals. In one such reaction in which dichloromethane was used as solvent there was detected among the products a significant quantity of bromodichloromethane. Write reactions showing a possible origin of this compound.

The Characteristic Substitution Reactions in Benzene

Among aliphatic compounds (derivatives of alkanes), the introduction of functional groups by substitution of hydrogen in a hydrocarbon is of virtually no significance. Free radical halogenation is the only practical reaction, and the useful synthetic applications of this reaction are quite limited indeed (Chap. 11). The synthesis of derivatives of benzene, as well as other aromatic compounds, is in sharp contrast to the situation in the aliphatic series. The large resonance energy of benzene (Chap. 12) renders substitution of hydrogen the most important reaction of this compound. After attack of a positive group at a double bond, completion of addition would result in loss of the resonance stabilization of the aromatic system, so addition is not completed; loss of a proton occurs to give a substituted benzene as the product of the reaction (cf. Eq. 12-14). Furthermore, as will be developed in this chapter, there prove to be directive influences in benzene which allow preparation of polysubstituted benzenes of various orientations that may be desired. Thus, **the principal sources of all the derivatives of benzene are benzene and methylbenzenes.**

Prior to World War II, essentially the only primary source of benzene and the methylbenzenes was **coal tar,** the tarry distillate obtained when coal is heated in absence of air. The principal product of this pyrolysis is coke (about 75%), and the next most abundant product is coal gas (the gas used as a fuel in areas where natural gas is not available). The yield of coal tar varies with different samples of coal, but is usually no more than 3% of the weight of the coal. Thus coal tar may be regarded as a by-product of the steel industry, which consumes the major amount of the coke. In addition, benzene and its derivatives constitute only a small per cent of coal tar, and only a few of the substituted benzenes are isolable as pure starting materials for synthesis. The major constituents of coal tar are compounds in the naphthalene series (Chap. 29), higher condensed ring compounds (Chap. 30), and heterocyclic nitrogen compounds (Chaps. 31 through 33).

The principal benzene derivatives obtainable from coal tar are the following:

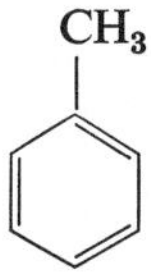

Toluene 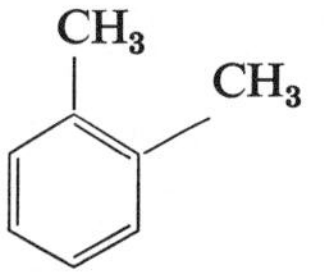   o-Xylene 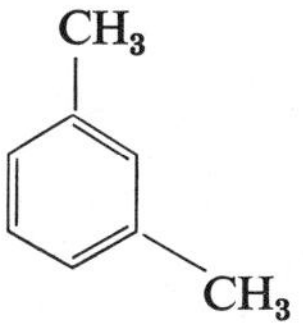   m-Xylene

p-Xylene 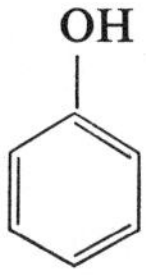   Phenol 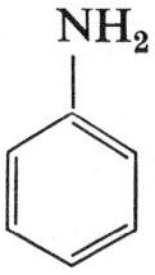   Aniline

The demand for benzene itself is greatly increased by the fact that most of the phenol and aniline consumed in the chemical industry is made from benzene; the amount of these substances available from coal tar is far below demand. This is another illustration of the function of benzene as the ultimate source of its derivatives. As will be discussed in Chapter 19, aniline is among the most important intermediates for synthesis of many benzene derivatives.

During and since World War II, the demand for the starting materials mentioned in the above paragraph has become considerably greater than the supply available from the coal tar produced as a by-product in the steel industry. Fortunately, methods have been developed for obtaining benzene, toluene, and the xylenes from the alkanes found in petroleum. One toluene plant constructed in the United States during World War II produced more toluene from petroleum (for manufacture of TNT, trinitrotoluene) than the entire coal tar industry of the nation. The conversion of alkanes to benzene derivatives involves dehydrogenation and cyclization, a combined process known as *cyclodehydrogenation*. Catalysts have been found which will promote such reactions at high temperatures, and it has been customary to feed the catalytic units with suitable mixtures of alkanes (sometimes cycloalkanes), then separate the desired aromatic compounds from the effluent mixture. A typical process is conversion of *n*-heptane to toluene, Eq. 1. Similarly, *n*-hexane yields benzene and *n*-octane yields a mixture of xylenes and ethylbenzene.

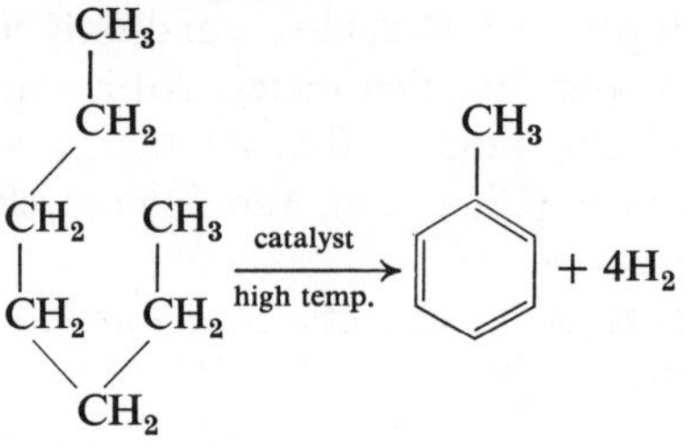

$$
\text{catalyst, high temp.} \qquad + 4H_2 \tag{1}
$$

Nomenclature

The naming of benzene derivatives involves very little not already described in the aliphatic series, but a few things should be studied at this time. Several of the common benzene derivatives have common names, and these should be learned, for they are used as the basis for naming more highly substituted derivatives. Examples are the substances listed as available from coal tar. Others will be mentioned as the compounds are studied.

When the benzene ring becomes a radical, it is called **phenyl;** for example, aniline may be called phenylamine. A further rather confusing point is that the benzyl radical is the phenylmethyl radical, thus:

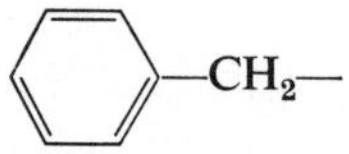

The various substituents on benzene are named in the same manner discussed for aliphatic compounds. For example, toluene may be called methylbenzene, and the xylenes are dimethylbenzenes. When two substituents are present, three orientations are possible, as illustrated in the case of the xylenes. The three orientations are known as *ortho*, *meta*, and *para*, and these are designated by the prefixes *o*-, *m*-, and *p*-. The names beneath the formulas for the xylenes show the orientation for each of these names. These prefixes are applied similarly when each substituent is named separately, as in the following examples.

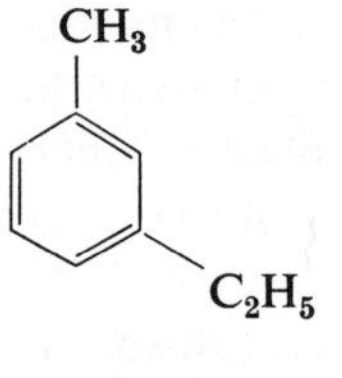

m-Ethyltoluene 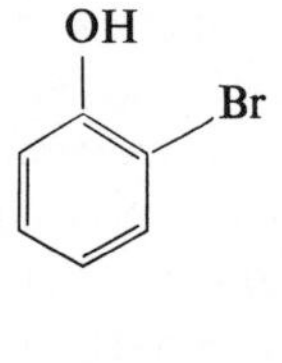   *o*-Bromophenol 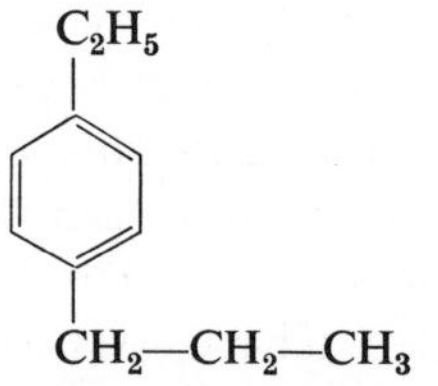   *p*-Ethyl-*n*-propylbenzene

When two substituents are named separately, as in *p*-ethyl-*n*-propylbenzene, the substituents are most properly placed in alphabetical order; however, there is no advantage to this convention except for indexing purposes. In ordinary

chemical writing, the names are placed in any convenient order. If one substituent is part of the basic name, as in *m*-ethyltoluene, the other substituent
must be placed first.

When more than two substituents are present, all substituents are located
by number. The numbering is started on a carbon bearing a substituent, and
proceeds around the ring in the direction giving the smallest numbers to the
carbons bearing substituents. Any carbon bearing a substituent may be chosen
as carbon-1 unless this leads to larger numbers than necessary. Also, in use
of names such as toluene and phenol, the carbon bearing the substituent on
which the name is based must be carbon-1. Examples will help to clarify these
principles. It should be noted that location by number of the methyl in toluene

2-Bromo-3-nitrotoluene

1-Nitro-3-chloro-4-ethylbenzene
or 1-Ethyl-2-chloro-4-nitrobenzene

not 1-Nitro-4-ethyl-5-chlorobenzene
or 1-Chloro-2-ethyl-5-nitrobenzene

is unnecessary, for the carbon bearing this group must be designated carbon-1,
as mentioned above. The objection to the latter two names for the second
example is that they lead to larger numbers than are necessary. Actually, the
name 1-nitro-3-chloro-4-ethylbenzene is not strictly correct, for the *sum* of the
numbers is greater than in 1-ethyl-2-chloro-4-nitrobenzene.

No further new principles need be learned for naming of benzene derivatives, but application of the general principles of nomenclature to aromatic
compounds should be practiced.

Orientation and Rate of Substitution in Benzene

Before the specific substitution reactions may be studied with understanding it is necessary to consider the factors controlling the relative rates of
substitution and the orientation of substituents entering the benzene ring. Early
in the study of aromatic compounds, it was observed that the **orientation (*ortho*,
meta, or *para*) of a second group entering the benzene ring is determined by the
nature of the group already present in the ring.** Influence of the entering group
is minor. It was further observed that one group of substituents directs a
second substituent predominantly to the *meta* position, while another group of
substituents has a directing influence giving predominantly a mixture of the
ortho and para isomers. Thus, there are only two types of directing influence:
meta-directing and *ortho,para*-directing. This directing influence is not 100%
effective, but it is rarely less than 90% effective; it nearly always results in a
product from which a pure compound may be isolated in the case of a *meta*-
director. Of course there is an additional problem of separation in the case of
ortho,para-directors, and this will be the subject of further discussion.

Rules of substitution

1. If the atom attached to the aromatic ring is relatively positive, the substituent is *meta*-directing; if the atom attached to the ring is relatively negative, the substituent is *ortho,para*-directing.

2. Presence in the ring of a *meta*-director always makes the rate of substitution much slower than in benzene. Presence of an *ortho,para*-director makes substitution in the ring faster, except for the case of halogen which gives slightly slower substitution.

These rules are based on experimental observation, extending over many years; however, they may be correlated on the basis of modern theories of reaction mechanism and resonance stabilization of molecules. Before this correlation is undertaken, however, it is desirable to amplify the basic rules somewhat.

On the basis of our discussions thus far of negative and positive groups or atoms in a molecule, we may develop the following tabulation of common functional groups:

o,p-Directing	*m*-Directing

—F, —Cl, —Br, —I
 	
—CH$_3$, —C$_2$H$_5$, etc
 	
—OH, —OCH$_3$, —OR
 	
—NH$_2$, —NH—C—R
           ‖
           O
	(structural formulas for nitro, sulfonic acid, trialkylammonium, nitrile, carboxylic acid, ester, amide, and ketone groups)

The only group which might not be classified readily in the above tabulation is the alkyl group; however, if one considers the polarity of the C—H bond, he concludes that the hydrogen is the positive end of the dipole. Thus, carbon is relatively negative, and this interpretation proves to fit well with the general correlations to be presented below. There has been discussion of the negative character of halogen, oxygen and nitrogen. In addition, the carbonyl group has been presented frequently as a dipole with the carbon the positive end thereof. The first three of the *meta*-directors actually carry a positive charge on the atom by which the group is attached to another atom. The first of the *meta*-directors is the **nitro** group, of essentially no importance in aliphatic chemistry but among the most important functional groups in benzene derivatives.

It should be mentioned at this time that there are a very few groups which cannot be classified, a priori, on the basis of the first rule of substitution. These include phenyl as a substituent and the alkene linkage, —CH=CH—, both of which are *ortho,para*-directors. These will be discussed later, at appropriate points.

The second rule of substitution, having to do with rate, is of considerable interest in connection with basic correlations of the principles underlying directive influence. In addition, this matter is of considerable importance for predicting position of substitution in rings already having two or more substituents. For this purpose, it is convenient to consider the following expression of relative rates as promoted by the indicated substituents:

$$
\begin{array}{lll}
\text{OH} & ortho,para\text{-directors} & \\
\text{or} \quad > \text{phenyl} > & \text{and} & > meta\text{-directors} \\
\text{NH}_2 & \text{unsubstituted benzene} &
\end{array}
$$

The differences indicated are those great enough to be of practical use in synthesis; differences which exist within the groups are rarely great enough to be of use in synthesis and are not worth remembering for most kinds of work.

These principles may be illustrated by considering the following molecules, where the principal positions of a third substitution are indicated by arrows.

The 2-position in 3-nitrotoluene is not indicated because steric hindrance in this position would slow up substitution sufficiently to cause a preponderance of substitution at the 4- and 6-positions. It is obvious that further substitution in 2-bromotoluene is not a promising route of synthesis, on account of the large number of isomers to be expected, but a third substitution in any of the other examples will lead to only two isomers, the same number obtained in the second substitution. Such applications of the substitution rules are necessary in all multistep syntheses in the benzene series. A further important consideration is separability of isomers, discussed in the next section.

Separation of Isomeric Benzene Derivatives

Separation of compounds containing a different number of substituents is usually easy on account of the difference in boiling point accompanying the difference in molecular weight, but separation of isomeric compounds is often difficult. This consideration is of particular significance on account of the regular occurrence of mixtures of *ortho* and *para* isomers. Various special methods are used, especially in industry, for separation of specific mixtures, but the only generally reliable method for separating such mixtures is by fractional distillation. Even if one isomer is a less soluble solid which can be separated by fractional crystallization, the more soluble isomer is usually not separable in a pure condition. Thus differences in boiling points of the *ortho* and *para* isomers become a matter of much significance, and a rather general rule is as follows: *ortho and para isomers usually do not differ sufficiently in boiling point to permit practical separation by distillation unless one of the substituted groups is nitro, in which case separation by fractional distillation is nearly always practical.* Nearly any isomeric pairs may be used to illustrate this generality, but the chloro- and nitrotoluenes are appropriate:

Boiling points

o-Chlorotoluene	159.5°
p-Chlorotoluene	162.2°
o-Nitrotoluene	222°
p-Nitrotoluene	238°

In planning syntheses for preparation of pure compounds, one may take advantage of any separations which he happens to know are feasible, but the only general principle on which he can depend is the separability of isomeric aromatic nitro compounds. This lends great significance to the nitro compounds, for the fortunate combination of known reactions, especially those discussed in Chapter 19, makes possible synthesis of nearly any desired benzene derivative from an appropriate pure nitro compound. This good fortune is increased by the fact that nitro is a *meta*-director; there is no trouble with a second substitution proceeding as fast as the first.

Basic Correlations of Directive Influence in Benzene

As has been discussed in Chapter 12, substitution in benzene proceeds according to the sequence shown in Eq. 2, where B^+ represents the positive

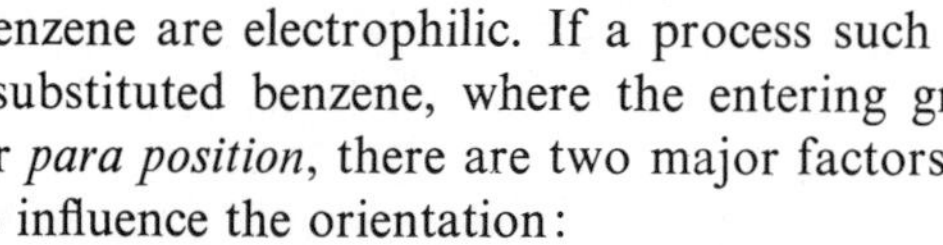

$$+ H^+ \qquad (2)$$

(transition state)

group entering the benzene ring. Virtually all the important substitution reactions in benzene are electrophilic. If a process such as shown in Eq. 2 is applied to a substituted benzene, where the entering group may occupy an *ortho, meta,* or *para position*, there are two major factors that may reasonably be expected to influence the orientation:

1. Since the entering group is positive, if any factor tends to make one position have a higher electron density (be more negative), substitution should be more rapid at the more negative position. This consideration applies to the so-called "ground state" of the molecule, which is the normal molecule in solution prior to reaction; therefore, it is concerned only with the relative tendency of the entering positive group to approach one position or the other. The next item, concerned with the probability of a reaction occurring when the entering group approaches, is no doubt of much greater significance.

2. Any factor which makes the transition state of lower energy for one position or the other will cause substitution to favor the position with the lower-energy transition state. This follows from the fact that a lower energy of activation causes a faster rate of reaction.

Since *ortho,para*-directors give a mixture of products substituted in these two positions, it might be presumed that the same considerations apply in the two positions. This proves to be the case, and it is convenient to consider a comparison between *meta* and one of the other positions, so the discussion will be directed first to a consideration of the *meta* and *ortho* positions.

Nitrobenzene is a convenient compound for consideration of the two factors operative in determining directive influence, and the charge distribution in the ground state may be considered first. By employing charge separation in the benzene ring, such resonance forms as shown in Group A and additional similar ones may be considered; however, it will be noted that these forms give

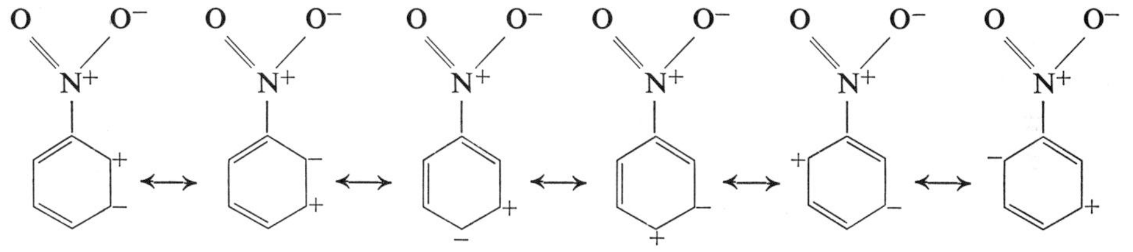

(Group A)

no indication of a difference in charge at the various positions. The plus or minus charge appears on each carbon in the same number of resonance forms of the same type. If, however, there be considered resonance forms (Group B) involving electron transfer from the ring to the substituent, some pertinent conclusions may be reached. Two things may be noted: first, in all these

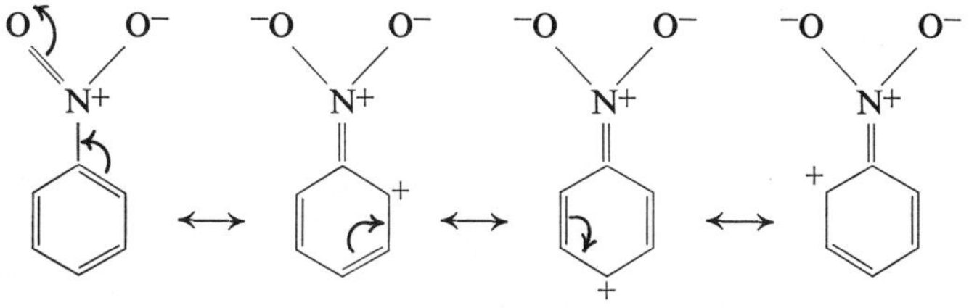

(Group B)

resonance forms, electrons are transferred out of the ring so the total electron density in the ring has been reduced; second, each charged form has a plus charge in the *ortho* or *para* position. This would indicate that substitution would be slowed down by the low electron density in the ring, and that a positive group would prefer the *meta* position in order to avoid the still lower electron density in the *ortho* and *para* positions. The nitro group is predicted, then, to be a *meta*-director, and to give the low rate of substitution characteristic of *meta*-directors.

In further consideration of the resonance forms in Group B, it should be noted that such forms cannot be written to put the plus charge in the *meta* position and keep all valences satisfied. Furthermore, shifting electrons towards the ring by putting the electron pair from the double bond on nitrogen instead of oxygen would give resonance forms of such high energy (plus charge on oxygen) that they would not make a significant contribution to the character of the resonance hybrid (cf. Chap. 12). Finally, in both Group A and Group B, all forms could be written with the double bond to the other oxygen in the nitro group, but such forms would have no influence on the conclusions to be reached. Such forms merely indicate that the nitro group is resonance-stabilized, and this is consistent with the stable character of this group.

Next, let us consider **resonance forms for the transition state** in *ortho* substitution (Group C) and *meta* substitution (Group D). It may be noted that for *ortho* substitution (Group C), one resonance form has a plus charge on the

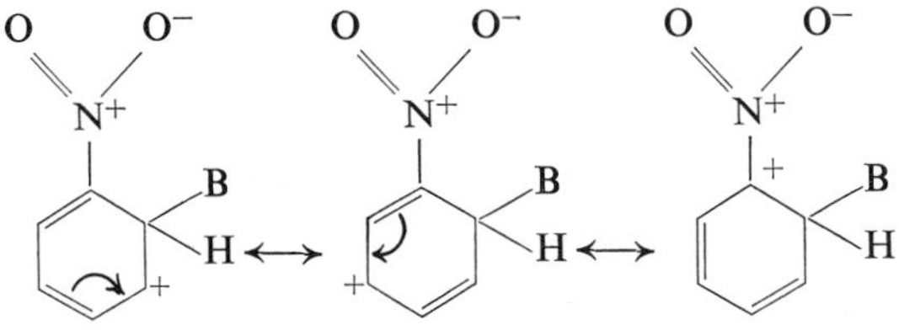

(Group C)

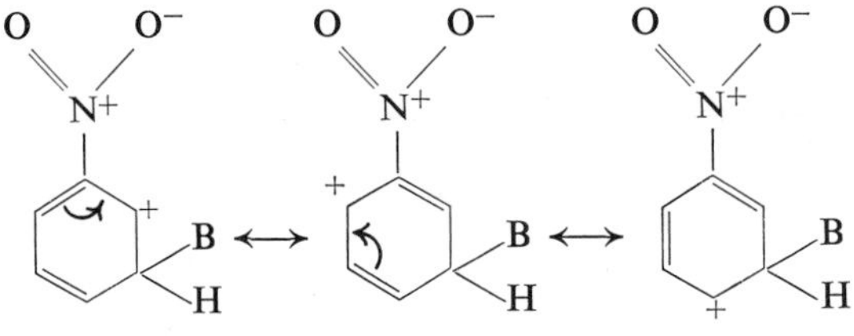

(Group D)

carbon attached to nitrogen, while in *meta* substitution (Group D), no resonance form has a plus charge on the carbon attached to nitrogen. Since like charges repel, it follows that the transition state for *meta* substitution is of lower energy; therefore, this position of substitution would be favored.

All considerations, then, indicate that nitrobenzene should be a *meta*-director, which it is.

The same considerations which have been detailed for nitrobenzene obviously apply to all groups in which there is adjacent to the ring a polar double bond with the positive end orientated towards the ring. The polarity of the carbonyl and cyano groups is demonstrated by dipole moment measurements, as well as the direction of addition of reagents (hydrogen attacks oxygen or nitrogen). The resonance forms with electrons withdrawn from the ring would have the following features:

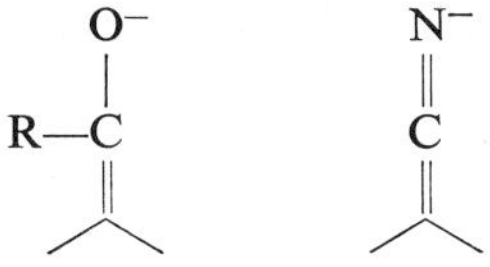

$$\underset{\substack{|\\R-C\\ \diagdown}}{\overset{\substack{O^-\\||}}{}} \qquad \underset{\substack{C\\||\\ \diagdown}}{\overset{\substack{N^-\\||}}{}}$$

In the case of a *meta*-director not doubly-bonded, as in a quaternary ammonium salt such as phenyl trimethylammonium ion, only the arguments

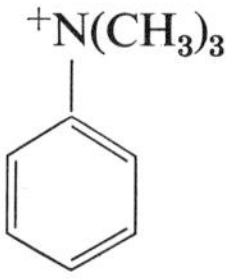

$$^+N(CH_3)_3$$

concerning the transition state apply. Since such compounds are strong *meta*-directors it may be concluded that the factors concerned with the transition state are the more important ones.

In the case of most of the *ortho,para*-directors, the same arguments as applied to *meta*-directors are valid, but the predicted direction of electron transfer is into the ring, and the regions of high electron density are *ortho* and *para*. This is consistent with an accelerated rate of substitution in the *ortho* and *para* positions. As a representative example, phenol may be considered. The oxygen has eight electrons around it, so cannot accommodate any more, but it can give electrons to the ring, as indicated in the resonance forms in Group E.

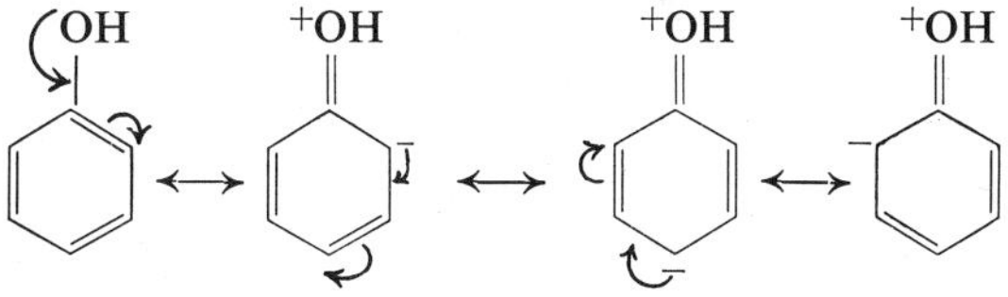

(Group E)

Thus the high electron density in the *ortho* and *para* positions should make these positions attractive to an entering positive group.

As regards the energy of the transition state, the resonance forms in Group C show that *ortho* substitution renders the carbon attached to the substituent more positive. When the attached atom is the electronegative oxygen (concerning *inductive* effect of hydroxyl, cf. Chap. 13), this should lower the energy of the transition state and thus favor *ortho* substitution. If one writes forms similar to Group C for *para* substitution, it turns out that the positions of charge are the same. In addition to the resonance forms shown in Group C, there may be considered still another resonance form when the substituent is a group such as hydroxyl which may donate electrons to the ring via resonance:

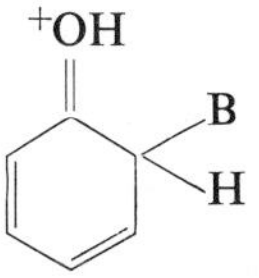

This possibility leads to the prediction of a still lower energy in the transition state, and this is undoubtedly responsible for the very high rate of substitution in phenols and amines.

All the *ortho,para*-directors with nitrogen or oxygen attached to the ring would be predicted as having the observed directing influence by application of the same reasoning detailed for phenol. There remain halogen and alkyl, which have been the source of considerable discussion in the chemical literature.[1]

Halogen should be *ortho,para*-directing by application of the same arguments as applied to phenol; there may be considered the same types of resonance forms as in Group E. The anomaly is the slightly slower rate of substitution in halogen-substituted benzenes, in spite of the displacement of electrons into the ring by contribution of resonance forms such as shown in Group E. Perhaps the best explanation is that resonance contribution of these forms is so small that it is negligible, and is outweighed by the fact that halogen is a powerful electron-attracting group by an inductive (electrostatic) effect. This increased negativity would strengthen the *ortho,para* direction by lowering the energy of the transition state (a highly negative group attached to the positive carbon indicated in Resonance Group C). At the same time, the general withdrawal of electrons from the ring would lower the rate of substitution. The electron-withdrawing character of halogen is indicated rather clearly by increase of the acidic strength in α-bromo acids (cf. Chap. 13). In summary, then, halogen is no undue strain on the theory if it be assumed that its resonance contribution via forms as in Group E is negligible.

The case of an alkyl substituent such as methyl cannot be treated via any resonance forms such as apply in Groups B and E for the apparent reason that all electrons around the carbon in methyl (or other attached alkyl) are involved in single bonds to other atoms. An effort to avoid this limitation has been introduced in the form of "no-bond resonance" or "hyperconjugation," wherein there are considered resonance forms such as the following:

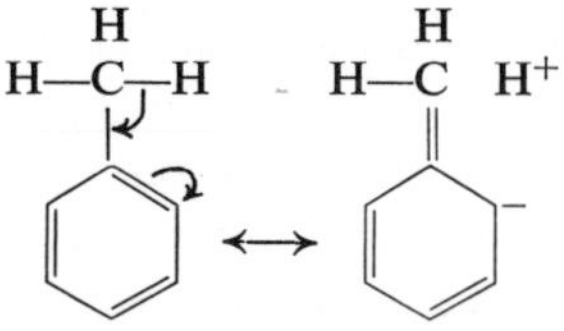

For a period of years, hyperconjugation was a rather popular explanation of various phenomena, in spite of the fact that it is a considerable extrapolation of the basic theory of electron delocalization, as applied to unsaturated systems. It would appear, however, that there have been reported no phenomena which may be explained by hyperconjugation more adequately than by other general theories requiring no special modification for the specific cases. In the case of

---

[1] The effect of the methyl group on substitution in benzene and on the properties of numerous other molecules has been presented by Prof. Paul D. Bartlett of Harvard University in an interesting article, "The Chemical Properties of the Methyl Group," *J. Chem. Ed.*, **30**, 22 (1953).

substitution in alkylbenzenes, hyperconjugation appears contraindicated. Among other objections, it would predict no *ortho,para*-directing influence for *tert*-butylbenzene, which has no hydrogens on the carbon attached to the ring.[2] Actually the *tert*-butyl group is an *ortho,para*-director, although less effective than methyl at increasing rate of substitution.

The directive effect of methyl may be satisfactorily correlated with our general theory if it be recognized that the only effect is in the transition state. As has been noted earlier, the activation energy required to reach the transition state is always the most important consideration, by a wide margin. The fact that toluene substitutes only about six times faster than benzene indicates a modest increase in electron density in the ring. It is known that toluene has a dipole moment with the negative end toward the ring. This is consistent with the fact that hydrogen is strongly electropositive, hence the electrons shared by carbon and hydrogen would be more toward the carbon than the hydrogen. This means that each C—H bond is polar with the negative end toward carbon. This would make carbon relatively negative, hence favor a lower energy for the *ortho, para* transition state, as shown in Resonance Group C. Thus *ortho,para* substitution at a slightly accelerated rate in alkylbenzenes may also be correlated on the basis of the same theory used to explain directing influences of other groups.

An interesting feature of the above explanation of the directing influence of methyl is that it also explains the directing influencing of *tert*-butyl. In this group, the dipolar C—H bonds are one atom removed from the carbon attached to the ring, also at an angle to the plane of the ring, but there are three times as many of them. This situation would certainly be expected to lead to a larger dipole moment for the *tert*-butylbenzene molecule as a whole, and it does prove to have about twice the dipole moment of toluene. The insulation of the dipolar bonds from the ring by an additional carbon, however, decreases the displacement of electrons into the ring and decreases the negative character of the carbon attached to the ring.

Although some details of directing influence in the benzene ring cannot be predicted by the principles developed above, the major features seem well correlated. Even in detail, there are no experimental observations in conflict with predictions. Orientation in substitution is determined to some extent by the relative electron density at ring positions in the ground state; however, both rate and orientation in substitution are determined to a major extent by the energy levels of the respective transition states.

Halogenation

As has been discussed in Chapter 12, ferric halide will generate positive chlorine or bromine (cf. Eq. 12-13), and thus lead to substitution of halogen in

---

[2] Advocates of hyperconjugation proposed to circumvent this discrepancy by invoking "second-order hyperconjugation," which was defined as "no-bond resonance" involving two carbon atoms.

benzene. Since bromobenzene is substituted only slightly more slowly than benzene, further substitution occurs, as shown in Eq. 3. Only a small amount of trisubstitution occurs under the mild conditions indicated in Eq. 3, and use

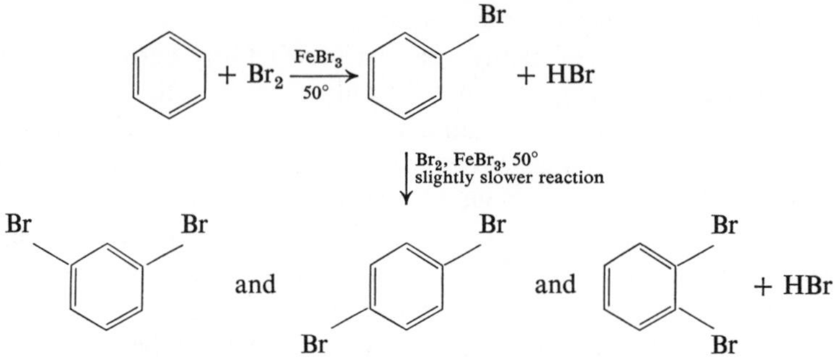

(3)

(trace formed)   (principal products)

of excess of benzene will result in a rather good yield of bromobenzene. As has been discussed previously, separation of bromobenzene from dibromobenzenes by distillation is not difficult; however, separation of the *o*- and *p*-dibromobenzenes is not practical, except that a part of the higher-melting *para* isomer may be separated by crystallization. Preparation of the pure isomers of dibromobenzene is accomplished by other synthetic methods to be discussed in Chapter 19.

Chlorination of benzene proceeds in a manner entirely analogous to bromination; however, **iodination** occurs without a Lewis acid as catalyst. Benzene is able to displace iodide ion from molecular iodine (Eq. 4), without

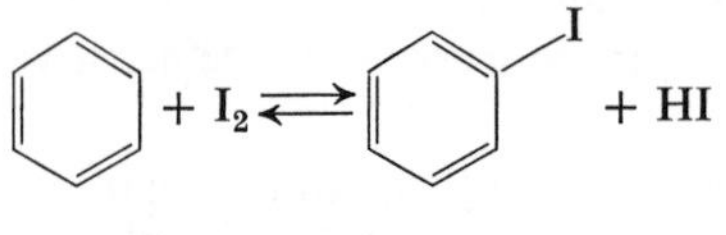

(4)

assistance of a Lewis acid. In contrast with bromination and chlorination, however, the iodination reaction is reversible. Yields in a process such as shown in Eq. 4 are poor unless hydrogen iodide is removed. For many aromatic compounds, which are not oxidized readily, hydrogen iodide may be removed by oxidation with nitric acid (Eq. 5), and this has the additional advantage of

$$4HI + 2HNO_3 \rightarrow 2I_2 + N_2O_3 + 3H_2O \tag{5}$$

reconverting the iodide ion to iodine, available for further substitution.

Another device for preventing reversal of the iodination reaction is use of iodine chloride (Eq. 6). This device is used with compounds susceptible to oxidation.

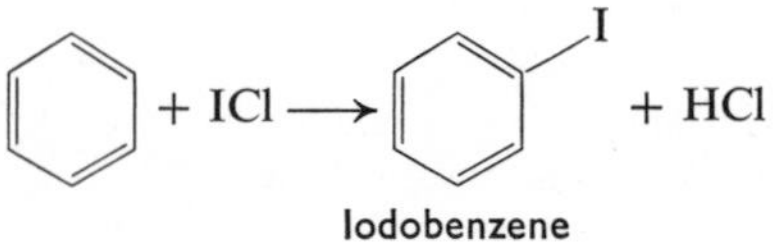

Iodobenzene

(6)

Halogenation of alkylbenzenes. Since ring substitution in aromatic compounds is an ionic reaction, depending on generation of a positive entering group, and alkane substitution is a free radical reaction (review Chap. 11), either type of reaction may be accomplished with rather clean-cut exclusion of the other. In general, ring-halogenation (Eq. 7) is of little value, because of the

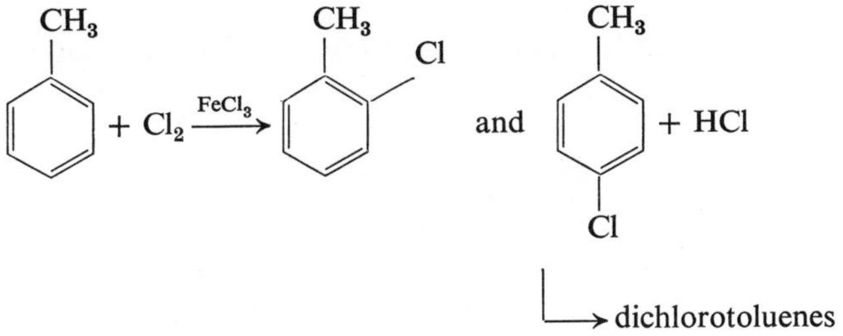

impracticality of separating the mixture of isomers (cf. Chap. 19 for practical methods). Halogenation of toluene in the alkyl group (known as *side chain halogenation*) is of use (Eq. 8), although its principal application is industrial.

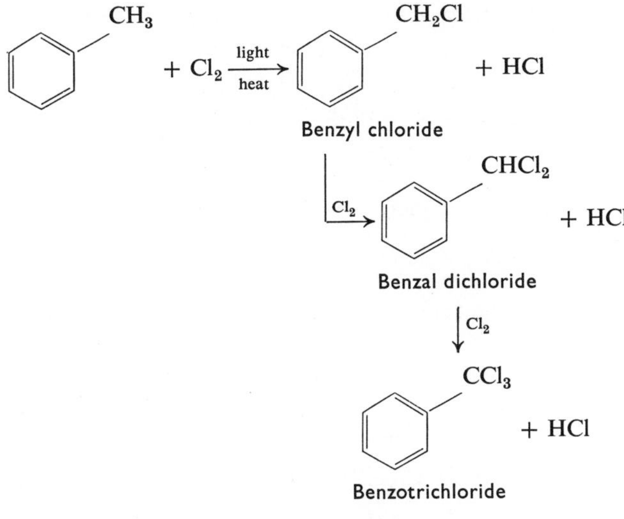

Use of excess of toluene leads to benzyl chloride as the principal product. Industrially, any benzal dichloride and benzotrichloride that are formed may be hydrolyzed to yield benzaldehyde and benzoic acid, respectively. (Why are these products obtained on hydrolysis?)

Certain brominations of alkylbenzenes are useful for yielding a single product because of the fact that *bromine* (in contrast to chlorine) *extracts a tertiary hydrogen more easily than a secondary one, and a primary one at the slowest rate.* These differences, dependent on the higher activation energy of hydrogen abstraction by bromine, are sufficient to allow a rather clean-cut reaction such as shown in Eq. 9. 1-Bromo-1-phenylethane is not easily obtained in other ways. Except in structures where monosubstitution gives a single

$$\text{C}_6\text{H}_5\text{CH}_2\text{—CH}_3 + \text{Br}_2 \xrightarrow[\text{heat}]{\text{light}} \text{C}_6\text{H}_5\text{CH}\text{—CH}_3 \overset{|}{\underset{\text{Br}}{}} + \text{HBr} \qquad (9)$$

compound, the side chain halogenation is not useful. For example, bromination of *n*-butylbenzene would give an inseparable mixture of secondary bromides.

Nitration

Since substitution in benzene occurs with a positive group, the negative nitrate ion, resulting from ordinary ionization of nitric acid, does not substitute. In certain solvents, however, nitric acid gives the positive *nitronium ion*, and this does substitute fairly readily in benzene. Concentrated sulfuric acid has proved to be a particularly useful solvent for nitrations, and ionization in this solvent is believed to occur as follows:

$$\underset{\substack{\text{Nitronium} \\ \text{ion}}}{\text{HNO}_3 + 2\text{H}_2\text{SO}_4 \longrightarrow \text{NO}_2^+} + \underset{\substack{\text{Hydronium} \\ \text{ion}}}{\text{H}_3\text{O}^+} + 2\text{HSO}_4^- \qquad (10)$$

The hydronium ion is nothing more than a hydrated proton; so Eq. 10 may be regarded as the sum of Eqs. 10a and 10b.

$$\text{HNO}_3 + \text{H}_2\text{SO}_4 \longrightarrow \text{NO}_2^+ + \text{H}_2\text{O} + \text{HSO}_4^- \qquad (10a)$$

$$\text{H}_2\text{SO}_4 + \text{H}_2\text{O} \longrightarrow \text{H}_3\text{O}^+ + \text{HSO}_4^- \qquad (10b)$$

It is of interest that nitric acid is functioning as a base in the reaction shown in Eq. 10a. The reason for including the ionization of a mole of sulfuric acid (Eq. 10b) in Eq. 10 is that four moles of ions are produced by dissolving one mole of nitric acid in excess sulfuric acid (as shown by the freezing point depression observed). When the nitronium ion displaces a proton from an aromatic compound, the reaction may be represented as in Eq. 11.

$$\text{Ar}\text{—H} + {}^+\text{NO}_2 \longrightarrow \text{Ar}\text{—NO}_2 + \text{H}^+ \qquad (11)$$

If Eq. 10a is added to Eq. 11, we get Eq. 12, which gives the net reagents consumed and the products formed. It is customary, for simplicity, to write

$$\text{Ar}\text{—H} + \text{HNO}_3 \longrightarrow \text{Ar}\text{—NO}_2 + \text{H}_2\text{O} \qquad (12)$$

nitration reactions in this manner, with sulfuric acid on the arrow as a solvent and catalyst; but it should be borne in mind that nitration can occur only in an environment which furnishes the nitronium ion (or possibly some other positive ion).

When benzene is nitrated in sulfuric acid solvent, the net reaction shown in Eq. 13 is secured.

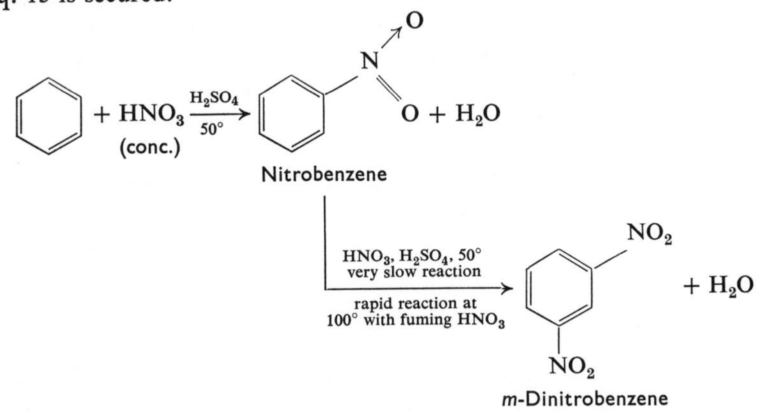

$$\text{Benzene} + HNO_3 \xrightarrow[\text{(conc.)}]{\substack{H_2SO_4 \\ 50°}} \text{Nitrobenzene} + H_2O$$

Nitrobenzene

(13)

$$\xrightarrow[\substack{\text{rapid reaction at} \\ 100° \text{ with fuming } HNO_3}]{\substack{HNO_3, H_2SO_4, 50° \\ \text{very slow reaction}}} m\text{-Dinitrobenzene} + H_2O$$

m-Dinitrobenzene

The much slower rate of the second nitration is characteristic of substitution in a benzene substituted with a *meta*-director. A very high yield of monosubstitution may be secured, and the product is easily separated in a pure condition. Under more drastic conditions, as indicated in the lower line of Eq. 13, an equally satisfactory preparation of m-dinitrobenzene is available.

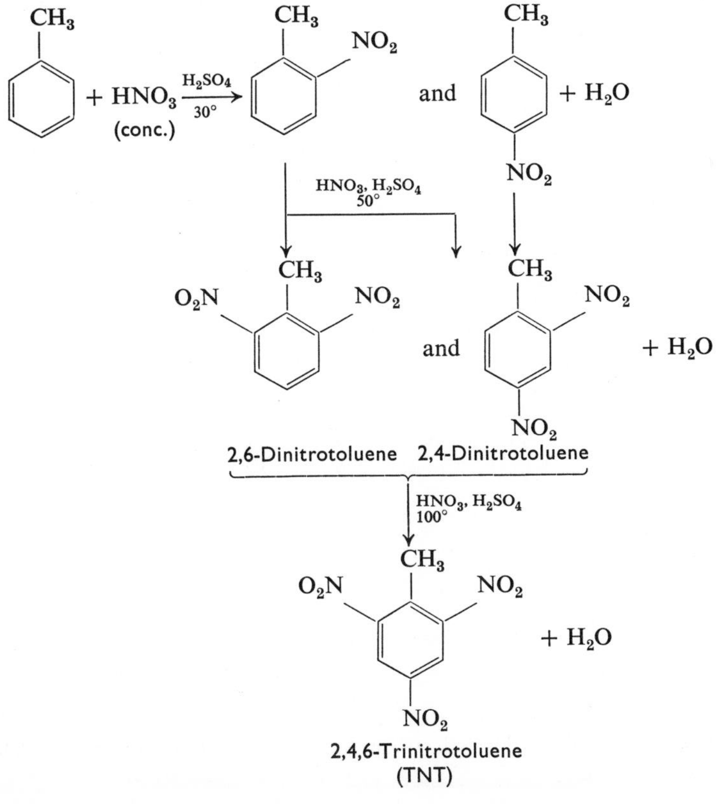

$$\text{Toluene} + HNO_3 \xrightarrow[\text{(conc.)}]{\substack{H_2SO_4 \\ 30°}} \text{(o-nitrotoluene)} \quad \text{and} \quad \text{(p-nitrotoluene)} + H_2O$$

$$\xrightarrow[\substack{HNO_3, H_2SO_4 \\ 50°}]{} \text{2,6-Dinitrotoluene} \quad \text{and} \quad \text{2,4-Dinitrotoluene} + H_2O \quad (14)$$

2,6-Dinitrotoluene   2,4-Dinitrotoluene

$$\xrightarrow[\substack{HNO_3, H_2SO_4 \\ 100°}]{} \text{2,4,6-Trinitrotoluene (TNT)} + H_2O$$

2,4,6-Trinitrotoluene
(TNT)

Nitration of toluene, as outlined in Eq. 14, is a very useful reaction which illustrates several things of interest. Comparison of the conditions indicated in Eqs. 13 and 14 shows the effect of the *o,p*-director in acceleration of substitution. Further, each step in Eq. 14 may be secured in a clean-cut manner, on account of the depressing effect of the *m*-director on rate of substitution. As discussed above the isomeric nitro compounds may be readily separated. On account of the considerable bulk of the nitro group, no doubt responsible for the difference in boiling point of isomers, a steric effect also appears in the substitution reactions. The *o*-nitrotoluene is formed in considerably smaller amount than the *p*-isomer, under the conditions in Eq. 14, and the 2,6-dinitrotoluene is formed in even lower ratio.

The mononitrotoluenes are of very great significance as intermediates for making other substituted benzenes, as will be developed in the next chapters. Trinitrotoluene has been used in very large amounts as a military explosive.[3]

Nitration of phenol illustrates the extremely large effect of hydroxyl in accelerating substitution. As shown in Eq. 15, substitution occurs without

$$\text{(15)}$$

heating in nitric acid diluted with water. In such a solution the principal ionization of nitric acid is the familiar one giving the nitrate ion and a proton

---

[3] The great utility of TNT as a high explosive lies in its insensitivity to shock. It will not detonate if struck with a hammer on an anvil, dropped a distance of five miles on concrete, or shattered with rifle bullets. The only reliable way to shoot TNT is with another charge of a more sensitive explosive. Although this insensitivity to shock is a great advantage for use in bombs or nose charges in shells, the accompanying low rate of detonation of TNT is a disadvantage. It does not give the Munroe effect, which refers to the effect in a cone-shaped charge of explosive that results in most of the force of the blast going towards the base of the cone. As mentioned in Chap. 14, footnote 4, PETN has a sufficiently high rate of detonation to be used in shaped charges; however, this explosive is detonated by rifle fire and therefore unsuitable for bombs. Only about 500 pounds of TNT can be shot in one bomb, the remainder is merely blown around. For larger bombs, there was developed during World War II the

explosive commonly known as RDX, which is 50% more powerful than TNT and will detonate in any amount. When mixed with about an equal amount of TNT, RDX is rendered sufficiently insensitive to withstand rifle fire, and this mixture was used in aerial bombs.

(or hydronium ion). The concentration of the nitronium ion is so minute that its presence cannot be demonstrated; however, it is probably this very small concentration that gives rapid nitration of phenol. Since nitration introduces a *meta*-director, disubstitution is negligible.

Separation of the nitrophenols is especially easy, for the *ortho* isomer is rather volatile with steam, and the *para* isomer is essentially non-volatile. This remarkable and very useful difference in steam-volatility of the *ortho* and *para* isomers is observed in all nitrophenols and nitroamines, and to a smaller extent in halophenols. The difference in volatility in steam distillation is greater than the difference in vapor pressures of the two isomers. This is caused by the very low solubility of the *ortho* isomer in water and the consequent heterogeneous distillation. Both differences between the isomers (solubility and vapor pressure) are ascribed to the fact that in the *ortho* isomer the proton is held *between* the oxygen in the nitro group and the oxygen attached to the aromatic ring. The effect is that of the proton being bonded to both oxygens. In such a structure, the resultant ring is said to be a **chelate ring** and the hydrogen is termed **chelated.** This type of bonding may be interpreted as hydrogen bonding, as indicated in formula A; however, the bond direction to one oxygen must be so far out of a parallel line with the bond to the other oxygen that the hydrogen bond would be much weaker (cf. Chap. 13) than the phenomena demand. It seems more

(A)   (B)   (C)

appropriate to regard the holding of the chelated hydrogen between two oxygens as a result of resonance stabilization (Formulas B and C). With the hydrogen at a midpoint, Formulas B and C differ only in positions of electrons, hence qualify as resonance forms. These forms, then, would contribute to the character of the molecule and, among other things, would prevent intramolecular hydrogen bonding in the *ortho* isomer. This would result in a much higher vapor pressure for the *ortho* isomer, for decrease in vapor pressure is an expected and well-documented effect of intramolecular hydrogen bonding (cf. Chap. 13). Furthermore, cross hydrogen bonding with solvent (in this case water) is a well-known phenomenon which greatly increases solubility in the solvent. Prevention of this in the *ortho* isomer, on account of chelation, leads to the observed low solubility in water.

There is additional evidence for (or manifestation of) resonance stabilization in the chelated *ortho* isomer. As mentioned, Formulas B and C, as resonance forms, should contribute to the character of the molecule. One such character is the bright yellow color of *o*-nitrophenol, as contrasted to the nearly colorless *p*-nitrophenol. It is well-known that structures such as shown in

Formulas D and E are colored some shade of yellow or red (benzoquinones; cf. Chap. 20), and in resonance form C, *o*-nitrophenol has a structure of this

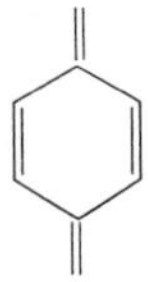

(D) 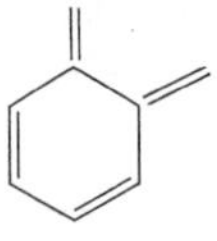   (E) 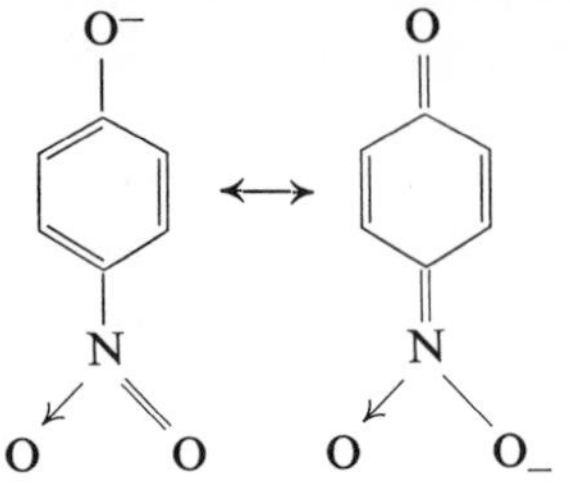   *p*-Nitrophenolate ion

type. Such structures cannot be written for *p*-nitrophenol (nearly colorless), but can be written for the *p*-nitrophenolate anion, as shown above. Interestingly enough, *p*-nitrophenol is an indicator; its solution gives a sharp change from colorless to deep yellow when the *p*H becomes high enough to convert the phenol to its anion! It should be understood that the indicated resonance forms for the anion become possible only when the oxygen-hydrogen bond is broken—this leaves the electron pair free for delocalization.

Sulfonation

The **naming** of sulfonic acids, as illustrated for the compounds in Eqs. 16, 18, and 19, depends on addition of *-sulfonic acid* to the name of the hydrocarbon or hydrocarbon derivative. It is the same as one system for naming carboxylic acids (cf. Chap. 13). As a substituent, the sulfonic acid group is termed *sulfo*.

In contrast to halogenation and nitration, *sulfonation of benzene is a reversible reaction*, as shown in Eq. 16. The mechanism which supplies the

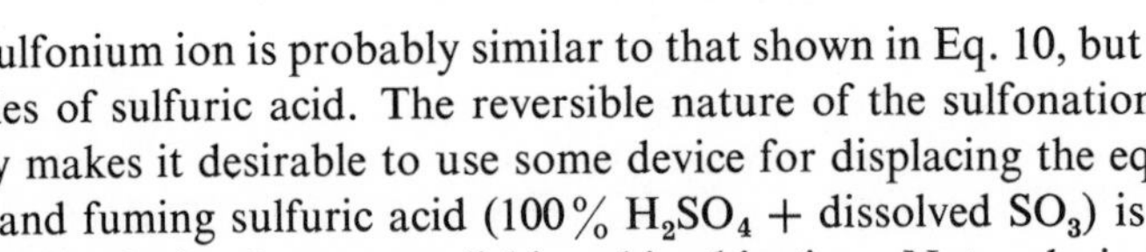

Benzenesulfonic acid

positive sulfonium ion is probably similar to that shown in Eq. 10, but involving three moles of sulfuric acid. The reversible nature of the sulfonation reaction frequently makes it desirable to use some device for displacing the equilibrium forward, and fuming sulfuric acid (100% H_2SO_4 + dissolved SO_3) is a particularly effective device for accomplishing this objective. Not only is the water removed (Eq. 17), in addition, sulfuric acid (on the left of the equilibrium in Eq. 16) is generated.

$$SO_3 + H_2O \longrightarrow H_2SO_4 \tag{17}$$

The sulfo group proves to be particularly effective in reducing electron density in the ring, so a second substitution occurs only under rather drastic conditions (Eq. 18). A third substitution of sulfo in benzene is barely possible, strictly impractical; most of the organic material is decomposed under the drastic conditions required.

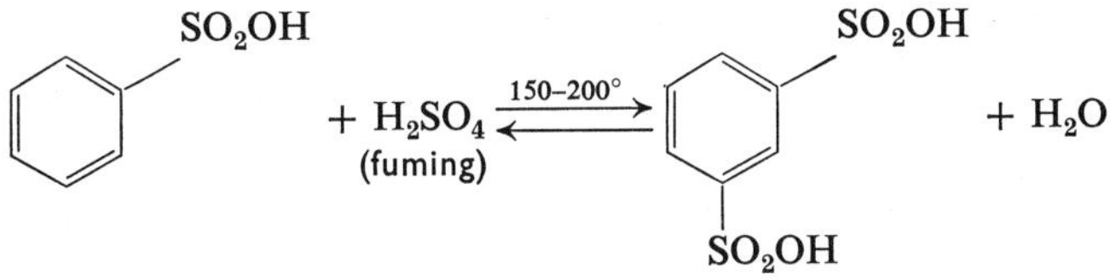

$$\text{C}_6\text{H}_5\text{SO}_2\text{OH} + \text{H}_2\text{SO}_4 \underset{}{\overset{150\text{--}200°}{\rightleftarrows}} \text{(m-C}_6\text{H}_4(\text{SO}_2\text{OH})_2) + \text{H}_2\text{O} \qquad (18)$$

H_2SO_4
(fuming)

m-Benzenedisulfonic acid

In reflection of the activating influence of the *o,p*-directors, toluene is sulfonated under milder conditions (Eq. 19) than is benzene (Eq. 16); indeed,

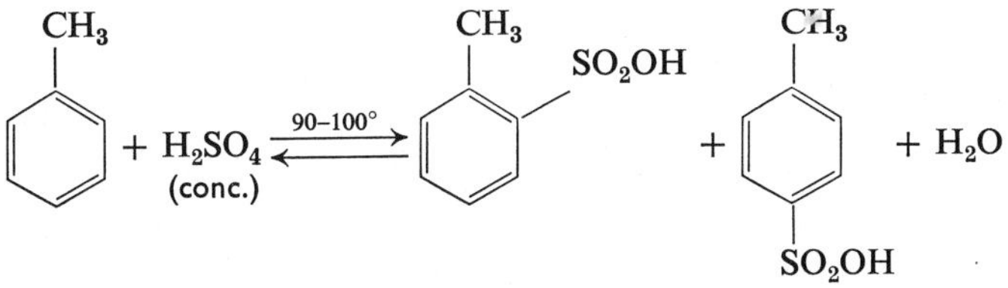

$$\text{C}_6\text{H}_5\text{CH}_3 + \text{H}_2\text{SO}_4 \underset{}{\overset{90\text{--}100°}{\rightleftarrows}} \text{(o-CH}_3\text{C}_6\text{H}_4\text{SO}_2\text{OH}) + \text{(p-CH}_3\text{C}_6\text{H}_4\text{SO}_2\text{OH}) + \text{H}_2\text{O} \qquad (19)$$

H_2SO_4
(conc.)

o-Toluene-
sulfonic acid

p-Toluene-
sulfonic acid

concentrated sulfuric acid is preferable for sulfonation of toluene. Use of fuming acid promotes excessive disulfonation.

The inclusion of temperatures in the equations for aromatic substitution is not intended to indicate that such details are worth remembering specifically. These data are included to illustrate the extent to which aromatic substitution may be controlled. Further, it is worthwhile to remember the types of substitution which proceed readily under very mild conditions and those which require drastic conditions.

The Friedel and Crafts Reaction

The substitution reaction discovered by Friedel and Crafts near the beginning of the twentieth century has been of great value for substitution of alkyl or acyl groups into aromatic compounds. As will be developed below, acylation has by far the greater scope in synthesis.

For the substitutions of alkyl and acyl, a Lewis acid is utilized to extract halogen from the appropriate halide and leave the positive fragment which is reactive towards substitution in benzene.[4] Although ferric halides were found to be effective for generation of a positive species for halogenation of benzene, ferric salts have found little use in the Friedel and Crafts reaction. The most potent and widely used catalyst is anhydrous aluminum chloride. When a milder reagent is desired, zinc chloride or stannic chloride has been used. The ion-generating reactions with aluminum chloride are shown in Eqs. 20 and 21, while a general substitution is shown in Eq. 22. The catalyst is regenerated as

$$R\text{—}Br + AlCl_3 \rightleftharpoons R^+ + {}^-AlCl_3Br \tag{20}$$

$$\underset{\displaystyle O}{R\text{—}\overset{\|}{C}\text{—}Cl} + AlCl_3 \longrightarrow \underset{\displaystyle O}{R\text{—}\overset{\|}{C}{}^+} + {}^-AlCl_4 \tag{21}$$

$$Ar\text{—}H + R^+ \longrightarrow Ar\text{—}R + H^+ \tag{22}$$

$$H^+ + {}^-AlCl_4 \longrightarrow HCl + AlCl_3 \tag{23}$$

shown in Eq. 23, so the substitution reactions may be conveniently written as net reactions with the Lewis acid shown as a catalyst. This practice is followed in the following sections.

Alkylation by the Friedel and Crafts Reaction

Ethylbenzene may be conveniently synthesized by the reaction outlined in Eq. 24. Toluene can be synthesized similarly, but the synthesis is of no sig-

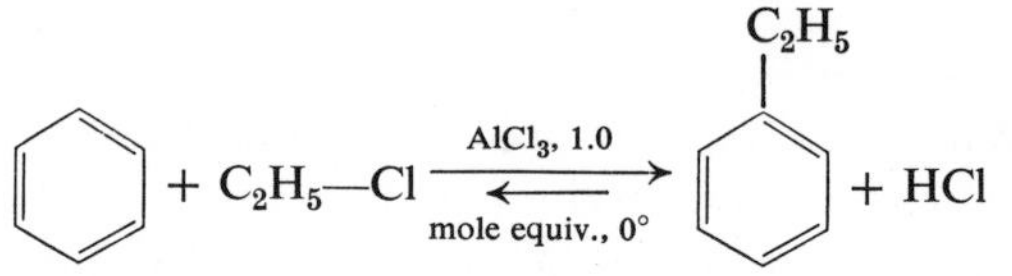

$$+ C_2H_5\text{—}Cl \underset{\text{mole equiv., } 0°}{\overset{AlCl_3,\ 1.0}{\rightleftharpoons}} \quad + HCl \tag{24}$$

nificance on account of the large-scale production of toluene by methods previously mentioned.

---

[4] A considerable amount of investigation, especially by H. C. Brown of Purdue University and F. R. Jensen of the University of California at Berkeley, has been directed towards examination of the details of the Friedel and Crafts reaction. In most cases, there appears to be involvement of a positive ion of the sort represented in Eq. 20; however, in some cases the mechanism may be more complex. In alkyl halides, for example, there may sometimes occur a reaction of a concerted nature, i.e., an assisted displacement reaction (cf. Chap. 6). If this type of reaction should occur, the Lewis acid would be pulling the halogen as the aromatic compound is acting as a nucleophile and displacing the halogen. In some instances, with acid chlorides, the intermediate species may be a salt of the acid chloride and the Lewis acid of the following structure:

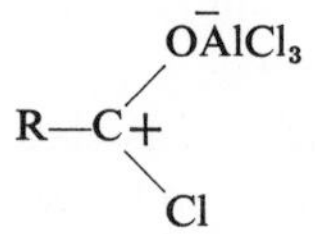

$$R\text{—}\underset{\diagdown\ Cl}{\overset{\diagup\ \overset{-}{O}AlCl_3}{C+}}$$

The alkylation of benzene by a reaction of the type shown in Eq. 24 is subject to certain severe limitations which may be briefly outlined:

1. The reaction occurs satisfactorily with benzenes substituted with *ortho,para*-directors, but *fails to occur* to a practical extent if a *meta*-director is present in the ring.

2. The reaction is reversible, and this leads to complications when poly-substitution is attempted. Proper conditions for a specific synthesis must be determined. If large amounts of aluminum chloride are used, or higher temperatures are employed, *meta* orientation is often obtained, probably by sequences such as that shown in Eq. 25. At high temperature with excess aluminum chloride, 1,3,5-trisubstituted benzenes

$$(25)$$

can be obtained in moderate yields under specific conditions. Also, toluene or xylene may be converted to a mixture of polymethylbenzenes. This has been of use in isomerizing xylenes; also the rather insoluble 1,2,4,5-tetramethylbenzene may be crystallized from the mixture of polymethylbenzenes which may be obtained.

The *meta* isomer is formed under conditions allowing attainment of equilibrium because of its energy being lower than the *ortho* or *para* isomer. As has been discussed, the *ortho* and *para* isomers are formed more rapidly with an *o,p*-director in the ring; however, the *meta* isomer is a more stable compound. It follows that the *meta* isomer will accumulate in a reversible process if sufficient time is allowed. Similarly, in sulfonation of toluene, if the reaction is allowed to proceed for a long time at high temperature, the *m*-toluenesulfonic acid becomes the principal product of the reaction. As shown in Eq. 19, essentially none of the *meta* isomer is formed under ordinary conditions for sulfonation of toluene.

3. Since the carbonium ion is the intermediate in the alkylation reaction (Eqs. 20 and 22), rearrangement occurs whenever a more stable or equally stable ion is available. As discussed in Chapter 6, stability of the carbonium ion decreases in the order: tertiary, secondary, primary. It follows that such rearrangements as shown in Eqs. 26 and 27 will occur. With higher *n*-alkyl halides, the various possible *sec*-alkylbenzenes will be formed, so the reaction becomes of no value at all for preparation of a pure compound.

From the above considerations, it follows that the alkylation of benzene by the Friedel and Crafts reaction is not a general reaction. It is of use for synthesis of certain specific compounds, including those mentioned above.

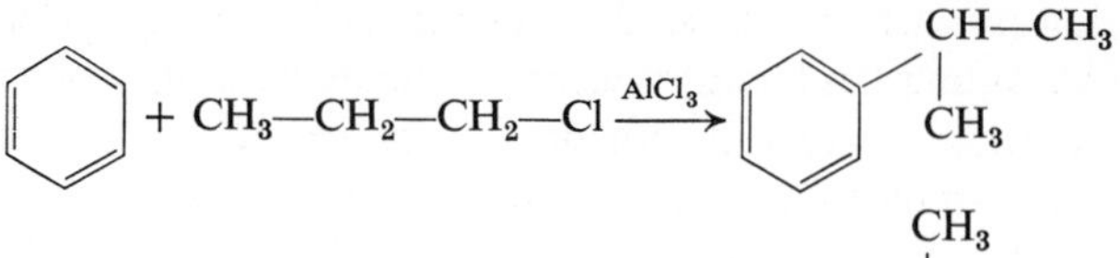

$$\text{C}_6\text{H}_6 + \text{CH}_3\text{—CH}_2\text{—CH}_2\text{—Cl} \xrightarrow{\text{AlCl}_3} \text{C}_6\text{H}_5\text{—CH(CH}_3\text{)—CH}_3 + \text{HCl} \quad (26)$$

$$\text{C}_6\text{H}_6 + \text{CH}_3\text{—CH(CH}_3\text{)—CH}_2\text{—Cl} \xrightarrow{\text{AlCl}_3} \text{C}_6\text{H}_5\text{—C(CH}_3\text{)}_2\text{—CH}_3 + \text{HCl} \quad (27)$$

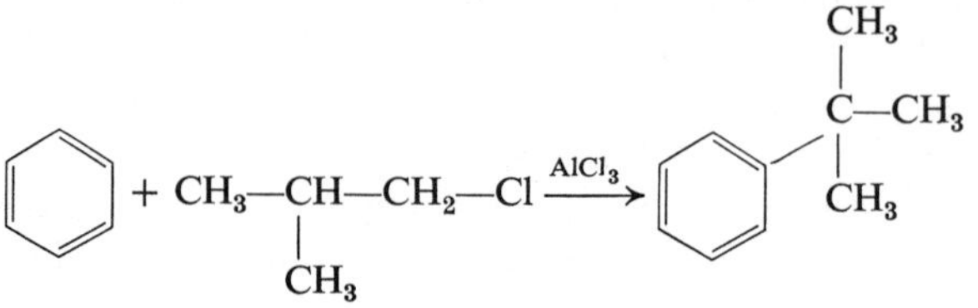

Acylation by the Friedel and Crafts Reaction

The application of the Friedel and Crafts method to acylation may be illustrated by synthesis of the simplest aromatic ketone (Eq. 28). The name

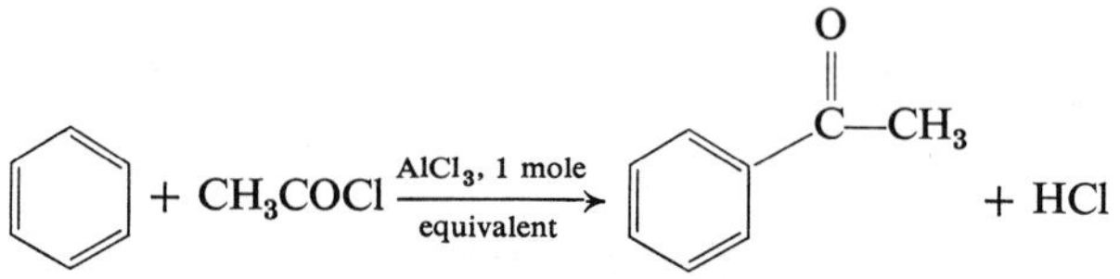

$$\text{C}_6\text{H}_6 + \text{CH}_3\text{COCl} \xrightarrow[\text{equivalent}]{\text{AlCl}_3,\ 1\ \text{mole}} \text{C}_6\text{H}_5\text{—C(=O)—CH}_3 + \text{HCl} \quad (28)$$

Acetophenone

indicated in Eq. 28 for methyl phenyl ketone, or acetylbenzene, is a rather unattractive type of nomenclature which is rather widely used. For example, ethyl phenyl ketone is called propiophenone.

Advantages of the acylation reaction may be cited by reference to the numbered disadvantages of the alkylation reaction:

1. and 2. Since the Friedel and Crafts reaction does not occur at a significant rate on *meta*-substituted compounds, there is no difficulty with polysubstitution; the mono-acylation product is obtained in excellent yield.

3. The positive acylonium ion does not rearrange; so the "expected" product is obtained from the synthesis.

In addition to the above-cited merits of the acylation reaction, there is also the fact that substitution in benzene derivatives containing an *ortho,para*-director goes largely in the *para* position, as in Eq. 29. The predominance of

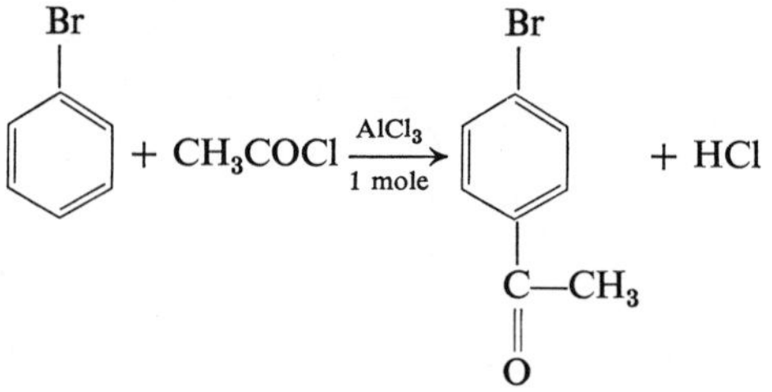

$$\text{C}_6\text{H}_5\text{Br} + \text{CH}_3\text{COCl} \xrightarrow[\text{1 mole}]{\text{AlCl}_3} \text{Br—C}_6\text{H}_4\text{—C(=O)—CH}_3 + \text{HCl} \quad (29)$$

p-Bromoacetophenone
or *p*-Bromophenyl methyl ketone

para substitution is believed due to the fact that the carbonyl group forms a complex with the aluminum chloride, and this complex is so bulky that *ortho* substitution (adjacent to the substituent already present) is discouraged by steric hindrance. Complex formation results from attraction of the Lewis acid (electron acceptor) for the electron-rich oxygen of the carbonyl group. The complex is bound firmly enough to inactivate the aluminum chloride as a catalyst; so there must be used at least one mole of aluminum chloride per mole of carbonyl group, as is indicated in Eqs. 28 and 29.

Acid anhydrides may be used in the acylation reaction if two moles of aluminum chloride are used (1 mole per carbonyl group), but open-chain anhydrides are rarely used, because all except acetic anhydride are more expensive than the corresponding acid chlorides. The cyclic anhydrides are frequently used, however (Eq. 30), for they lead to types of compounds very

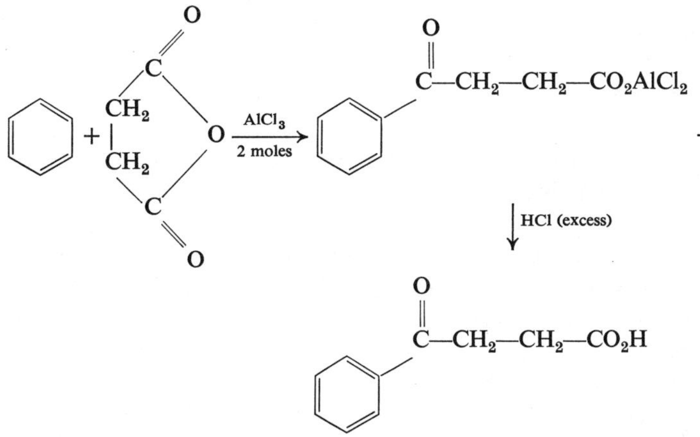

$$\text{C}_6\text{H}_6 + \text{(succinic anhydride)} \xrightarrow[\text{2 moles}]{\text{AlCl}_3} \text{C}_6\text{H}_5-\overset{\text{O}}{\underset{}{\text{C}}}-\text{CH}_2-\text{CH}_2-\text{CO}_2\text{AlCl}_2 + \text{HCl}$$

$$\downarrow \text{HCl (excess)} \tag{30}$$

$$\text{C}_6\text{H}_5-\overset{\text{O}}{\underset{}{\text{C}}}-\text{CH}_2-\text{CH}_2-\text{CO}_2\text{H}$$

β-Benzoylpropionic acid

useful in synthesis. Any type of cyclic anhydride usually gives excellent yields in this reaction. Utilization of the aroylpropionic acids in synthesis will be discussed frequently in later chapters.

Since preparation of most alkylbenzenes by direct alkylation is defeated by rearrangement, it should be mentioned at this time that the acylbenzenes, readily obtainable by acylation, may be reduced in excellent yield by the Clemmensen method or the Wolff-Kishner method (cf. Chap. 15). For illustration, the synthesis of *p*-chloro-*n*-hexylbenzene would follow the sequence outlined in Eq. 31.

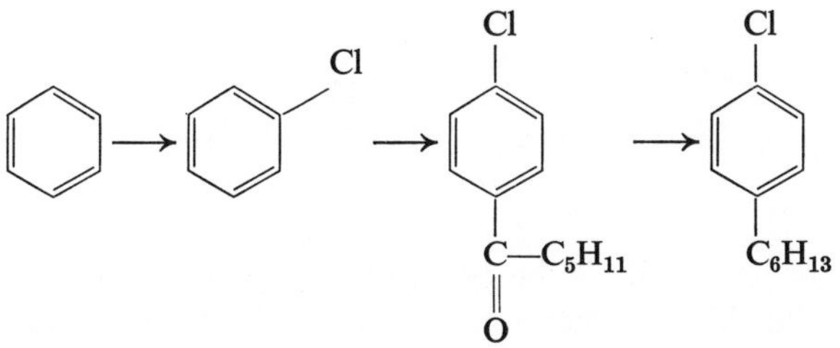

$$\text{C}_6\text{H}_6 \rightarrow \text{C}_6\text{H}_5\text{Cl} \rightarrow \text{(p-Cl-C}_6\text{H}_4\text{-CO-C}_5\text{H}_{11}) \rightarrow \text{(p-Cl-C}_6\text{H}_4\text{-C}_6\text{H}_{13}) \tag{31}$$

Variants of the Friedel and Crafts Reaction

Certain reactions of considerable importance in synthesis do not actually use an acid chloride, but no doubt proceed by reaction mechanisms involving attack of an acylonium ion or the equivalent on an aromatic nucleus.

Gattermann–Koch aldehyde synthesis. Although formyl chloride is not a stable compound (cf. Chap. 14, footnote 2) the components of this molecule (carbon monoxide and hydrogen chloride) will give a substitution reaction with a benzene derivative activated by an *o,p*-director (Eq. 32). Usually

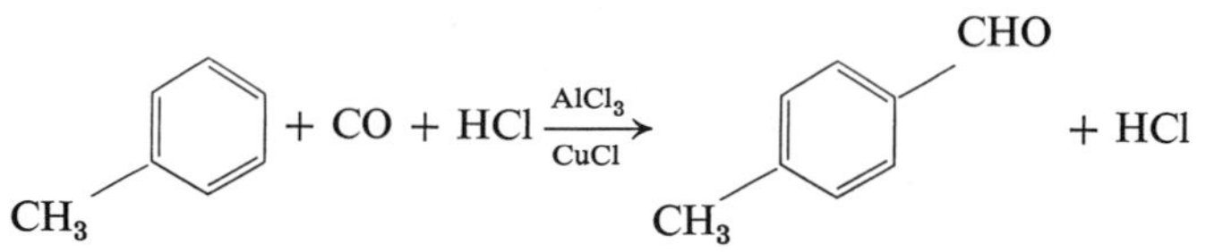

$$\text{CH}_3\text{-C}_6\text{H}_4 + CO + HCl \xrightarrow[\text{CuCl}]{\text{AlCl}_3} \text{CHO-C}_6\text{H}_4\text{-CH}_3 + HCl \qquad (32)$$

a mixed catalyst is used for this reaction, as shown. Although hydrogen chloride appears on both sides of Eq. 32, it would not be realistic to omit it from the reaction. This reaction will not occur without an activating group in the ring; however, the limited activation of alkyl is sufficient.

Gattermann aldehyde synthesis. The Gattermann-Koch reaction is usually satisfactory; however, it involves handling carbon monoxide, which is a rather dangerous gas (colorless, odorless, and accumulative in its poisoning action). If the benzene ring is substituted with hydroxyl or methoxyl (highly activating groups), there may be used the Gattermann synthesis which employs hydrogen cyanide (Eq. 33). Hydrogen cyanide (boiling point 26°) has an

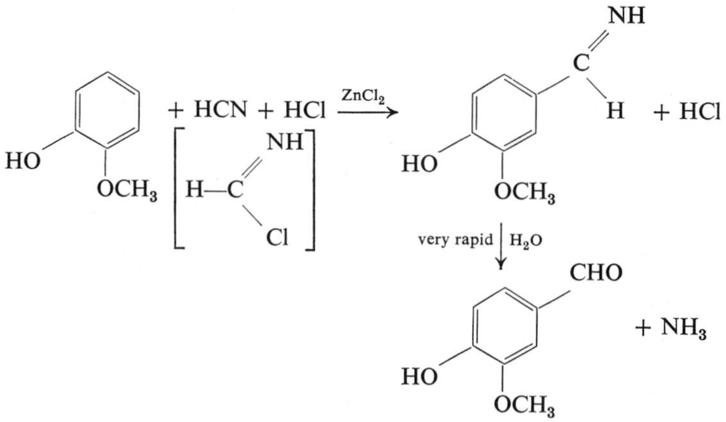

$$(33)$$

appreciable odor, especially if the operator is smoking, and is less hazardous than carbon monoxide. Furthermore, it is usually satisfactory to generate the hydrogen cyanide and the catalytic agent *in situ* by use of zinc cyanide, as in Eq. 34.

$$Zn(CN)_2 + 2HCl \longrightarrow 2HCN + ZnCl_2 \tag{34}$$

The product of the reaction shown in Eq. 33, vanillin, is one of the active flavor components in vanilla extract. The synthetic components are now used almost exclusively in foods. Synthesis of phenols will be discussed later (Chaps. 19 and 20).

Condensation of trichloroacetaldehyde. If the positive character of the carbonyl in an aldehyde is greatly increased by proximity to the trichloromethyl group (electron withdrawal by chlorine), the protonated species (conjugate acid) becomes sufficiently reactive to attack benzene. The type of net reaction obtained is illustrated in Eq. 35, wherein is shown synthesis of the

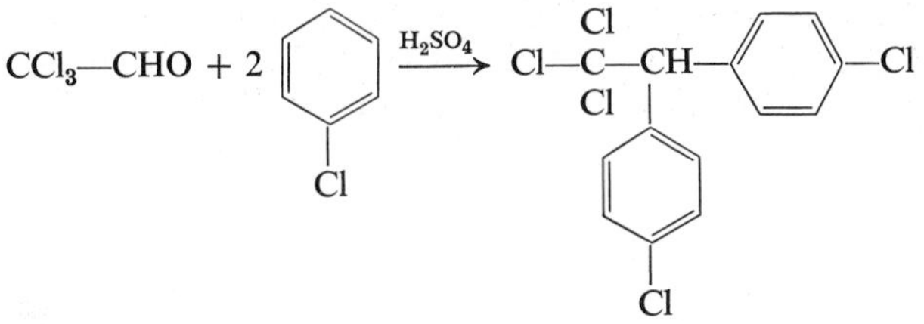

$$CCl_3{-}CHO + 2 \underset{\displaystyle{Cl}}{\bigcirc} \xrightarrow{H_2SO_4} Cl{-}\underset{\displaystyle Cl}{\overset{\displaystyle Cl}{C}}{-}CH{\Big\langle}\bigcirc{\Big\rangle}{-}Cl \tag{35}$$

Trichloroacetaldehyde
(chloral)

1,1-Bis-(*p*-chlorophenyl)-
2,2,2-trichloroethane
(DDT)

insecticide DDT (abbreviation of the rather vague name, dichlorodiphenyltrichloroethane). A usual substitution of the protonated aldehyde in benzene would give the carbinol, $CCl_3{-}\underset{\displaystyle OH}{CH}{-}Ar$. The oxonium salt of this intermediate would dissociate quite readily to give the resonance-stabilized benzyl carbonium ion, $CCl_3{-}\underset{+}{CH}{-}Ar$, which would again substitute in the aromatic ring to give the final product.

EXERCISES

I. Write one correct name for each of the following compounds. It will prove convenient to use the common name, benzoic acid, which is accepted in the IUC system in place of benzenecarboxylic acid.

(a) 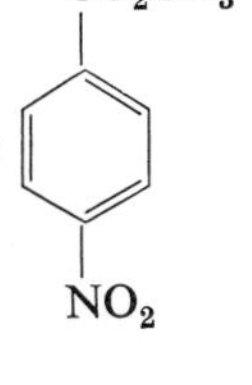 (CO$_2$CH$_3$ / NO$_2$ benzene structure)

(b) 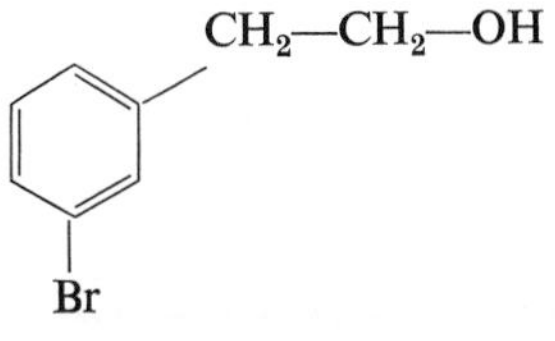 (Br / CH$_2$—CH$_2$—OH benzene structure)

(c) 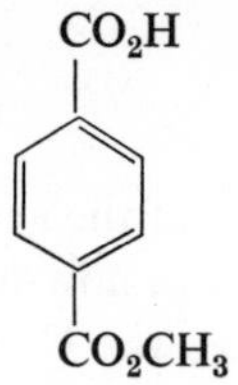

(d) 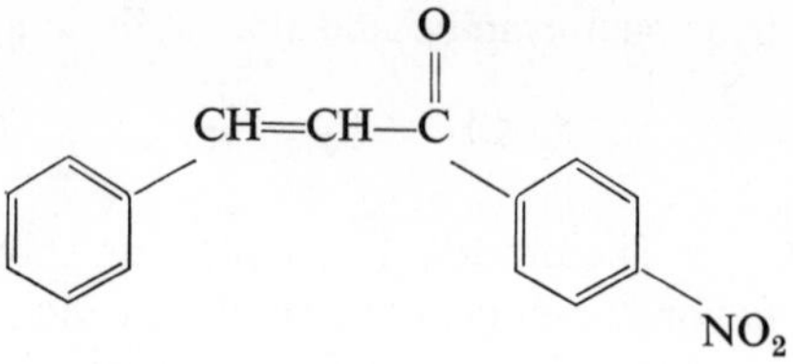

(e) 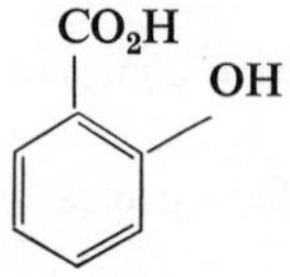

(f) 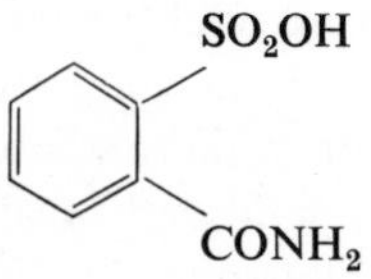

2. Suppose that each of the following compounds were nitrated under conditions appropriate for causing mononitration. At what position or positions would major substitution occur? How many isomers would result in significant quantity in each case?

(a) 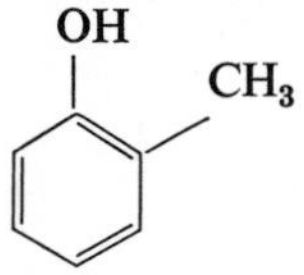

(b) 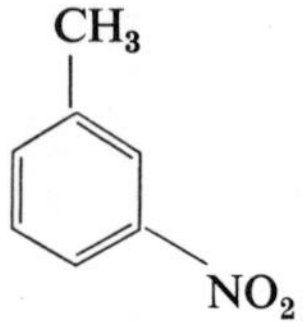

(c) 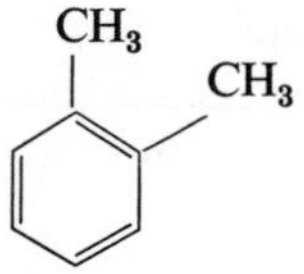

(d) 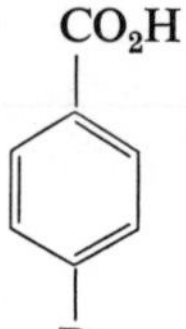

3. Indicate practical methods for converting benzene to each of the following compounds, in one or more steps, using any desired reagents.

(a) 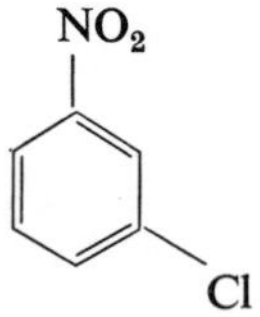

(b) 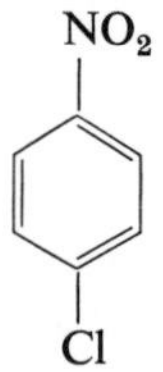

(c) 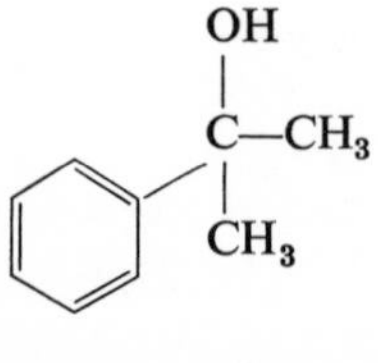

(d) 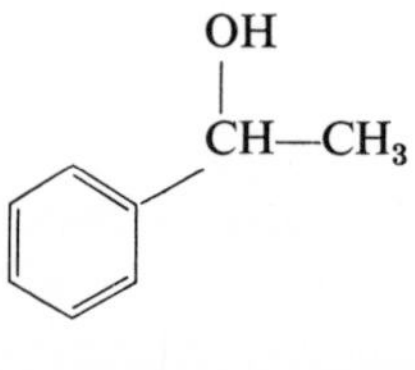

(e)

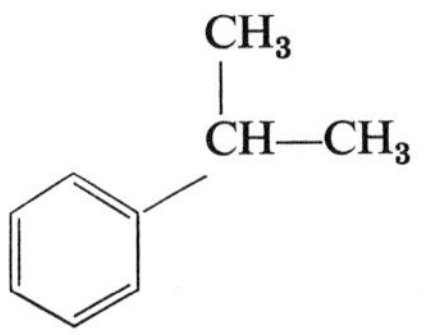

CH$_3$

CH—CH$_3$

(f)

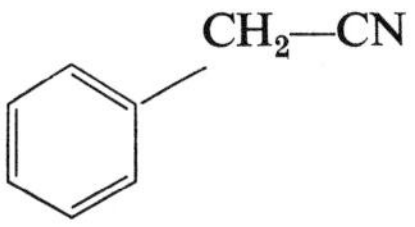

CH$_2$—CN

(g)

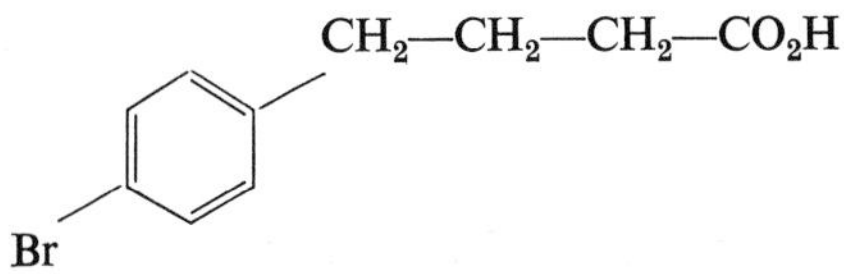

CH$_2$—CH$_2$—CH$_2$—CO$_2$H

Br

(h)

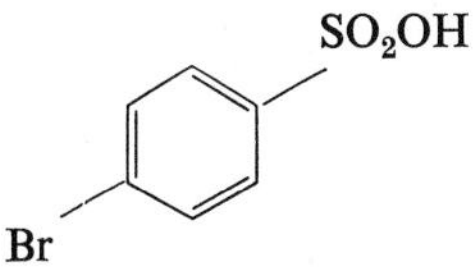

SO$_2$OH

Br

4. Write resonance forms which indicate that *meta* substitution would be expected in acetophenone. Consider both criteria for predicting directing influence.

5. Write resonance forms which indicate that toluene should be an *ortho,para-* director. Consider transition states for both *ortho* and *para* substitution.

6. Write resonance forms showing the chelate ring in *o*-nitroaniline.

7. Outline by equations a practical method for accomplishing the following conversion. Any desired reagents may be used, but the product should be obtained in a condition reasonably free of isomers.

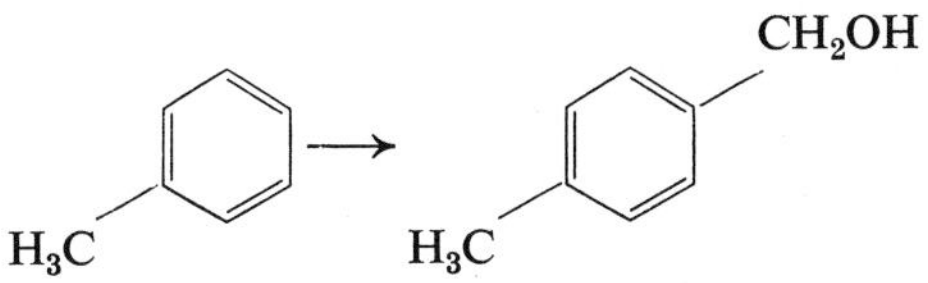

H$_3$C

$\longrightarrow$

CH$_2$OH

H$_3$C

18

Reactions and Characteristics of the Primary Products of Aromatic Substitution

Since most other aromatic compounds are synthesized directly or indirectly from the ones prepared by substitution, it is appropriate to consider next the properties and reactions of the primary substitution products. Further substitution in these compounds follows principles presented in the preceding chapter; therefore, the present chapter will be devoted primarily to reactions involving alteration of the functional group. The alkylbenzenes give few generally significant reactions other than substitution; however, there will be discussed the stable free radicals and ions which become possible when an alkane is highly substituted with aromatic groups.

In addition to the classes of aromatic compounds considered in the present chapter, there remain amines (Chap. 19), phenols (Chap. 20) and aromatic carboxylic acids (Chap. 21).

Aryl Halides

The aryl halides (halogenated aromatic compounds) differ from the other types of compounds discussed in the present chapter in that the most widely applicable synthesis of them is not direct substitution. The most useful syntheses of aryl halides are the Sandmeyer and Gattermann reactions which use primary aromatic amines as starting materials (Chap. 19). *Replacement of hydroxyl by halogen*, which is the most widely used synthesis of alkyl halides, *is rarely applicable to synthesis of aryl halides.* Except in instances where a pure isomer may be obtained by direct substitution, the aryl halides are usually made from an aromatic amine.

Reactions of Aryl Halides

The displacement reaction (S_N2 reaction) is quite difficult in the aromatic series, even with halogen as the leaving group. This is a consequence of the donation of electrons by halogen to the aromatic ring by resonance, the same phenomenon discussed in Chapter 12 for vinyl halides. This lowers the electron density on halogen and thus discourages its leaving as a negative group. It may be mentioned that this statement is not contrary to the observation that halogen lowers electron density in the benzene ring and thus slows up substitution. The resonance effect partially counterbalances the electrostatic attraction of electrons so that the electron density on halogen remains lower than is the case when halogen is attached to an alkyl group and there is no competing process for shifting electron density. The difficulty in accomplishing displacement of halogen in aryl halides is responsible for major differences in synthetic routes in the aromatic and aliphatic series.

Since the displacement reaction is nucleophilic attack on the carbon bearing halogen, the slowness of the reaction is alleviated if this carbon is made more positive by substituents in the ring.[1] A nitro group is a particularly powerful electron-withdrawing group, hence causes a general reduction of electron density in the ring. In addition, there is a specific lowering of electron density on the carbon bearing halogen if the nitro group is *ortho* or *para*. This may be deduced by consideration of the following resonance forms:

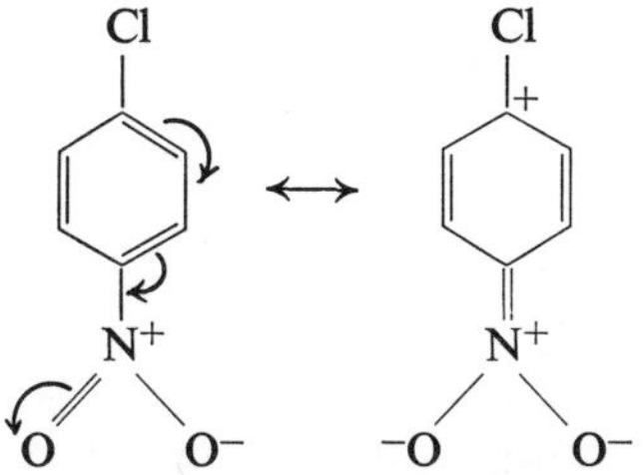

Of course similar resonance forms may be written for the *ortho* position. With one *ortho* or *para* nitro group, the usual displacement reactions of halogen (by hydroxyl or alkoxyl) can be accomplished with some difficulty, and presence

---

[1] The "activation" of aromatic halides by various substituents in the ring has been studied by Professor Joseph Bunnett, now at Brown University but at the University of North Carolina when most of these investigations were carried out. A paper including discussion of some of Bunnett's results as well as those of other workers is that by Bunnett, Moe, and Knutson, *J. Am. Chem. Soc.* **76,** 3936 (1954).

of two or three nitro groups in these positions makes the rate comparable to that in the aliphatic series. This will be illustrated in the discussion of phenol synthesis below.

Presence of a second halogen in the ring also decreases electron density in the ring, hence increases rate of displacement. This is a general inductive effect, however, and is in addition to the effect of halogen in increasing electron density at positions *ortho* and *para* to it. The operation of these two effects is noted in rates of alkaline hydrolysis of one halogen in the dichlorobenzenes. The *p*-dichlorobenzene is hydrolyzed about twenty times as rapidly as chlorobenzene, but the *meta* and *ortho* isomers are hydrolyzed about forty times as rapidly as chlorobenzene. The inductive effect is stronger in the *ortho* isomer than in the *meta*, but the resonance effect in the *ortho* isomer partially neutralizes the inductive effect; so the rates turn out to be about the same in the *ortho* and *meta* isomers.

Displacement of halogen by hydroxyl (phenol synthesis). When the halogen is not activated by presence of electron-withdrawing groups in the ring, displacement by hydroxyl is very difficult. It is accomplished industrially by use of extreme conditions (Eq. 1). Since phenol is weakly acidic (cf. Chap.

$$\text{C}_6\text{H}_5\text{Cl} + \text{HOH} \xrightarrow[\substack{3000 \text{ p.s.i.} \\ \text{pressure}}]{\text{NaOH, } 320°} \text{C}_6\text{H}_5\text{OH} + \text{HCl} \qquad (1)$$
(as salts)

20), both it and the hydrochloric acid shown in Eq. 1 are actually obtained from the alkaline reaction mixture as salts.

With *o*- or *p*-nitrochlorobenzenes, hydrolysis under laboratory conditions is feasible (Eq. 2), and 2,4,6-trinitro-1-chlorobenzene hydrolyzes almost as easily as an acid chloride.

$$\text{(}o\text{-Cl-C}_6\text{H}_4\text{-NO}_2) + \text{HOH} \xrightarrow[\text{low pressure}]{\text{NaOH, } 140°} \text{(}o\text{-HO-C}_6\text{H}_4\text{-NO}_2) + \text{HCl} \qquad (2)$$
(as salts)

Replacement of halogen by cyano (nitrile synthesis). Aromatic halogen cannot be successfully replaced with cyano by use of sodium cyanide, as can be done in the aliphatic series; however, good yields can usually be realized by use of cuprous cyanide under the rather strenuous conditions shown in Eq. 3.

$$\text{C}_6\text{H}_5\text{Cl} + \text{CuCN} \xrightarrow[250°, \text{ pressure}]{\text{pyridine catalyst}} \text{C}_6\text{H}_5\text{CN} + \text{CuCl} \qquad (3)$$

Cyanobenzene
or benzonitrile

It should be emphasized that the process in Eq. 3, utilizing the covalently bonded cuprous cyanide, is not a simple displacement reaction. The mechanism of the reaction is complicated and not understood, but it is clearly not a displacement reaction. The pressures required for the cuprous cyanide reaction are easily handled in the laboratory, and the process is effective with chlorides, bromides, or iodides. Hydrolysis of the cyanide proceeds as has been described for aliphatic nitriles (Chap. 13), and this constitutes a good synthesis of aromatic carboxylic acids.

Grignard reagents. Aromatic chlorine is inert to reaction with magnesium, when the reaction is carried out in diethyl ether in the usual way; however, aryl bromides and iodides do react to form Grignard reagents in a normal manner. The bromides are especially useful (Eq. 4). The arylmagnesium

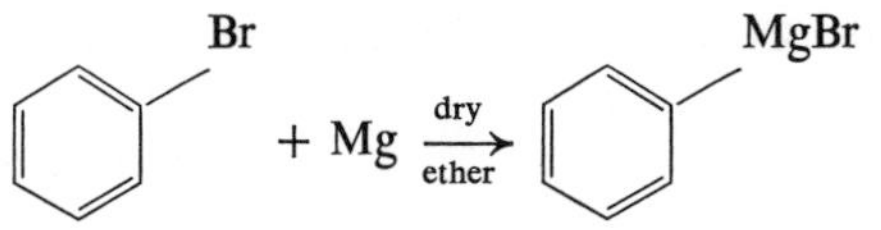

$$\text{(4)}$$

halides give all the reactions that have been discussed for Grignard reagents—with carbon dioxide, aldehydes, ketones, acid chlorides, esters, and nitriles. They are quite useful for making a variety of compounds in the aromatic series, and constitute a major utility of aromatic halides. Other groups may be in the aromatic ring provided that they do not react with the Grignard reagent. *Since all polar multiple bonds do react with the Grignard reagent*, this eliminates the *meta*-directing groups.

The inertness of chlorine[2] towards formation of a Grignard reagent may be turned to considerable advantage, for a bromochlorobenzene may be put through a stepwise sequence such as outlined in Eq. 5.

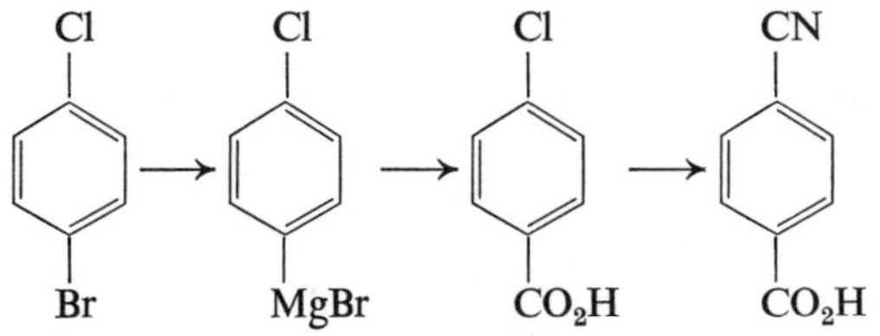

$$\text{(5)}$$

The aromatic chlorine will react with lithium to give a lithium reagent, as shown in Eq. 6. In most reactions, the lithium derivative gives the same products as the Grignard reagent, and they have proved to be very useful intermediates

---

[2] It was reported in 1957 [H. E. Ramsden, A. E. Balint, W. R. Whitford, I. I. Walburn and R. Cserr, *J. Org. Chem.* **22,** 1202 (1957)] that an aryl chloride will react with magnesium if there is used as solvent the cyclic ether, tetrahydrofuran. The Grignard reagent so formed appears to be normal in all reactions, so this provides an alternative to use of lithium in order to secure an organometallic reagent from an aryl chloride.　　　　　　　　　　　　　　　　　　Tetrahydrofuran

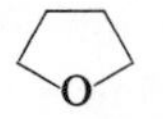

for conversion of the aryl chlorides to other aromatic derivatives. In one reaction, the lithium derivative gives a different product from the Grignard reagent. Whereas carbonation of a Grignard reagent gives a carboxylic acid

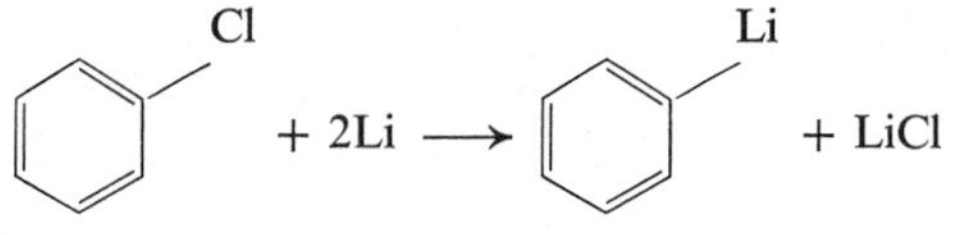

$$
\begin{array}{ccc}
\text{Cl} & & \text{Li} \\
\bigcirc\!\!-\!\! & + \ 2\text{Li} \longrightarrow & \bigcirc\!\!-\!\! & + \ \text{LiCl}
\end{array}
\qquad (6)
$$

(Eq. 13-16), the chief product from a lithium reagent is a symmetrical ketone (Eq. 7). The Grignard reagent fails to give this reaction at a significant rate because of the insolubility of the magnesium salt of the carboxylic acid.

$$
\text{R—Li} + \text{R—CO}_2\text{Li} \longrightarrow \text{R—}\!\!\underset{\substack{| \\ \text{R}}}{\overset{\substack{\text{OLi} \\ |}}{\text{C}}}\!\!\text{—OLi} \xrightarrow{\text{H}_2\text{O}} \text{R—}\!\!\underset{\substack{|| \\ \text{O}}}{\text{C}}\!\!\text{—R} + 2\text{LiOH}
\qquad (7)
$$

Nitro Compounds

Reduction is the only reaction of aromatic nitro compounds which is of general interest; this process may lead to several types of compounds, including the very useful primary aromatic amines. The amines give so many useful reactions (Chap. 19) that their precursors, the nitro compounds, become the most widely synthesized intermediates in the benzene series. The ease of purification of nitro compounds (cf. Chap. 17) is an additional important factor in their usefulness.

Reduction to Primary Amines

Complete reduction of a nitro compound to give a primary amine, indicated in Eq. 8, may be accomplished in a really large variety of procedures.

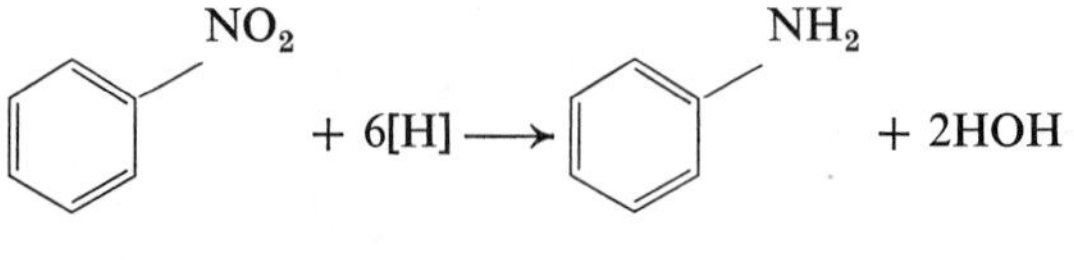

$$
\begin{array}{ccc}
\text{NO}_2 & & \text{NH}_2 \\
\bigcirc\!\!-\!\! & + \ 6[\text{H}] \longrightarrow & \bigcirc\!\!-\!\! & + \ 2\text{HOH}
\end{array}
\qquad (8)
$$

Among the successful methods are (a) chemical reduction in acidic, basic, or neutral medium, employing such agents as zinc and acid, tin and acid, iron and water with catalytic amounts of acid, or sodium and alcohol; (b) catalytic hydrogenation, employing nearly any catalyst, including nickel, platinum, copper chromite, or palladium; (c) electrolytic reduction in neutral or alkaline medium. In general, catalytic hydrogenation is likely to be most useful, but chemical reduction is sometimes able to avoid reduction of other groups attacked by the catalytic method. The essentially neutral iron and water reduction

is often an especially good method for chemical reduction; it avoids side reactions encountered in acid or alkaline media. Electrolytic reduction may be
more useful than the relatively small investigation of it would suggest.

Intermediate Reduction Products

Although the primary amine is by all odds the most important reduction
product of the nitro group, several different intermediate reduction products
may be obtained by use of suitable reagents. In connection with chemical
oxidation or reduction, it is well established on an empirical basis that when more
than one stage is possible, as in the reduction, A → B → C, *the compound
obtained depends on which reducing agent is used, not how much of it is used.* This,
of course, differs sharply from other types of reaction, where relative rates of
the consecutive reactions depend in part on the concentrations of the reactants.
For example, in bromination of benzene (Eq. 17-3), the use of excess of bromine
encourages formation of dibromobenzenes. In a reduction, a given reaction
will occur only if the **oxidation-reduction potential** of the reducing agent is equal
to or in excess of that for the compound being reduced. Oxidation-reduction
potentials of inorganic ions have been determined and tabulated under a set of
standard conditions, and these data are very useful in determining which
reactions will occur and which ones cannot occur. In organic reactions, such
data have been applied on a very limited basis, partly because of the frequency
with which heterogeneous reaction systems are used and partly because the
oxidation-reduction potential of a given substance varies very greatly in different solvents. With organic molecules, the reaction obtained with a given
reducing agent under certain conditions remains almost entirely empirical. The
only prediction possible concerning the reducing agent to use is that which can
be based on data published for analogous compounds. A given functional
group will behave in the same way, however, in different molecules unless there
are present groups causing a substantial shift in electron density in the molecule.
An important instance of this latter situation follows.

Reduction of one of two identical nitro groups. In general, it is not
possible to secure reaction with only one of two identical groups; i.e., one
group will not react more or less completely while the second remains inert.
This is reasonable, since the groups should react at the same rate if they are
identical groups. If the groups are near each other, however, they may affect
each other's rates of reaction, as discussed earlier in this chapter for hydrolysis
of dichlorobenzenes. In the case of two nitro groups in the same benzene ring,
reduction of the first group occurs in an aromatic ring substituted by a powerful
electron-withdrawing group, the nitro group. Reduction of the second nitro
group, after the first has been reduced, occurs in an aromatic ring substituted
with a powerful electron-donating group, the amino group. Thus, it would
seem possible that there might be a preferential reduction of one nitro group,
and this proves to be the case. Ammonium polysulfide or sodium sulfide are
commonly used (Eq. 9), and yields are good. The nitro groups may be in any

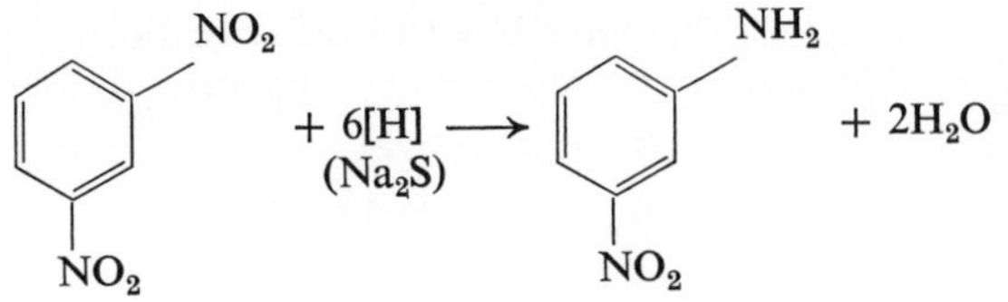

$$\text{NO}_2\text{-benzene-NO}_2 + 6[\text{H}] \xrightarrow[(\text{Na}_2\text{S})]{} \text{NH}_2\text{-benzene-NO}_2 + 2\text{H}_2\text{O} \qquad (9)$$

orientation, but it should be noted that if the two nitro groups are not identical a mixture of products results (Eq. 10).

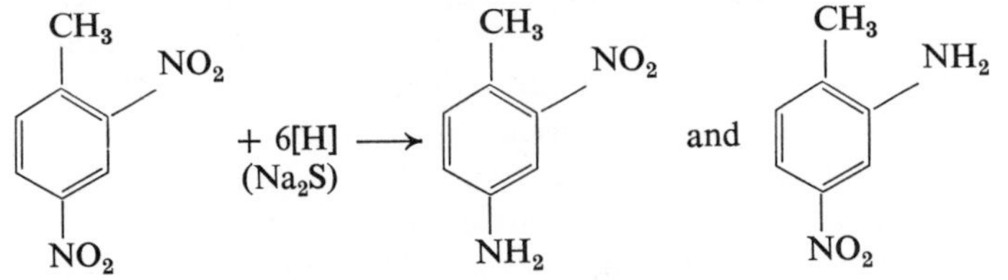

$$\text{CH}_3\text{-benzene-NO}_2,\text{NO}_2 + 6[\text{H}] \xrightarrow[(\text{Na}_2\text{S})]{} \text{CH}_3\text{-benzene-NO}_2,\text{NH}_2 \quad \text{and} \quad \text{CH}_3\text{-benzene-NH}_2,\text{NO}_2 \qquad (10)$$

Reduction in acid medium. The intermediate products formed in acid medium are outlined in Eq. 11, and reagents suitable for yielding one of the

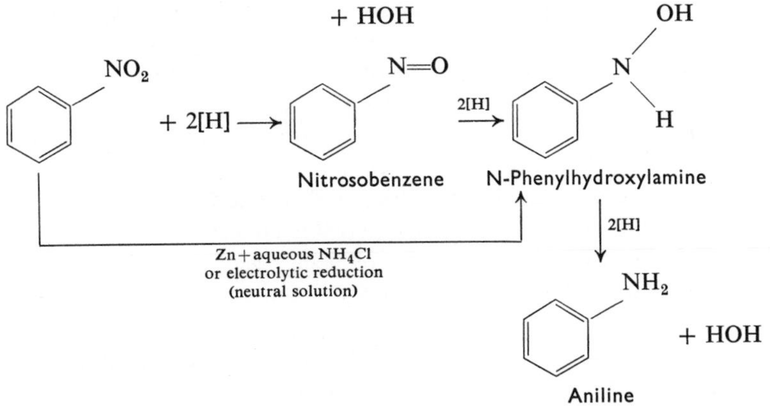

$$\text{C}_6\text{H}_5\text{NO}_2 + 2[\text{H}] \longrightarrow \underset{\text{Nitrosobenzene}}{\text{C}_6\text{H}_5\text{N}{=}\text{O}} \xrightarrow{2[\text{H}]} \underset{\text{N-Phenylhydroxylamine}}{\text{C}_6\text{H}_5\text{N}(\text{OH})\text{H}}$$

+ HOH

Zn + aqueous NH$_4$Cl
or electrolytic reduction
(neutral solution)

$$\xrightarrow{2[\text{H}]} \underset{\text{Aniline}}{\text{C}_6\text{H}_5\text{NH}_2} + \text{HOH} \qquad (11)$$

intermediates are shown. Under all conditions tried, nitrosobenzene is reduced more rapidly than nitrobenzene; therefore it has not been possible to isolate nitrosobenzene from this reduction. Nitrosobenzene may be obtained from N-phenylhydroxylamine by oxidation with dichromate or ferric ion, however, and reduction of nitrosobenzene under the conditions shown in Eq. 11 gives phenyl-hydroxylamine. For this reason and others, nitrosobenzene is believed to be an intermediate in the reduction of nitrobenzene.

Certain substituted N-phenylhydroxylamines are useful as photographic developers; however, a larger use of them is for *rearrangement to p-aminophenols*, as shown in Eq. 12. The *p*-aminophenols are also employed as photographic developers, and have numerous other uses; an important one is for synthesis of benzoquinones, described in Chapter 20.

Occurrence of the *p*-aminophenol rearrangement can be a serious side reaction when reduction to aniline is carried out in strongly acid solution.

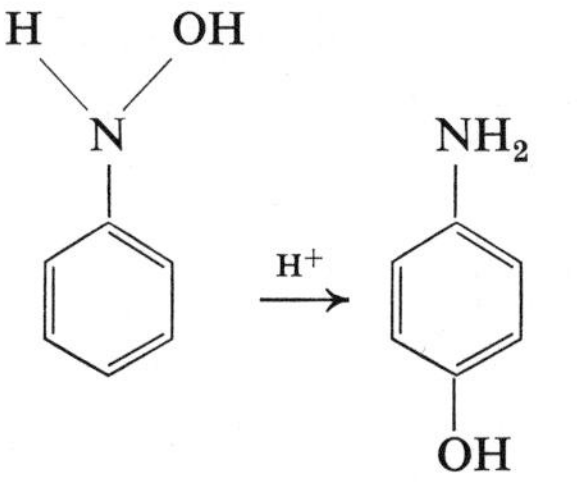

$$
\text{(12)}
$$

Reduction in alkaline medium. When reduction is carried out in alkaline medium, the two intermediate products shown in Eq. 11 condense with each other (Eq. 13) more rapidly than they are reduced. It follows that products

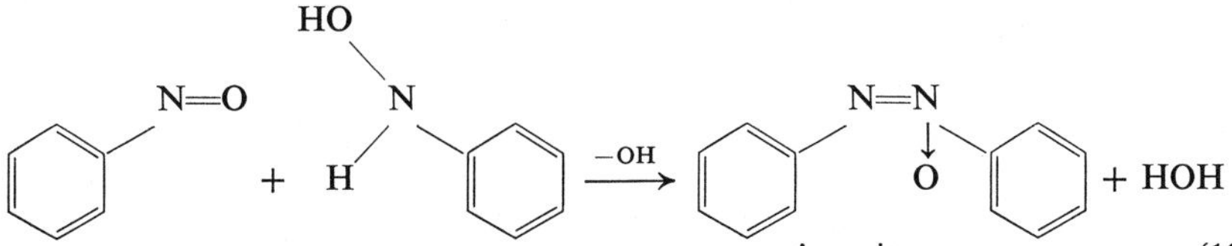

Azoxybenzene   (13)

obtained in alkaline medium will be those obtained by further reduction of azoxybenzene. The intermediates obtainable in alkaline medium, and certain reagents yielding them, are shown in outline form in Eq. 14.

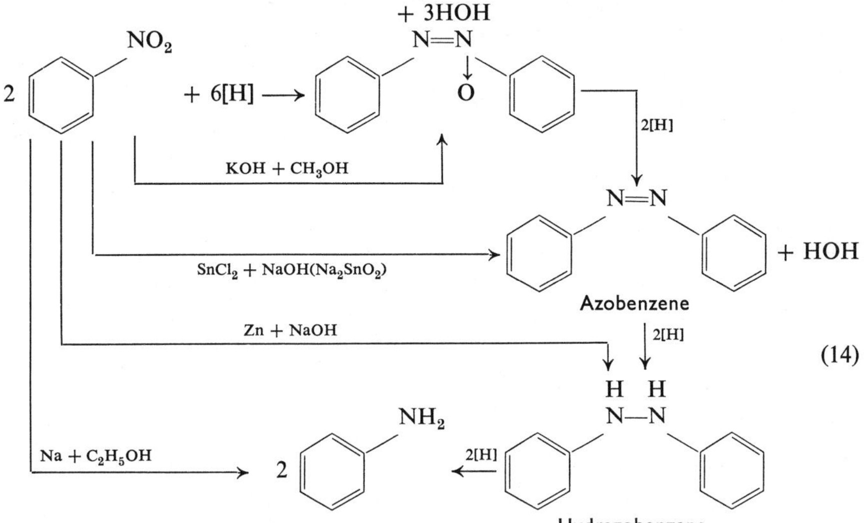

$$
\text{(14)}
$$

The processes shown in Eq. 14 are the chief methods used for obtaining the types of intermediate compounds shown. Of these intermediates, the most useful type is hydrazobenzene, which gives the interesting and useful **benzidine**

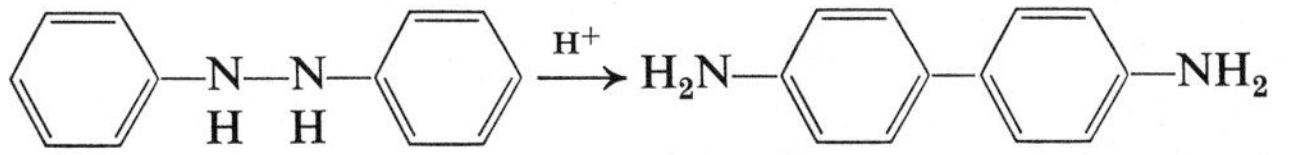

$$
\text{(15)}
$$

Benzidine or 4,4′-diaminobiphenyl

rearrangement, shown in Eq. 15. This rearrangement occurs in the *para* position; so rearrangement of 2,2'-dimethylhydrazobenzene (from reduction of *o*-

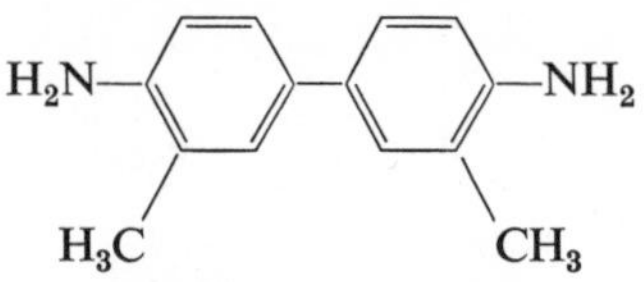

3,3'-Dimethylbenzidine

nitrotoluene) gives 3,3'-dimethylbenzidine. The benzidines find considerable use in making dyes (cf. Chap. 19).

Sulfonic Acids

The sulfonic acids are strong acids, that is, completely ionized in solution, and their properties are those of compounds containing an ionic bond. They are nearly always solids, frequently decompose on melting, and have such a low volatility that they cannot be distilled in the ordinary sense. They are usually nearly insoluble in organic solvents and so soluble in water that crystallization is difficult. Furthermore, the highly corrosive free acids are frequently hygroscopic and therefore difficult to store. For these reasons, the sulfonic acids are commonly isolated as their sodium or potassium salts, which are neutral compounds usually amenable to isolation by crystallization from water. It will be noted below that most of the important reactions of these compounds are conveniently carried out on the salts.

The Acidity of Sulfonic Acids

As has been mentioned previously (Chap. 12), the acidity of all types of organic acids, except sulfonic acids and related compounds, may be satisfactorily explained on the basis of resonance stabilization of the anion. There is some evidence that the sulfonic acid group can exhibit resonance by virtue of accommodating ten valence electrons around the nucleus of sulfur. Although the lower molecular weight elements, containing electrons only in the first two principal energy levels, may have a maximum of eight electrons involved with valence, the larger atoms may have more. For example, phosphorus pentachloride, PCl_5, is a well-known stable compound in which phosphorus has ten valence electrons. Resonance forms for the sulfonate anion would be of the following type:

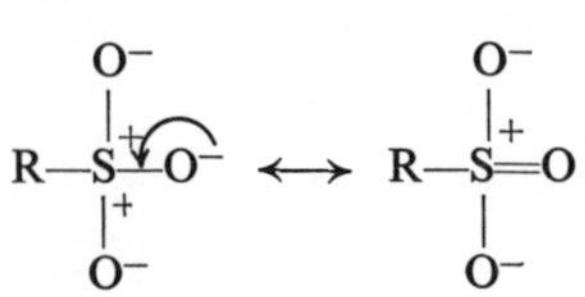

Two other similar forms have the double bond to the other oxygens. This theory seems quite inadequate to explain the complete dissociation of sulfonic acids, however, for the associated acid (hydrogen on one oxygen in above formula) has only one less resonance form than the anion.

Perhaps the best explanation of the high acidity of sulfonic acids lies in the double positive charge on the central sulfur, which is surrounded by negatively charged oxygens in the anion. This highly charged central nucleus would be expected to displace electrons toward it to such an extent as to decrease the charge on the surrounding oxygens and thus lower their attraction for a proton. This explanation is similar to the most probable explanation of the dissociation of halogen acids in solution. Halogen is so prone to hold electrons and withdraw them from surrounding atoms with which it is bonded that hydrogen readily leaves as a proton when a polar solvent helps stabilize the separated ions by solvation. The electron-attracting capacity of halogen is demonstrated in its effect on rate of benzene substitution (Chap. 17) and its effect on ionization of halogen acids (Chap. 13).

Characterization of Sulfonic Acids

Since sulfonic acids cannot be distilled in the ordinary sense and have poorly defined melting points, the two chief characteristics by which compounds are ordinarily identified are missing. The usual procedure for characterizing sulfonic acids is to convert them to derivatives which do have definite melting points.

One simple device which is frequently successful is forming a salt with an amine. The molecular weight of such salts is high enough to cause the one electrovalence to be such a small percentage of the compound that the covalent character becomes sufficiently dominant to give well-defined melting points. The amine frequently used is p-toluidine (p-methylaniline), and the salt is of the following structure:

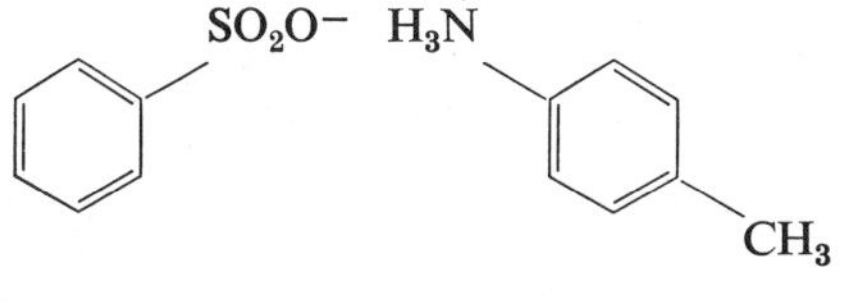

If the amine salts do not give satisfactory melting points, the amide of the sulfonic acid may be formed. The simple amides are very frequently solids which give sharp melting points. The amide must be formed from the acid chloride in the sulfonic acid series, and the acid chloride is usually prepared from the acid or its salt and phosphorus pentachloride (Eq. 16). Other methods of forming acid chlorides and amides, effective in the carboxylic acid series, *are not satisfactory in the sulfonic acid series*. If a substituted amide is desired, an amine can be used instead of ammonia in the last step of Eq. 16.

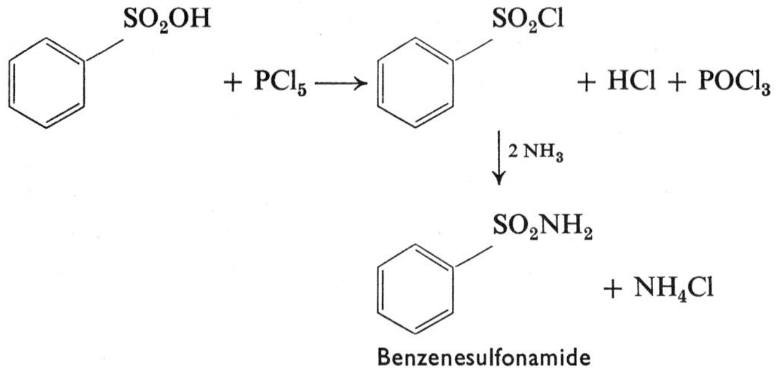

$$SO_2OH + PCl_5 \longrightarrow SO_2Cl + HCl + POCl_3$$

$$\downarrow 2\,NH_3$$

$$SO_2NH_2 + NH_4Cl$$

(16)

Benzenesulfonamide

Reactions Involving Replacement of the Sulfonic Acid Group

Sulfonic acids are sufficiently stable to allow use of the very strenuous conditions usually necessary to replace a group attached to the aromatic ring. Furthermore, the sulfonation reaction is reversible (cf. Chap. 17); so the sulfonic acid group can be removed by hydrolysis.

Hydrolytic removal of the sulfonic acid group is nothing more than the reversal of sulfonation (Eq. 17-16). The removal, carried out under conditions shown in Eq. 17, is sometimes desired after the sulfonic group has been put into

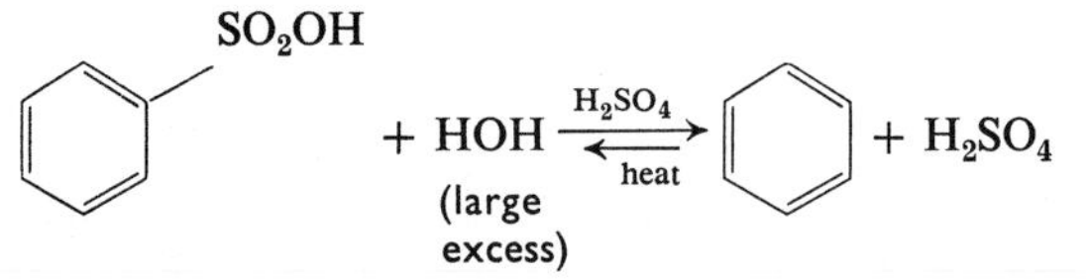

$$SO_2OH + HOH \underset{\text{heat}}{\overset{H_2SO_4}{\rightleftarrows}} + H_2SO_4$$

(large excess)

(17)

a ring to block a substitution position and thus allow a second substitution to occur at another point. This device is not used as often as is substitution of nitro and later removal after reduction to amino. The latter device will be specifically illustrated in the next chapter.

Replacement by hydroxyl (phenol synthesis). Fusion of sulfonic acid salts with potassium hydroxide usually gives an excellent yield of phenol. The process is shown in Eq. 18. Since phenols are weak acids, the free phenol is obtained by solution of the cooled melt with water and addition of a strong acid. This process gives good yields for various substituted sulfonic acids and

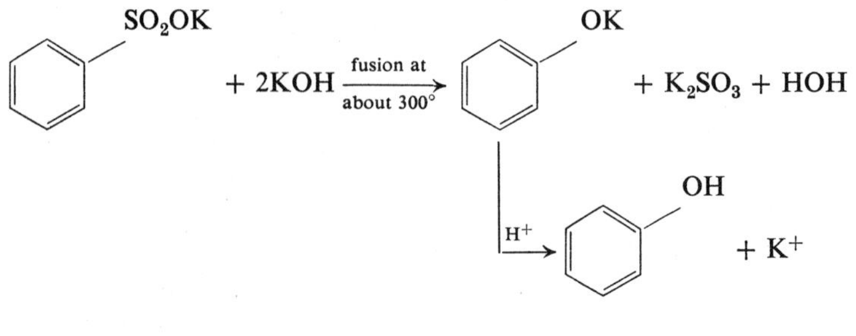

$$SO_2OK + 2KOH \xrightarrow[\text{about }300°]{\text{fusion at}} OK + K_2SO_3 + HOH$$

$$\downarrow \overset{H^+}{\longrightarrow} OH + K^+$$

(18)

for disulfonic acids. It fails with compounds containing groups such as the aldehyde group which are unstable to hot alkali.

Replacement by cyano. This reaction requires such drastic conditions (Eq. 19) that the yields are usually poor. It is occasionally used in the benzene

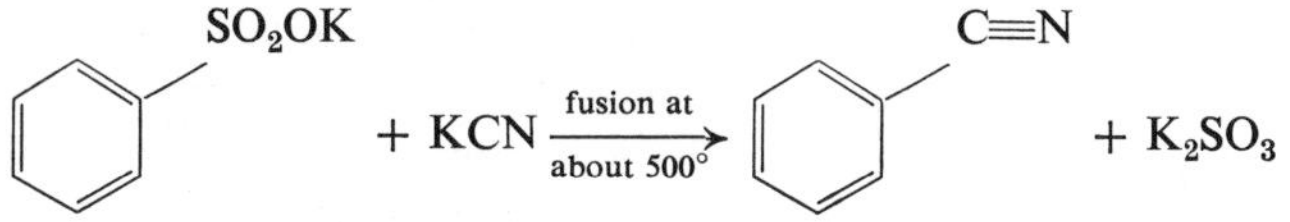

$$\underset{\text{SO}_2\text{OK}}{\bigcirc} + \text{KCN} \xrightarrow[\text{about 500}^\circ]{\text{fusion at}} \underset{\text{C}\equiv\text{N}}{\bigcirc} + \text{K}_2\text{SO}_3 \qquad (19)$$

series, but is more common in the naphthalene series (cf. Chap. 29) where obtaining of nitriles through the halide (Eq. 3) or the amine (Eq. 19-50) is sometimes not feasible.

Formation and Reactions of Functional Derivatives of Sulfonic Acids

The sulfonic acids form the same types of functional derivatives as do carboxylic acids; that is, acid chlorides, esters, and amides. In the sulfonic acid series, however, the derivatives are always much less reactive than are the corresponding carboxylic acid derivatives. Where similar reactions are exhibited, rates are much lower in the sulfonic acid series. The amides and esters are always formed from the acid chlorides.

Sulfonyl chlorides. The preparation of sulfonyl chlorides from the acids has been described in Eq. 16. It is sometimes convenient to prepare the acid chlorides by use of chlorosulfonic acid, and this process is described in connection with synthesis of aminosulfonamides (Eq. 26).

The sulfonyl chlorides react with compounds containing hydrogen on oxygen or nitrogen, as do carboxylic acid chlorides (cf. Chap. 14), but at a much lower rate. For example, benzenesulfonyl chloride reacts with cold water to give the sulfonic acid during a period of a few days, and reacts during a few minutes with boiling water. A sulfonyl chloride can be precipitated from a reaction mixture with water, then dried, without appreciable loss.

In contrast with the sulfonic acids, the sulfonyl chlorides can be readily reduced to give either sulfinic acids (Eq. 20) or thiophenols (Eq. 21). These

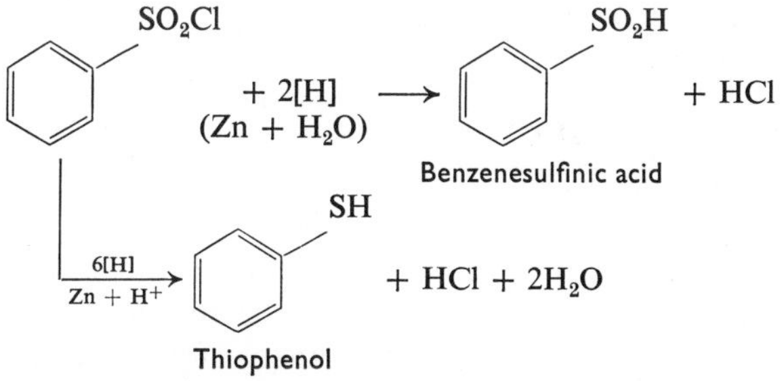

$$\underset{\text{SO}_2\text{Cl}}{\bigcirc} \begin{array}{c} + 2[\text{H}] \\ \text{(Zn + H}_2\text{O)} \end{array} \longrightarrow \underset{\text{SO}_2\text{H}}{\bigcirc} + \text{HCl} \qquad (20)$$

Benzenesulfinic acid

$$\xrightarrow[\text{Zn + H}^+]{6[\text{H}]} \underset{\text{SH}}{\bigcirc} + \text{HCl} + 2\text{H}_2\text{O} \qquad (21)$$

Thiophenol

reactions constitute important methods for preparation of these classes of compounds. The thiophenols are weakly acidic, on account of resonance stabilization of the anion (cf. Chap. 20 concerning acidity of phenols) and, in addition, the strongly electron-attracting character of sulfur.

The sulfinic acids are weak acids, not completely ionized in solution as are the sulfonic acids. This may be interpreted as due to removal of one charge from the central sulfur atom in the anion. The structure of the associated sulfinic acid is subject to some uncertainty. The method of preparation (Eq. 20) would suggest structure A since the halogen removed by reduction is definitely

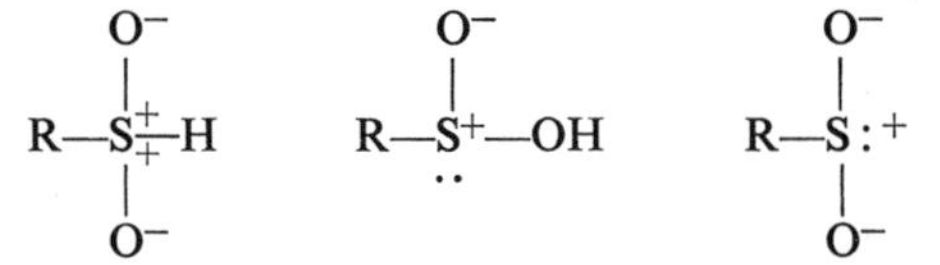

$$
\begin{array}{ccc}
\text{O}^- & \text{O}^- & \text{O}^- \\
| & | & | \\
\text{R}-\overset{+}{\underset{+}{\text{S}}}-\text{H} & \text{R}-\overset{+}{\text{S}}-\text{OH} & \text{R}-\overset{+}{\text{S}}: \\
| & \ddots & | \\
\text{O}^- & & \text{O}^- \\
\text{(A)} & \text{(B)} & \text{Sulfinate anion}
\end{array}
$$

on sulfur; however, this is not a reliable criterion. Regardless of whether A or B is the correct structure for the associated acid, the anion would have the structure shown. Since the acid does ionize to some extent, the hydrogen has ample opportunity to become attached to the atom regarded by it as most favorable. There is some reason to doubt that the positively charged proton would prefer the positively charged sulfur rather than the negatively charged oxygen (however, cf. Exercise 2 of this chapter).

This discussion of the structure of sulfinic acids is included partly to demonstrate that deduction of structure from method of preparation may be hazardous. For similar reasons, it is also hazardous to deduce structure entirely on the basis of structures of products formed from chemical reactions of a given compound. In both instances, uncertainty may arise because of occurrence of reactions (especially rearrangements) in addition to the reaction anticipated.

Sulfonic acid esters. As has been mentioned previously, the esters cannot be satisfactorily prepared by direct esterification; the sulfonyl chloride must be used, as shown in Eq. 22. The sulfonic esters do not exhibit the nu-

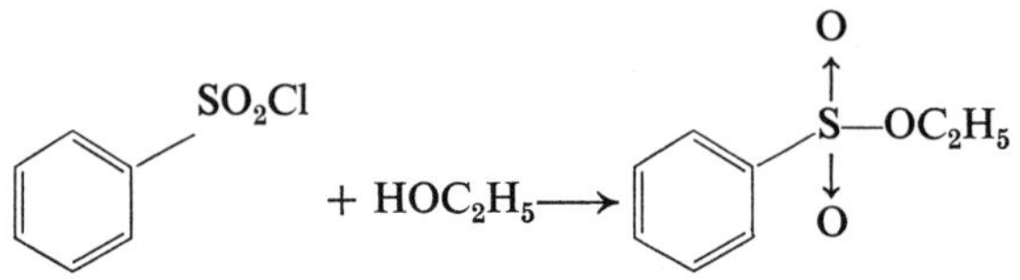

$$
\text{C}_6\text{H}_5\text{SO}_2\text{Cl} + \text{HOC}_2\text{H}_5 \longrightarrow \text{C}_6\text{H}_5\text{SO}_2\text{OC}_2\text{H}_5 \tag{22}
$$

Ethyl benzenesulfonate

merous useful reactions shown by the esters of carboxylic acids. In the reactions which they give, cleavage occurs between oxygen and alkyl; in other words, the sulfonate anion is displaced from alkyl. This is the reaction that has been described for sulfate esters (cf. Eq. 14-30 and accompanying discussion). Such a displacement is sometimes of utility, for synthesis of the sulfonate ester from the alcohol (Eq. 22) does not involve rupture of the bond between oxygen and carbon in the alcohol. This becomes of importance in instances where displacement of hydroxyl with halogen by usual methods results in carbonium ion formation and resultant rearrangement (cf. Chap. 6). The only practical method for converting a secondary alcohol to the corresponding bromide, *with no rearrangement at all*, is *via* the sulfonate ester, as in Eq. 23.

$$C_3H_7\!-\!CH\!-\!CH_3 + Ar\!-\!SO_2Cl \longrightarrow C_3H_7\!-\!CH\!-\!OSO_2\!-\!Ar + HCl$$
$$\underset{OH}{|} \qquad\qquad\qquad\qquad \underset{CH_3}{|} \quad \Big\downarrow {\scriptstyle Br^-}$$

$$C_3H_7\!-\!CH\!-\!Br + Ar\!-\!SO_2O^- \quad (23)$$
$$\underset{CH_3}{|}$$

Sulfonic esters may be saponified to give the sulfonic acids, but the reaction is much slower than with carboxylic acids.

Sulfonamides. Preparation of sulfonamides has already been indicated in Eq. 16. Naming of N-substituted sulfonamides follows the same principles used to name amides of carboxylic acids, as shown in the following examples.

m-Chloro-N-ethyl-
benzenesulfonamide

N-Ethyl-N-methyl-
benzenesulfonamide

Benzenesulfonamide
anion

If at least one hydrogen is present on the nitrogen of a sulfonamide, the compound is weakly acidic. This may be ascribed to attraction of the doubly charged sulfur for electrons, which is sufficient to displace the electrons in nitrogen enough to overcome the normal tendency of nitrogen to donate electrons and thus be basic (cf. Chap. 19).

The sulfonamides are of little interest for their chemical reactions, but certain of the sulfonamide derivatives have proved of considerable interest in medicine. Two of these are probably worthy of mention although their use has declined considerably since about 1945.

The sodium salt of N-chloro-*p*-toluenesulfonamide may be prepared as shown in Eq. 24. The *p*-toluenesulfonamide is prepared from the sulfonyl chloride, in turn secured by chlorosulfonation (cf. Eq. 26) of toluene. Both the *ortho* and *para* isomers are obtained, but are separable (for utilization of the *ortho* isomer, cf. Eq. 21-13). Chloramine T is an effective and noncorrosive antiseptic agent. This effect is probably due to the fact that the water in tissues causes a slow reversal of Eq. 24 to give a constantly renewed supply of the sodium hypochlorite, which is germicidal.

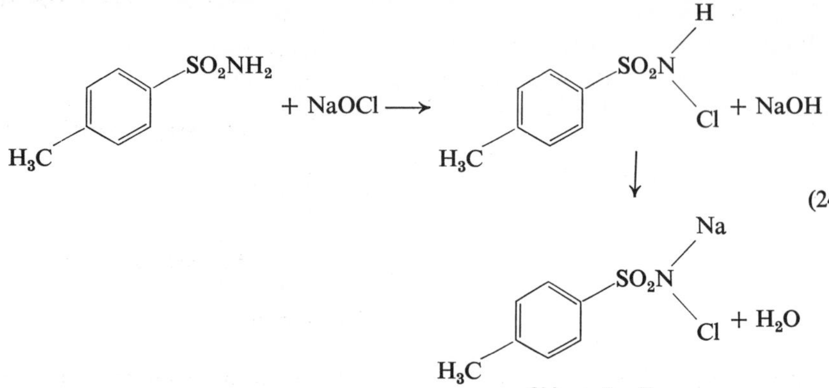

Chloramine T

$$(24)$$

The **p-aminobenzenesulfonamides,** known as "sulfa drugs," were widely used for a period as agents to kill bacterial infections. They are administered orally. A drawback to these agents is the specific sensitivity to them which has been developed by many people; however, they have remained the most effective agents against certain infections. The first of these drugs was the simple amide of p-aminobenzenesulfonic acid (sulfanilic acid), whose chemical and trade name is sulfanilamide. Synthesis of this compound will serve to illustrate a general method for obtaining sulfa drugs.

The synthesis of sulfanilamide cannot proceed directly from the acid chloride of sulfanilic acid, for the acid chloride would react with the amino group of another molecule, and this process would continue to give a polymer. The amino can be protected by acylation, however, and the protecting group can be removed after the acid chloride has been formed and allowed to react. The sequence for forming sulfanilamide is shown in Eq. 26 and the acetylation of aniline is shown in Eq. 25. The process in Eq. 26 includes certain interesting reactions. In the first line of this equation is shown the process of substitution of the sulfonic acid group and formation of its acid chloride in one sequence, by use of the mono-acid chloride of sulfuric acid (chlorosulfonic acid). This is believed to involve two steps: (a) reaction of the acid chloride in a Friedel and Crafts type of reaction to give the sulfonic acid and hydrogen chloride, (b) conversion of the sulfonic acid to the acid chloride by a second molecule of chlorosulfonic acid (which goes to sulfuric acid). The final step in the sequence in Eq. 26 illustrates the slower rate of reaction of sulfonic acid derivatives. The carboxylic amide is readily hydrolyzed with essentially no attack on the sulfonamide; so

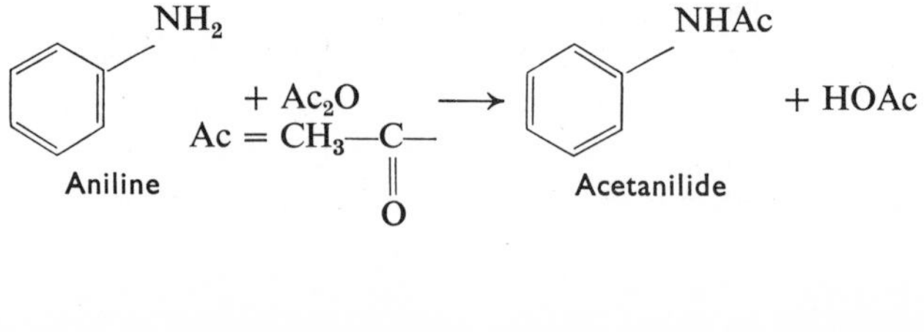

$$(25)$$

Aniline $Ac = CH_3-\overset{\displaystyle O}{\underset{\displaystyle \|}{C}}-$ Acetanilide

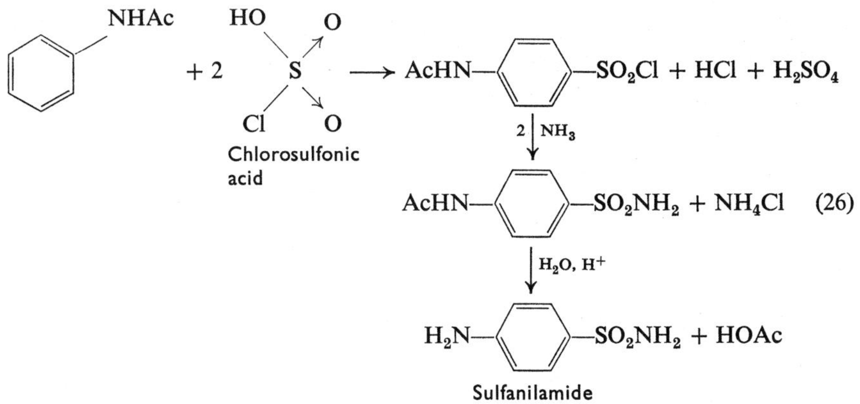

$$\text{C}_6\text{H}_5\text{NHAc} + 2 \; \underset{\substack{\text{Chlorosulfonic} \\ \text{acid}}}{\overset{\substack{\text{HO} \quad \text{O}}}{\text{S}}} \longrightarrow \text{AcHN}\!\!-\!\!\bigcirc\!\!-\!\!\text{SO}_2\text{Cl} + \text{HCl} + \text{H}_2\text{SO}_4$$

$$\xrightarrow{2 \; \text{NH}_3} \text{AcHN}\!\!-\!\!\bigcirc\!\!-\!\!\text{SO}_2\text{NH}_2 + \text{NH}_4\text{Cl} \quad (26)$$

$$\xrightarrow{\text{H}_2\text{O}, \; \text{H}^+} \text{H}_2\text{N}\!\!-\!\!\bigcirc\!\!-\!\!\text{SO}_2\text{NH}_2 + \text{HOAc}$$

Sulfanilamide

the protecting group is removable from the amino without injury to the rest of the molecule.

The various substituted sulfonamides which have been used as chemotherapeutic agents can be synthesized by substitution of a primary amine for ammonia in Eq. 26, second step. Examples of useful drugs and the amines from which they are formed follow:

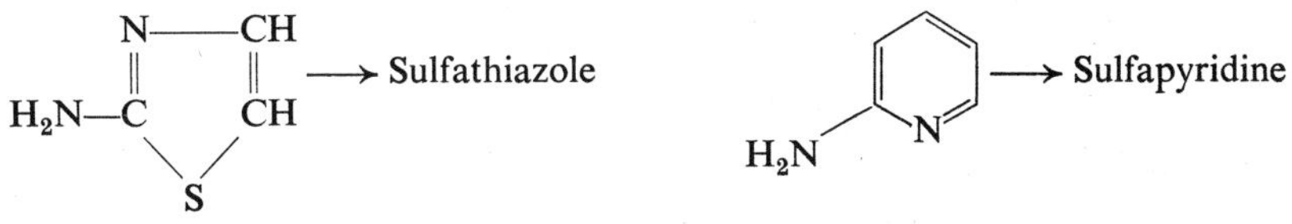

$$\text{H}_2\text{N}\!-\!\text{C}\overset{\text{N}\!-\!\text{CH}}{\underset{\text{S}}{\big\|\quad\big\|}}\text{CH} \longrightarrow \text{Sulfathiazole}$$

2-Aminothiazole

$$\text{H}_2\text{N}\!\!-\!\!\bigcirc\!\!\text{N} \longrightarrow \text{Sulfapyridine}$$

2-Aminopyridine

It should be mentioned that other methods of synthesis of the sulfa drugs have been devised, and some of the amines that have been used are of somewhat more complicated structure.

Stable Free Radicals, Carbonium Ions and Carbanions

The Friedel and Crafts reaction on carbon tetrachloride results in replacement of only three halogens (Eq. 27); steric hindrance blocks reaction of the fourth chlorine, so that the product of the reaction is triphenylmethyl chloride.

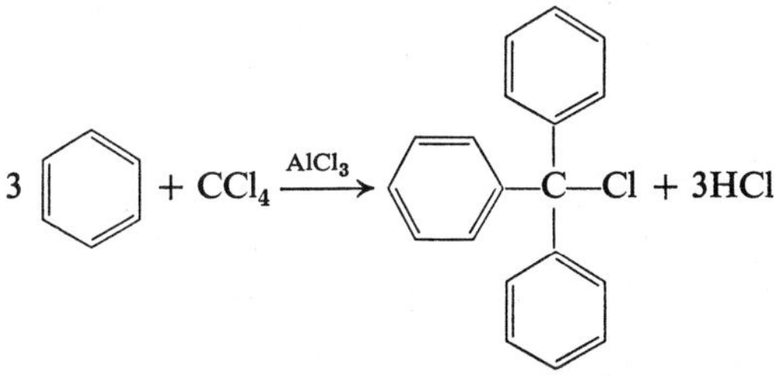

$$3 \; \text{C}_6\text{H}_6 + \text{CCl}_4 \xrightarrow{\text{AlCl}_3} (\text{C}_6\text{H}_5)_3\text{C}\!-\!\text{Cl} + 3\text{HCl} \quad (27)$$

In 1901, Moses Gomberg, then Professor of Chemistry at the University of Michigan, carried out the reaction shown in Eq. 28 in order to get hexaphenyl-

$$
\underset{\underset{C_6H_5}{|}}{\overset{\overset{C_6H_5}{|}}{2C_6H_5-C-Cl}} + 2Ag \longrightarrow \underset{\underset{H_5C_6}{|}\;\underset{C_6H_5}{|}}{\overset{\overset{H_5C_6}{|}\;\overset{C_6H_5}{|}}{C_6H_5-C-C-C_6H_5}} + 2AgCl \tag{28}
$$

ethane. The coupling of two molecules of a halide by reaction with a metal is a well-known type of reaction, called a Wurtz reaction, although it is of little general importance because it is chiefly useful for synthesis of hydrocarbons. The mechanism of the conversion is uncertain. The reaction is mentioned here because of the remarkable properties which Gomberg reported for the product of the coupling reaction. They were not the properties expected at that time for hexaphenylethane.

Instead of being rather inert, as might be expected for a hydrocarbon, Gomberg's coupling product proved to be a very reactive substance, which combined rapidly with many reagents, including the oxygen of air. The most striking property was that the solid crystalline substance was white, but its solutions were orange. Evaporation of the orange-colored solution left the white crystals. Furthermore, the depth of color of the solution was dependent on the temperature. Determination of the molecular weight of the substance in solution gave a value substantially lower than that calculated for the hexaphenyl-ethane formula, and *the molecular weight also varied with temperature*. It soon became apparent that this behavior could be explained only by dissociation of hexaphenylethane in solution (Eq. 29). The associated hexaphenylethane is the

$$
\underset{\underset{H_5C_6}{|}\;\underset{C_6H_5}{|}}{\overset{\overset{H_5C_6}{|}\;\overset{C_6H_5}{|}}{C_6H_5-C-C-C_6H_5}} \rightleftharpoons \underset{\underset{C_6H_5}{|}}{\overset{\overset{C_6H_5}{|}}{C_6H_5-C\cdot}} + \underset{\underset{C_6H_5}{|}}{\overset{\overset{C_6H_5}{|}}{\cdot C-C_6H_5}} \tag{29}
$$

colorless substance which crystallizes from solution, while the orange free radicals give the solution its color. The position of the equilibrium depends on temperature.

The color of the free radical may be rationalized on the basis of resonance forms such as the following:

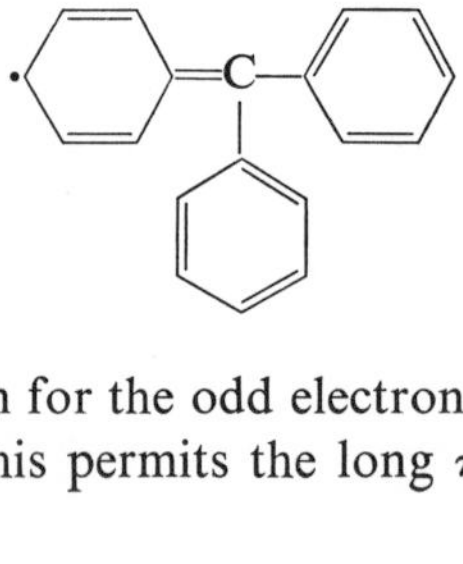

Similar forms may be written for the odd electron in each of the nine available *ortho* and *para* positions. This permits the long π-electron orbitals characteristic of colored substances.

Resonance stabilization of the free radical appears to be the major factor in lowering the energy of the radical to such an extent that dissociation of the carbon-carbon bond occurs. The carbon-carbon bond has such a large bond energy that dissociation can occur only if some factor causes a large lowering of the energy of the radicals. The steric crowding of so many large groups around a carbon helps the dissociation some, for this lowers the bond energy; but the major factor is resonance stabilization of the radicals. Several lines of investigation have established these factors in their relative importance; but two observations may be used as illustrations. First, if resonance stabilization of the radical is decreased by replacement of several of the phenyl groups in hexaphenylethane with cyclohexyl radicals (sterically larger than phenyl), there results a compound which does not dissociate in solution. Second, if resonance possibilities are increased by replacing phenyl with naphthyl, dissociation is increased. Tri-α-naphthylmethyl, shown below, is a free radical even in the crystalline condition, as shown by the deep violet color of the solid.

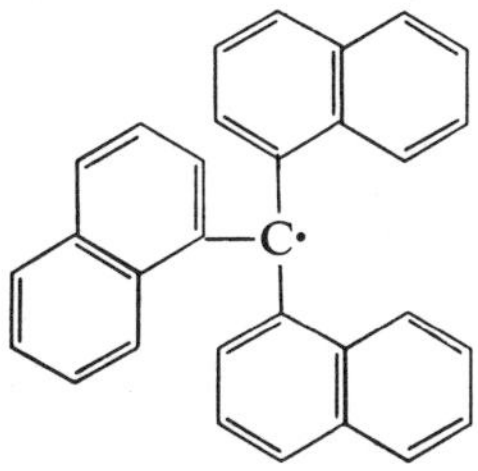

tri-α-Naphthylmethyl

The existence of free radicals sufficiently stable to be isolated and studied has had a profound effect on the thinking of organic chemists. In particular, the reality of free radicals as reaction intermediates (cf. Chap. 11) seems well established. The major difference between a methyl radical and a triphenyl-methyl radical is that the latter has its energy lowered by resonance to such an extent that it does not have the exceedingly high order of reactivity of the methyl radical. By experiments in flowing gas streams, it has been shown that free methyl radicals do exist, but the average life of such a radical is only about one one-hundredth of a second. If nothing else is present for reaction, two radicals will join to form a stable molecule, one of the reactions discussed in Chapter 11.

In a free radical the bond hybridization is sp^2; for only three electrons in carbon are engaged in bonding; therefore, all the bonds are in a plane, with the p orbital containing the lone electron at right angles to that plane. The carbonium ion, similarly, is "flat," but the carbanion probably retains its tetrahedral configuration, with the unshared electron pair in one orbital.

Other types of stable free radicals have been discovered. Perhaps the simplest of all is diphenylnitrogen, from dissociation of tetraphenylhydrazine, as shown in Eq. 30.

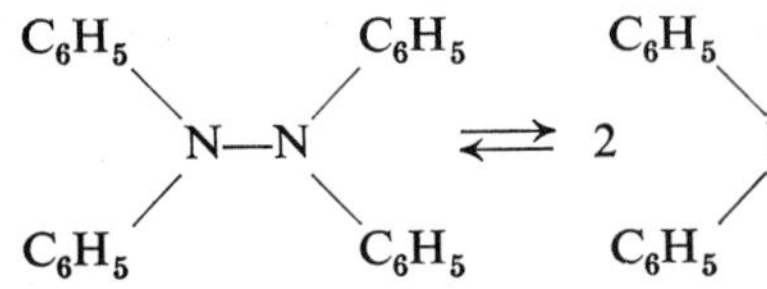

$$C_6H_5\diagdown \diagup C_6H_5 \qquad \qquad C_6H_5\diagdown$$
$$N—N \qquad \rightleftarrows 2 \qquad N\cdot \qquad\qquad (30)$$
$$C_6H_5\diagup \diagdown C_6H_5 \qquad\qquad C_6H_5\diagup$$

Stable carbonium ions and carbanions. Just as the free triphenyl-methyl radical is stabilized by resonance, the free cation or anion may also be similarly stabilized. Although hexaphenylmethane dissociates into free radicals in such solvents as benzene, dissociation into ions appears not to occur, even in ionizing solutions. The triphenylmethyl carbonium ion is obtained in solutions of triphenylmethyl chloride, for such solutions react with silver nitrate to give silver chloride in the manner of inorganic chlorides.

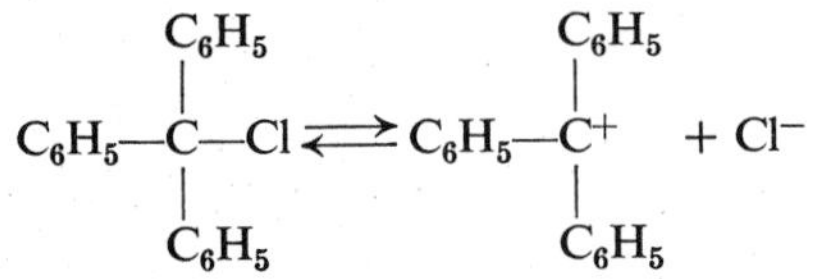

$$
\begin{array}{ccc}
& C_6H_5 & C_6H_5 \\
& | & | \\
C_6H_5—C—Cl & \rightleftarrows C_6H_5—C^+ & + \; Cl^- \\
& | & | \\
& C_6H_5 & C_6H_5
\end{array}
\qquad (31)
$$

The triphenylmethyl carbanion may also be obtained in certain ways, for example by reaction of triphenylmethane with sodium in liquid ammonia, Eq. 32.

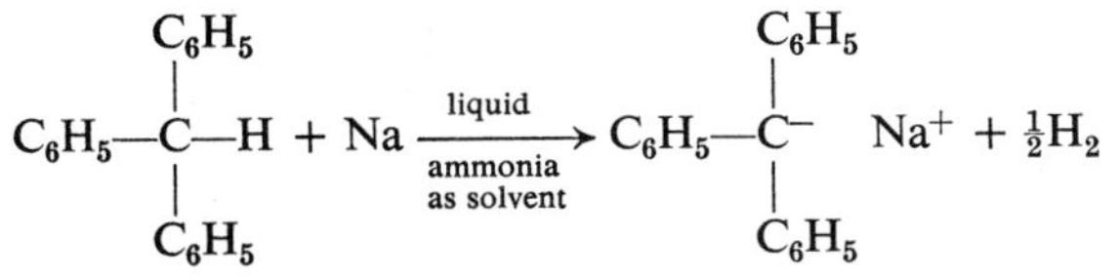

$$
\begin{array}{ccc}
C_6H_5 & & C_6H_5 \\
| & \text{liquid} & | \\
C_6H_5—C—H + Na & \xrightarrow[\text{as solvent}]{\text{ammonia}} & C_6H_5—C^- \quad Na^+ + \tfrac{1}{2}H_2 \\
| & & | \\
C_6H_5 & & C_6H_5
\end{array}
\qquad (32)
$$

Electron withdrawal by the accumulation of phenyl groups renders the hydrogen sufficiently acidic to react with sodium in a highly ionizing solvent. The liquid ammonia solution of triphenylmethyl carbanion is colored deep red.

Aromatic Aldehydes and Ketones

The aromatic aldehydes and ketones, with carbonyl attached directly to the aromatic ring, differ little from the aliphatic compounds. Principal differences in reactions are dependent on the fact that the adjacent aromatic ring eliminates hydrogens alpha to the carbonyl. Since this eliminates condensations of the aldol type (cf. Chap. 15), certain other reactions become possible, and these will be mentioned in the present section.

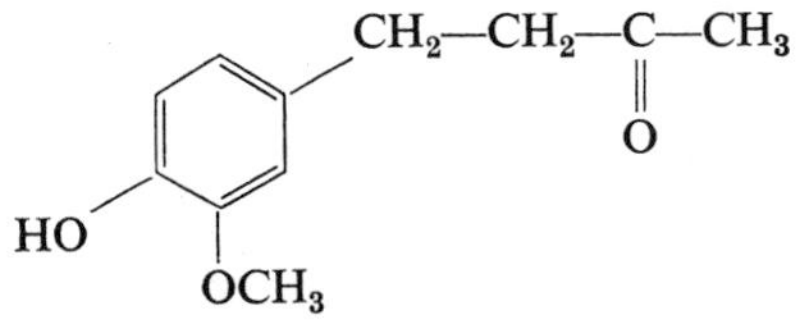

Zingerone

Substantial numbers of aromatic aldehydes and ketones occur in plants, and certain of them are flavoring components of natural spices. The synthesis of vanillin, occurring in vanilla extract, has already been mentioned (Eq. 17-33). A similar ring structure is present in zingerone, responsible for the flavor of ginger.

Synthesis of Aromatic Aldehydes and Ketones

Aldehydes with *para*-oriented *o,p*-directors in the ring may be made by the modifications of the Friedel and Crafts reaction discussed in the preceding chapter (Eqs. 17-32 and 17-33). The Rosenmund reduction, widely used for synthesis of aliphatic aldehydes (Eq. 15-2), is also useful for synthesis of aromatic aldehydes. It may be applied in presence of other reducible groups, even the nitro group (Eq. 33). It is of interest that although the reaction shown in Eq. 33

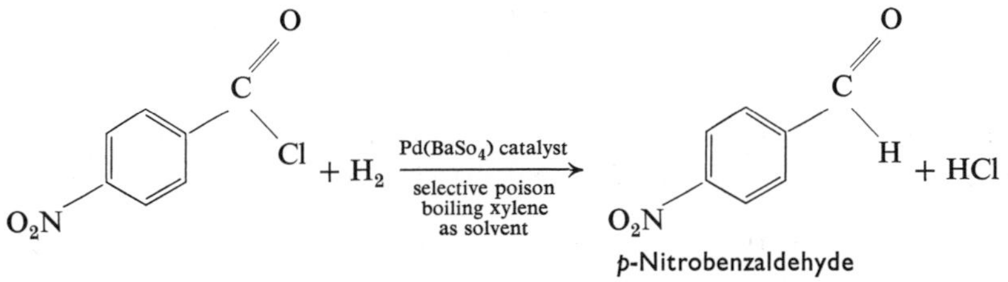

p-Nitrobenzaldehyde

gives a rather good yield, *o-nitrobenzoyl chloride fails completely in the Rosenmund reduction.* This is probably caused by formation of cyclic compounds by reaction of an intermediate in the reduction with the adjacent nitro group; however, nothing certain is known concerning the reasons for failure of this reaction.

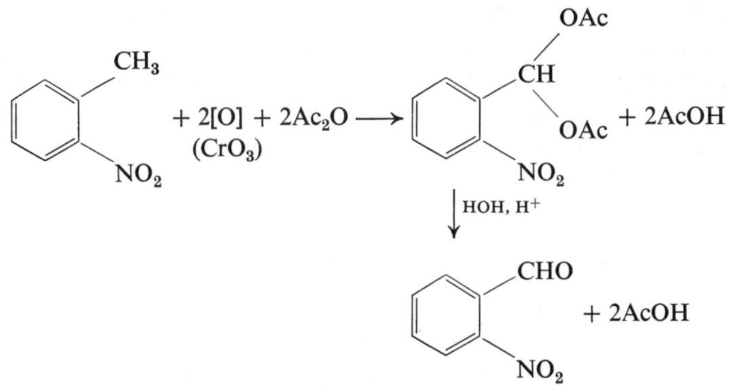

Since *o*-nitrobenzaldehyde is a rather important compound (cf. synthesis of quinolines, Chap. 32), there will be mentioned a rather unusual type of synthesis which is applicable to it. Although an aldehyde is oxidized much more readily than a methyl group substituted on the aromatic ring, it is possible to secure a poor yield of aldehyde derivative by running the oxidation in acetic anhydride solution (Eq. 34). As the aldehyde is formed, it is converted to the diacetate, a derivative similar to the acetal but bearing two ester groups on a single carbon rather than two ether groups. As in the case of the acetal, acid hydrolysis of the diacetate is facile, as shown in Eq. 34. The yield of *o*-nitrobenzaldehyde in this process is only about 20%, but this is probably the best available synthesis. This relatively simple compound is surprisingly difficult to secure.

Ketones are most easily synthesized by the Friedel and Crafts reaction, as discussed in Chapter 17; however, this procedure is able to yield only the *para* isomer from a benzene substituted with an *o,p*-director. For other orientations, or with *meta*-directors in the ring, the same synthetic procedures are used as have been discussed for the strictly aliphatic ketones (Chap. 15). Most useful methods are the Grignard reaction with a nitrile or with an acid chloride in presence of ferric chloride. The latter method is known to be useful in presence of carbonyl groups; however, its utility in presence of the nitro group has not been reported. Since nitro is such an important functional group in the aromatic series, and the Grignard reagent reacts with it readily, an additional ketone synthesis which is effective in presence of the nitro group will be described. This involves use of an organocadmium reagent, which may be easily prepared from the Grignard reagent (Eq. 35). The choice of R—Cd—Cl in Eq. 35 is arbitrary;

$$R\text{—}MgX + CdCl_2 \longrightarrow R\text{—}CdCl + MgXCl \tag{35}$$

use of two moles of Grignard reagent to one of cadmium chloride gives R—Cd—R, whose reactions appear to be the same as R—Cd—Cl. The importance of the organocadmium reagent is that it reacts sluggishly if at all with any type of polar multiple bond, but gives a rapid reaction with an acid chloride (Eq. 36). The reactions shown in Eqs. 35 and 36 are normally carried out in sequence in

m-Nitropropiophenone

the same reaction vessel, so the process is not laborious. This is the only use of the organocadmium reagent, but it is an important one. The reason for the selective reaction of the cadmium reagent with an acid chloride depends on presence of the magnesium halide formed in Eq. 35. This weak Lewis acid is able to extract the halogen from an acid chloride to give the acylonium ion which then reacts with the cadmium reagent. The actual sequence, then, is that shown in Eq. 37. Thus, the reaction of the organocadmium reagent is closely related to the Friedel and Crafts reaction; the difference is that the acylonium ion attacks the organocadmium reagent rather than an aromatic nucleus.

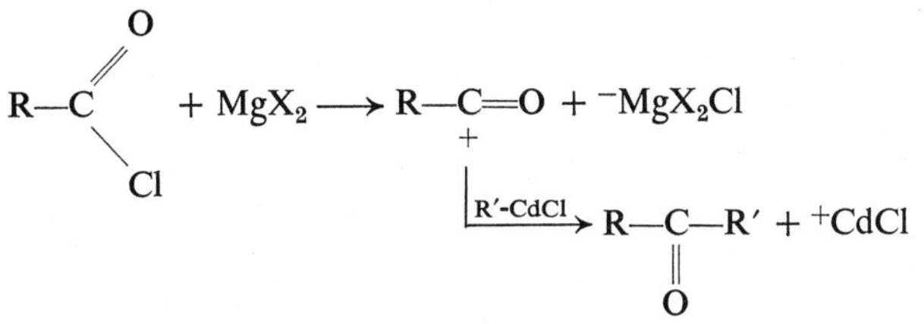

$$
R-C\overset{\displaystyle O}{\underset{\displaystyle Cl}{\big\backslash}} \ + \ MgX_2 \longrightarrow R-\overset{+}{C}{=}O \ + \ ^-MgX_2Cl
$$

$$
\xrightarrow{\ R'\text{-CdCl}\ } R-\underset{\underset{\displaystyle O}{\|}}{C}-R' \ + \ ^+CdCl \tag{37}
$$

Reactions of Aromatic Aldehydes and Ketones

Of course the aromatic aldehydes and ketones give the reactions characteristic of the carbonyl group, as discussed in Chapter 15, so these reactions should be reviewed. In addition, a few other reactions become possible because of absence of alpha hydrogens in the aromatic aldehydes. The **cross Cannizzaro reaction** has already been discussed (Eq. 15-48). The **cross aldol condensation,** previously mentioned for use with formaldehyde (Eq. 15-50), may also be applied satisfactorily with an aromatic aldehyde (Eq. 38). There is only a single

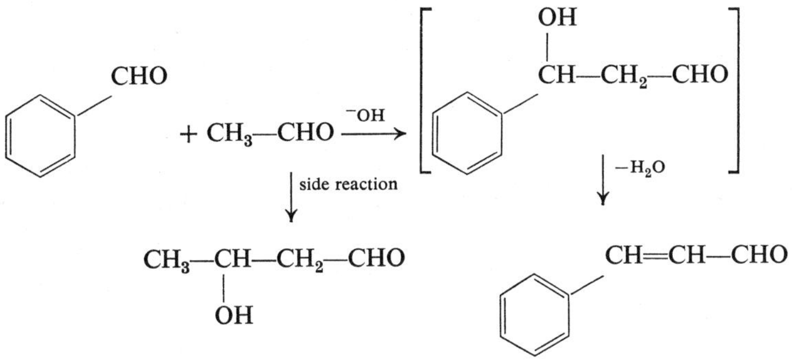

Cinnamic aldehyde

$$\tag{38}$$

by-product which may usually be separated easily from the desired aromatic condensation product, on account of a difference in molecular weight. It is worthy of note that the aldol product, which is also a benzyl alcohol, is so easily dehydrated that it is difficult to isolate the hydroxy aldehyde. The unsaturated aldehyde is the normal reaction product, as shown. This easy dehydration is probably an E2 elimination, *very seldom* observed for elimination of water. Its occurrence in the presently discussed instance no doubt results from two factors: the alpha hydrogens in an aldehyde are somewhat acidic (Chap. 15) hence easily abstracted by base to initiate elimination; hydroxyl leaves very easily on account of incipient formation of a benzyl carbonium ion which is resonance stabilized. The combination of these factors is enough to produce concerted elimination of water by the usual type of transition state for E2 elimination:

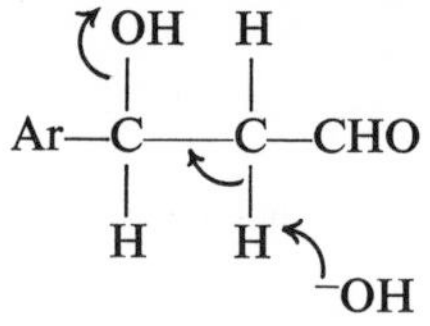

$$\text{Ar}-\overset{\overset{\displaystyle \textrm{OH}}{|}}{\underset{\underset{\displaystyle \textrm{H}}{|}}{\textrm{C}}}-\overset{\overset{\displaystyle \textrm{H}}{|}}{\underset{\underset{\displaystyle \textrm{H}}{|}}{\textrm{C}}}-\textrm{CHO} \qquad {}^{-}\textrm{OH}$$

Since ketones give an aldol condensation that is highly reversible, they work especially well in a cross reaction with an aromatic aldehyde. In addition, the first step in Eq. 39 is more rapid than the second, so either benzalacetone or

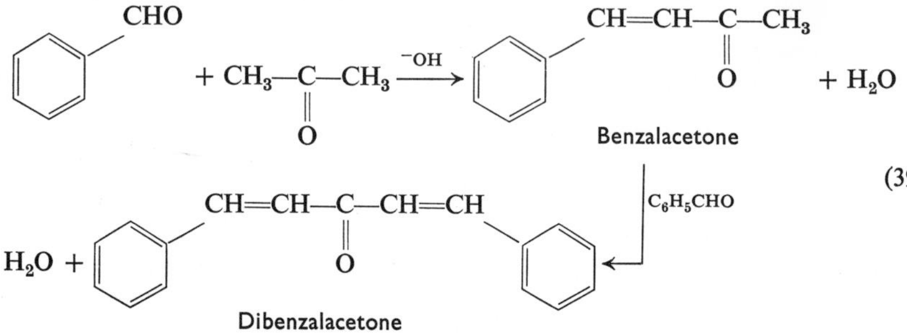

Benzalacetone

Dibenzalacetone

(39)

dibenzalacetone may be secured in good yield, depending on the concentration of reagents.

Benzoin condensation. A condensation of the type shown in Eq. 40 applies only to aromatic aldehydes, for potassium cyanide is sufficiently basic

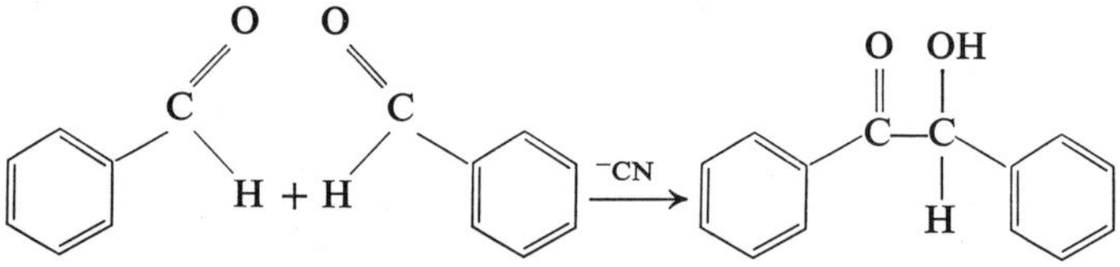

(40)

to give the aldol condensation with aldehydes having alpha hydrogens. Schematically, the benzoin condensation consists of addition of the hydrogen and carbonyl from one molecule of benzaldehyde to the carbonyl group of another molecule, but the actual mechanism is a rather interesting one which involves several steps. The specific catalytic effect of the cyanide ion depends on a rather unique combination of properties: (1) the nucleophilicity of cyanide is just right to allow attack on carbonyl in the first step of the reaction (Eq. 40a) and dissociation in the last step (Eq. 40c); (2) cyanide is an unsaturated group, which allows resonance stabilization of the anion formed in the intermediate step (Eq. 40b).

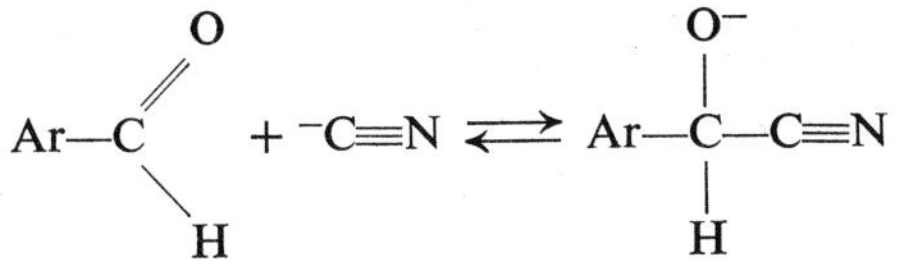

$$\text{Ar-}\overset{\displaystyle O}{\underset{\displaystyle H}{\overset{\|}{C}}} + \;^-C{\equiv}N \;\rightleftarrows\; \text{Ar-}\overset{\displaystyle O^-}{\underset{\displaystyle H}{\overset{|}{C}}}\text{-C}{\equiv}N \qquad (40a)$$

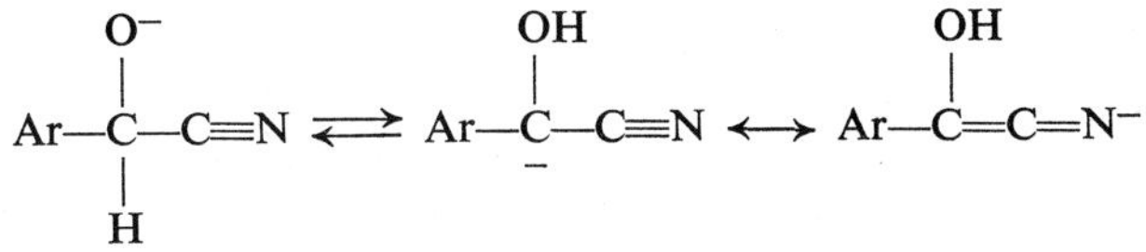

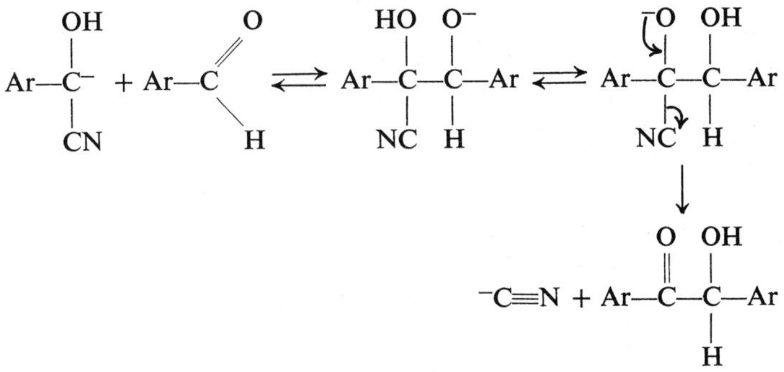

$$\text{Ar-}\overset{\displaystyle O^-}{\underset{\displaystyle H}{\overset{|}{C}}}\text{-C}{\equiv}N \;\rightleftarrows\; \text{Ar-}\overset{\displaystyle OH}{\overset{|}{C}}\text{-C}{\equiv}N \;\longleftrightarrow\; \text{Ar-}\overset{\displaystyle OH}{\overset{|}{C}}{=}C{=}N^- \qquad (40b)$$

$$\text{Ar-}\overset{\displaystyle OH}{\underset{\displaystyle CN}{\overset{|}{C^-}}} + \text{Ar-}\overset{\displaystyle O}{\underset{\displaystyle H}{\overset{\|}{C}}} \;\rightleftarrows\; \text{Ar-}\overset{\displaystyle HO}{\underset{\displaystyle NC}{\overset{|}{C}}}\overset{\displaystyle O^-}{\underset{\displaystyle H}{\overset{|}{C}}}\text{-Ar} \;\rightleftarrows\; \text{Ar-}\overset{\displaystyle O}{\underset{\displaystyle NC}{\overset{|}{C}}}\overset{\displaystyle OH}{\underset{\displaystyle H}{\overset{|}{C}}}\text{-Ar} \qquad (40c)$$

$$\downarrow$$

$$^-C{\equiv}N + \text{Ar-}\overset{\displaystyle O}{\overset{\|}{C}}\overset{\displaystyle OH}{\underset{\displaystyle H}{\overset{|}{C}}}\text{-Ar}$$

The fully aromatic α-hydroxy ketone, such as formed in Eq. 40, is commonly known as a benzoin; however, a more general name for an α-hydroxy ketone is **acyloin.**

Since an acyloin is very easily oxidized (Eq. 15-10), very mild reagents may be used to convert a benzoin to a benzil (Eq. 41). Chief interest in compounds of the benzil type is the remarkable rearrangement which they give in alkali, known as the **benzilic acid rearrangement** (Eq. 42). The mechanism of the benzilic acid rearrangement (Eq. 42a) bears some similarity to the benzoin

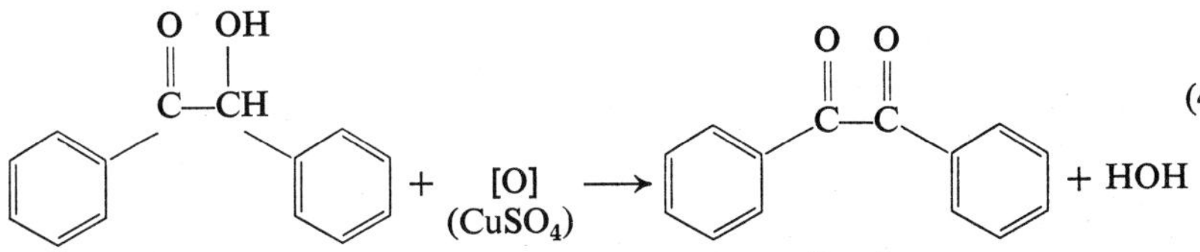

$$(41)$$

Benzil

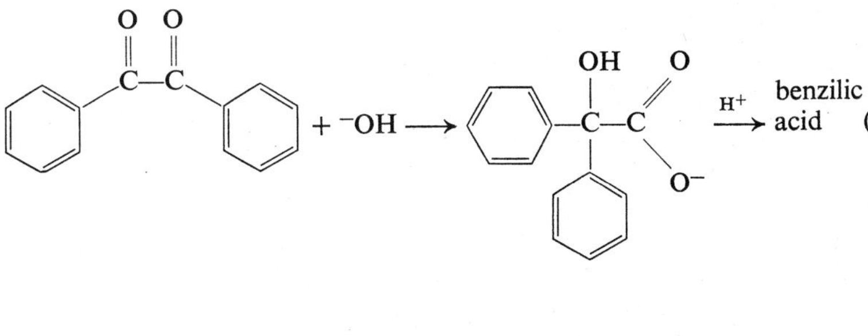

$$(42)$$

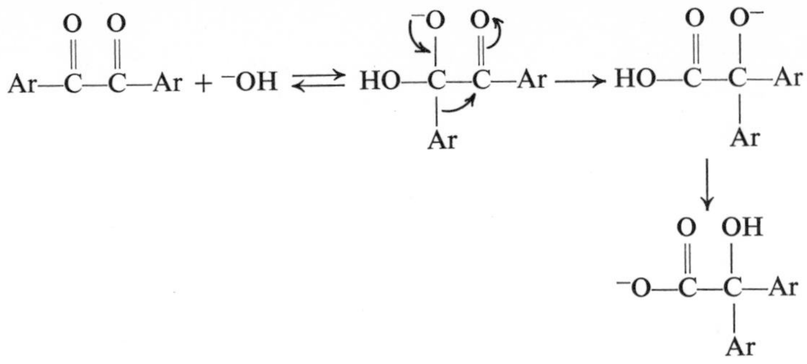

$$Ar-\overset{\overset{O}{\|}}{C}-\overset{\overset{O}{\|}}{C}-Ar + {}^{-}OH \rightleftarrows HO-\overset{\overset{{}^{-}O}{|}}{C}-\overset{\overset{O}{\|}}{C}-Ar \longrightarrow HO-\overset{\overset{O}{\|}}{C}-\overset{\overset{O^{-}}{|}}{C}-Ar$$

(42a)

$$\overset{\overset{O}{\|}}{{}^{-}O}-C-\overset{\overset{OH}{|}}{C}-Ar$$

condensation; however, a very important difference concerns migration of the aromatic group to the adjacent carbon. The driving force behind this rearrangement is migration of a carbanion to an adjacent atom of relatively low electron density, in this case the carbonyl carbon. Among the numerous other rearrangements depending on this same type of group migration are the Hofmann hypobromite reaction (Chap. 19) and the Beckmann rearrangement (next section).

A principal utilization of acids of the benzilic type is for synthesis of diphenylacetic acids. Powerful reducing agents such as phosphorus and hydriodic acid will reduce the hydroxyl function directly.

Beckmann rearrangement of ketoximes. This rearrangement can be applied to aliphatic ketones, but has been studied principally with aromatic ketones. It occurs in the presence of acids or acid chlorides of strong acids, and the net reaction is that shown in Eq. 43.

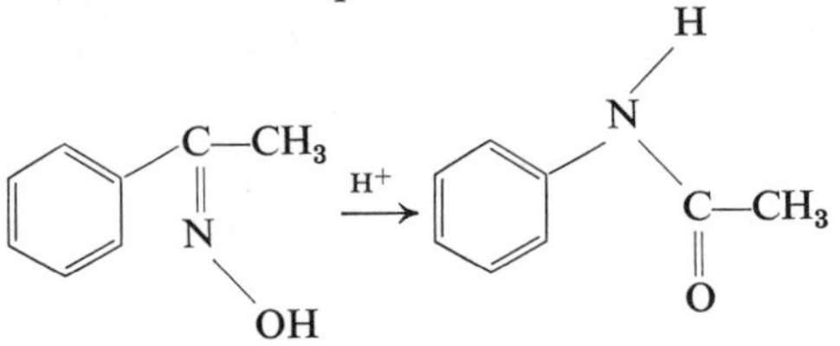

(43)

If rotation around the carbon-nitrogen double bond is restricted, it follows that a ketoxime or aldoxime may exist in two geometrically isomeric forms. This has proved to be the case, and such isomers have been isolated in the aromatic series. This is one reason that the rearrangement has been more

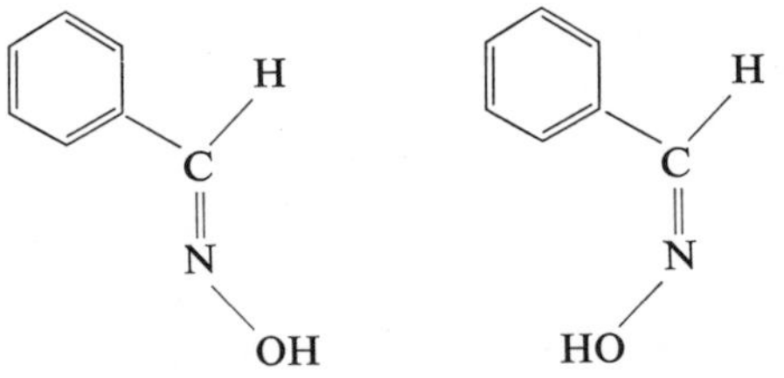

syn-Benzaldoxime   *anti*-Benzaldoxime

extensively investigated with aromatic ketoximes. For aldoximes, the one with hydroxyl on the same side with hydrogen is called *syn* and the other *anti.*

In the Beckmann rearrangement, it has been found that the group *anti* to hydroxyl is the one that migrates. This gives a backside displacement of the protonated hydroxyl (Eq. 44) as the rearrangement step.[3] This differs from a

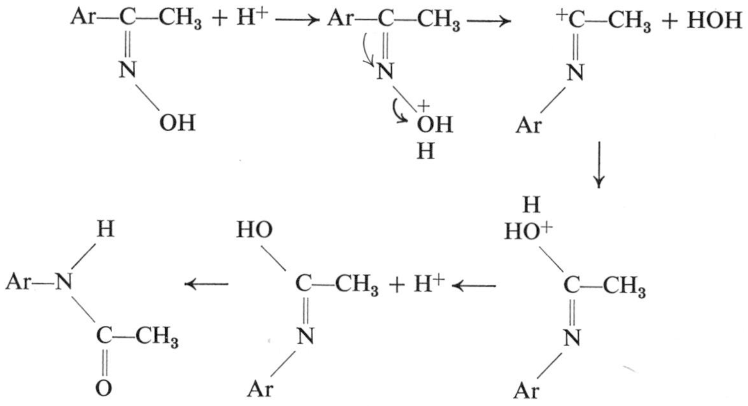
Ar—C—CH₃ + H⁺ ⟶ Ar—C—CH₃ ⟶ ⁺C—CH₃ + HOH
N
OH
N
OH
H
N
Ar
H
HO⁺
C—CH₃
N
Ar
HO
C—CH₃ + H⁺
N
Ar
H
Ar—N
C—CH₃
O
(44)

(Enol form of amide)

simple S_N2 reaction only in that the displacement is accomplished by a group migrating from an adjacent carbon rather than a group entering from outside the molecule. This type of rearrangement involves migration of a negative group (i.e., carbon with an attached electron pair) to an adjacent atom of low electron density. There are many examples of such migrations. Those previously described are the benzilic acid rearrangement (preceding section) and the rearrangement of a carbonium ion (cf. Chap. 6 and numerous subsequent discussions).

In a few types of compounds, the Beckmann rearrangement has been of synthetic use, usually for synthesis of an amine or acid by hydrolysis of the amide formed by rearrangement.

Oximes of aldehydes ordinarily do not give a rearrangement of the Beckmann type, but such reactions have been reported with polyphosphoric acid as the catalyst.

EXERCISES

1. Write three resonance forms for the sulfonate anion and two for the sulfinate anion, assuming that sulfur can accommodate ten valence electrons.

---

[3] Equation 44 does not include some of the known details of the mechanism of the Beckmann rearrangement or different types of intermediates involved with certain catalysts. An understandable summary of what is known about this rearrangement has been presented by Prof. C. R. Hauser of Duke University and D. S. Hoffenberg in *J. Org. Chem.*, **20**, 1482 (1955).

2. Write the possible resonance forms for a sulfinic acid (neglecting any resonance with the nucleus; use R— to represent the nucleus) when (a) hydrogen is on sulfur, (b) hydrogen is on oxygen. Does this suggest any factor that might tend to work against the normal tendency of hydrogen to become attached to negative oxygen rather than positive sulfur? If the hydrogen is on sulfur in the sulfinic acids, will the anion have any more resonance forms than the associated acid?

3. Arrange the following compounds in order of increasing ease of displacement of the chlorine by a negative group.

(a) *p*-Chlorotoluene.
(b) 3-Nitro-4-chlorotoluene.
(c) 2-Nitro-4-chlorotoluene.
(d) 3,4-Dinitro-1-chlorobenzene.
(e) 1,3-Dichloro-4-nitrobenzene.⎫
(f) 1,4-Dichloro-3-nitrobenzene.⎬ (Which chlorine displaced more easily?)
(g) 2,4-Dinitro-1-chlorobenzene.

4. Outline practical syntheses for each of the following compounds, starting with either a compound available from coal tar or a monosubstituted benzene derivative. So long as continuity is maintained, any desired reagents may be used to accomplish the conversions. Routes should be chosen so as to give the compounds free of inseparable isomers.

(a)

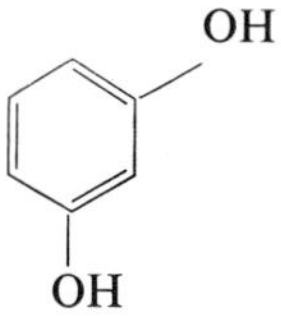

OH

OH

(b)

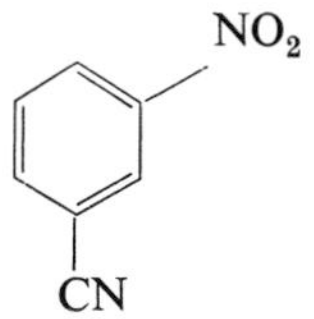

NO$_2$

CN

(c)

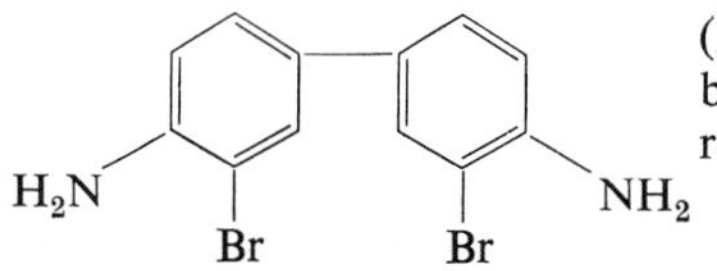

H$_2$N   Br   Br   NH$_2$

(Remember the benzidine rearrangement)

(d)

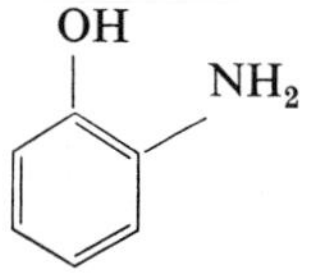

OH   NH$_2$

(e)

OH

NH$_2$

(f)

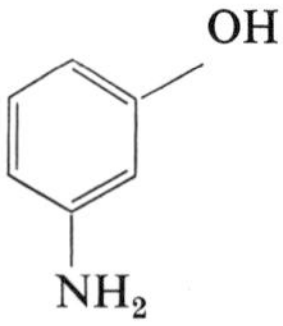

OH

NH$_2$

(g)

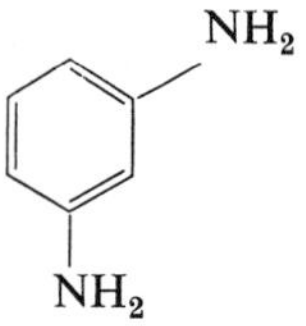

NH$_2$

NH$_2$

(h)

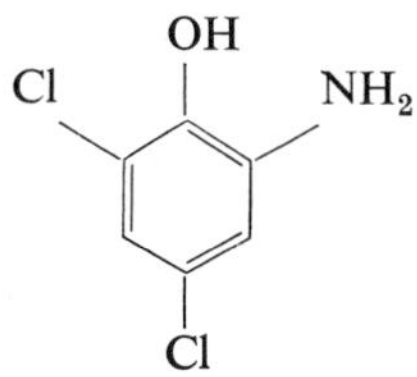

Cl   OH   NH$_2$

Cl

(i)

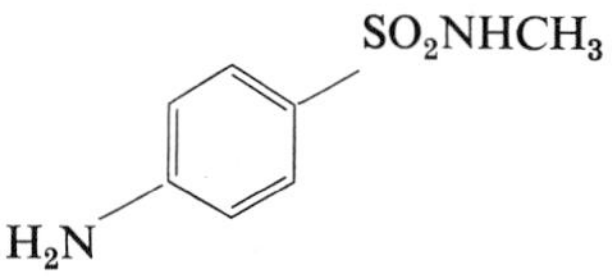

SO$_2$NHCH$_3$

H$_2$N

(j)

CO$_2$H

Br

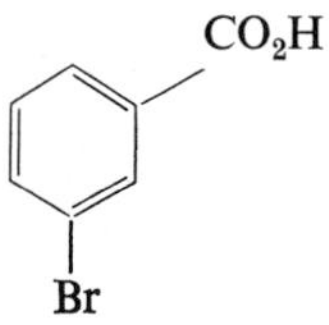

(k) 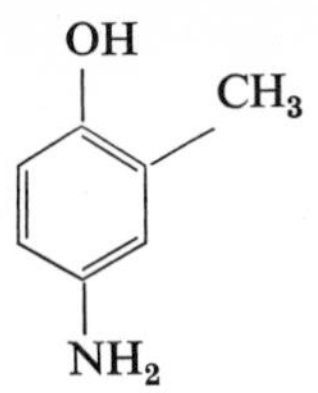 2-methyl-4-aminophenol structure: benzene ring with OH at top, CH$_3$ ortho, NH$_2$ at bottom (para to OH)

(l) 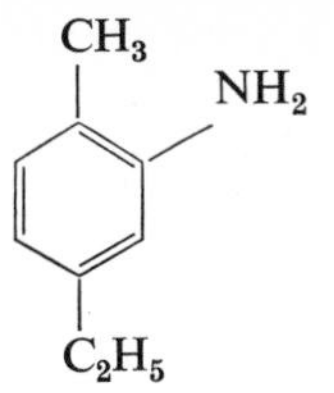 benzene ring with CH$_3$ at top, NH$_2$ ortho, C$_2$H$_5$ at bottom

(m) 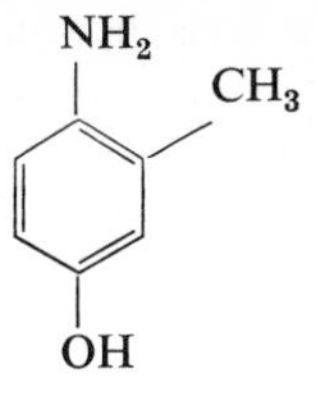 benzene ring with NH$_2$ at top, CH$_3$ ortho, OH at bottom

(n) 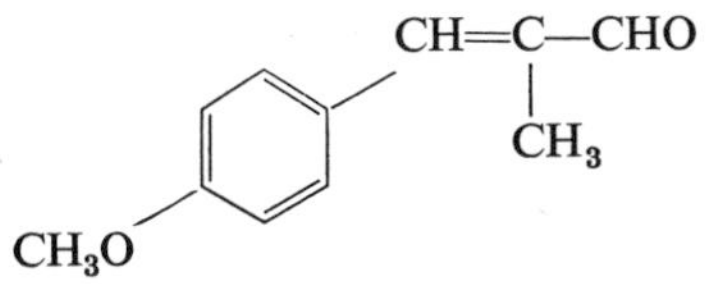 benzene ring with CH$_3$O substituent and CH=C(CH$_3$)—CHO substituent

(o) benzene ring with H$_3$C and CH$_2$—CH$_2$—CH$_2$—C(=O)—CH$_3$ substituents

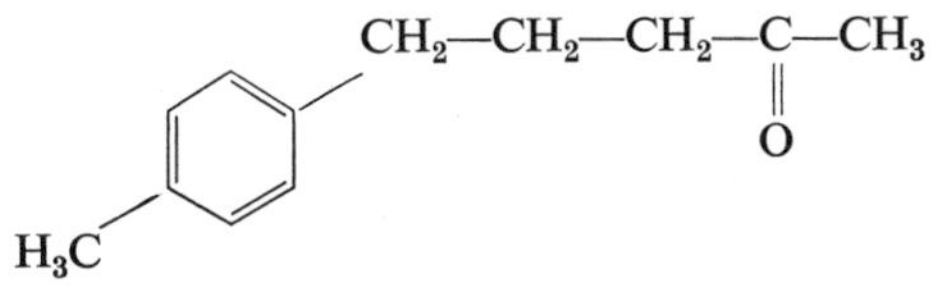

(p) 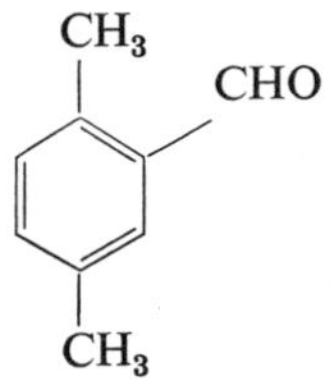 benzene ring with CH$_3$ at top, CHO ortho, CH$_3$ at bottom

(q) 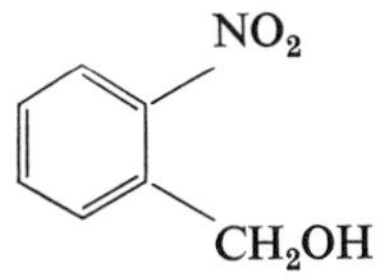 benzene ring with NO$_2$ and CH$_2$OH substituents (ortho)

5. Name all the organic compounds whose syntheses are requested in Exercise 4.

6. Outline a synthetic sequence by which p-chlorobromobenzene may be converted to p-ethylbenzoic acid.

7. Outline a sequence by which you can separate a mixture of the following compounds without using fractional crystallization or fractional distillation.

(a) Sulfanilamide.
(b) N-Methylbenzenesulfonamide.
(c) N,N-Dimethylbenzenesulfonamide.
(d) Aniline.

8. If 1,2,3,5-tetrabromobenzene were subjected to basic hydrolysis, which bromine would you expect to be displaced most easily by hydroxyl?

9. Write the formulas for all the compounds that would result from a benzoin condensation of p-methylbenzaldehyde with benzaldehyde.

10. Starting with phenol, outline a practical synthesis of zingerone. In this process, it may be assumed that the *ortho* and *para* isomers of methoxybenzenesulfonic acid are separable.

11. Salicylaldehyde is considerably more volatile than p-hydroxybenzaldehyde. Suggest a plausible explanation of this.

12. Outline two independent routes (proceeding through different intermediates) for conversion of toluene to p-propionyltoluene.

13. Write three resonance forms for diphenylnitrogen, besides that shown in Eq. 30.

14. Starting with benzene, outline a synthesis of hexa-(*p*-ethylphenyl)ethane.

15. Explain, using any indicated resonance forms to support your explanation, why the liquid ammonia solution of the triphenylmethyl carbanion would be expected to be colored.

16. Diethylcadmium is moderately volatile, so it may be distilled and obtained in a pure form after it is prepared from a Grignard reagent. A pure sample of diethylcadmium fails to react with benzoyl chloride at a significant rate. Explain this behavior.

Amines, the Most Important Organic Bases

The amines, resulting from replacement of one or more hydrogens in ammonia, are by far the most important of the organic bases. Oxygen-containing compounds such as the alcohols and ethers are basic, as has been discussed in several earlier chapters, but they are weaker bases than water. Thus, the basic function is commonly regarded as a secondary characteristic of the oxygen derivatives. The limited number of structures giving basicity to organic compounds is in marked contrast to the situation in acids, for numerous organic structures yield significantly acidic compounds.

The **quaternary ammonium bases,** also to be discussed in this chapter, are very closely related to the amines. The relationship is analogous to that between ammonium hydroxide and ammonia. The *imines* (cf. Eq. 14-21) and *imino esters* (cf. Eq. 14-19) are less important types of bases which are also closely related to the amines.

The aromatic amines are much more important in synthesis than are the aliphatic ones, partly because of the highly activating effect of the amino group on substitution in the ring and partly because of the useful reactions of the diazonium salts formed from a primary aromatic amine and nitrous acid. Discussion of these reactions will constitute an important part of the present chapter.

The aromatic amines usually have a pronounced but mild odor, in sharp contrast to the strong and offensive odor so characteristic of aliphatic amines. On the other hand, the aliphatic amines have important functions in biological systems (see below), whereas the aromatic amines are usually rather toxic when ingested. The toxicity of the aromatic amines is normally of a lower order than that of such substances as hydrogen cyanide; however, most aromatic amines are too toxic to be used safely as drugs. The aminosulfonamides, described in the preceding chapter, are toxic, but less so to man than to bacteria. The acetyl derivative of aniline, acetanilide, is a rather effective analgesic, but significantly more toxic than aspirin (*o*-acetoxybenzoic acid).

Nomenclature

The amines are classified as *primary*, *secondary*, or *tertiary*, according to the number of radicals attached to nitrogen. Substitution of a fourth radical gives a quaternary ammonium base. The terminology applied in distinguishing

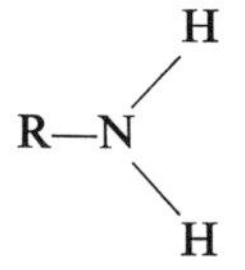

$$R-N\begin{array}{c}H\\\\H\end{array} \qquad R-N\begin{array}{c}R'\\\\H\end{array} \qquad R-N\begin{array}{c}R'\\\\R''\end{array} \qquad \left[\begin{array}{c}R'\\|\\R-N-R'''\\|\\R''\end{array}\right]^{+} {}^{-}OH$$

Primary amine	Secondary amine	Tertiary amine	Quaternary ammonium base

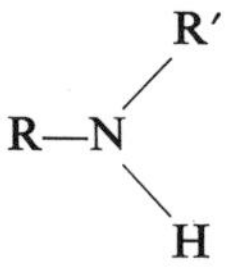

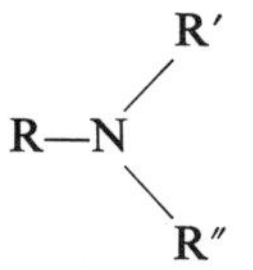

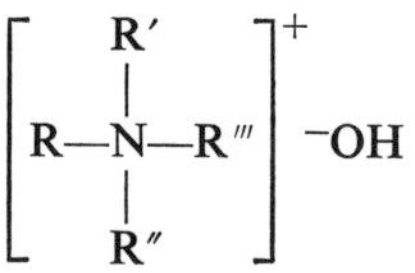

between types of amines should be clearly differentiated from that used in classifying alcohols or alkyl radicals in general. A secondary amine has two organic radicals *attached to nitrogen;* if these radicals are alkyl, they may be primary, secondary, or tertiary. Examples may be used to illustrate the distinctions involved.

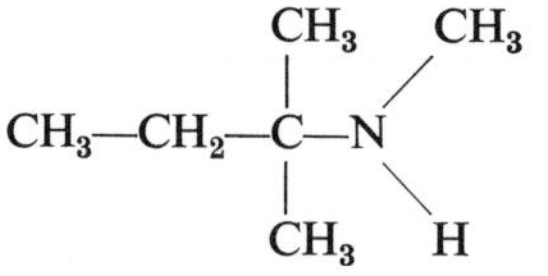

$$CH_3-CH_2-\underset{\underset{CH_3}{|}}{\overset{\overset{CH_3}{|}}{C}}-N\begin{array}{c}CH_3\\\\H\end{array}$$

A secondary amine

$$CH_3-CH_2-\underset{\underset{CH_3}{|}}{CH}-$$

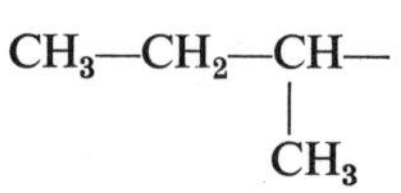

A secondary alkyl radical

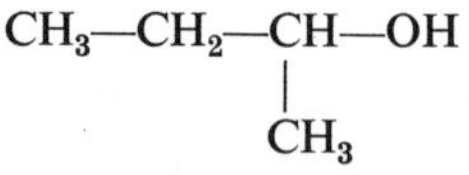

$$CH_3-CH_2-\underset{\underset{CH_3}{|}}{CH}-OH$$

A secondary alcohol

$$CH_3-CH_2-\underset{\underset{CH_3}{|}}{CH}-NH_2$$

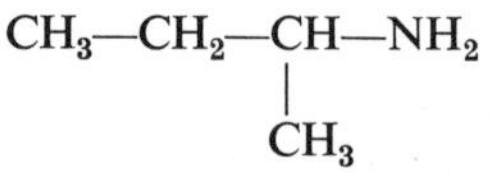

A primary amine

Amines are ordinarily named by combining as a prefix to "amine" the names of the radicals attached to nitrogen. A few examples follow:

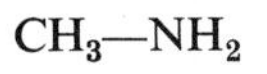

$$CH_3—NH_2 \qquad CH_3—\overset{\overset{\displaystyle CH_3}{|}}{\underset{\underset{\displaystyle CH_3}{|}}{C}}—NH_2 \qquad C_2H_5—N\overset{\displaystyle H}{\underset{\displaystyle CH_3}{<}}$$

Methylamine 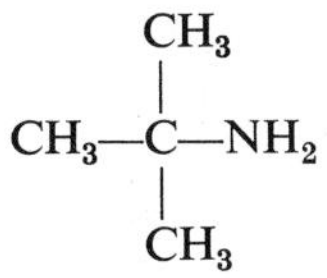   *tert*-Butylamine 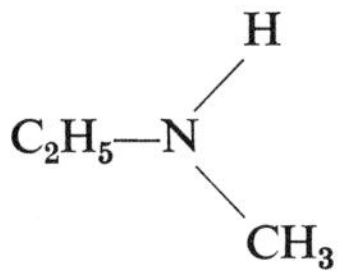   Ethylmethylamine

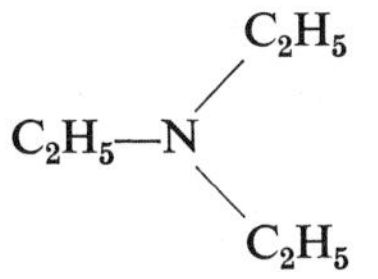

$$C_2H_5—N\overset{\displaystyle C_2H_5}{\underset{\displaystyle C_2H_5}{<}}$$

Triethylamine

A large number of the amines are sufficiently simple to be named by this system. With the exception of amines containing the isopropyl group, a very few are known which contain more than one secondary or tertiary alkyl attached to nitrogen. Quaternary ammonium bases are named similarly:

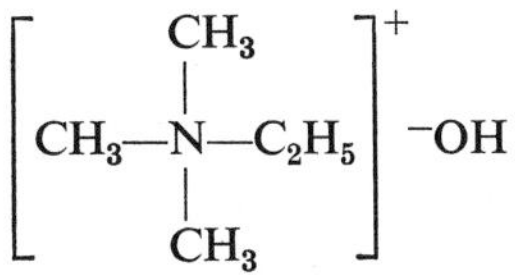

$$\left[CH_3—\overset{\overset{\displaystyle CH_3}{|}}{\underset{\underset{\displaystyle CH_3}{|}}{N}}—C_2H_5 \right]^+ \quad {}^-OH$$

Ethyltrimethylammonium hydroxide

In complex amines, the IUC nomenclature is ordinarily used, and the —NH_2 group is named as the substituent *amino*. Secondary and tertiary amines are named as in the following examples. In the first example, note that

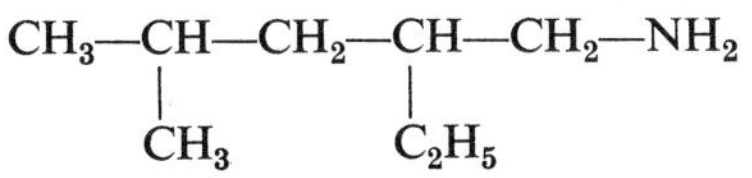

$$CH_3—\overset{\overset{\displaystyle CH_3}{|}}{\underset{\underset{\displaystyle CH_3}{|}}{CH}}—CH_2—\overset{\overset{}{}}{\underset{\underset{\displaystyle C_2H_5}{|}}{CH}}—CH_2—NH_2 \qquad HO—CH_2—CH_2—CH_2—N\overset{\displaystyle CH_3}{\underset{\displaystyle CH_3}{<}}$$

1-Amino-2-ethyl-4-methylpentane 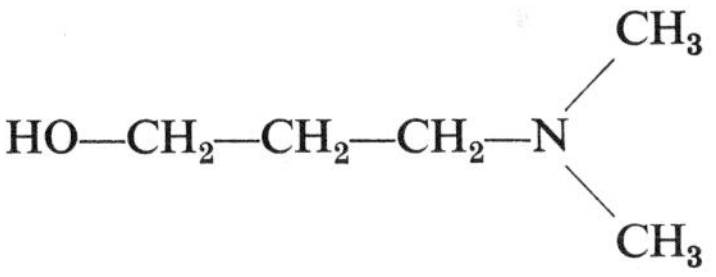   3-Dimethylamino-1-propanol

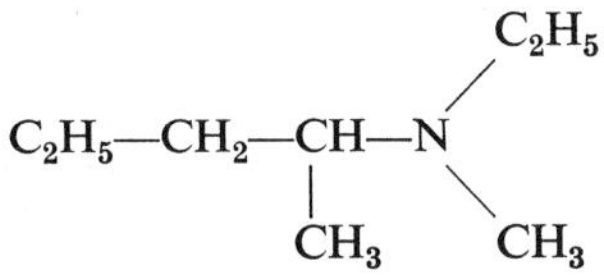

$$C_2H_5—CH_2—\overset{}{\underset{\underset{\displaystyle CH_3}{|}}{CH}}—N\overset{\displaystyle C_2H_5}{\underset{\displaystyle CH_3}{<}}$$

2-Ethylmethylaminopentane

the longest carbon chain is not used as the basis of the name but rather the longest chain containing the carbon to which the functional group is attached. This is a basic rule of nomenclature, which is very useful. It avoids the awkward necessity of naming the group —CH_2—NH_2. In case there seems likelihood of ambiguity, the radicals attached to amino may be specified by appropriate use of parentheses. For example, the last name above may be clarified as follows: 2-(ethylmethylamino)pentane.

Natural Occurrence of Organic Bases

Organic bases occur widely in nature, and some of them are very important compounds. Of particular importance are the amino acids (Chap. 25) and the heterocyclic compounds which contain nitrogen in a ring (Chaps. 31 through 33); however, many acyclic bases are also of biological significance. Among the latter are derivatives of the quaternary ammonium base, choline. The choline ion is essential to many phases of metabolism, and acetylcholine is

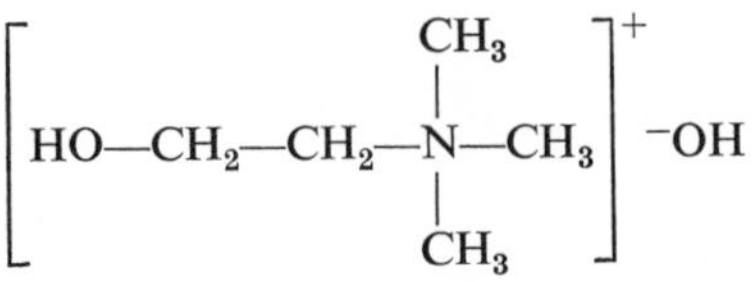

$$\left[HO-CH_2-CH_2-\overset{\overset{\displaystyle CH_3}{|}}{\underset{\underset{\displaystyle CH_3}{|}}{N}}-CH_3 \right]^+ \ ^-OH$$

Choline

$$\left[CH_3-\overset{\overset{\displaystyle O}{||}}{C}-O-CH_2-CH_2-\overset{\overset{\displaystyle CH_3}{|}}{\underset{\underset{\displaystyle CH_3}{|}}{N}}-CH_3 \right]^+ \ ^-OH$$

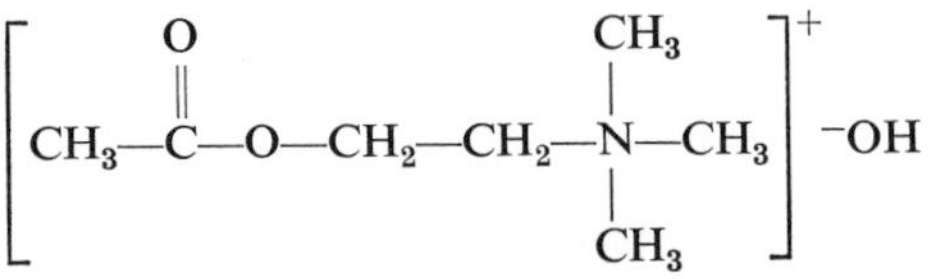

Acetylcholine

the hormone which depresses blood pressure. It is balanced in the animal organism by another hormone, epinephrine, which raises blood pressure. These hormones also exert several other more complicated effects in animal metabolism. The action of acetylcholine is kept localized by certain enzymes which promote its hydrolysis to choline. Acetylcholine, when free in the body fluids, is among the most poisonous substances known; therefore any substance interfering with the acetylcholine-destroying enzymes is also very toxic. Included among such toxic agents are certain phosphonic acid derivatives known as *nerve gases* (cf. Chap. 34).

Choline occurs in a combined form in a variety of lipid (cf. Chap. 14) known as a **phospholipid,** an essential type of compound occurring in the brain, spinal cord, and other strategic places. Typical phospholipids are the compounds known as **lecithins.** Since a lecithin contains both the acidic phosphoric acid group and the basic quaternary ammonium grouping, in neutral solution

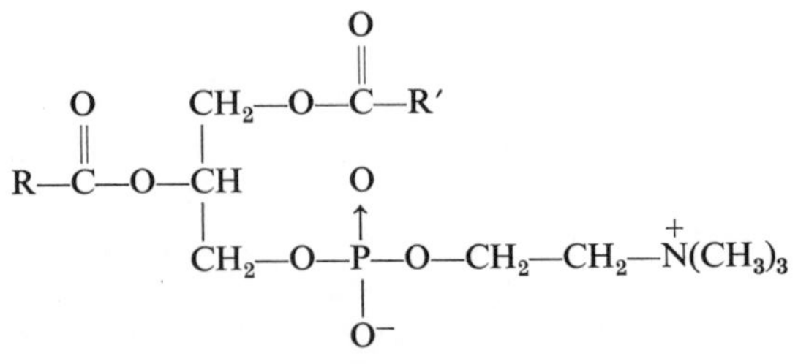

$$
\begin{array}{l}
\qquad\qquad\qquad\qquad \overset{\displaystyle O}{\underset{\displaystyle ||}{}} \\
\qquad\quad\ \overset{\displaystyle O}{\underset{\displaystyle ||}{}} \quad CH_2-O-C-R' \\
R-C-O-CH \qquad\ O \\
\qquad\quad\ | \qquad\qquad\ \uparrow \\
\qquad\quad\ CH_2-O-\underset{\underset{\displaystyle O^-}{|}}{P}-O-CH_2-CH_2-\overset{+}{N}(CH_3)_3
\end{array}
$$

An α-lecithin

the compound is an intramolecular salt, as in the formula illustrating an α-lecithin. Like the naturally occurring triglycerides (cf. Chap. 14), the lecithins are always found in mixtures containing several different fatty acids (different R groups in the formula shown). Also, the phosphoric acid may occur as the ester of the center hydroxyl in glycerol, in which case the compound is known as a β-lecithin.

Certain diamines are produced in the decay of flesh, and the foul odor of decaying flesh is due largely to putrescine and cadaverine.

$$H_2N—(CH_2)_4—NH_2 \qquad H_2N—(CH_2)_5—NH_2$$
Putrescine   Cadaverine

Geometry of the Nitrogen Atom

Reference to Table 3-1 (review of Chap. 3 is recommended) will recall the fact that nitrogen has three electrons in the $2p$ energy level, hence may form three covalent bonds by sharing these electrons. Since the bond directions for the p orbitals form angles of 90° with each other (cf. Fig. 3-3), the valence directions in nitrogen might be expected to form angles of 90° with each other. Actually, nitrogen is such a small atom that mutual repulsion of the attached atoms always causes the valence directions to be spread considerably beyond the 90° angle. The similar situation existing in oxygen is shown in Fig. 3-6. Even in ammonia, with three hydrogens attached to nitrogen, the valence angles of nitrogen are spread to about 106°, as shown in Fig. 1. In a substance such as

Fig. 1. Valence angles in ammonia.

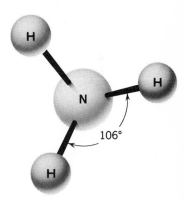

trimethylamine, the angles become even greater. In each case, the bond angles vary somewhat depending on the amount of crowding of the atoms attached to nitrogen, but in all cases the angle is near the 109.5° characteristic of the sp^3 hybridized orbitals by which carbon is bonded. Thus the directions of the three valences in trivalent nitrogen are near those of three valences of carbon, but the fourth valence in trivalent nitrogen is lacking; the additional electron pair is in a $2s$ orbital. The distortion of the "normal" valence angles which occurs in all trivalent nitrogen compounds may well be responsible for the difficulty which has been experienced in getting more than one secondary or tertiary radical attached to the nitrogen atom.

Since the bond angles in trivalent nitrogen are quite close to those in sp^3 hybridization, these bonds are frequently regarded as having the character of the sp^3 hybrid. This idea is based on the principle that bond character may be deduced from knowledge of the angle between bond directions. If the trivalent nitrogen bonds are regarded as of sp^3 character, this means that one s electron and the three p electrons are hybridized, while the remaining s electron is included in one orbital to give the non-bonding pair. As mentioned above, however, the valence characteristics in trivalent nitrogen seem to fit better the concept that the bond directions are distorted from the normal directions for p-orbitals.

In pentavalent nitrogen, there are four covalences, and the bond angles are similar to those in carbon. Since the fourth covalence is formed by nitrogen donating both electrons, it seems realistic to regard nitrogen as forming its four covalent bonds with one $2s$ and three $2p$ electrons (cf. Chap. 3, bond structure in ammonium salts). If these electrons enter hybridized orbitals, there result the sp^3 orbitals, the same situation existent in the bonding carbon atom. There is much experimental evidence that the nitrogen and carbon atoms have very similar geometry.

Basicity of Amines and Quaternary Ammonium Bases

The base strength of an amine, like that of ammonia, is commonly defined as a function of the amount of hydroxide ion furnished in water solution. Hydroxide ion is generated from a base of the ammonia type on account of the reaction with water which is shown in Eq. 1. In accordance with the Lewis

$$R—NH_2 + HOH \rightleftarrows R—\overset{+}{N}H_3 + {}^-OH \qquad (1)$$

concept of a base as an electron donor, it may be said that the more potent the base at displacing hydroxyl from water the further forward is the equilibrium in Eq. 1 and the larger is the concentration of hydroxide ion. Further, the basic ionization constant, K_b, actually represents the equilibrium constant for Eq. 1, thus:

$$K_b = \frac{[R—\overset{+}{N}H_3][^-OH]}{R—NH_2} \qquad (2)$$

Since water is present in large amount as solvent, it is not included in the expression for K_b. It should be noted that the basic ionization constant differs from the acid ionization constant,[1] in that the latter represents equilibrium in dissociation of the acidic species to give a proton and anion.

The reversal of Eq. 1 may be regarded as displacement of the nitrogen base from hydrogen by hydroxide ion, or as dissociation of the cation to give the amine and a proton (see below); in either case, a nitrogen-hydrogen bond in the cation must be ruptured. If all the hydrogens have been replaced to yield

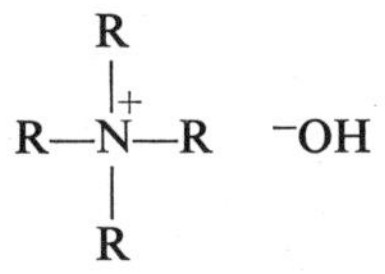

$$
\begin{array}{c}
R \\
| \\
R\!-\!\overset{+}{N}\!-\!R \quad {}^{-}OH \\
| \\
R
\end{array}
$$

a quaternary ammonium base, it becomes necessary to rupture a carbon-nitrogen bond in order to give reversion to a species not involving the hydroxide ion. The activation energy for displacement of nitrogen from carbon is sufficiently high that hydroxide is unable to promote the reaction except at high temperature. The quaternary ammonium hydroxide, therefore, is a strong base; it gives a mole of hydroxide ion in solution for each mole of base. This is in contrast to amines which are weak bases on account of the existence of the equilibrium shown in Eq. 1.

The Concept of pK_a in Bases

Although base strength is frequently assessed in terms of the basic dissociation constant, K_b, for many purposes it proves still more convenient to consider the acid dissociation constant for the cation, as in Eq. 3 (for convenience in writing, the ammonium ion is used instead of an amine ion). In the

$$
{}^{+}NH_4 \rightleftarrows NH_3 + H^{+} \tag{3}
$$

Lewis sense, the cation is accepting electrons from the proton, whereas in the classical sense the cation is dissociating to give a proton. Thus, the equilibrium constant for Eq. 3 is

$$
K_a = \frac{[NH_3][H^{+}]}{[{}^{+}NH_4]} \tag{4}
$$

---

[1] If the acid is regarded, not as simply dissociating, but as reacting with water to give the hydronium ion:

$$
H\!-\!A + HOH \rightleftarrows A^{-} + H_3O^{+}
$$

then the acid and base dissociation constants become of similar character. In dilute water solution, however, the proton is not cleanly hydrated by a single molecule of water as depicted in the equation above. There is rapid equilibrium between free protons and hydronium ions, and both ions are solvated with additional water. As has been discussed previously, all ions are normally stabilized by solvation.

By a straightforward treatment, it is possible to show that K_a for the cation and K_b for the base are related by the ion product of water, K_w, which is $[H^+][^-OH]$ or 10^{-14}. For this purpose, Eq. 2 (written for ammonia) is solved for the ammonium ion, as follows:

$$[^+NH_4] = \frac{K_b[NH_3]}{[^-OH]} \tag{5}$$

If the value for the ammonium ion in Eq. 5 is substituted in Eq. 4,

$$K_a = \frac{[NH_3][H^+][^-OH]}{K_b[NH_3]} = \frac{[H^+][^-OH]}{K_b} = \frac{K_w}{K_b} \tag{6}$$

By substitution of the value for K_w, the experimentally determined values for K_b may be used to easily calculate values for K_a. Furthermore, pK_a may be defined as for acids (cf. Chap. 13, footnote 3), in which sense $pK_a = \log(1/K_a)$.

In illustration of the use of these simple relations, we may calculate the K_a for ammonium ion as 5.5×10^{-10} and the pK_a as 9.24, by use of the experimentally determined value of K_b for ammonia, which is 1.8×10^{-5}.

The **advantages of the pK_a scale** for weak bases may be summarized as involving the following:

1. The pH at which one-half the amine is in the form of the ammonium salt is numerically equal[2] to the pK_a. Thus, for ammonia in aqueous solution at pH 9.24, half the substance is present as the ammonium ion and half as ammonia. It may also be shown by simple calculation that at pH 8.24, 90% of the base is converted to the cation, while at pH 7.24, 99% of the base is present as the cation. Thus, at pH 5, the concentration of free ammonia becomes so low that the solution may be boiled without significant loss of ammonia.

2. It is more readily apparent, and easily calculated, that weakly basic amines require concentrated acid to obtain conversion to the cation (i.e., the salt).

3. It is possible to quickly compare bases of very different basicities, as will be encountered among the organic bases. It is even possible to relate on the same scale such diverse species as acetic acid and anilinium ion.

4. The K_a relation does not require water solution, whereas the expression for K_b is based on water supplying hydroxide (cf. Eqs. 1 and 2). Limitation to water solvent is especially unsatisfactory on account of the insolubility in water of the great majority of amines.

Certain of these advantages will be apparent in comparing the different basicities of the compounds listed in Table 1.

---

[2] This relationship may be demonstrated directly, as was done for acid dissociation (Chap. 13, footnote 3). In Eq. 4, if $[NH_3]$ is equal to $[^+NH_4]$, then $K_a = [H^+]$, so $\log(1/K_a) = \log(1/[H^+])$ or $pK_a = pH$.

Relative Base Strengths of Amines

The base strengths of amines vary greatly, depending on the groups substituted on nitrogen, and major differences may be well correlated on the basis of predictable electron displacements within the molecules. Illustrative values are assembled in Table 1.

Since an alkyl group is an electron donor, but a weak one (refer to rate of substitution in benzene, or acidity of α-methyl acids), substitution of hydrogen in ammonia by an alkyl would be predicted to increase the base strength of ammonia. Further, different alkyl groups should be similar. Both these expectations are realized, as shown in the first three entries in Table 1. In the case of a phenylamine, however, where the following type of resonance interaction with the ring is possible:

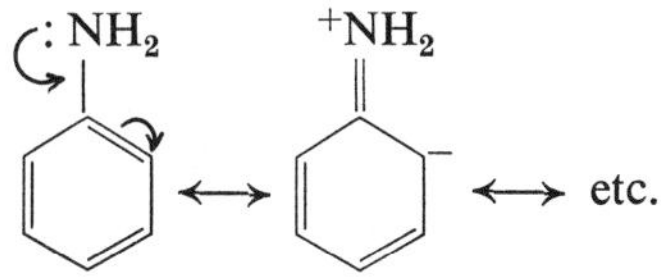

a significant reduction of electron density on nitrogen would be predicted. A decrease in electron density on nitrogen would, in turn, decrease potency of the base as an electron donor, hence weaken the base strength. It may be observed that the drop in K_b for aniline is about six powers of ten (most easily noted as a decrease of about 6 in pK_a). This is consistent with the large increase in rate of substitution in benzene when there is an amino in the ring. If a second phenyl is substituted on nitrogen, to give diphenylamine, the compound becomes almost neutral, insoluble in a dilute solution of strong acid. Triphenylamine is strictly neutral, exhibits no evidence of basic properties.

Table I. Selected Values for Basicities of Amines and Acidities of Ammonium Ions

Amine	K_b	K_a	pK_a
Ammonia	1.8×10^{-5}	5.5×10^{-10}	9.24
Methylamine	4.0×10^{-4}	2.5×10^{-11}	10.6
n-Proplyamine	4.7×10^{-4}	2.1×10^{-11}	10.7
Aniline (phenylamine)	4.0×10^{-10}	2.5×10^{-5}	4.6
p-Methylaniline	1.6×10^{-9}	6.0×10^{-6}	5.22
o-Chloroaniline	4.1×10^{-12}	2.4×10^{-3}	2.62
p-Chloroaniline	5.6×10^{-11}	1.8×10^{-4}	3.75
m-Nitroaniline	4.1×10^{-12}	2.4×10^{-3}	2.6
p-Nitroaniline	1.0×10^{-13}	1.0×10^{-1}	1.0

For the reasons described above, substitution of methyl in the aromatic ring should cause a small shift of electron density towards amino. This minor shift in electron density is reflected in a modest increase (0.6) in the pK_a of the methylaniline shown in Table 1.

In the case of chlorine in the aromatic ring, it has been stated (Chap. 17) that the net effect is electron withdrawal from the ring; donation of electrons by resonance interaction is outweighed by the powerful inductive effect of halogen. This results in a decrease in base strength. Furthermore, the reduction in base strength is greatest for the *o*-chloroaniline, where the inductive effect is stronger (halogen closer to nitrogen) but the resonance effect is the same as for the *para* position.

The *meta* and *para* isomers of nitroaniline are included to illustrate the effect of position of substitution and its correlation with predictions based on examination of resonance forms. As has been discussed in Chapter 17, nitro is a powerful electron-withdrawing group, and this is evidenced by a significant reduction in base strength in the nitroanilines. It is of further interest that the pK_a of the *para* isomer is 1.6 lower than for the *meta* isomer. This may reasonably be ascribed to the possibility for resonance interaction between amino and nitro in the *para* (or *ortho*) position but not in the *meta* position:

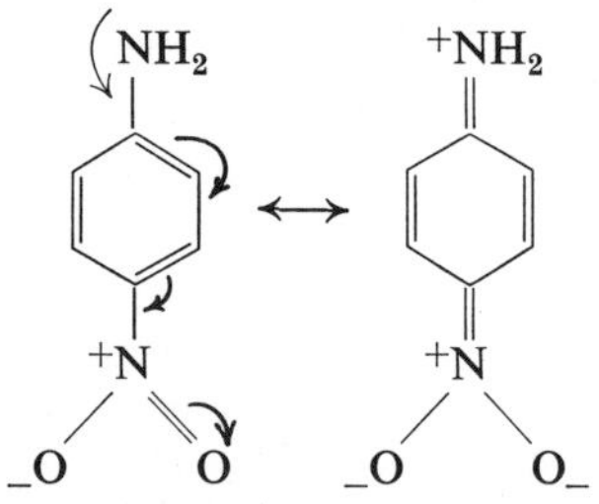

The substituent effects are multiplied when there is substitution of more than one electron-withdrawing group. For example, 2,4-dinitroaniline is barely basic, insoluble in dilute solution of a strong acid, while 2,4,6-tribromoaniline is essentially neutral.

Salts of Amines and Quaternary Ammonium Bases

Since the salts of amines (Eq. 7) contain a fully ionic electrovalence, they tend to be soluble in water and insoluble in organic solvents. This permits

$$R-NH_2 + HCl \longrightarrow R-\overset{+}{N}H_3 + Cl^- \tag{7}$$

separation of the amines from non-basic compounds by the same procedures described for the alkali salts of carboxylic acids (Chap. 13). After other organic compounds have been extracted from the water solution of the amine salt, the amine may be recovered from the salt by use of a strong base (Eq. 8). Association

$$R-\overset{+}{N}H_3\overset{-}{Cl} + Na\overset{+}{O}\overset{-}{H} \rightleftarrows R-NH_2 + HOH + Na\overset{+}{C}\overset{-}{l} \tag{8}$$

$$\updownarrow$$

$$R-\overset{+}{N}H_3\overset{-}{O}H$$

of the amine and water give the alkylammonium and hydroxide ions so that the ions on the right of the equilibria are the same as those on the left; however, it is realistic to write such an equation, for the concentration of ions on the right is greatly reduced by the fact that the amine associates with water to only a small extent (note values for K_b in Table 1). Furthermore, unless the amine is of rather low molecular weight it will be insoluble in water and thus displace both equilibria in Eq. 8 to yield the free amine. In practice, amines may be recovered from their salts as easily as may carboxylic acids.

The quaternary ammonium bases also form salts, and the reaction is drawn forward by formation of water which is essentially un-ionized (Eq. 9).

$$\overset{+}{R_4N}\overset{-}{OH} + \overset{+}{H}\overset{-}{Cl} \longrightarrow \overset{+}{R_4N}\overset{-}{Cl} + HOH \tag{9}$$

Since a quaternary ammonium base is completely ionized, as is its salt, treatment of the salt with sodium hydroxide merely adds additional ions to the solution. An equation such as *Eq. 10 represents nothing more than an arbitrary re-pairing*

$$\overset{+}{R_4N}\overset{-}{Cl} + \overset{+}{Na}\overset{-}{OH} \rightleftarrows \overset{+}{R_4N}\overset{-}{OH} + \overset{+}{Na}\overset{-}{Cl} \tag{10}$$

of the ions. In order to free a quaternary ammonium base from its salt, it is necessary to choose conditions under which the inorganic salt is insoluble. Conditions which have been used to give precipitation of the inorganic salts are outlined in Eqs. 11 and 12. Since the quaternary ammonium hydroxides are

$$\overset{+}{R_4N}\overset{-}{Cl} + \overset{+}{K}\overset{-}{OH} \xrightarrow[\text{solvent}]{\text{ethanol}} \overset{+}{R_4N}\overset{-}{OH} + \underline{KCl} \tag{11}$$

$$\overset{+}{R_4N}\overset{-}{Cl} + AgOH \xrightarrow[\text{solvent}]{\text{water}} \overset{+}{R_4N}\overset{-}{OH} + \underline{AgCl} \tag{12}$$

usually quite soluble in water, the base must be recovered by evaporation of the filtrate from removal of the inorganic salt. The quaternary ammonium salts and bases are also non-volatile, in contrast to the volatile amines.

The processes shown in Eqs. 11 and 12 are commonly used for preparation of quaternary ammonium hydroxides, because synthetic methods for the quaternary ammonium ion actually apply to the salts (see below).

Synthesis of Amines

Synthesis of secondary and tertiary amines is nearly always accomplished from primary amines, so principal emphasis is on synthesis of the primary amines. There will be considered first, however, the general method yielding all three classes of amines in a sequence of reactions.

General Synthesis of Quaternary Salts and the
Three Classes of Amines

As discussed in Chapter 6, ammonia and amines are sufficiently good nucleophiles to displace halogen from an alkyl halide (Eq. 6-4), to yield the amine salt. There was no further elaboration of this process in Chapter 6; however, in view of the previous discussion in the present chapter, it is apparent that the salt formed in such a displacement would equilibrate with the salt of the base involved in the original displacement. This would give the sequence depicted in Eq. 13, if ammonia and an alkyl halide were used. The equilibrium

$$NH_3 + R{-}Br \longrightarrow R{-}\overset{+}{N}H_3\overset{-}{Br} \underset{}{\overset{NH_3}{\rightleftarrows}} R{-}NH_2 + \overset{+}{N}H_4\overset{-}{Br} \qquad (13)$$

shown in Eq. 13 is that of a salt and a base with the alternate salt and base. The position of equilibrium will depend on the difference in base strength of the two bases (cf. Table 1), so in the present case will not be displaced to a major extent in either direction. An examination of Eq. 13 reveals that the starting alkyl halide and the resultant alkylamine must be in the reaction mixture together, so there is nothing to prevent the occurrence of the reaction shown in Eq. 14— as well as those shown in Eqs. 15 and 16. Ratio of reactants is virtually the only

$$R{-}NH_2 + R{-}Br \longrightarrow R_2\overset{+}{N}H_2\overset{-}{Br} \underset{}{\overset{NH_3 \text{ or} \atop \text{an amine}}{\rightleftarrows}} R_2NH + \overset{+}{N}H_4\overset{-}{Br} \qquad (14)$$

$$R_2NH + R{-}Br \longrightarrow R_3\overset{+}{N}H\overset{-}{Br} \underset{}{\overset{NH_3 \text{ or} \atop \text{an amine}}{\rightleftarrows}} R_3N + \overset{+}{N}H_4\overset{-}{Br} \qquad (15)$$

$$R_3N + R{-}Br \longrightarrow R_4\overset{+}{N}\overset{-}{Br} \qquad (16)$$

control over distribution of products in this series of reactions, although steric hindrance slows the rates of the follow reactions. At the completion of the reaction, sodium hydroxide is added in order to free the amines from their salts (cf. Eq. 8).

The process described above, with use of excess alkyl halide, is an excellent **synthesis of quaternary ammonium salts** unless the reactions are blocked by hindrance. With a secondary alkyl halide, or with a primary alkyl halide having a branch in the 2-position, there is difficulty in pushing the reaction beyond the primary amine stage. The pronounced effect of crowding in substitution on nitrogen has been discussed in a preceding section in this chapter.

Simple *n*-alkylamines are synthesized industrially by the above-described processes, for the classes of amines may be separated by fractional distillation if the alkyl is larger than methyl; however, **principal use of the method in the laboratory is for tertiary amines and quaternary ammonium salts.** The synthesis of tertiary amines is greatly improved by the fact that heating of the residue of alkali and quaternary salt remaining after removal of the amines converts the quaternary salt to tertiary amine in rather good yield. The process is an E2 elimination (cf. Chap. 9) which proceeds in the usual concerted manner, as shown in Eq. 17.

$$R\overset{\overset{\displaystyle H}{|}}{\underset{\underset{\displaystyle \overset{H}{}}{|}}{C}}-CH_2-\overset{+}{N}(CH_2-CH_2-R)_3 \longrightarrow R-CH{=}CH_2 + (R-CH_2-CH_2)_3N + HOH$$

$$^-OH \tag{17}$$

The reaction shown in Eq. 17 is known as the **Hofmann elimination.** It is occasionally used for synthesis of an alkene, but probably the greatest use, other than that presently discussed, has been for degradation of natural products. The amine, whether primary, secondary or tertiary, is exhaustively methylated (as in Eqs. 13 through 16), then the quaternary salt is heated with base to give the degradation to an alkene. The alkene may then be processed further for determination of structure. Frequently, the amine from the first degradation is subjected to additional Hofmann degradations, until all alkyl groups originally present have been eliminated as alkenes.

If reaction of the alkyl halide is carried out with a primary or secondary amine, instead of ammonia, tertiary amines or quaternary salts with two or three different R groups may be obtained. The net products are indicated in Eqs. 18 and 19.

$$R{-}Br + R'{-}NH_2 \longrightarrow R{-}\overset{\displaystyle H}{\underset{}{N}}{-}R' \quad \text{and} \quad R{-}\overset{\displaystyle R}{\underset{}{N}}{-}R' \quad \text{and} \quad R{-}\overset{\displaystyle R}{\underset{\displaystyle R}{\overset{+}{N}}}{-}R'Br^- \tag{18}$$

$$R{-}Br + R'{-}\overset{\displaystyle H}{\underset{}{N}}{-}R'' \longrightarrow R'{-}\overset{\displaystyle R}{\underset{}{N}}{-}R'' \quad \text{and} \quad R'{-}\overset{\displaystyle R}{\underset{\displaystyle R}{\overset{+}{N}}}{-}R''Br^- \tag{19}$$

Since displacement reactions do not occur with aryl halides (Chap. 18), an aromatic amine cannot be prepared from an aryl halide by the presently discussed method. An aromatic amine can be used, however, as the nucleophile, so the groups R' and R" in Eqs. 18 and 19 may be aromatic. This permits preparation of such amines as the following from a primary aromatic amine:

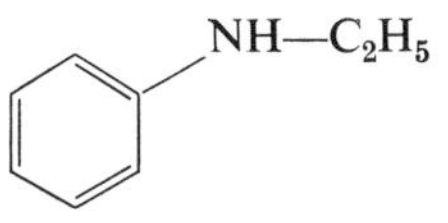

N-Ethylaniline

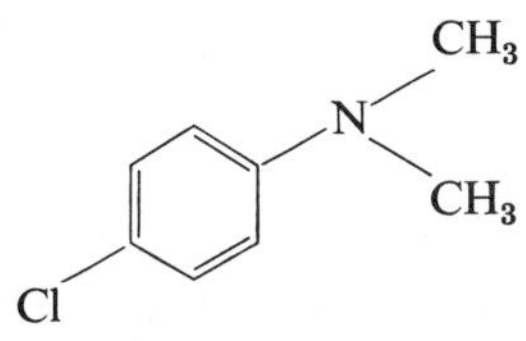

p-Chloro-N,N-dimethylaniline

Synthesis of Secondary Amines

Secondary amines are nearly always obtained from the primary amines. One satisfactory method for accomplishing this conversion, to yield a pure secondary amine, is presented in Eq. 20. Formation of the imine (cf. Chap. 15) is a common addition reaction of aldehydes, and catalytic hydrogenation of

$$R-C{\overset{O}{\underset{H}{\diagdown}}} + R'-NH_2 \longrightarrow [R-CH{=}N-R'] + HOH$$
(not isolated)

$$\xrightarrow{H_2, Pt} R-CH_2-\overset{H}{N}-R'$$

(20)

the double bond yields the amine. It may be noted that the synthesis in Eq. 20 is the same sequence as that of primary amines in Eq. 22. The R groups in the reactants may be either aliphatic or aromatic.

Synthesis of Primary Amines

Of the numerous syntheses which have been devised for primary amines, we will discuss four methods which will allow synthesis of primary amines from a variety of starting materials. The first two methods sometimes give small amounts of secondary amines as by-products, but this side reaction rarely interferes with the utility of the syntheses. All of these methods may be used with aliphatic amines, but the third method has been used very little for aliphatic compounds on account of the limited availability of aliphatic nitro compounds.[3] In contrast, reduction of nitro compounds is nearly always used for synthesis of aromatic amines (cf. Chap. 18). The final method to be discussed is occasionally used for an aromatic amine, but the first two methods cannot yield amines with the amino group attached to the aromatic ring.

Reduction of nitriles. Although this reduction may be accomplished with several different chemical agents, better yields are usually secured by catalytic hydrogenation (Eq. 21). Since nitriles may be prepared from alkyl

$$R-C{\equiv}N + 2H_2 \xrightarrow[\text{catalyst}]{\text{Pt or Ni}} R-CH_2-NH_2$$

(21)

---

[3] The only feasible laboratory synthesis of aliphatic nitro compounds is the reaction of an alkyl halide with silver nitrite:

$$R-CH_2-Br + AgNO_2 \longrightarrow R-CH_2-NO_2 + AgBr$$

Yields in this reaction tend to be quite poor on account of formation of the nitrite ester, $R-CH_2-ONO$, as major product. In 1954, Prof. Nathan Kornblum, of Purdue University, published a considerably improved procedure in *J. Am. Chem. Soc.*, **76**, 3209 (1954), for favoring formation of the nitro compound. In spite of this improvement, the aliphatic nitro compounds have not been widely used in synthesis.

Industrially available at a moderate cost are nitromethane, nitroethane, 1-nitropropane and 2-nitropropane. These compounds are obtained by a high temperature, free radical reaction between propane and nitric acid.

halides (Eq. 6-1) or acids (Eq. 14-18), the over-all amine synthesis may be accomplished either with or without chain extension by one carbon atom.

Reduction of oximes may be accomplished chemically (e.g., with sodium and ethanol), but catalytic hydrogenation (Eq. 22) is probably the best method.

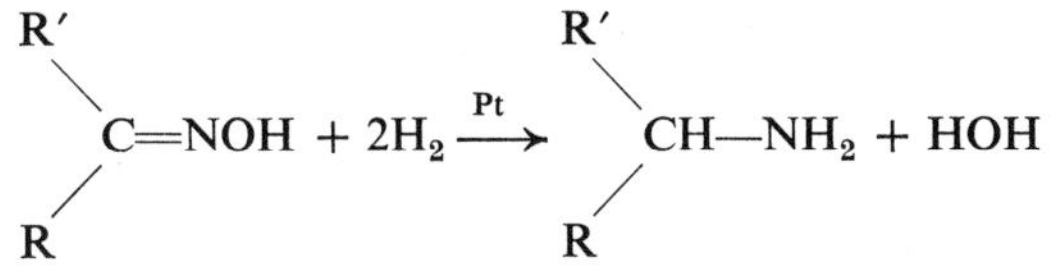

$$\begin{array}{c} R' \\ \diagdown \\ \diagup \\ R \end{array} C{=}NOH + 2H_2 \xrightarrow{\text{Pt}} \begin{array}{c} R' \\ \diagdown \\ \diagup \\ R \end{array} CH{-}NH_2 + HOH \qquad (22)$$

(R = H or alkyl)

The net synthesis in this case is from an aldehyde or ketone. If a ketone is the starting material the amine is primary but it is a *sec*-alkylamine.

Reduction of nitro compounds may be accomplished with numerous chemical reagents, as discussed in Chapter 18, but catalytic hydrogenation (Eq. 23) often gives a nearly quantitative yield.

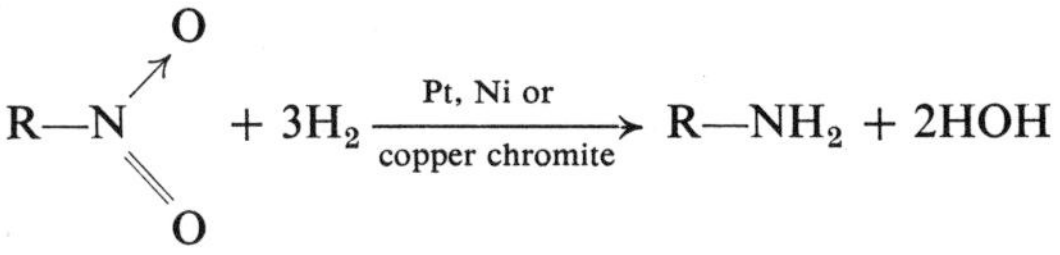

$$R{-}N\overset{\displaystyle O}{\underset{\displaystyle O}{\diagup}} + 3H_2 \xrightarrow[\text{copper chromite}]{\text{Pt, Ni or}} R{-}NH_2 + 2HOH \qquad (23)$$

Hofmann hyprobromite reaction. The net reaction for this process is shown in Eq. 24. An inspection of this equation makes it clear that a rather

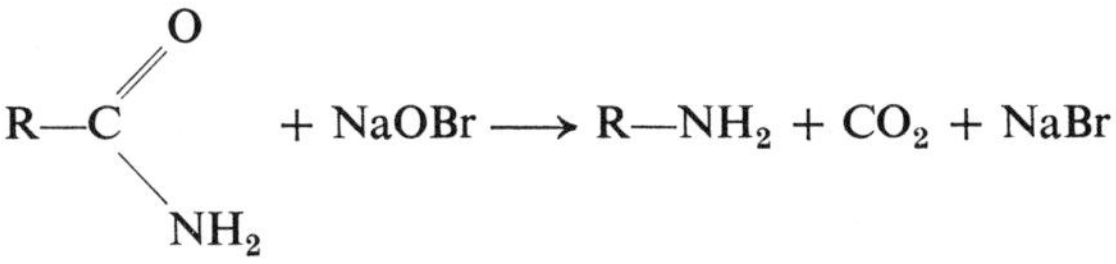

$$R{-}C\overset{\displaystyle O}{\underset{\displaystyle NH_2}{\diagup}} + NaOBr \longrightarrow R{-}NH_2 + CO_2 + NaBr \qquad (24)$$

unusual reaction has occurred, in that CO seems to have been extracted from between the R— and —NH$_2$. Since the procedure usually constitutes a good synthesis of amines, but requires rather special conditions in many instances, the mechanism of the reaction has been studied extensively. The mechanism seems now to be well understood, and is presented in the following sequence.

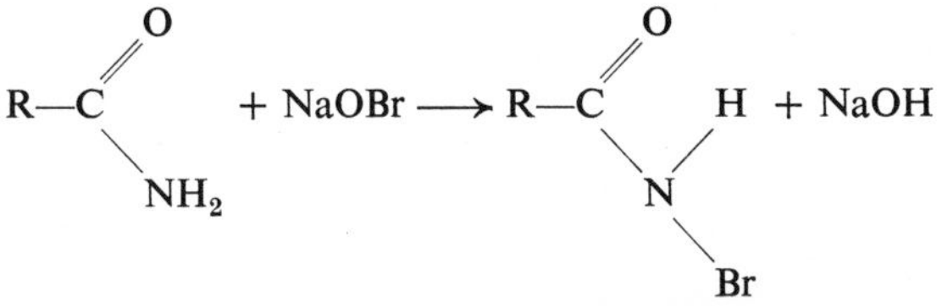

$$R{-}C\overset{\displaystyle O}{\underset{\displaystyle NH_2}{\diagup}} + NaOBr \longrightarrow R{-}C\overset{\displaystyle O}{\underset{\displaystyle N{-}Br}{\diagup}} H + NaOH \qquad (25)$$

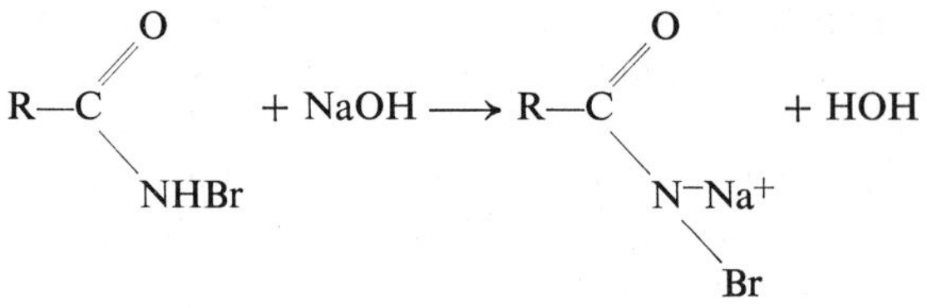

$$R-\overset{\displaystyle O}{\overset{\|}{C}}\diagdown_{NHBr} + NaOH \longrightarrow R-\overset{\displaystyle O}{\overset{\|}{C}}\diagdown_{N^-Na^+}\diagdown_{Br} + HOH \tag{26}$$

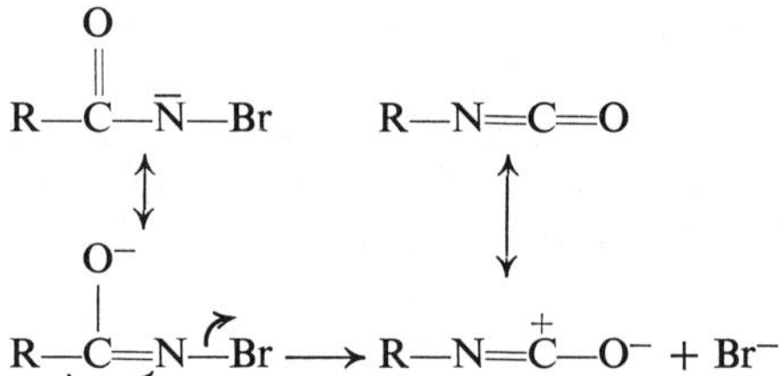

$$R-\overset{\displaystyle O}{\overset{\|}{C}}-\bar{N}-Br \qquad R-N=C=O$$
$$\updownarrow \qquad\qquad \updownarrow$$
$$\underset{O^-}{\overset{\displaystyle |}{R-C}}=N-Br \longrightarrow R-N=\overset{+}{C}-O^- + Br^- \tag{27}$$
$$\text{An isocyanate}$$

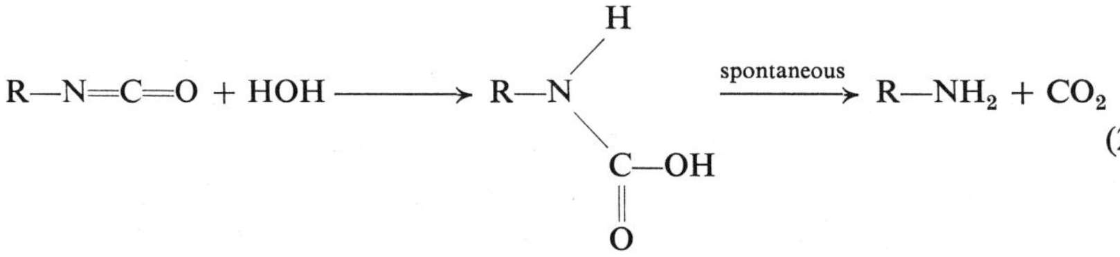

$$R-N=C=O + HOH \longrightarrow R-\overset{\displaystyle H}{\underset{\displaystyle C-OH}{N}} \xrightarrow{\text{spontaneous}} R-NH_2 + CO_2 \tag{28}$$
$$\underset{\displaystyle O}{\overset{\|}{}}$$
$$\text{A carbamic acid}$$
$$\text{(unstable)}$$

The key step in this sequence is the rearrangement shown in Eq. 27. This rearrangement involves displacement of halogen by migration of a negative group from an adjacent atom, the type of reaction involved in the Beckmann rearrangement (Eq. 18-44).

The primary product of the sequence outlined above is the isocyanate; the amine results only if the isocyanate is allowed to react with water. Although water is formed in Eq. 26, if an alcohol is used as solvent for the reaction it outnumbers the water so much that the final product becomes the product of the reaction of an isocyanate with the alcohol (Eq. 29). Urethanes are nothing

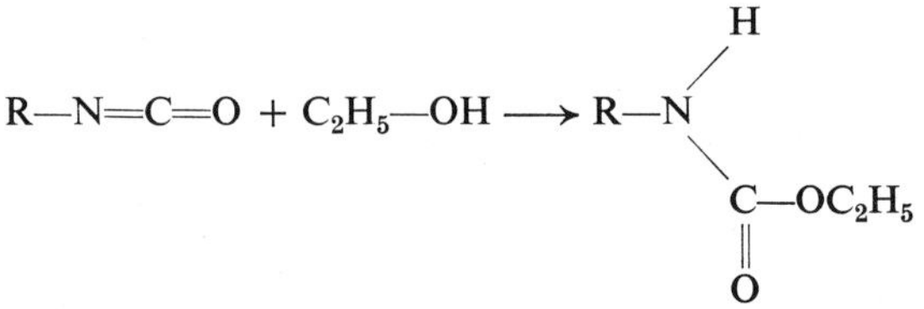

$$R-N=C=O + C_2H_5-OH \longrightarrow R-\overset{\displaystyle H}{\underset{\displaystyle C-OC_2H_5}{N}} \tag{29}$$
$$\underset{\displaystyle O}{\overset{\|}{}}$$
$$\text{A urethane}$$

more than carbamic esters; so hydrolysis of the urethane leads to the carbamic acid, which decarboxylates to give the amine. Better yields of aliphatic amines are nearly always secured[4] if the Hofmann reaction is carried out in alcohol, the urethane isolated, and the amine finally secured by hydrolysis.

It is worthy of note that a carbamic acid is nothing more than a mono-amide of carbonic acid, and its spontaneous decarboxylation is analogous to the behavior of carbonic acid. Furthermore, di-esters of carbonic acid are stable, as are urethanes, the esters of carbamic acids.

A final matter worthy of comment is the acidity of the N-bromo amide formed as an intermediate (cf. Eq. 26). Substitution of acyl on nitrogen, to form an amide, converts an amine to an essentially neutral compound. When the powerful electron-attracting halogen is also substituted on nitrogen, this withdraws electrons sufficiently to render the remaining hydrogen acidic. Acidity is also encouraged by resonance stabilization of the anion, as depicted in Eq. 27.

Reactions of Amines

General reactions of amines, applying to both aliphatic and aromatic compounds, consist principally of nucleophilic attack of three types: salt formation, displacement reactions, reaction with acid derivatives. The first two types of reaction, discussed in the present chapter, apply to all three classes of amines (primary, secondary, and tertiary). Reaction with acid derivatives, discussed in Chapter 14 (e.g., cf. Eq. 14-5), depends on loss of a hydrogen atom to yield a stable product; therefore, this type of reaction does not occur with a tertiary amine.

In order to complete discussion of amine reactions there will now be added the methods used to distinguish between classes of amines and, of particular importance, the reactions given only by aromatic amines.

Distinction between Classes of Amines

Of the reactions which reveal easily recognized differences in the three classes of amines, the best are the reaction with an aromatic sulfonyl chloride, discussed in Chapter 18, and the reaction with nitrous acid, not previously discussed.

---

[4] A major side reaction occurring when the amine is formed directly is reaction of the isocyanate with the amine to yield a disubstituted urea.

$$R—N{=}C{=}O + R—NH_2 \longrightarrow R—NH—\underset{\overset{\|}{O}}{C}—NH—R$$

As may be seen in Eqs. 28 and 29, as well as the reaction just mentioned, the characteristic reaction of an isocyanate involves nucleophilic attack on the multiply-bonded carbon. The reaction is completed by addition of a proton to nitrogen. Addition of the proton to oxygen may occur, but this yields the enol form of the product, and the keto form is always more stable, as discussed previously.

Hinsberg test. Reaction of benzenesulfonyl chloride with an amine is the basis for the most widely used method for distinguishing between classes of amines, both aliphatic and aromatic. As mentioned in Chapter 18, sulfonyl chlorides react with amines or ammonia (Eq. 18-16) to give sulfonamides, provided the amine has at least one hydrogen on nitrogen. Thus the reaction with the three classes would yield the following results:

From Primary Amine: *From Secondary Amine:* 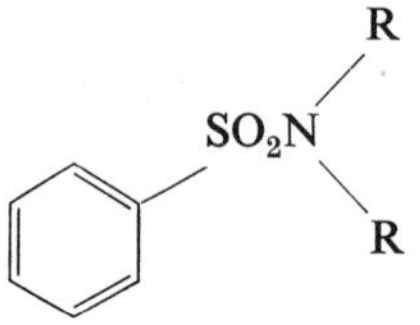   *From Tertiary Amine:*

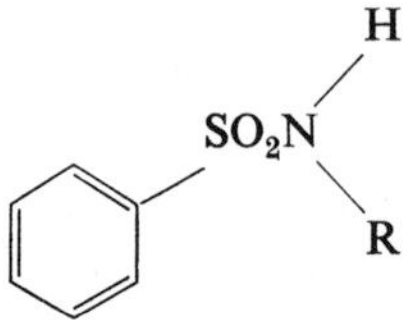

$$\text{SO}_2\text{N} \Big\langle {}^H_R \qquad \text{SO}_2\text{N} \Big\langle {}^R_R \qquad$$

No reaction, hence recovery of R—N—R

If it be recalled that sulfonamides bearing at least one hydrogen on nitrogen are acidic (cf. Chap. 18), it follows that results of the reaction with the sulfonyl chloride may be interpreted as follows:

(a) If the reaction product is acidic, the amine was primary.
(b) If the reaction product is neutral, the amine was secondary.
(c) If the reaction product is basic (unreacted amine), the amine was tertiary.

In practice, the Hinsberg test gives results that are definitive and easily interpreted with nearly all amines.

Reactions with nitrous acid may also be used to distinguish between classes of amines, although the reactions given by aromatic amines are different from those given by aliphatic amines. For both types of amine, for reaction in aqueous media, interpretation of results is the same, as follows:

(a) If a gas (nitrogen) is evolved, after warming for an aromatic amine, the amine is primary.
(b) If the product of reaction is a neutral substance, the amine is secondary.
(c) If the product of the reaction is a base, the amine is tertiary.

The reactions on which these interpretations depend must be considered separately for each class of amine. For the primary amine, there is formed the type of compound known as a diazonium salt, which is so unstable for an aliphatic amine that it decomposes as formed, even below zero degrees, (Eq. 30). For an aromatic amine, this salt is stable at $0°$ (Eq. 30). This useful inter-

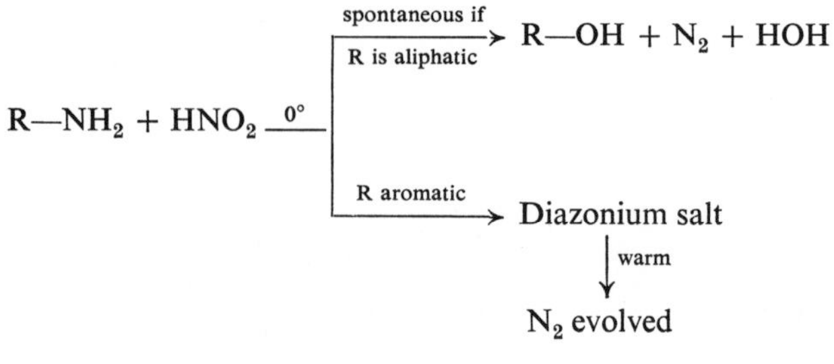

$$\text{R—NH}_2 + \text{HNO}_2 \xrightarrow{0°}$$

spontaneous if R is aliphatic $\longrightarrow$ R—OH + N_2 + HOH

R aromatic $\longrightarrow$ Diazonium salt $\xrightarrow{\text{warm}}$ N_2 evolved

(30)

mediate in the aromatic series will be discussed in some detail in a later section in this chapter.

Secondary amines give substitution of nitroso on nitrogen (Eq. 31) for both aliphatic and aromatic compounds. Presence of the electron-withdrawing

$$R—NH—R' + HONO \longrightarrow \underset{\underset{NO}{|}}{R—N—R'} + HOH \qquad (31)$$

nitroso group on the nitrogen destroys its electron-donating capacity to the extent that an N-nitrosoamine is neutral.

Tertiary aliphatic amines fail to react with nitrous acid, hence the amine is recovered from the reaction. Aromatic amines give substitution of nitroso in the ring (Eq. 32); hence, the product of this reaction is also basic.

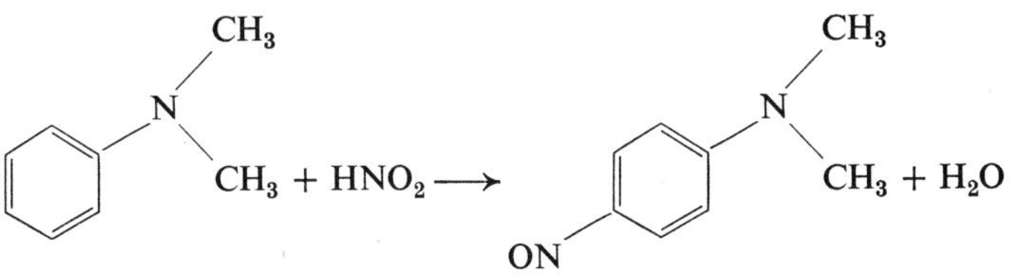

p-Nitroso-N,N-dimethylaniline

Nitrosation of tertiary aromatic amines goes almost entirely *para*, and is sometimes of use in synthesis in instances where *para* substitution is desired; however, serious side reactions sometimes defeat the synthetic utility of the reaction. The reaction used for illustration in Eq. 32 goes in good yield, and reduction of the nitroso group constitutes the best synthesis of p-dimethyl-aminoaniline.

Substitution Reactions of Aromatic Amines

Presence in the ring of the basic, strongly electron-donating amino group gives rise to several special features in aromatic substitution; so there is needed some supplementation of the general discussion of aromatic substitution in Chapter 17.

Halogenation of amines is of relatively limited usefulness. Amines are so readily oxidized that this reaction competes with halogen substitution, especially in chlorination. Bromination proceeds fairly well, but so rapidly (even without an iron catalyst) that frequently the only product isolable in good yield is the one with all available *ortho* and *para* positions filled. Bromination of aniline proceeds as in Eq. 33.

Since the medium for the reaction shown in Eq. 33 becomes rapidly more acidic, the amines are present in equilibrium with their salts; the more basic the amine, the further the equilibrium is shifted towards the salt. Halogenation lowers the basicity of the amine; therefore the ratio of free amine present becomes higher for the monohalogenated amine, still higher for the dihalogenated amine. Since the amine salts are *meta*-directors, halogenated very slowly, the higher concentration of halogenated amines increases the rate of their halogenation; hence the principal product is the trihalogenated amine.

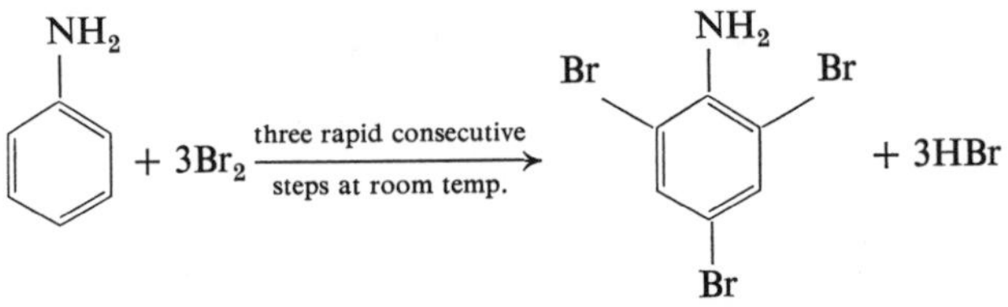

$$\text{(33)}$$

2,4,6-Tribromoaniline

Halogenation can be controlled well if the amine is first acetylated, then halogenated. The halogenated amine may finally be secured by hydrolysis.

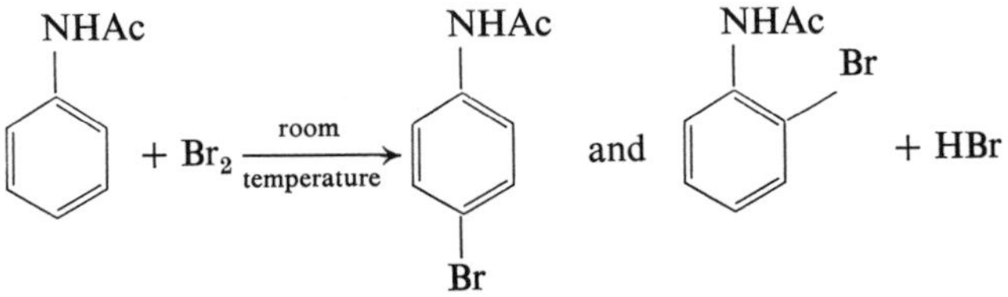

p-Bromoacetanilide (larger amount) *o*-Bromoacetanilide (smaller amount)

$$\text{(34)}$$

There is some dihalogenation, but a satisfactory yield of the mono-halogenated compound may be secured. At higher temperature, and with a larger ratio of bromine, dihalogenation may be obtained satisfactorily.

Nitration of amines is even less satisfactory than is halogenation. When nitration is carried out in strong acid, the salt of the amine is the principal species present; however, aromatic amines are such weak bases that the salt is dissociated to some extent, as in Eq. 35. Although very little of the free amine

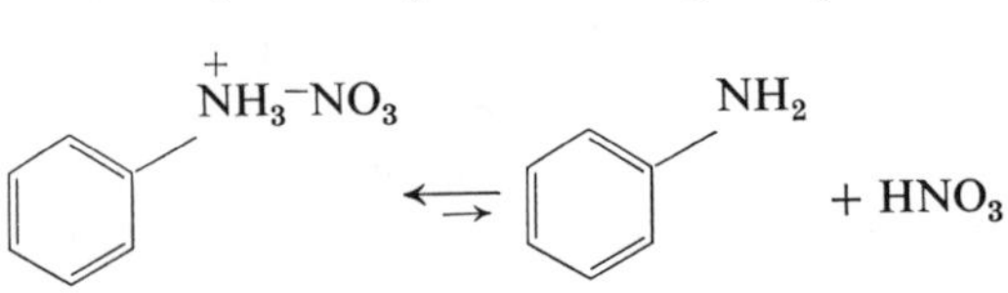

$$\text{(35)}$$

is present, its rate of reaction is vastly faster than the ion, for the $^{+}NH_3$ grouping is a *meta*-director (cf. Chap. 17). The result is a reaction giving all three substitution isomers, with the *meta* in somewhat larger amount. Furthermore, oxidation is a serious side reaction.

As in the case of halogenation, nitration is best carried out on the acetylated amine. Since nitro is a *meta*-director, clean-cut mono-substitution may be obtained. In sulfuric acid as solvent, principal substitution is in the *para* position (Eq. 36), and hydrolysis gives a good yield of *p*-nitroaniline. At higher

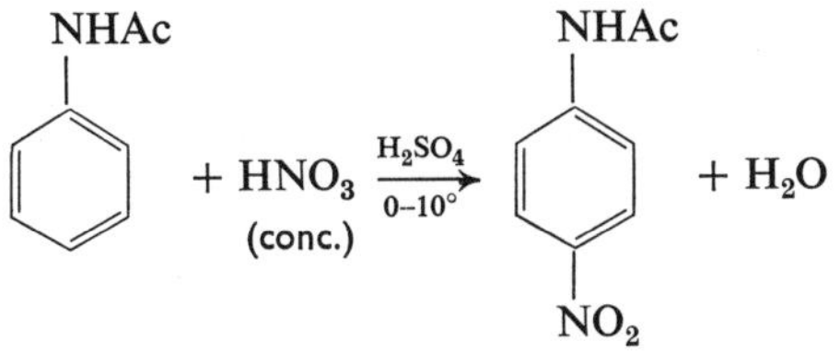

$$
\text{NHAc} + \text{HNO}_3 \;\xrightarrow[\text{0–10°}]{\text{H}_2\text{SO}_4}\; \text{NHAc-NO}_2 + \text{H}_2\text{O} \tag{36}
$$

(conc.)

temperature, 2,4-dinitroacetanilide may be secured and hydrolyzed to 2,4-dinitroaniline.

Sulfonation. Direct introduction of the sulfonic acid group into the ring does not occur, but the salt of the amine and sulfuric acid dehydrates to the sulfamic acid on heating; and this rapidly rearranges to give almost entirely the *p*-aminobenzenesulfonic acid (sulfanilic acid), which is present largely as the intramolecular salt, as shown in Eq. 37. Sulfanilic acid is manufactured in

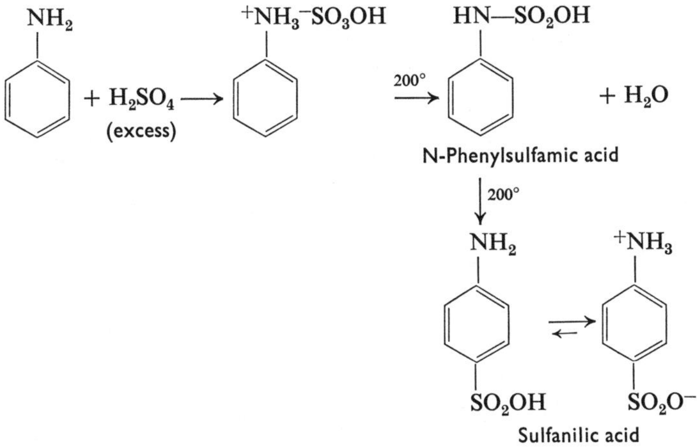

$$
\text{NH}_2 + \text{H}_2\text{SO}_4 \longrightarrow \text{}^+\text{NH}_3{}^-\text{SO}_3\text{OH} \;\xrightarrow{200°}\; \text{HN--SO}_2\text{OH} + \text{H}_2\text{O}
$$

(excess)

N-Phenylsulfamic acid

$$
\Big\downarrow 200° \tag{37}
$$

$$
\text{NH}_2\text{--SO}_2\text{OH} \;\rightleftharpoons\; \text{}^+\text{NH}_3\text{--SO}_2\text{O}^-
$$

Sulfanilic acid

considerable quantity by this process. It is used in the manufacture of several dyes by the coupling procedure described later in this chapter (Eq. 52).

The Friedel and Crafts reaction with tertiary amines, such as N,N-dimethylaniline, is beset by such serious side reactions that the method is rarely of synthetic utility. The Friedel and Crafts reaction is not applicable to primary and secondary amines, for alkylation or acylation occurs on nitrogen (synthesis of secondary amines, acylation of amines).

Triphenylmethane dyes. Under strenuous conditions, a tertiary aromatic amine will give a condensation reaction with an aromatic aldehyde which is similar to a Friedel and Crafts reaction. A rather similar reaction of trichloro-acetaldehyde has been described (Eq. 17-35). An illustrative reaction of this type with a tertiary amine is shown in Eq. 38. A major reason for interest in

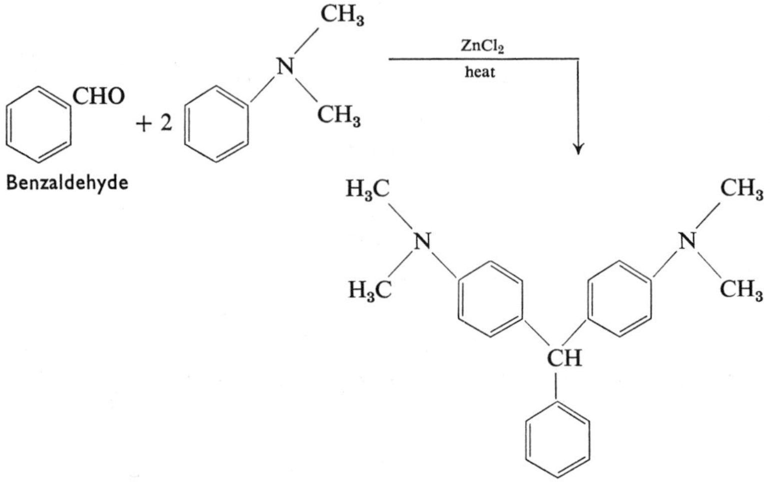

(38)

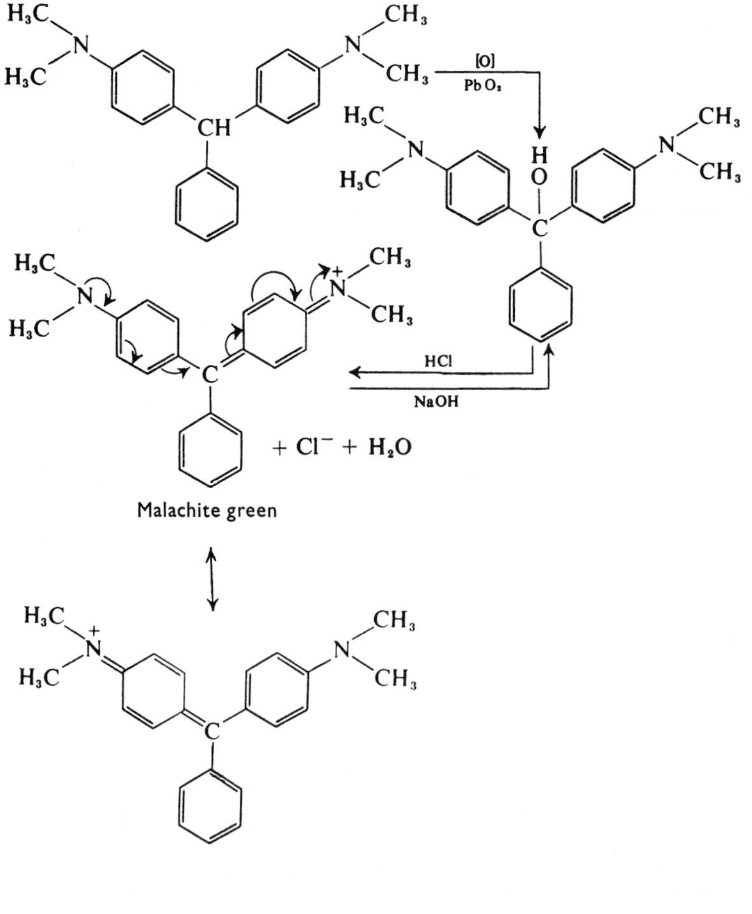

(39)

Malachite green

this reaction is that the highly substituted central carbon atom in the product is subject to an oxidation which yields a tri-arylcarbinol, as illustrated in Eq. 39. The product of the lead peroxide oxidation in Eq. 39 is an aliphatic alcohol; however, the presence of the three aromatic rings on the carbinol carbon renders the hydroxyl so labile that dissociation of the oxonium salt occurs quite readily to leave a carbonium ion. The ease of removing hydroxyl is no doubt due to resonance stabilization of the resultant positive ion. Resonance forms may be written with the plus charge in any *ortho* or *para* position, but forms in which nitrogen is acting as a base by donating electrons should be the most important forms; so these are shown in the lower lines of Eq. 39.

The resonance forms shown for malachite green indicate the maximum extent of the orbitals of the π-electrons. Extended orbitals of this sort are usually responsible for color in organic compounds. The azo dyes, discussed later in this chapter, will be noted to have extended π-orbitals.

The carbinol which gives the malachite green salt with acid does not ionize to give hydroxyl ion, although it gives a salt with acid; so it is known as a *pseudo base* (imitation base). Since the colored salt also gives the colorless pseudo base on treatment with sodium hydroxide, the pseudo base is sometimes called the *leuco base* (colorless base).

By use of substituted amines and aldehydes, triphenylmethane dyes of different shades may be secured.

Diazotization and Reactions of Diazonium Compounds

As has been mentioned, the most important reaction of primary aromatic amines is that with nitrous acid. This process, known as **diazotization,** is carried out in strongly acid medium (Eq. 40). Benzenediazonium chloride is a salt, and

$$\text{(C}_6\text{H}_5)\text{NH}_3\text{Cl} + \text{HONO} \xrightarrow[0°]{\text{H}^+} (\text{C}_6\text{H}_5)\text{N}_2\text{Cl} + 2\text{H}_2\text{O} \qquad (40)$$

if some other acid is used the anion of that acid will be present. When dry, diazonium salts are dangerous explosives, since they are very sensitive to shock and are likely to detonate unexpectedly. In solution, they are entirely safe, and reactions are nearly always carried out on the freshly prepared salt in solution.

The structure of the diazonium group is complicated by the fact that it changes with the *p*H of the solution, and investigation of this structure has been the subject of research by several chemists.[5] It seems likely that the equilibria

---

[5] The interpretation of diazonium equilibria presented here is based largely on the investigation by the Swiss chemists, Wittwer and Zollinger, reported in *Helv. Chim. Acta*, **37**, 1954 (1955).

occurring in a solution of a diazonium salt are as represented in Eq. 41.

$$\text{Ar}-\overset{+}{\text{N}}\!\!\equiv\!\!\text{N} + {}^-\text{OH} \underset{K_1}{\overset{}{\rightleftharpoons}} \text{Ar}-\text{N}\!\!=\!\!\text{N}-\text{OH} \underset{K_2}{\overset{{}^-\text{OH}}{\rightleftharpoons}} \text{Ar}-\text{N}\!\!=\!\!\text{N}-\text{O}^- + \text{HOH} \quad (41)$$

$$K_1 \ll K_2$$

Since the value for the equilibrium constant K_1 is much smaller than that for K_2, it follows that any concentration of alkali which shifts the first equilibrium forward appreciably will displace the second equilibrium much more. This means that the concentration of the intermediate *diazoic acid* is always vanishingly small. The two significant species in the solution are the *diazonium cation* and the *diazotate anion*. It follows that the diazonium salt may be properly regarded as a dibasic acid, but the second acidic function is formed only after reaction of the first. Below pH 4.5, there appears to be no significant concentration of the diazotate ion, and above pH 13 there is no significant concentration of the diazonium ion. Between these two values, the concentration of diazonium ion drops by a factor of about 10^2 for each unit increase in the value of the pH. From these considerations, it follows that most reactions dependent on the diazonium ion would be favored in strong acid solution. This is actually the case for all reactions except that with cyanide ion (Eq. 50) and the coupling reaction (Eq. 52). These are favored in weakly acidic or neutral solution, for the other component is inactivated in strongly acid solution; therefore reaction occurs best near neutrality where there is some concentration of each of the reactive species. In strongly alkaline solution, coupling will not occur, for the diazotate ion becomes the only significant species. A reaction of the diazotate ion will be discussed in Chapter 28.

Phenol synthesis. The diazonium ion reacts with water, and this is why the diazotization is carried out at $0°$. At this temperature, reaction with water is sufficiently slow to allow time for other reactions if they are desired. If the phenol is desired, warming the diazonium solution gives rapid conversion to phenol (Eq. 42), with evolution of nitrogen, as mentioned in connection with

$$\underset{\text{warm}}{\overset{\text{H}^+}{\longrightarrow}}$$

(Eq. 42 — structures: benzene with N_2^+ + HOH → benzene with OH + H^+ + N_2)   (42)

the test for primary amines (Eq. 30). This reaction usually gives only a moderately good yield of phenol (50–65%), but many substituted phenols are best made by this process, for it makes possible conversion of the easily purified nitro compound to the phenol. It is important that the medium be strongly acidic and that diazotization be completed before the solution is warmed, otherwise coupling with the phenol (Eq. 50) becomes a very serious side reaction.

Reduction of the diazonium salt may be accomplished to give either of two products, depending on the reagent used.

(a) HYDRAZINE SYNTHESIS may be accomplished by reduction with either sulfur dioxide or stannous chloride in acidic solution (Eq. 43). Phenyl-

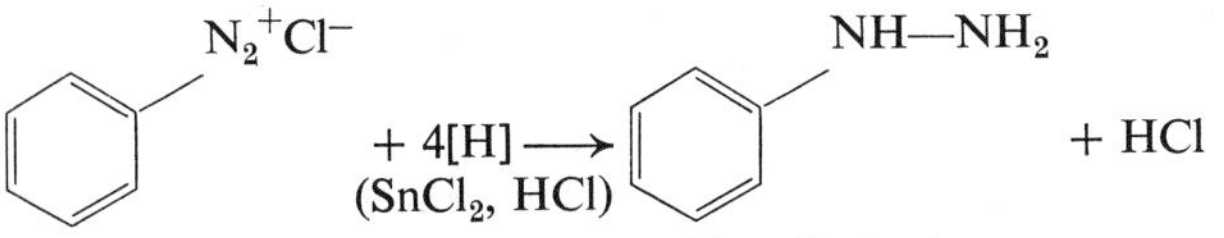

$$\text{C}_6\text{H}_5\text{—N}_2^{+}\text{Cl}^{-} + 4[\text{H}] \xrightarrow{(\text{SnCl}_2, \text{HCl})} \text{C}_6\text{H}_5\text{—NH—NH}_2 + \text{HCl} \quad (43)$$

Phenylhydrazine

hydrazine is an important sugar reagent (Chap. 23), and is also used to make solid derivatives of other aldehydes and ketones (cf. Eq. 15-7). Various substituted hydrazines, also of use as carbonyl reagents, can be made by employing the appropriate substituted diazonium salt in the process shown in Eq. 43.

(b) REMOVAL OF THE DIAZONIUM GROUP BY REDUCTION has been accomplished with several reagents, but hypophosphorous acid has been found to give the best results (Eq. 44).

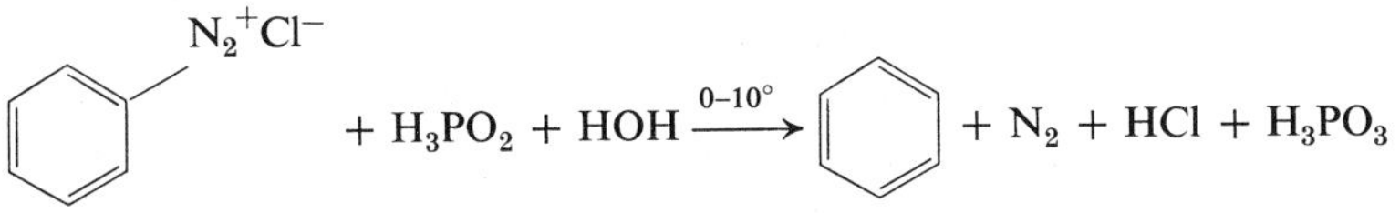

$$\text{C}_6\text{H}_5\text{—N}_2^{+}\text{Cl}^{-} + \text{H}_3\text{PO}_2 + \text{HOH} \xrightarrow{0\text{--}10°} \text{C}_6\text{H}_6 + \text{N}_2 + \text{HCl} + \text{H}_3\text{PO}_3 \quad (44)$$

Although removal of a group from the ring might appear, at first consideration, a rather useless process, it proves to be a rather convenient procedure for several types of synthesis. It is especially useful for accomplishing the synthesis of *meta*-substituted compounds by a sequence such as the following:

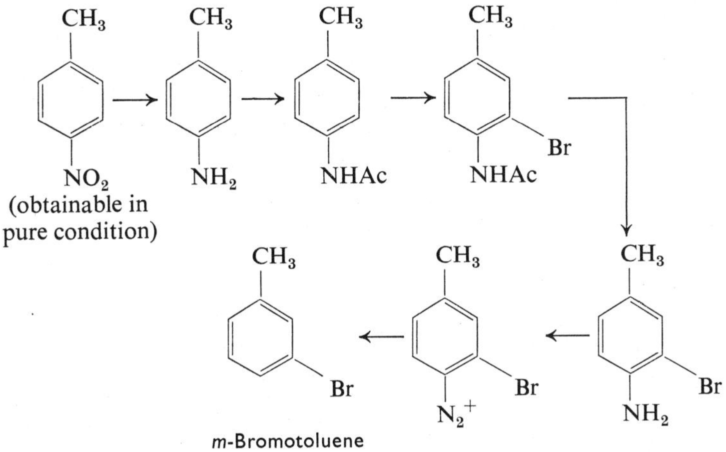

(45)

m-Bromotoluene

Although several steps are involved in this process, the reactions are experimentally simple and give good yields. For synthesis of *m*-bromotoluene and many related compounds (cf. Exercises at the end of this chapter), the route shown in Eq. 45 is about the only one available.

Sandmeyer and Gattermann reactions. The reactions in this group are catalyzed by copper (Gattermann reactions) or cuprous salts (Sandmeyer reactions). The products secured with the two catalysts are the same, and the cuprous salts are usually more effective. The more important substituents which may be introduced by these reactions are the halogens and cyano. The rather complicated mechanisms of these reactions are only partly understood.

(1) SUBSTITUTION OF HALOGEN. All of the common halogens, including fluorine, may be substituted by this process. Satisfactory conditions are indicated in Eqs. 46 through 49. In Eqs. 46 and 47, it may be noted that the only

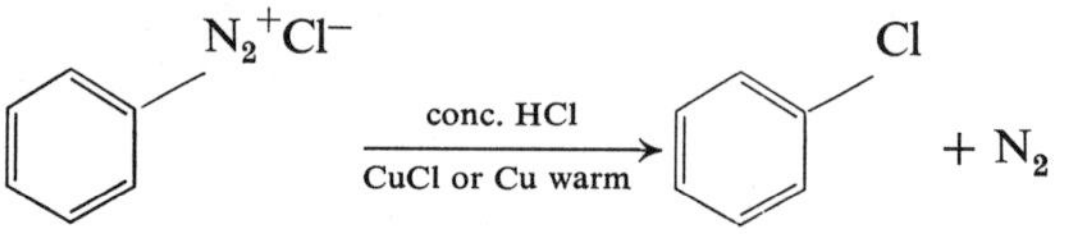

$$
\underset{\text{CuCl or Cu warm}}{\overset{\text{conc. HCl}}{\longrightarrow}} \quad \text{Cl} \quad + \text{N}_2 \tag{46}
$$

$$
\underset{\text{CuBr or Cu warm}}{\overset{\text{conc. HBr}}{\longrightarrow}} \quad \text{Br} \quad + \text{N}_2 \tag{47}
$$

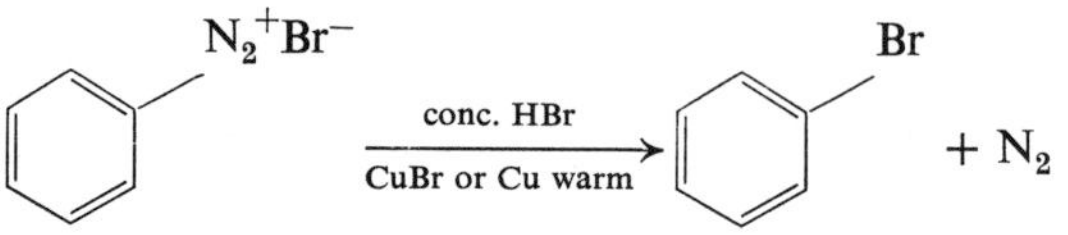

$$
\underset{\text{warm}}{\overset{\text{H}_2\text{SO}_4}{\longrightarrow}} \quad \text{I} \quad + \text{N}_2 \tag{48}
$$

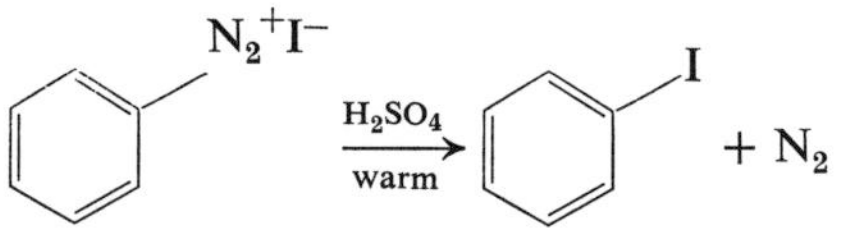

$$
\text{N}_2{}^+\text{Cl}^- + \text{HBF}_4 \longrightarrow \text{N}_2\text{BF}_4 + \text{HCl}
$$
Fluoroboric acid   (precipitates)

heat | dry solid

$$
\text{F} \quad + \text{N}_2 + \text{BF}_3 \tag{49}
$$

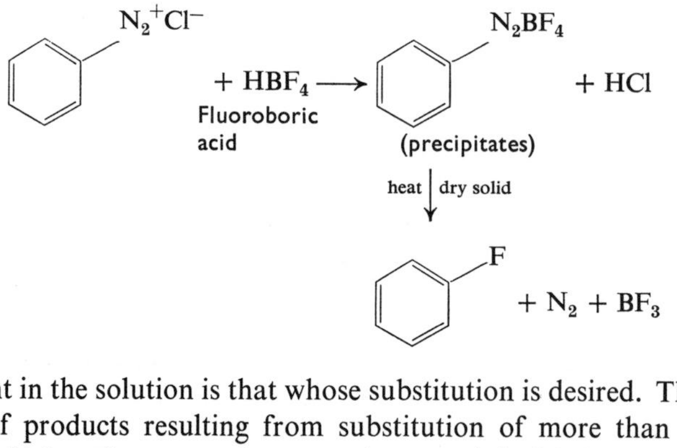

anion present in the solution is that whose substitution is desired. This prevents formation of products resulting from substitution of more than one anion. Hydriodic acid is rather expensive; so only enough iodide is used to form the iodobenzene, and the hydrogen ion is increased to the desired value with sulfuric acid. This is successful because the sulfate and hydrogen sulfate anions do not substitute in the Sandmeyer reaction. Actually, iodide substitutes so readily that no catalyst is needed, but this reaction is commonly included among the Sandmeyer and Gattermann reactions.

The substitution of fluorine is worthy of special comment, for this is one of the few methods for introducing fluorine into the aromatic ring. Also, the diazonium fluoroborate is one of the few diazonium salts which is quite insoluble in water and one of the few which it is safe to heat in a dry state. Even with this salt, the heating is often done in a long narrow tube so that only a small portion of the salt is heated at one time.

(2) SUBSTITUTION OF CYANO (NITRILE SYNTHESIS). This reaction gives a poorer yield than does halogen substitution, for it must be carried out near neutrality (Eq. 50). This lowers the concentration of the diazonium ion (cf.

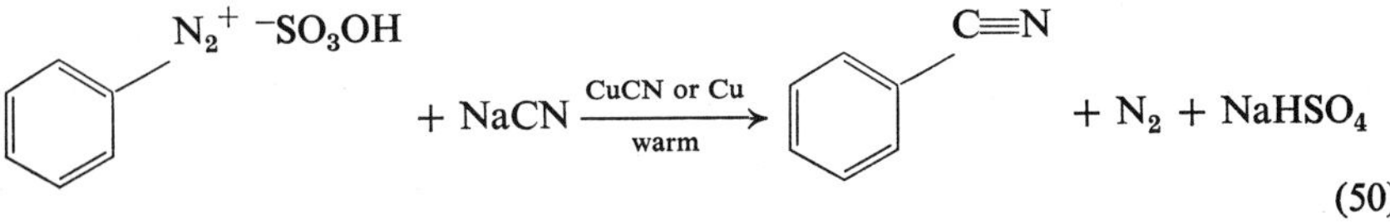

$$ \text{(50)} $$

Eq. 41) and leads to side reactions. The relatively high pH cannot be avoided, however, for hydrogen cyanide is such a weak acid that it does not furnish sufficient cyanide ions for the reaction. At higher pH, the ionized cyanide salt is formed.

The *particular significance* of the Sandmeyer reactions is for forming pure isomers in instances where other substitution routes lead to inseparable mixtures of isomers. As an illustration, synthesis of pure *o*-bromotoluene may be considered. It was pointed out in Chapter 17 that direct bromination of toluene leads to an inseparable mixture of the *ortho* and *para* isomers, but nitration of toluene gives a readily separable mixture of *ortho* and *para* isomers. Conversion of the nitro compound to the halogen derivative would then follow the sequence

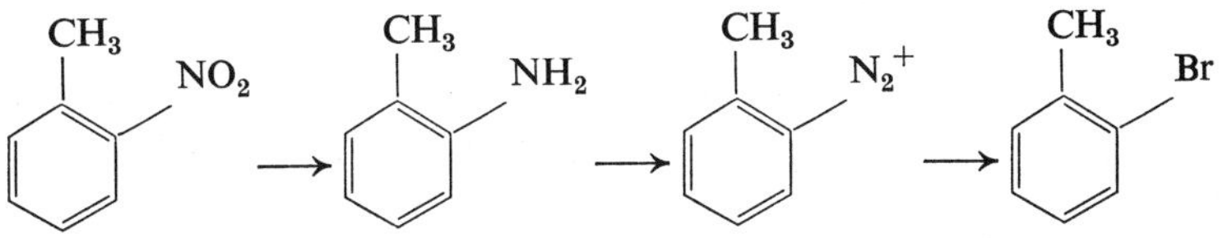

(pure isomer)

$$ \text{(51)} $$

outlined in Eq. 51. The great utility of the replacement reactions of the diazonium group will become apparent in solving the synthetic problems included in the Exercises at the end of this chapter.

Coupling reaction. This reaction occurs most rapidly near neutrality or in slightly acidic solution. The medium is often buffered with sodium acetate as shown in Eq. 52, but in some instances, it is satisfactory to simply add alkali as the reaction proceeds.

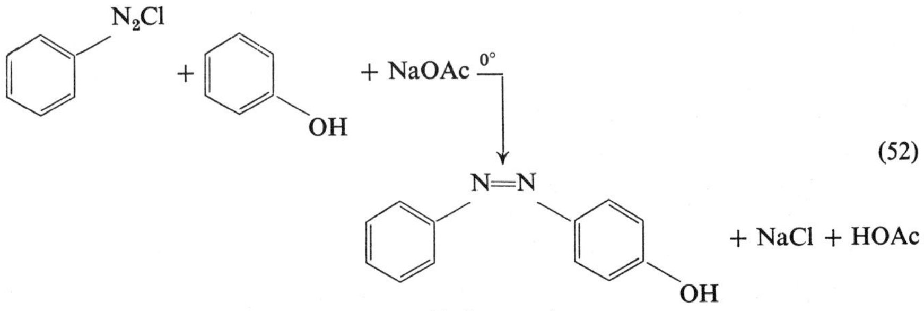

$$ \text{(52)} $$

p-Hydroxyazobenzene

The coupling reaction occurs only with highly activated benzene derivatives, i.e., phenols and amines. With tertiary amines, the reaction proceeds similarly to that shown in Eq. 52, to give the *p*-dialkylaminoazobenzene, but with amines having a hydrogen on nitrogen, coupling occurs initially on nitrogen. Warming in slightly acid solution gives rearrangement into the ring, as shown in Eq. 53.

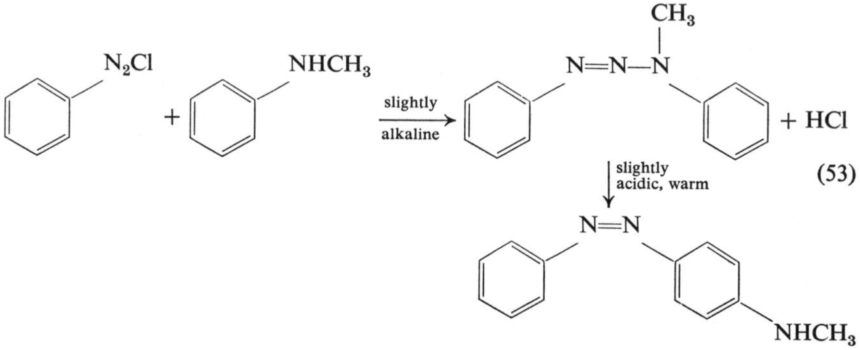

p-Methylaminoazobenzene

(53)

The coupling reaction goes *almost exclusively para* unless this position is occupied, in which case it will occur in the *ortho* position. If all positions *ortho* or *para* to the amino or hydroxyl are occupied by other groups, the coupling reaction will not occur.

The coupling reaction is of much commercial significance, for many of the substituted azo compounds are **commercially useful dyes.** They may be used for direct dyeing of silk and wool, and cotton may be dyed if the coupling process is carried out on the cloth by passing the cloth first into the amine or phenol solution, then into the solution of diazonium salt. Such a dye is said to be an "ingrain color." Some of the dyes used for foods are azo dyes, and the dyes in color film are also azo dyes. In photographic film, coupling is a part of the development process.

The azo grouping is responsible for the color of these compounds, and such a group is known as a **chromophore.** The shade of the color is affected by substituents in the benzene rings, and the substance is able to function as a dye and become attached to cloth only when salt-forming groups are in the ring (**auxochrome groups).** A large chemical industry is concerned with furnishing the intermediates (phenols and amines) for making dyes of many different shades. Most of the azo dyes are some shade of yellow or red, although shades approaching blue may be secured with certain structures. Many of the dye intermediates are naphthalene derivatives, and this interest has led to much of the development of naphthalene chemistry (cf. Chap. 29).

Although there is no object in learning the structures and trade names of large numbers of azo dyes at this time, certain examples may be used to illustrate the types of compounds encountered:

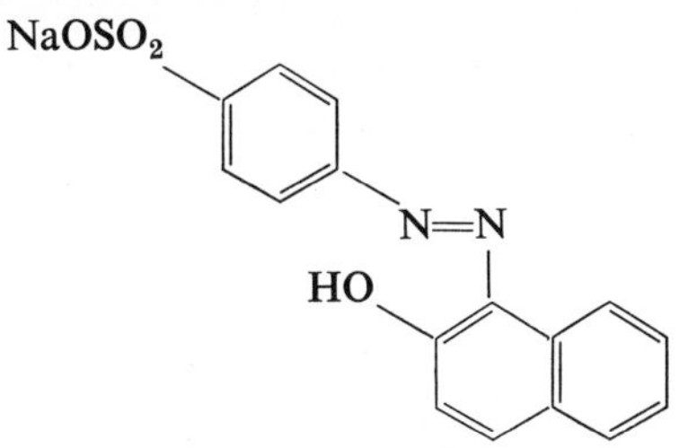

Orange II

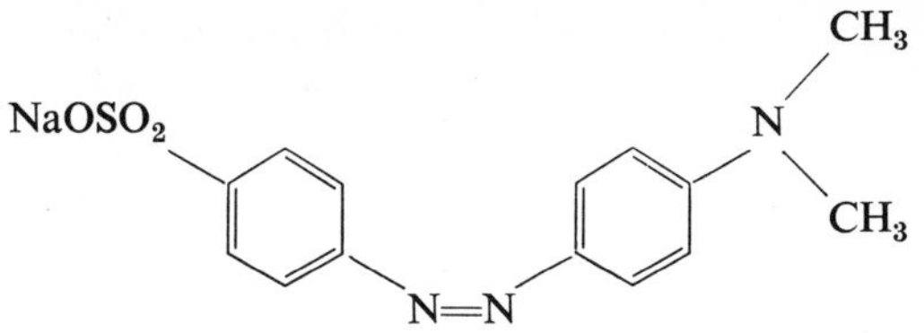

Methyl orange

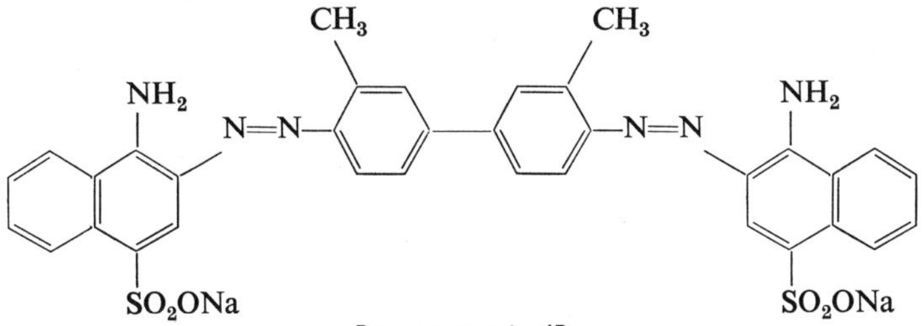

Benzopurpurin 4B

Inspection of these formulas will reveal the amines needed for diazotization and the agents with which coupling is carried out.

The azo compounds containing a sulfonic acid group and an amino group substituted in the rings give a change in color when passing from the salt of the acid to that of the amine; hence they have been used as indicators. Methyl orange, which is yellow in base and pink in acid, is an example of such a

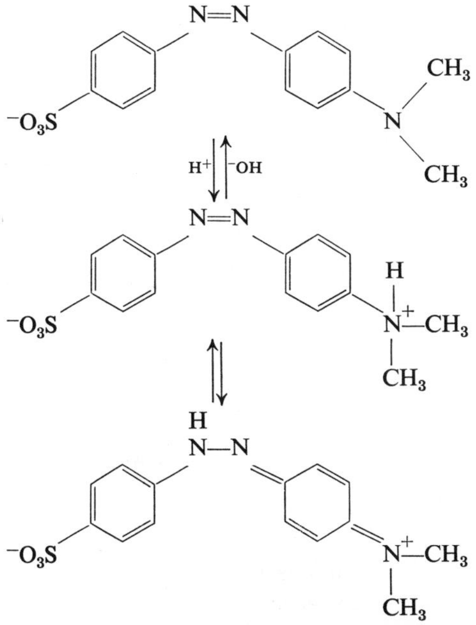

$$(54)$$

substance. The color change is believed due to the possibility for a different chromophore in the cation, as shown in Eq. 54. Since the pH at which the color change occurs is influenced by the substituents in the rings and type of rings present, indicators may be secured which change color at various hydrogen ion concentrations.

In addition to their extensive uses as dyes, the azo compounds have a utility in **synthesis of p-aminophenols.** Reduction of an azo compound leads to an amine (Eq. 18-14); so reduction of a p-hydroxyazobenzene leads to an aminophenol. Sodium hydrosulfite has proved very effective for this reduction, as in Eq. 55, which outlines the synthesis of 3-methyl-4-aminophenol from m-cresol, which occurs in coal tar.

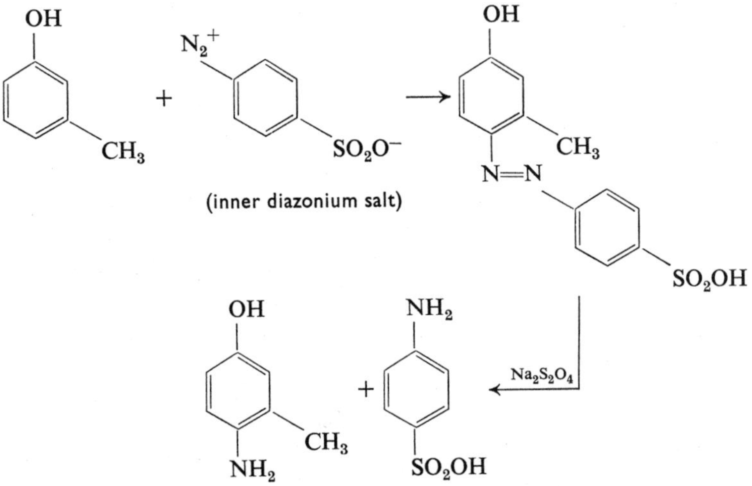

(inner diazonium salt)

(55)

Diazotized sulfanilic acid is especially useful as the coupling agent because sulfanilic acid can be easily separated as its water-soluble sodium salt in bicarbonate solution, which will not convert the weakly acidic aminophenol to its salt.

The synthesis of 4-amino-3-methylphenol could also be accomplished by nitration and reduction of the nitro group, but the yield by this route is much lower. Nitration does not occur exclusively in the *para* position as does coupling.

EXERCISES

I. Give one name for each of the following compounds.

(a) CH_3—CH—CH_2—N—CH_2—CH_3
　　　　 |　　　 |
　　　 CH_3　 CH—C_2H_5
　　　　　　　 |
　　　　　　 CH_3

(b) 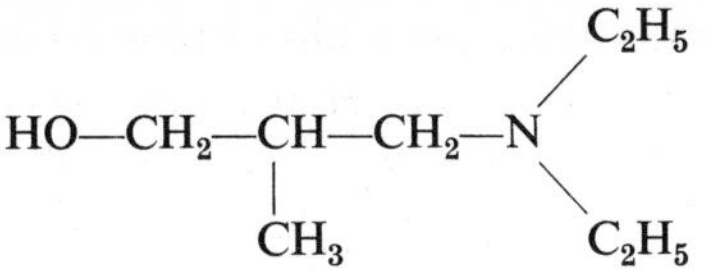 $HO-CH_2-CH-CH_2-N\begin{smallmatrix}C_2H_5\\\\C_2H_5\end{smallmatrix}$

            $|$
           CH_3

(c) $C_2H_5-\overset{+}{\underset{\underset{CH_3}{|}}{\overset{\overset{CH_3}{|}}{N}}}-\underset{\underset{CH_3}{|}}{CH}-CH_3$ ^-OH

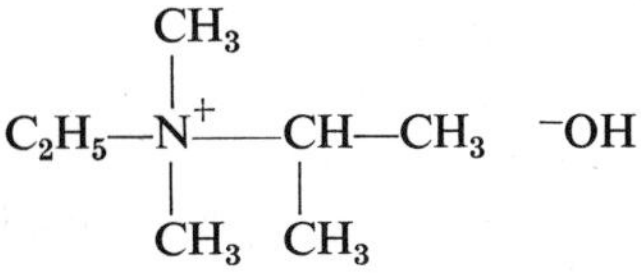

(d) 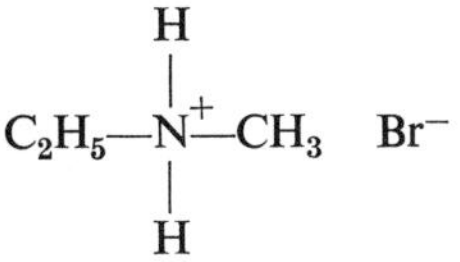 $C_2H_5-\overset{+}{\underset{\underset{H}{|}}{\overset{\overset{H}{|}}{N}}}-CH_3$ Br^-

(e) 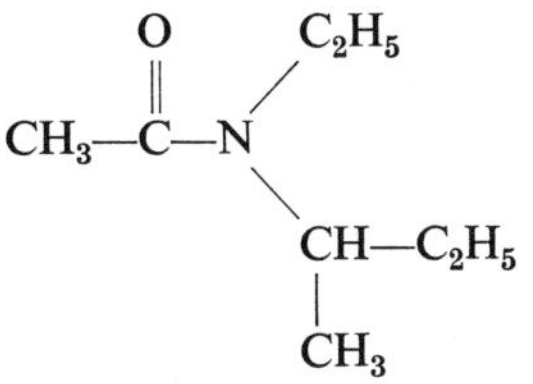 $CH_3-\overset{\overset{O}{\|}}{C}-N\begin{smallmatrix}C_2H_5\\\\CH-C_2H_5\\|\\CH_3\end{smallmatrix}$

(f) 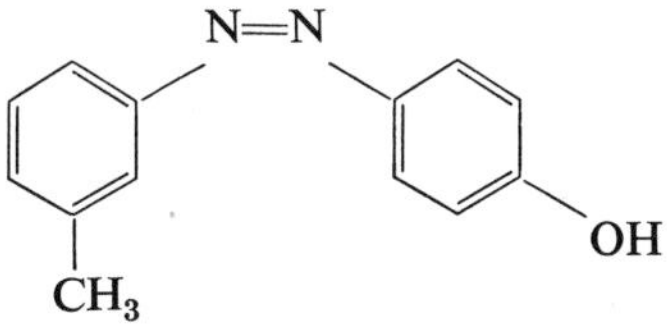 [benzene ring with CH_3 substituent]$-N{=}N-$[benzene ring]$-OH$

(g) 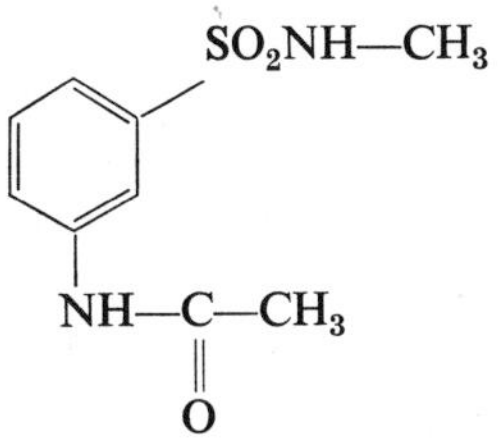 [benzene ring with SO_2NH-CH_3 substituent and $NH-\overset{\overset{}{C}}{\underset{O}{\|}}-CH_3$ substituent]

2. Outline by a flow sheet a method for separating the following compounds and obtaining each in a pure condition: *n*-hexylamine, caproic acid, *n*-hexyl alcohol.

3. If you were given six test tubes, each known to contain a different one of the following six compounds, how could you determine by qualitative tests the identity of the compound in each tube? Write balanced equations for the tests.

(a) *n*-Nonylamine.
(b) *n*-Nonyl alcohol.
(c) *n*-Heptylethylamine.

(d) *n*-Hexylethylcarbinol.
(e) Tri-*n*-propylamine.
(f) Di-*n*-propylethylcarbinol.

4. Let us suppose that you have isolated from a natural product a compound of unknown structure. The analysis and molecular weight determination show the molecular formula, $C_8H_{15}O_3N$. The compound is neutral (does not dissolve in cold acid or cold alkali to any greater extent than in water). Hydrolysis of the compound gives three compounds: one acidic, one basic, and one neutral.

The acidic compound is a white crystalline solid which, on treatment with acetic anhydride, gives a solid anhydride. This solid anhydride, on reaction with methanol, gives only one organic compound, which proves to be an acid with an equivalent weight of 132.

The basic compound has the molecular formula C_2H_7N, and on treatment with nitrous acid nitrogen gas is evolved.

The neutral compound gives an acid with the same number of carbon atoms, when it is oxidized with an agent such as permanganate. When the neutral compound is treated with sodium hypoiodite, iodoform is produced.

Write the structural formula for the compound isolated from the natural product.

5. Indicate syntheses of the following compounds from starting materials containing no more than two carbon atoms.

(a) 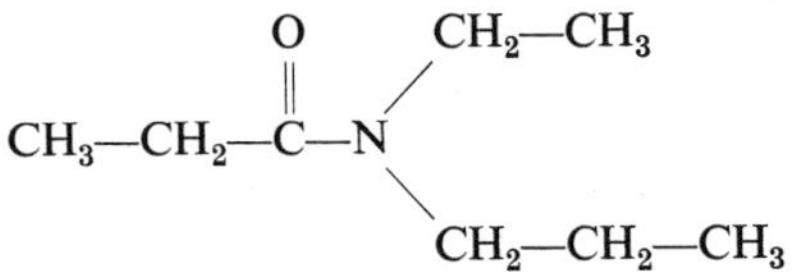
$$CH_3-CH_2-\overset{\overset{\displaystyle O}{\|}}{C}-N\overset{\displaystyle CH_2-CH_3}{\underset{\displaystyle CH_2-CH_2-CH_3}{<}}$$

(b) 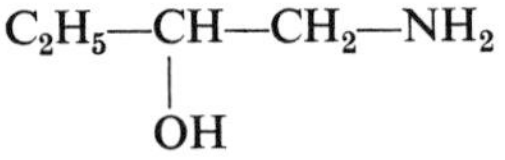
$$C_2H_5-\underset{\underset{\displaystyle OH}{|}}{CH}-CH_2-NH_2 \qquad \textit{(via propionaldehyde)}$$

(c) $H_2N-(CH_2)_4-NH_2$

(d) 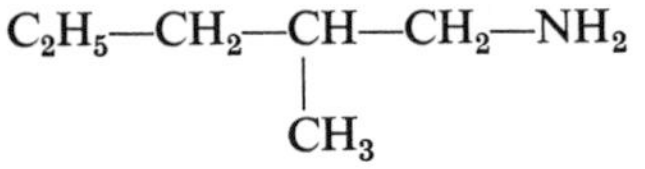
$$C_2H_5-CH_2-\underset{\underset{\displaystyle CH_3}{|}}{CH}-CH_2-NH_2 \qquad \begin{array}{l}\textit{(via aldol condensation}\\\textit{of propionaldehyde)}\end{array}$$

(e) 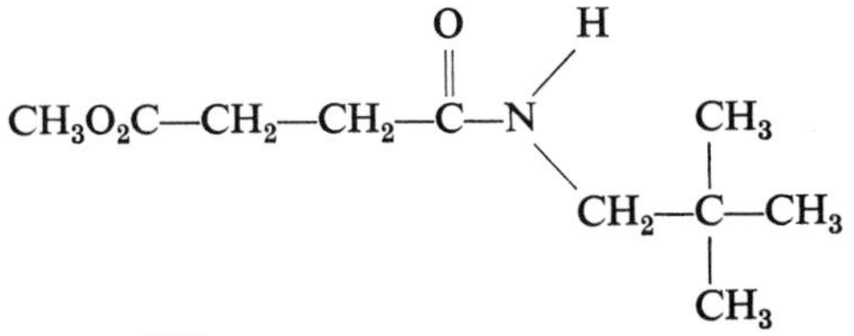
$$CH_3O_2C-CH_2-CH_2-\overset{\overset{\displaystyle O}{\|}}{C}-N\overset{\displaystyle H}{\underset{\displaystyle CH_2-\underset{\underset{\displaystyle CH_3}{|}}{\overset{\overset{\displaystyle CH_3}{|}}{C}}-CH_3}{<}}$$

(f) 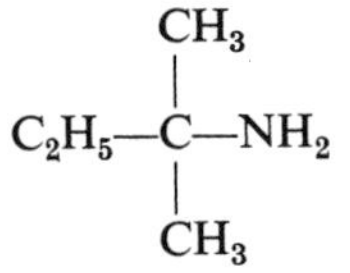
$$C_2H_5-\underset{\underset{\displaystyle CH_3}{|}}{\overset{\overset{\displaystyle CH_3}{|}}{C}}-NH_2$$

(Note to (e) and (f): Reaction of a tertiary halide with either cyanide or ammonia fails to give any of the expected product, that is, the major product obtained when the halide is primary. Explain this behavior—after reviewing Chapter 6, if necessary.)

6. For each of the following pairs of compounds, indicate which is the stronger base.

(a) *p*-Nitroaniline, *m*-nitroaniline.
(b) Diphenylamine, 2,4,6-tribromoaniline.

(c) 2,3-Dibromoaniline, 2,3-dimethylaniline.
(d) 2,3-Dibromoaniline, 2,4-dibromoaniline.

7. By use of qualitative tests and basic strengths, distinguish between the following amines.

(a) Tri-*n*-propylamine.
(b) Phenyldimethylamine (N,N-dimethylaniline).
(c) *p*-Methylaniline (*p*-toluidine).
(d) N-Methylaniline.

8. Starting with substances available from coal tar, indicate by equations three independent routes for synthesis of 3-methyl-4-aminophenol. Equations need not be balanced but all necessary reagents and conditions should be indicated. There should be indicated methods adaptable for separation of any isomeric mixtures encountered.

9. Using as starting materials only compounds available from coal tar, indicate practical syntheses of the following compounds. Practical syntheses do not include those which give an inseparable mixture of isomers or those which give much poorer yields than alternative methods which have been discussed. For parts (b) through (g) particular attention should be paid to synthetic possibilities starting with various compounds in the sequence termed Eq. 45 in this chapter.

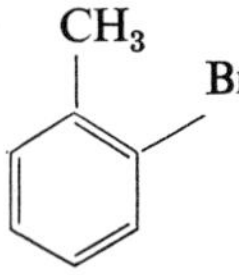

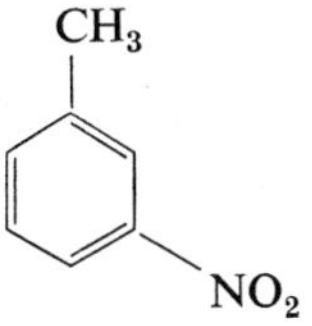

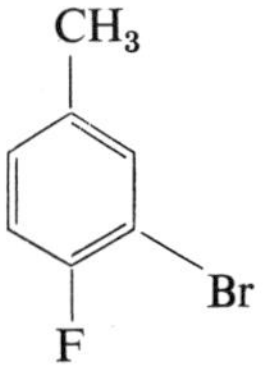

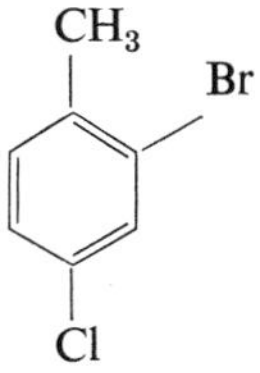

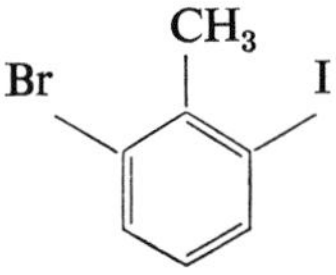

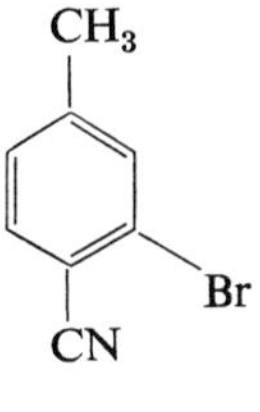

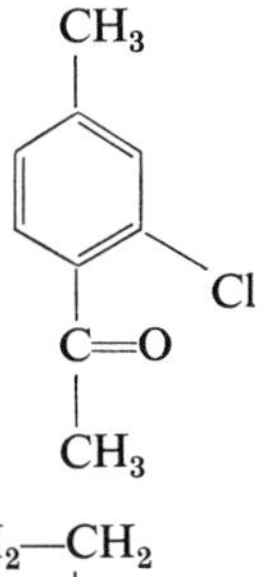

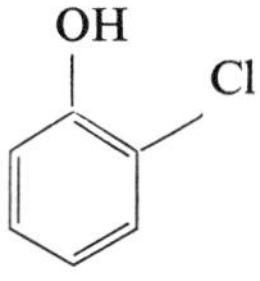

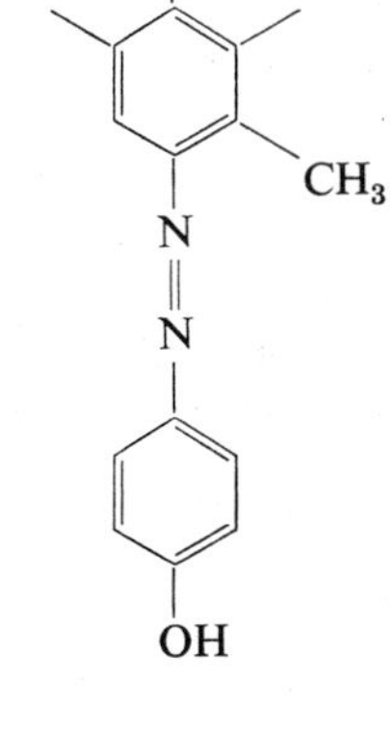

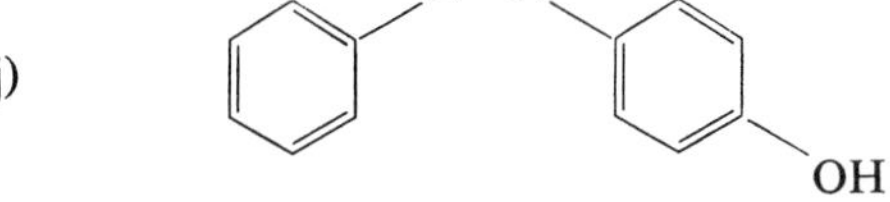

(k) 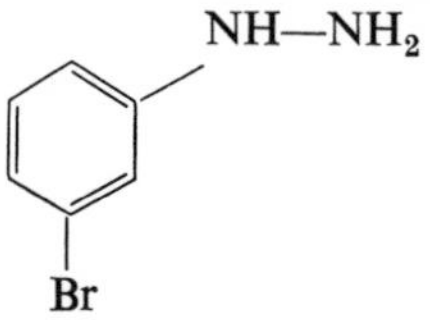

(l) 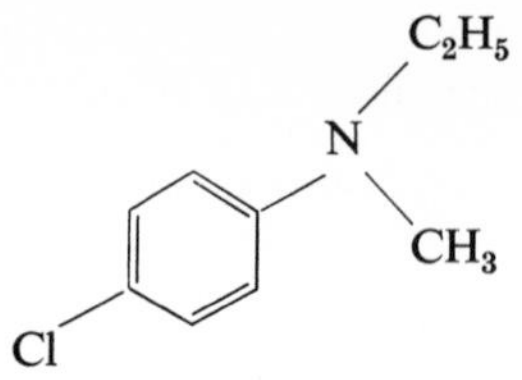

10. (a) Outline a synthesis from benzene of the starting materials required to synthesize a dye differing from malachite green only in having a *p*-nitro group substituted in the ring which is unsubstituted in malachite green.
(b) Write five resonance forms for the malachite green cation, in addition to those shown in Eq. 39.
(c) If it be assumed that the species initiating the reaction shown in Eq. 38 is the product of attack of zinc chloride as a Lewis acid on the aldehyde, outline plausible steps that might reasonably be involved in this over-all reaction.

Chapter 2

Phenols and Benzoquinones

The phenols, including the aminophenols, are important intermediates for synthesis of various useful aromatic compounds. Probably the largest tonnages of phenols are consumed in the dye industry (cf. Chap. 19). The benzoquinones are actually not aromatic compounds, but they are prepared by oxidation of amines or phenols, hence profitably studied in connection with the reactions of these compounds.

Phenol itself is a highly corrosive substance, known as *carbolic acid* in the drug industry. On the skin, it causes disagreeable burns which heal slowly. When ingested in significant quantity, it causes a slow and painful death. Many of the substituted phenols occur in nature, and some of them are highly toxic. For example, the agents responsible for the skin reactions caused by poison ivy and poison oak[1] are phenols. Others of the naturally occurring phenols are relatively nontoxic in comparison with the parent substance. Examples are

---

[1] The toxic agent in the poison oak and poison ivy sap is a mixture of phenols having large alkyl groups (some unsaturated) substituted in the ring. These very toxic materials have been studied extensively by Prof. C. R. Dawson of Columbia University. Separation of the complex mixture by the technique of chromatography has been described by Dawson in an article in *Nature*, **171**, 841 (1953), and a general description of this work has been reported by him in *Record of Chem. Progress*, **15**, 39 (1954).

eugenol and thymol, which occur widely in plants. They may be readily isolated from oil of cloves and oil of thyme, respectively. The natural hormone, epinephrine, is a phenol with an amino group in the side chain.

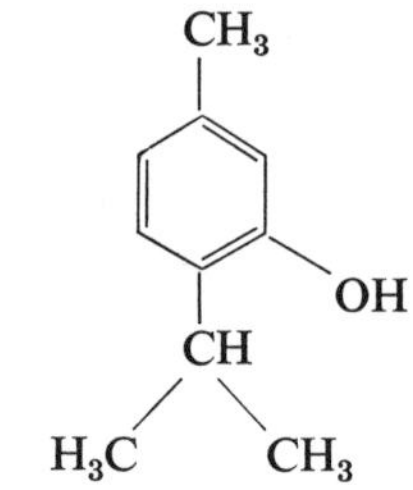

Thymol

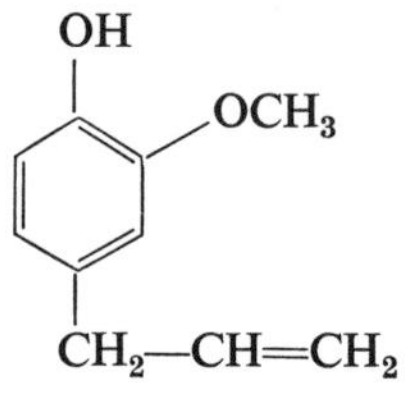

Eugenol

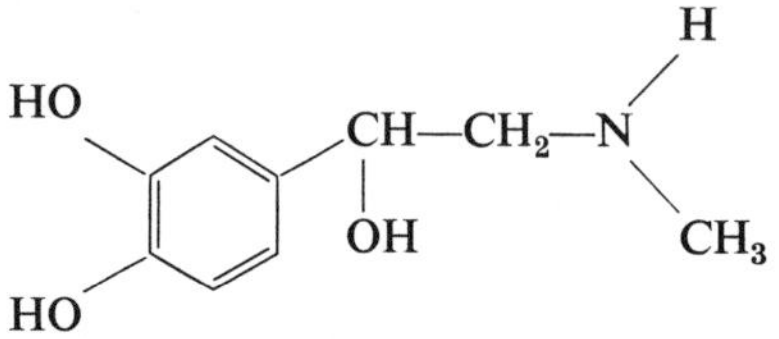

Epinephrine

Although phenols occur in coal tar, phenol itself is used in such large quantity that most of the industrial consumption of it is synthesized from benzene (cf. Eq. 18-1). In contrast, coal tar is a commercial source of the three isomeric cresols (methylphenols). The *m*-cresol is especially troublesome to synthesize from benzene or toluene.

Acidity of Phenols

The phenols are weakly acidic compounds, in contrast with the alcohols which do not ionize in water solution. This difference may be anticipated, for the phenolate anion is stabilized by resonance, as shown in the following formulas:

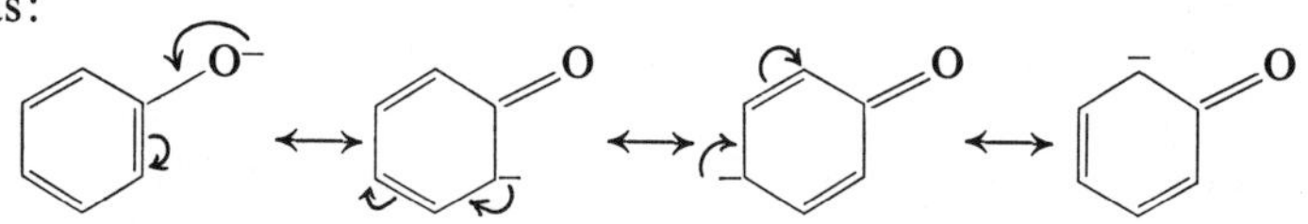

The phenols are very weakly acidic, less so than carbonic acid, unless electron-withdrawing groups are substituted in the *ortho* or *para* positions. Just as electron withdrawal reduces the basic strength of amines (Chap. 19), it increases the acidic strength of phenols, and this is not a small effect. 2,4,6-Trinitrophenol (picric acid), whose pk_a is 0.8, is a stronger acid than phenol (pK_a 9.9) by a factor of one billion.

The weakly acidic nature of most phenols may be turned to good advantage for their separation from neutral material and also carboxylic acids. Since both phenols and carboxylic acids occur rather widely in complex mixtures in nature, their separation is of particular significance. If a solution of organic compounds is extracted with an aqueous solution of strong alkali (sodium or potassium hydroxide), both phenols and carboxylic acids form salts which dissolve in the alkali. If carbon dioxide is passed into the alkaline solution, the phenols (weaker acids than carbonic acid, pK_a 6.5 for first ionization) are freed from their salts while the carboxylic acids remain as their soluble salts. After separation of the phenols, the carboxylic acids can then be freed from their salts by addition of a strong acid such as sulfuric acid.

It should be noted that a phenol may be regarded as the enol form of a ketone:

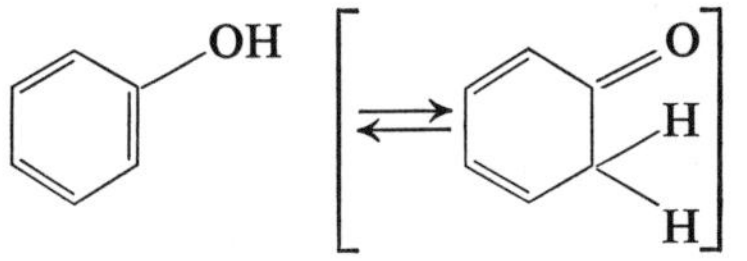

Whereas most ketones exist almost entirely in the keto form (cf. Chap. 15), most phenols appear to be entirely in the enol form, for they do not give reactions of the carbonyl group. This seems a reasonable circumstance, for the resonance stabilization of benzene is lost in the keto form. The trihydroxybenzene, phloroglucinol, does give reactions of the carbonyl group, hence must exist in equilibrium with a small amount of the keto form:

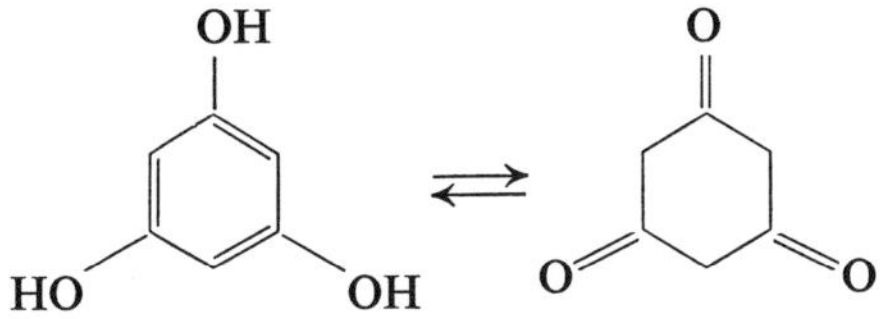

This behavior of phloroglucinol is no doubt caused by the fact that the loss of the benzene resonance energy occurs only once, while the gain of energy in going from enol to keto forms occurs three times. This reduces the energy of the 1,3,5-cyclohexanetrione to the point that the equilibrium is shifted in its favor to some extent.

Synthesis of Phenols

The principal methods used for synthesis of phenols and substituted phenols have been discussed in previous chapters. They are:

1. Alkali fusion of sulfonic acids, Eq. 18-18.

2. Hydrolysis of diazonium salts, Eq. 19-42.

3. Hydrolysis of aryl halides, Eqs. 18-1 and 18-2.

The first two methods can be applied to synthesis of a wide variety of phenols. The last-named method is limited principally to phenols substituted with nitro in the *ortho* or *para* positions, and the industrial synthesis of phenol itself.

Reactions of Phenols

Substitution reactions. As has been mentioned previously (Chap. 17), phenol substitutes quite readily, and this is sometimes a disadvantage when monosubstitution is desired.

HALOGENATION is useful principally in those instances where substitution in all the open *ortho* and *para* positions is desired. For example, *o*-cresol may be converted in high yield to 4,6-dibromo-*o*-cresol (Eq. 1).

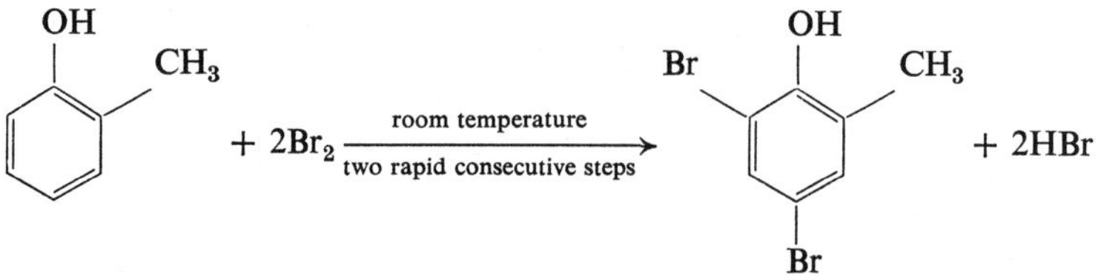

$$\text{(structure)} + 2Br_2 \xrightarrow[\text{two rapid consecutive steps}]{\text{room temperature}} \text{(structure)} + 2HBr \quad (1)$$

NITRATION often gives only moderate yields because of the ease with which most phenols are oxidized with nitric acid, but the reaction finds considerable use on account of the facile separation of *ortho* and *para* isomers (cf. Eq. 17-15, and following discussion). Sometimes it is more profitable to nitrate a halogen-substituted benzene, hydrolyze the mixture of nitro compounds, then separate the resultant *o*- and *p*-nitrophenols.

SULFONATION proceeds in moderately good yields, and can be utilized to secure either the *ortho* or *para* isomer (Eq. 2). Sulfonation occurs much more

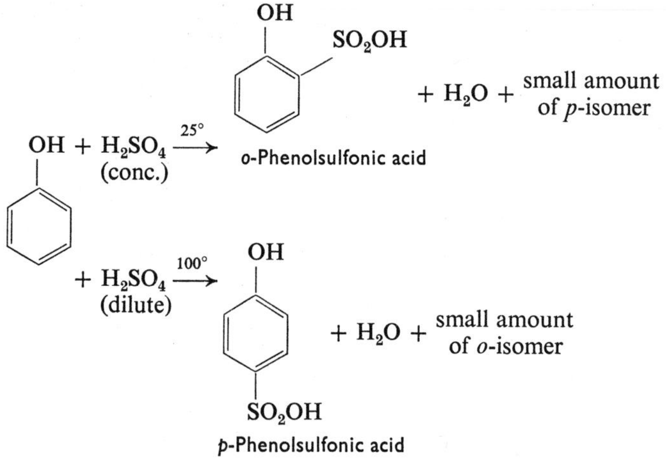

$$\text{OH} + H_2SO_4 \xrightarrow{25°} \text{(o-Phenolsulfonic acid)} + H_2O + \begin{array}{l}\text{small amount}\\ \text{of } p\text{-isomer}\end{array}$$

$$\text{(phenol)} + H_2SO_4 \xrightarrow{100°} \text{(p-Phenolsulfonic acid)} + H_2O + \begin{array}{l}\text{small amount}\\ \text{of } o\text{-isomer}\end{array} \quad (2)$$

o-Phenolsulfonic acid

p-Phenolsulfonic acid

rapidly in the *ortho* position; however, the *para* isomer is of substantially lower energy, quite possibly because of steric interference of the bulky sulfo group. Thus, in anhydrous sulfuric acid where only the water formed in the reaction is present, reversal of the sulfonation reaction is not significant, so the initially formed ortho isomer may be obtained as the principal product. In somewhat diluted sulfuric acid, at a sufficiently high temperature to facilitate attainment of equilibrium, the lower energy *para* isomer accumulates as the principal

o-Phenolsulfonic acid $\quad\quad\quad\quad\quad\quad\quad$ *p*-Phenolsulfonic acid

$$\text{o-Phenolsulfonic acid} \overset{\longrightarrow}{\longleftarrow} \text{Phenol} + H_2SO_4 \overset{\longrightarrow}{\longleftarrow} \text{p-Phenolsulfonic acid} \quad (3)$$

+ HOH $\quad\quad\quad\quad\quad\quad\quad\quad\quad\quad\quad\quad\quad$ + HOH

product. The equilibria involved are shown in Eq. 3, in which the lower arrows summarize the net position of equilibrium.

Friedel and Crafts reactions. As in the case of primary and secondary amines, reaction of an alkyl halide or acyl halide is with the active hydrogen, thus oxygen-substituted compounds are obtained (ethers or phenol esters). Actually the ethers and esters are not satisfactorily made in this way, but are made by the procedures discussed later in this chapter.

The products that would be obtained by a Friedel and Crafts reaction can be secured by either of two indirect routes, as in Eqs. 4 and 5.

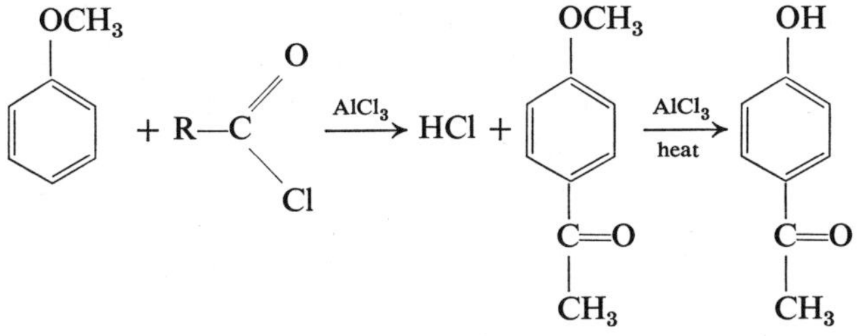

(+ smaller amount
of o-isomer)

$$(4)$$

Other acids (aluminum chloride is a Lewis acid), especially hydriodic acid, may be used to cleave the ether, in which case the phenol is obtained, not the halide as is the case with aliphatic ethers (cf. Eq. 6-20). If desired, the ether group may be left as protection to the hydroxyl until after additional reactions have been carried out on the carbonyl.

The rearrangement shown in Eq. 5 is called the **Fries rearrangement.**

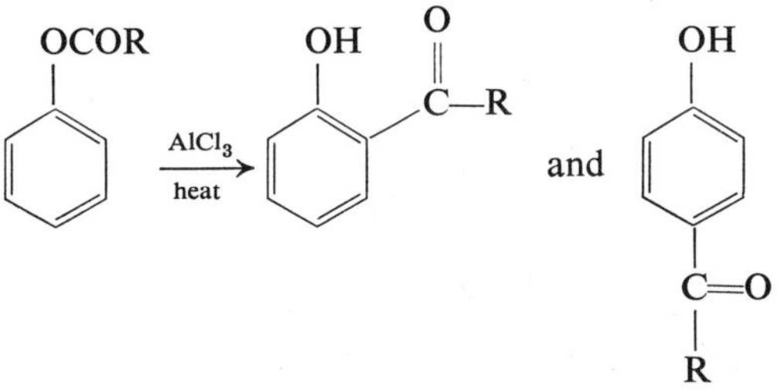

$$(5)$$

The ratio of isomers can sometimes be adjusted by change in temperature, but it is rarely that one isomer is highly favored. Separation of the two isomers by distillation is simple, on account of hydrogen bonding in the *ortho* isomer (cf. nitrophenols, Chap. 17).

Condensation with aldehydes. The ease of substitution of hydrogen in phenols is so great that there occur condensations with aldehydes which resemble cross aldol condensations (cf. Eq. 15-50). The greatest significance of such reactions is a continuation of the condensation with formaldehyde to form polymers, as shown in Eq. 6. The type of reaction shown may occur in any or

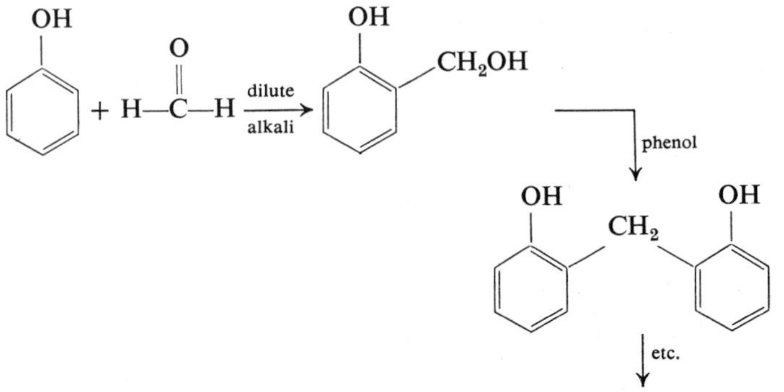

(6)

all of the *ortho* and *para* positions to give a highly cross-linked polymer. Bakelite is such a material.

A similar reaction of cyclic anhydrides with phenols will be discussed in Chapter 21.

Kolbe reaction. This procedure actually involves initial reaction with the oxygen function, but rearrangement into the ring occurs. It may be noted that the first step in Eq. 7 is entirely analogous to the reaction of a Grignard

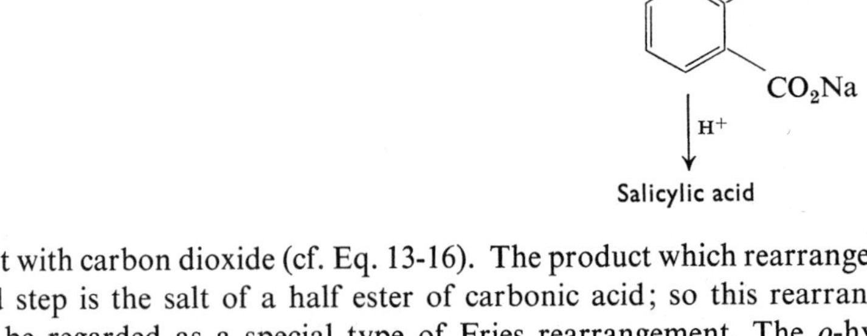

(7)

Salicylic acid

reagent with carbon dioxide (cf. Eq. 13-16). The product which rearranges in the second step is the salt of a half ester of carbonic acid; so this rearrangement might be regarded as a special type of Fries rearrangement. The *o*-hydroxy-benzoic acid is usually the dominant isomer when the Kolbe synthesis is carried

out as shown. The mechanism of the Kolbe rearrangement is not well understood; it is especially obscure why use of the potassium salt tends to give the
para isomer.

Salicylic acid is manufactured in quantity for synthesis of its acetyl
derivative (*o*-acetoxybenzoic acid), usually marketed under the name aspirin.
This analgesic is that most widely used for relief of superficial pain.

Reimer-Tiemann reaction. This synthesis gives rather poor yields and is
limited to preparation of *o*-hydroxybenzaldehydes; however, these structures
have numerous uses. The net conversion is shown in Eq. 8. The *para*-isomer is a

$$
\text{C}_6\text{H}_5\text{OH} + \text{Cl}-\overset{\text{Cl}}{\underset{\text{Cl}}{\text{C}}}-\text{H} + 3\text{KOH} \longrightarrow \text{C}_6\text{H}_4(\text{OH})(\text{CHO}) + 3\text{KCl} + 2\text{H}_2\text{O} \quad (8)
$$

minor by-product in this reaction. It is known that the aldehyde is formed by
alkaline hydrolysis of the benzal dichloride (Eq. 9). The mechanism of formation of the benzal dichloride is of considerable interest, for it involves a type

$$
\text{C}_6\text{H}_4(\text{OH})(\text{CHCl}_2) + 2^-\text{OH} \longrightarrow 2\text{Cl}^- + \left[\text{C}_6\text{H}_4(\text{OH})\overset{\text{OH}}{\underset{\text{OH}}{\text{CH}}} \right] \longrightarrow \text{C}_6\text{H}_4(\text{OH})(\text{CHO}) + \text{HOH} \quad (9)
$$

of reaction intermediate, known as a **carbene,** which is occasionally of importance as a reaction intermediate and has not yet been discussed. A carbene
contains a neutral carbon atom which is covalently bonded to two other atoms
and has, in addition, two non-bonding electrons. The distinction between a
carbanion and a carbene should be noted; the carbanion bears a negative
charge, whereas the carbene is neutral. A common mechanism leading to the
highly reactive carbene species is **α-elimination** of halogen acid by base. This
type of elimination, in which both atoms are eliminated from the same carbon
atom, occurs most readily when two or more electron-attracting groups are
substituted on a single carbon atom. As shown in the reaction with chloroform
(Eq. 10), this is not a concerted elimination; the anion is intermediate. The
characteristic reaction of a carbene is **insertion,** going between two atoms and

$$
\text{HO}^- \smallfrown \text{H}-\text{CCl}_3 \longrightarrow \text{HOH} + {}^-\overset{\text{Cl}}{\underset{\text{Cl}}{\text{C}}}\text{Cl} \longrightarrow :\text{CCl}_2 + \text{Cl}^- \quad (10)
$$

becoming bonded to each of them, as shown in Eq. 11. Insertion occurs more readily in a carbon-hydrogen bond than in a carbon-carbon bond, and the reaction displays no sensitivity to steric hindrance. The reason for preference

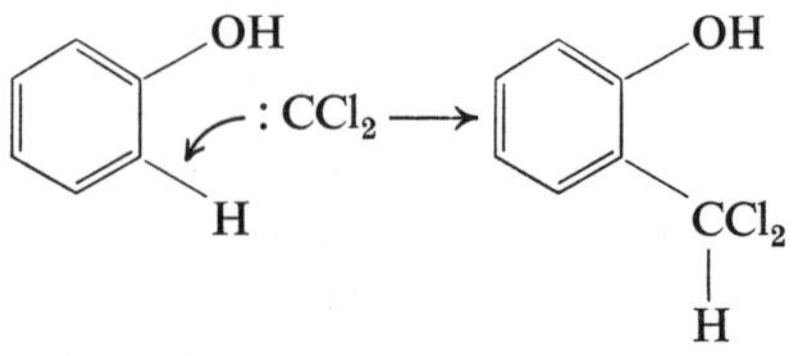

$$\text{(11)}$$

for the *ortho* position in a phenol is not clear, but this isomer is formed in larger amount. The insertion reaction of carbenes tends to be relatively indiscriminate, however, and this is the reason that yields of a single compound are always poor in reactions involving this intermediate. It is only in relatively special situations that the reactions are of synthetic utility, for synthesis of compounds that are even more difficult to secure by other routes. The o-hydroxybenzaldehydes are illustrative.

The carbene may be formed as a side reaction in some processes and lead to a serious lowering of yield in the desired reaction. The dehydrohalogenation of α-bromo acids with *t*-butoxide (Eq. 16-19) sometimes gives rather poor yields, and the principal cause of this seems to be carbene formation and the resultant host of products.

Functional derivatives of phenols. Traditionally, **esters** of phenols and carboxylic acids have been prepared by reaction of the phenol with an acid chloride (Eq. 12), although acetic anhydride is often used to make acetates

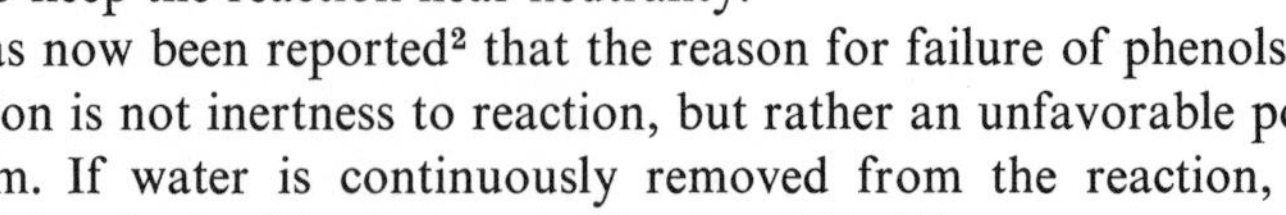

$$\text{(12)}$$

on account of its cheapness. Since the phenolate anion is more nucleophilic than the phenol, alkali is frequently added during the course of the acylation in order to keep the reaction near neutrality.

It has now been reported[2] that the reason for failure of phenols in direct esterification is not inertness to reaction, but rather an unfavorable position of equilibrium. If water is continuously removed from the reaction, excellent yields may be obtained in direct esterification (Eq. 13).

---

[2] R. D. Offenhauer, *J. Chem. Educ.*, **41**, 39 (1964), reported that a nearly quantitative yield of ester was obtained when equimolar amounts of *p*-cresol and hexanoic acid were heated for 22 hours under reflux with 4 grams of concentrated sulfuric acid per mole of reactants, as water was continuously removed by azeotropic distillation with toluene.

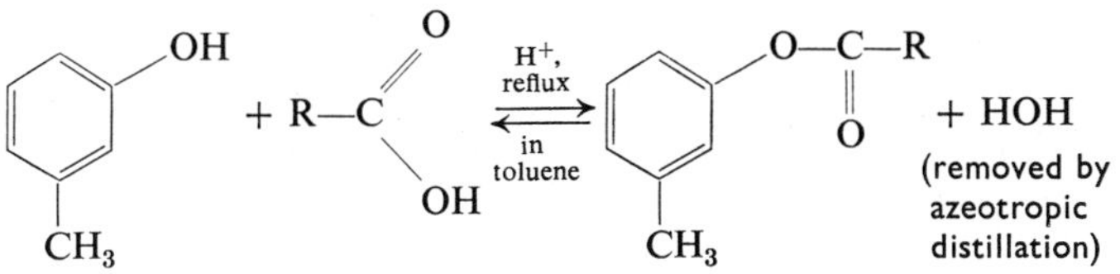

$$\text{(structure: m-cresol)} + R-C\overset{O}{\underset{OH}{\big\langle}} \quad\underset{\substack{\text{in} \\ \text{toluene}}}{\overset{\substack{H^+, \\ \text{reflux}}}{\rightleftarrows}}\quad \text{(structure: aryl ester)} \quad O-C-R \;+\; HOH \qquad (13)$$

(removed by
azeotropic
distillation)

Ethers of phenols are always made by the Williamson synthesis, which is quite convenient, for the salt of the phenol is made by treatment with sodium hydroxide (in contrast with alcohols, where the alkoxide must be prepared with metallic sodium, Eq. 2-1). Alkyl halides are commonly used for higher alkyl ethers (Eq. 14), but methyl ethers are usually made with dimethyl sulfate (Eq. 15). As has been mentioned earlier (cf. Eq. 14-30), dimethyl sulfate is

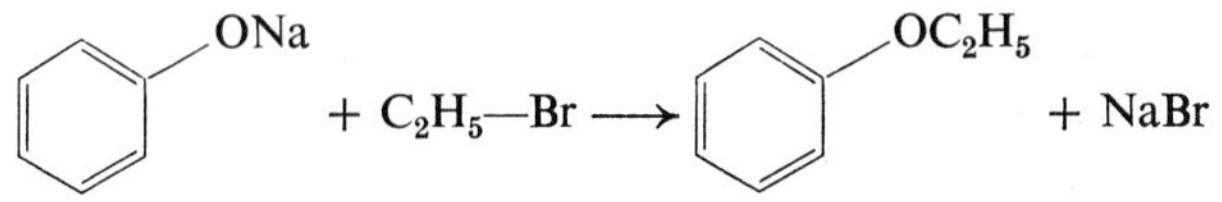

$$\text{(C}_6\text{H}_5\text{ONa)} + C_2H_5-Br \longrightarrow \text{(C}_6\text{H}_5\text{OC}_2\text{H}_5)} + NaBr \qquad (14)$$

Ethyl phenyl ether

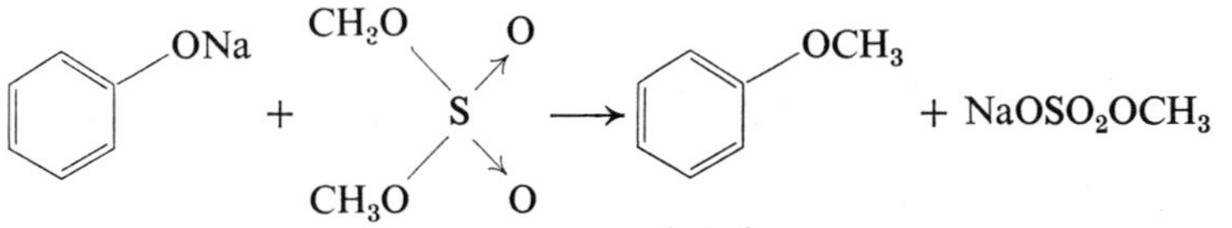

$$\text{(C}_6\text{H}_5\text{ONa)} + \underset{CH_3O}{\overset{CH_3O}{\big\rangle}}S\underset{O}{\overset{O}{\big\langle}} \longrightarrow \text{(C}_6\text{H}_5\text{OCH}_3)} + NaOSO_2OCH_3 \quad (15)$$

Anisole

cheaper than methyl iodide and is more reactive in the displacement reaction. Methyl bromide and chloride are inconvenient to use on account of their being gases. The only drawback to the sulfate is its high toxicity. Formation of methyl ethers is worthy of specific comment, for this is the ether ordinarily formed when protection of the phenol group is desired (for example, cf. Eq. 4).

Benzoquinones

It has been stated in this chapter and the preceding one that phenols and amines are unstable to oxidation, but oxidation of the benzene ring has not yet been discussed in detail. Actually, the unsubstituted benzene ring can be oxidized, but with extreme difficulty. It is believed that the first product of this oxidation is benzoquinone, as shown in Eq. 16, but this substance is more easily oxidized than benzene and cannot be isolated from this reaction. Since oxidation consists of removal of electrons, it might be expected that electron-withdrawing groups would stabilize the ring to oxidation and electron-donating groups would sensitize the ring to oxidation. This proves to be the case. The strongly electron-donating groups, amino and hydroxy, make the ring so

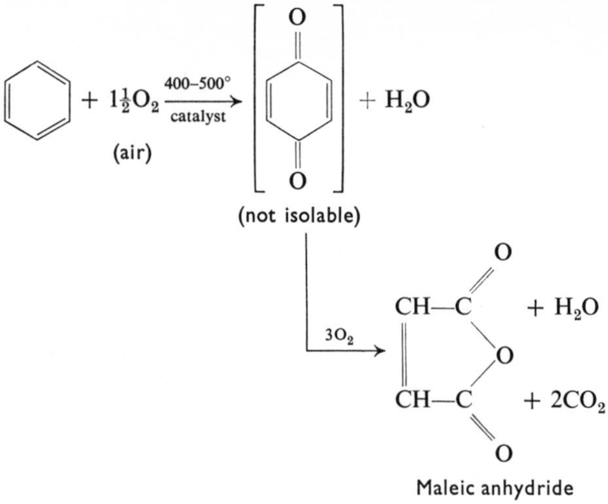

$$\text{benzene} + 1\tfrac{1}{2}O_2 \xrightarrow[\text{catalyst}]{400-500°} \left[\text{1,4-benzoquinone} \right] + H_2O$$

(air)

(not isolable) (16)

$$\xrightarrow{3O_2} \text{Maleic anhydride} + H_2O + 2CO_2$$

Maleic anhydride

unstable to oxidation that it is attacked by agents mild enough to permit isolation of quinone. The equations are shown:

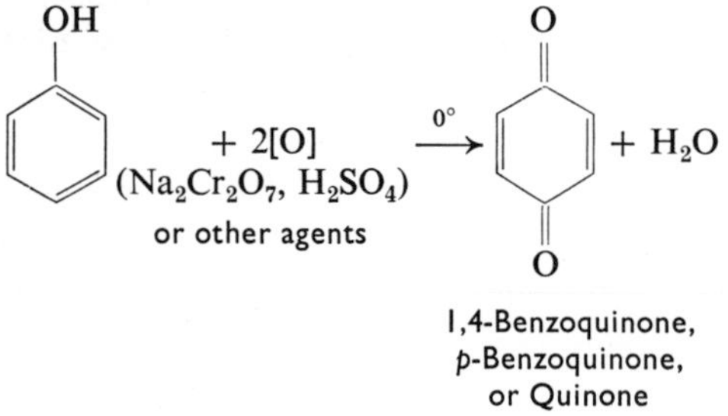

$$\text{phenol (OH)} + 2[O] \; (Na_2Cr_2O_7, H_2SO_4) \text{ or other agents} \xrightarrow{0°} \text{1,4-benzoquinone} + H_2O$$

(17)

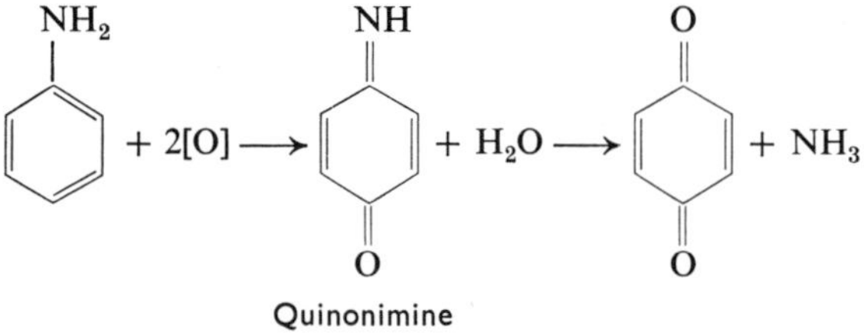

1,4-Benzoquinone,
p-Benzoquinone,
or Quinone

$$\text{aniline (NH}_2) + 2[O] \longrightarrow \text{Quinonimine (NH)} + H_2O \longrightarrow \text{benzoquinone (O)} + NH_3$$

(18)

Quinonimine

The quinonimine, initial product of the oxidation of an amine, is so easily hydrolyzed that it can be isolated only under strictly anhydrous conditions. With aqueous oxidizing media, the amine gives the same product as the phenol.

The processes shown in Eqs. 17 and 18 give rather poor yields (5–30%) of quinones, principally because high molecular weight products result from coupling of the free radical initially formed by removal of hydrogen from the oxygen or nitrogen. This radical may be represented as a resonance hybrid, and may couple at any of the positions indicated in the resonance forms:

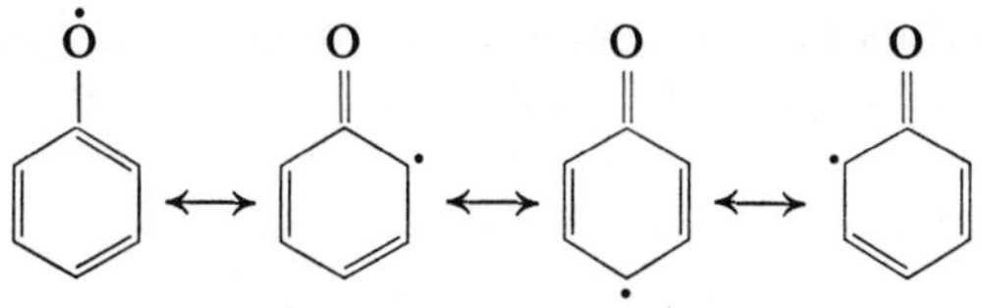

Actually, benzoquinone itself is made industrially by the process shown in Eq. 18; the cheapness of aniline offsets the poor yield in the reaction. A few other quinones are made in this way, from readily available amines or phenols. Another use of this oxidation has been the location of a substituent *para* to the hydroxyl or amino, in a compound of unknown structure. Any group *para* to the hydroxyl or amino is eliminated in the oxidation, as is illustrated in Eq. 19.

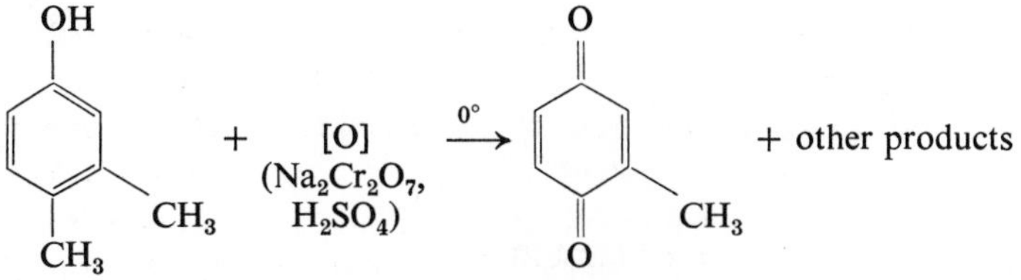

2-Methyl-1,4-
benzoquinone
or Toluquinone

If the *para* group is halogen, the yield in the oxidation becomes somewhat better (40–60%), and if a second hydroxyl or amino is in the *para* position, excellent yields can usually be obtained. The process shown in Eq. 21 is that

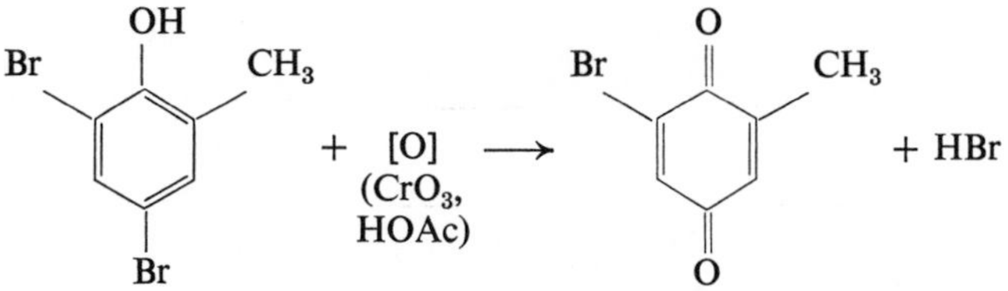

6-Bromotoluquinone

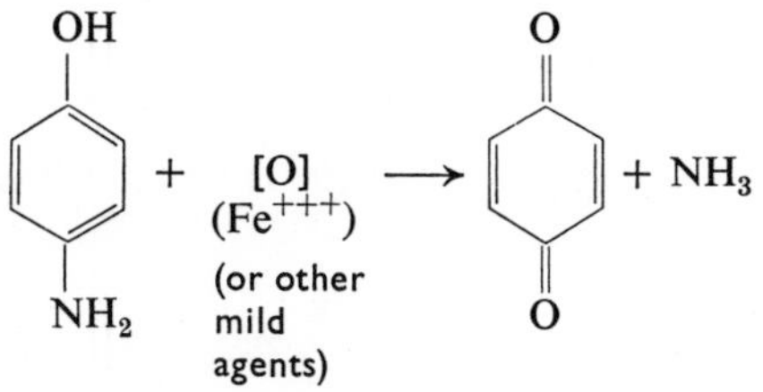

most widely applied to high-yield synthesis of *p*-benzoquinones. The 1,4-diamines or 1,4-dihydroxybenzenes may also be oxidized in excellent yield, but it is rarely that the diamine is easily obtained, and the 1,4-dihydroxybenzenes are nearly always obtained by reduction of the quinone (cf. below). Thus the *p*-aminophenol is an important intermediate for quinone synthesis. There have been discussed three methods of securing the *p*-aminophenols: nitration of a phenol and reduction, diazo coupling of a phenol and reduction, the hydroxylamine rearrangement.

Properties and Reactions of *p*-Benzoquinones

The quinones are relatively unstable compounds which are always colored some shade of yellow or red. They are nearly always solids, and many of them form beautiful, brilliantly colored crystals. They are sensitive to acids and alkali, also to light. The decomposition products are usually higher molecular weight; so steam distillation of the relatively volatile quinones is a favorite method for their purification. Presence of halogen in the ring increases the stability of quinones; even 6-bromotoluquinone is sufficiently stable to be handled conveniently and to be reasonably stable to storage. Quinones with unsaturated substituents such as nitro and carboxyl have rarely been made, and are quite unstable.

A quinone and a hydroquinone will frequently form a complex known as a **quinhydrone.** These complexes, which are colored very deeply, usually green-black, contain a molecule of each component. The manner in which complexing is accomplished is not entirely clear, but hydrogen bonding seems a reasonable possibility:

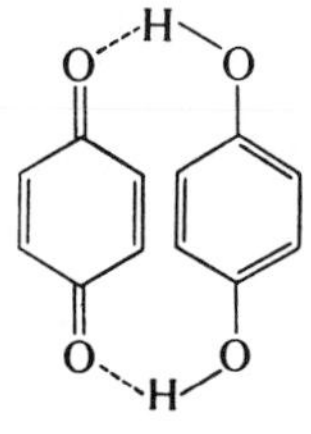

Quinones sometimes occur in nature, but most of the naturally occurring ones are of relatively complex structure, and frequently belong to the naphthalene series of compounds. An example is vitamin K, one of the factors

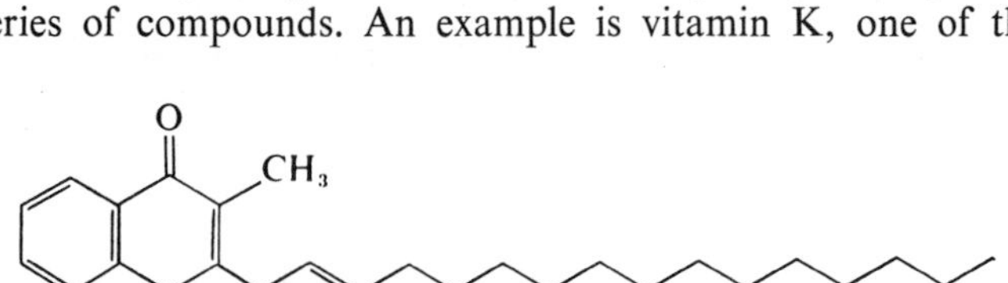

Vitamin K

necessary for blood clotting. The $C_{20}H_{39}$ side chain in vitamin K is the **phytyl** group, built up from four isoprene units (cf. Chap. 11). This unit is found in many natural products, including the rather prevalent phytol.

The highly conjugated system of double bonds in quinones gives them a considerable reactivity towards many reagents. Two reactions which are especially important will be mentioned at this time.

Reduction. A variety of agents will reduce a quinone to the corresponding **hydroquinone.** Sodium hydrosulfite is especially useful (Eq. 22). The

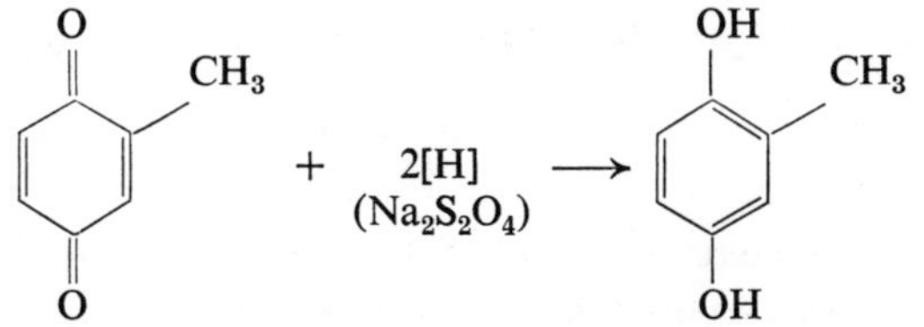

$$+ \quad \underset{(Na_2S_2O_4)}{2[H]} \quad \longrightarrow \quad \tag{22}$$

Toluhydroquinone
(2-Methyl-1,4-
dihydroxybenzene)

1,4-dihydroxybenzenes, or hydroquinones, are nearly always made by reduction of the corresponding quinones. Thus nearly any amine or phenol may be converted to the corresponding hydroquinone, and *p*-aminophenols may be converted in high yield.

1,4-Addition. Various polar reagents, sometimes with the help of catalysts, may be added to quinones in a 1,4-manner. Halogen acid may be used to indicate the type of reaction (Eq. 23). In case addition is carried out

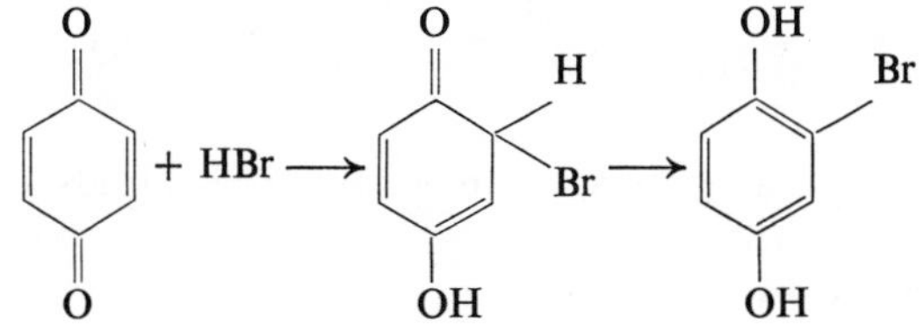

$$+ \; HBr \longrightarrow \qquad \longrightarrow \qquad \tag{23}$$

with a substituted quinone, such as toluquinone, any one of three products may be formed (entering group *ortho, meta,* or *para* to group already present). The separation and analysis of the products has been somewhat complicated; but the principal product seems to have the two substituents *para.* For example, toluquinone and hydrogen chloride give 5-chlorotoluhydroquinone. This type of

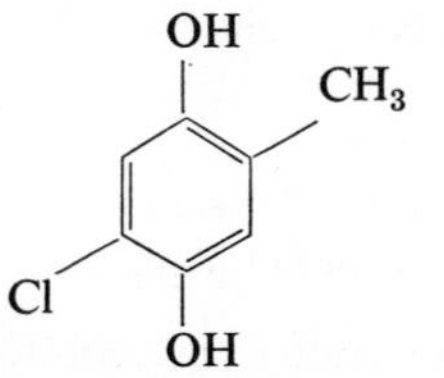

5-Chlorotoluhydroquinone

reaction has been applied to alcohols, amines, acid chlorides, acetic acid, and other reagents. The usefulness of the reaction has been limited in some instances by the occurrence of the following equilibrium:

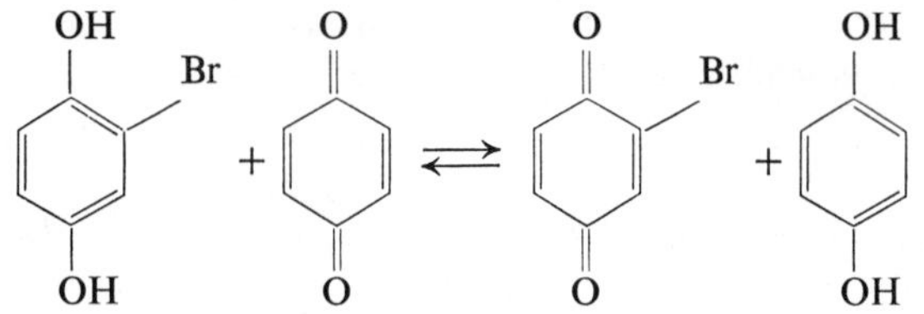

$$(24)$$

The substituted quinone resulting in Eq. 24 may add halogen acid and thus lead to the disubstituted hydroquinone, and this may lead in turn to trisubstituted hydroquinone. This sort of mixture is sometimes very difficult to separate.

o-Benzoquinones

There are structurally possible quinones in which the oxygen functions are in *ortho* positions, and a few of them have been prepared. They are much less stable than the *p*-quinones; in fact, they are even unstable to water. They are obtained by oxidation of an *o*-dihydroxybenzene with a mild agent in presence of a drying agent, as shown in Eq. 25 for 4-methyl-1,2-benzoquinone. Since

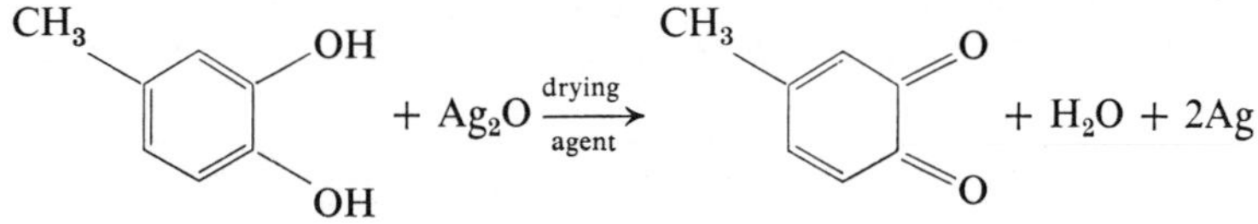

$$+ H_2O + 2Ag \quad (25)$$

anhydrous conditions are necessary, an *o*-aminophenol leads not to the quinone but to the quinonimine.

m-Benzoquinones are not structurally possible.

EXERCISES

1. Write structural formulas for the following compounds.

(a) 4-Pentadecyl-1,2-dihydroxybenzene.
(b) 2-Methyl-5,6-dibromo-1,4-benzoquinone.
(c) 3,5-Dibromotoluquinone.
(d) Tetrabromo-1,2-benzoquinone.
(e) 2-Methyl-4-hydroxybenzenesulfonic acid.
(f) Ethyl 2-methyl-4-phenylbenzenesulfonate.

2. The dihydroxybenzenes are rather important compounds. They are catechol (or pyrocatechol), the 1,2-isomer; resorcinol, the 1,3-isomer; and hydroquinone, the

1,4-isomer. Outline practical syntheses of the three dihydroxybenzenes, starting with materials available from coal tar.

3. Without using fractional crystallization, outline a practical separation of a mixture of the following compounds: (a) *p*-nitrophenol, (b) *o*-nitrophenol, (c) sulfanilic acid, (d) anisole.

4. For picric acid, write three resonance forms illustrating shift of electrons from the phenolic oxygen to oxygen on a nitro group.

5. Starting with monosubstituted derivatives of benzene, outline practical syntheses of each of the following compounds. There should be used methods which give a practical yield of the desired compounds not admixed with inseparable isomers. When separation of isomers is necessary, the method that will accomplish the separation should be indicated.

(a)

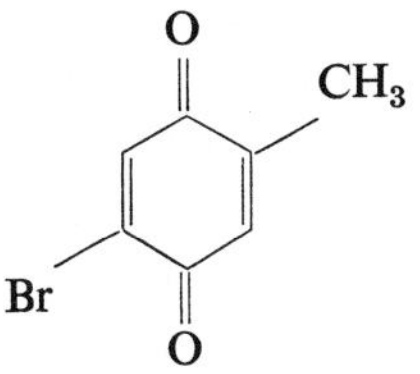

(b)

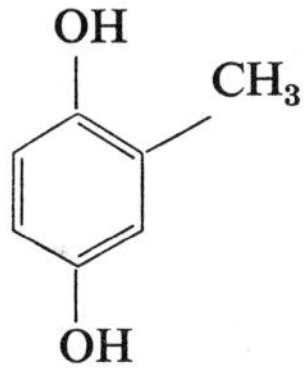

(c)

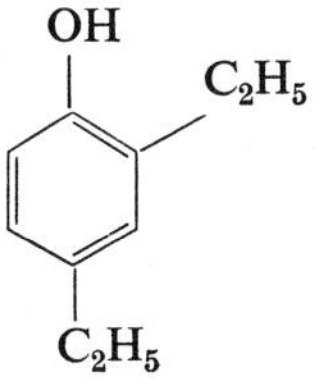

(d)

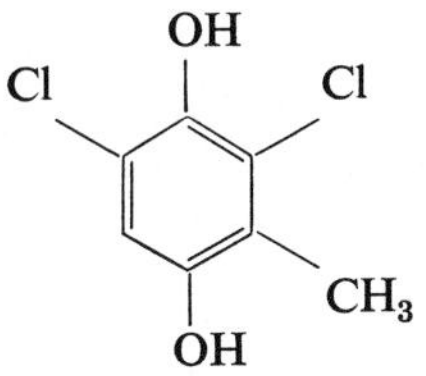

(e)

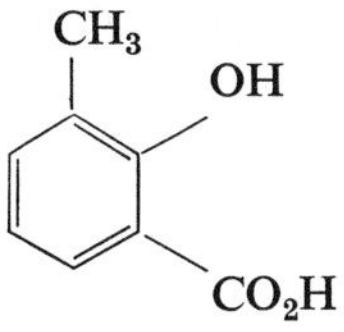

(f)

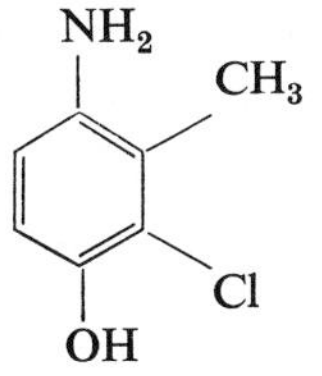

(g)

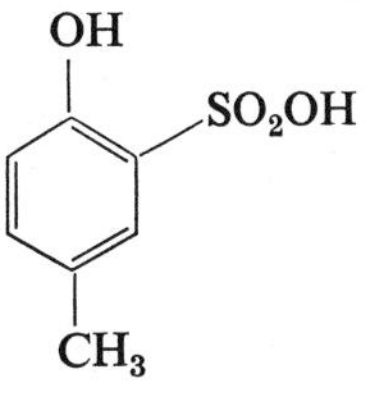

(h)

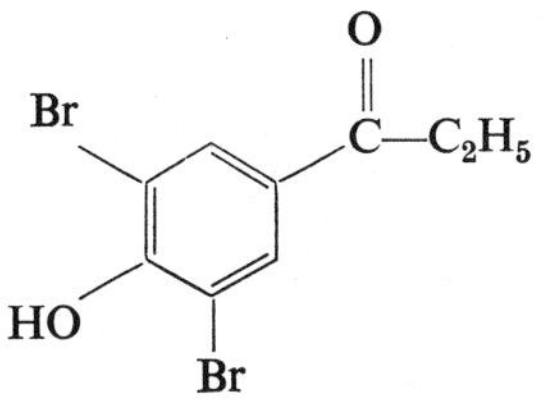

(i)

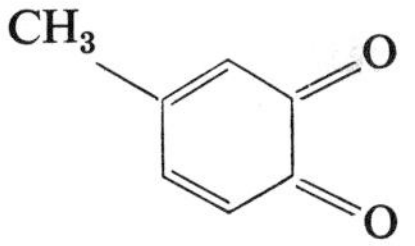

(j)

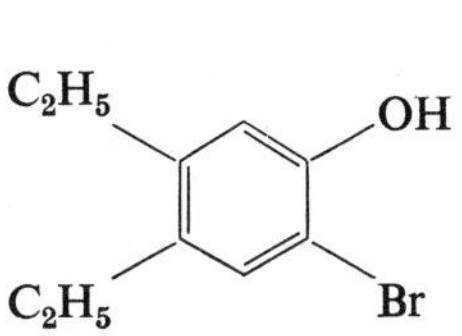

(k)

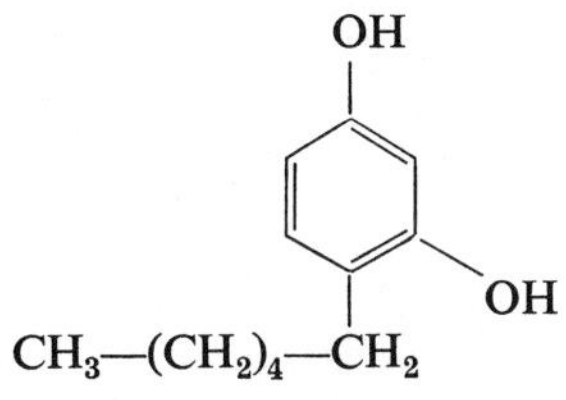

6. (a) Write the balanced chemical equations for the steps involved in cleavage of anisole with hydriodic acid (review Chap. 6). (b) Bearing in mind that aluminum chloride is a Lewis acid and noting the form of the equations in part (a), write reasonable balanced equations for cleavage of anisole with aluminum chloride.

7. A rather useful reaction of quinones, known as the Thiele-Winter reaction is illustrated in the following balanced equation:

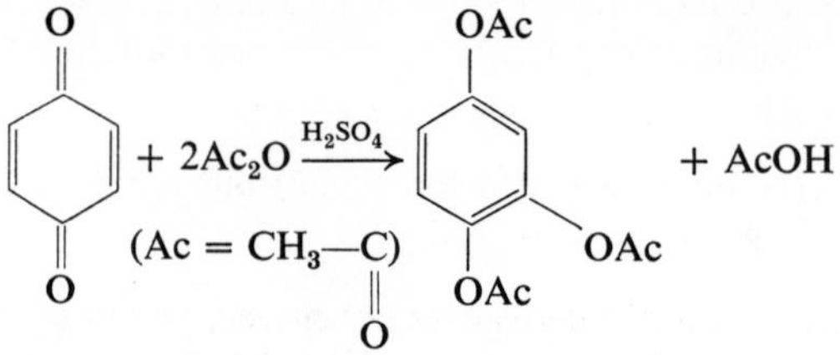

Write a series of steps showing a plausible mechanism for this conversion. In writing this mechanism, bear in mind the 1,4-addition reaction of quinones, and consider that traces of water will be present in the reaction mixture so that some acetic acid will be present at the beginning of the reaction.

Aromatic Carboxylic Acids

The aromatic carboxylic acids differ from the aliphatic ones in relatively few respects; however, some of the differences are worthy of consideration. Since nearly all aromatic compounds, including benzene itself, are somewhat toxic, the aromatic acids are not suitable as food. As discussed in Chapter 14, the aliphatic acids are the chief components of fats, one of the major classes of foodstuffs. Although the aromatic acids are not suitable as foods, they are a relatively nontoxic class of aromatic compounds. Several grams of benzoic

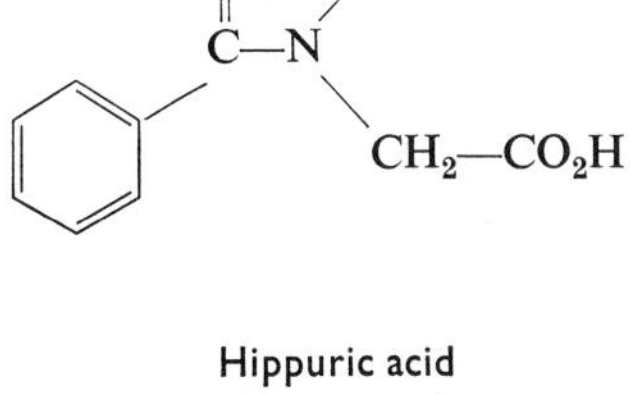

Hippuric acid 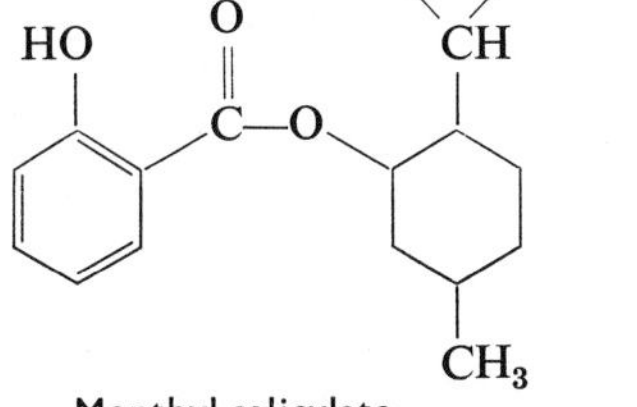   Menthyl salicylate

acid may be ingested with no ill effects; it is detoxified in the body by conversion to hippuric acid. Numerous aromatic carboxylic acids occur in nature or have important biological functions. *p*-Aminobenzoic acid appears to be essential for the metabolic process of certain bacteria, and 2-hydroxy-4-aminobenzoic acid (4-aminosalicylic acid) interferes with the metabolism of such bacteria. The derivatives of salicylic acid are especially interesting. Aspirin (acetylsalicylic acid) has already been mentioned in Chapter 20; and methyl salicylate is the naturally occurring oil of wintergreen. Menthyl salicylate has the remarkable property of screening out the ultraviolet radiation of sunlight so effectively that it gives protection against sunburn, even prevents sun tan, for several hours (until it is decomposed by a photochemical reaction).

Properties of Aromatic Carboxylic Acids

The aromatic acids do not have the disagreeable odor so characteristic of the lower molecular weight aliphatic acids. Benzoic acid has a distinct, but not unpleasant odor. The alkali metal salts of the aromatic acids do not have the properties of soaps, in contrast with the salts in the aliphatic series.

Since the benzene ring is prone to withdraw electrons from a substituent group, **benzoic acid is a somewhat stronger acid than aliphatic carboxylic acids.** The ionizable hydrogen is two atoms removed from the ring, however, so the increase in acid strength is modest. The pK_a of benzoic acid is 4.18, in comparison with 4.85 for octanoic acid. Electron-withdrawing groups in the ring increase acid strength, but the effect is less dramatic than in the phenols (Chap. 20) where the ionizable hydrogen is closer to the ring. The effects of electron delocalization by resonance and by the inductive effect are illustrated by pK_a values for o-nitrobenzoic acid (2.21), m-nitrobenzoic acid (3.46) and p-nitrobenzoic acid (3.40). In the case of the chlorobenzoic acids, where the inductive effect is dominant, acid strength simply drops off with distance from carboxyl to halogen; pK_a values for the o-, m- and p-isomers are 2.89, 3.82, 4.03.

The aromatic acids are relatively high-melting compounds; apparently all those investigated are solids. Lower-melting compounds are obtained when phenyl is substituted in an aliphatic side chain rather than attached directly to carboxyl.

Nomenclature

The naming of aromatic acids follows the previously discussed methods. The basis of the name is always the common name for an aromatic acid, and the carbon carrying carboxyl is considered as carbon-1 in all cases.

2-Hydroxyterephthalic acid

4-Nitrophthalic anhydride

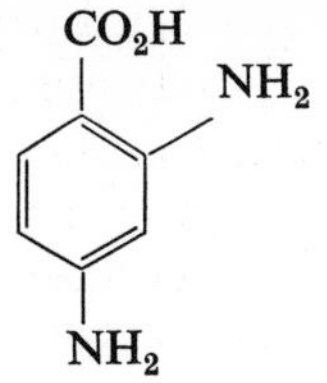

4-Aminoanthranilic acid

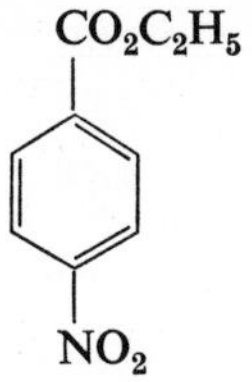

Ethyl p-nitrobenzoate

Synthesis

Several of the significant methods for preparation of aromatic acids have already been discussed, but one new method will be added.

From aryl bromides, via the Grignard reagent:

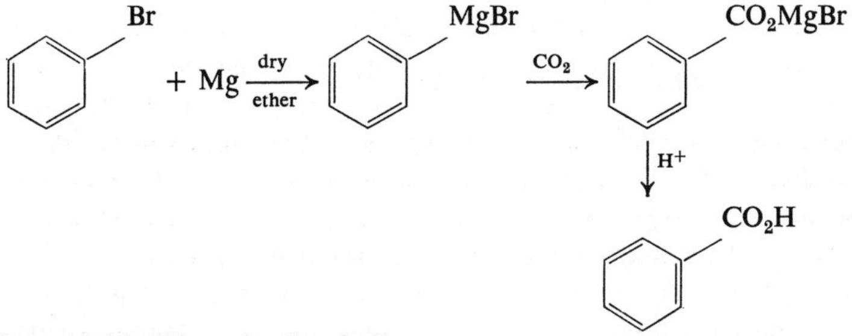

$$(1)$$

From aryl halides, via the nitrile:

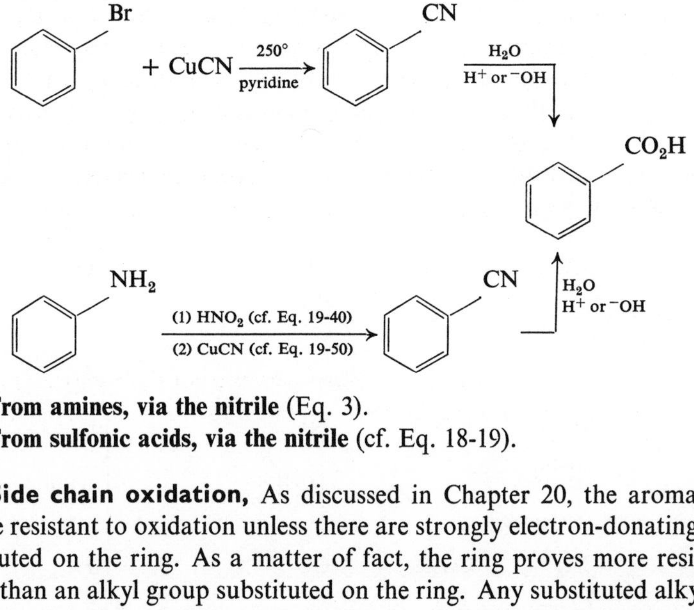

$$(2)$$

$$(3)$$

From amines, via the nitrile (Eq. 3).

From sulfonic acids, via the nitrile (cf. Eq. 18-19).

Side chain oxidation, As discussed in Chapter 20, the aromatic ring is quite resistant to oxidation unless there are strongly electron-donating groups substituted on the ring. As a matter of fact, the ring proves more resistant to attack than an alkyl group substituted on the ring. Any substituted alkyl group will be removed by oxidation and a carboxyl will be formed in its place. Larger groups are sometimes oxidized in connection with structural studies, but methyl is the group usually oxidized for synthetic purposes. The procedure shown in Eq. 4 usually gives a good yield, and is often a convenient method for synthesis of various substituted benzoic acids. One should remain alert to the fact that presence of hydroxyl or amino makes the ring so susceptible to oxidation that quinones are secured (Eq. 20-17), not aromatic carboxylic acids.

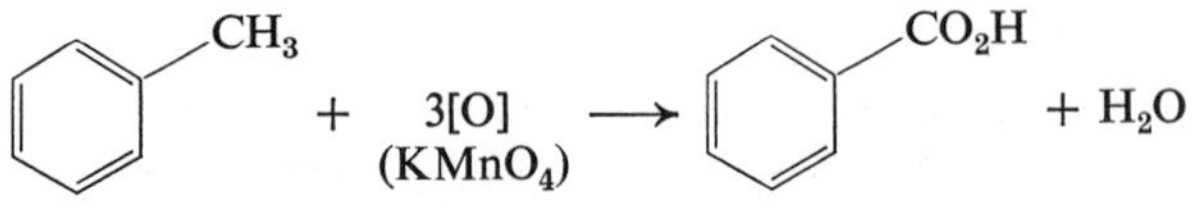

$$\text{(with } + \ 3[O] \ (\text{KMnO}_4) \longrightarrow \text{gives CO}_2\text{H} + \text{H}_2\text{O} \qquad (4)$$

Choice among the methods outlined for synthesis of acids depends largely on the type of compound available for synthesis of the particular acid desired. In the benzene series, the syntheses from amines and sulfonic acids are used only when other routes are inapplicable, for yields are relatively low. Certain useful reaction sequences for obtaining substituted acids are indicated in the following section.

Reactions of Aromatic Carboxylic Acids

Functional derivatives of the aromatic acids are formed by the same methods discussed for aliphatic acids in Chapters 13 and 14, and the reactions of these derivatives parallel those of the aliphatic compounds. Reactions of acid derivatives involving the alpha hydrogens (such as α-bromination, Eq. 16-2) naturally do not occur with aromatic acids, for there are no alpha hydrogens.

Substitution reactions of aromatic acids and their functional derivatives are those to be expected from compounds containing a *meta*-directing substituent in the ring. *Meta*-substituted acids can be obtained by direct substitution in the acid, while *ortho*- or *para*-substituted acids must be made by way of converting some *ortho,para*-director to the carboxyl group. Reference to the section on synthesis will reveal that halogen, amino, or methyl can be conveniently converted to carboxyl. The following chart illustrates a few synthetic routes for preparing *para*-substituted aromatic carboxylic acids. *Ortho*-substituted acids can be similarly prepared by use of appropriate *ortho*-substituted starting materials.

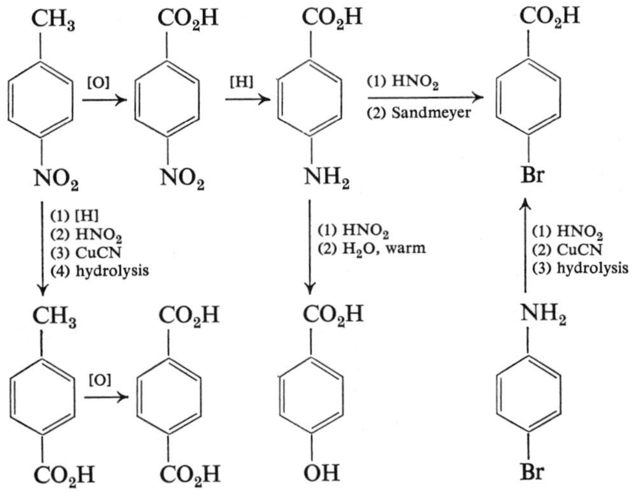

Phthalic Acid and Related Compounds

Phthalic acid, some of its reaction products, and certain closely related compounds are of sufficient importance to justify specific consideration.

Industrial Preparation of Phthalic Acid

Until recently, phthalic acid was prepared almost entirely by oxidation of naphthalene, from coal tar, as shown in Eq. 5.

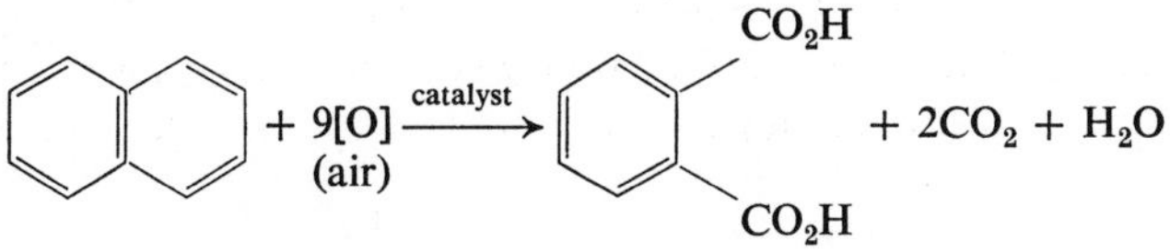

$$\text{Naphthalene} + 9[O] \xrightarrow{\text{catalyst}} \text{Phthalic acid (} CO_2H, CO_2H \text{)} + 2CO_2 + H_2O \qquad (5)$$

The demand for phthalic acid has become so great that the supply from naphthalene is inadequate, and it is now made also by a second process depending on oxidation of o-xylene, obtained by cyclodehydrogenation of octane from petroleum.

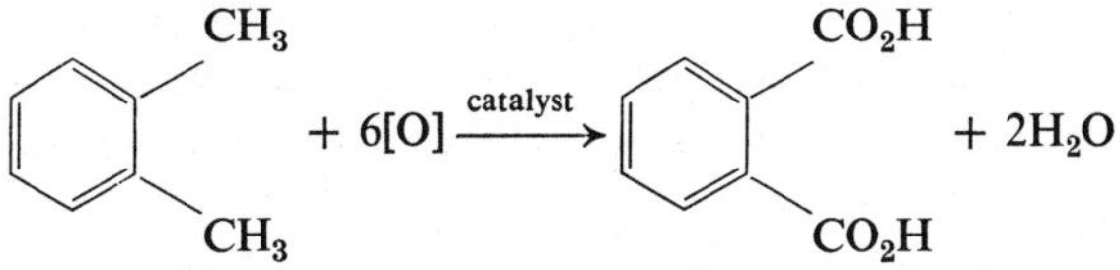

$$\text{(} CH_3, CH_3 \text{)} + 6[O] \xrightarrow{\text{catalyst}} \text{(} CO_2H, CO_2H \text{)} + 2H_2O \qquad (6)$$

Oxidation of p-xylene, also obtained by cyclodehydrogenation, usually followed by rearrangement (cf. Chap. 17), yields the p-dicarboxybenzene, terephthalic acid, Eq. 7.

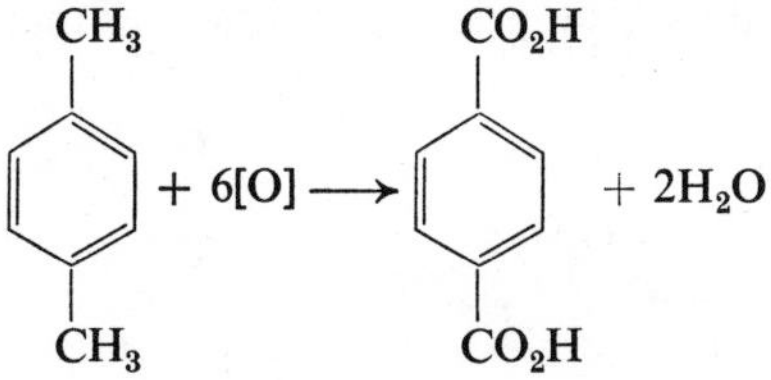

$$\text{(} CH_3, CH_3 \text{)} + 6[O] \longrightarrow \text{(} CO_2H, CO_2H \text{)} + 2H_2O \qquad (7)$$

Polymers from Phthalic and Terephthalic Acids

Polymers of phthalic acid with polyhydroxy compounds, such as glycerol or pentaerythritol, are highly branched, tough polymers of particular use in protective coatings. Such polymers are called **alkyd resins.** A typical resin of this sort is obtained from glycerol and phthalic acid or anhydride, Eq. 8.

If terephthalic acid is converted to a polymeric ester with a polymethylene glycol, $HO-(CH_2)_n-OH$, a linear polymer results, and these polymers have proved very useful, indeed, for spinning fibers for making cloth. Such polymers differ from Nylon only in that the functional group is ester rather than amide.

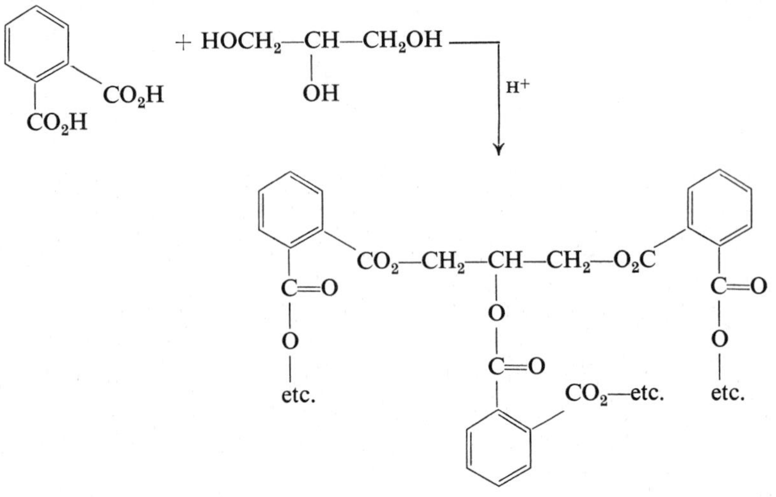

(8)

The most useful of the linear poly-esters appears to be Dacron (pronounced "day-kron"), the polymer with ethylene glycol.

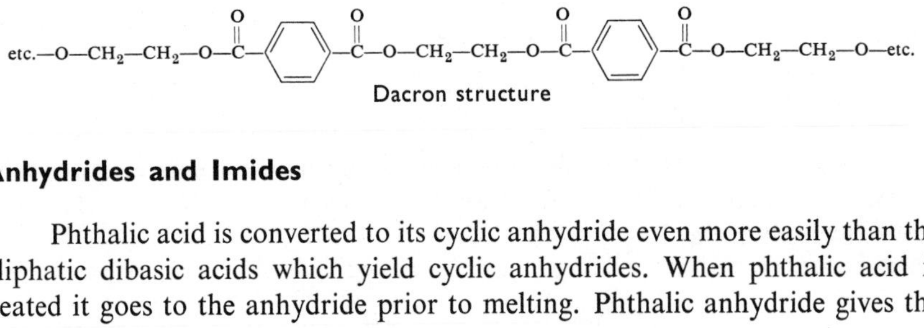

Dacron structure

Anhydrides and Imides

Phthalic acid is converted to its cyclic anhydride even more easily than the aliphatic dibasic acids which yield cyclic anhydrides. When phthalic acid is heated it goes to the anhydride prior to melting. Phthalic anhydride gives the

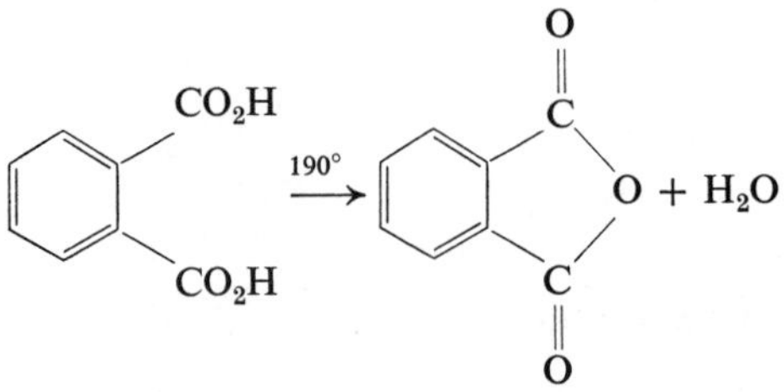

(9)

various useful reactions characteristic of aliphatic cyclic anhydrides (Eqs. 14-7 and 14-8), as well as certain others to be discussed later in this chapter.

Phthalimide is an interesting compound formed readily by heating phthalic anhydride with ammonia (Eq. 10). Presumably the imide is formed by way of an intermediate amido acid which recyclizes.

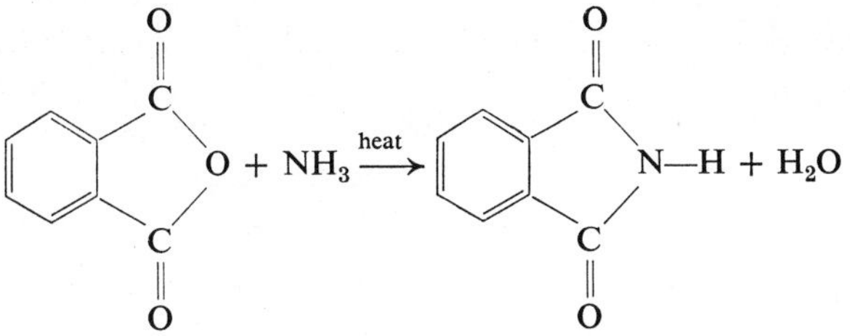

$$\text{(10)}$$

It has previously been mentioned that replacement by acyl of one hydrogen in a basic amine converts it to a neutral amide, $R\text{—}C\text{—}NH_2$. Further, if a
hydrogen in an amine is replaced by a sulfonyl group, the electron attracting power of the sulfonyl group (cf. Chap. 18) is sufficient to render the hydrogens on nitrogen acidic. Substitution of two acyl groups on a single nitrogen also renders the remaining hydrogen on nitrogen acidic. This may be ascribed reasonably to resonance stabilization of the anion:

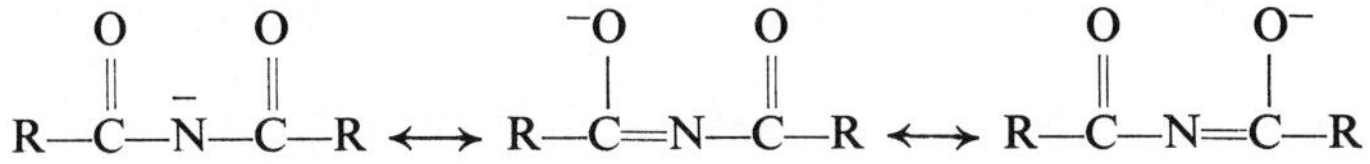

It will be noted that the second acyl group makes possible a larger orbital for electron delocalization, and, in addition, two of the resonance forms are structurally identical. As discussed in Chapter 12, both these factors contribute to greater resonance stabilization of the anion, hence greater acidity for the acid. Phthalimide, as well as other imides, proves to be sufficiently acidic to form a salt with potassium hydroxide in aqueous media (Eq. 11). The phthalimide

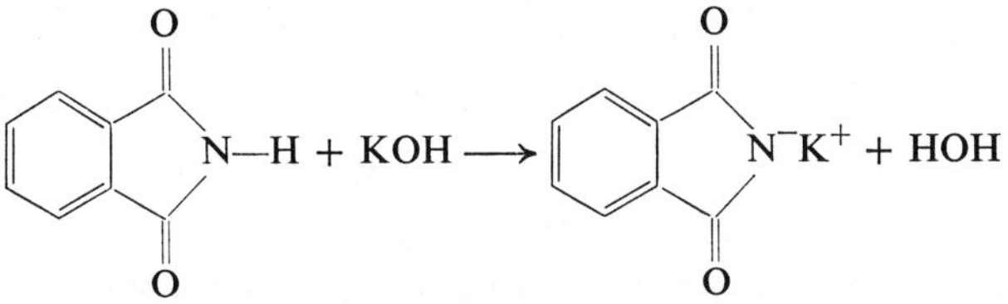

$$\text{(11)}$$

anion is useful for securing substitution on nitrogen by way of a displacement reaction (Eq. 12) similar to an amine synthesis (cf. Chap. 19).

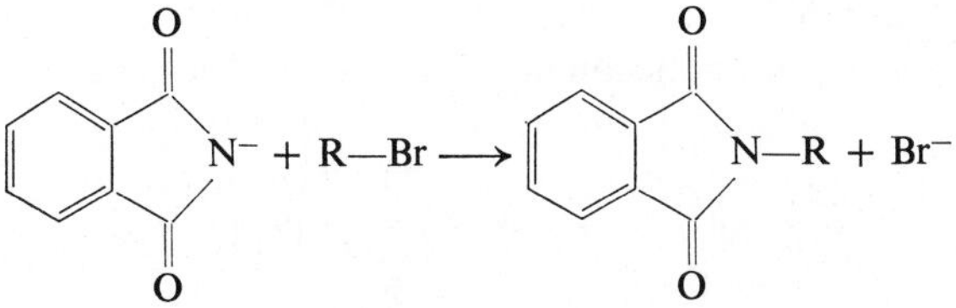

$$\text{(12)}$$

Sweetening agents. Saccharin, a non-nourishing sweetening agent, is the sodium salt of a mixed imide from a sulfonic and a carboxylic acid. The sequence for its synthesis is shown in Eq. 13. Although saccharin is rather bitter

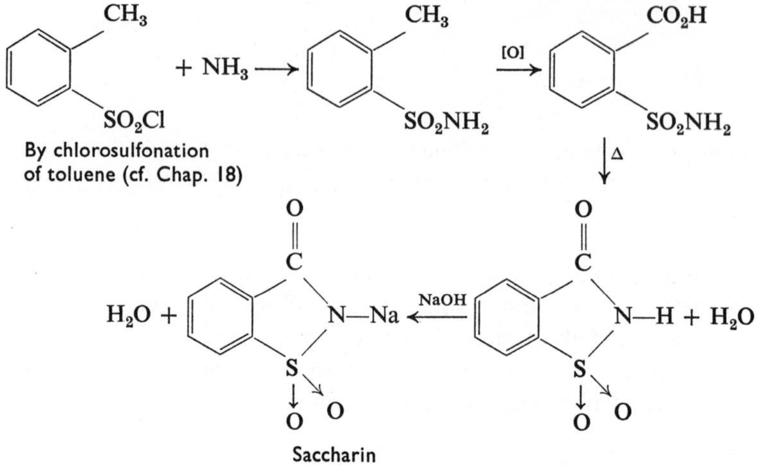

By chlorosulfonation of toluene (cf. Chap. 18)

(13)

Saccharin

in concentrated solution, in dilute solution it is about 750 times sweeter than sucrose (table sugar). There appears to be no objection to use of saccharin as a sweetening agent in food, except that it is not nourishing. In view of the danger to health of excessive weight, more widespread use of non-nourishing sweetening agents would appear desirable in many countries. Another rather widely

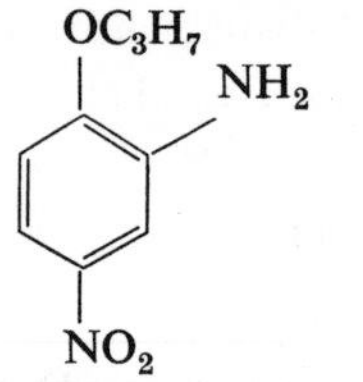

2-*n*-Propoxy-5-nitroaniline 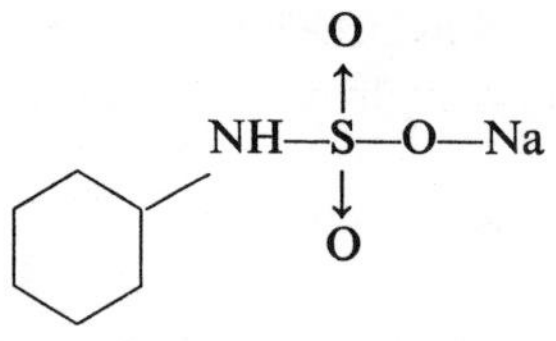   Sodium N-cyclohexylsulfamate

used non-nourishing sweetening agent is the salt of N-cyclohexylsulfamic acid (Sucaryl). The phenol ether, 2-*n*-propoxy-5-nitroaniline, is about 4,000 times as sweet as sucrose but has some toxicity.

Phthaleins. In presence of a Lewis acid, phthalic anhydride will condense with phenols in a reaction not dissimilar to the condensation of aromatic aldehydes with tertiary aromatic amines (Eq. 19-38). The reaction with phenol itself gives phenolphthalein, Eq. 14. In the lower line of this equation is shown the conversion in alkali which makes phenolphthalein an indicator. Generation of the quinoid structure and opening of the lactone ring probably occurs in a concerted process involving the transition state shown in Eq. 15.

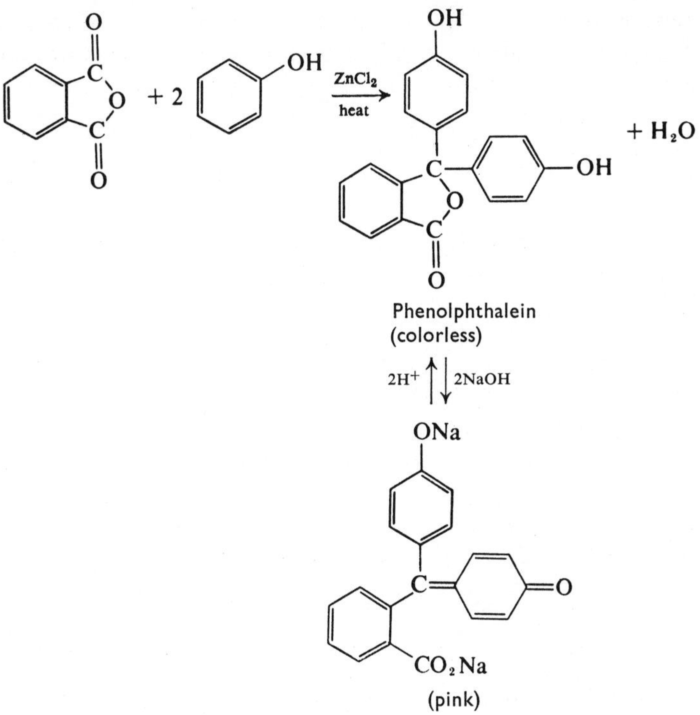

$$+ H_2O \qquad (14)$$

Phenolphthalein
(colorless)

$$2H^+ \uparrow \downarrow 2NaOH$$

(pink)

$$+ HOH \qquad (15)$$

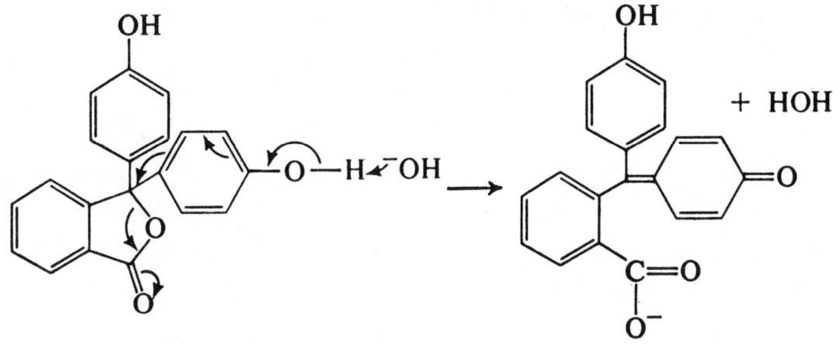

In the anion of the phenolic salt, there is possible the electron delocalization shown in the following partial formulas:

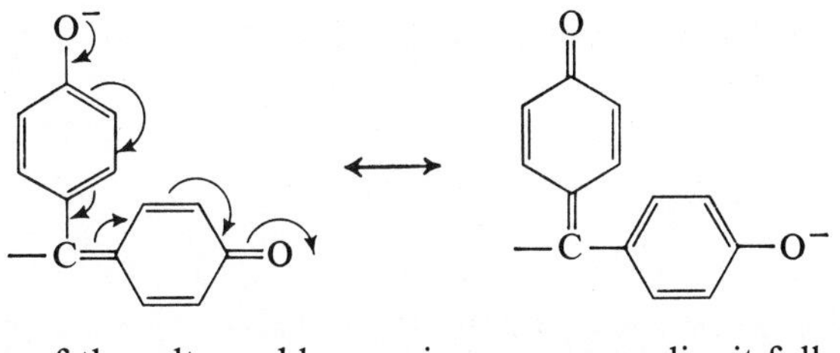

Since ionization of the salt would occur in aqueous media, it follows that both rings have quinonoid character and there is the extensive system of conjugated double bonds characteristic of compounds absorbing light in the visible region of the spectrum.

If resorcinol is condensed with phthalic anhydride, a similar reaction takes place, except that water is lost to give an additional ring as shown in Eq. 16.

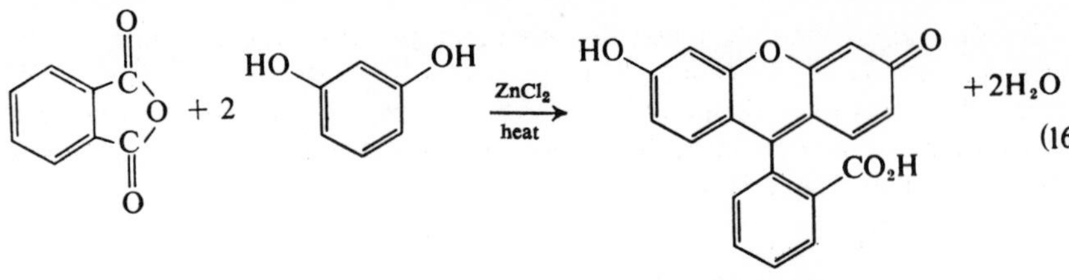

Fluorescein

The lactone ring in fluorescein is indicated as open, for the substance is highly colored, even in acid solution. Salts of fluorescein are dyes, but not fast dyes. Eosin, tetrabromofluorescein, is a red dye used in biological stains and red ink, and as a silk and wool dye. Since both end-rings in fluorescein should have quinonoid character (see above discussion of phenolphthalein), it is of interest that bromination to make eosin fills the *ortho* positions in both oxygen-substituted rings, as would be predicted. Use of substituted phthalic anhydrides leads to dyes of different shades.

Acids with Carboxyl in the Side Chain

When the carboxyl group is not attached directly to the aromatic nucleus, but is separated by one or more carbons, the properties of aliphatic acids become more or less dominant. For example, phenylacetic acid has an offensive odor, reminiscent of the lower aliphatic acids. The alkali salts of the side chain acids become soapy only when as many as four or five carbons separate carboxyl and phenyl. The salts of γ-phenylbutyric acid are not noticeably soapy, but the salts of ϵ-phenylcaproic acid definitely show properties of soaps.

Synthesis of the side-chain acids follows patterns common in the aliphatic series. Examples are shown in Eqs. 17 and 18. Usual methods of aliphatic

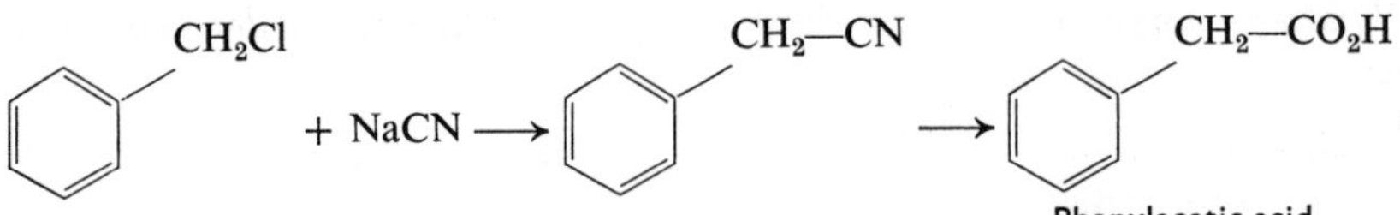

Phenylacetic acid

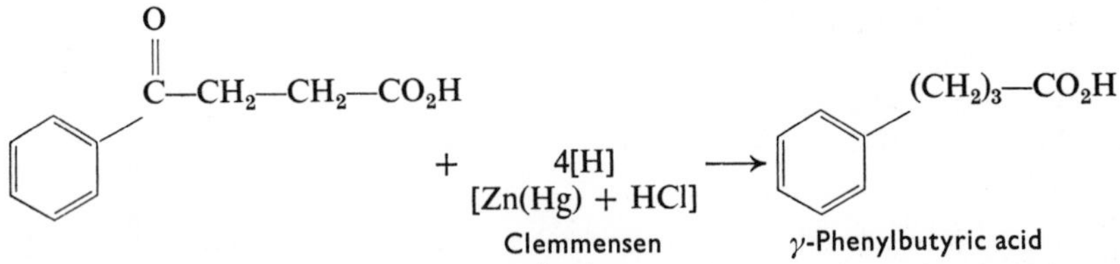

Clemmensen reduction γ-Phenylbutyric acid

chemistry may be used for chain extension of these acids or synthesis of derivatives and other classes of compounds.

EXERCISES

1. Starting with monosubstituted derivatives of benzene or compounds available from coal tar, outline by equations (not balanced but with conditions and reagents indicated) practical syntheses of each of the following compounds. Any desired reagents may be used to accomplish the conversions. Synthetic methods discussed in Chapter 19 should be reviewed.

(a) 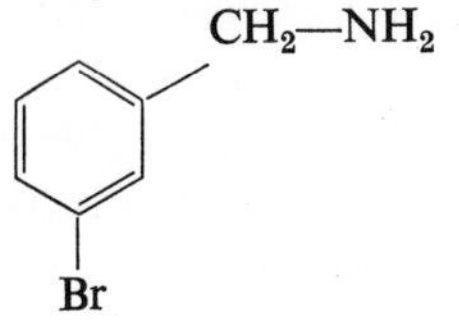 [structure: benzene ring with CH$_2$—NH$_2$ group and Br]

(b) 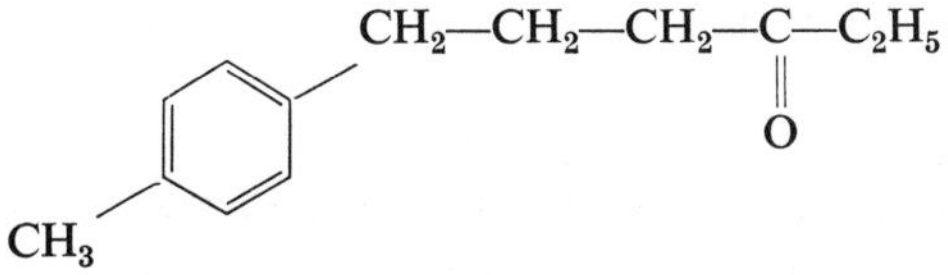 [structure: benzene ring with CH$_2$—CH$_2$—CH$_2$—C($=$O)—C$_2$H$_5$ and CH$_3$]

(c) [structure: benzene ring with CO$_2$H, Br, Br]

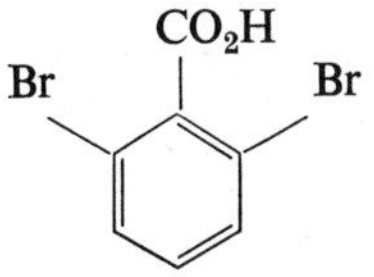

(d) 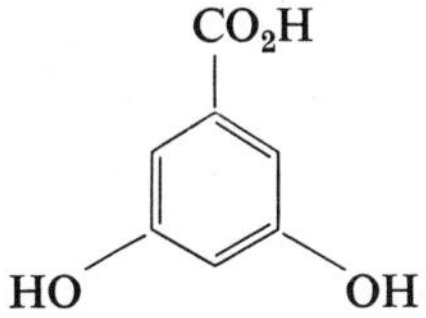 [structure: benzene ring with CO$_2$H, HO, OH]

(e) 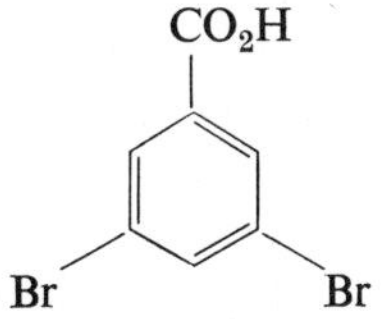 [structure: benzene ring with CO$_2$H, Br, Br]

(f) [structure: benzene ring with CO$_2$H, Br, Cl, F]

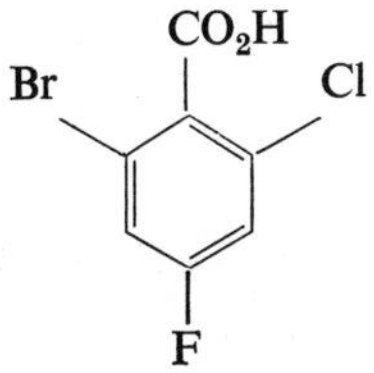

(g) 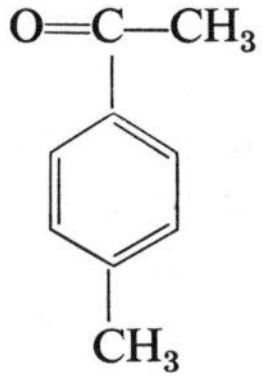 [structure: benzene ring with O$=$C—CH$_3$, CH$_3$]

(h) 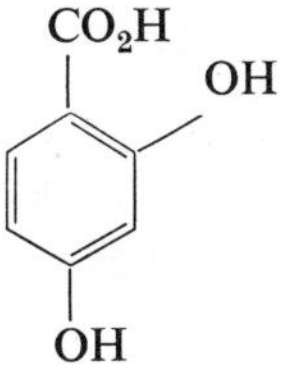 [structure: benzene ring with CO$_2$H, OH, OH]

(i) 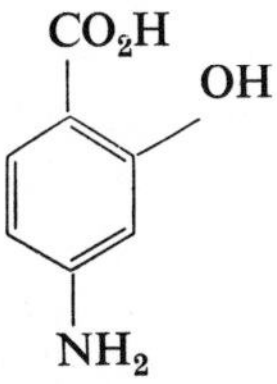 [structure: benzene ring with CO$_2$H, OH, NH$_2$]

2. Write resonance forms indicating that fluorescein should brominate in both end rings.

3. Predict which of the following will be stronger acids than benzoic acid, and which will be weaker.

(a) *p*-Hydroxybenzoic acid.
(b) *m*-Bromobenzoic acid.
(c) 3,5-Dinitrobenzoic acid.
(d) *m*-Methylbenzoic acid (*m*-toluic acid).
(Note: The acidities of the acids listed above are related to that of benzoic acid in the manner predicted from consideration of electronic displacements. In monosubstituted acids, however, the effects are usually small, and are frequently outweighed by factors that are poorly understood; for example, *o*-toluic acid (pK_a 3.89) is actually a stronger acid than is benzoic acid. *Ortho* substitution is especially prone to increase the acid strength.)

4. Would you predict that phthalimide is a stronger or weaker acid than the imide from which saccharin is made?

5. Give three different routes, with no intermediate compounds in common, for conversion of benzene to benzonitrile (cyanobenzene).

6. Outline a synthesis, starting with benzene, for the sweetest compound mentioned in this chapter. Assume that isomeric nitro amines, like other isomeric nitro compounds, are separable.

7. Starting with one of the xylenes, outline synthetic methods for securing each of the following half esters in an essentially homogeneous condition. Mention any special conditions for synthesis or special methods for purification which may be required. Remember the influence of steric factors on rate of reaction.

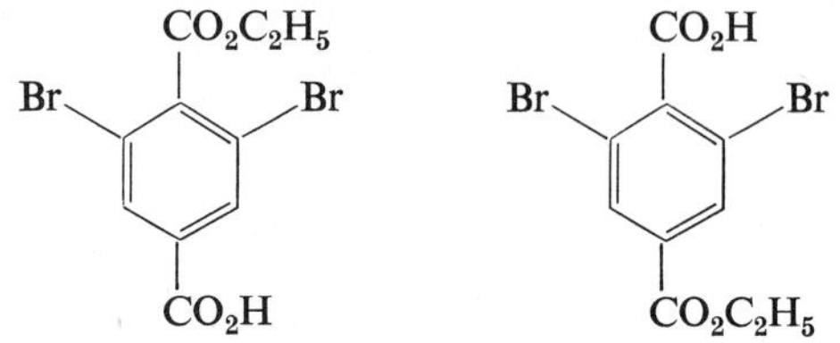

Name each of the above compounds.

8. Using as starting materials one of the xylenes and one of the cresols, outline a practical synthesis of the following substituted phenolphthalein.

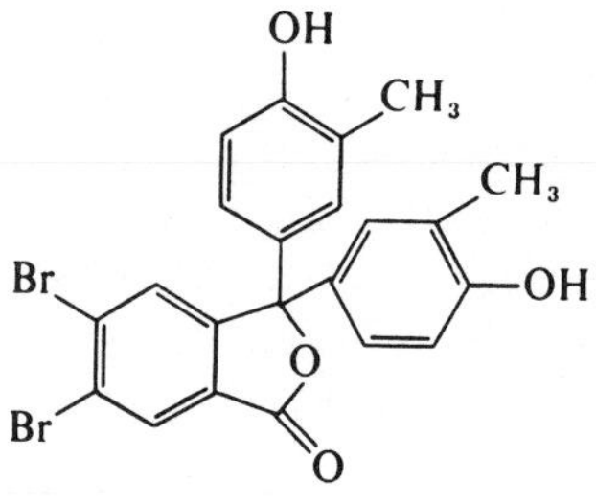

Chapter

22

Optical Isomerism

Stereoisomers differ from each other, not in the order in which the atoms are linked together, but in the positions in space of the atoms relative to each other. In Chapter 7, it was mentioned that stereoisomers are commonly classified in two broad categories, **geometrical isomers and optical isomers.** Both of these types of stereoisomers have been widely observed in organic compounds.

At this time it becomes appropriate to restrict somewhat the definition of geometric isomers by stating that they are stereoisomers whose isomerism does not depend on asymmetry in the molecule. This extension of the definition of geometric isomers becomes necessary in order to exclude optical isomers, because **optical isomers are molecules possessing an asymmetric structure.**

Fundamental Basis of Optical Isomerism

Any object, including an organic molecule, whose geometrical shape is such that it contains no plane of symmetry, may exist in forms which are mirror images of each other but are otherwise identical. Such an object, containing no plane of symmetry, is said to be **asymmetric.** The extremely rare type of structure in which asymmetry is eliminated by presence of a center of symmetry or axis of symmetry is of insufficient importance to be considered in the present discussion. The best and most common illustration of asymmetric structure is furnished by the right and left hands. Inspection will reveal that it is not possible to pass an imaginary plane through one of your hands in such a position that each object on one side of the plane is matched by an identical object on the other side of the plane. Thus your hands are asymmetric and may exist in mirror image forms. If your hands are placed directly opposite each other at equal distances from an imaginary plane, each part of one hand may be placed opposite the same part of the other hand. Thus the two together can give a symmetrical whole, but each is asymmetric. Similarly, any organic molecule which is asymmetric may exist in two forms which are mirror images of each other but are otherwise identical. Such mirror image molecules are a specific type of optical isomer known as **enantiostereoisomers or enantiomorphs.** The shorter, equivalent terms, **enantiomers or optical antipodes,** are more frequently used.

The most common cause of asymmetry in an organic molecule is presence of one or more **asymmetric carbon atoms,** and we will confine our present discussion to this type of asymmetry. A type of asymmetry arising from restricted rotation will be described near the end of this chapter, and another type will be presented in Chapter 28. An asymmetric carbon atom may be easily detected, for it is an atom attached to four different groups. The asymmetry resulting from presence of such an asymmetric carbon atom is shown in Fig. 1, in which the atoms indicated as A, B, D, and E may be any atoms or

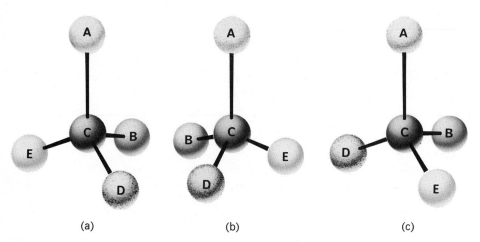

(a) (b) (c)

Fig. I. Model of a molecule containing an asymmetric carbon, which is designated by C. The other spheres, labeled A, B, D, and E, may be any atoms (or groups of atoms) so long as they all differ from each other. If any two of these atoms are the same, the molecule is not asymmetric because a plane of symmetry may be passed midway between the like atoms. The molecules shown in (b) and (c) are identical with each other and are the mirror image of the molecule shown in (a).

groups of atoms so long as they differ from each other. In this figure, (a) and (b) are mirror images, as may be seen by comparing the positions of the opposing atoms. In order to see that the molecule in (b) is indeed not identical with that in (a), it is necessary only to rotate the model in (b) to the position in (c), where the atom B is in the same position relative to the carbon as is the case in (a). It will be noted that the positions of the atoms D and E are exchanged in (a) and in (c). Finally, one should realize that if any two groups in (a) are exchanged there results the mirror image shown in (b) and (c). These relationships become especially clear if such models as shown in Fig. 1 are set up with molecular model kits of the type mentioned in Chapter 3. Such a model kit is a nearly indispensable adjunct for the study of this chapter and the two following chapters.

Physical Properties of Enantiomorphs

Since enantiomorphs, or enantiostereoisomers, are identical with each other in all respects except for their mirror image relationship, it is not surprising that their physical properties are identical except for one physical property dependent on the asymmetry. The boiling points, melting points, refractive indices, densities, colors, etc. of enantiomorphs are identical. The property that is different is rotation of the plane of polarized light; so this property should be discussed without further delay.

Optical activity. A compound is said to be **optically active** if it can rotate the plane of polarization of plane[1] polarized light, and an asymmetric molecule can do this. Although the principles involved in polarized light are discussed in detail in courses in elementary physics, the nature of polarized light will be presented here in very elementary form.

The principles involved in polarization of light are shown in diagrammatic form in Fig. 2. It will be noted, from a study of the legend under this figure, that the significant characteristic of plane polarized light is that all light in the beam is vibrating in a single plane. If such a beam of light is passed through a solution of an optically active compound (or a pure optically active liquid) the plane of polarization is rotated in a manner such as shown in Fig. 2(c). The observed angle through which the plane of polarization is rotated is termed α.

Polarized light may be secured in several ways, but the device giving the most homogeneous plane polarized light is known as a Nicol prism (pronounced like the metal, nickel). An ordinary beam of light passed through a Nicol prism comes out plane polarized; in other words, the Nicol prism transmits only that component of the wave motion vibrating in a single plane. If this beam of polarized light is directed into a second Nicol prism with its polarizing plane at right

---

[1] There are other types of polarized light, such as circularly polarized light; however, when no qualifying adjective is used, the expression "polarized light" is assumed to mean plane polarized light.

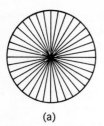 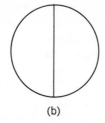 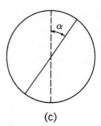

(a)   (b)   (c)

Fig. 2. Diagram indicating the nature of polarized light. In (a) is shown a cross section of a beam of ordinary light traveling directly toward the observer. Vibration of the light is at right angles to the direction of travel, but not otherwise orientated; hence the direction of vibration may be in any direction across the beam, as shown by the numerous lines in (a). In (b) is shown a beam of polarized light, where the only direction of vibration is the direction shown by the cross-line. This direction is the *plane of polarization*. In (c) is shown the same beam with the plane of polarization rotated to the position shown by the solid line. The angle between the original plane of polarization (dashed line) and the plane of polarization after rotation is indicated by α.

angles to the first, no light at all will pass through. Thus if the beam of polarized light is passed through a solution of an asymmetric compound, a second Nicol prism can be used to detect the amount the plane of polarization has been rotated. The device used for this purpose is known as a **polarimeter,** and a cross-sectional diagram of such a device is shown in Fig. 3. In practice, such instruments vary from simple ones costing a few hundred dollars to precision instruments costing several thousands of dollars and able to detect angles of rotation as low as 0.0002° of arc.

As might be expected, each of a pair of enantiomorphs rotates the plane of polarized light an *equal amount but in opposite directions*. This follows logically from the fact the substances differ only in being mirror images. It has been universally (although arbitrarily) agreed that the direction of rotation is *positive*, (+), if the direction of rotation is *clockwise* as viewed by an observer looking

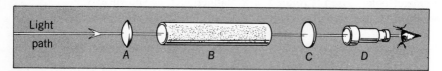

Fig. 3. Polarimeter in cross section. *A*, Nicol prism known as the *polarizer*; *B*, tube containing the compound being examined for optical activity; *C*, Nicol prism known as the *analyzer* and placed in a rotating mount from which degrees of arc may be read; *D*, eyepiece through which the light is viewed as *C* is rotated to a position of minimum darkness. In order to give improved accuracy, most instruments are much more complicated than indicated in this diagram, although the principles remain the same. In particular, a split-beam arrangement is used so that the final setting is made by matching two adjacent fields.

at the beam of light approaching him. It follows that the rotation shown in Fig. 2(c) is a positive rotation. Conversely, a *counterclockwise* rotation is termed *negative*, (−). In addition, a positive rotation is frequently termed *dextro*, and a negative rotation is termed *levo*.[2] The application of these terms to organic nomenclature will be discussed in a subsequent section.

The **optical rotation** is a very valuable physical constant for establishing the identity of a compound, especially since it also tells whether the compound is the dextro or levo form. If the rotation is to be used as a physical constant, it is clear that the units of measurement must be specified. For example, density is weight per unit volume. For optical rotations, the term used is **specific rotation,** which is the optical rotation expressed in degrees when the light path in the solution is 1 decimeter (10 centimeters) and the concentration of the solution is 1 gram per milliliter. Such concentrations of solute are ordinarily unobtainable in practice, and even a pure liquid frequently has a density less than unity, but the specific rotation may be calculated if the rotation is observed at any known concentration. The rotation also varies slightly with the wavelength of light used and the temperature; so these must be specified. The complete formula for calculating an optical rotation may be expressed as follows:

$$[\alpha]_{\text{wavelength}}^{\text{temp.}} = \frac{\alpha}{(l)(c)} \tag{1}$$

In this formula $[\alpha]$ is the specific rotation, and α is the rotation observed when the light passes through a solution of length l (in decimeters) in which the concentration of active compound is c (in grams per milliliter). The temperature is expressed in degrees centigrade. The wavelength of light is usually given in Ångstrom units unless there is used the yellow line from a sodium arc, known as the "D line" of sodium. In this latter case, "D" is used instead of a wavelength, for convenience.

A final point to be mentioned is that the rotation may be different in different solvents, and may not be strictly proportional to concentration in rare instances. Thus a complete expression for reporting an optical rotation in the chemical literature usually takes a form such as the following:

$$[\alpha]_{\text{D}}^{25} = +24.7° \ (c = 0.10 \text{ g./ml. in chloroform}) \tag{2}$$

This means that at 25°, using the D line of sodium light, the specific rotation was 24.7° of arc when the rotation was observed in chloroform solution and the concentration was approximately 0.10 gram per milliliter. If no units of concentration are specified, they are assumed to be g./100 ml.; thus, the expression in parentheses in Eq. 2 might appear as ($c = 10$, chloroform). When rotation is

---

[2] Dextro and levo are derived from Greek words meaning "right" and "left." There is evident no philosophical or practical reason why the clockwise rotation should be called positive or associated with the direction, right; however, the usage has evolved and become standard in all countries where the artistic science of chemistry is pursued.

observed on a pure liquid, c in Eq. 1 is replaced by d, the density of the liquid, for density is defined in terms of grams per milliliter; also the expression in parentheses in Eq. 2 becomes "homogeneous" or "neat."

Although specific rotation is the term commonly used as a characteristic physical constant of a compound, comparison of rotations of different compounds becomes much more meaningful if there is used an expression based on molecular weight rather than weight. For such purposes, the specific rotation is conveniently converted to **molecular rotation** by Eq. 3.

$$[M] = \frac{([\alpha])(\text{mol. wt.})}{100} \tag{3}$$

Inclusion of 100 in Eq. 3 is purely for convenience, to keep the numbers of a convenient order of magnitude. Temperature, wavelength, etc. are expressed for molecular rotation in the same manner as for specific rotation.

Mixed melting point behavior of enantiomorphs. As has already been pointed out, the physical properties of enantiomorphs are identical except that the two forms rotate the plane of polarized light in opposite directions. It follows, then, that the dextro and levo forms of a substance have identical melting points. The fact remains, however, that *the dextro and levo forms are different substances;* therefore a mixture of the two shows a depressed melting point just as do mixtures of other substances. A simple melting point diagram for an enantiostereoisomeric pair is shown in Fig. 4(a), where the eutectic point occurs at an equimolar mixture of the two isomers. A mixture of equal amounts of dextro and levo forms is known as the **racemic substance.** Naturally, a racemic substance shows no optical rotation. On numerous occasions, the racemic substance is not simply a **racemic mixture** of two kinds of crystals which gives the melting point diagram of the sort shown in Fig. 4(a). Instead, there may be a new type of crystal lattice formed in which both of the enantiomorphs are incorporated, usually in a 1:1 ratio. Such a substance is called a **racemic compound.** In this case, a double melting point diagram is obtained, as in Fig. 4(b). The right side is a characteristic diagram of mixtures of the racemic compound and the dextro compound, while the left side is a similar diagram for the levo compound. Since the racemic compound is another kind of crystal, its melting point has no fixed relationship to that of the dextro and levo compounds; it may be higher, lower, or the same. Furthermore, other physical properties of the racemic compound, such as solubility, may differ from those of the enantiomorphs; so the racemic compound is often separable from the enantiomorphs.

This section, concerned with the behavior of optical isomers on melting, should be studied carefully. These matters are especially important in connection with identification of natural products (nearly always optical isomers) by comparison of melting points with those of substances of known structure. The melting point behavior of enantiomorphs also makes it clear that they really are different compounds, even though all their physical properties save one are identical.

Fig. 4. Melting-point diagrams for mixtures of enantiostereoisomers. In (a) is shown the simple diagram resulting when the racemic substance is a mixture. In (b) is shown the type of diagram exhibited by a pair of enantiomorphs forming a racemic compound. In this example, the racemic compound has a slightly higher melting point than the dextro and levo forms; however, this is not always the case. The racemic compound may have the same melting point as the enantiomorphs, or a lower melting point.

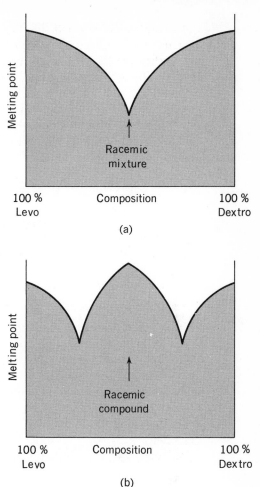

Configurational Formulas and Nomenclature

Naming of enantiomorphs. Large numbers of the compounds already studied are capable of existing in enantiomorphic forms, and the naming of these substances in optically active forms is rather simple. It is necessary only to place (+) or (−) before the usual name.[3] For example, lactic acid and α-methylbutyric acid in the dextro and levo forms, respectively, would be (+)-lactic acid and (−)-α-methylbutyric acid.

---

[3] In the literature prior to about 1940, there was very limited use of (+) and (−) to indicate direction of rotation. There were used, instead, dextro and levo, expressed by *d*- and *l*- before the name. This designation is not recommended at all at the present time, however, for the capital letters, D- and L-, have a different significance to be discussed in connection with relative configuration. Use of capital letters and lower-case letters to indicate rather different things tends to lead to confusion.

Conventions used in writing configurational formulas. As has been mentioned in Chapter 7, the structure of a compound describes the order in which the atoms are linked together, while the configuration describes the relative positions of the atoms in space. The spatial arrangement of atoms is best observed in molecular models, next best in three-dimensional drawings such as in Fig. 1; however, these devices are rather time-consuming, and many situations may be visualized by use of projection formulas according to certain conventions which are rather widespread. When a single asymmetric carbon is present, it is convenient to illustrate spatial relationships by use of an Alexander projection, the semiprojection formula which has been described in Chapter 3. The two enantiomorphs of lactic acid are shown as follows:

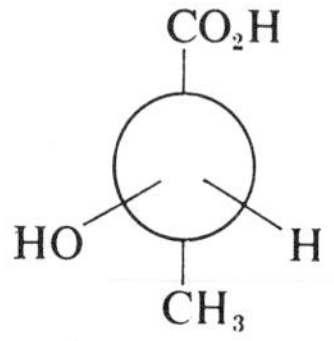

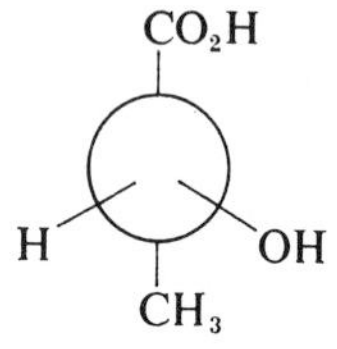

If the asymmetric carbon is visualized as a sphere (in a model, for example) with carboxyl standing straight up and the methyl group back of the sphere, then the hydroxyl and hydrogen will be projecting forward and to each side. In the one case, hydroxyl is on the right (of the viewer), in the other case on the left. It is highly recommended that this model be set up with a molecular model kit so that these relationships will be clear.

A further simplification of the formulas shown above is often convenient, especially when molecules with several asymmetric carbons are being considered. This consists of a complete projection of the above formulas, as shown below:

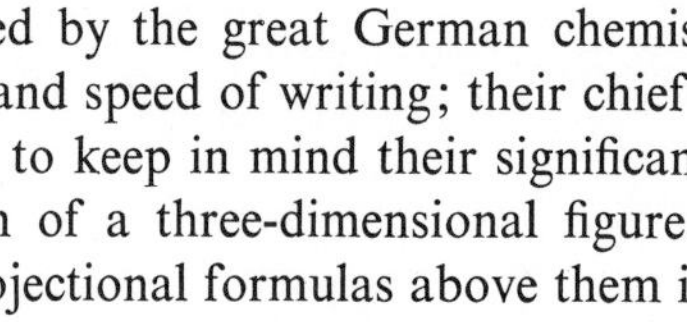

Formulas of this type are sometimes called Fischer projection formulas, for they were first suggested by the great German chemist, Emil Fischer. Their principal virtue is ease and speed of writing; their chief drawback is that some imagination is required to keep in mind their significance, especially that they are a planar projection of a three-dimensional figure. Comparison of these formulas to the semiprojectional formulas above them is very helpful.

Absolute configuration. The two optical antipodes of many molecules, including lactic acid, have been obtained, and the two substances have equal but opposite optical rotations. It has not been possible on the basis of first principles,[4] however, to decide which of the configurational formulas should be assigned to the molecule with the dextro rotation. The matter is complicated by the common observation that a relatively small change in a group two or three atoms distant from the asymmetric carbon can cause a change in the sign of rotation. For example, the following conversion has been observed:

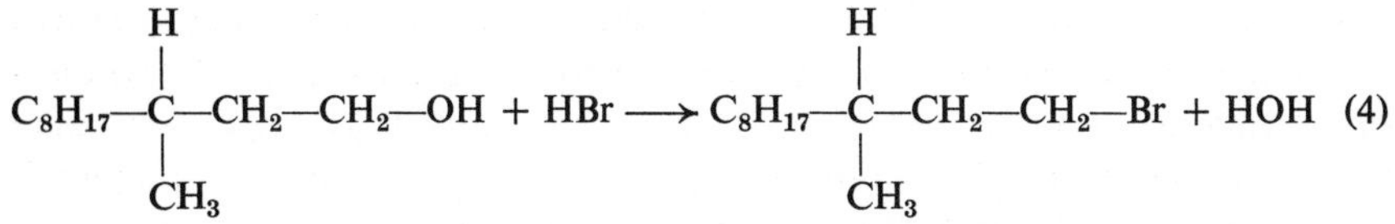

$$\underset{\substack{| \\ CH_3 \\ \text{(+)-3-Methyl-1-hendecanol} \\ [\alpha]_D^{25} = +4.1°}}{\overset{\overset{H}{|}}{C_8H_{17}-C-CH_2-CH_2-OH}} + HBr \longrightarrow \underset{\substack{| \\ CH_3 \\ \text{(−)-3-Methyl-1-hendecyl bromide} \\ [\alpha]_D^{25} = -5.2°}}{\overset{\overset{H}{|}}{C_8H_{17}-C-CH_2-CH_2-Br}} + HOH \quad (4)$$

In this example, none of the bonds on the asymmetric carbon has been ruptured; hence it is clear that the sign of rotation has changed without the configuration of the groups changing. Change in the nature of one of the groups gives a change in sign, even with the same configuration in the two molecules. As a matter of fact, there is known at least one molecule, methyl hydrogen β-methyl-glutarate,

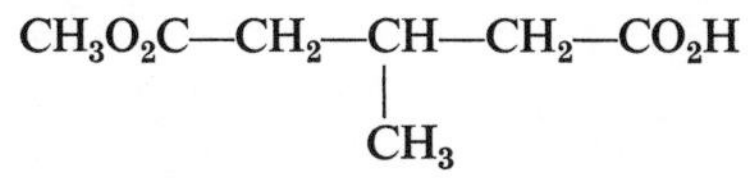

$$\underset{\substack{| \\ CH_3}}{CH_3O_2C-CH_2-CH-CH_2-CO_2H}$$

whose sign of rotation changes with temperature. It follows from all this that the sign of rotation supplies no information about the configuration of the molecule, at least, no information subject to direct and reliable interpretation.

It is possible to learn the **relative configuration** of molecules, however, if one molecule can be converted into the other, as in Eq. 4. We know that the bromide obtained in this reaction has the same configuration as the alcohol from which it was made. In case a group attached directly to the asymmetric carbon is displaced in a reaction not involving a carbonium ion as intermediate (cf. Chap. 6), we know that *inversion of configuration* takes place (cf. Fig. 6-1), that is, one configuration is changed to the other. This may or may not result in a change in sign of rotation. In case a carbonium ion is involved as an intermediate in a reaction involving the asymmetric carbon, the geometry of the molecule is unlikely to be maintained, since only three groups are attached to the carbon in a carbonium ion. When the fourth group becomes attached, either of the possible configurations may result, and statistics hold (except in certain

---

[4] In recent years, considerable progress has been made in devising a set of principles by which the sign of optical rotation of an enantiomorph may be deduced from knowledge of its structural formula. Stated differently, these principles may be used to assign the proper formula of the two optical antipodes to the one with a dextro rotation. These principles, known as "Brewster's Rules," do not always give the "right answer," but they represent considerable progress. These rules have been proposed by Professor J. H. Brewster, of Purdue University.

special limiting situations) since the number of molecules is so large. A product formed *via* a carbonium ion usually consists of equal amounts of $(+)$ and $(-)$ forms, hence shows no optical rotation. Such a process, starting with an active compound and ending with a racemic substance, is termed **racemization.**

Sufficient knowledge of reaction mechanisms has been accumulated (e.g., cf. Chap. 6) that it is possible to convert many optically active compounds, without racemization, and thus establish their relative configurations. Near the end of the nineteenth century, in connection with his study of the stereochemistry and structures of carbohydrates (cf. Chap. 23), Emil Fischer proposed that glyceraldehyde be used as a basic reference point for establishing relative configuration of other compounds. He further proposed that the configuration depicted in the right-hand formula below be arbitrarily assigned to that glyceraldehyde having a dextro rotation. All compounds having this configuration are said to belong to the dextro series, regardless of the direction of rotation of polarized light, and this configuration is indicated in names by use of a small capital letter, D- for DEXTRO. Similarly, L- is used for LEVO.

$$
\begin{array}{cc}
\underset{\text{L-Glyceraldehyde}}{
\begin{array}{c}
\text{O} \\
\parallel \\
\text{C--H} \\
\\
\text{HO} \qquad \text{H} \\
\text{CH}_2\text{OH}
\end{array}}
&
\underset{\text{D-Glyceraldehyde}}{
\begin{array}{c}
\text{O} \\
\parallel \\
\text{C--H} \\
\\
\text{H} \qquad \text{OH} \\
\text{CH}_2\text{OH}
\end{array}}
\end{array}
$$

$$
\begin{array}{cc}
\text{CHO} & \text{CHO} \\
| & | \\
\text{HO--C--H} & \text{H--C--OH} \\
| & | \\
\text{CH}_2\text{OH} & \text{CH}_2\text{OH} \\
\text{L-Glyceraldehyde} & \text{D-Glyceraldehyde}
\end{array}
$$

Fischer's assignment of the right-hand formula above to the dextrorotatory glyceraldehyde was purely arbitrary, since at that time there was no way of securing any information about the absolute configuration of a molecule. Some sixty years later, application of the techniques of x-ray diffraction has established Fischer's arbitrary choice as the correct one. D-Glyceraldehyde has the configuration shown in the right-hand formula above! It follows that proof of the configuration of an optical isomer relative to glyceraldehyde also establishes the absolute configuration of that molecule. Since large numbers of compounds have had their configurations relative to glyceraldehyde established, the proof of the absolute configuration of glyceraldehyde was an important milestone in the study of stereochemistry.

It proves necessary to adopt certain conventions in order to have a uniform system of classifying compounds as belonging to the D- or L-series. The basic convention is that when the asymmetric molecule is placed so that an aldehyde group, or closely related group such as carboxyl, is directed up, with hydrogen and hydroxyl extending forward and to each side, then the D-isomer has hydroxyl on the right of the viewer facing the molecule. This is the position of the molecules shown in the Alexander projections of the glyceraldehydes. Furthermore, as stated above, the dextrorotatory glyceraldehyde has been found to have the configuration described above as the D-isomer. In illustration of this system, we may consider Fischer projections of a few compounds as follows:

$$
\begin{array}{ccc}
\text{CO}_2\text{H} & \text{CO}_2\text{H} & \text{CO}_2\text{H} \\
| & | & | \\
\text{H—C—OH} & \text{H—C—OH} & \text{HO—C—H} \\
| & | & | \\
\text{CH}_3 & \text{CH}_2\text{—CO}_2\text{H} & \text{C}_2\text{H}_5 \\
\text{D-Lactic acid} & \text{D-Malic acid} & \text{L-}\alpha\text{-Hydroxybutyric acid}
\end{array}
$$

It is apparent that extensive application of the above-described system for classifying enantiomorphs as DEXTRO or LEVO requires numerous additional conventions. For example, what about a molecule containing no hydroxyl? The only two extensions of the conventions that are appropriate for present consideration are: (a) if amino is present and hydroxyl absent, then the position for amino is considered in the same way as described for hydroxyl; (b) if both hydroxyl and amino are absent, but a hydrogen is present on the asymmetric carbon, then the isomer with hydrogen on the left (as in D-glyceraldehyde) is the D-isomer. In actual practice, greatest application of these conventions has been to compounds containing either hydroxyl or amino on the asymmetric carbon, for a great many of the important natural products contain these groups.

The system of relating absolute configurations to D-glyceraldehyde (or some other compound which has been related to D-glyceraldehyde) has been of much use, and is widely applied; however, it should be clearly understood that this system depends on a series of conventions, of which the most important have been outlined above. Furthermore, it must be recognized as entirely possible for uncertainty and disagreement to arise because of the possibility for ambiguity. An illustration will be presented. D-Malic acid (formula above) is assigned the D-configuration on the grounds that conversion to the aldehyde group of the carboxyl attached to the asymmetric carbon and conversion of the lower group to —CH$_2$OH gives the glyceraldehyde that is dextrorotatory.[5] Let us consider, however, the possibility that by some multistep process there might be accomplished the conversion indicated in Eq. 5. Although the formula for D-malic acid in Eq. 5 has been "turned over" (rotated in space 180°), in order to illustrate the point, this obviously does not change the configuration of the molecule. Nevertheless, by conversion of —CH$_2$—CO$_2$H to —CHO and conversion of —CO$_2$H to —CH$_2$OH (distinctly feasible

---

[5] Actual accomplishment of these conversions is a tedious, multistep process, but no matter how long and indirect the process, the relationship is established by ultimately effecting the stated conversions without racemization.

conversions, incidentally), it appears that we have shown that this malic acid actually belongs to the L-series—it can be converted to L-glyceraldehyde. It follows that in addition to the conventions already mentioned, there must be some understanding about *which* group is converted to the aldehyde group, etc. Unfortunately, the necessary conventions have never been developed and generally accepted.

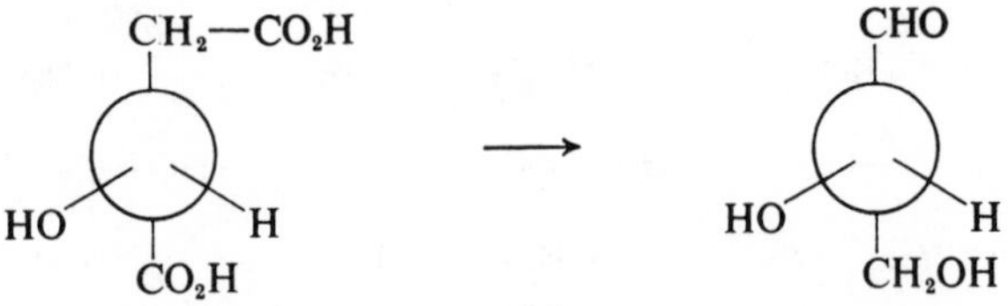

$$
\begin{array}{ccc}
\underset{\text{D-Malic acid}}{\overset{\text{CH}_2\text{—CO}_2\text{H}}{\text{HO} \quad \text{H}}} & \longrightarrow & \underset{\text{L-Glyceraldehyde}}{\overset{\text{CHO}}{\text{HO} \quad \text{H}}}
\end{array} \tag{5}
$$

The necessity, illustrated above, for a series of conventions in relating optical isomers to one of the glyceraldehydes, and inadequacy of the conventions has led to the development of another system of classifying optical antipodes. Although this new system requires a large amount of definition, it has been clearly defined,[6] and it has proved sufficiently valuable that its basic concepts should be understood by the student of elementary organic chemistry.

The Sequence Rule

Since the application of the Sequence Rule for specifying absolute configuration involves principles different from those employed in the Fischer system described above, it is necessary to use different symbols to indicate dextro and levo; otherwise, it would not be possible to know which systems were being applied. In the Sequence Rule system, levo (counterclockwise) is indicated by *S* (from the Latin, *sinister*, meaning left) and dextro (clockwise) is indicated[7] by *R*. As a first step in the assignment of *R*- or *S*- to a configuration, it is necessary to consider the basic sequence rule by which the four groups attached to the asymmetric carbon are placed in order: **the four groups attached to the asymmetric atom are placed in the inverse order of the atomic numbers of**

---

[6] The system for specifying absolute configuration known as the Sequence Rule was first proposed in 1951 [R. S. Cahn and C. K. Ingold, *J. Chem. Soc.*, 612 (1951)], but it received very little attention until a further expansion and clarification was presented five years later by R. S. Cahn, C. K. Ingold and V. Prelog, *Experientia*, **12**, 81 (1956). A convenient summary and illustration of the basic principles of the Sequence Rule has been published by R. S. Cahn, *J. Chem. Educ.*, **41**, 116 (1964).

[7] The symbol *R* was selected because it is the first letter of the Latin word, *rectus*, although *rectus* actually means straight. The word right appears to derive from the Anglo Saxon *riht*. There is probably an etymological relationship between *riht* (as well as similar words in several languages) and *rectus* developed in the sense: right means straight (as opposed to crooked), and straight is right (as opposed to wrong), and the right side of the body (as opposed to the wrong side) is that in which the muscular action is usually the strongest.

the atoms attached to the asymmetric atom. Thus, the group with the atom of highest atomic number is placed first (and termed *a*), the next highest is *b*, the third is *c*, and the lowest is *d*. This may be illustrated by considering the simple asymmetric molecule, 1-bromo-1-chloroethane (formula I), where the sequence

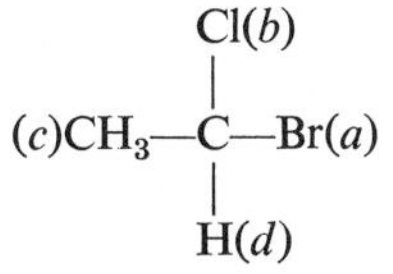

$$
\begin{array}{c}
\text{Cl}(b) \\
| \\
(c)\text{CH}_3\!\!-\!\!\text{C}\!\!-\!\!\text{Br}(a) \\
| \\
\text{H}(d) \\
| \\
\text{I}
\end{array}
$$

assigned is indicated by the letters in parentheses; bromine is the highest atomic number, hence is *a*, while hydrogen is lowest and is therefore *d*. In the methyl group, it is carbon which is attached to the asymmetric atom, so this group is *c*.

Assignment of the *R*- and *S*-configuration. Assignment of the configuration involves two steps, of which the first is: the molecule is viewed in the direction of the valence bond between the asymmetric carbon and the group assigned as *d*, with *d* behind the asymmetric carbon. In other words, the viewer looks "down the bond" from the asymmetric carbon to *d*, with the other three groups projecting towards him and to the sides like the three legs of a tripod being viewed from the bottom. This may be illustrated by considering an Alexander projection of 1-bromo-1-chloroethane, as shown in II. One would

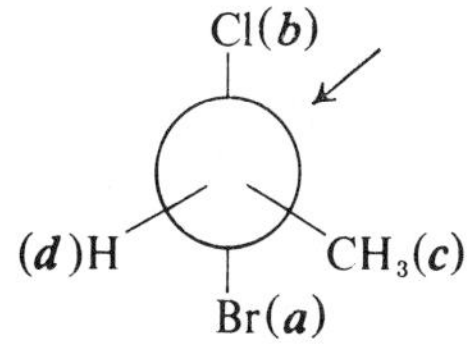

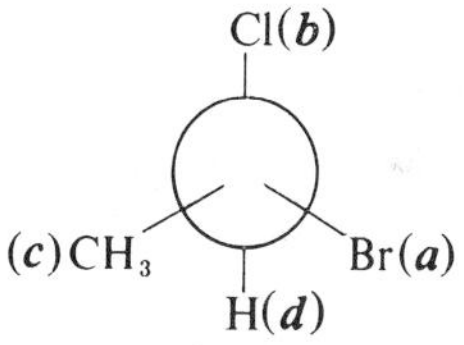

look "down the C—H bond" by looking in the direction of the arrow while standing somewhat behind the plane of the paper. If the molecule is rotated one-third revolution about a vertical axis (direction of the C—Cl bond) so that the hydrogen is behind, the position shown in III results. For the position shown in III, one would look down the C—H bond from a position in front of the paper and a little above the molecule.

The molecule is assigned the *R*-configuration if the groups *a*, *b*, and *c* are **in a clockwise sequence when the molecule is viewed down the bond from the asymmetric atom to *d*.** This follows the idea that the dextro or right-handed direction is clockwise. Similarly, if the groups *a*, *b*, and *c* lie in a counterclockwise sequence the molecule has the *S*-configuration. Assignment of the configuration is quite simple if one has a model, for he can simply look at the model from the side opposite the group of lowest atomic number (*d*) and note whether *a*, *b* and *c* lie in a clockwise or counterclockwise sequence. For deciding the configuration from viewing a projection on a plane surface, the Alexander projection with group *d* behind (as in III) is probably most easily managed, for the groups in question lie in a circle in the way that one is accustomed to viewing a clock. Thus, the molecule shown in III has the *S*-configuration—as one proceeds from *a* to *b* to *c* he is going in a counterclockwise direction. It is also the case that a projection in a Fischer sense, where the *S*-1-bromo-1-chloro-ethane[8] is written as in IV, can be quickly assigned as just described for the

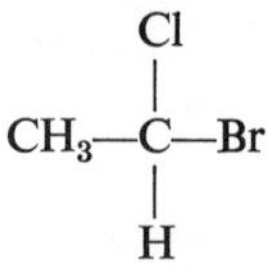

$$
\begin{array}{c}
Cl \\
| \\
CH_3—C—Br \\
| \\
H
\end{array}
$$

IV

Alexander projections. A Fischer projection can be made easily, however, only after the molecule has been "rotated" in the proper position to put group *d* behind. In an Alexander projection, this "rotation" can be easily made "on paper" without getting the groups misplaced. This matter will be illustrated below, in considering a few necessary extensions of the basic rules in this section.

Assignment of configuration in larger molecules. In order to assign configuration in any molecule, numerous sub-rules must be developed; however, consideration of two types of structure makes possible assignment of configuration in an adequate variety of molecules for present purposes.

(1) SATURATED CHAINS AND RINGS. In many instances (most molecules, in fact), assignment of sequence cannot be accomplished by application of the basic rule, for two atoms attached to the asymmetric atom may be the same. In such instances, sequence is determined by considering the next atoms in the chain. For example, the molecule shown in V would be assigned the sequence depicted in V-s. Both —CH_3 and —CH_2OH have carbon attached to the

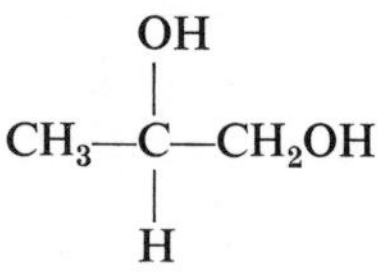

$$
\begin{array}{cc}
\begin{array}{c}
OH \\
| \\
CH_3—C—CH_2OH \\
| \\
H
\end{array}
&
\begin{array}{c}
a \\
| \\
c—C—b \\
| \\
d
\end{array} \\
V & V\text{-}s
\end{array}
$$

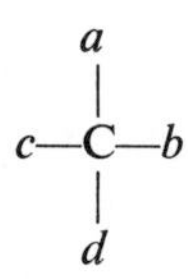

asymmetric atom; however, the next atoms in —CH_3 are all hydrogen, which is of lower atomic number than oxygen attached to the carbon in —CH_2OH. Thus, —CH_2OH is assigned *b*. If formula V is a Fischer projection, this molecule has, then, the *R*-configuration.

---

[8] Although Cahn recommends that *R*- and *S*- be written in parentheses when included as part of a name, he notes that "no difficulty is likely if . . . *R* and *S* are written . . . without parentheses." Since there appears to be no advantage to use of the parentheses they are omitted in the present book.

According to the principle just discussed, a tertiary alkyl always takes priority over secondary alkyl, which in turn takes priority over a primary group. This follows since the tertiary alkyl has three carbons attached to the carbon by which the radical is joined, a secondary radical has two carbons so attached, and a primary one has only a single carbon so attached.

In case of a branched chain in which different atoms are attached at the point of branching, sequence is assigned according to the usual basis of priority; that is, the chain is selected which carries the atom of highest atomic number. In illustration of this principle, the structure shown in VI is assigned as in VI-s.

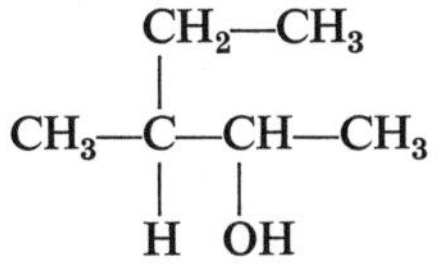

$$CH_2\!-\!CH_3$$
$$|$$
$$CH_3\!-\!C\!-\!CH\!-\!CH_3$$
$$| \quad |$$
$$H \quad OH$$

VI (S-configuration)

$$b$$
$$|$$
$$c\!-\!C\!-\!a$$
$$|$$
$$d$$

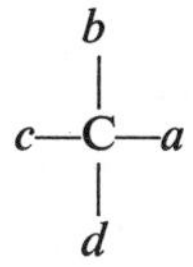

VI-s

Since the right-hand group has both —OH and —CH$_3$ attached to the carbon adjacent to the asymmetric atom, assignment is made on the basis of oxygen which has the higher atomic number than carbon. This makes the right-hand group a, as assigned. Similarly, ethyl is assigned as b, since only hydrogens are present in the methyl group.

Rings are assigned in the same manner as are branches, as illustrated by VII and VII-s. In the ring, one carbon next to the point of branching carries

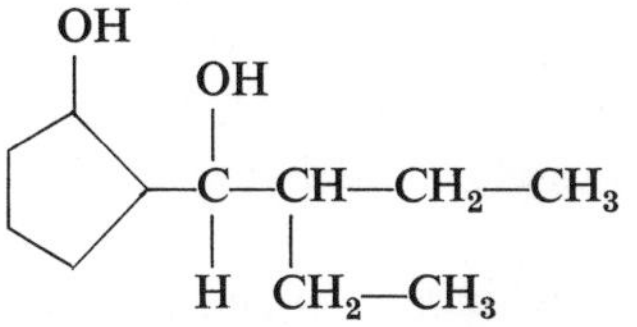

$$OH$$
$$OH$$
$$|$$
$$C\!-\!CH\!-\!CH_2\!-\!CH_3$$
$$| \quad |$$
$$H \quad CH_2\!-\!CH_3$$

VII (S-configuration)

$$a$$
$$|$$
$$b\!-\!C\!-\!c$$
$$|$$
$$d$$

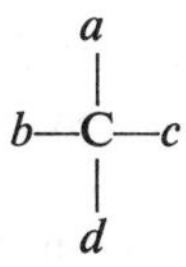

VII-s

hydroxyl, so this takes preference and the 2-hydroxycyclopentyl group is assigned as b. If additional asymmetric carbons are to be assigned, such as those in the cyclopentane ring, the same system is applied. Molecules with more than one asymmetric carbon will be considered somewhat later in this chapter.

(2) UNSATURATED GROUPS. The convention adopted for multiple bonds is: atoms joined by a double bond are considered as duplicated, while those joined by a triple bond are regarded as triplicated. This is best understood by considering simple illustrations. For example, in the carbonyl group, C=O, it is considered that carbon is joined to two oxygens and that oxygen is joined to two carbons. Thus, for application of the Sequence Rule, carbonyl is treated as C—O. Sequence is then assigned on this basis. Thus, the following priorities

$$| \quad |$$
$$O \quad C$$

would occur (highest priority on left, lowest on right), as deduced in the usual way, including consideration of the number of oxygens on carbon:

Functional group

Sequence rule equivalent

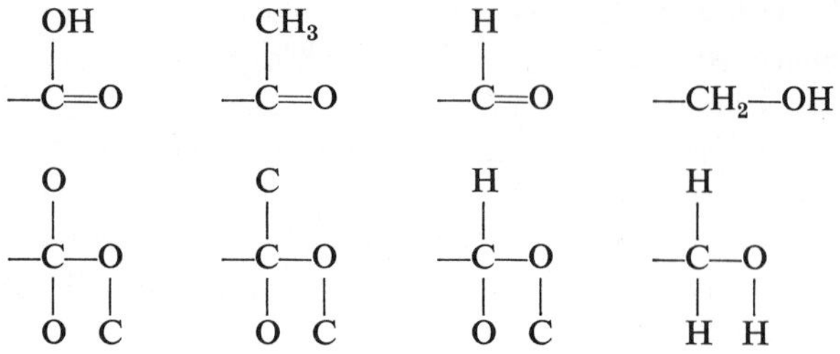

In illustration of the application of the Sequence Rule to multiply-bonded compounds, consideration of D-glyceraldehyde is instructive. In formula VIII is shown the Alexander projection of this molecule with hydroxyl on the right

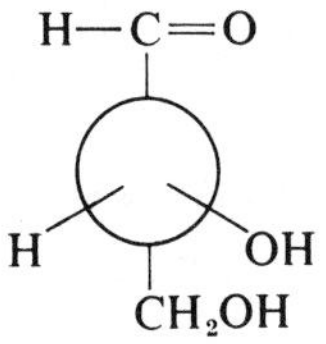

VIII

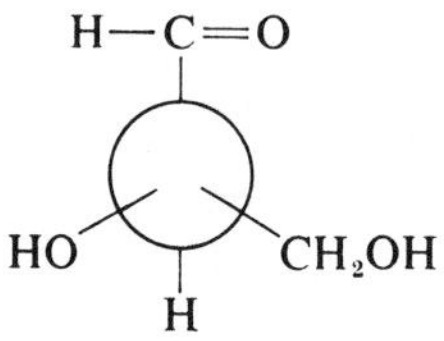

IX

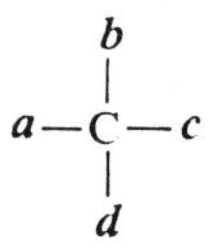

IX-s

and the aldehyde group up, as customary in the Fischer conventions. In IX is shown the molecule rotated to the position convenient for Sequence Rule assignment. As noted in the equivalences tabulated above, —CHO takes precedence over —CH_2OH. Thus, D-glyceraldehyde is also classified as *R*-glyceraldehyde.

As a final point in connection with the Sequence Rule system for classification of configuration, it should be mentioned that, although this system avoids ambiguities such as arise in application of the Fischer conventions, there can arise confusing situations requiring careful consideration. For example, if the aldehyde group in D-glyceraldehyde should be reduced to methyl, to yield structure X, it is clear that the absolute configuration of X and of IX

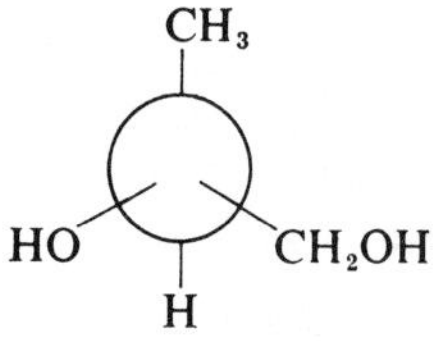

X

(*S*-configuration)

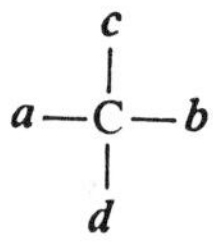

X-s

are the same. Nevertheless, sequence assignment as shown in X-s makes clear that X must be assigned the *S*-configuration.

Diastereoisomers

Diastereoisomers (frequently shortened to diastereomers) are geometric isomers whose isomerism does not depend on restriction of rotation about a bond. This distinguishes them from the *cis* and *trans* isomers that occur in alkenes or in cyclic compounds. Although diastereomers of the type classified as *erythro* and *threo* have already been encountered in connection with addition to alkenes (Chap. 9), additional discussion is pertinent at this time, for most diastereomers (but not all, as discussed below) also exist as optical isomers; that is, they are usually asymmetric.

By their very nature, the optically active diastereoisomers have more than one asymmetric carbon, so several optical isomers become possible. Unless the molecule has elements of symmetry as a whole, as in the *meso* compounds discussed below, the total number of optical isomers may be calculated: if the molecule has n asymmetric carbons, the number of optical isomers is 2^n. For consideration of a compound with two asymmetric carbons, hence existing in four optical isomers, a suitable example is α-chloro-α′-hydroxysuccinic acid. Fischer projection formulas for the four isomers are shown in structures XI to XIV. Understanding of the discussion of these structures is greatly facilitated

CO_2H	CO_2H	CO_2H	CO_2H
$Cl-C-H$	$H-C-Cl$	$H-C-Cl$	$Cl-C-H$
$H-C-OH$	$HO-C-H$	$H-C-OH$	$HO-C-H$
CO_2H	CO_2H	CO_2H	CO_2H
XI	XII	XIII	XIV

by construction of models of them. It may be noted that XI and XII are optical antipodes, as are XIII and XIV; however, XI is neither identical with nor a mirror image of either XIII or XIV. Thus, XI and XII are the optically isomeric forms of one geometric isomer, the *threo* isomer, while XIII and XIV are the optical antipodes of the *erythro* isomer.[9] Thus, all four structures are optical isomers, for they are asymmetric molecules; but certain of them are mirror image pairs, while others are also geometric isomers.

In view of the isomeric relationships just discussed, isomers XI and XII will have identical physical properties except for rotating the plane of polarized light in opposite directions, as will isomers XIII and XIV. On the other hand, geometric isomers usually have different physical properties, so XI or XII may be expected to differ from XIII or XIV in such characteristics as melting point,

---

[9] The distinction between *erythro* and *threo* isomers should be reviewed in Chapter 9; however, it may be mentioned in summary that the *erythro* isomer is the one in which a maximum number of like atoms on the adjacent asymmetric carbons may be lined up one beneath the other. In XIII and XIV, for example, both —H and —CO_2H may be orientated one above the other, whereas in XI and XII the hydrogens are on opposite sides when carboxyls are orientated one above the other.

boiling point, and solubility. This is a very important matter in connection with separation of isomers, and its application to separation of optical isomers will be discussed below. If a mixture of all four of the presently discussed isomers were obtained in a synthesis, ordinary methods of separation such as crystallization, distillation, or gas chromatography would be likely to furnish separation of the two DL-mixtures, one consisting of XI and XII, the other of XIII and XIV. Each of these DL-mixtures would exhibit no optical rotation, for equal amounts of the mirror images would be present. Furthermore, the D- and L-isomers could not be separated by ordinary methods on account of their identical physical properties. This separation requires a subterfuge, usually involving conversion to geometric isomers (see optical resolution below).

Meso compounds. If a molecule has a symmetrical structure as a whole, it cannot exist as mirror images even though it may contain asymmetric carbons. Such a structure is termed a meso compound. The situation is best understood by considering an example, and the historically important[10] tartaric acid is a good illustration. Alexander projections for the three isomeric tartaric acids follow:

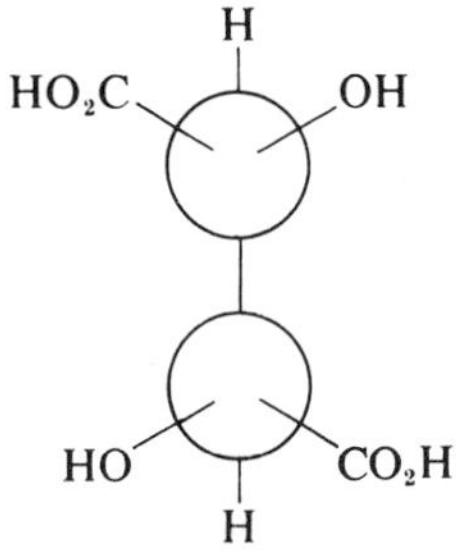

S,S-Tartaric acid	R,R-Tartaric acid	R,S-Tartaric acid or meso-Tartaric acid
XV	XVI	XVII

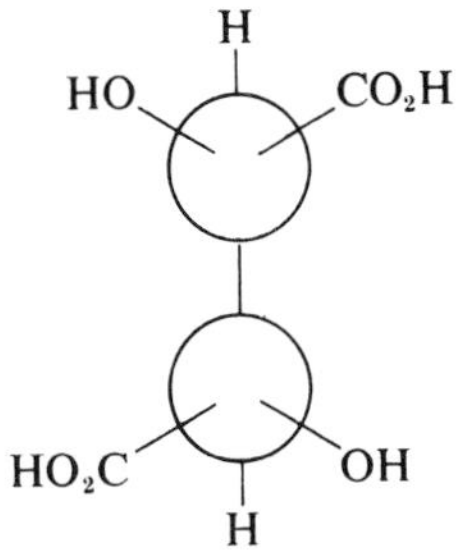

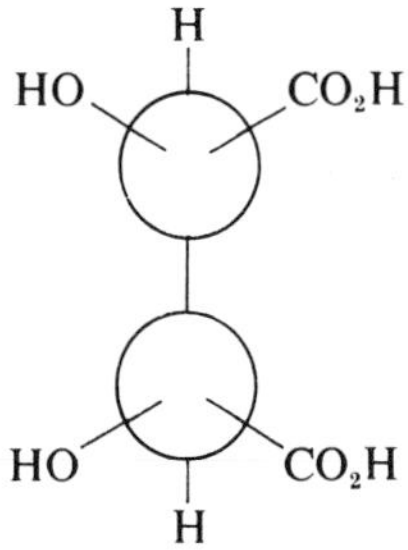

In these projections, the hydrogens have been placed to the rear so that the Sequence Rule may be readily applied.[11] If sequence assignments are made, we obtain the following (in each, c is the asymmetric carbon atom):

---

[10] The early work of Louis Pasteur on optically active organic compounds, and the first separation of optical isomers, involved the tartaric acids. The tartaric acid occurring as a precipitate in wine vats is the R-(+)-tartaric acid. Equal amounts of the R- and S- forms give a racemic compound rather than a mixture.

[11] Since several tons of printer's ink have been expended in futile arguments as to whether XV or XVI should be termed D-tartaric acid, the present discussion is based on application of the Sequence Rule, which does not encounter ambiguities as do the Fischer conventions applied to molecules with more than one asymmetric carbon.

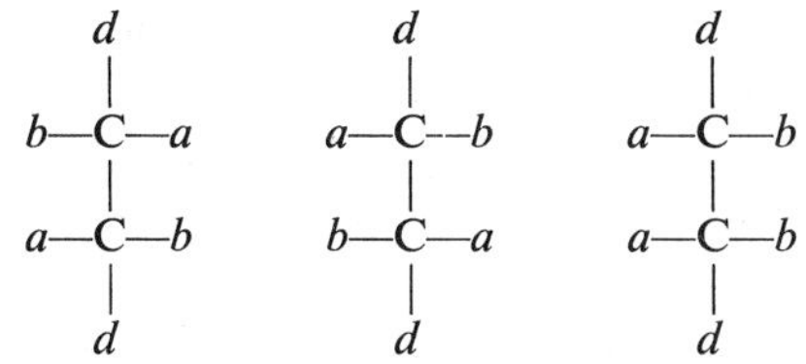

$$
\begin{array}{ccc}
d & d & d \\
| & | & | \\
b-C-a & a-C-b & a-C-b \\
| & | & | \\
a-C-b & b-C-a & a-C-b \\
| & | & | \\
d & d & d \\
\text{XV-s} & \text{XVI-s} & \text{XVII-s}
\end{array}
$$

Thus, XV and XVI are asymmetric molecules which are optical antipodes, one with S-configuration at both asymmetric carbons and the other with R-configurations. Structure XVII is a geometric isomer of the pair of enantiomers and is a meso form, optically inactive because it has a plane of symmetry. This plane is perpendicular to the bond between the central carbons, midway between these atoms; each group above this plane is matched by one beneath it.

Optical Isomerism in *cis,trans* Isomers and in Allenes

In the case of *cis* and *trans* isomers in alkenes, asymmetry cannot occur at one double bond, for each unsaturated carbon has only three groups on it. In case there is an asymmetric carbon in addition to an alkene linkage, as in 5-methyl-2-heptene (XVIII), then four stereoisomers result. Both the *cis* and *trans*

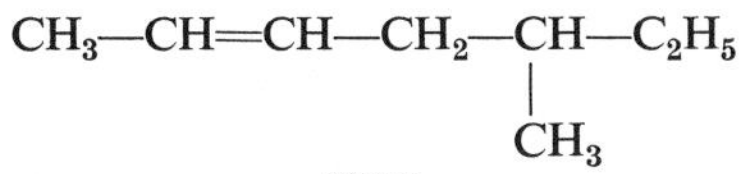

$$
CH_3-CH{=}CH-CH_2-CH-C_2H_5
$$
$$
\underset{\text{XVIII}}{\overset{|}{CH_3}}
$$

forms exist as R- and S-isomers.

Allenes. If double bonds are on adjacent carbons, with the center carbon doubly-bonded to each adjacent carbon, this structure is known as an **allene.** If an allene has different groups attached to each terminal carbon in the allene group, a special type of molecular asymmetry results so that R- and S-forms occur. This can be illustrated in the simple allene, 3,5-dimethyl-3,4-heptadiene (XIX).

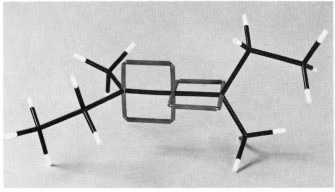

XIX

The central carbon in the unsaturated trio is involved in two π-bonds, therefore its hybridization is *sp*. It follows that the two sigma bonds form an angle of 180°, so the unsaturated carbons lie in a straight line, as the molecule is depicted above. Furthermore, the two pi orbitals attached to the center unsaturated carbon must lie in planes at right angles to each other, as is the case in an alkyne (cf. Chap. 10). As the molecule is shown, the alkyl groups on the right side are in the plane of the paper, and the alkyl groups on the left side of the molecule are in a plane at right angles to the plane of the paper. Construction of a model will quickly clarify the geometry of the allenic structure. The center carbon has the same geometry as in an alkyne (*sp* hybridization) and the terminal unsaturated atoms of the allene structure have sp^2 hybridization. In this structure, with different groups attached to the terminal unsaturated carbons, there is no plane of symmetry. For example, the plane of the paper bisects symmetrically all of the molecule except the left end—here there is ethyl on one side and methyl on the other. All efforts to locate a plane of symmetry in a model prove unsuccessful. It is of interest that allenes have been found, experimentally, to be optically active. A particularly interesting example is the highly unsaturated acid, mycomycin (cf. Chap. 10, footnote 1), which contains no asymmetric carbon but proves to rotate the plane of polarized light; it is optically active, therefore asymmetric. Acid-catalyzed isomerization of the allenic structure in mycomycin to an alkyne destroys the optical activity.

Cyclic structures. In the case of cyclic structures containing two or more asymmetric carbons, the geometric isomers exist as optical antipodes unless the molecule has a plane of symmetry, as in *meso* structures. These relations may be illustrated with the 1,2-cyclopentanediols, wherein the *cis* isomer (XX) is optically inactive and the *trans* isomer is asymmetric, therefore

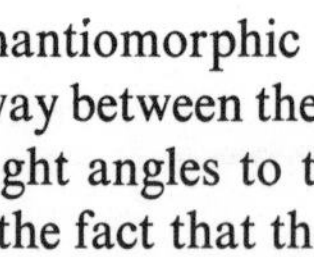

cis
XX

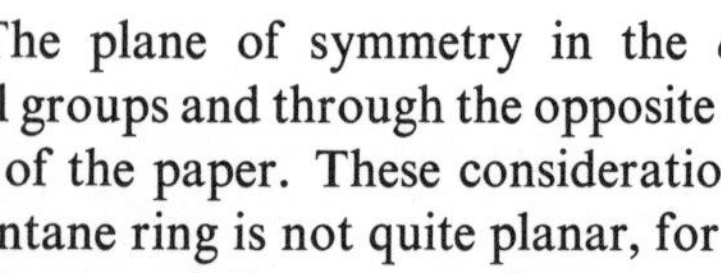

trans
XXI

exists in enantiomorphic forms. The plane of symmetry in the *cis* isomer passes midway between the hydroxyl groups and through the opposite methylene group, at right angles to the plane of the paper. These considerations are unaffected by the fact that the cyclopentane ring is not quite planar, for molecular vibrations cause rapid transfer of the out-of-plane atoms from one side to the other of the plane containing the other atoms. The structures in formulas XX and XXI may be conveniently represented as in XX-p and XXI-p, where the projection of the cyclopentane ring is used, or in XX-d and XXI-d where the large dot is used to represent a hydrogen which is above the plane of the paper (refer to discussion in Chap. 7).

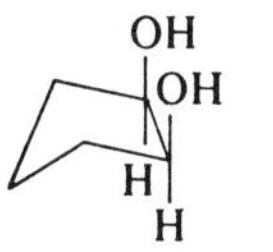

In **six-atom** rings, which exist almost entirely in a chair configuration, symmetry or asymmetry in the molecule is most easily assessed in planar projections such as discussed above for the five-atom rings, in spite of the fact that conformational formulas seem to indicate otherwise at first inspection. For example, formulas XXII and XXII′, for *cis*-1,2-cyclohexanediol, are indeed

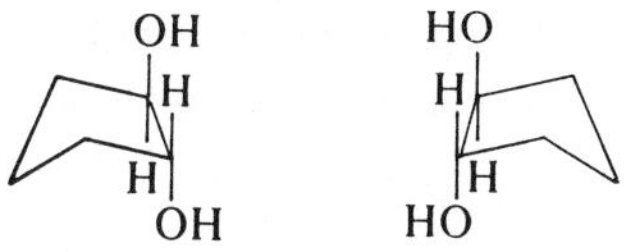

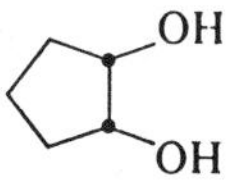

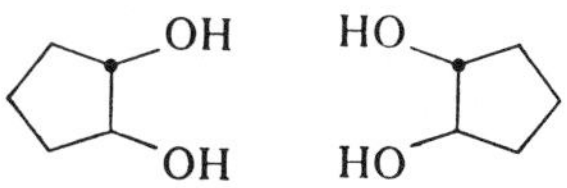

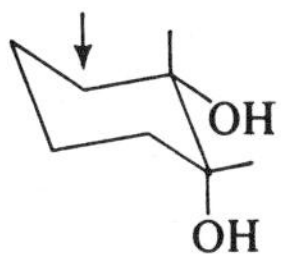

mirror images of each other, which would appear, at first consideration, to demonstrate that the molecule is asymmetric. If XXII′ is rotated 180° around a vertical axis, so as to make the rings congruent, it will be noted that the lower hydroxyl groups are also congruent, but the upper hydroxyl group will be on the "front" carbon in the rotated formula. The pertinent factor, which has been ignored thus far in these considerations, is that the cyclohexane ring is in rapid equilibrium with the conformation resulting from "flipping" the rings (refer to discussion in Chap. 7). If formula XXII′ is flipped, conformation XXII′-f results. If this formula is now rotated 120° about a vertical axis until the axial hydroxyl is congruent with this group in XXII, it will be noted that the equatorial hydroxyls are also congruent, and the carbons marked by an arrow come to the same position. Indeed, the two formulas are completely identical. This identity is obscured somewhat in the projections of the chair conformation because the lengths of the middle bonds in the formulas are exaggerated for pictorial reasons. Examination of Framework Molecular Models of the *cis*-1,2-cyclohexanediol will make it quite evident that a *cis*-disubstituted cyclohexane is not asymmetric unless the two substituted groups are different. On account of rapid equilibration of the two chair conformations, the planar projection yields correct deductions concerning asymmetry.

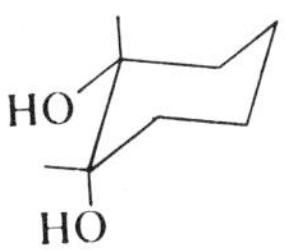

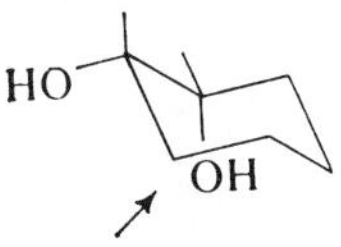

In the case of the *trans*-1,2-disubstituted cyclohexanes, the structure is asymmetric as has been noted above for the cyclopentanes. The conformational formulas for *trans*-1,2-cyclohexanediol are **XXIII-*S*** and **XXIII-*R***. It is immediately apparent that flipping of these formulas will not give identity, for

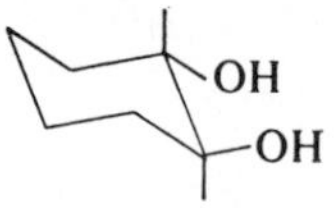

XXIII-S 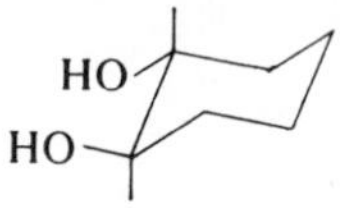   XXIII-R

either flipped structure has two axial hydroxyl groups. This is in contrast with the *cis* isomer, in which there is one axial and one equatorial hydroxyl. Thus, flipping of the *cis* isomer does not alter the type of hydroxyls present; only the positions of the axial and equatorial hydroxyls are changed (refer to formulas **XXII'** and **XXII'-f**).

In the case of a 1,3-disubstituted cyclohexane such as 1,3-cyclohexanediol, it is immediately apparent that the *cis* isomer has a plane of symmetry, even in the conformational projection (**XXIV**), while it is also apparent that the *trans*

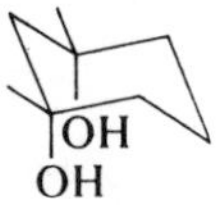

XXIV 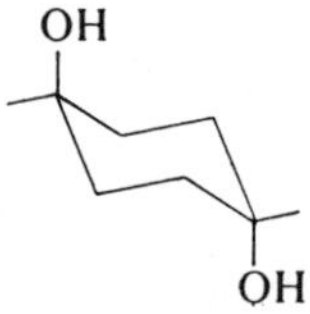   XXV

1,3-isomer cannot have a plane of symmetry. In the 1,4-cyclohexanediols, even the *trans* isomer (**XXV**) has a plane of symmetry, the plane through the valence directions of the two hydroxyls. Since this plane bisects the ring as well as the two substituents, the molecule is also symmetrical when the 1- and 4- substituents are different. In the 1,2- and 1,3-disubstituted cyclohexanes, both *cis* and *trans* isomers are asymmetric if the two substituents are different.

In the case of **decalins** (two cyclohexane rings fused together), both the *cis* and *trans* isomers (**XXVI-c** and **XXVI-t**) are optically inactive because each

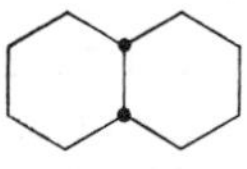

XXVI-c 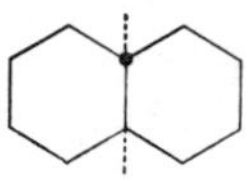   XXVI-t 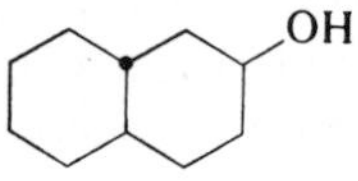   XXVII

has a plane of symmetry. The *cis* isomer has two planes of symmetry at right angles to the plane of the paper, while the *trans* isomer has a plane of symmetry at right angles to the paper as indicated by the dotted line in the formula. It may also be noted that each of the carbon atoms in this plane has two identical groups on it. If a single hydrogen is substituted in one ring, however, as in formula **XXVII**, the symmetry of either a *cis* or *trans* decalin is destroyed. Formula **XXVII** contains three asymmetric carbons, for the two groups on the central carbon atoms are no longer identical.

Optical Resolution

The separation of enantiostereoisomers is known as **optical resolution.** It is an important process, for a synthesis which creates an asymmetric carbon gives exactly equal amounts of the R- and S-forms. This is because the exceedingly large number of molecules involved allows a statistically perfect distribution. For example, synthesis of an asymmetric molecule is shown in Eq. 6. Either of the two alpha hydrogens may be replaced by bromine; therefore,

$$CH_3-CH_2-CO_2H + Br_2 \xrightarrow{PBr_3} CH_3-CH-CO_2H + HBr \qquad (6)$$
$$\underset{\displaystyle Br}{\big|}$$

exactly equal amounts of the R- and S-forms are produced. Since the physical properties of the optical antipodes on which separation might be based are identical, their separation must depend on special procedures known as optical resolution.

Methods for optical resolution. Although several methods have been explored and used for partial resolution, only three methods have given enantiomorphs in a state of "optical purity" (term used to indicate complete absence of the enantiomorph). Of these only the one named last below has been widely applied.

1. The first optical resolution was accomplished by Louis Pasteur, who picked out by hand the different shaped crystals of certain salts of the tartaric acids. This was made possible because of the very large well-formed crystals developed by these salts. Unfortunately, this process is largely of historical significance; there have been few, if any, additional resolutions by this method.

2. Since biological processes are highly stereospecific, on account of the asymmetric enzymes involved (cf. Chap. 25), it is quite often the case that one enantiomer enters a metabolic process and the other does not. If a microorganism can be found that feeds on a compound, it will usually eat one enantiomorph and leave the other alone. Isolated enzymes will also make such a differential attack, on some occasions. This type of resolution has some significant uses, but finding the correct organism or enzyme is often difficult; also one of the isomers is destroyed.

3. Conversion of the enantiostereoisomers to diastereoisomers, separation of the diastereoisomers, and regeneration of the enantiomers is the sequence most widely used and most successful. The process is successful only when several favorable situations can be realized:

(a) A suitable optically active substance, usually a natural product, must be available.

(b) The reaction giving the diastereoisomers must be reasonably easy and proceed in high yield; also regeneration of the original enantiomorphs must be reasonably satisfactory. There must be no racemization involved in either of these chemical reactions.

(c) The diastereoisomers must be separable. Crystallization is nearly always used, and this means that the substances must be well-defined crystalline solids of sufficiently different solubilities.

The process meeting requirement (b) best is salt formation, and its suitability is greatly enhanced by occurrence of numerous active acids and bases in nature. The scheme for separation of enantiomorphic acids is outlined:

L-acid   L-acid·D-base ⎫ diastereoisomers, must
 +   + D-base ⟶   +   ⎬ be separable if process
D-acid   D-acid·D-base ⎭ is to succeed

   (available in | fractional
   nature) | crystallization

L-acid·D-base   D-acid·D-base
   | H+ | H+ (strong acid)

L-acid + D-base salt   D-acid + D-base salt

This process has been widely used for resolving three types of compounds:
(a) Acids with active bases, as outlined.
(b) Bases with active acids by similar procedure.
(c) Alcohols by prior conversion to half esters, as in Eq. 7.

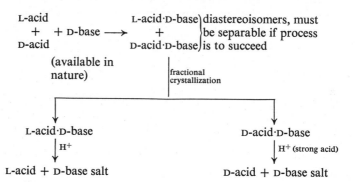

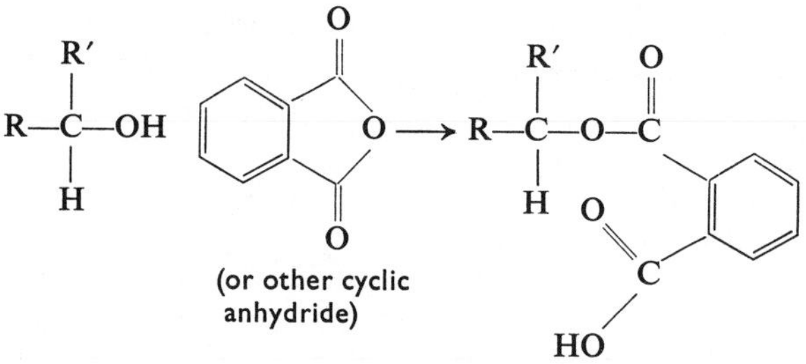

(7)

(or other cyclic anhydride)

Since reaction of an alcohol with an anhydride involves nucleophilic attack of the oxygen in the alcohol on the carbonyl group (cf. Chap. 14), there is no rupture of a bond to the asymmetric carbon in the alcohol, so absence of racemization is assured. The acidic function in the half ester can be used to effect resolution by the scheme outlined for a simple acid; then the optically active alcohol may be secured by saponification of the half ester. Since saponification involves attack of base on the carbonyl carbon, again there is no hazard of racemization.

For resolution of an alcohol in which the asymmetric carbon is not attached directly to hydroxyl, resolution via the half ester is entirely practical; however, separation of the diastereomers usually proves to be more difficult than is normal in such structures as shown in Eq. 7. In general, tertiary alcohols cannot be resolved via the half ester, for anhydrides usually react to dehydrate a tertiary alcohol. Little interest has been associated with resolution of tertiary alcohols, because conversion to the bromide, normally required for use in synthesis, proceeds by an S_N1 mechanism. As previously mentioned, this results in racemization of the asymmetric center.

Syntheses with Optically Active Compounds

Since most natural products of biochemical or medicinal interest are optical isomers, syntheses of optically active compounds have been of truly enormous interest. Acids, bases, and alcohols have been the principal types of compounds available as pure optical isomers by resolution, so conversions of these compounds to other structures have been the synthetic pathways for laboratory synthesis of optically active compounds. This rather advanced topic in organic synthesis can be only introduced at this time, but it should be particularly emphasized that knowledge of reaction mechanism becomes of extreme importance in this kind of work. As has already been described, simple displacement reactions lead to optical inversion, while any reaction in which the asymmetric carbon becomes a carbonium ion leads to racemization. Another important reaction leading to racemization is formation of the Grignard reagent. The mechanism of this process is not known, but it seems probable that the Grignard reagent may be formed as in Eq. 8. In the ion pair intermediate, the carbon has only three groups attached to it, with an electron pair in the fourth

$$
\underset{\underset{H}{|}}{\overset{\overset{R'}{|}}{R-C-Br}} \quad :Mg \longrightarrow \underset{\underset{H}{|}}{\overset{\overset{R'}{|}}{R-C:^-}} \ BrMg^+ \longrightarrow RR'CH-MgBr \tag{8}
$$

orbital. This structure could not hold its asymmetry, so the magnesium could become attached to either side of the carbanion to give the *RS*-mixture.

Whenever a carbon atom, in a synthetic intermediate, becomes attached to only three groups, its asymmetry is nearly always lost; when a fourth group attacks, in most structures it will form equal amounts of the two optical isomers. The carbonium ion is such an intermediate. Another illustration of racemization is an aldol condensation with a carbonyl compound having an asymmetric carbon in the α-position. This process involves conversion to the resonance-stabilized enolate ion, as shown in Eq. 9, so racemization of the

$$
\underset{\underset{CH_3}{|}}{\overset{\overset{H}{|}}{R-C-C}}\overset{O}{\underset{H}{\diagdown}} + B^- \rightleftarrows \underset{\underset{CH_3}{|}}{\overset{\overset{-}{|}}{R-C-C}}\overset{O}{\underset{H}{\diagdown}} \longleftrightarrow \underset{\underset{CH_3}{}}{R-C=C}\overset{O^-}{\underset{H}{\diagup}} \tag{9}
$$
$$
+ \ BH
$$

asymmetric center ensues. Similarly, any process involving enolization of a carbonyl compound will result in racemization of an asymmetric carbon in the α-position.

An illustrative sequence of the sort that might be involved in a synthesis from an optically active alcohol is outlined in Eqs. 10 and 11. With phosphorus

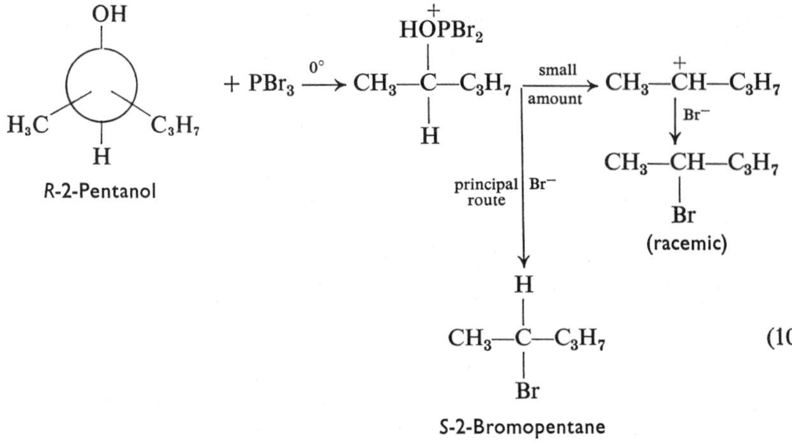

$$\text{(10)}$$

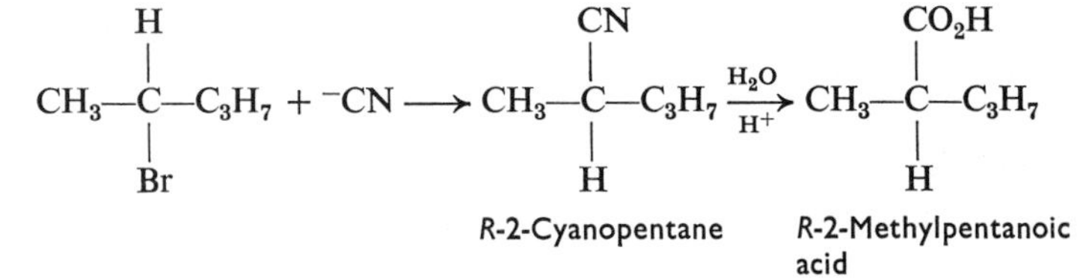

S-2-Bromopentane

$$\text{(11)}$$

R-2-Cyanopentane   R-2-Methylpentanoic acid

tribromide at low temperature, the assisted displacement would be the principal route, but some dissociation to the carbonium ion occurs, so the product would be contaminated with some RS-2-bromopentane. Displacement by cyanide is a clean-cut S_N2 reaction, so no further racemization would occur. Likewise, the hydrolysis in acid would not involve the asymmetric center, so again no further racemization would occur. Formation of enol in acidic medium is so slow that it would have no significant effect. If, however, basic hydrolysis were used, rapid equilibration with the enolate ion from both nitrile and amide would occur during the hydrolysis, so complete racemization of the asymmetric center would be likely. The few per cent of RS-compound in the final product could probably be removed by crystallization of a solid derivative of the 2-methylpentanoic acid. Unless the RS-substance proved to be a racemic compound much less soluble than the R-isomer, this purification would present no difficulty. Occasionally, one has bad luck and the RS-compound is a remarkably insoluble substance. In such cases, the difficulty can usually be circumvented by trying another—perhaps still another—solid derivative of the acid.

Asymmetric induction. In instances where there has been obtained a pure optical isomer, generation in synthesis of another asymmetric center may result in formation of much larger amounts of one diastereoisomer. This phenomenon, known as asymmetric induction, depends largely on steric factors, and it must be emphasized that it can occur only if a pure optical antipode has been obtained in some way and is used as starting material in the synthesis. Hydrogenation of ring compounds is a type of reaction in which prediction of the effect of steric factors has been rather successful. If a pure optical isomer of 2-ethyl-3-methyl-1-cyclopentene could be secured in some way, hydrogenation would be predicted to give as principal product the *cis*-1-ethyl-2-methylcyclopentane (Eq. 12). Adsorption would occur preferentially with the methyl group

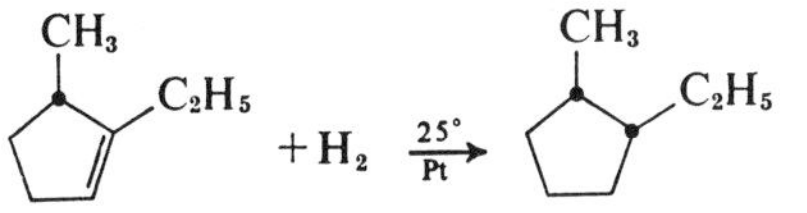

$$\text{(structures)} + H_2 \xrightarrow[\text{Pt}]{25°} \qquad\qquad (12)$$

on the asymmetric carbon directed away from the catalyst. Addition of hydrogen to the double bond on the side adsorbed on the catalyst, as the ethyl group goes away from the catalyst, would give the *cis*-1-ethyl-2-methylcyclopentane as *predominantly one optical isomer*. If the optical antipode of the starting material were used, the product would be the mirror image of that shown in Eq. 12, while racemic starting material would yield *RS-cis*-1-ethyl-2-methylcyclopentane.

EXERCISES

I. Define or clearly illustrate each of the following terms.

(a) Enantiostereoisomers.
(b) Diastereoisomers.
(c) Optical isomers.
(d) Geometric isomers.
(e) Racemic compound.
(f) Racemic mixture.
(g) Racemic substance.
(h) Racemization.
(i) Meso compound.
(j) Asymmetric induction.

(k) Optical resolution.
(l) Optical rotation.
(m) Molecular rotation.
(n) Asymmetric carbon.
(o) Asymmetric molecule.
(p) D-Configuration.
(q) S-Configuration.
(r) Inversion of configuration.
(s) Fischer projection.
(t) Alexander projection.

2. Write projection formulas for all the stereoisomers of each of the following compounds. Any type of formula may be used, so long as it shows the stereoisomerism. Use of the large dot to indicate a hydrogen which is "up" is probably the most convenient representation for the cyclic structures, but Framework Molecular Models are likely to be almost indispensable for understanding the isomerism possible.

(a) $CH_3-CH=CH-\underset{\underset{CH_3}{|}}{CH}-C_2H_5$

(b) $CH_3-\underset{\underset{CH_3}{|}}{C}=CH-\underset{\underset{CH_3}{|}}{CH}-CH_3$

(c) $CH_3-\underset{\underset{OH}{|}}{CH}-\underset{\underset{OH}{|}}{CH}-CH_3$

(d) $CH_3-\underset{\underset{OH}{|}}{CH}-\underset{\underset{O-\overset{\overset{\parallel}{O}}{C}-CH_3}{|}}{CH}-CH_3$

(e)

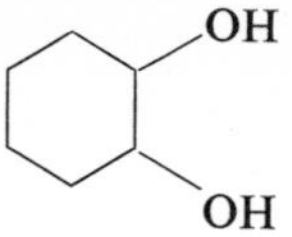

(f)

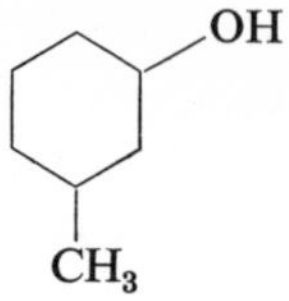

(g)

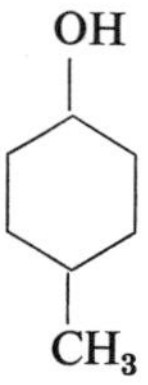

(h) $HO{-}CH_2{-}CH{-}CH{-}CO_2H$ with OH OH

(i)

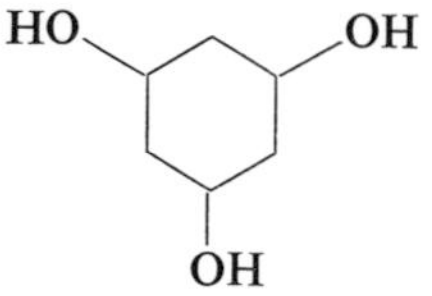

(j)

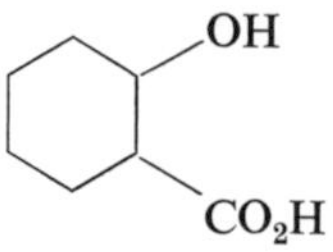

(k)

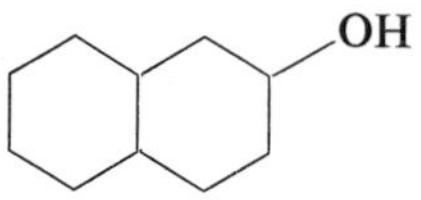

3. For each part of Exercise 2, indicate which formulas are *cis*, *trans* isomers, which are enantiostereoisomers, and which are diastereoisomers.

4. Write one or two sentences explaining the meaning of the following expression:

$$[\alpha]_D^{25} = -25.9° \ (c = 0.12 \text{ g./ml. in acetone})$$

5. Outline by equations and any indicated diagrams how the following conversion may be accomplished.

$$C_2H_5{-}CHO \longrightarrow C_2H_5{-}CH{-}CH_3 \quad (\text{in } R\text{-configuration})$$
$$OH$$

6. Starting with the *R*-2-butanol, prepared as in Exercise 5, outline a practical synthesis of *R*-3-methylpentylamine. Mention any special procedure that may be necessary to secure the product in a state of optical purity.

7. If you should have available both enantiostereoisomers of a solid compound, how could you discover whether the two form a racemic mixture or a racemic compound if an equimolar mixture of the two should prove to melt lower than the melting point of the pure isomers?

8. Write a structural formula (configurational formulas not requested) for each of the following.

(a) A compound which exhibits both geometrical and optical isomerism.
(b) A compound which has two asymmetric carbons but exhibits no optical rotation.
(c) A cyclic compound which exists as *cis* and *trans* forms, neither of which is an asymmetric molecule.
(d) A cyclic compound which exists as *cis* and *trans* forms, both of which are asymmetric molecules.

9. Draw Alexander projections for the *S*-configuration of each of the following structures.

(a)

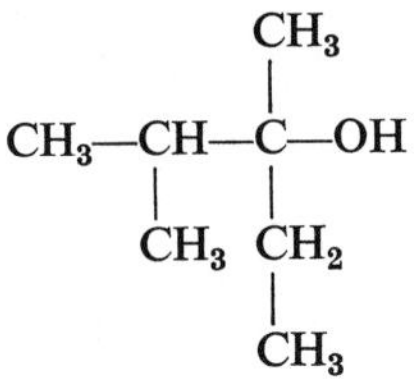

$$CH_3—\underset{\underset{CH_3}{|}}{CH}—\underset{\underset{\underset{\underset{CH_3}{|}}{CH_2}}{|}}{\overset{\overset{CH_3}{|}}{C}}—OH$$

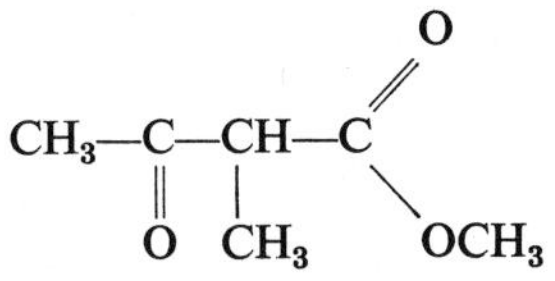

(b)

$$CH_3—\underset{\underset{O}{||}}{C}—\underset{\underset{CH_3}{|}}{CH}—\overset{\overset{O}{\diagup}}{C}\diagdown_{OCH_3}$$

(c)

$$\overset{\overset{H\diagdown \quad \diagup O}{C}}{\underset{\underset{CH_2—OH}{|}}{\underset{\underset{CH—OH}{|}}{CH—OH}}}$$

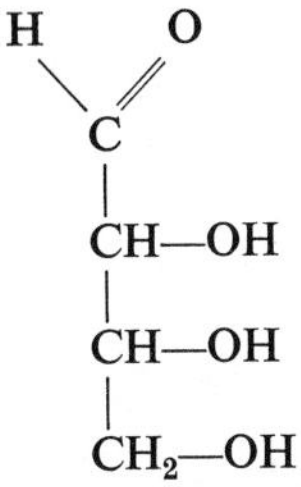

(show *S*-configuration for both asymmetric carbons)

(d)

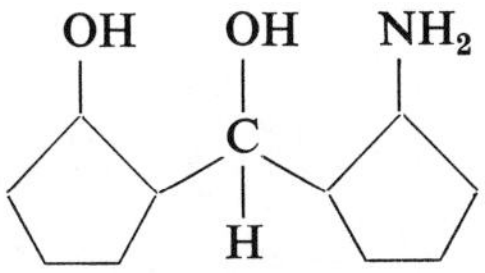

$$\overset{\overset{OH \qquad OH \quad NH_2}{|}}{\underset{\underset{H}{|}}{C}}$$

(show configuration of center asymmetric carbon only)

10. Assign the *R*- or *S*-configuration to the starting material drawn in Eq. 12. Assign configurations to both asymmetric carbons in the product of this reaction.

Monosaccharides, the Basic Structural Unit in Carbohydrates

Carbohydrates are a very important class of compounds, both industrially and biologically. They constitute one of the three major classes of foodstuffs, and the people of most countries depend to a large extent on carbohydrates to furnish the fuel to run their biological systems. The carbohydrates include such well-known substances as sugars, starch, and cellulose. The name originated long ago before anything was known of structural chemistry, and it originated from the observation that the empirical formulas for carbohydrates may be regarded as a combination of carbon and water. For example, the sugar glucose is $C_6H_{12}O_6$ or $C_6(H_2O)_6$. Actually, it turns out that the true structure of carbohydrates has nothing at all in common with this concept. The disaccharides and polysaccharides are built up of two or more units of the basic structural unit known as a monosaccharide. Carbohydrates of sufficiently low molecular weight to be soluble in water (principally mono- and disaccharides) are usually called sugars. The present chapter will be devoted to a study of the monosaccharides, the least complex of the sugars.

The Structure of Glucose

Glucose, which is one of the more common monosaccharides, has the empirical formula $C_6H_{12}O_6$. It is sometimes called grape sugar or dextrose.

The structure of glucose may be deduced from the following reactions which it has been found to give.

(a) Vigorous reduction with a powerful agent such as phosphorus and hydrogen iodide gives an isolable amount of 2-iodo-*n*-hexane; therefore the carbon chain is unbranched.

(b) It reacts with carbonyl reagents such as hydroxylamine, also it is oxidized by mild agents to give an acid with the same number of carbons. It follows that an aldehyde group is present.

(c) Acetylation with acetic anhydride gives a pentaacetate; therefore five hydroxyl groups are present.[1]

If it be remembered that compounds with more than one hydroxyl group on a carbon are unstable, it follows that glucose has one hydroxyl on each carbon except the carbon in the aldehyde group. The structural formula of glucose must therefore be

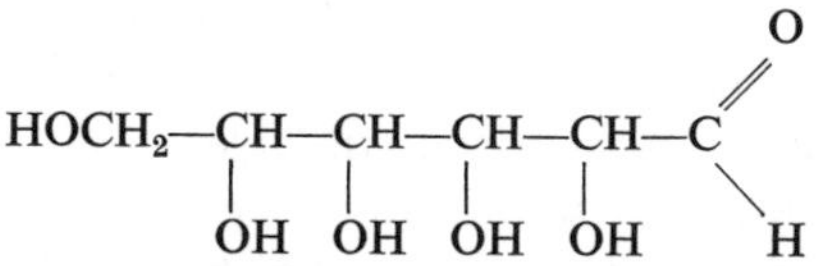

$$\text{HOCH}_2\text{—CH—CH—CH—CH—C}\diagup^{\textstyle O}_{\diagdown \text{H}}$$
$$\qquad\ \ \ \ |\ \ \ \ \ |\ \ \ \ \ |\ \ \ \ \ |$$
$$\qquad\ \ \ \text{OH\ \ OH\ \ OH\ \ OH}$$

Although this structural formula may be deduced from the relatively small amount of information just cited, there remains the problem of determining the constitution (configuration of the asymmetric carbons), for the glucose formula contains no less than *four* asymmetric carbons. It follows that the above structural formula may exist in *sixteen* stereoisomeric forms. It is also the case that several other naturally occurring sugars have the same structural formula as glucose; the only difference is in configuration. Thus configuration becomes very important in the study of carbohydrates.

Configurational Formulas

Determination of the configurational formulas of the sugars was a very laborious task, requiring thousands of man-hours of time. The ultimate solution of this puzzle is a monument to the ingenuity of man. Much of this work was directed by Emil Fischer near the beginning of the twentieth century, and he was later awarded the Nobel prize in chemistry for these investigations. The configurations of the sugars were deduced by reactions interrelating them with each other and with molecules containing fewer asymmetric carbon atoms. Finally, absolute configurations were established by determining the relationships to the glyceraldehydes. The reasoning is not too involved for us to consider at the present time, but is rather time-consuming, so the established

---

[1] The conclusion based on the results of acetylation was correct, although the reaction is more involved than was realized at that time. As will be discussed subsequently in this chapter, one hydroxyl which is acetylated is a hemi-acetal hydroxyl.

configuration will be presented. It is customary to write configurational formulas for sugars in the manner illustrated for glucose, with the aldehyde group

$$
\begin{array}{ccc}
& \text{CHO} && \text{CHO} \\
& | \\
\text{H}-&\text{C}-\text{OH} && \text{H}-\!\!\!-\text{OH} \\
& | \\
\text{HO}-&\text{C}-\text{H} && \text{HO}-\!\!\!-\text{H} \\
& | & \text{or} \\
\text{H}-&\text{C}-\text{OH} && \text{H}-\!\!\!-\text{OH} \\
& | \\
\text{H}-&\text{C}-\text{OH} && \text{H}-\!\!\!-\text{OH} \\
& | \\
& \text{CH}_2\text{OH} && \text{CH}_2\text{OH}
\end{array}
$$

Glucose

up. This is a Fischer projection formula of the type discussed in Chapter 22 for more simple compounds. If we first consider the lower asymmetric carbon (carbon-5 when numbering is started with the aldehyde group), according to the principles previously discussed for writing projection formulas, —CH$_2$OH is back and carbon-4 is up, while hydrogen and hydroxyl are forward, one on each side. To consider the whole molecule, all the carbons are placed in a plane, with the hydrogens and hydroxyls all projecting toward the viewer. For the specific configuration possessed by glucose, the hydrogens and hydroxyls fall to the right and left of this plane as shown in the projection. A model of this molecule should be constructed from a model kit and compared with the projection formula. When this is done, it will be noted that when all the carbons are oriented so that hydrogens and hydroxyls are forward, the carbons turn into a ring on account of the 109° valence angle of carbon. Thus the projection formula written for sugars not only projects the hydroxyls and hydrogens onto a plane surface but also visualizes the ring of carbons as "unrolled." These relationships should be fixed well in mind by comparing projection formulas with the actual models.

In the assignment of relative configurations to sugars, they are classified according to the relative configuration of carbon-5 (the lower asymmetric carbon in the projection formula); therefore glucose, which has the lower asymmetric carbon of the Dextro configuration as shown in the projection formula, is termed D-glucose. Since the rotation of the molecule is positive, the full name is D-(+)-glucose, but glucose is commonly used, since the mirror image, L-(−)-glucose, is not a naturally occurring sugar. Diastereoisomers of glucose have other names.

There is considerable merit to application of the Sequence Rule in defining configurations in the sugar series. In order to classify D-glucose in the R- or S-series, we may consider the Alexander projection (I) of the bottom asymmetric carbon atom. Since carbon-6 has one oxygen and two hydrogens attached to it, while carbon-4 carries an oxygen and carbon, the top group becomes b. Rotation to the viewing position gives the projection shown is I-s, where the

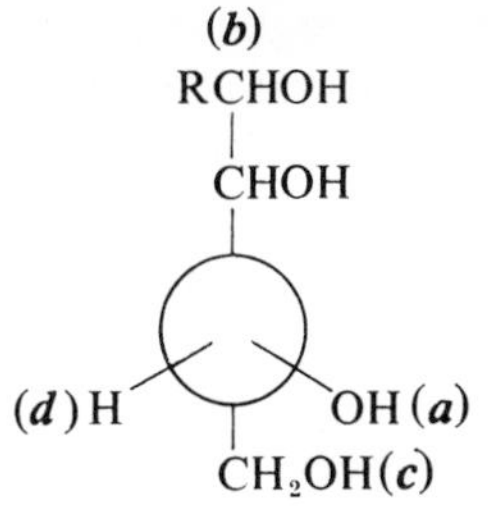

(b)
RCHOH
|
CHOH

(d)H OH (a)

CH₂OH(c)

I

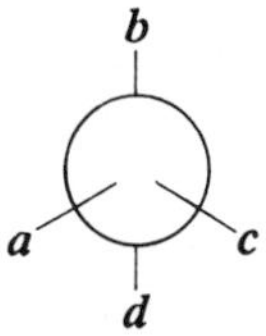

b

a c

d

I-s

R- configuration is revealed by the clockwise sequence. Thus, D-glucose may also be designated as R-glucose.

Conformational Formulas in Cyclic Forms of Monosaccharides

The formula giving the structure and constitution of glucose contains a great deal of information about this molecule; however, one important feature is still lacking. This additional structural feature was revealed relatively early in the work on the carbohydrates by the reaction products of glucose and methanol in the presence of an acid catalyst. These are the conditions for acetal formation from an aldehyde, a reaction previously discussed (Eqs. 15-31, 15-32, and 15-33). For comparison purposes, the normal net reaction of an aldehyde to form an acetal is repeated in Eq. 1 (acid catalysis is not essential but accelerates

$$
R-C\overset{O}{\underset{H}{\diagup}} + CH_3OH \underset{H^+}{\rightleftharpoons} R-CH\overset{OH}{\underset{OCH_3}{\diagup}} \underset{CH_3OH,\ H^+}{\rightleftharpoons} R-CH\overset{OCH_3}{\underset{OCH_3}{\diagup}} + HOH \quad (1)
$$

the reaction). It may be noted that the aldehyde reacts with two molecules of alcohol to yield the acetal. With excess alcohol, the equilibria are shifted well forward to yield the final product.

The reaction of glucose with methanol gave results, outlined in Eq. 2, which differ in two significant respects from the usual acetal formation. First,

$$
\underset{\text{Glucose}}{C_6H_{12}O_6} + \underset{\text{(excess)}}{CH_3OH} \overset{H^+}{\longrightarrow} \underset{\text{(two isomers)}}{C_7H_{14}O_6} + HOH \quad (2)
$$

only *one* mole of alcohol reacted per mole of glucose, even with a large excess of alcohol. Secondly, *two* isomeric products were obtained. These results strongly suggest that glucose exists in solution, at least in part, as a hemi-acetal with one of its own hydroxyls. This indication has been fully substantiated by more than half a century of investigation of the carbohydrate structures.

If glucose is in equilibrium with a cyclic hemi-acetal form, there remains the problem of learning which hydroxyl is involved. Since five- and six-membered rings are the most stable sizes, it may be presumed that one of these rings is formed, but it was not until the decade beginning in 1920 that the British chemist, W. N. Haworth, was able to demonstrate conclusively[2] that the oxygen on carbon-5 is the one involved in hemi-acetal formation in monosaccharides. The method used by Haworth is discussed later in this chapter. This gives a six-membered ring and at the same time results in carbon-1 becoming asymmetric (attached to four different groups). There would actually be formed, then, two stereoisomeric hemi-acetals, differing in the configuration of carbon-1, and this accounts for the two acetals formed by the process shown in Eq. 1. The equilibrium between the aldehyde form of glucose and the two hemi-acetal forms is illustrated in Eq. 3, in which conformational formulas for the two hemi-acetals are used. As shown in this equation, the form of glucose with the higher optical rotation has been designated the α-isomer. The use of conformational formulas makes it possible to remember the constitutions of the sugars

$$
\begin{array}{ccccc}
\text{α-R-Glucose} & \rightleftharpoons & \begin{array}{c} \text{CHO} \\ \text{H—OH} \\ \text{HO—H} \\ \text{H—OH} \\ \text{H—OH} \\ \text{CH}_2\text{OH} \end{array} & \rightleftharpoons & \text{β-R-Glucose}
\end{array} \tag{3}
$$

α-R-Glucose
$[\alpha]_D = +109.6°$

β-R-Glucose
$[\alpha]_D = +20.5°$

with very little effort, so certain features of these formulas should be noted with care. After discussion of these features, interesting aspects of the glucose equilibrium will be described.

Examination of a molecular model (cf. Fig. 1) makes it especially clear that in the conformational formula for β-*R*-glucose *every substituent occupies an equatorial position*.[3] This is all that need be remembered in order to write a correct formulation for glucose, showing the correct configuration for each

---

[2] Since the influential Emil Fischer had declared (on the basis of very meager evidence) that hemi-acetal linkage was at carbon-4, Haworth's findings were accepted with some reluctance. The results of the brilliant series of researches by Haworth and his students were eventually summarized by him in a book, *The Constitution of Sugars*, Arnold and Co., London, 1929.

[3] If the β-*R*-glucose ring be flipped to the other chair conformation, then every substituent will occupy an axial position. In view of the information presented in Chapter 7 concerning the higher energy of the axial positions, especially in the case of 1,3-diaxial substitution, the glucose molecule will be almost entirely in the chair conformation shown. Thus, this conformation should always be written. As a memory aid in learning the constitutions of other carbohydrates, it is quite desirable to always write the same conformation for the ring, with the oxygen in the same position. In writing structures for polysaccharides, as discussed in Chapter 24, it becomes necessary to write the rings in different positions, but even this becomes much more simple if one has become accustomed to viewing the rings in a certain position. An important feature of the conformational formulas is that the same groups remain equatorial or axial, no matter what position may be adopted for the ring. These positions are changed only if the ring is flipped to the other conformation.

Fig. I. Framework Molecular Model of β-R-glucose. It is of particular importance to note that each equatorial substituent is *trans* to those on each side of it. For the position shown for the molecule, the I- and 3-hydroxyls as well as the terminal hydroxymethylene group are above the ring carbons to which they are joined, while the 2- and 4-hydroxyls are below the ring carbons.

asymmetric carbon. The α-*R*-glucose, which has the opposite configuration at carbon-1, has the hemi-acetal hydroxyl in the axial position. By use of the information contained in the configurational formula for glucose, it is also possible to write a correct Fischer projection for the open-chain form of glucose, by remembering one point. Each hydroxyl that is *down* in the conformational formula (as written in Eq. 3) is on the *right* in the Fischer projection (as a memory aid, dextro and down begin with the same letter). If any uncertainty arises as to whether an equatorial hydroxyl is above or below the ring in the conformational formula, this uncertainty can be resolved immediately by noting the direction of the axial position on the same carbon; the equatorial position is on the opposite side from the axial position at any carbon. Location of the hydroxyl on carbon-5 in the open-chain formula does not follow from the above considerations, since this oxygen is turned into the ring in the cyclic structures. This is no problem to remember, however, since the family to which the glucose belongs is determined by the configuration of this carbon. The *R*- or D-glucose has this hydroxyl on the right in the Fischer projection. Similarly, all D-sugars have this hydroxyl on the right, consequently have the —CH_2OH group in the equatorial position in the cyclic structure.

Equilibration in Glucose Solutions

It has been observed in numerous instances that cyclic structures with five- or six-atom rings are of lower energy than similar open-chain structures.

Among other examples already discussed are the lactones (Chap. 16). Thus, it would be expected that the equilibria in Eq. 3 would be in favor of the hemiacetal forms of the sugars. This proves to be the case; in water solution, the aldehyde form is estimated to be present to the extent of only about 0.024%, truly a trace amount. Furthermore, substituents in the axial position are subject to more steric interference than those in the equatorial position (cf. Chap. 7). This factor should cause the β-glucose to be present in the equilibrium mixture in larger amount, and this also proves to be the case. The equilibrium in water at room temperature is about 37% α-R-glucose and 63% β-R-glucose.

Calculation of the relative abundance in solution of the α- and β-forms of glucose may be based on the optical rotation of the equilibrium mixture, for it has been possible to isolate the two pure cyclic forms in the crystalline condition. Painstaking experimentation has discovered conditions of solvent and temperature under which one form is significantly less soluble. As this form separates by crystallization, equilibrium is re-established and more of the less soluble form crystallizes. By solution of a pure isomer, and immediate determination of the rotation, the values for the two forms which are included in Eq. 3 have been measured. As the solution stands, the rotation changes until there is reached, usually after several hours, the equilibrium value of about 52.7° for the specific rotation. Such a change in optical rotation as a solution stands is known as **mutarotation.** This phenomenon is regarded as a clear indication of some type of change in structure.

Since equilibration of the three forms of glucose (cf. Eq. 3) occurs in solution, removal of one form by a chemical reaction (or physical means such as crystallization; cf. above) can eventually result in all the sugar reacting in that one form. Subsequently we will discuss reactions in which all the sugar reacts as an aldehyde, in spite of the small concentration of that form. In acetal formation, shown by empirical formulas in Eq. 2, the acid catalysis accelerates the rate of equilibration as well as acetal formation, so the two acetals are formed in equilibrium concentration dependent on their relative energy contents. Acetals of sugars are known as **glycosides,** while those of glucose are known as **glucosides.** In Eq. 4 the conformational formulas are given for the products of acetal formation with glucose.

$$R\text{-Glucose} + CH_3OH \xrightarrow{H^+} \qquad \text{and} \qquad (4)$$

(equilibrium in Eq. 3)

Methyl α-R-glucoside   Methyl β-R-glucoside

Planar Ring Projections of Sugar Formulas

The representation of sugars in conformational formulas has been practiced very little prior to about 1960, so most of the literature prior to that time (and some of it since then) utilizes projections of planar rings. The type of projection nearly always used is shown in formulas II and III. The hydroxyls that are on the right in the Fischer projection are depicted as down in the planar projection when the hemi-acetal carbon is on the right and the ring oxygen is behind. In addition, the 1-hydroxyl is down in the α-D-glucose. This type of

representation is entirely effective for showing the configuration at each atom; however, each of these configurations must be remembered separately, either in the Fischer projection or the planar ring projection. Furthermore, if the ring is rotated about an axis across the ring—for example, if the ring in formula III is rotated 180° on a transverse axis—every group that was up becomes down and vice versa. When such rotations become necessary in order to put together the formulas of polysaccharides (next chapter), it becomes quite difficult to keep all the groups in the proper position. This is in considerable contrast to the situation in the conformational formulas where one can remember the *R*-glucose configuration with essentially no effort, since all substituents are equatorial. Furthermore, the substituents remain equatorial no matter in what position the ring may be placed.

Classification of Sugars

Sugars containing the carbonyl group at the end of the chain, as in glucose, are termed **aldehydo** sugars, while those containing the carbonyl within the chain are termed **keto** sugars. Many of the monosaccharides contain six carbons, as does glucose, and are called **hexoses.** Other natural sugars contain five carbons, and are called **pentoses.** Either natural or synthetic sugars with some other number of carbons are named similarly, i.e., **heptoses, octoses,** etc. Although the "total synthesis" of a sugar, building up one asymmetric atom at a time, is so laborious that it has been attempted only in connection with determination of configurations, natural sugars have been built up to higher molecular weights by a process discussed later in this chapter.

Combinations of the above names are used. For example, glucose is an **aldohexose.**

Naturally Occurring Monosaccharides

Although many dozens of monosaccharides have been found in nature, only a few occur widely. For present purposes, it is sufficient to learn the names and configurational formulas of one aldopentose, two aldohexoses (besides glucose), and one ketohexose. The formulas for these sugars are given

in cyclic form, as the β-isomer. All these sugars, which occur relatively abundantly in nature, have the *R*- or D-configuration for the lower asymmetric

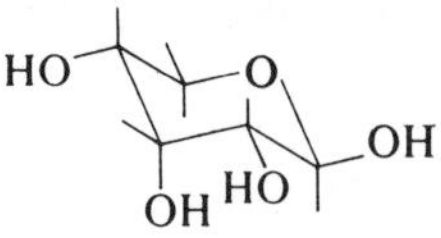

IV	V	VI
β-R-Ribose	β-R-Mannose	β-R-Galactose

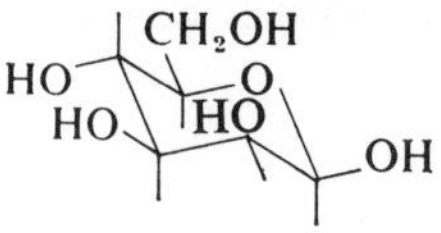

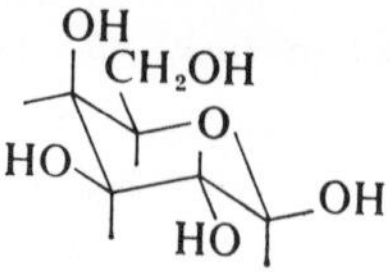

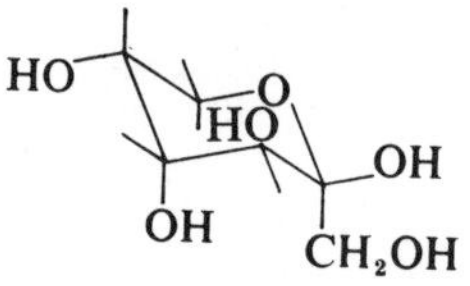

VII 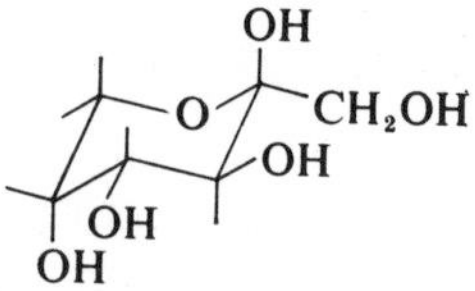   VII′

β-R-(−)-Fructose

carbon, hence are classified as belonging to that series. All are dextrorotatory,
except for fructose, hence the inclusion of the direction of rotation in the name
for fructose. On account of its unusual levo rotation, fructose is sometimes
called levulose.

In all the monosaccharides whose formulas are shown, Haworth demonstrated that the hemi-acetal (or hemi-ketal for fructose) is formed by reaction
with the hydroxyl delta to the carbonyl. Such hemi-acetals, with a ring of six
atoms, are said to be **pyranose** forms.[4] Although hemi-acetals with five-atom
rings are uncommon in the monosaccharides (cf. discussion of fructose below),
these structures are encountered frequently in the disaccharides (next chapter).
They are termed **furanose** forms of the sugars.

It is of considerable interest that glucose, which has the maximum number
of substituents in the lower-energy equatorial positions, is by far the most
abundant of the naturally-occurring sugars. It seems reasonable to expect that
the natural evolutionary processes might result in the most stable of the sugar
configurations becoming the most abundant.

If the differences between each of these formulas and glucose are noted,
it proves rather easy to remember the structures. The pentose, **ribose** (IV),
presents no problem since all three of its fixed hydroxyls are down (the 1-hydroxyl
is up in the β-isomer). This places the hydroxyl at carbon-3 in the axial position.
There is no substituent on the ring at carbon-5 because only five carbons are
present (the end group is —CH_2O—).

---

[4] The terms "pyranose" and "furanose" arise from attachment of carbohydrate endings
to the names of the cyclic compounds, pyran and furan:

Pyran 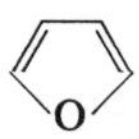   Furan

Mannose (V) differs from glucose only at carbon-2, where the hydroxyl is axial in mannose. Sugars which differ only in the configuration of the carbon adjacent to the aldehyde group (hemi-acetal group in the cyclic form) are known as **epimers;** therefore, mannose and glucose are epimers. Any process which changes one epimer to the other, or equilibrates the two, is known as **epimerization.** As discussed in the preceding chapter, enolization is a process which results in epimerization.

Galactose (VI) also differs from glucose at only one asymmetric center, carbon-4; the hydroxyl in this position is axial. Thus, the structure of each of the aldohexoses follows from remembering one item.

Fructose (VII) does not differ from glucose in the configuration of its asymmetric carbon atoms; however, the carbonyl is at carbon-2, and this gives the hemi-acetal form a rather different set of characteristics. Carbon-6 is in the ring, so —CH_2— occurs at the position where —CH_2OH is a substituent in the aldohexoses, and the —CH_2OH substituent occurs at the hemi-ketal carbon. This results in a shift of the hydroxyl substituents by one ring-atom so that two of the fixed hydroxyls become axial. Furthermore, if hydroxyl at the hemi-ketal in the β-isomer is placed in the equatorial position, as is the case in the aldohexoses, the bulky —CH_2OH group becomes axial. For the reasons just detailed, the more stable conformation for fructose results when the ring is flipped, as in VII'. In this latter conformation, only two hydroxyls are axial. Although it is probably most appropriate to write β-R-fructose in the lower energy conformation (VII'), the other conformation (VII), in which the other common sugars are more stable, is the most convenient form in which to remember the proper configuration. Actually, *a significant percentage of the fructose molecules in solution exist in the furanose form.* In absence of perturbing factors, the hemi-acetal with a six-atom ring is of substantially lower energy than that with a five-atom ring; however, the interference between axial substituents in the pyranose form of fructose (even in conformation VII') is sufficient to negate the normal advantage of the six-atom ring. Thus, both furanose forms and pyranose forms of fructose are in equilibrium in solution.

In order to rapidly assess the sugar configuration that is predicted to be most stable, the use of an **"instability number"** has been introduced. These numbers are assigned on the basis of three structural features, of which the two that occur most often are defined as follows: for each axial substituent (other than hydrogen) there is assigned an instability number of 1; for each axial —CH_2OH which is on the same side as another axial substituent, there is assigned an instability number of 1.5 instead of 1. Thus, for the two conformations of β-R-fructose, VII has an instability number of 3.5, while VII' has 2. In instances where conformational equilibria have been measured, by use of nuclear magnetic resonance to locate the positions of the hydrogens, the relative abundances of the conformations have been in approximate agreement with the estimates from the semi-quantitative instability numbers.

In the case of α-R-fructose, the two conformations are represented by VIII and VIII'. In the case of VIII the instability number is 3, whereas the value for VIII' is 2. Thus, again the flipped conformation, VIII', is evaluated as the

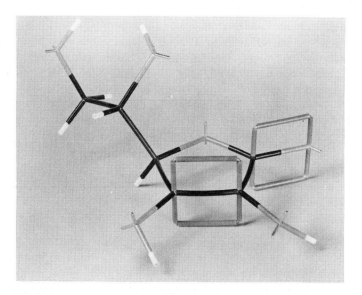

VIII   VIII′

more stable, although by a smaller margin than for the β-isomer. The ratio between these two conformations should be approximately 2:1. It may be recalled that in the case of the α- and β-isomers of R-glucose, where the difference in instability number of the more stable conformations is unity, the two isomers in solution were in the ratio 63:37. In the glucose isomers, the flipped conformations would have such high instability numbers (4.5 and 5.5) that they would contribute little in the equilibria.

Ascorbic acid. Although the most abundant naturally occurring derivatives of monosaccharides are the higher molecular weight disaccharides and polysaccharides, there are other important derivatives of monosaccharides found in nature. These include the antibiotic, streptomycin, and the vitamin,

Fig. 2. Framework Molecular Model of the S-ascorbic acid molecule. Cross sections in the π-orbitals of the two double bonds (alkene and carbonyl) are shown, to illustrate the fact that the ring is at right angles to the planes representing the largest cross sections of the π-orbitals. With the ring oxygen behind and the carbonyl group to the right (customary orientation for viewing a monosaccharide ring), the side chain is turned up so that carbon-5, of S-configuration, is above the ring. A Fischer projection in this position shows the hydroxyl to the right. It is of interest to verify the S-configuration for carbon-5 by assigning groups a, b, c, and d.

riboflavin (vitamin B_2). Another vitamin, ascorbic acid (vitamin C), is a derivative of an *S*-sugar. This structure, which is shown in Fig. 2, is an unsaturated γ-lactone, so the hydroxyl groups at carbon-2 and carbon-3 are enolic. The five-atom ring is a flat structure with the two enolic hydroxyls and the carbonyl oxygen in the same plane as the ring. The asymmetric carbon outside the ring is carbon-5 and has the *S*-configuration. The asymmetric carbon in the ring has the *R*-configuration. The enol form must be the dominant structure in ascorbic acid, in view of the acidity of the molecule; however, there is probably some equilibration in solution with the hydroxy ketone forms shown in Eq. 5.

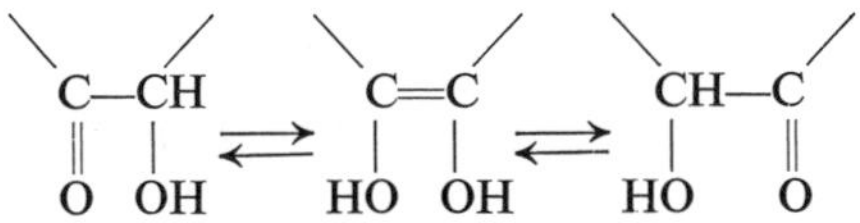

$$
\begin{array}{ccccc}
\diagdown\,\diagup & & \diagdown\,\diagup & & \diagdown\,\diagup \\
\mathrm{C-CH} & \rightleftarrows & \mathrm{C=C} & \rightleftarrows & \mathrm{CH-C} \\
\|\ \ | & & |\ \ | & & |\ \ \| \\
\mathrm{O\ \ OH} & & \mathrm{HO\ \ OH} & & \mathrm{HO\ \ O}
\end{array}
\tag{5}
$$

The *S*-ascorbic acid is manufactured from *R*-glucose by an ingenious series of reactions in which group transformations are accomplished so as to make carbon-2 in glucose the carbon-5 in ascorbic acid. This maneuver from the *R*- to *S*-series is illustrated in Eq. 6, where the Fischer projection of

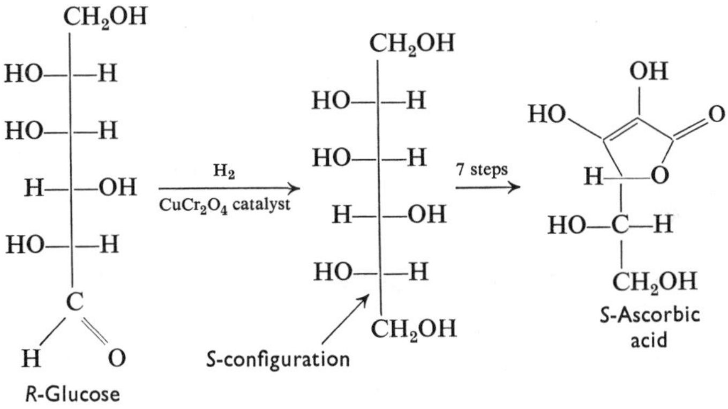

$$\tag{6}$$

R-Glucose → S-configuration → S-Ascorbic acid (Eq. 6)

glucose is "turned over" in order to illustrate the nature of the conversions. It is essential that the asymmetric carbons in ascorbic acid be of the correct configuration; otherwise, the biological activity is lost.

Chemical Reactions of Monosaccharides

It should be emphasized at the outset that treatment of sugars with alkali gives complicated reactions leading to large numbers of products. Among other reactions involved are a reverse of the aldol condensation and epimerization via the enol. In reactions where sugars are expected to give a good yield of a single product, alkali must be avoided. Especially in hydrolyses, acid catalysis should be used; however, vigorous treatment with acid may also lead to deep-seated reactions (Eqs. 17 and 18).

As has been discussed at some length in connection with equilibrium between the different forms of a sugar, if one form reacts faster than the others, derivatives of that form will be obtained. In addition, if one direction of reaction is irreversible and others are reversible a single product may result. This latter factor is responsible for the substantial number of transformations of sugars that result from reaction of the trace amount of aldehyde form present in the equilibrium mixture. In the reactions discussed below in which the open-chain form of the sugar is responsible for the reaction products, the starting sugar is written in this form.

Ester formation. Esters of sugars may be prepared by the methods used for the other esters (cf. Chap. 14), and good yields are obtained if acylation is carried out with either an anhydride or an acid chloride. The hemi-acetal forms are the species that react more rapidly, and a mixture of the alpha and beta forms of the acyl derivatives is usually obtained unless a pure alpha or beta sugar is used under special conditions of esterification. If, however, the equilibrium mixture of sugars is acetylated with acetic anhydride in presence of sodium acetate as catalyst, a nearly pure sample of the beta derivative is obtained, as shown for glucose in Eq. 7. The nearly exclusive formation of the beta

$$R\text{—Glucose} + 5Ac_2O \xrightarrow{\text{NaOAc}} \quad + 5HOAc \quad (7)$$

(equilibrium mixture as in Eq. 3)

Pentaacetyl-β-R-glucose

derivative is attributable to the fact that when the hemi-acetal hydroxyl is in the less hindered equatorial position it reacts considerably more rapidly than does the axial hydroxyl. Since acetic anhydride reacts rapidly with any water that might be present in the reagents, there is also no acid-catalyzed equilibration between the alpha and beta forms of the ester.

Ethers of sugars. If the methyl glycoside (acetal) of a sugar is formed (Eq. 4), hydrolysis of this derivative is not catalyzed by base, as usual for acetals (cf. Chap. 15). This allows ether formation by conversion of hydroxyl to the anion with base, and utilization of this nucleophile in a displacement reaction (cf. Eqs. 6-3 and 14-30 for ether syntheses). Conversion of methyl β-R-glucoside

$$+ 4(CH_3)_2SO_4 + 4NaOH \longrightarrow \quad (8)$$

$$+ 4NaOSO_2OCH_3 + 4HOH$$

to the tetramethyl ether[5] is shown in Eq. 8. Ethers of this sort were very important in the work of Haworth and co-workers in determining ring size in the cyclic structures for sugars. This utility depends on the fact that the acetal methoxyl is readily hydrolyzed with acid catalysis, as usual for acetals, but the other ether groups are not easily hydrolyzed by acid, as normal for simple ethers (cf. Chap. 6). Thus, acid hydrolysis of the methyl tetramethylglucoside gives the tetramethylglucose, which equilibrates with a small amount of the aldehyde form of the sugar (Eq. 9). Vigorous oxidation of the tetramethyl

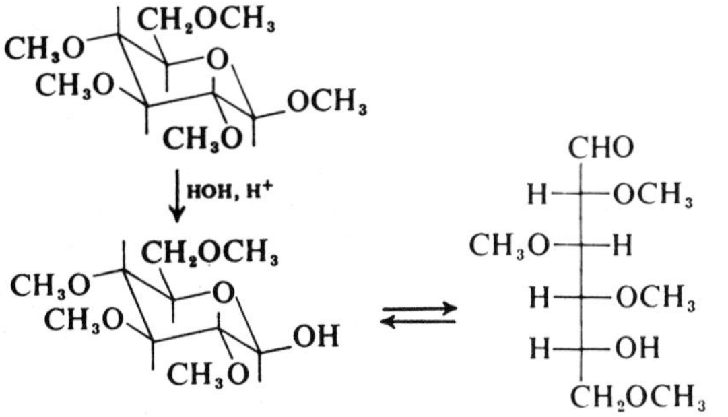

$$
\begin{array}{c}
\text{(structure: pyranose ring with } CH_2OCH_3, CH_3O, CH_3O, OCH_3, CH_3O) \\
\downarrow \text{HOH, H}^+ \\
\text{(structure: pyranose ring with } CH_2OCH_3, CH_3O, CH_3O, OH, CH_3O)
\end{array}
\rightleftharpoons
\begin{array}{l}
\text{CHO} \\
\text{H---OCH}_3 \\
\text{CH}_3\text{O---H} \\
\text{H---OCH}_3 \\
\text{H---OH} \\
\text{CH}_2\text{OCH}_3
\end{array}
\qquad (9)
$$

sugar, for example with nitric acid, will first oxidize the secondary alcohol to a ketone and the aldehyde to an acid. The oxidation will continue further, however, and cleave the ketone on either side of carbonyl to give two acids as shown in Eq. 10. Oxidative cleavage of ketones has been discussed in Chapter

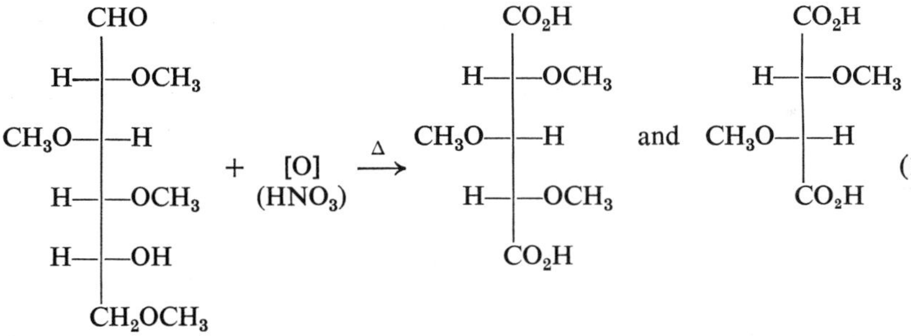

$$
\begin{array}{l}
\text{CHO} \\
\text{H---OCH}_3 \\
\text{CH}_3\text{O---H} \\
\text{H---OCH}_3 \\
\text{H---OH} \\
\text{CH}_2\text{OCH}_3
\end{array}
\; + \; \begin{array}{c} [O] \\ (\text{HNO}_3) \end{array} \xrightarrow{\Delta}
\begin{array}{l}
\text{CO}_2\text{H} \\
\text{H---OCH}_3 \\
\text{CH}_3\text{O---H} \\
\text{H---OCH}_3 \\
\text{CO}_2\text{H}
\end{array}
\; \text{and} \;
\begin{array}{l}
\text{CO}_2\text{H} \\
\text{H---OCH}_3 \\
\text{CH}_3\text{O---H} \\
\text{CO}_2\text{H}
\end{array}
\qquad (10)
$$

---

[5] Formation of ethers of sugars in this way is a rather slow process, for the concentration of anion of an alcohol in equilibrium with sodium hydroxide is relatively small, and hydroxide is highly competitive in the displacement reaction. Sodium is commonly used to secure the anion of alcohols for use in ether synthesis, but this route is not practical for use with carbohydrates on account of their insolubility in solvents not containing acidic hydrogens that also react with sodium. In recent years, the remarkable solvent properties of dimethyl sulfoxide, $CH_3\text{---}S\text{---}CH_3$, have greatly simplified the formation of ethers of sugars. Not only will this
$\downarrow$
O
solvent dissolve such compounds as sugars and inorganic reagents, it also greatly accelerates rate of reaction. In the best procedure using dimethyl sulfoxide as solvent, methyl iodide is used as alkylating agent and silver oxide is used as base. Pull of the silver ion on halogen facilitates the displacement by alkoxide.

15 (cf. Eqs. 15-17 and 15-18). Since the acids resulting from the oxidation shown in Eq. 10 have respectively four and five carbons in the chain, it follows that the hydroxyl group was on carbon-5, and the carbon-5 was involved in hemi-acetal formation.

Oxidation of sugars. (1) DETECTION OF THE CARBONYL GROUP. The carbonyl group in sugars is detectable by usual methods described in Chapter 15. Usually, this involves the use of either Fehling's solution (Eq. 15-8) or Tollens' reagent (Eq. 15-9). Neither of these methods distinguishes between aldo and keto sugars, for α-hydroxy ketones are readily attacked by either reagent (cf. Eq. 15-10). Furthermore, the product of the reaction is not a single substance, as is the case with simple aldehydes, on account of the extensive reaction occurring with alkali, which is present in these test solutions. The principal use of the test is for detection of "reducing sugars" in solution[6] (the oxidizing agent is reduced). If the oxidation test is negative on a sugar, this is another useful application, for this shows absence of a carbonyl group, a situation encountered in certain disaccharides (cf. next chapter).

(2) OXIDATION TO MONO-ACIDS. Mild oxidizing agents, such as bromine in a buffered aqueous solution, give a clean-cut oxidation of the sugar hemi-acetal to the lactone (Eq. 11). The six-atom lactone ring, in contrast with the hemi-acetal ring, is less stable than the five-atom lactone ring; so equilibration

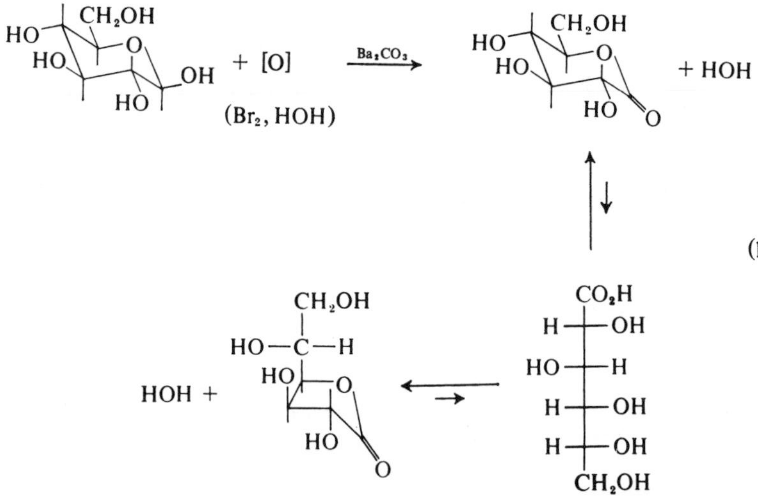

(11)

The test with Fehling's solution is that commonly used to detect sugar in the urine of diabetics, who are lacking in the enzyme necessary for oxidation of sugars in the metabolic process. Under a standardized set of conditions, the weight of cuprous oxide precipitated may be used as a quantitative determination of reducing sugars in solution. The sugar being determined must be known, however, for different sugars reduce different amounts of cupric ion under the same conditions. This is a striking demonstration of the different properties of diastereoisomers.

of the δ-lactone with the hydroxy acid results in conversion to the more stable γ-lactone. The generic name for a sugar mono-acid is **glyconic acid,** while the specific acid from glucose is known as **gluconic acid.** Gluconic acid lactone is written to indicate that the five-atom ring is not quite planar, as has been discussed for rings of this size (cf. Chap. 7). This is in contrast to the unsaturated ring present in *S*-ascorbic acid (cf. Fig. 1). If the lactone ring is written with the oxygen behind and the carbonyl on the right, as had been our practice in viewing the hemi-acetal rings, the side chain is pulled up, so that the convention of the Fischer projection shows the hydroxyl on the left for the *R*-configuration. Assignment of sequence to the substituents on carbon-5 will reveal that this is the *R*-configuration that is written in Eq. 11.

An oxidation of mannose similar to that shown in Eq. 11 gives **mannonic acid,** while galactose gives **galactonic acid.**

3. OXIDATION TO DI-ACIDS. More vigorous oxidation of a sugar will attack the primary alcohol preferentially to the secondary hydroxyls, so that the di-acid, known as a **glycaric acid,** is obtained. Nitric acid, under less vigorous conditions than required for Eq. 10, will yield a glycaric acid, as illustrated for glucose in Eq. 12. Lactone formation from **saccharic acid** occurs, but it is not shown in Eq. 12, for a lactone may form with either carboxyl.

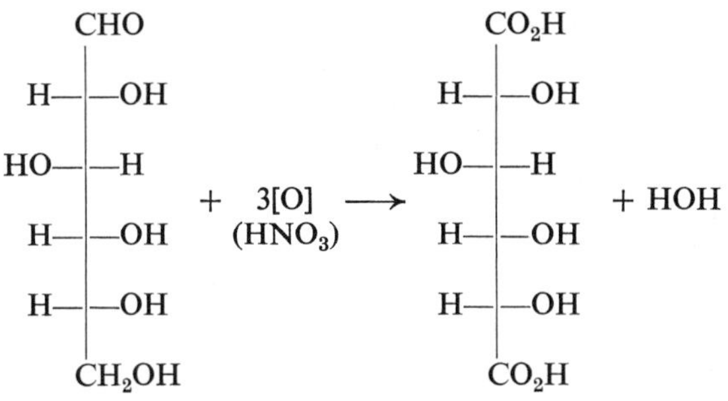

$$
\begin{array}{cc}
\text{CHO} & \text{CO}_2\text{H} \\
\text{H——OH} & \text{H——OH} \\
\text{HO——H} & \text{HO——H} \\
\text{H——OH} \quad +\ 3[\text{O}] \longrightarrow & \text{H——OH} \quad +\ \text{HOH} \\
\text{H——OH} \quad (\text{HNO}_3) & \text{H——OH} \\
\text{CH}_2\text{OH} & \text{CO}_2\text{H}
\end{array}
\tag{12}
$$

Similarly to the reaction shown in Eq. 12, mannose yields **mannosaccharic acid,** and galactose yields **mucic acid.** The latter acid is of interest since it is optically inactive in spite of having four asymmetric carbons. The molecule has a plane of symmetry, which is indicated by the dotted line in formula IX;

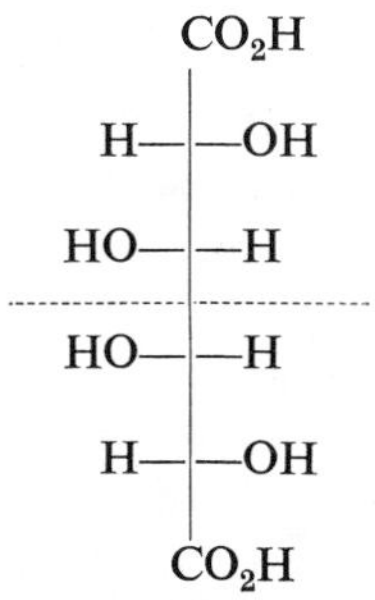

$$
\begin{array}{c}
\text{CO}_2\text{H} \\
\text{H——OH} \\
\text{HO——H} \\
\text{HO——H} \\
\text{H——OH} \\
\text{CO}_2\text{H}
\end{array}
$$

Mucic acid
IX

the plane of symmetry is perpendicular to the plane of the paper in the projection. The optical inactivity of mucic acid was a key part of the evidence on which the configuration of galactose was originally assigned. The symmetrical structure is also responsible, no doubt, for the remarkably low solubility of mucic acid in water. The sugars and derivatives, as a result of such a high oxygen content, are usually very soluble in water. This water-insolubility of mucic acid renders nitric acid oxidation an excellent and simple *test reaction for galactose.*

Reduction of sugars with various agents leads to the hexahydroxy compounds. Catalytic hydrogenation has been used to accomplish this conversion (cf. Eq. 6 for sorbitol synthesis); however, electrolytic reduction has been found to be especially economical for the industrial preparation of **sorbitol** from glucose and **mannitol** from mannose. These compounds have many uses of which one is as a *humectant* (agent for preventing a material from drying out).

Reaction with phenylhydrazine. Of the various carbonyl reagents, phenylhydrazine and ring-substituted phenylhydrazines have been of greatest utility in the sugar series. The initial reaction is formation of a phenylhydrazone, as usual for aldehydes or ketones (cf. Eq. 15-7). Unless this initial reaction product precipitates from solution, further reaction occurs (as outlined below in Eq. 14), so the precipitation of a phenylhydrazone has proved of considerable diagnostic value in recognizing sugars and also in separating them. With the unsubstituted phenylhydrazine in water solution, *only mannose has been observed to give a precipitate of phenylhydrazone.* The reaction is shown in Eq. 13.

Mannose phenylhydrazone (13)

Substituted phenylhydrazines have been found which will yield insoluble phenylhydrazones with various other sugars. The utility of the hydrazones in separating sugars is a consequence of the fact that hydrolysis of the hydrazone gives the parent sugar from which the derivative was made.

If excess of phenylhydrazine is used in reaction with a sugar, those sugars giving soluble phenylhydrazones (all sugars but mannose) give further reaction to yield an **osazone.** For most sugars the osazone crystallizes from water solution as bright yellow crystals. The over-all conversion for glucose is shown in Eq. 14. The net result is oxidation of the secondary alcohol at carbon-2 to carbonyl, followed by hydrazone formation with the carbonyl. The mechanism of osazone formation has been the subject of considerable investigation, but the

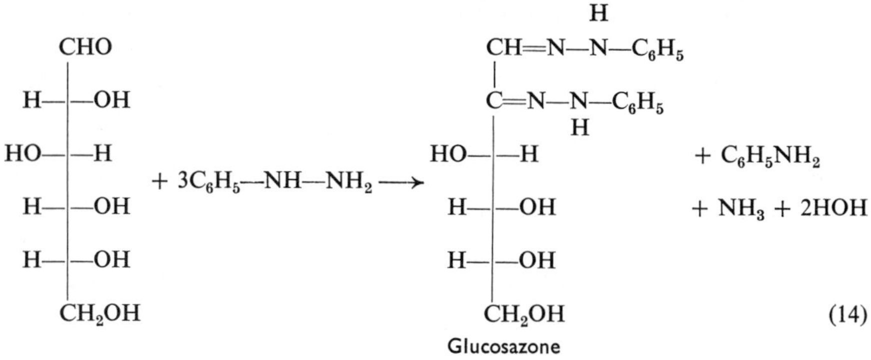

$$
\begin{array}{c}
\text{CHO} \\
\text{H}\!\!-\!\!\text{OH} \\
\text{HO}\!\!-\!\!\text{H} \\
\text{H}\!\!-\!\!\text{OH} \\
\text{H}\!\!-\!\!\text{OH} \\
\text{CH}_2\text{OH}
\end{array}
\;+\; 3C_6H_5\!\!-\!\!NH\!\!-\!\!NH_2 \longrightarrow
\begin{array}{c}
\overset{H}{\text{CH}=N\!\!-\!\!N\!\!-\!\!C_6H_5} \\
\underset{H}{\text{C}=N\!\!-\!\!N\!\!-\!\!C_6H_5} \\
\text{HO}\!\!-\!\!\text{H} \\
\text{H}\!\!-\!\!\text{OH} \\
\text{H}\!\!-\!\!\text{OH} \\
\text{CH}_2\text{OH}
\end{array}
\quad
\begin{array}{l}
+\; C_6H_5NH_2 \\
+\; NH_3 + 2HOH
\end{array}
\qquad (14)
$$

Glucosazone

details of the intermediate steps remain uncertain. There has also been considerable discussion and investigation of why the process stops after attack on carbon-2. Prevention of further reaction by precipitation of the osazone can hardly be the proper explanation, for a few disaccharides give water-soluble osazones, and further reaction does not occur in these cases under normal conditions. A critical examination of the data on osazone formation[7] has led to the conclusion that the insolubility of the osazone, as well as inhibition of further reaction, is caused by the existence of the osazone as the stable chelated structure (cf. Chap. 17, in connection with nitrophenols) shown in formula X.

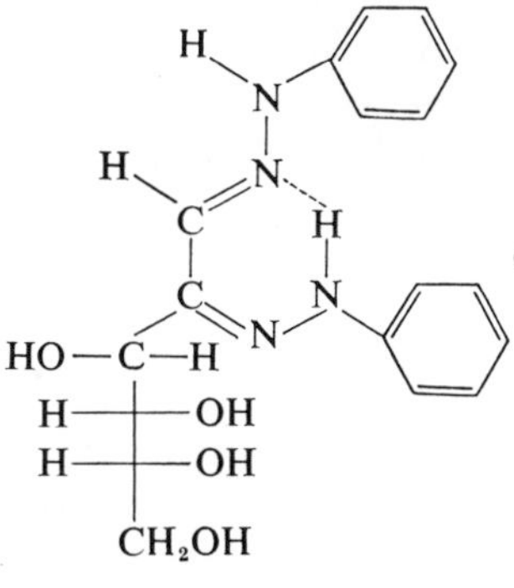

Glucosazone
X

If osazone formation is applied to fructose, carbon-1 proves to be the point of oxidation, so there is formed glucosazone, the identical compound to that formed from glucose. Of course this relationship was of great utility in establishing the relative configurations of these two sugars. It also turns out that the *rate* of osazone formation is different for these two sugars, so this may be used to distinguish between them in aqueous solution.

---

[7] L. Mester, *Advances in Carbohydrate Chemistry*, Vol. XIII, Academic Press, New York: (1958), p. 129.

In several of the above reactions, detection of sugars in aqueous solution has been emphasized. This is of significance on account of the great difficulty frequently associated with isolation of the pure crystalline sugars from their syrupy water solutions. Water-insoluble, crystalline derivatives and reliable tests on aqueous solutions have been of great value in sugar chemistry.

As may be noted by inspection of the formula for glucosazone, hydrolysis of an osazone does not yield the parent sugar from which the osazone was formed. Instead, there is obtained a 1-aldo-2-keto sugar, a structure known as an "osone." For this reason, osazone formation is of no value for separating sugars except in the form of that derivative.

Building higher sugars. Conversion of a sugar to the next higher one, which has been of much significance in establishing relative configurations,

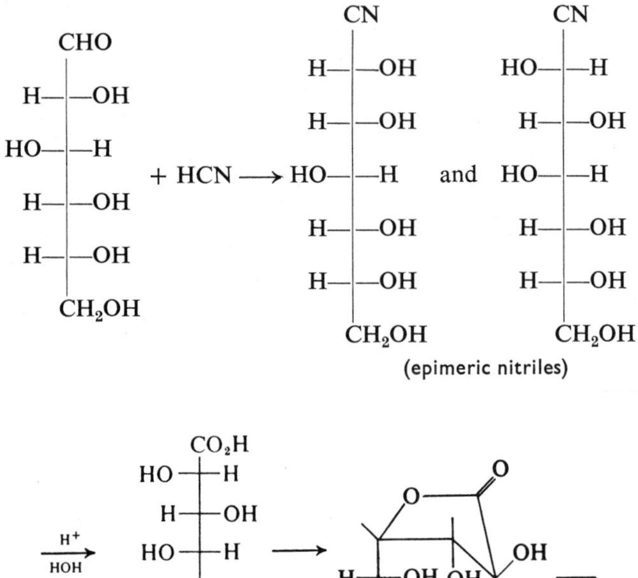

$$
\begin{array}{c}
\text{CHO} \\
\text{H——OH} \\
\text{HO——H} \\
\text{H——OH} \\
\text{H——OH} \\
\text{CH}_2\text{OH}
\end{array}
\;+\; \text{HCN} \longrightarrow\;
\begin{array}{c}
\text{CN} \\
\text{H——OH} \\
\text{H——OH} \\
\text{HO——H} \\
\text{H——OH} \\
\text{H——OH} \\
\text{CH}_2\text{OH}
\end{array}
\;\text{and}\;
\begin{array}{c}
\text{CN} \\
\text{HO——H} \\
\text{H——OH} \\
\text{HO——H} \\
\text{H——OH} \\
\text{H——OH} \\
\text{CH}_2\text{OH}
\end{array}
\tag{15}
$$

(epimeric nitriles)

$$
\begin{array}{c}
\text{CN} \\
\text{HO——H} \\
\text{H——OH} \\
\text{HO——H} \\
\text{H——OH} \\
\text{H——OH} \\
\text{CH}_2\text{OH}
\end{array}
\xrightarrow[\text{HOH}]{\text{H}^+}
\begin{array}{c}
\text{CO}_2\text{H} \\
\text{HO——H} \\
\text{H——OH} \\
\text{HO——H} \\
\text{H——OH} \\
\text{H——OH} \\
\text{CH}_2\text{OH}
\end{array}
\longrightarrow
\tag{16}
$$

Na(Hg), HOH

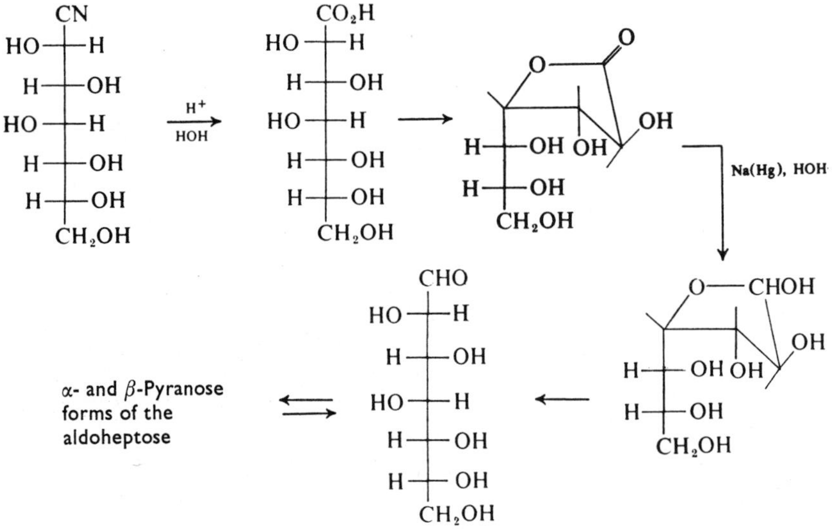

α- and β-Pyranose forms of the aldoheptose

$$
\begin{array}{c}
\text{CHO} \\
\text{HO——H} \\
\text{H——OH} \\
\text{HO——H} \\
\text{H——OH} \\
\text{H——OH} \\
\text{CH}_2\text{OH}
\end{array}
$$

(furanose forms of the aldoheptose)

has been accomplished in several ways. The most successful method is probably that known as the **Kiliani synthesis,** which is outlined in Eqs. 15 and 16, as applied to glucose. The reactions involved have been studied earlier in application to more simple structures, except for the reduction with sodium amalgam of a lactone to a hemi-acetal. Since the hemi-acetals with six-atom rings are more stable, when the furanose forms equilibrate with the open-chain aldehyde sugar, this in turn equilibrates with the pyranose forms until all the heptoses have been converted to the more stable pyranose sugars.

As discussed in the preceding chapter, asymmetric induction will usually cause formation of unequal amounts of the epimers in a reaction such as shown in Eq. 15 or the reduction in Eq. 16; however, there is nearly always some of each isomer formed. Since these are diastereoisomers, they are usually separable, so that one of them can be separated and used for subsequent steps, as shown in Eq. 16. Of course the stereoisomeric heptoses may be equilibrated through the open-chain form, as shown in Eq. 16, so the ratio of isomers obtained on reduction of the lactone is of no consequence.

By the methods shown in Eqs. 15 and 16, pure sugars with as many as nine carbons have been synthesized. The large number of steps, and the necessity for separating mixtures of diastereoisomers combined to make the effort required for this work quite impressive.

Distinction between a pentose and a hexose may be accomplished by heating the sugar with hydrochloric acid. The reactions are shown in Eqs. 17 and 18. Reasonable mechanisms may be formulated for these reactions, but it is

$$C_5H_{10}O_5 \xrightarrow[\text{HCl}]{\text{heat}} \begin{array}{c} \text{CH——CH} \\ \| \qquad \| \\ \text{CH} \quad \text{C—CHO} \\ \diagdown \diagup \\ \text{O} \end{array} + 3HOH \qquad (17)$$

Furfural

$$C_6H_{12}O_6 \xrightarrow[\text{HCl}]{\text{heat}} \begin{array}{c} \text{CH}_3\text{—C—CH}_2\text{—CH}_2\text{—CO}_2\text{H} \\ \| \\ \text{O} \end{array} + HCO_2H + HOH \qquad (18)$$

Levulinic acid

probably not profitable to discuss them at this time. In addition to their test value (pentoses give a neutral product, hexoses acidic products), these reactions are of commercial significance. Both levulinic acid and furfural are cheap articles of commerce, and furfural is starting material for synthesis of numerous important chemicals.[8]

---

[8] Oat hulls, not regarded as edible by man, contain polysaccharides made up of pentoses; so the Quaker Oats Co. is a major supplier of furfural to the chemical market.

EXERCISES

I. Define or illustrate clearly each of the following terms.

(a) Aldopentose
(b) Epimers.
(c) Osazone.
(d) Ketohexose.
(e) Pyranose form of a sugar.
(f) Mutarotation.
(g) Phenylhydrazone.

(h) Glycoside.
(i) Glycaric acid.
(j) Constitution.
(k) Reducing sugar.
(l) Lactone.
(m) An *R*-sugar.
(n) A D-sugar.

2. If you were given four test tubes, each containing a different one of the following sugars, how could you most easily establish the identity of each sugar by qualitative tests?

(a) *R*-Ribose.
(b) *R*-Fructose.

(c) *R*-Mannose.
(d) *R*-Galactose.

3. Write a configurational formula for each of the following.

(a) A glycaric acid which is a meso molecule.
(b) A pentose which, on chain extension by the Kiliani synthesis, will give an epimeric mixture containing *R*-mannose.
(c) A vitamin which is a carbohydrate derivative.

4. If you were given an aqueous solution containing a mixture of *R*-glucose, *R*-galactose and *R*-mannose, how could you separate the *R*-mannose and obtain the sugar in a pure condition? Give equations for any reactions used for this purpose.

How could you prove that a constituent of the above-described mixture is *R*-galactose?

5. Outline a synthesis of the following aldoheptose, starting with a sugar mentioned in this chapter. Assume that any epimeric mixtures encountered in this synthesis can be separated.

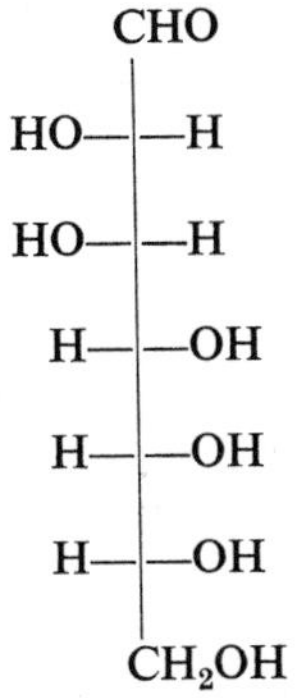

$$
\begin{array}{c}
\text{CHO} \\
\text{HO—}\!\!\!-\!\!\!\text{H} \\
\text{HO—}\!\!\!-\!\!\!\text{H} \\
\text{H—}\!\!\!-\!\!\!\text{OH} \\
\text{H—}\!\!\!-\!\!\!\text{OH} \\
\text{H—}\!\!\!-\!\!\!\text{OH} \\
\text{CH}_2\text{OH}
\end{array}
$$

6. There was isolated from natural sources a sugar of unknown configuration, and it was shown to be an aldotetrose. It was subjected to the chain extension process starting with addition of hydrogen cyanide to the aldehyde group, and this gave an epimeric pair of aldopentoses. Neither of these aldopentoses was *R*-ribose or *S*-ribose.

One of the epimeric aldopentoses was again subjected to the chain extension process, and there was obtained an epimeric mixture of aldohexoses, one of which was *R*-galactose (proved by oxidation with nitric acid).

Write configurational formulas (conformations for hexoses) for the beta forms (furanose for the tetrose, pyranose for the others) of the one tetrose, two pentoses, and two hexoses mentioned above. Assign instability numbers for the two conformations of each hexose.

7. Write conformational formulas for the alpha and beta isomers of the sugar synthesized in Eq. 16, and for that sugar to be synthesized in Exercise 5. Also write these formulas with the rings flipped to the other conformation. Assign instability numbers to each formula.

24

Disaccharides and Polysaccharides

The study of the monosaccharides is of fundamental importance because they are the building blocks from which the disaccharides and polysaccharides are constructed; however, the most important of the naturally occurring carbohydrates are the higher molecular weight compounds. Not only is the number of different di- and polysaccharides large, but the total weight of such compounds produced in nature is very great indeed. In the present chapter, we will consider a few of these compounds in order to study their structures and properties.

As their names imply, the disaccharides are built from two monosaccharide units, while the polysaccharides contain more than two such units. It is sometimes convenient to designate carbohydrates built from three or four monosaccharide units as tri- or tetrasaccharides. It turns out that the majority of natural carbohydrates contain either two of the basic structural units or else a rather large number of units; however, there have been found in nature several trisaccharides, including the antibiotic, streptomycin.

Lactose, a Typical Disaccharide

The sugar lactose, occurring in cow's milk, may be regarded as a typical disaccharide. Although skimmed (defatted) milk contains 4.5–5% of lactose (and only about 4% of protein), milk does not have a pronounced sweet taste, for lactose is not one of the sugars imparting a strong sweet taste.

Structure of lactose. If lactose is hydrolyzed with dilute acid, there are formed equal amounts of the two monosaccharides R-glucose and R-galactose. These sugars may be characterized by such tests as described in Chapter 23; so the nature of the components of lactose is readily determined. Since monosaccharides contain hydroxyl and carbonyl groups, and acetals are readily hydrolyzed by acid (cf. Chaps. 15 and 23), it might be suspected that a disaccharide is an acetal, and this proves to be the case. Although the experimental details of proof of structure of this acetal are rather numerous and complex, the principles involved may be outlined as follows.

1. If lactose is oxidized with a mild agent attacking only the aldehyde group present (Eq. 23-11), and the oxidized sugar is hydrolyzed, the products obtained are gluconic acid and galactose. Since the galactose unit was not oxidized and the glucose unit was oxidized, it follows that the aldehyde group in galactose was the one combined as an acetal in the disaccharide.

2. If all the hydroxyls in lactose are converted to methyl ethers by the procedure described in the preceding chapter (Eq. 23-8), and the methylated product is hydrolyzed with dilute acid, the glucose derivative formed is 2,3,6-trimethylglucose, shown in the accompanying formula in the open-chain form. This structure may be established by oxidative cleavage, as has been described in Eq. 23-10.

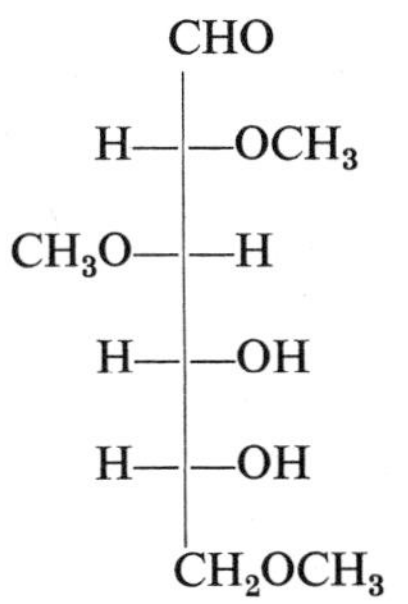

$$
\begin{array}{c}
\text{CHO} \\
\text{H——OCH}_3 \\
\text{CH}_3\text{O——H} \\
\text{H——OH} \\
\text{H——OH} \\
\text{CH}_2\text{OCH}_3
\end{array}
$$

2,3,6-Trimethylglucose

Since acid hydrolysis cleaves the acetal linkage but not an ether linkage, if the hydroxyl at carbon-5 is assumed to have been combined in the hemi-acetal form of glucose (this has been demonstrated), it may be concluded that the hydroxyl at carbon-4 was the one combined in the acetal linkage with galactose to form lactose.

3. The galactose derivative formed on hydrolysis of methylated lactose is 2,3,4,6-tetramethylgalactose; so hemi-acetal formation at the 5-position (as in free galactose) is demonstrated.

4. The remaining unknown factor in the lactose formula is the configuration at carbon-1 in the galactose unit of lactose. Is the acetal

(analogous to the glucose derivatives shown in Eq. 23-4) the alpha or the beta form? The method commonly used for determining this feature of configuration is enzymatic hydrolysis. Since enzymes are optically active, a given enzyme usually promotes reaction with only one of the two possible stereoisomers. Lactose is hydrolyzed in the presence of an enzyme known to attack the beta acetal linkage, therefore the acetal linkage in lactose has the beta configuration.

From the above items of evidence, the structure of lactose is that represented in the following conformational formula.

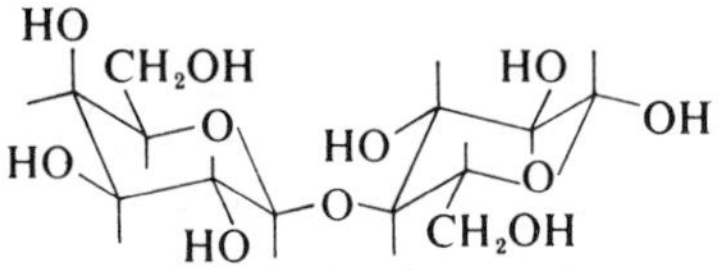

Lactose
(with glucose unit in β-form)

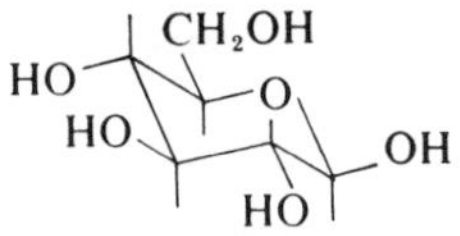

β-R-Glucose

In order to write the lactose formula with realistic valence angles for the acetal oxygen (oxygen between the rings) it is necessary to rotate the glucose unit from the normal position in which it is viewed. For comparison, the β-R-glucose structure is written in the normal position in the formula beside the lactose formula. As described in the preceding chapter, "turning over" the configurational formulas in writing polysaccharide structures presents no problems, for the equatorial (or axial) positions for hydroxyl are not changed. In particular, it should be noted that the glucose unit in the lactose formula has not been flipped to the alternate conformation; the formula in the position shown on the right has simply been rotated so that the right-hand carbon is up and the ring oxygen is forward.

As is apparent from its formula, lactose is a reducing sugar, for the hemiacetal group in the glucose unit is free to equilibrate with a small amount of the aldehyde form. Lactose will, therefore, give an osazone; also, the aldehyde group may be oxidized to carboxyl. As cited above, oxidation of the aldehyde group in galactose provided evidence that the hemi-acetal group is in the glucose unit. A part of the lactose in solution will have the isomeric α-configuration for the glucose unit, but a larger amount will have the lower-energy β-configuration at carbon-1, which is that shown in the formula.

Sucrose

Although several disaccharides occur in nature, the most common one is ordinary table sugar, sucrose, which is obtained commercially from either sugar cane or sugar beets. From either source, it is obtained in a very high state of purity and marketed at a surprisingly low price. There is no difference between the products from the two sources.

The basic structural features of sucrose may be deduced from two observations: on hydrolysis, it gives equal amounts of glucose and fructose; it does not reduce Fehling's solution. The latter observation shows that acetal formation occurs between the two hemi-acetal hydroxyls; otherwise one hemiacetal would be free to equilibrate with the aldehyde form, which would be oxidized by Fehling's solution. This structural feature has rendered rather difficult the determination of configuration at the two carbons joined to the acetal oxygen; however, it now seems established that the linkage to glucose is alpha, that to fructose is beta. A final surprising feature of the sucrose structure involves the ring size in the fructose unit. This has been shown to be the furanose ring, although the fructose formed by hydrolysis of sucrose rapidly equilibrates, via the keto form, with the pyranose ring structures described for fructose in Chapter 23. The ring size in the fructose unit of sucrose was established in the usual way: complete methylation of the disaccharide, hydrolysis to the methylated monosaccharides, and finally oxidation of the methylated fructose so obtained. The structural features of natural sucrose are shown in the formula below, in which the fructofuranose unit is written in the usual fashion with the ketal carbon to the right and the ring oxygen behind. In this formula, it is

Sucrose
(Hemi-acetal linkage is β- to fructose, α- to glucose)

necessary to turn the glucose unit around, but this generates no confusion with the conformational ring structure; all substituents remain equatorial except for the alpha linkage at the acetal carbon.

Since sucrose contains a unit of fructose, the sweetest of the common monosaccharides, it is not surprising that sucrose is a sweet sugar.

Polysaccharides

The polysaccharides occur in great variety in nature and are of much industrial significance. The most important and well known of the polysaccharides are starch, one of the most basic foodstuffs, and cellulose. Starch occurs widely but is especially abundant in tubers such as potatoes and in cereals such as wheat and corn. Cellulose and the complex substance known as lignin are the chief components of wood, while cotton is nearly pure cellulose. Also included among the polysaccharides are the vegetable gums, such as gum arabic and cherry gum; chitin, in the exoskeletal structures of crustacea; ivory nut mannan; and many other diverse substances.

The technology of the utilization of polysaccharides is a large subject beyond the scope of our present studies, but it may be mentioned that cellulose especially has numerous uses other than for making paper and cotton cloth. Cellulose can be modified to make the kind of cloth known as rayon, and when the hydroxyls are acetylated there may be fabricated the type of transparent films used for making photographic film. Nitrated cellulose (hydroxyls converted to nitrate esters), known as guncotton or nitrocellulose, is widely used in smokeless powder, the principal propellant for firearms. Partially nitrated cellulose, known as pyroxylin, has been employed as a base for various plastics, and has been widely utilized in lacquers such as those used on automobiles.

In addition to the polysaccharides composed of hexoses, such as those just mentioned, there are also numerous polysaccharides built of pentoses. These include such well-known substances as oat hulls, corncobs, peanut hulls, and straw. A major industrial utilization of these materials is for hydrolysis to the component pentoses, which are in turn converted to the industrially important chemical furfural (cf. Eq. 23-17).

The structures of a large number of the polysaccharides have been determined, and they contain many features of interest; however, our present discussion must be limited to a brief consideration of cellulose and starch, representative polysaccharides which are the most important of the group.

Cellulose

Hydrolysis of cellulose gives only one sugar, glucose, and the application of the methylation procedure described in connection with the lactose structure shows that the acetal linkage between the glucose units always involves the hydroxyl on carbon-4. The configuration of the acetal link is beta; so cellulose may be regarded as composed of long chains of glucose units joined by beta linkages through the 1- and 4-positions.

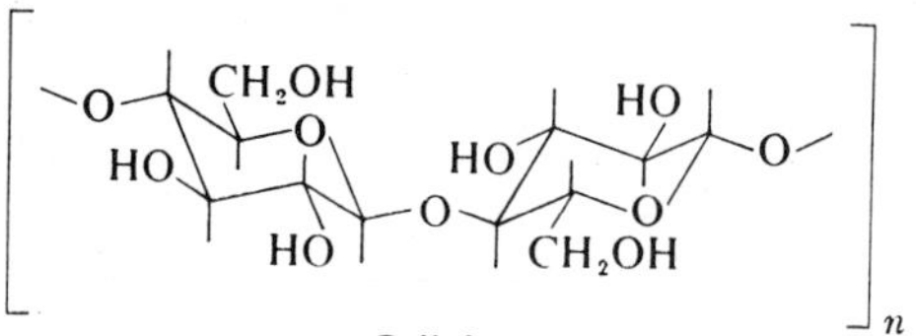

Cellulose

One of the most successful methods for determining the molecular weight of such large molecules as cellulose is by study of the rate of sedimentation of the material in the very high-speed centrifuge known as an ultracentrifuge. This method has shown that cellulose from various sources is always a mixture of chains of various lengths. Molecular weights have been found to fall largely in the range 300,000 to 500,000, which corresponds to about 1,700 to 2,800 glucose units. Examination of cellulose by x-ray diffraction has shown that the long chains lie parallel to each other, and it seems probable that hydrogen bonding (cf. Chap. 13) is a major contributor to the forces holding these chains together in bundles so strongly as to result in the great mechanical strength characteristic of cellulose. The long chains naturally tend to give cellulose the fibrous nature observed in cotton and wood. The strong intermolecular hydrogen bonding is also probably responsible for the extreme insolubility of cellulose; otherwise, a substance with such a high percentage of oxygen might be expected to be somewhat soluble in water, or at least to disperse as a colloid.

Carnivorous mammals, including man, do not have enzymes capable of promoting hydrolysis of the beta acetal linkage in cellulose; therefore it passes through the digestive tract unchanged. Certain animals, especially ruminants (cud-chewing animals) such as the cow, have bacteria in the digestive tract which can hydrolyze the beta link in cellulose. This is a very nice arrangement, for the animal can digest the glucose liberated by the bacteria and thus derive nourishment from cellulose.

Starch

Hydrolysis of starch gives only one monosaccharide, glucose, as does cellulose; however, the acetal linkages in starch are alpha. The difference in acetal linkage is a very important difference between cellulose and starch, for mammals have enzymes capable of hydrolyzing the alpha-linked units of starch and are able, therefore, to utilize starch as food.

Starch also differs from cellulose in that some of the polysaccharide chains in starch are "branched," that is, there are present glucose units having more than one hydroxyl combined in acetal formation with other units of glucose. The branched chains give different physical properties to the molecules, and certain precipitation procedures have been used to separate the branched from the unbranched starch molecules. The fraction consisting almost entirely of straight chains, termed **amylose,** is of lower molecular weight. Study of the molecular weight by use of the ultracentrifuge has indicated a range of about 20,000 to 225,000, which is considerably lower than the molecular weight range in cellulose. Acetal linkage in the amylose fraction is at the 4-position; so the structure is the same as that of cellulose except that the configuration at carbon-1 is alpha.

The branched-chain fraction of starch, termed **amylopectin,** has a molecular weight range of 200,000 to 1,000,000, even higher than that of cellulose. The methylation procedure has been used to determine that the position of the second acetal formation, leading to branching, is at carbon-6; so the branching may be indicated as follows:

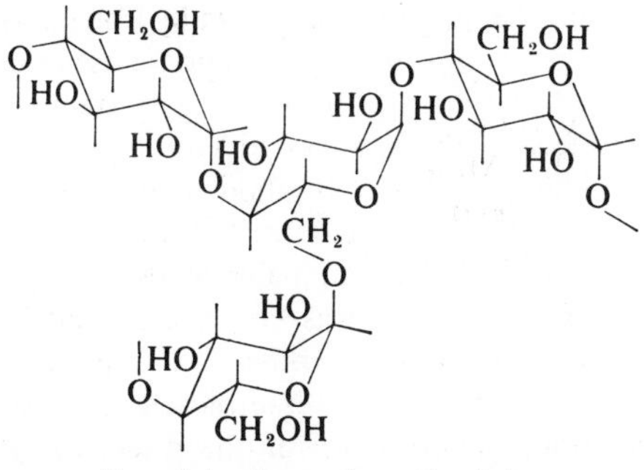

Branch in the amylopectin chain

The average number of branches per molecule is not known with accuracy, but varies with the source of the starch, as does the ratio of amylose to amylopectin.

From this brief discussion, it may be seen that the structure of starch is not only more complicated than is that of cellulose, but is also much more variable.

EXERCISES

1. Write the equation for the hydrolysis of sucrose, showing equilibration of the furanose form of fructose with the equilibrium mixture in which the free mono-saccharide exists. All formulas should be configurational ones, and pyranose structures should be written as the more stable conformation.

2. There is found in several plants, including sugar beets, a small amount of the trisaccharide known as raffinose. The structure has been shown to be that resulting from alpha acetal formation between the pyranose form of galactose and the hydroxyl on carbon-6 in the glucose unit of sucrose. Write the configurational formula for raffinose.

3. There occurs in several fungi, such as mushrooms, a disaccharide known as tre-halose. It gives only glucose on hydrolysis, it does not reduce Fehling's solution, and the methylation procedure has shown that the glucose units are both in the pyranose form. This information limits trehalose to a single structure, but three configurations are possible for the acetal formation. Write formulas for the three possible configurations.

4. Enzymatic hydrolysis of the amylose component of starch yields a disaccharide known as maltose. Write the configurational formula for maltose.

5. Suppose that amylopectin is completely methylated so as to convert all hydroxyls to methyl ethers, then this methylated product is hydrolyzed with dilute acid. Write configurational formulas (aldehyde forms) for the dimethylglucose, the trimethyl-glucose, and the tetramethylglucose (from one end of the polysaccharide chain) that will result.

6. Write the equation, using configurational formulas, for the reaction that occurs when lactose is heated with dilute nitric acid.

7. Let us suppose that there was isolated from the fruit of a tropical plant an unknown sugar which did not reduce Fehling's solution. On hydrolysis with aqueous acid, there were obtained a pentose and a hexose. By appropriate use of enzymatic hydrolysis, it was determined that the acetal linkages to both sugars are alpha.

When the hexose from hydrolysis was added to an aqueous solution of phenyl-hydrazine there was obtained, after only about a minute at room temperature, a precipitate. This precipitate was characterized by melting point and mixed melting point as the phenylhydrazone of a common aldohexose.

Characterization of the pentose was not so easy, but it was accomplished by extending the chain by use of the Kiliani synthesis. This procedure yielded an epimeric mixture of hexoses which, on oxidation with nitric acid, gave the insoluble mucic acid.

Write the configurational formula for the disaccharide, assuming that each monosaccharide unit is in the pyranose form.

Amino Acids, Proteins, and Nucleic Acids

Proteins are no doubt the most important type of organic molecules. Not only are they the basic structural material in animal organisms; they are also the basic molecules on which animal metabolism depends. The enzymes and many hormones are proteins, while other proteins serve as carriers for oxygen, lipids, or the all-important nucleic acids. The high molecular weights and unusual structures of proteins render them not subject to the usual manipulative methods of organic chemistry. Much of our current understanding of protein structures and functions has resulted from application of the methods of physical chemistry.

Amino acids are the building blocks from which the high molecular weight proteins are constructed, in somewhat analogous fashion to the manner in which polysaccharides are built up from monosaccharides. The structures of amino acids are more simple than those of monosaccharides, however, and the amide linkages by which proteins are built are not subject to the complexity of the acetal linkages in polysaccharides. The complexity of the protein structures, especially their great variety, derives from the considerable number of different amino acids and from the secondary bonding forces which determine the specific shapes of proteins.

Amino acids, the building blocks from which proteins are made, will be discussed first, as a necessary introduction to the study of protein structures.

Amino Acids

Although there may be various types of amino acids, such as amino sulfonic acids, the term amino acid is normally understood to mean amino carboxylic acid unless some other type is specified. The amino group may be substituted at any point along the carboxylic acid chain, but the compounds of importance in proteins are α-amino acids; therefore, this type has been the subject of most study and will receive most of our attention. As will be developed, many amino acids found as constituents of proteins have another functional group, in some instances another amino group; however, the α-amino function is always present.

Nomenclature used with amino acids follows the normal usages that have been previously described; however, virtually all the amino acids from proteins have received common names. Although there is no obvious advantage to learning all these common names in a study of elementary organic chemistry, names and structures of some of the important and representative acids should be learned. A few illustrations follow, and others will be presented in connection with the discussion of proteins.

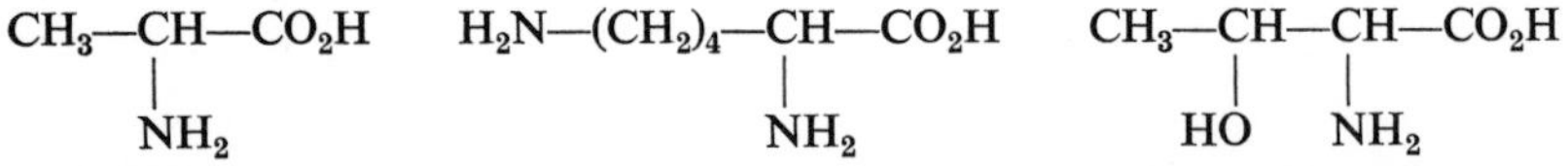

$$CH_3-CH-CO_2H$$
$$|$$
$$NH_2$$

α-Aminopropionic acid
or Alanine

$$H_2N-(CH_2)_4-CH-CO_2H$$
$$|$$
$$NH_2$$

α,ε-Diaminocaproic
acid or Lysine

$$CH_3-CH-CH-CO_2H$$
$$|\quad\quad|$$
$$HO\quad NH_2$$

α-Amino-β-hydroxy-
butyric acid or Threonine

All the natural amino acids except glycine, aminoacetic acid, have at least one asymmetric carbon, the alpha carbon. Except in a few abnormal polypeptides the naturally-occurring amino acids have the L-configuration at the α-carbon, hence are designated as belonging to the L-series. Only four natural amino acids have an additional asymmetric carbon besides the α-carbon, so the α-carbon is used as the basis for designating the configuration rather than the carbon most remote from carboxyl. This is contrary to the convention employed in the sugars. If an L-amino acid such as L-alanine is assigned according to the sequence rule, it proves to also have the S-configuration. This assignment is illustrated:

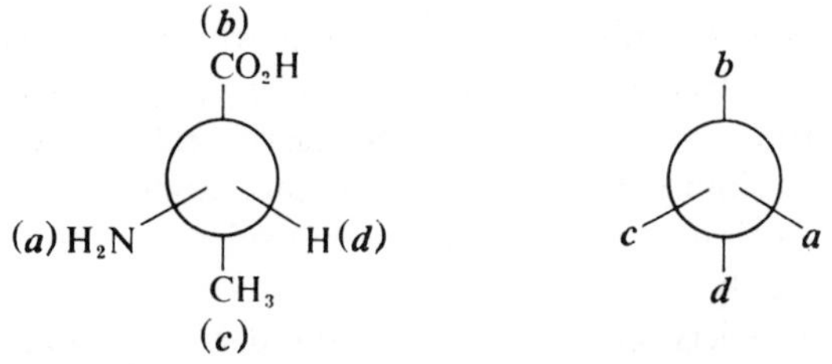

S-Alanine

(viewing position)

Of course the direction of rotation of the amino acids may be either dextro or levo.

When an amide is formed by linkage between amino in one amino acid and carboxyl in another, the product is called a **peptide,** and this is the linkage by which proteins are built up. A peptide of two amino acid units is a dipeptide, one with three a tripeptide, with four a tetrapeptide, etc., employing the same prefixes used in the hydrocarbon names. Any peptide with several amino acid units is termed a **polypeptide,** and a polypeptide of rather high molecular weight is a **protein.** The dividing line between a polypeptide and a protein is not clearly defined and is, indeed, rather arbitrary. There is no particular need for a precise division between polypeptides and proteins. A polypeptide is named, ordinarily, by use of the common names of the amino acids in sequence, starting with the acid having a free amino, as illustrated:

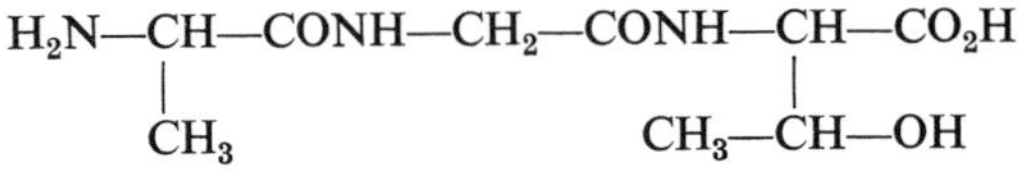

$$H_2N-CH-CONH-CH_2-CONH-CH-CO_2H$$
$$\quad\ \ | \qquad\qquad\qquad\qquad\quad\ |$$
$$\quad\ \ CH_3 \qquad\qquad\qquad CH_3-CH-OH$$

or   H-Ala-Gly-Thr-OH

Alanylglycylthreonine

Since proteins are of such high molecular weight, and the linkage between amino acids is always the peptide linkage, the sequence is often indicated in the shorthand method illustrated at the right of the condensed structural formula. In most instances, the first three letters of the amino acid are used for the abbreviation. In one case, cysteine, *Cy* is used to indicate all the amino acid except the sulfur; in another case, isoleucine, *Ileu* is the abbreviation. Since the abbreviation refers to $-NH-CHR-CO-$ in a polypeptide formula, $H-$ is affixed to the amino end and $-OH$ to the carboxyl end.

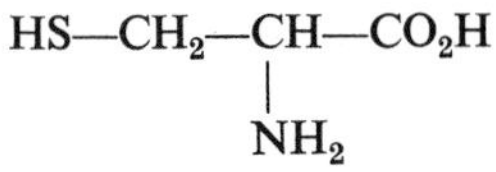

$$HS-CH_2-CH-CO_2H$$
$$\qquad\qquad\ \ |$$
$$\qquad\qquad\ \ NH_2$$

Cysteine

$$CH_3-CH-CH_2-CH-CO_2H \qquad CH_3-CH_2-CH-CH-CO_2H$$
$$\qquad\ \ | \qquad\qquad | \qquad\qquad\qquad\qquad\qquad | \qquad\ |$$
$$\qquad\ \ CH_3 \qquad\ NH_2 \qquad\qquad\qquad\qquad H_3C \quad\ NH_2$$

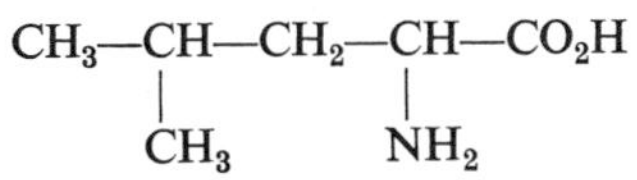

Leucine 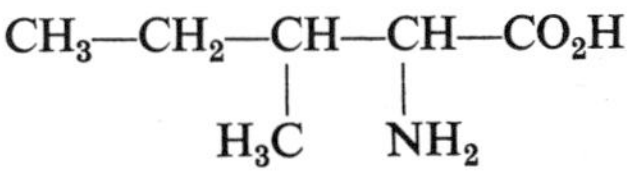   Isoleucine

A common structure in proteins is junction of two cysteine molecules via a disulfide linkage to give the diamino dicarboxylic acid, cystine.

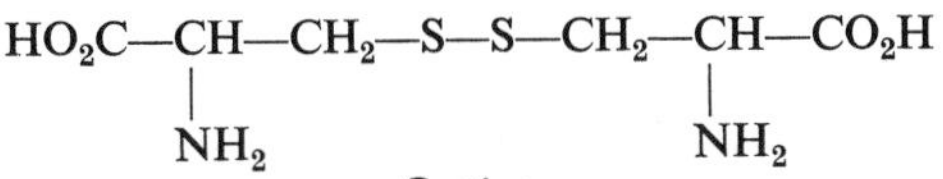

$$HO_2C-CH-CH_2-S-S-CH_2-CH-CO_2H \qquad HO-Cy-S-S-Cy-OH$$
$$\qquad\quad | \qquad\qquad\qquad\qquad\qquad\qquad | \qquad\qquad\qquad\quad\ | \qquad\qquad |$$
$$\qquad\quad NH_2 \qquad\qquad\qquad\qquad\quad\ NH_2 \qquad\qquad\qquad\ H \qquad\quad\ H$$

or

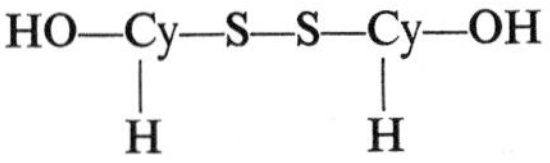

Cystine

Structure of Amino Acids

Since an amino acid contains both an acidic and a basic group, the principal species existing in solution is an inner salt, a structure often designated as a **zwitterion.** Both the basic and acidic groups are weak ones; so there is equilibrium with a very small amount of the acid-base form, as shown in Eq. 1. Even though the amount of acid-base form is extremely small (actually less than 0.001 % for most amino acids), if this form reacts readily with some

$$\underset{\substack{+NH_3}}{R-CH-C}\underset{O^-}{\overset{O}{\diagup}} \quad \rightleftharpoons \quad \underset{NH_2}{R-CH-CO_2H} \tag{1}$$

reagent, equilibrium tends to be re-established, so all the amino acid may eventually react in the acid-base form. The situation is rather reminiscent of that occurring in the monosaccharides (cf. Chap. 23). Reactions of the two forms of the amino acids will be discussed below.

The zwitterion form of the amino acids is that which crystallizes from solution, so solid amino acids are in this form. Conversion of the amino acid to a salt with another acid or base (cf. Eqs. 4 and 5) renders the substance more soluble; so the lowest solubility occurs at the pH where inner salt formation is at a maximum. This pH varies somewhat for different amino acids, depending on the exact structure. The pH at which a given amino acid has the lowest solubility, hence maximum inner salt formation, is termed the **isoelectric point** for that amino acid.

The **physical properties** of amino acids are those to be expected of salts, that is, low volatility and high melting point. Most of them are nonvolatile in the ordinary sense and have such high melting points that they decompose on melting. By way of illustration, we may draw a comparison with bromoacetic acid, which boils at about 208° and melts at 50°. Since ethyl bromide boils at 38° and ethylamine boils at 17°, aminoacetic acid might be expected to boil lower than bromoacetic acid. On account of the zwitterion structure, however, aminoacetic acid is nonvolatile and melts with decomposition at about 235°.

Synthesis of Amino Acids

Numerous methods have been devised for synthesis of amino acids, including special methods for the more complicated natural amino acids. At the present time, there will be mentioned two methods, based on reactions previously discussed, which are applicable to synthesis of a variety of the simple 2-aminoalkanoic acids.

The general synthesis of amines from alkyl halides and ammonia (Eq. 19-13) works especially well for amino acids. Synthesis of valine is outlined in Eq. 2. The equilibrium shown in this sequence is a realistic one, not just a re-pairing of ions, for the zwitterion is an inner-neutralized ion. In addition, the zwitterion of the amino acid usually precipitates from the aqueous ammonium hydroxide solution in which the reaction is normally carried out. At the completion of the reaction, the pH may be adjusted to the isoelectric point in order to secure maximum precipitation of the product. In the synthesis of amino acids, further substitution to give a secondary amine (cf. Eq. 19-14) has little tendency to occur on account of the difficulty in securing substitution of two *sec*-alkyl groups on nitrogen. Thus, steric interference with the second substitution renders the yield in preparation of α-amino acids better than normal in preparation of *n*-alkylamines.

$$CH_3-CH-CH-CO_2H + 2NH_3 \longrightarrow CH_3-CH-CH-CO_2NH_4$$

$$\begin{array}{cc} CH_3 & Br \end{array} \qquad\qquad\qquad\qquad \begin{array}{cc} CH_3 & {}^+NH_3Br^- \end{array}$$

α-Bromoisovaleric acid

$$CH_3-CH-CH-CO_2{}^- + NH_4Br \qquad (2)$$

$$\begin{array}{cc} CH_3 & {}^+NH_3 \end{array}$$

Valine

A second synthesis of amino acids may be based on the reaction of ammonia and hydrogen cyanide with an aldehyde. The imine, $R-CH=NH$, which is formed from the aldehyde and ammonia, will add hydrogen cyanide in the same manner that an aldehyde does. Thus, the product is an α-aminonitrile, which may be hydrolyzed by usual methods to the amino acid (Eq. 3).

$$R-\overset{\overset{\displaystyle O}{\|}}{C}\diagdown_H + HCN + NH_3 \longrightarrow R-\underset{\underset{\displaystyle NH_2}{|}}{CH}-C\equiv N \xrightarrow{HOH,\ H^+} R-\underset{\underset{\displaystyle {}^+NH_3}{|}}{CH}-CO_2{}^- + {}^+NH_4$$

$$+ HOH \qquad\qquad\qquad\qquad\qquad (3)$$

The processes shown in Eqs. 2 and 3 give, of course, the *RS*-amino acids. If the naturally occurring *S*-amino is desired, the methods of optical resolution must be used (Chap. 22). Usually the N-acetyl derivative of the amino acid is the most convenient species for resolution by conversion to a salt with an optically active base.

Reactions of Amino Acids

Salt formation. If an amino acid is treated with a strong acid or base, there is some direct neutralization of the acid-base form of the amino acid (cf. Eq. 1); however, the principal species in solution is the zwitterion, and this is probably the principal reactant. Thus, a strong base frees the weakly basic amine from its salt, as in Eq. 4, while a strong acid frees the weak acid from its salt, as in Eq. 5. The nature of these reactions is best understood if they are

$$R-\underset{\underset{\displaystyle {}^+NH_3}{|}}{CH}-CO_2{}^- + NaOH \rightleftarrows R-\underset{\underset{\displaystyle NH_2}{|}}{CH}-CO_2{}^-Na^+ + HOH \qquad (4)$$

$$R-\underset{\underset{\displaystyle {}^+NH_3}{|}}{CH}-CO_2{}^- + HCl \longrightarrow R-\underset{\underset{\displaystyle {}^+NH_3Cl^-}{|}}{CH}-CO_2H \qquad (5)$$

compared with the equation for freeing of a simple amine from its salt (Eq. 19-8) and the equation for liberation of a carboxylic acid from its salt (Eq. 13-2).

Reactions of the carboxyl group. In general, the carboxyl in an amino acid will react with the same reagents with which simple carboxylic acids react (cf. Chap. 13), unless there is some interfering reaction with the amino group. Among the more important of these reactions is esterification (Eq. 6). Since

$$R-CH-CO_2H + CH_3OH \overset{H^+}{\rightleftharpoons} R-CH-CO_2CH_3 + HOH \qquad (6)$$
$$\underset{NH_2}{|} \qquad\qquad\qquad \underset{NH_2}{|}$$

formation of the ionic zwitterion is not possible in the ester, the esters of amino acids have about the volatility to be expected of such covalently linked compounds. One consequence of this structural feature is that the esters may be separated by fractional distillation, and this device was the first to be used for separation of the mixtures of amino acids obtained from hydrolysis of proteins. This method has now been supplanted, especially in work with very small quantities, by other techniques.[1]

Derivatives of the carboxyl group cannot be prepared by way of the acid chloride, for amines react rapidly with acid chlorides. If the acid chloride should be prepared, there would rapidly ensue a polymerization of the type shown in Eq. 7.

$$nR-\underset{NH_2}{\underset{|}{CH}}-\overset{O}{\overset{\|}{C}}\diagdown Cl \longrightarrow R-\underset{NH_2}{\underset{|}{CH}}-\overset{O}{\overset{\|}{C}}-\underset{H}{\underset{|}{N}}-\underset{R}{\underset{|}{CH}}-\overset{O}{\overset{\|}{C}}-\underset{H}{\underset{|}{N}}-\underset{R}{\underset{|}{CH}}-\overset{O}{\overset{\|}{C}}-etc. \qquad (7)$$

Reactions of the amino group. The most important reaction of the amino group is acylation; in fact, this is the reaction shown in Eq. 7 which results in the polymerization of an amino acid chloride. The amino group may be acylated in a normal manner with a simple acid chloride, as in Eq. 8. The acid chloride of the acylated amino acid is stable to intramolecular reaction, for the amino group has been protected; therefore, it may be used to acylate another

---

[1] Of the several methods developed for separation of the complex mixtures of amino acids resulting from protein hydrolysis, the most useful have been dependent on the various techniques of partition between two phases, known as chromatography. In gas phase chromatography, where there is partitioning between the gas phase and solution in a liquid, the esters of amino acids have been separated successfully in very small quantities. The most successful methods, however, have employed liquid phase chromatography, using partition of the amino acids either on an adsorptive agent or on an ion exchange resin. These methods have been developed primarily from the researches of Dr. Stanford Moore and Dr. William H. Stein, of the Rockefeller Institute. A description of the general application of the various techniques of chromatography may be found in the book by Prof. H. G. Cassidy, of Yale University, entitled *Fundamentals of Chromatography*, Interscience Publishers, New York, 1957.

$$CH_3-\overset{\displaystyle O}{\underset{\displaystyle Cl}{C}} + CH_3-\underset{\underset{\displaystyle NH_2}{|}}{CH}-CO_2H \longrightarrow CH_3-\underset{\underset{\displaystyle N}{|}}{CH}-CO_2H \qquad (8)$$

$$\underset{\displaystyle H}{\diagup}\overset{\displaystyle }{\underset{\displaystyle }{N}}\underset{\displaystyle C-CH_3}{\diagdown}$$

α-Acetaminopropionic
Acid or Acetylalanine

amino acid, as outlined in Eq. 9. If so desired, the product in Eq. 9 may be converted to the acid chloride and allowed to react with still another amino

$$CH_3-\underset{\underset{\displaystyle NHAc}{|}}{CH}-CO_2H + SOCl_2 \longrightarrow CH_3-\underset{\underset{\displaystyle NHAc}{|}}{CH}-\overset{\displaystyle O}{\underset{\displaystyle Cl}{C}} \quad\xrightarrow{H_2N-CH_2-CO_2H}$$

$$\qquad (9)$$

$$CH_3-\underset{\underset{\displaystyle NHAc}{|}}{CH}-\overset{\displaystyle O}{\overset{\displaystyle \|}{C}}-\overset{\displaystyle H}{\overset{\displaystyle |}{N}}-CH_2-CO_2H$$

Acetylalanylglycine

acid; in fact, the process could be repeated until there had been built up a long-chain polypeptide with its initial amino acid acetylated.

Synthesis of polypeptides. Polypeptides may be synthesized by the basic process described in the preceding section; however, certain elaborations are necessary for really satisfactory results. Two principal modifications are of importance: there must be used a protecting acyl group which may be cleaved without cleavage of the amide groups in the peptide chain; other acid derivatives are preferable to the acid chloride as intermediates for amide formation.

One of the more successful acylating groups for protection of the amino group has been the *carbobenzoxy group* (often designated as *Cbz* in formulas). This group is introduced by acylation with carbobenzoxy chloride, which is the reaction product of phosgene (carbonyl dichloride) and one mole of benzyl alcohol. Use of a large excess of the acid chloride leads to a reasonable yield of the mono-ester (Eq. 10). This reagent, which has become commercially

$$\underset{\displaystyle }{\bigcirc}\text{—}CH_2OH + \underset{\text{(excess)}}{Cl-\overset{\displaystyle O}{\overset{\displaystyle \|}{C}}-Cl} \longrightarrow \underset{\displaystyle }{\bigcirc}\text{—}CH_2O-\overset{\displaystyle O}{\overset{\displaystyle \|}{C}}-Cl + HCl \quad (10)$$

available, reacts with amino acids in the normal fashion shown for a simple acid chloride in Eq. 8.

The utility of the carbobenzoxy group lies in the fact that it may be cleaved by reductive methods, including catalytic hydrogenation, which do not affect the other amide linkages in the molecule. The products of hydrogenation of a carbobenzoxy derivative are shown in Eq. 11. Initial products of the

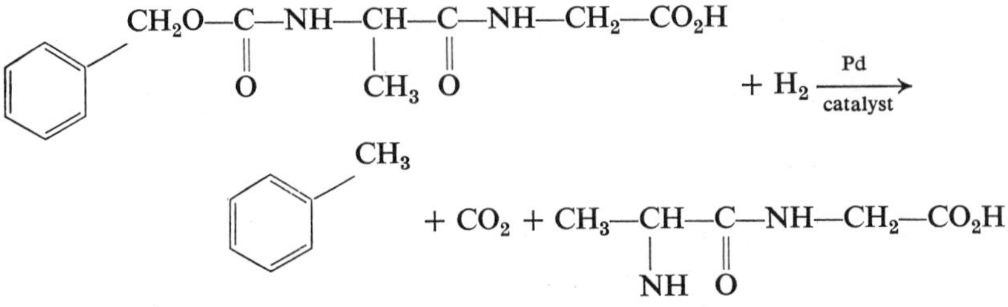

$$
\text{C}_6\text{H}_5\text{—CH}_2\text{O—C—NH—CH—C—NH—CH}_2\text{—CO}_2\text{H} \;+\; \text{H}_2 \xrightarrow[\text{catalyst}]{\text{Pd}}
$$

$$
\text{C}_6\text{H}_5\text{—CH}_3 \;+\; \text{CO}_2 \;+\; \text{CH}_3\text{—CH—C—NH—CH}_2\text{—CO}_2\text{H} \tag{11}
$$

Alanylglycine

hydrogenation are toluene and the carbamic acid, HO_2C—NH—R, but the latter species spontaneously decarboxylates as usual (cf. Eq. 19-28).

Use of the acid chloride as an intermediate in peptide synthesis (cf. Eq. 9) is sometimes unsatisfactory because other functions in the amino acid are sensitive to the reagent forming the acid chloride; however, a more persistent difficulty arises from the fact that acid chlorides give a particularly rapid equilibration with the enol form (Eq. 12). In the case of an optically active

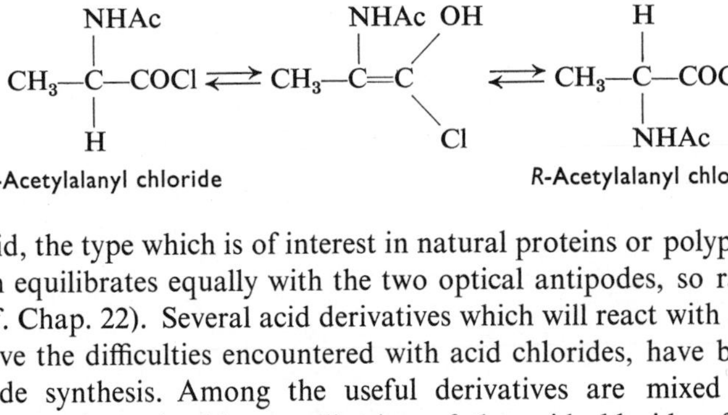

$$
\text{CH}_3\text{—C—COCl} \rightleftharpoons \text{CH}_3\text{—C}\!=\!\text{C} \rightleftharpoons \text{CH}_3\text{—C—COCl} \tag{12}
$$

S-Acetylalanyl chloride   R-Acetylalanyl chloride

amino acid, the type which is of interest in natural proteins or polypeptides, the enol form equilibrates equally with the two optical antipodes, so racemization results (cf. Chap. 22). Several acid derivatives which will react with amines, but do not give the difficulties encountered with acid chlorides, have been utilized for peptide synthesis. Among the useful derivatives are mixed anhydrides which may be formed without utilization of the acid chloride of the amino acid as intermediate. The mixed anhydride from the commercially available ethyl chlorocarbonate, formed as in Eq. 13, has been widely used. Triethyl-

$$
\text{R—CO}_2\text{H} + \text{Cl—C—OEt} \xrightarrow{(\text{C}_2\text{H}_5)_3\text{N}} \text{R—C} \Big\langle \begin{array}{c} \text{O} \\ \text{O—C—OEt} \\ \parallel \\ \text{O} \end{array} \;+\; (\text{C}_2\text{H}_5)_3\overset{+}{\text{N}}\text{H}\overset{-}{\text{Cl}} \tag{13}
$$

amine is utilized in this reaction as a base which will give the anion of the acid but will not react irreversibly with the acid chloride (cf. Chap. 19).

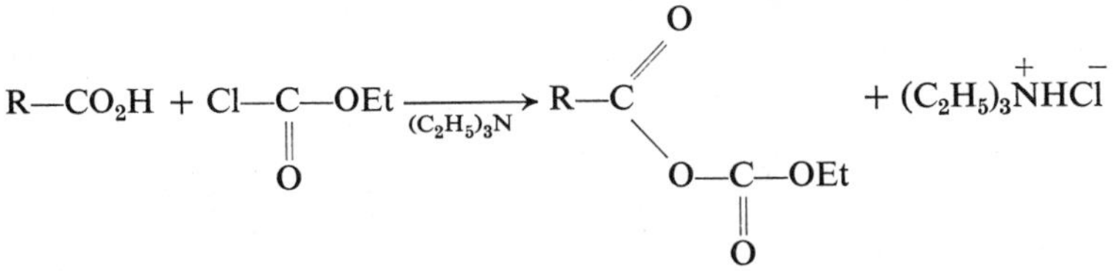

The methods discussed in this section are summarized by the sequence shown in Eq. 14 for synthesis of a dipeptide. Reaction of the mixed anhydride with the amino group gives the amide and the half ester of carbonic acid. The latter is unstable (as is carbonic acid) and dissociates to the alcohol and carbon dioxide. Higher peptides are obtained similarly, by use of additional steps prior to final cleavage of the carbobenzoxy group.

$$CH_3-CH-CH_2-CH-CO_2H + Cbz-Cl \longrightarrow CH_3-CH-CH_2-CH-CO_2H$$
$$\overset{|}{CH_3} \qquad \overset{|}{NH_2} \qquad\qquad\qquad \overset{|}{CH_3} \qquad \overset{|}{NH-Cbz}$$

$$\xrightarrow[Cl-CO_2C_2H_5]{Et_3N} CH_3-CH-CH_2-CH-\overset{\overset{O}{\|}}{C}-O-\overset{\overset{O}{\|}}{C}-OC_2H_5 \xrightarrow{H-Ala-OH}$$
$$\overset{|}{CH_3} \qquad \overset{|}{NH-Cbz}$$

(14)

$$CH_3-CH-CH_2-CH-\overset{\overset{O}{\diagup}}{C} \qquad\qquad + CO_2$$
$$\overset{|}{CH_3} \qquad \overset{|}{NH} \qquad \overset{|}{NH-CH-CO_2H}$$
$$\qquad\qquad \overset{|}{Cbz} \qquad\qquad \overset{|}{CH_3} \qquad + C_2H_5OH$$

$$\downarrow H_2, Pd$$

$$CH_3-CH-CH_2-CH-\overset{\overset{O}{\|}}{C}-\overset{\overset{H}{|}}{N}-CH-CO_2H$$
$$\overset{|}{CH_3} \qquad \overset{|}{NH_2} \qquad\qquad \overset{|}{CH_3}$$

Leucylalanine

Proteins

Proteins are one of the three classes of foodstuffs and may be used as fuel by animal organisms; however, their functions as structural material and for other special purposes such as mentioned at the beginning of this chapter render them of particular significance. Each species of animal builds a set of specific proteins characteristic of that species; another species builds a different set of proteins. Each species also builds a very large number of different proteins, different ones for each organ and each part of an organ. When one considers the number of species of animals, birds, fish, and reptiles, then adds the virtually endless numbers of insects and microorganisms, he may begin to wonder, perhaps, how there could be so many millions of different proteins. He may also wonder how the pattern of synthesis is so faithfully monitored by each species. A brief consideration, as presented below, makes it clear that there is little danger of the number of possible proteins becoming exhausted. The biological control of protein synthesis is an incredibly complicated matter into which man is beginning to gain a little insight, as will be discussed in connection with nucleic acids.

The number of amino acids which are rather common and occur in many proteins amounts to twenty, and some dozen additional amino acids have been found in at least one polypeptide or protein. Hydrolysis of a single protein rarely gives less than seventeen amino acids. Molecular weights for the basic unit in proteins are frequently as high as 15,000, sometimes higher. For purposes of illustrating the number of proteins possible, let us consider a structure so simple that it would normally be called a polypeptide, one built from one molecule of ten different amino acids. The number of possible combinations of the amino acids is easily calculated by simple mathematics, for the number of possible sequences of arrangement of n things is factorial n. Thus, for ten amino acids, we have $10 \times 9 \times 8 \ldots \times 1$, or 3,628,800. A similar calculation for eighteen or twenty amino acids, each taken a few times rather than only once, will obviously lead to a number of a size whose significance is beyond comprehension. We may comprehend, however, that the number of possible proteins is rather properly described as infinite.

It has become possible, using such methods as described below and applying tremendous manpower, to learn the sequence of amino acids in several proteins, although all details of the structure are not well known. The synthesis of a polypeptide of the size of natural proteins, and learning to arrange it in the proper conformation (see below) has become the subject of experimentation. Certain proteins have been "synthesized" by recombination of fragments, and there is speculation that "total syntheses" of proteins may be accomplished by the end of the twentieth century. If this could actually be accomplished for numerous proteins, the principal constituent substances of a simple microorganism would be in hand, but there would remain the baffling mystery of what makes a thing alive. It seems clear that any discussions of synthesis of a living thing must remain pure fantasy until man has developed scientific tools that are as yet beyond his imagination. Research in the field of proteins is indeed difficult, but probably the most important area of scientific investigation. The methods required are mostly those of physics and physical chemistry. In particular, there are needed radically new methods of attack.

Physical Properties, Isolation, and Classification of Proteins

Proteins usually form aggregates (see below) of more than one basic molecular unit. This renders the effective molecular weights so high that usually they do not form true solutions but form colloidal solutions or suspensions in water, as well as in a few organic solvents with special properties. Living cells consist largely of proteins and water. On account of their properties, the separation and characterization of proteins do not yield to the ordinary methods of organic chemistry. Separations are accomplished by precipitation with increasing concentrations of salt in the solution or addition of organic solvents, or by use of high-speed centrifugation (*ultracentrifugation*). Proteins, like amino acids, are least soluble at their isoelectric points, since some free amino and carboxyl groups are usually present. Thus, adjustment of pH will sometimes cause precipitation of one protein while others are left in solution until the *p*H is altered.

The use of **counter-current distribution** has been among the more effective procedures for difficult separations of proteins. Its value was dramatically demonstrated in 1952 when applied by L. C. Craig, of the Rockefeller Institute, for separation of a pure sample of the hormone insulin. The principle of this method may be illustrated by considering a row of ten separatory funnels containing a solution of the mixture in the first funnel and equal portions of the same solvent in the others. The contents of each funnel, starting with that containing the mixture, are extracted in turn with a portion of a solvent immiscible with the first solvent. Thus, the components of the mixture are distributed between the two phases on each extraction, and the first lot of the second solvent is followed by nine more portions. In the separation of difficult mixtures, hundreds of "transfers" are made in a machine which shakes the mixtures, then transfers them automatically. Finally, after the counter-current distribution, each lot of solvent must be examined for homogeneity of its content of solute.

The isolation of natural proteins is especially complicated by the fact that they are **denatured** by heat, as well as numerous chemical agents including strong acids and alkalis. The principal process involved in denaturation is of a physical nature, as discussed below in connection with structural considerations; however, chemical reactions are sometimes involved. In particular, free sulfhydryl groups (—SH) are frequently formed, presumably from reduction of the disulfide link in cystine. Denaturation always decreases solubility. A cooked egg illustrates the kinds of changes that occur in denaturation. A few natural proteins have been isolated in a crystalline condition, but no denatured protein has been obtained crystalline.

Criteria of purity. Not only is the separation of a pure protein difficult; it is also quite difficult to know whether the material obtained is in a homogeneous condition. The usual criteria for purity and identity do not apply to proteins, for the substances have no boiling points or melting points, and most other physical constants are not meaningful. Solubility characteristics, and especially rate of sedimentation in the ultracentrifuge, have been the principal devices used for characterization of a protein. More recently, **electrophoresis** has been applied with considerable success. This applies to rate of migration in the electric field in an electrolytic cell. The rate of movement is influenced not only by the size and shape of the molecule but also by the number and kind of ionized groups. In several instances, electrophoresis has detected nonhomogeneity in a protein preparation which had been classified by other methods as a pure species.

Classification of proteins. On account of the difficulties which have been outlined, proteins cannot be classified in such conventional ways as applied to other organic molecules. Classification has been based largely on physical properties. For example, the **fibrous proteins** are highly insoluble species, with fiber-like characteristics. They include such things as skin, hair and feathers. Another class is that of the **globular proteins,** which are soluble species of relatively globular shape. They include a large number of well-known types such as egg albumin and the blood plasma proteins. More detailed group classifications may be found in textbooks of biochemistry or reference works on organic chemistry. The classifications are largely for operational convenience.

Proteins which contain no non-protein parts are termed simple proteins (a rather inappropriate name!), while those which have combined in their structures non-protein parts known as **prosthetic groups** are called **conjugated proteins.** Many of the most important proteins are conjugated ones. Among these are **hemoglobin,** the oxygen-carrier of the blood which contains **hemin** as the prosthetic group. Hemin is a complex molecule containing four substituted pyrrole nuclei and one atom of iron per molecule. In the oxidized form, hemin has the bright red color characteristic of arterial blood, while in the reduced form (after delivery of the oxygen) it has the dark color of venous blood. Hemin has a structure rather closely related to chlorophyll, the pigment responsible for photosynthesis in green plants. The most important of the conjugated proteins are the **nucleoproteins** which are constituents of the nuclei of cells and contain the **nucleic acids,** the subject of later discussion in this chapter.

Amino Acids from Proteins

Either acidic or basic hydrolysis of proteins cleaves the amide linkages and yields the constituent amino acids. Basic hydrolysis gives equilibration of the amides with a small amount of the enol forms, hence causes racemization at the alpha position. For this reason, acid hydrolysis must be used if optically active amino acids are desired. On the other hand, two amino acids, cystine and tryptophan, are decomposed by heating with strong acid, so the quantitative determination of these components must be made after basic hydrolysis or

Tryptophan

enzymatic hydrolysis. Hydrolysis catalyzed by enzymes is slow and usually incomplete; however, it is of great utility, not only to permit isolation of sensitive components, but also to yield polypeptides which are fragments of the original protein (cf. sequence determination below).

There are three types of amino acids from proteins: neutral, basic, and acidic. All those mentioned thus far, except for lysine, are *neutral amino acids*, in that there are present one amino group and one carboxyl group. Tryptophan has a second amino group in the indole nucleus, but this is so very weakly basic that tryptophan is regarded as a neutral amino acid. Other interesting amino acids are proline, thyroxine and phenylalanine (α-amino-β-phenylpropionic acid).

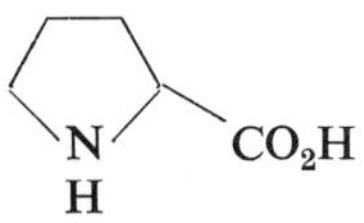

Proline 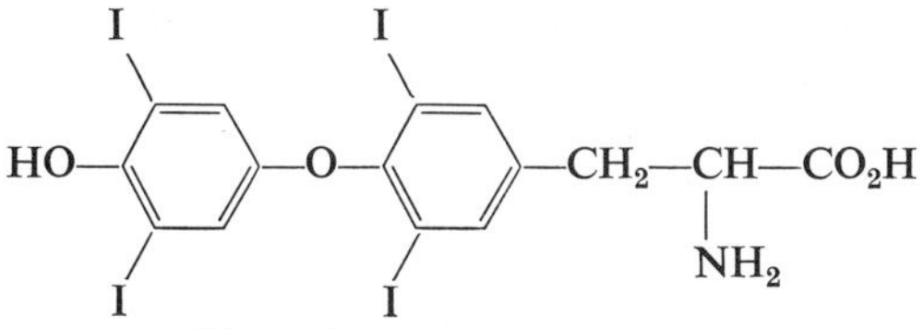   Thyroxine

The interesting feature of proline is the secondary alpha amino group. The only other natural amino acid having a secondary amino group in the alpha position is hydroxyproline, which has hydroxyl substituted in the ring opposite carboxyl.

Thyroxine is actually not a common amino acid, but an interesting and important one. Its only occurrence is in thyroglobulin, the protein hormone which is responsible for increasing the rate of metabolism. Excessive production of thyroglobulin in the thyroid gland leads to various disorders resulting from too high a rate of metabolism, while a lack of this hormone leads to the ennui resulting from too low a rate of metabolism.

Basic amino acids contain one carboxyl group and more than one amino group. Lysine, previously mentioned, is one example, and histidine is another. Histidine, which contains the heterocyclic imidazole ring system, is of considerable interest. On decarboxylation, it leads to **histamine,** which is believed

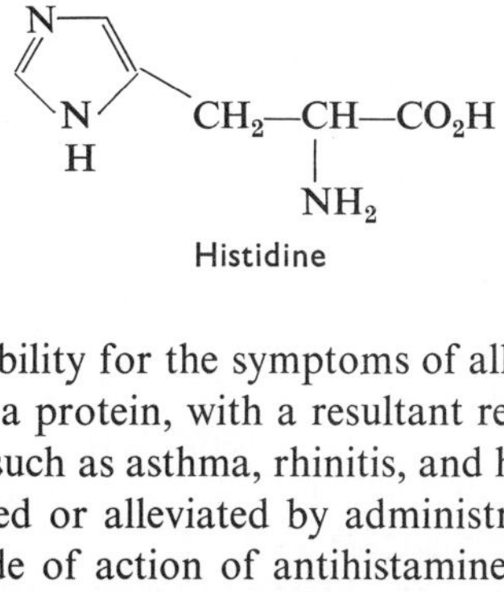

Histidine

to bear a major responsibility for the symptoms of allergy. Allergy is the result of extreme sensitivity to a protein, with a resultant release of histamine, which gives allergic symptoms such as asthma, rhinitis, and hives. The effects of histamine are often neutralized or alleviated by administration of drugs known as antihistamines. The mode of action of antihistamines is not well understood, although their substitution for histamine in some process seems indicated. All these drugs are tertiary diamines with either two or three carbons between the two amino groups. The presence of three carbon atoms between the primary and secondary amino groups in histidine may be noted.

When a basic amino acid occurs in a protein, the second amino group may be free, in which case the protein is rendered basic unless there are present more free carboxyls than amino groups. The second amino group has been found combined in a peptide linkage, to create a branched-chain structure, in some polypeptides; however, this type of cross-linkage has not been demonstrated in molecules of sufficiently high molecular weight to be regarded as proteins.

The common type of cross-linkage in proteins is the disulfide bond, —S—S—, which joins the two parts of cystine. This disulfide linkage may be formed by oxidative coupling of the sulfhydryl groups in two molecules of cysteine.

Acidic amino acids contain one amino group and two carboxyl groups. Only the two whose formulas are shown have been isolated.

$$HO_2C—CH_2—CH_2—CH—CO_2H \qquad HO_2C—CH_2—CH—CO_2H$$
$$\underset{NH_2}{|} \qquad\qquad\qquad\quad \underset{NH_2}{|}$$

Glutamic acid   Aspartic acid

The carboxyl adjacent to the amino group is that ordinarily involved in peptide bond formation, and the second carboxyl is frequently present as the simple amide. Hydrolysis of the protein yields ammonia from these simple amide groups, so determination of ammonia in the hydrolysate reveals the number of unsubstituted amide groups present.

The monosodium salt of glutamic acid, often marketed as MSG, has very interesting properties as a condiment. In particular, it improves the flavor of meat—makes it taste more like meat.

Essential amino acids. In view of the fact that living organisms can accurately synthesize all the various proteins in their structures, it seems somewhat surprising that animals are unable to synthesize certain of the amino acids. These are known as essential amino acids, for the animal must eat proteins containing them in order to live. Such proteins are obtained by eating other animals or plants containing these amino acids. Plants are the ultimate source. The proteins themselves are not the essential ingredients, for they are taken apart in the digestive process (by enzymatic hydrolysis) and used to fabricate the particular proteins characteristic of the species involved. Amino acids may also be burned to furnish energy. Ingested proteins are never incorporated directly into the tissue of the animal ingesting them. Furthermore, it has been established that proteins in the animal body are being built up and torn down continuously so that there is a rather rapid turnover of amino acids. Certain of the essential amino acids, such as histidine, are rather complex, but others such as lysine, are relatively simple.

It has also been found that different species have different requirements of essential amino acids. Histidine, for example, appears essential to rats but not to man. Rats have been most extensively studied, and there have been found ten amino acids essential to their growth. Only eight of these appear to be essential to man.

Structure Determination in Proteins

As the structures of proteins have become better understood, the complexity of these structures has grown more apparent. The structural features are described in four categories known as the **primary, secondary, tertiary, and quaternary structures.** The secondary and tertiary structures are concerned with conformation, while the primary structure involves the identity of the amino acids present and the sequence of their linkage. Thus, the primary structure is the type of structure of general applicability to organic molecules. Determination of the number and kind of amino acids present has depended largely on their separation by methods discussed earlier in this chapter. Determination of the molecular weight of the protein unit and the sequence in which the amino acids are linked are also necessary in order to define the primary structure.

Molecular weight of proteins. On account of the high molecular weight of proteins and their solubility characteristics, usual methods of determining molecular weight are not applicable. Development of the very high-speed centrifuge, the ultracentrifuge, by the Swedish chemist, The Svedberg, prior to 1930 gave a means of securing sedimentation from solution of such large molecules as proteins. Since rate of sedimentation is a function of the size of the molecule, molecular weights could be calculated. By this device, very high molecular weights were determined for many proteins, as high as 50,000,000 for some viruses. These molecular weights are accurate for the size of the particles being observed; however, subsequent studies have revealed that several (or many) of the basic molecules of the protein are frequently held together by some type of intermolecular forces (the quaternary structure; see below). These aggregates are the particles observed in ultracentrifugation; hence, the molecular weights determined by rate of sedimentation do not represent the size of the basic molecules.

Determination of the basic molecular size has proved rather difficult, and often has been accomplished only when the amino acid sequence has been established. Frequently, a **minimal molecular weight** can be established when the quantitative and qualitative analysis for amino acids and other components in the hydrolysate have been accomplished. For example, hemoglobin can contain no less than one atom of iron per molecule, and on this basis the minimal molecular weight is about 17,000. Similarly, minimal molecular weights may be based on the fact that no less than one molecule of a given amino acid may be present. In particular, except in a cyclic polypeptide, there must be at least one **terminal amino acid,** the amino acid at the end of the chain whose amino group is uncombined in a peptide linkage. In the case of branched-chain proteins, there might be two terminal amino acids which are the same, but this is unlikely unless other structural features indicate a symmetrical structure. In many instances, the minimal molecular weights, especially those based on determination of the terminal amino acid, have proved to be the actual molecular weight of a single molecule (within the precision of the experimental methods). Illustrative of the relationships just discussed, the enzyme insulin has a molecular weight by sedimentation of about 35,000, whereas the minimal molecular weight was determined as about 6,500. Determination of the complete structure of insulin by F. Sanger gave a molecule with a molecular weight of 5,734 (linkage of 48 amino acid molecules).

Amino acid sequence in proteins. The basic scheme which has been successful for determination of amino acid sequence in proteins consists of: (a) partial hydrolysis to give polypeptide fragments of various sizes and locations in the protein structure, (b) separation of the polypeptides by chromatographic methods or the closely related counter-current distribution, (c) determination of the sequence in the polypeptides, especially di- and tripeptides, (d) fitting together overlapping pieces to work out the protein structure in the manner of solving a jigsaw puzzle. The most basic tool for determining the sequence in the small polypeptides is the end-group analysis, i.e., determining the component amino acid whose amino group is uncombined.

End-group analysis depends on allowing the polypeptide (or protein) to react with some compound to give a nitrogen-carbon linkage which is able to survive hydrolysis of the peptide linkages. The amino acid from hydrolysis which has the N-substituted group is, then, the terminal amino acid in the polypeptide or protein. The most useful method has been formation of a secondary amine by use of 2,4-dinitrofluorobenzene, for the bright yellow amino acid which is substituted with the dinitrophenyl group is easily separated and recognized. Furthermore, the formation of the secondary amine occurs under mild conditions on account of activation of the fluorobenzene by the *o*- and *p*-nitro groups (cf. Chap. 18). The sequence by which the structure of a dipeptide would be established as alanylglycine is shown in Eq. 15.

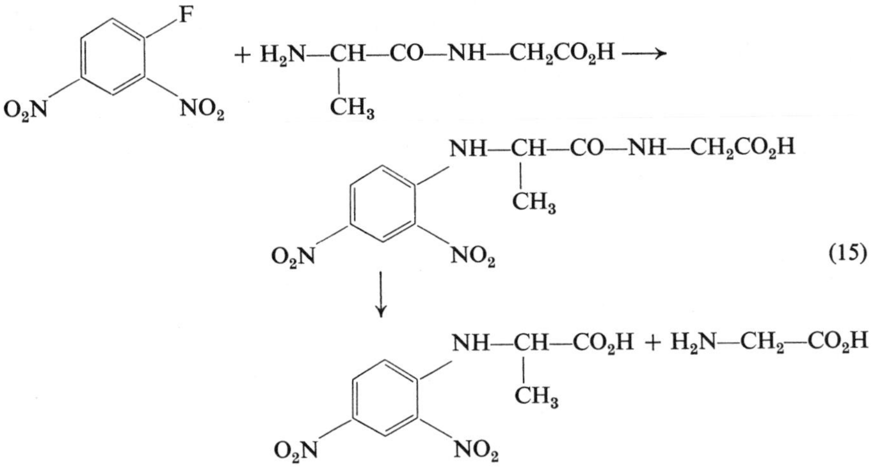

$$+ \ H_2N-CH-CO-NH-CH_2CO_2H \longrightarrow$$
with side chain CH_3 on the CH

$$NH-CH-CO-NH-CH_2CO_2H$$
with side chain CH_3

(15)

$$\downarrow$$

$$NH-CH-CO_2H \ + \ H_2N-CH_2-CO_2H$$
with side chain CH_3

In a larger polypeptide, or even a protein, the end-group is similarly established as that amino acid carrying the dinitrophenyl group after hydrolysis.

Determination of the amino acid sequence in a protein may be illustrated by considering a heptapeptide whose hydrolysis gave one molecule each of the seven amino acids A, B, C, D, E, F, and G. The experimental observations will be further defined as in the following items:

   1. End-group analysis showed F to be the terminal amino acid in the heptapeptide.

2. On partial hydrolysis with an enzyme, several di- and tri-peptides were obtained and separated. End-group tagging and hydrolysis of several of these showed the following compositions, with the end-group that listed first in each instance: (a) F(AG), (b) F—A, (c) A(CG), (d) C(BE), (e) E(BD).

Since F is followed by A [as in (b)], and peptide (a) contains G, we have the initial sequence F—A—G. We also have peptide (c), which extends the sequence to F—A—G—C. Since (d) is C(BE) and (e) is E(BD), B is after E, so we have the sequence —C—E—B—D. This completes the structure as F—A—G—C—E—B—D. Note that the structure may be deduced without use of the dipeptide.

Although the experimental data for this heptapeptide were summarized above in four sentences, thousands of man-hours of expert experimentation would be required to secure these data. In order to secure the data necessary to assign the primary structure to the protein hormone insulin[2] an awe-inspiring expenditure of man-power was required in order to determine the sequence for forty-eight molecules of amino acids. The structure includes two overlapping rings of amino acids which are formed from the disulfide linkages in three molecules of cystine.

Secondary structure. After determination of the amino acid sequence in a protein, there remains the question of the manner in which the molecule is disposed in space. The conformation in a single molecule, directed specifically towards the relative positions of amino acids which are near each other in space, is the secondary structure. It has been determined, largely by x-ray diffraction and study of optical rotation, that the most common conformation for proteins is helical. Unfortunately, pictures or diagrams of various models of proteins fail to communicate anything significant concerning the nature of the helical structure.[3] Their nature can be visualized rather well, however, by considering that the chains of amino acids are wound into a helix in the manner of the paper that is wound to make a mailing tube. In the most stable helix for S-amino acids, known as the **right-handed α-helix,** the spiraling of the polypeptide chain is in the sense of a right-handed thread on a screw, with the terminal amino group up. The principal factor contributing to the stability of the α-helix is hydrogen bonding of the carbonyl of one amino acid to the —N—H grouping in another amino acid suitably located along the spiral. For the α-helix, the

---

[2] Insulin, the hormone secreted by the pancreas, is required for metabolism of carbohydrates. In diabetes, there is a deficiency of this hormone, which is signaled by the appearance in the urine of glucose and other products of incomplete metabolism of sugars. The symptoms of diabetes are relieved by administration of the amount of insulin carefully determined as necessary to make up the deficiency. This treatment results in a spectacular relief of the symptoms, but no cure for diabetes is known, in terms of restoration of the ability of the pancreas to produce insulin.

[3] If sufficient pieces are available, it is possible to construct realistic models of the protein helix with the Framework Molecular Models. By use of tubes of appropriate lengths, hydrogen bonds can be inserted so that helices of considerable length can be conveniently held in place.

properly spaced locations occur in the amino acids in the first and third positions, second and fourth positions etc. This results in a spiral of the polypeptide linkages, with all —N—H and C=O groupings mutually hydrogen-bonded, and with the groups attached to the α-carbons projecting along the outside of the helix. This gives a relatively rigid structure, with certain groupings in definitely orientated positions with respect to each other. This matter is very important in connection with the function of proteins as hormones and enzymes (see below). The orientations would be entirely different with an *R*-amino acid rather than an *S*-structure, hence the specificity of the *S*-configuration in biological functions.

A major factor in the denaturation of proteins (see above) is "unwinding" of the helical structure to give a more or less randomly coiled polypeptide structure. This naturally destroys any biological function of the protein that depends on the proper spacing of groups, and it has been consistently noted that denaturation "kills" any biological function of the protein. Unwinding of the helix has been observed to greatly decrease the optical rotation of a protein or polypeptide. Studies on synthetic polypeptides, prepared from optically active amino acids, have shown that magnitude of optical rotation may be used as an accurate index of the amount of helical structure in the polypeptide, and this has also been of value in studying denaturation of proteins. In some instances, carefully controlled heating causes a partial unwinding of the helix, and subsequent cooling results in restoration of the helix.

Tertiary and quaternary structures in proteins are concerned with relative positions of remote parts of one or more molecules. **Tertiary structure** refers to the over-all folding of a single molecule, the manner in which a chain is oriented when not held in a helix. It deals with conformation as applied to parts of the molecule which are rather distant from each other in the amino acid sequence. Limited data on tertiary structures have become available from *x*-ray diffraction and light scattering. The **quaternary structure** refers to the forces by which the basic protein molecules are held together in aggregates. Relatively little of a detailed nature is known of the quaternary structure; however, the forces holding the aggregates together are probably any of several types of secondary valence forces, such as hydrogen bonding, chelation, and electrostatic attraction. The quaternary structure of proteins is mainly responsible for the gross shape of the aggregates observed in ultracentrifugation.

Enzymes

Enzymes are the catalysts by means of which living organisms are able to carry out the manifold complicated chemical processes on which life depends. All enzymes are proteins, but some of them owe their activity to a prosthetic group. Many of the prosthetic groups have been identified, and they frequently consist of nitrogen compounds in which nitrogen occurs in a ring (heterocyclic nitrogen compounds). The term **coenzyme** is frequently applied to the prosthetic group in conjugated proteins which are enzymes.

Enzymes are classified largely on the basis of the types of reactions which they catalyze. For example, enzymes which promote hydrolysis are known collectively as **hydrolases.** There is further subdivision among the **hydrolases.** For example, enzymes which promote hydrolysis of fats (glycerides) are known as **lipases,** named from the term lipid. Enzymes involved in reductions are known as **reductases,** while those concerned with oxidations are **oxidases.** The enzymes involved in the oxidation-reduction reactions have prosthetic groups which are oxidized as the **substrate** (material undergoing reaction) is reduced, and vice versa.

The manner in which enzymes act as such remarkable catalysts, which promote reactions under much milder conditions than possible in the laboratory, is not entirely understood, but the essential feature involves a specific orientation of the substrate on the enzyme. Forces of surface energy may be involved,

Fig. 1. Diagram illustrating failure of one enantiostereoisomer (in b) to fit the contact points of an enzyme (in a), which are fit by the other enantiostereoisomer (in c).

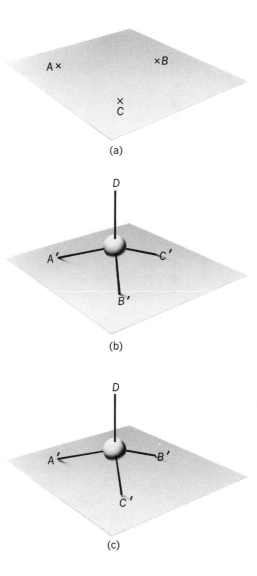

as in the case of catalytic hydrogenation. In any case, the "active sites" on the enzyme involve relatively small areas and are specifically oriented in an asymmetric sense on account of the asymmetry in the enzymes. The contact with the enzyme in an asymmetric manner may be successfully interpreted in the sense of a three-point contact. An illustration of this concept, in terms of the necessity for the correct diastereoisomer in biological processes, is presented in Fig. 1. If the points of contact with the protein are indicated by the points A, B, and C in Fig. 1(a), the asymmetric molecule in Fig. 1(c) will fit with A′, B′, and C′ in contact with A, B, and C. It is clear that the mirror image in Fig. 1(b) cannot fit properly with the contact points on the protein. This concept is also consistent with the observation that biological action of a molecule is intimately associated with its geometrical shape. The shape of the molecule is sometimes more important than the exact functional groups present.

Toxins are proteins which are poisonous to the animal organism. Many of them are lethal in exceedingly small doses; in fact, several of the most poisonous substances known are proteins. These include the venom of poisonous snakes and the toxins of many of the pathogenic bacteria. It seems probable that the action of toxins is a catalytic one, as in the case of enzymes, except that the toxin disrupts or blocks some action of an enzyme which is necessary in metabolism. Snake venoms are known to contain enzymes whose action is tissue-destroying.

Nucleic Acids

Nucleoproteins are conjugated proteins occurring in the nuclei of cells. The non-protein part of the nucleoproteins consists of complicated structures known as nucleic acids. It is established with considerable reliability that the nucleic acids carry the "code" by which the sequence of amino acids in protein synthesis is determined. These molecules, then, are responsible for the inherited characteristics transmitted from parent to offspring by the genes in cells. In view of these characteristics, the nucleic acids, as well as the nucleoproteins, have been intensively investigated.

Viruses have been the most thoroughly investigated nucleoproteins, on account of their ability to cause infection in the manner of a living organism and, indeed, to reproduce. As a matter of fact, the basic precept that the test of a living organism is ability to reproduce results in classification of a virus as living. The virus appears to reproduce, however, by using the protein-synthesizing mechanism of the host organism to synthesize the virus proteins under direction of the virus nucleic acids. The virus nucleic acids furnish the template for synthesis of themselves, as well as the accompanying proteins. The usual composition of the aggregates of nucleoproteins is largely protein, with the nucleic acid comprising a small percentage of the total. The nucleic acid molecule is of much higher molecular weight, however, than the basic protein molecule.

The **tobacco mosaic virus,** which may be obtained in a crystalline condition, has been extensively investigated. The weight of the aggregates determined in ultracentrifugation is very high, about 50,000,000. The basic protein molecule, however, is a great deal smaller. The total sequence of the 158 amino acid molecules in this protein has been determined, and this gives the basic protein molecule a molecular weight of about 17,500. In contrast, the tobacco mosaic virus nucleic acid has a molecular weight of about 2,000,000. Since the aggregate is about 94% protein, it follows that many protein molecules are associated with each nucleic acid molecule.

Structure of Nucleic Acids

Nucleic acids are made up of a sugar, phosphoric acid, and cyclic nitrogen bases. Two pentoses are the only sugars that have been found in the nucleic acids, and only one of the two is found in a given nucleic acid, never both in the same nucleic acid. One of the sugars is *R*-ribose (cf. Chap. 23), and the other is desoxyribose, which differs from ribose in lacking hydroxyl on carbon-2. A methylene group, rather than H—C—OH, occurs at position-2 in desoxyribose. The nucleic acids containing ribose are known as **ribonucleic acids,** abbreviated as **RNA,** while the nucleic acids containing desoxyribose are termed **desoxyribonucleic acids,** or **DNA.** The different functions of DNA and RNA in controlling protein synthesis, reproduction, and inheritance are becoming understood to a small extent, but these matters are beyond our present discussion of the chemistry of these fascinating substances.

The primary structure of a nucleic acid consists of a chain of sugar units, linked by phosphate ester groupings, and having nitrogen bases attached to the sugar units instead of the acetal linkage present in polysaccharides. A chain showing two sugar units in an RNA is illustrated:

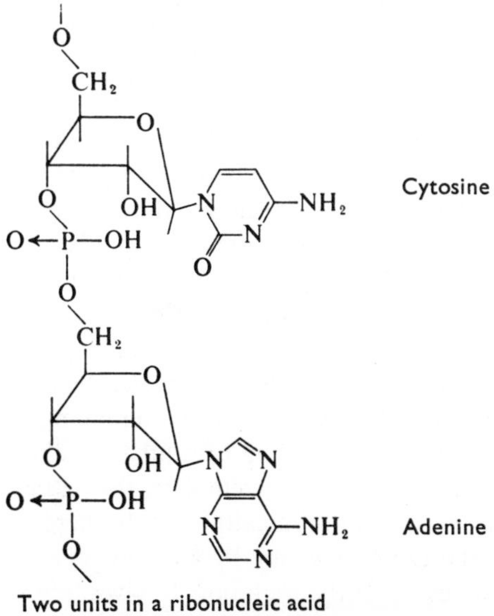

Two units in a ribonucleic acid

It will be noted that the ribose units in the RNA have the furanoside ring structure rather than the pyranoside ring characteristic of uncombined mono-saccharides. The two heterocyclic bases shown in the illustrative section of the RNA chain are among the four bases that are most abundant in RNA. The DNA molecules contain large amounts of three other bases besides adenine and cytosine, five bases total. Additional bases occur as minor components in the nucleic acids. The six-membered ring containing two nitrogen atoms in the orientation shown in cytosine is the **pyrimidine** ring system, while the bicyclic system in adenine is the **purine** ring system. All the bases in DNA and RNA are either pyrimidines or purines.

The hydrolysis of a nucleic acid with acid catalysis cleaves the phosphate ester with the primary alcohol considerably faster than that with the secondary alcohol, presumably because of the greater steric hindrance at the secondary position. This gives as a major product of the acid-catalyzed hydrolysis a sugar monophosphate, a structure known as a **nucleotide.** It may be seen that the nucleotides are building blocks from which the nucleic acids are constructed, just as the monosaccharides are the units from which polysaccharides are built

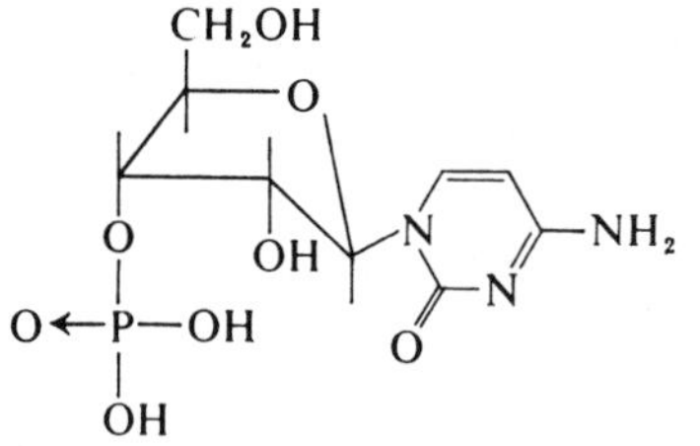

A nucleotide 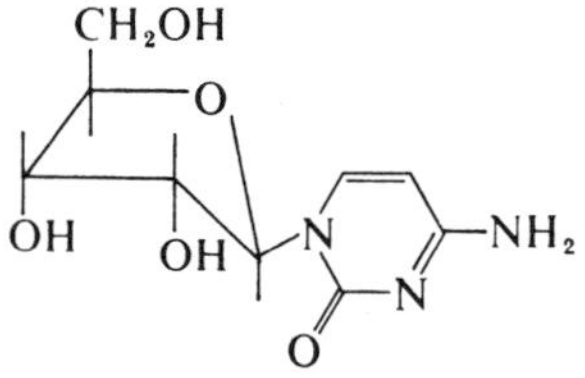   A nucleoside

and amino acids are the species from which proteins are built up. More vigorous hydrolysis of a nucleotide will cleave the phosphate ester linkage, without opening the ring of the carbohydrate unit, to give a **nucleoside.**

By x-ray diffraction, it has been possible to learn the secondary structure of a DNA molecule. This structure proves to be helical, but more complicated than the protein type of helix, in that the DNA consists of two right-handed helices that are intertwined, one with the 3-phosphate linkage below the sugar (as in the nucleotide formula shown above), the other with the 3-phosphate linkage above the sugar. Thus, the two spirals are intertwined with one proceeding in the sense of a right-handed thread down, the other a right-handed thread up. The spiral turns relatively slowly so that about ten nucleotide units are involved in a single complete turn. As in proteins, the spiral is stabilized by hydrogen bonding. The DNA molecule, then, consists of the double spiral with a base attached at each unit. Different patterns of base arrangements constitute different codes leading to synthesis of different proteins. So long as there is no damage to the DNA template, the pattern of proteins synthesized in each generation is monitored faithfully. If there is an accident, perhaps the shattering of the DNA structure by a cosmic ray or by man-made radiation, a mutation may result. If the mutation survives, there is evolution.

EXERCISES

1. Write the formula for a heptapeptide containing six different amino acids, and containing two cross links, one due to presence of lysine and the other due to presence of cystine.

2. Write the equations for synthesis of a tripeptide from three different amino acids, one of which is an acidic amino acid.

3. Outline by means of equations, not necessarily balanced but with all conditions and reagents indicated, how the following amino acids could be synthesized from the indicated starting materials. So long as continuity is maintained, any desired reagents may be used.

(a) $HC\equiv CH \longrightarrow$ glycine

(b) $CH_3-CH-CH_2OH \longrightarrow$ leucine
$\qquad\quad |$
$\qquad\;\; CH_3$

(c) $H_2C=CH_2 \longrightarrow$ aspartic acid

(Assume mono-bromination of succinic acid in the Hell-Volhard-Zelinsky reaction.)

4. An octapeptide isolated after partial hydrolysis of a protein was subjected to investigation designed to learn the sequence of amino acids in it. Reaction of the peptide with 2,4-dinitrofluorobenzene, followed by complete hydrolysis yielded the dinitrophenyl derivative of alanine along with the amino acids: leucine, isoleucine, glycine, threonine, glutamic acid, histidine, and tryptophan. There was also obtained one mole equivalent of ammonia. Partial hydrolysis, followed by separation of polypeptides, yielded four tripeptides, whose end-group analysis and hydrolysis yielded the following combinations: Thr(Gly, Ileu), Ileu(Gly, Try), Ala(Glu, Thr), and Gly(His, Try).

Write the primary structure for the octapeptide, using the condensed structural formulas for the amino acid units.

5. Define or clearly illustrate each of the following terms.

(a) Decapeptide.
(b) Carbobenzoxy chloride.
(c) Essential amino acid.
(d) Basic amino acid.
(e) *S*-Amino acid.
(f) α-Helix.
(g) Nucleotide.
(h) Nucleoprotein.
(i) Conjugated protein.
(j) Prosthetic group.
(k) Virus.
(l) Denaturation.
(m) Secondary structure of a protein.
(n) Disulfide cross link.
(o) Coenzyme.
(p) Purine ring system.
(q) Analysis for terminal amino acid.
(r) Racemization via enol formation.

26

Addition Reactions of Enolate Ions

The nature of the enolate ion was discussed in some detail in Chapter 15, in connection with the aldol condensation of aldehydes and ketones. The enolate ion may engage in addition reactions, or in displacement reactions, just as is the case for other negative species. In the case of the aldol condensation (cf. Eq. 15-39), the important step in which two aldehydes become joined involves addition of the enolate ion from one molecule to the carbonyl group of another. For convenience, this process is again shown in Eq. 1. Since

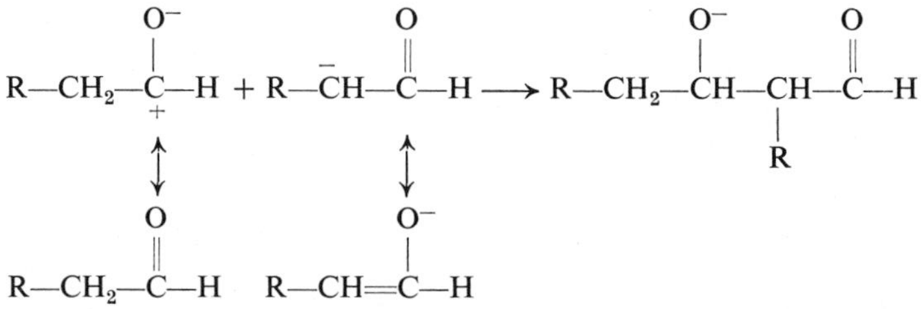

$$
\underset{\substack{\uparrow \\ \downarrow \\ \underset{\substack{\| \\ R-CH_2-C-H}}{O}}}{\overset{\overset{O^-}{|}}{\underset{+}{R-CH_2-C-H}}} + \underset{\substack{\uparrow \\ \downarrow \\ \underset{\substack{| \\ R-CH=C-H}}{O^-}}}{\overset{\overset{O}{\|}}{R-\bar{C}H-C-H}} \longrightarrow \underset{\substack{| \\ R}}{\overset{\overset{O^-}{|}}{R-CH_2-CH-CH}}-\overset{\overset{O}{\|}}{C}-H \qquad (1)
$$

addition reactions of this type may be used to build larger molecules rapidly by joining two relatively large pieces, the syntheses possible are much more diversified than most of those discussed in earlier chapters. Several of the enolate additions, commonly termed "condensations," will be discussed in the present chapter, while important displacement reactions of enolate ions will be discussed in the next chapter.

A considerable variety of enolate condensations has been developed, depending on appropriate selection of the enolate ion and the unsaturated group to be attacked by the ion. Many of these reactions are of the "cross" type; that is, the enolate ion is generated from one variety of molecule, while the unsaturated group (carbonyl or nitrile) attacked by the ion is from another species. The cross reactions are successful, however, only if the components are properly chosen. Factors involved in such cross reactions have already been discussed in Chapters 15 and 18.

The Claisen Ester Condensation

Esters will engage in condensation reactions in much the same manner as will aldehydes; however, it is necessary to use a base strong enough to give some enolate ion from the very weakly acidic ester, and a base which will not hydrolyze the ester to acid. An acid is readily converted to the carboxylate anion by a base, and the carboxylate anion is converted to an enolate ion only with extremely strong base under vigorous conditions, for such a di-anion has like charges in overlapping orbitals, a rather high-energy situation:

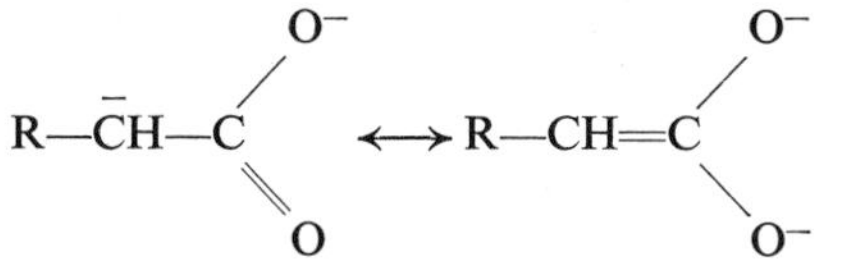

$$R-\overset{-}{C}H-\overset{O^-}{\underset{O}{C}} \longleftrightarrow R-CH=\overset{O^-}{\underset{O^-}{C}}$$

Thus, the ester condensations must be carried out in absence of water and with a suitable base. The metallic alkoxides have been most widely used. If the alkoxide is formed from the same alcohol as the ester, a mixture of esters is avoided. A typical net conversion, applied to ethyl acetate, is shown in Eq. 2.

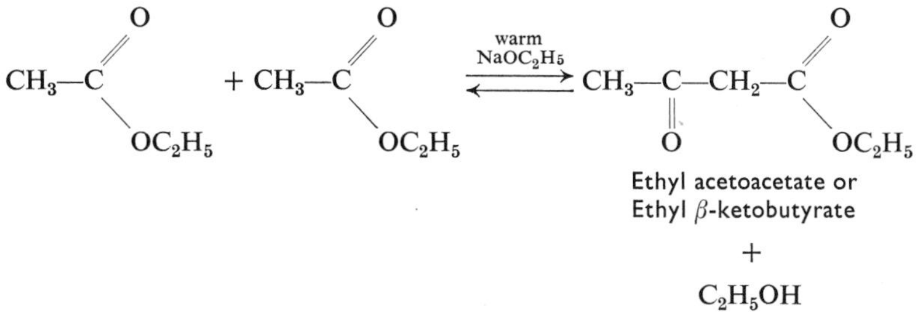

$$CH_3-\overset{O}{\underset{OC_2H_5}{C}} + CH_3-\overset{O}{\underset{OC_2H_5}{C}} \underset{\text{warm}}{\overset{NaOC_2H_5}{\rightleftarrows}} CH_3-\overset{O}{\underset{O}{C}}-CH_2-\overset{O}{\underset{OC_2H_5}{C}} \qquad (2)$$

Ethyl acetoacetate or
Ethyl β-ketobutyrate

$$+$$

$$C_2H_5OH$$

The mechanism of the reaction involves a typical attack of the enolate ion on the carbonyl in a molecule not converted to the enolate ion (Eq. 3). The initial product is an alkoxide ion, which may dissociate directly to give the β-keto ester. There may be some exchange of the hemi-ketal ion (initial product in Eq. 3) with ethanol to give the hemi-ketal; however, as discussed in Chapter 15, a hemi-ketal which is not a cyclic one dissociates almost entirely in favor of the alcohol and ketone. Thus, this alternate possible route yields the same product as the route shown in Eq. 3.

$$
\begin{array}{c}
\text{CH}_3\text{—C}\!\!\begin{array}{c}\nearrow\text{O}\\ \searrow\text{OC}_2\text{H}_5\end{array}\\
+\\
\overset{-}{\text{CH}_2}\text{—C}\!\!\begin{array}{c}\nearrow\text{O}\\ \searrow\text{OC}_2\text{H}_5\end{array}
\end{array}
\rightleftharpoons
\begin{array}{c}
\overset{\text{O}^-}{\underset{\text{CH}_2\text{—CO}_2\text{C}_2\text{H}_5}{\text{CH}_3\text{—C—OC}_2\text{H}_5}}
\end{array}
\rightleftharpoons
\begin{array}{c}
\overset{\text{O}}{\overset{\|}{\text{CH}_3\text{—C—CH}_2\text{—CO}_2\text{C}_2\text{H}_5}}\\
+\\
\text{C}_2\text{H}_5\text{O}^-
\end{array}
\qquad (3)
$$

In actuality, the β-keto ester shown as the final product in Eqs. 2 and 3 is obtained only after water is added to the completed reaction. In the presence of the strong base, sodium ethoxide, a β-keto ester is converted to a major extent to the enolate ion (Eq. 4), for the β-keto ester is a much stronger acid than a simple ketone or ester. This follows logically from the fact that electron delocalization in the β-keto ester anion, as in the resonance forms in Eq. 4,

$$
\underset{\text{O}}{\overset{\|}{\text{CH}_3\text{—C—CH}_2\text{—CO}_2\text{C}_2\text{H}_5}} + {}^-\text{OC}_2\text{H}_5 \rightleftharpoons \underset{\text{O}}{\overset{\|}{\text{CH}_3\text{—C—}\overset{-}{\text{C}}\text{H—CO}_2\text{C}_2\text{H}_5}}
$$

$$
\underset{\text{O}^-}{\text{CH}_3\text{—C}{=}\text{CH—CO}_2\text{C}_2\text{H}_5} \qquad (4)
$$

$$
\underset{\text{O}}{\overset{\|}{\text{CH}_3\text{—C—CH}{=}\text{C}}}\!\!\begin{array}{c}\nearrow\text{O}^-\\ \searrow\text{OC}_2\text{H}_5\end{array}
$$

occurs in a much larger orbital than possible in the mono-unsaturated compounds. This lowers the energy of the enolate ion, thus increases acidity of the carbonyl compound. Since the product of the Claisen condensation competes successfully for the base used as catalyst, at least one equivalent of ethoxide for two moles of starting ester must be used so that base will be sufficient to convert all the starting ester to product. Since this condensation is reversible, as are most enolate addition reactions, it is often an advantage to use an excess of base and to remove the alcohol formed as a product.

Other types of compounds with two unsaturated groups on a single carbon are also relatively acidic, as is the case with β-keto esters. The most important of these is the di-ester of malonic acid, the three-carbon dibasic acid. This substance will be utilized in reactions discussed later in this chapter. It figures especially prominently in the enolate displacements discussed in the next chapter.

The β-keto esters are also of much importance in synthesis, on account of their relatively acidic methylene group, so the Claisen condensation becomes a useful reaction for supplying this type of synthetic intermediate. It should be borne in mind that the ester obtained in a simple condensation (one ester used, as in Eq. 2) has the following form:

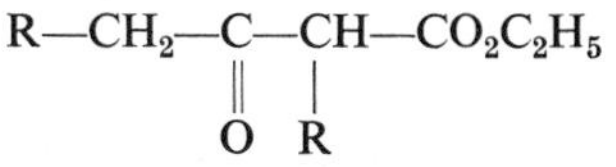

$$R-CH_2-\underset{\underset{O}{\|}}{C}-\underset{\underset{R}{|}}{CH}-CO_2C_2H_5$$

If the R groups are different, then the compound can be obtained only in a cross condensation, and this fails to yield the desired compound in separable form unless components can be chosen so as to avoid some of the four reactions normally possible. For example, condensation of ethyl acetate with ethyl propionate will yield four esters:

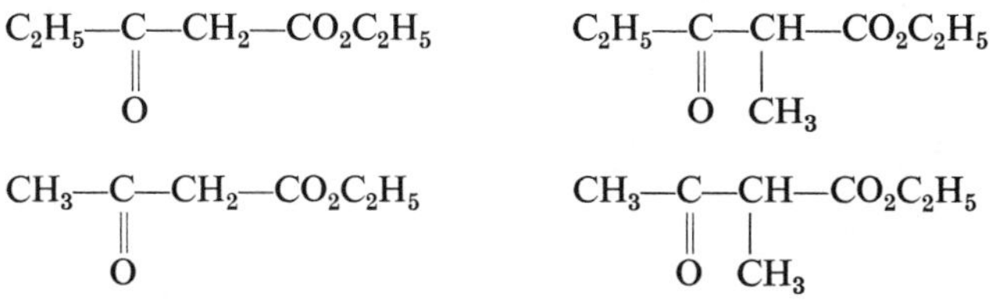

$$C_2H_5-\underset{\underset{O}{\|}}{C}-CH_2-CO_2C_2H_5 \qquad C_2H_5-\underset{\underset{O}{\|}}{C}-\underset{\underset{CH_3}{|}}{CH}-CO_2C_2H_5$$

$$CH_3-\underset{\underset{O}{\|}}{C}-CH_2-CO_2C_2H_5 \qquad CH_3-\underset{\underset{O}{\|}}{C}-\underset{\underset{CH_3}{|}}{CH}-CO_2C_2H_5$$

Since one of the cross products is the desirable compound (otherwise a cross condensation would not be attempted), the very low yield is complicated by the fact that separation of the desired product is difficult if at all possible. The cross products, on the upper left and lower right, are isomeric, so their physical properties are likely to be sufficiently similar to render separation difficult.

A **cross condensation** becomes practical if one ester has no alpha hydrogens, for this eliminates two products, including one of the cross products. Most commonly used in cross condensations are ethyl formate (Eq. 5) and esters of aromatic acids (Eq. 6). In the reaction shown in Eq. 5, the yield of

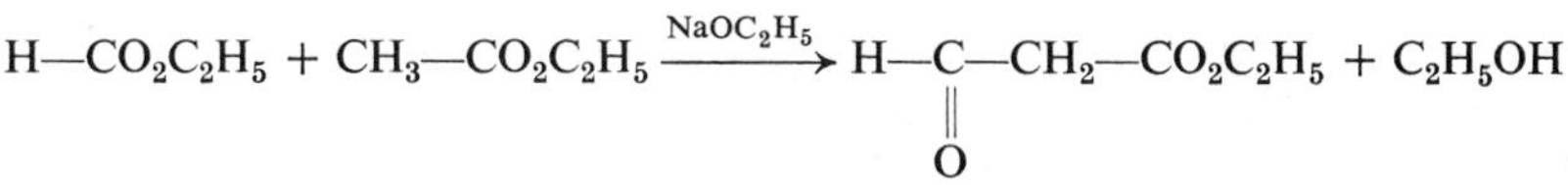

$$H-CO_2C_2H_5 + CH_3-CO_2C_2H_5 \xrightarrow{NaOC_2H_5} H-\underset{\underset{O}{\|}}{C}-CH_2-CO_2C_2H_5 + C_2H_5OH$$

$$(5)$$

Ethyl formylacetate

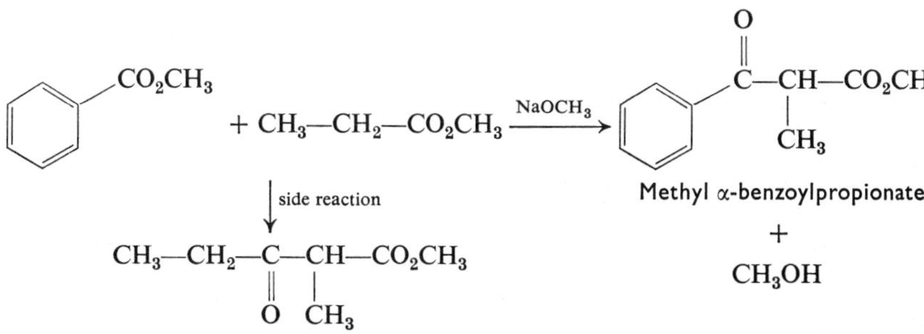

(6)

Methyl α-benzoylpropionate

+

CH₃OH

side reaction

$$CH_3-CH_2-\underset{\underset{O}{\|}}{C}-\underset{\underset{CH_3}{|}}{CH}-CO_2CH_3$$

ethyl formylacetate is quite good, for the carbonyl group in ethyl formate is so highly reactive that the condensation of ethyl acetate with itself is a minor side reaction. In the reaction shown in Eq. 6, formation of methyl α-propionyl-propionate is a major side reaction; however, separation of this compound from the desired product is no problem on account of the significantly higher molecular weight of the methyl α-benzoylpropionate. In addition, an excess of the cheap methyl propionate may be used so that a good yield may be secured on the basis of methyl benzoate. This factor would become still more important if a substituted benzoate (more expensive) were used.

Ester condensation with aldehydes. The carbonyl in an aldehyde is considerably more reactive than that in an ester. This is reflected in the observation that the aldol condensation occurs rapidly at room temperature or below, whereas the Claisen ester condensation is very sluggish unless heated moderately. It follows that an excellent cross condensation may be secured between an ester and an aldehyde with no alpha hydrogens. Thus, cinnamate esters may be secured in excellent yield (Eq. 7). At a temperature near zero

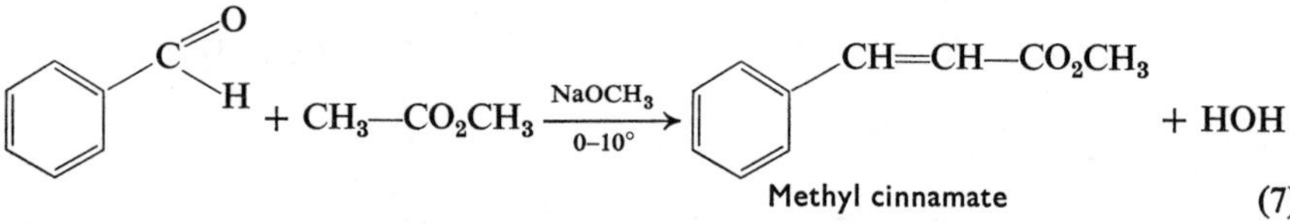

$$
\text{PhCHO} + CH_3-CO_2CH_3 \xrightarrow[0-10°]{NaOCH_3} \text{Ph-CH=CH-CO}_2CH_3 + HOH
$$

Methyl cinnamate (7)

degrees, there is essentially no condensation of the ester with itself, so the cinnamate is obtained in high yield. As usual when a benzyl alcohol is obtained as initial product in a condensation, the dehydrated compound is the final product of the reaction.

Perkin Condensation

This condensation is a cross reaction between an aromatic aldehyde (no alpha hydrogens) and an acid anhydride. The catalyst is the sodium salt of a carboxylic acid. The most simple Perkin condensation is shown in Eq. 8. The weakly basic sodium carboxylate no doubt gives a low concentration of enolate ion of the anhydride, so a rather high temperature is required to accomplish the reaction. The condensation involved in Eq. 8 differs from that in Eq. 7 only in that the ester is replaced with the anhydride. The initial products of the

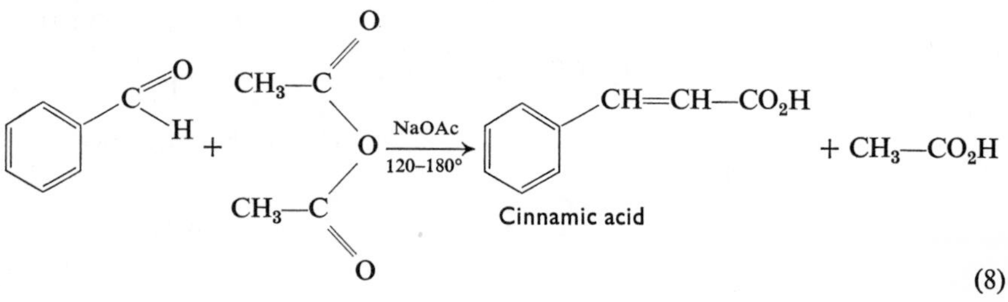

$$
\text{PhCHO} + (CH_3CO)_2O \xrightarrow[120-180°]{NaOAc} \text{Ph-CH=CH-CO}_2H + CH_3-CO_2H
$$

Cinnamic acid (8)

condensation may be regarded as the mixed anhydride and water, in which case water would hydrolyze the mixed anhydride to give two moles of acid as shown in the net reaction. It is likely, however, that reaction between the mixed anhydride and the sodium acetate also yields acetic anhydride and the sodium salt of cinnamic acid, for this type of equilibrium is known to occur. For example, if the catalyst is the salt of a different acid than that in the anhydride, the equilibrium shown in Eq. 9 occurs. It seems necessary that the mixed

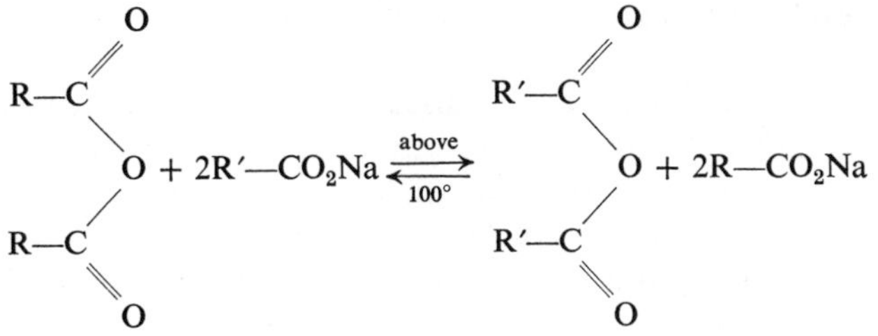

$$
\begin{matrix}
\text{R—C} \\ \text{R—C}
\end{matrix}\Bigg\rangle\text{O} + 2\text{R}'\text{—CO}_2\text{Na} \underset{100°}{\overset{\text{above}}{\rightleftharpoons}} \begin{matrix}
\text{R}'\text{—C} \\ \text{R}'\text{—C}
\end{matrix}\Bigg\rangle\text{O} + 2\text{R—CO}_2\text{Na} \qquad (9)
$$

anhydride be an intermediate in this equilibrium. Unless the equilibrium happens to lie quite far in one direction, and condensation is desired with the anhydride on the favored side, it obviously becomes necessary to use the same acid for both anhydride and salt. Otherwise the product will be a mixture of two cinnamic acids. In illustration, if propionic anhydride is condensed with benzaldehyde, using sodium acetate as catalyst, the product is likely to be a mixture of cinnamic acid and α-methylcinnamic acid. For this reason, it is sometimes necessary to accept a low yield in the Perkin reaction, or else consume three moles of the acid (two in the anhydride, one in the salt). The choice will depend on ease of separation of the anticipated mixture and cost of the acid in question.

It should be noted that the Perkin condensation and the condensation of an ester with an aldehyde (Eq. 7) are competitive reactions. One gives the ester, while the other gives the acid. The Perkin reaction is applicable to a wider variety of aromatic aldehydes, but the aldehyde-ester reaction gives higher yields in many cases, with consumption of only one mole of the acid. The Perkin reaction requires a minimum of two moles of acid, since one mole of anhydride is consumed.

If the Perkin reaction is carried out with an o-hydroxybenzaldehyde, the

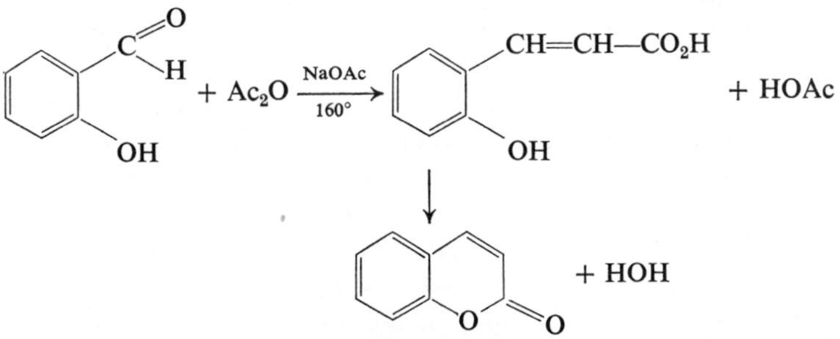

$$
\text{(o-hydroxybenzaldehyde)} + \text{Ac}_2\text{O} \xrightarrow[160°]{\text{NaOAc}} \text{(o-hydroxycinnamic acid, CH=CH—CO}_2\text{H)} + \text{HOAc} \qquad (10)
$$

$$\downarrow$$

Coumarin + HOH

initial product cannot be isolated because of the ease with which the lactone is formed (cf. Chap. 16 for discussion of lactones). Condensation of salicylaldehyde is shown in Eq. 10. Coumarin is manufactured for use in flavors and perfumes (odor of new-mown hay, it is said). Vanilla extract in current use is nearly always compounded from synthetic vanillin (cf. Eq. 17-33) and synthetic coumarin.

Michael Condensations

In the enolate condensations discussed thus far, the enolate ion has attacked the carbonyl carbon. If an α,β-unsaturated carbonyl compound is used, attack may occur at the β-position in the manner of a 1,4-addition. Such reactions are known as Michael condensations and a variety of them occur in satisfactory yield if the cross reaction is favored by use of an enolate from a more acidic compound such as a β-keto ester or malonic ester. Compounds of this acidity may be readily converted almost entirely to the enolate ion so that the principal carbonyl species remaining in the solution is the α,β-unsaturated compound. A typical condensation of this sort is shown in Eq. 11. This particular reaction gives an excellent yield, near 90%. The prin-

$$CH_3-CH=CH-CO_2CH_3 + \underset{CO_2CH_3}{\overset{CO_2CH_3}{CH_2}} \xrightarrow{NaOCH_3} \underset{\underset{CO_2CH_3}{\overset{|}{CH-CO_2CH_3}}}{\overset{|}{CH_3-CH-CH_2-CO_2CH_3}} \quad (11)$$

Methyl crotonate   Dimethyl malonate

cipal use of compounds such as the product in Eq. 11 involves the facile decarboxylation of malonic acids, which will be discussed in the final section in this chapter. The attack of the malonate ion on the unsaturated ester may be represented as in Eq. 12. The initial product is the enolate ion of the monoester; however, the alternate enolate ion of the malonic ester is of considerably lower energy; therefore a rapid proton exchange would occur to give the ion of greater resonance stabilization, shown in the lower line of Eq. 12. This ion is the product of the reaction, but is rapidly converted to the ester (product shown in Eq. 11) when water is added after the condensation is completed.

In Michael condensations with α,β-unsaturated ketones, the α-position of the ketone in the initial reaction product is so spaced with respect to the ester group that a second condensation to give a cyclic product usually occurs. A typical condensation of this type is the reaction between a malonic ester and mesityl oxide (Eq. 13). The initial product in Eq. 13 is capable of giving several enolate ions, but the one in which the ion is formed at the methyl group has a strategic location for attack on the carbonyl in the ester group to yield a ring of favored size (six atoms). Thus, this reaction occurs, and the product isolated is

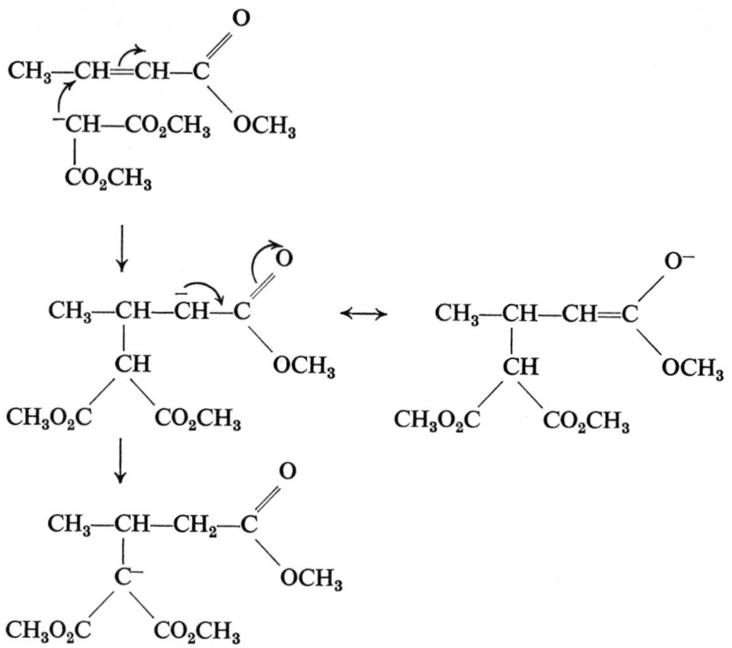

$$CH_3-CH=CH-C\overset{O}{\underset{OCH_3}{\diagdown}}$$
$$\underset{\overset{|}{CO_2CH_3}}{{}^-CH-CO_2CH_3}$$

$$\downarrow$$

$$CH_3-CH-\overset{-}{CH}-C\overset{O}{\underset{OCH_3}{\diagdown}} \quad\longleftrightarrow\quad CH_3-CH-CH=C\overset{O^-}{\underset{OCH_3}{\diagdown}} \qquad (12)$$

$$\underset{CH_3O_2C\quad CO_2CH_3}{\overset{|}{CH}} \qquad\qquad \underset{CH_3O_2C\quad CO_2CH_3}{\overset{|}{CH}}$$

$$\downarrow$$

$$CH_3-CH-CH_2-C\overset{O}{\underset{OCH_3}{\diagdown}}$$
$$\underset{CH_3O_2C\quad CO_2CH_3}{\overset{|}{\underset{\diagup\quad\diagdown}{C^-}}}$$

that shown in the lower line of Eq. 13. The α,β-unsaturated ketone used in Eq. 13 is readily available, for it is the product resulting from dehydration of the aldol condensation product from acetone.

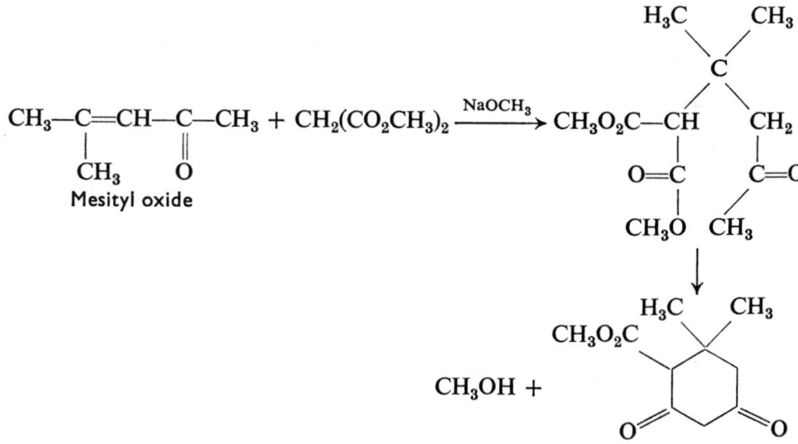

$$\underset{\substack{\overset{|}{CH_3}\quad\overset{\|}{O}\\ \text{Mesityl oxide}}}{CH_3-C=CH-C-CH_3} + CH_2(CO_2CH_3)_2 \xrightarrow{\text{NaOCH}_3} \begin{array}{c} H_3C\quad CH_3 \\ \diagdown\diagup \\ C \\ CH_3O_2C-\overset{|}{CH}\quad \overset{|}{CH_2} \\ \overset{\|}{O=C}\quad \overset{\|}{C=O} \\ \overset{|}{CH_3O}\quad \overset{|}{CH_3} \end{array}$$

$$\downarrow \qquad (13)$$

$$CH_3OH + \begin{array}{c} H_3C\quad CH_3 \\ CH_3O_2C\diagdown \\ \end{array}$$

Since the esters of malonic acid have been utilized in the Michael reactions described thus far, it should be mentioned that the dialkyl malonates are readily available from acetic acid, using reactions previously discussed (Eq. 14).

$$CH_3-CO_2H + Br_2 \xrightarrow[\text{PBr}_3]{\text{trace of}} Br-CH_2-CO_2H \xrightarrow{{}^-CN} NC-CH_2-CO_2H \qquad (14)$$

$$\downarrow \text{CH}_3\text{OH,H}^+$$

$$CH_3O_2C-CH_2-CO_2CH_3$$

If any of these steps seem unfamiliar, they should be reviewed by locating them via the index of the book. Dimethyl malonate and diethyl malonate are manufactured by this process and sold at a relatively modest price.

Cyanoethylation. Although the Michael condensation usually requires the enolate ion from a compound whose acidity is enhanced by two carbonyl groups, acrylonitrile, $CH_2=CH-C\equiv N$, is so very highly reactive that it will react sufficiently readily with less acidic compounds, such as aldehydes and ketones, to give a good cross reaction of the Michael type. Indeed, all available alpha hydrogens are replaced rapidly so that the only product isolated in satisfactory yield is that resulting from replacement of all alpha hydrogens.

$$C_3H_7-\underset{\underset{CH_3}{|}}{CH}-CHO + CH_2=CH-CN \xrightarrow{^-OH} C_3H_7-\underset{\underset{CH_2-CH_2-CN}{|}}{\overset{\overset{CH_3}{|}}{C}}-CHO \qquad (15)$$

2-(β-Cyanoethyl)-
2-methylpentanal

Thus, α-substituted aldehydes are often used (Eq. 15) to secure monosubstitution. In the case of an unsymmetrical ketone, there is difficulty with substitution on either side to give a mixture of products; however, a symmetrical ketone yields substitution of all hydrogens on one side of the carbonyl (Eq. 16). Presumably steric hindrance prevents substitution of the hydrogens on the other side, while the first cyanoethylation renders additional substitution on that side more rapid. The basic reason for the latter factor is not well understood.

$$CH_3-\underset{\underset{O}{\|}}{C}-CH_3 + 3CH_2=CH-CN \xrightarrow{^-OH} CH_3-\underset{\underset{O}{\|}}{C}-\underset{\underset{CH_2-CH_2-CN}{|}}{\overset{\overset{CH_2-CH_2-CN}{|}}{C}}-CH_2-CH_2-CN \quad (16)$$

In compounds such as obtained as products in Eqs. 15 and 16, the carbonyl group is so hindered that the nitrile may be hydrolyzed by boiling with concentrated acid or base, without affecting the carbonyl. If the product in Eq. 15 is used as starting material, final oxidation of the aldehyde then gives a dibasic acid of a type quite difficult to secure by other methods (Eq. 17).

$$C_3H_7-\underset{\underset{CH_2-CH_2-CN}{|}}{\overset{\overset{CH_3}{|}}{C}}-CHO \xrightarrow[\text{heat}]{\text{HOH, H}^+} C_3H_7-\underset{\underset{CH_2-CH_2-CO_2H}{|}}{\overset{\overset{CH_3}{|}}{C}}-CHO \xrightarrow{KMnO_4}$$

$$HO_2C-CH_2-CH_2-\underset{\underset{C_3H_7}{|}}{\overset{\overset{CH_3}{|}}{C}}-CO_2H \qquad (17)$$

α-Methyl-α-propylglutaric acid

On account of the variety of products obtainable, the cyanoethylation reaction has been among the most useful of the Michael condensations.

The Knoevenagel Reaction

A cross reaction may be secured between an aldehyde and one of the more acidic compounds such as malonic ester. The reaction occurs in either a 1:1 manner (Eq. 18) or a 1:2 manner (Eq. 19), depending on details of catalyst, temperature, solvent, and other variables. Usually, sufficient study can

$$
CH_3-CHO + \underset{\underset{CO_2C_2H_5}{|}}{\overset{\overset{CO_2C_2H_5}{|}}{CH_2}} \xrightarrow[\substack{such\ as \\ (C_2H_5)_3N}]{basic\ catalyst} CH_3-CH{=}\underset{\underset{CO_2C_2H_5}{|}}{\overset{\overset{CO_2C_2H_5}{|}}{C}} \quad + HOH \quad (18)
$$

$$
CH_3-CHO + 2\underset{\underset{CO_2C_2H_5}{|}}{\overset{\overset{CO_2C_2H_5}{|}}{CH_2}} \xrightarrow[catalyst]{basic} CH_3-\underset{\underset{CH-CO_2C_2H_5}{|}}{\overset{\overset{CH-CO_2C_2H_5}{|}}{CH}} \quad + HOH \quad (19)
$$

define conditions which yield either the 1:1 or 1:2 reaction in satisfactory yield, and in planning a synthesis it is reasonable to assume that either of the reactions may be secured. In practice, considerable experimentation is frequently required before suitable conditions can be found for the desired reaction; however, the products of the Knoevenagel reactions have many uses in synthesis.

As is indicated in Eqs. 18 and 19, an aldehyde with alpha hydrogens is successful in the Knoevenagel reactions when a more acidic compound is used as the second component. The much higher concentration of enolate ion from malonic ester competes successfully with the enolate ion from the aldehyde, although the latter will give side reactions, of course. A rather reactive ketone is also satisfactory in the Knoevenagel reaction; this includes methyl ketones and cyclic ketones. β-Keto esters are useful in 1:1 Knoevenagel reactions, but when the 1:2 reaction is attempted rather complex cyclic products result, on account of follow reactions such as that shown in Eq. 13.

The mechanism of the Knoevenagel reaction is rather interesting, in that the first step is a normal enolate condensation (Eq. 20) followed by loss of water, while the second step is a Michael condensation (Eq. 21). Loss of water in a facile manner occurs with esters having hydroxyl beta to two ester groups. This may well be an elimination of the E2 type (cf. Chap. 9), facilitated by the relatively high acidity of the hydrogen alpha to two ester groups. This compensates for the fact that hydroxyl is ordinarily too poor a leaving group to engage in an E2 elimination.

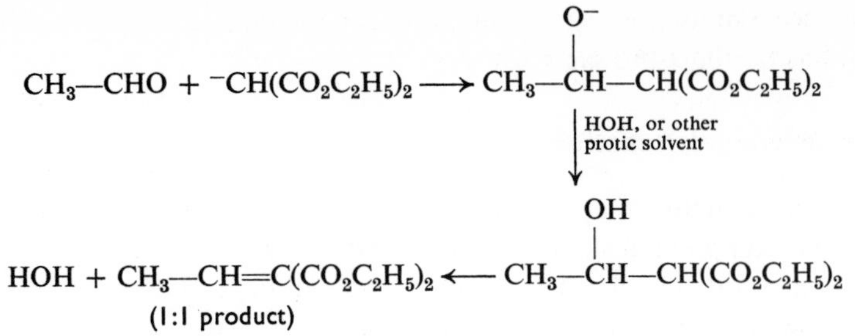

$$CH_3—CHO + {}^-CH(CO_2C_2H_5)_2 \longrightarrow CH_3—\overset{\overset{\displaystyle O^-}{|}}{CH}—CH(CO_2C_2H_5)_2 \qquad (20)$$

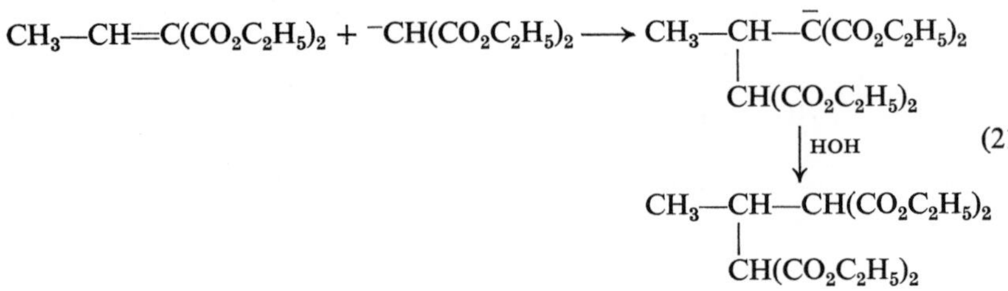

HOH, or other
protic solvent

$$HOH + CH_3—CH{=}C(CO_2C_2H_5)_2 \longleftarrow CH_3—\overset{\overset{\displaystyle OH}{|}}{CH}—CH(CO_2C_2H_5)_2$$
(I:I product)

$$CH_3—CH{=}C(CO_2C_2H_5)_2 + {}^-CH(CO_2C_2H_5)_2 \longrightarrow CH_3—\overset{\overset{\displaystyle }{|}}{CH}—\overset{\overset{\displaystyle }{|}}{\overset{-}{C}}(CO_2C_2H_5)_2$$
$$CH(CO_2C_2H_5)_2$$

HOH (21)

$$CH_3—\overset{\overset{\displaystyle }{|}}{CH}—CH(CO_2C_2H_5)_2$$
$$CH(CO_2C_2H_5)_2$$

Facile Decarboxylation of β-Keto Acids and Malonic Acids

Structures in which there is a carbonyl group beta to a carboxyl decarboxylate with unusual ease. In fact, a β-keto acid usually decarboxylates at room temperature, so that saponification of a β-keto ester, followed by acidification of the reaction mixture, results in vigorous evolution of carbon dioxide and formation of a ketone (Eq. 22). This ready loss of carbon dioxide occurs in

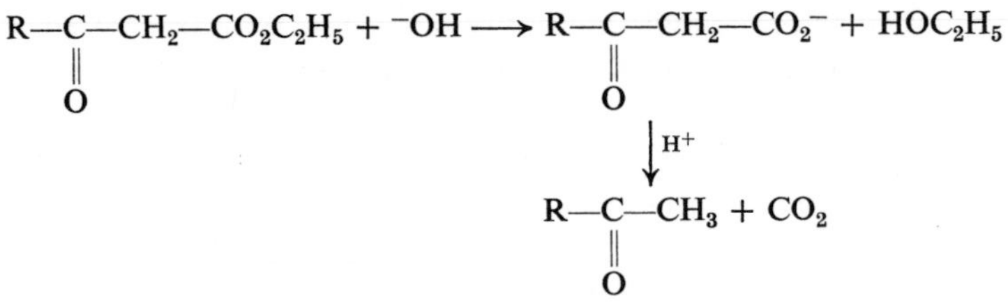

$$R—\overset{\overset{\displaystyle }{||}}{\underset{\underset{\displaystyle O}{}}{C}}—CH_2—CO_2C_2H_5 + {}^-OH \longrightarrow R—\overset{\overset{\displaystyle }{||}}{\underset{\underset{\displaystyle O}{}}{C}}—CH_2—CO_2{}^- + HOC_2H_5$$

H+

(22)

$$R—\overset{\overset{\displaystyle }{||}}{\underset{\underset{\displaystyle O}{}}{C}}—CH_3 + CO_2$$

the anion of the keto acid (Eq. 23), as the keto group is protonated. Although the keto group is protonated only in rather acidic solution, some anion of the

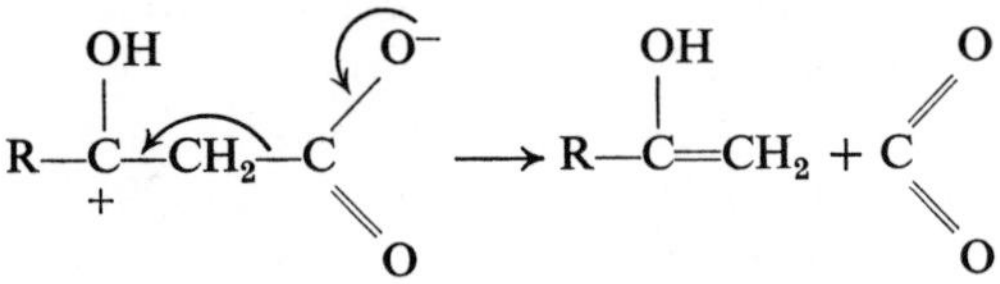

$$R—\overset{\overset{\displaystyle OH}{|}}{\underset{\underset{\displaystyle +}{}}{C}}{-}CH_2{-}C\overset{\diagup O^-}{\diagdown\!\!_O} \longrightarrow R—\overset{\overset{\displaystyle OH}{|}}{C}{=}CH_2 + C\overset{\diagup O}{\diagdown\!\!_O} \qquad (23)$$

carboxyl group would be formed by simple dissociation of carboxyl. The ease of loss of carbon dioxide is attributed to the fact that the other product besides the resonance-stabilized carbon dioxide molecule is the enol form of the ketone. Of course the enol form of the ketone will go rapidly to the keto form. If it were not for the adjacent carbonyl group, the other product would be a carbanion, which is a rather high-energy species.

Malonic acids also decarboxylate readily, but not so easily as the β-keto acids. Ordinarily, it is necessary to heat the malonic acid above 150°, but the yield of mono-acid is excellent. The malonic acid is usually heated alone for decarboxylation. Under these conditions, in absence of any ionizing solvent and strong acid, it is probable that the mechanism of transfer of a proton to the beta carbonyl is via a cyclic transition state (Eq. 24).

$$
\begin{array}{c}
\text{(Eq. 24)}
\end{array}
$$

$$R-CH_2-C\underset{\text{OH}}{\overset{\text{O}}{\diagdown}} \qquad (24)$$

$$R-CH=C\diagup_{\text{OH}}^{\text{}} + CO_2$$

The initial product is the enol form of the carboxylic acid. The basic mechanism in this decarboxylation is the same as that shown in Eq. 23 except that a specific proton is transferred.

Synthetic applications of facile decarboxylation. The relatively high acidity of the β-dicarbonyl compounds renders them useful in numerous synthetic reactions, some of which have been discussed in this chapter and others which will be discussed in the next chapter. In turn, the facile decarboxylation of the acids obtained by hydrolysis gives compounds of considerable use in synthesis. These applications may be illustrated by reference to compounds prepared in syntheses already described in this chapter.

Hydrolysis and decarboxylation of the product from Eq. 11 gives β-methylglutaric acid, and this constitutes the best synthesis of this compound (Eq. 25). Of course use of a higher molecular weight α,β-unsaturated ester in the

$$
\begin{array}{c}
CH_3-CH-CH_2-CO_2CH_3 + HOH \xrightarrow[\text{-OH}]{\text{H}^+ \text{ or}} CH_3-CH-CH_2-CO_2H \\
\qquad\quad | \qquad\qquad\qquad\qquad\qquad\qquad\qquad\qquad\quad | \\
\qquad\quad CH-CO_2CH_3 \qquad\qquad\qquad\qquad\qquad\quad CH-CO_2H \\
\qquad\quad | \qquad\qquad\qquad\qquad\qquad\qquad\qquad\qquad\quad | \\
\qquad\quad CO_2CH_3 \qquad\qquad\qquad\qquad\qquad\qquad\quad CO_2H \qquad (25) \\
\qquad\qquad\qquad\qquad\qquad\qquad\qquad\qquad\qquad\quad \downarrow\ 150\text{–}180° \\
CO_2 + HO_2C-CH_2-CH-CH_2-CO_2H \\
\qquad\qquad\qquad\qquad\qquad\quad | \\
\qquad\qquad\qquad\qquad\qquad\quad CH_3
\end{array}
$$

original Michael condensation will lead to a glutaric acid substituted with a group larger than methyl in the β-position.

An alternate synthesis of β-substituted glutaric acids utilizes products of the 1:2 Knoevenagel condensation. For example, hydrolysis and decarboxylation of the product of the reaction in Eq. 19 yields β-methylglutaric acid.

The two synthetic routes are competitive, but the Michael condensation is not troubled by an alternate reaction pathway (the 1:1 condensation in the Knoevenagel reaction).

The product of the reaction in Eq. 13 is a β-keto ester, so hydrolysis and acidification yields the cyclic diketone (Eq. 26). Since this product is a

$$
\begin{array}{ccc}
\underset{\displaystyle\text{(CH}_3\text{O}_2\text{C)}}{\overset{\displaystyle\text{H}_3\text{C}\quad\text{CH}_3}{\bigcirc}} & \xrightarrow[\text{(2) H}^+]{\text{(1) hydrolysis}} & \overset{\displaystyle\text{H}_3\text{C}\quad\text{CH}_3}{\bigcirc}
\end{array}
\tag{26}
$$

1,3-diketone, it gives reactions such as a 1:2 Knoevenagel condensation with aldehydes.

Hydrolysis and decarboxylation of the 1:1 Knoevenagel product gives interesting results, in that the β,γ-unsaturated acid is formed,[1] rather than the α,β-unsaturated acid which might be expected (Eq. 27).

$$
\underset{\displaystyle\text{CO}_2\text{C}_2\text{H}_5}{\overset{\displaystyle\text{CO}_2\text{C}_2\text{H}_5}{\text{R}-\text{CH}_2-\text{CH}=\text{C}}} + 2\,{}^-\text{OH} \longrightarrow \underset{\displaystyle\text{CO}_2^-}{\overset{\displaystyle\text{CO}_2^-}{\text{R}-\text{CH}_2-\text{CH}=\text{C}}}
$$

$$
\xrightarrow[\text{(2) heat}]{\text{(1) H}^+}
$$

$$
\begin{array}{l}
\text{CO}_2 + \text{R}-\text{CH}=\text{CH}-\text{CH}_2-\text{CO}_2\text{H} \\
+ \text{ minor amount of } \alpha,\beta\text{-} \\
\text{unsaturated isomer}
\end{array}
\tag{27}
$$

This synthesis is among the very few methods which yield a β,γ-unsaturated acid in relatively homogeneous condition. Reduction of the acid with lithium aluminum hydride (Eq. 28) yields the unsaturated alcohol, useful in various syntheses.

$$
\text{R}-\text{CH}=\text{CH}-\text{CH}_2-\text{CO}_2\text{H} + 4[\text{H}] \longrightarrow \text{R}-\text{CH}=\text{CH}-\text{CH}_2-\text{CH}_2\text{OH} + \text{HOH}
$$
$$
\text{(LiAlH}_4\text{)}
\tag{28}
$$

The Principle of Vinylogy

It has been discussed at some length that the enolate ion is stabilized by resonance, and condensation always occurs on the alpha carbon because this is the only carbon which can bear the charge in a resonance form. If there is a carbon-carbon double bond conjugated with the carbonyl group, then the

---

[1] This interesting double bond migration was investigated by Professor E. J. Corey (now of Harvard University) while he was on the chemistry faculty at the University of Illinois. The reference to the paper, in which a reasonable mechanism for the rearrangement was proposed, is E. J. Corey, *J. Am. Chem. Soc.*, **74**, 5897 (1952).

carbon just beyond the double bond may now bear the charge in a resonance form so that greater electron delocalization becomes possible. This may be illustrated with an α,β-unsaturated ester:

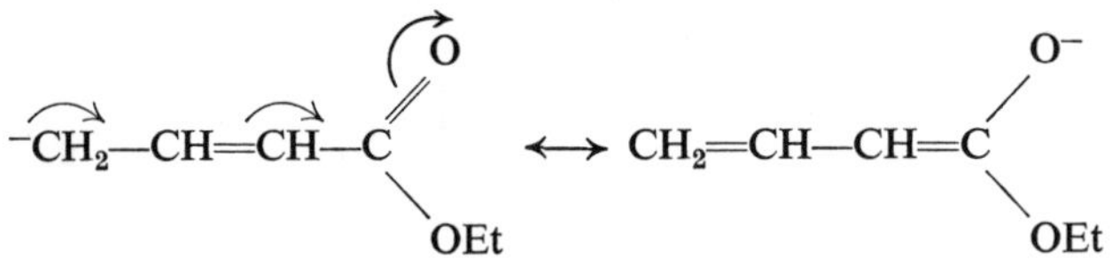

$$^-CH_2\!-\!CH\!=\!CH\!-\!C\!\!\begin{array}{c} \diagup\!\!O \\ \diagdown\!OEt \end{array} \quad \longleftrightarrow \quad CH_2\!=\!CH\!-\!CH\!=\!C\!\!\begin{array}{c} \diagup\!O^- \\ \diagdown\!OEt \end{array}$$

If the theory concerning reactivity of enolate ions is correct, we would expect such an ester as that shown above to give an ester condensation on the gamma carbon. *This proves to be the case;* the reaction shown in Eq. 29 occurs.

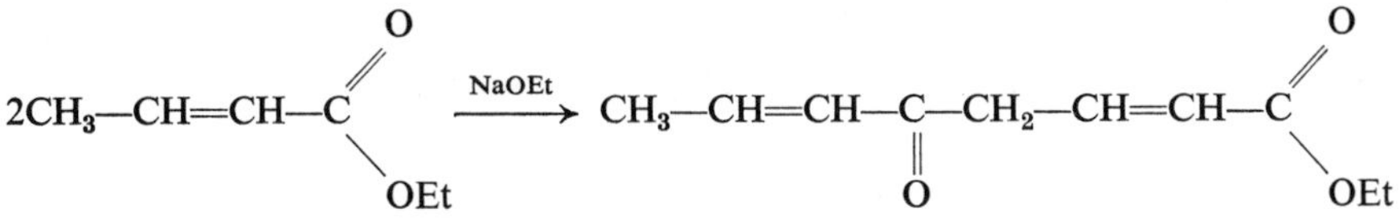

$$2CH_3\!-\!CH\!=\!CH\!-\!C\!\!\begin{array}{c} \diagup\!O \\ \diagdown\!OEt \end{array} \quad \xrightarrow{\text{NaOEt}} \quad CH_3\!-\!CH\!=\!CH\!-\!\underset{\displaystyle O}{\overset{\displaystyle O}{\|}}\!C\!-\!CH_2\!-\!CH\!=\!CH\!-\!C\!\!\begin{array}{c} \diagup\!O \\ \diagdown\!OEt \end{array}$$

$$(29)$$

This transfer of reactivity normal in the alpha position across a double bond (a vinyl group) is known as the principle of vinylogy. For a rapid empirical summing-up of reactivity in a molecule, it is convenient to realize that the molecule behaves as if the carbon-carbon double bond were absent and the groups on each side of it were attached to each other. This follows directly from the considerations of resonance stabilization.

It also follows that the principle of vinylogy should apply to longer systems of conjugated double bonds, and this has been observed. The following ester will condense on the carbon beyond the second double bond:

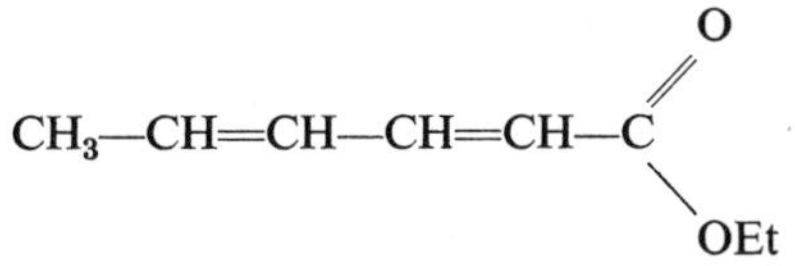

$$CH_3\!-\!CH\!=\!CH\!-\!CH\!=\!CH\!-\!C\!\!\begin{array}{c} \diagup\!O \\ \diagdown\!OEt \end{array}$$

The principle of vinylogy has been illustrated with esters, but it applies to all types of carbonyl compounds and nitriles. Other applications of it will be discussed later in connection with the chemistry of pyridine (Chap. 31) and quinoline (Chap. 32).

The reactions discussed in this chapter constitute an introduction to the enolate condensations. Pursuit of the manifold ramifications of these reactions, as well as the enolate displacements described in the next chapter, carries far into the complex synthetic methods being currently applied to synthesis of sex hormones, essential growth factors, and other types of biologically important compounds.

EXERCISES

1. Write all the equations involved if there is heated at 180° a mixture of benzaldehyde, propionic anhydride, and sodium *n*-butyrate.

2. Write resonance forms for the enolate ion of the ester

$$CH_3\text{---}CH_2\text{---}CH\text{=}CH\text{---}CH\text{=}CH\text{---}CO_2C_2H_5$$

3. Write equations for an ester condensation with an aldehyde which illustrates the principle of vinylogy.

4. Using as starting materials only aliphatic compounds with four or fewer carbon atoms, or monosubstituted aromatic compounds, outline by equations (not balanced, but with all conditions and reagents specified) practical syntheses of the following compounds.

(a) 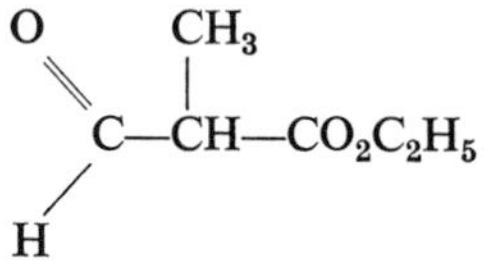
$$\begin{array}{c} O \quad\quad CH_3 \\ \diagdown\!\!\diagup \quad | \\ C\text{---}CH\text{---}CO_2C_2H_5 \\ \diagup \\ H \end{array}$$

(b)
$$\begin{array}{c} OH \\ | \\ C_3H_7\text{---}CH\text{---}CH\text{---}CH_2OH \\ | \\ C_2H_5 \end{array}$$

(c)
$$\begin{array}{c} O \\ \diagup\!\!\diagdown \\ \text{---}CH\text{=}CH\text{---}CH\text{=}CH\text{---}C \\ \diagdown \\ H \end{array}$$
(with a phenyl ring)

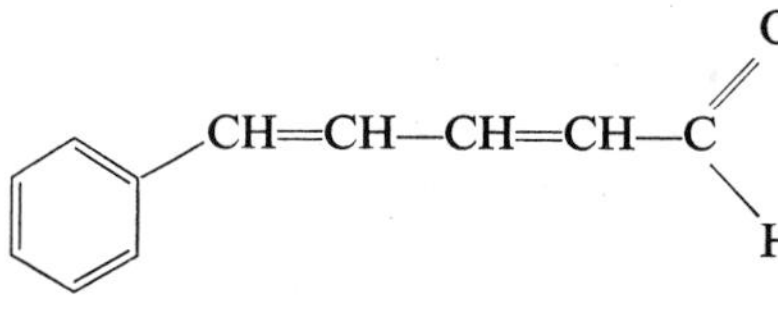

(d) 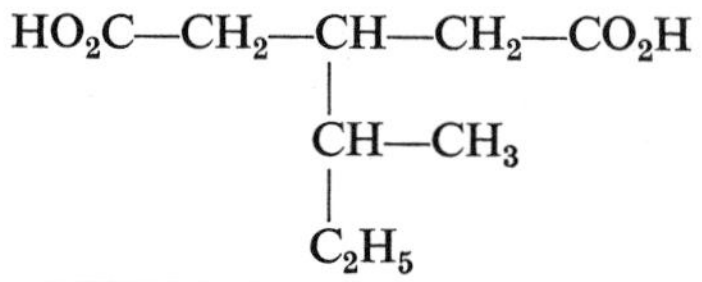
$$\begin{array}{c} HO_2C\text{---}CH_2\text{---}CH\text{---}CH_2\text{---}CO_2H \\ | \\ CH\text{---}CH_3 \\ | \\ C_2H_5 \end{array}$$

(e) 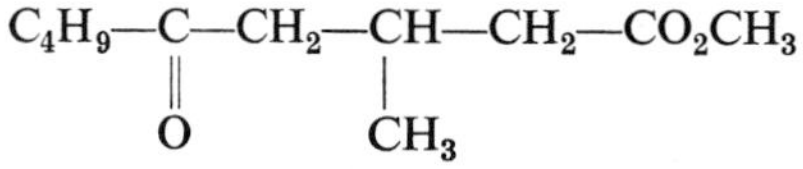
$$\begin{array}{c} C_4H_9\text{---}C\text{---}CH_2\text{---}CH\text{---}CH_2\text{---}CO_2CH_3 \\ \| \quad\quad\quad | \\ O \quad\quad\quad CH_3 \end{array}$$
(refer to Chap. 14 for synthesis of keto esters)

(f) 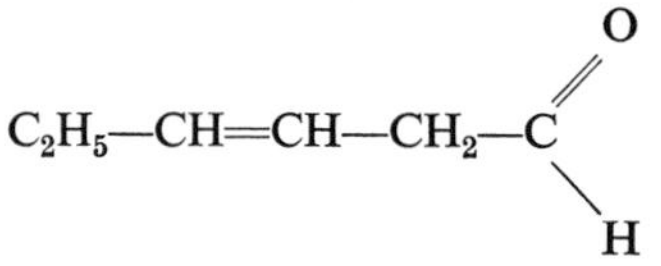
$$\begin{array}{c} O \\ \diagup\!\!\diagup \\ C_2H_5\text{---}CH\text{=}CH\text{---}CH_2\text{---}C \\ \diagdown \\ H \end{array}$$

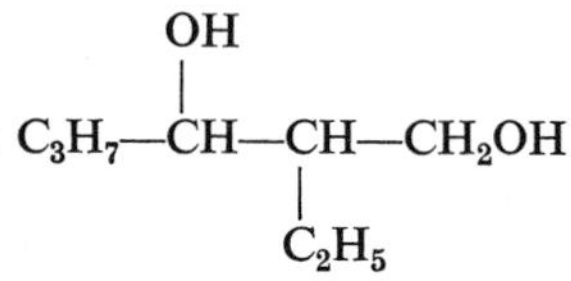

(g)
$$\begin{array}{c} C_2H_5 \\ | \\ HO_2C\text{---}C\text{---}CH_2\text{---}CH_2\text{---}CO_2CH_3 \\ | \\ C_4H_9 \end{array}$$

(h)
$$\begin{array}{c} CH_2\text{---}CH_2\text{---}CO_2CH_3 \\ | \\ HO_2C\text{---}C\text{---}CH_2\text{---}CH_2\text{---}CO_2CH_3 \\ | \\ CH_2\text{---}CH_2\text{---}CO_2CH_3 \end{array}$$
(consider hypohalite oxidation of methyl ketones, also steric hindrance)

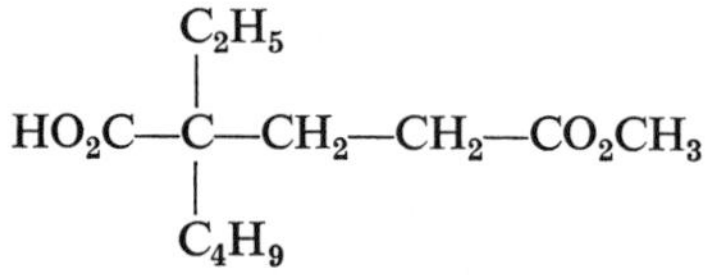

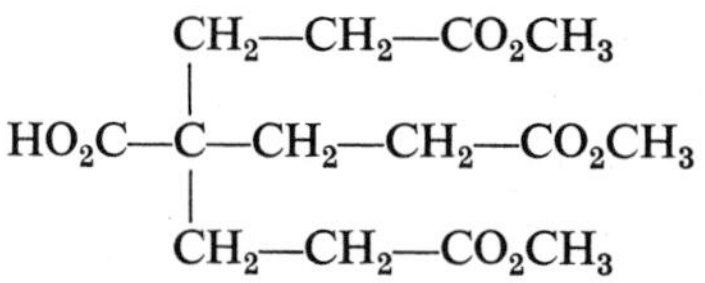

5. Name all the compounds whose formulas appear in Exercise 4.

Displacement Reactions of Enolate Ions

If a carbonyl compound is converted almost entirely to its enolate ion, so that very little of the carbonyl compound remains available for an enolate condensation, then the enolate ion may be used in a simple displacement reaction with an alkyl halide. The same considerations apply to nitriles, although they are used less frequently. If a dicarbonyl compound such as a β-keto ester or a malonic ester is utilized, nearly complete conversion to the enolate is simplified on account of the higher acidity of the ester. For example, if a malonic ester is treated with sodium ethoxide, the equilibrium (Eq. 1) is displaced

$$
\begin{array}{c}
\text{CO}_2\text{Et} \\
| \\
\text{CH}_2 \\
| \\
\text{CO}_2\text{Et}
\end{array}
+ \text{NaOC}_2\text{H}_5 \rightleftharpoons \text{Na}^+ +
\begin{array}{c}
\text{CO}_2\text{Et} \\
| \\
{}^-\text{CH} \\
| \\
\text{CO}_2\text{Et}
\end{array}
+ \text{EtOH} \qquad (1)
$$

(one resonance form
of the anion)

sufficiently far forward so that this device is usually satisfactory for forming the enolate ion for use in a displacement reaction. In the case of an alkylmalonate, it may be necessary to use a stronger base such as potassium *tert*-butoxide in order to displace the equilibrium sufficiently (cf. Eq. 7).

The sodium enolate is shown as ionized in Eq. 1, and it is probably the enolate ion that engages in the displacement reaction; nevertheless, the sodium derivative is probably associated to a large extent in solution. For example, this metallic derivative has an appreciable vapor pressure and can be distilled at low pressure, a behavior not characteristic of ionic compounds such as sulfonic acids or salts of carboxylic acids. In the associated molecule, there arises the question as to which atom (of those carrying a negative charge in the three principal resonance forms) is attached to the metal. Best evidence is that the metal is attached to oxygen and held in a chelate ring as follows:

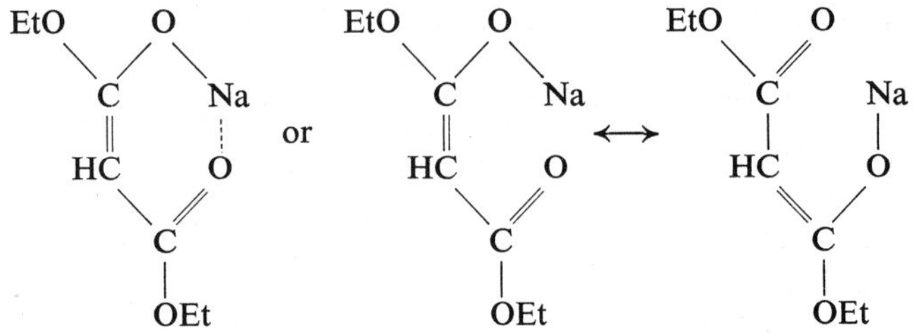

In the following sections of this chapter there will be discussed useful displacement reactions of the enolate ions from malonic esters, as well as β-keto esters, in addition to certain further conversions of the products of these reactions. In many instances, the enolate ion will be used in the reaction (as in Eq. 2), with the assumption that it has been secured by treating the ester with a sufficiently strong base.

Alkylation of Malonic Ester

The introduction of an alkyl group into a malonic ester is actually a straightforward simple displacement reaction of the S_N2 variety. The enolate ion serves as a nucleophile, as illustrated in Eq. 2. As in other displacement

$$
\begin{array}{c} CO_2Et \\ | \\ HC^- \\ | \\ CO_2Et \end{array} + CH_3-(CH_2)_3-Br \longrightarrow \begin{array}{c} CO_2Et \\ | \\ HC-C_4H_9 \\ | \\ CO_2Et \end{array} + Br^- \qquad (2)
$$

reactions, tertiary halides fail; however, secondary alkyl halides are almost as satisfactory as primary halides. Even in a primary halide, excessive hindrance can defeat the displacement. For example, neopentyl bromide (2,2-dimethyl-1-bromopropane) will not give displacement by such a bulky ion as the enolate ion. Aromatic halides will not give displacement, as usual, unless activated by at least two strongly electron-withdrawing groups. Since the S_N2 displacement is accompanied by inversion of configuration, if one starts with a secondary bromide of R-configuration the product is of S-configuration (Eq. 3). Normally, there is essentially no S_N1 component in the enolate displacements, thus no rearrangement or racemization during the reaction.

$$
\begin{array}{c}
\underset{\displaystyle \overset{\displaystyle CH_3}{|}}{\underset{\displaystyle \overset{|}{H}}{C_6H_{13}\!-\!C\!-\!Br}} +
\underset{\displaystyle \overset{\displaystyle CO_2Et}{|}}{\underset{\displaystyle \overset{|}{CO_2Et}}{^-CH}}
\longrightarrow
\underset{\displaystyle \overset{\displaystyle H}{|}}{\underset{\displaystyle \overset{|}{CH_3}}{C_6H_{13}\!-\!C\!-\!CH(CO_2Et)_2}} + Br^-
\end{array} \qquad (3)
$$

R-2-Bromooctane   Diethyl S-1-methylheptylmalonate

The displacement reactions of the enolate ions are *not reversible*, in sharp contrast with the enolate addition reactions; however, there is nearly always some **dialkylation as a side reaction**, when mono-alkylation of malonic ester is carried out. This occurs on account of the equilibrium shown in Eq. 4. This

$$
\underset{\displaystyle \overset{\displaystyle CO_2Et}{|}}{\underset{\displaystyle \overset{|}{CO_2Et}}{R\!-\!C\!-\!H}} +
\underset{\displaystyle \overset{\displaystyle CO_2Et}{|}}{\underset{\displaystyle \overset{|}{CO_2Et}}{H\!-\!C^-}}
\;\rightleftharpoons\;
\underset{\displaystyle \overset{\displaystyle CO_2Et}{|}}{\underset{\displaystyle \overset{|}{CO_2Et}}{R\!-\!C^-}}
+
\underset{\displaystyle \overset{\displaystyle CO_2Et}{|}}{\underset{\displaystyle \overset{|}{CO_2Et}}{H\!-\!C\!-\!H}}
\qquad (4)
$$

equilibrium is set up as soon as any of the substituted malonate is formed during the alkylation, and the position of the equilibrium is a function of the relative acidity of the two malonic esters. Fortunately, the equilibrium is normally in favor of the unsubstituted malonate ion. Reaction of the anion on the right of Eq. 4 yields the dialkylated malonate (Eq. 5). Since the equilibrium

$$
\underset{\displaystyle \overset{\displaystyle CO_2Et}{|}}{\underset{\displaystyle \overset{|}{CO_2Et}}{R\!-\!C^-}}
+ R\!-\!Br \longrightarrow
\underset{\displaystyle \overset{\displaystyle CO_2Et}{|}}{\underset{\displaystyle \overset{|}{CO_2Et}}{R\!-\!C\!-\!R}}
+ Br^-
\qquad (5)
$$

in Eq. 4 is developed as soon as some substituted malonate is formed, the substituted ion is in the solution with the alkyl halide, so there is nothing to prevent the reaction shown in Eq. 5. By the law of mass action, if excess malonic ester is used for the alkylation, the equilibrium in Eq. 4 is displaced to the left, thus the amount of dialkylation is reduced. In addition, excess of malonic ester displaces the equilibrium in Eq. 1 to the right, thus reduces the amount of ethoxide ion present when the alkyl halide is added. This reduces two additional side reactions (Eq. 6) which result from reaction of the alkyl

$$
R\!-\!CH_2\!-\!CH_2\!-\!Br + {}^-OEt \left[
\begin{array}{l}
\longrightarrow R\!-\!CH_2\!-\!CH_2\!-\!O\!-\!Et + Br^- \\
\longrightarrow R\!-\!CH\!=\!CH_2 + HOEt + Br^-
\end{array}
\right.
\qquad (6)
$$

halide with sodium ethoxide to give either displacement or elimination. For these reasons, there is normally used an excess of malonic ester in the mono-alkylation reaction.

When a substituted malonate is alkylated a second time, a better yield is probable if a stronger base than sodium ethoxide is used, and potassium *tert*-butoxide is the most commonly used reagent (Eq. 7).

$$C_4H_9\!-\!\underset{\underset{\displaystyle CO_2Et}{|}}{\overset{\overset{\displaystyle CO_2Et}{|}}{C}}\!-\!H \;+\; KO\!-\!\underset{\underset{\displaystyle CH_3}{|}}{\overset{\overset{\displaystyle CH_3}{|}}{C}}\!-\!CH_3 \;\rightleftharpoons\; K^+\,\overset{\overset{\displaystyle CO_2Et}{|}}{\underset{\underset{\displaystyle CO_2Et}{|}}{C}}\!-\!C_4H_9 \;+\; HOC(CH_3)_3 \qquad (7)$$

$$\xrightarrow[C_3H_7Br]{} \quad C_3H_7\!-\!\underset{\underset{\displaystyle CO_2Et}{|}}{\overset{\overset{\displaystyle CO_2Et}{|}}{C}}\!-\!C_4H_9 \;+\; KBr$$

Sodium *tert*-butoxide is not used because *tert*-butyl alcohol is so weakly acidic that it reacts with sodium very sluggishly.

By the methods discussed above, good yields of either monoalkyl- or dialkylmalonates may be obtained, and either or both the alkyl groups may be secondary. These compounds have numerous uses in synthesis, of which two will be discussed in the next section.

Utilization of Substituted Malonic Esters in Synthesis

Synthesis of monobasic acids. A major use of the malonic ester derivatives, whether obtained by some condensation reaction (Chap. 26) or by alkylation, is for hydrolysis and decarboxylation to a monobasic acid. Conversion of a dialkylmalonate to an α-alkyl acid is shown in Eq. 8. In planning

$$C_2H_5\!-\!\underset{\underset{\displaystyle CO_2Et}{|}}{\overset{\overset{\displaystyle CO_2Et}{|}}{C}}\!-\!C_4H_9 \;+\; 2HOH \xrightarrow[\substack{\text{or basic}\\\text{catalysis}}]{\text{acidic}} C_2H_5\!-\!\underset{\underset{\displaystyle CO_2H}{|}}{\overset{\overset{\displaystyle CO_2H}{|}}{C}}\!-\!C_4H_9 \;+\; 2EtOH$$

$$\xrightarrow{180°} C_4H_9\!-\!\underset{\underset{\displaystyle C_2H_5}{|}}{CH}\!-\!CO_2H \;+\; CO_2 \qquad (8)$$

2-Ethylhexanoic acid
or
n-Butylethylacetic acid

the synthesis of a carboxylic acid by way of alkylation of malonic ester, it is convenient to remember that the malonic ester moiety contributes the α-carbon and carboxyl group. Thus, if the acid to be synthesized is named as a derivative of acetic acid, the alkyl groups appearing in the name are the ones with which malonic ester should be alkylated. For synthesis of *n*-butylethylacetic acid (Eq. 8), malonic ester must be alkylated with *n*-butyl and with ethyl.

If a secondary halide is used for alkylation of malonic ester, this eventually yields a monobasic acid with a β-substituent. To make the acid shown at the top of p. 485, alkylation would be with ethyl bromide and with 2-bromooctane. Finally, it should be noted that alkylation with an *n*-alkyl halide, followed by hydrolysis and decarboxylation, yields a normal acid with two more carbon atoms than the starting alkyl halide. Thus, a two-carbon chain extension has been accomplished.

$$CH_3-(CH_2)_5-\overset{\overset{\displaystyle C_2H_5}{|}}{CH}-\overset{\overset{\displaystyle }{|}}{\underset{\underset{\displaystyle CH_3}{|}}{CH}}-CO_2H$$

Polyfunctional compounds containing halogen have been widely used for preparing more complicated structures than obtained by use of simple alkyl halides. Bromo ethers and bromo ketones are useful, but **bromo esters** are especially useful, partly because they may be secured in considerable variety. The synthesis of several types of bromo acids or esters has been discussed in Chapter 16. Bromo esters may be secured from the acids by normal esterification provided that hydrogen bromide is used as the acid catalyst so that displacement of halogen during the esterification process is avoided.

If an α-bromo ester is used as the alkylating agent, then a succinic acid derivative is obtained, as in the illustrative sequence[1] in Eq. 9. Use of bromo

$$CH_3-\overset{\overset{\displaystyle CO_2Et}{|}}{\underset{\underset{\displaystyle CO_2Et}{|}}{C^-}} + C_2H_5-\overset{\overset{\displaystyle }{|}}{\underset{\underset{\displaystyle Br}{|}}{CH}}-CO_2Et \longrightarrow CH_3-\overset{\overset{\displaystyle EtO_2C}{|}}{\underset{\underset{\displaystyle EtO_2C}{|}}{C}}-\overset{\overset{\displaystyle C_2H_5}{|}}{CH}-CO_2Et + Br^- \qquad (9)$$

$$\xrightarrow[\text{(2) } -CO_2]{\text{(1) [HOH]}} HO_2C-\overset{\overset{\displaystyle C_2H_5}{|}}{CH}-\overset{\overset{\displaystyle }{|}}{\underset{\underset{\displaystyle CH_3}{|}}{CH}}-CO_2H$$

α-Ethyl-α′-methylsuccinic acid

esters with the halogen more remote from carboxyl gives dibasic acids with a correspondingly larger number of carbons between carboxyls. Furthermore, certain types of branched-chain bromo esters can be prepared by reactions discussed previously. A sequence starting with β-methylglutaric acid (synthesis in Chap. 26) is outlined in Eqs. 10 and 11. It should be noted that the anhydride

$$HO_2C-CH_2-\overset{\overset{\displaystyle }{|}}{\underset{\underset{\displaystyle CH_3}{|}}{CH}}-CH_2-CO_2H \xrightarrow{\text{heat}} CH_3- \underset{\overset{\displaystyle O}{\|}}{\overset{\overset{\displaystyle O}{\|}}{}} \xrightarrow{CH_3OH} \qquad (10)$$

$$CH_3O_2C-CH_2-\overset{\overset{\displaystyle }{|}}{\underset{\underset{\displaystyle CH_3}{|}}{CH}}-CH_2-CO_2H \xrightarrow[\substack{\text{(2) AgNO}_3 \\ \text{(3) Br}_2\text{, CCl}_4 \text{ solvent}}]{\text{(1) }^-\text{OH to pH 10}} CH_3O_2C-CH_2-\overset{\overset{\displaystyle }{|}}{\underset{\underset{\displaystyle CH_3}{|}}{CH}}-CH_2Br$$

---

[1] In the second step in Eq. 9 are used convenient symbols for the oft-repeated processes of hydrolysis and decarboxylation. For hydrolysis, with either acid or basic catalysis and no special conditions, [HOH] is used, while $-CO_2$ (minus carbon dioxide) is used to indicate decarboxylation by simple heating.

may be used for a high yield synthesis of half ester when a glutaric or succinic acid is being used, and that a single half ester is obtained when the dibasic acid

$$
\begin{array}{c}
\underset{|}{CO_2Et} \\
\underset{|}{CH_2} \\
CO_2Et
\end{array}
\xrightarrow[\text{(2) } C_4H_9\text{—Br}]{\text{(1) NaOEt}}
\underset{\underset{CO_2Et}{|}}{C_4H_9\text{—CH}}
\xrightarrow[\substack{\text{(2) bromide} \\ \text{from Eq. 10}}]{\text{(1) KOC (CH}_3)_3}
\underset{\underset{CO_2Et}{|}}{C_4H_9\text{—}\overset{\overset{CO_2Et}{|}}{C}\text{—}CH_2\text{—}\overset{\overset{CH_3}{|}}{CH}\text{—}CH_2CO_2CH_3}
$$

$$
\Big\downarrow \substack{\text{(1) [HOH]} \\ \text{(2) } -CO_2} \qquad (11)
$$

$$
HO_2C\text{—}\overset{\overset{\displaystyle |}{C_4H_9}}{CH}\text{—}CH_2\text{—}\overset{\overset{\displaystyle |}{CH_3}}{CH}\text{—}CH_2\text{—}CO_2H
$$

2-Butyl-4-methylhexanedioic acid

used as starting material is symmetrical. Such a procedure would be of no value for use with α-methylglutaric acid, for this compound would lead to two half esters:

$$
CH_3O_2C\text{—}\overset{\overset{\displaystyle CH_3}{|}}{CH}\text{—}CH_2\text{—}CH_2\text{—}CO_2H
\qquad
HO_2C\text{—}\overset{\overset{\displaystyle CH_3}{|}}{CH}\text{—}CH_2\text{—}CH_2\text{—}CO_2CH_3
$$

4-Methoxycarbonylpentanoic acid   2-Methyl-4-methoxycarbonylbutanoic acid

The sequences of reactions outlined in this section give some idea of the versatility of syntheses depending on alkylation of a malonic ester. The products of these reactions may be used for further conversions using previously discussed reactions. In particular, the acids obtained from the above-discussed processes may be subjected to the various conversions discussed in Chapters 13, 14, and 26. In addition, aldehydes or ketones obtained from the acids may be utilized in syntheses discussed in Chapters 15 and 26.

Synthesis of barbituric acids. The pyrimidine ring system, mentioned in Chapter 25 as present in certain component parts of nucleic acids, occurs in many other compounds of considerable biological importance. Among these compounds are the **barbituric acids,** which are 2,4,6-trioxypyrimidines. The

Pyrimidine

2,4,6-Trioxypyrimidine
or Barbituric acid

presence of three oxygen functions in the ring encourages equilibration with the keto form (refer to discussion of phloroglucinol in Chap. 20), while presence of nitrogen in the rings also encourages equilibration with the keto form (or amide form, in this instance). In view of the relatively significant amounts of both keto and hydroxy forms in the barbituric acids, as well as other pyrimidines, the oxygen function is designated as *oxy*.

Many of the 5,5-disubstituted barbituric acids have considerable clinical importance as **hypnotics** (compounds inducing sleep),[2] and these are frequently synthesized from an appropriately substituted malonic ester. Synthesis of the 5-ethyl-5-(1-methylbutyl)barbituric acid, known by the trade name of Nembutal, is shown in Eq. 12. Nembutal is especially useful in some situations on account

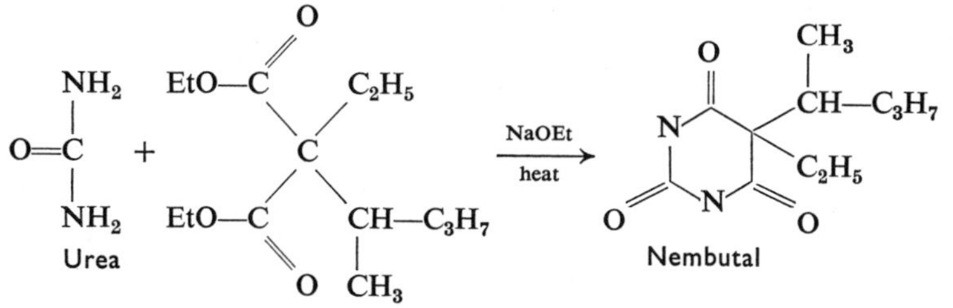

$$
\begin{array}{c}
\text{Urea} + \text{malonic ester} \xrightarrow[\text{heat}]{\text{NaOEt}} \text{Nembutal}
\end{array}
\tag{12}
$$

of its relatively rapid onset and the short duration of its action. For longer duration of action, Amytal is useful. It has ethyl and isoamyl substituted in the 5-position of barbituric acid. Numerous other barbiturates are marketed as hypnotics, under various trade names.

Acylation of Malonic Ester

Enolate ions react with acid chlorides in much the same manner of other nucleophiles (cf. Eq. 14-1 and Eqs. 14-3 through 14-6). Thus, the over-all conversion is substitution of the halogen by the enolate grouping. Of course an alcohol or other protic solvent must be avoided, for the acid chloride would react rapidly with such solvents. A typical acylation is shown in Eq. 13, in which

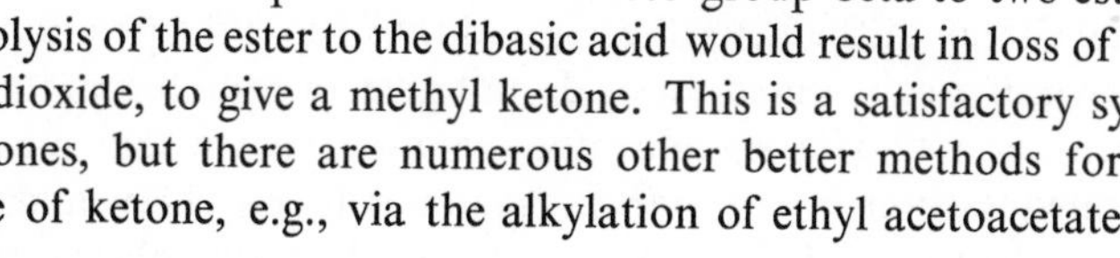

$$
\begin{array}{c}
C_3H_7-C(=O)Cl + {}^-CH(CO_2Et)_2 \longrightarrow C_3H_7-C(=O)-CH(CO_2Et)_2 + Cl^-
\end{array}
\tag{13}
$$

Diethyl butyrylmalonate

it may be noted that the product has the keto group beta to two ester groups. Thus, hydrolysis of the ester to the dibasic acid would result in loss of two moles of carbon dioxide, to give a methyl ketone. This is a satisfactory synthesis of methyl ketones, but there are numerous other better methods for synthesis of this type of ketone, e.g., via the alkylation of ethyl acetoacetate described on p. 489.

---

[2] Although the "barbiturates" have been widely used as hypnotics, they are actually rather dangerous and unsatisfactory. They are physiologically addicting and are also sufficiently toxic that an overdose can cause death. For this reason, the search continues for more satisfactory sleep-inducing drugs, and the use of barbiturates is rigidly controlled.

If an alkyl-acyl-malonate could be hydrolyzed to the di-acid, this would decarboxylate to a higher ketone; however, this conversion has not been accomplished. When such a malonic ester is treated with base, attack occurs on the keto group in preference to the ester groups, presumably on account of steric hindrance, and the reverse of the Claisen condensation occurs (Eq. 14).

$$\tag{14}$$

Since a carboxylic acid is a much stronger acid than malonic ester, the original products from reversal of the Claisen condensation (upper line of Eq. 14) go rapidly to the carboxylate anion and malonic ester. The latter is, of course, saponified by the base. Since the carboxylate anion does not have a reactive carbonyl group, also does not readily give an enolate ion as previously discussed, the reaction goes to completion in a reverse direction to the Claisen ester condensation. If the starting material in Eq. 14 were made by acylation of the substituted malonate (as in Eq. 13), then the attempted hydrolysis would give conversion to the malonic acid and monobasic acid corresponding to the starting materials in Eq. 13. This is a futile process, so the hydrolysis and decarboxylation of the acyl-alkyl-malonates fail. If hydrolysis with acid is attempted, a similar cleavage in the reverse Claisen sense occurs.

In view of the discussion in the preceding paragraph, it should be noted that, in principle, a keto ester such as the product in Eq. 13 or the starting material in Eq. 14 may be synthesized by a cross Claisen condensation between the malonic ester enolate ion and the mono-ester. The equilibrium in such a condensation proves to be not significantly forward, so that, in actuality, the reaction does not occur. It is probable that this shift in equilibrium is caused by steric interference between the several large groups on a single carbon, which increases the energy of the keto di-ester and thus shifts the position of equilibrium. In general, α-substituted esters do not give an equilibrium in the Claisen ester condensation that is significantly forward. This would mean that the tetrasubstituted carbon in the starting material in Eq. 14 would result in a particularly high energy. This is consistent with the actual observation that the reverse Claisen condensation becomes so rapid that it takes precedence over simple ester hydrolysis.

In spite of the failure of hydrolysis of the acyl-malonates, they become rather useful in synthesis if a different type of cleavage is applied. Heating of this type of compound with a strong acid under anhydrous conditions gives selective cracking of one ester group so that a simple β-keto ester results. The naphthalenesulfonic acid shown as catalyst in Eq. 15 is especially useful, for it is

$$\underset{\underset{O}{\overset{\|}{}}}{R-C}-\underset{\overset{}{CO_2Et}}{CH} \xrightarrow[\substack{\text{catalytic amount} \\ \text{heat}}]{\text{(naphthalenesulfonic acid, } SO_2OH)} R-\underset{\overset{\|}{O}}{C}-CH_2-CO_2Et + CO_2 + CH_2{=}CH_2 \qquad (15)$$

easily obtained in anhydrous condition and is essentially non-volatile. Heating of a carboxylic ester, especially in presence of a strong acid, cracks it to the carboxylic acid and alkene. This occurs more readily with the malonic ester, and the resultant β-keto acid decarboxylates immediately to give the simple β-keto ester. It will be noted that the process in Eq. 15 gives a β-keto ester of a type not obtainable from the Claisen ester condensation (cf. Chap. 26). Such keto esters are quite useful in the alkylation procedures described below.

Ketone Synthesis from β-Keto Esters

β-Keto esters may be alkylated by procedures essentially identical to those described earlier for malonic ester. A mono-alkylation is shown in Eq. 16, and the process may be repeated, if desired, to give a dialkylated β-keto ester. The β-keto ester used as starting material in Eq. 16 is ethyl acetoacetate, cheaply

$$CH_3-\underset{\overset{\|}{O}}{C}-CH_2-CO_2Et + {}^-OC_2H_5 \longrightarrow CH_3-\underset{\overset{\|}{O}}{C}-\overset{-}{C}H-CO_2Et \xrightarrow{C_3H_7-Br} \qquad (16)$$

$$CH_3-\underset{\overset{\|}{O}}{C}-\underset{\overset{|}{C_3H_7}}{CH}-CO_2Et$$

Ethyl α-acetylvalerate

available commercially from the simple Claisen condensation of ethyl acetate. Other esters available from the Claisen condensation have the form,

$$R-CH_2-\underset{\overset{\|}{O}}{C}-\underset{\overset{|}{R}}{CH}-CO_2Et,$$

as discussed in Chapter 26. In addition, the method described in the preceding section gives straight-chain higher β-keto esters which may be used in the alkylation reaction.

As discussed in Chapter 26, β-keto acids decarboxylate very easily, so hydrolysis of the β-keto ester yields a ketone. If mild conditions are used for the hydrolysis (Eq. 17), reversal of the Claisen condensation (Eq. 14) is only a side reaction. It is seen that the net process outlined in Eqs. 16 and 17 constitutes a **ketone synthesis.** If ethyl acetoacetate is used, a methyl ketone results, while a higher straight-chain keto ester yields a higher ketone. If the β-keto ester is alkylated once, a straight-chain ketone results, while a second alkylation yields an α-substituted ketone, as in Eq. 17. Of course one α-alkyl is obtained in the

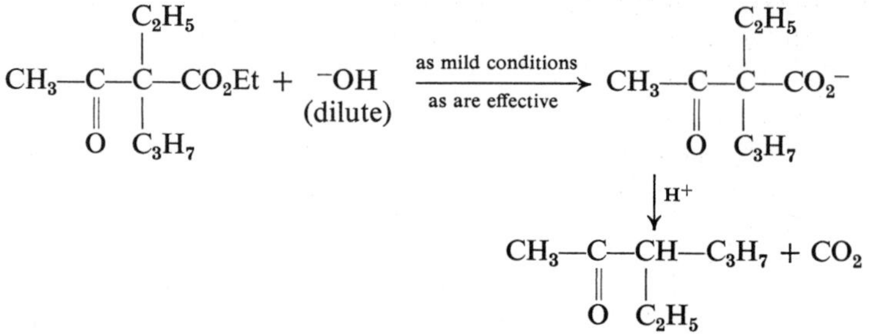

$$
\begin{array}{cc}
\underset{\underset{\overset{\|}{O}}{\overset{C_2H_5}{|}}}{CH_3-\underset{|}{C}-\underset{|}{C}-CO_2Et} + {}^-OH & \xrightarrow[\text{as are effective}]{\text{as mild conditions}} \underset{\underset{\overset{\|}{O}\ \ C_3H_7}{|}}{CH_3-C-\underset{|}{C}-CO_2^-}
\end{array}
$$

$$\Big\downarrow \text{H}^+ \tag{17}$$

$$
CH_3-\underset{\overset{\|}{O}}{C}-\underset{\overset{|}{C_2H_5}}{CH}-C_3H_7 + CO_2
$$

β-keto ester from the Claisen condensation unless acetate is the ester condensed. These processes constitute a versatile ketone synthesis in which the yields are rather good. This synthesis should be added, then, to the methods discussed in Chapter 15.

Enolate Ions from Monofunctional Ketones

A monofunctional, unsaturated compound may be converted sufficiently completely and rapidly to the enolate ion for use in a displacement reaction only if a very strong base is used. In addition, the displacement is obtainable in high yield only if the condensation reaction of the particular species involved does not give an equilibrium that is well forward. Thus, aldehydes are rarely satisfactory, for the aldol condensation goes rapidly and the equilibrium is well forward. Esters or nitriles may be used under certain conditions; however, the most useful of the monofunctional compounds are ketones. As mentioned in Chapter 15, the aldol condensation of ketones gives an equilibrium rather unfavorable to the condensation product. Even with ketones, certain problems are encountered. Of particular importance is the fact that a ketone has two positions alpha to the carbonyl group, so the enolate ion may form on either side, unless one alpha carbon bears no hydrogen atoms. Most satisfactory results are obtained with a symmetrical ketone, and the cyclic ketones have been most widely used in synthesis. Alkylation of cyclohexanone is shown in Eq. 18.

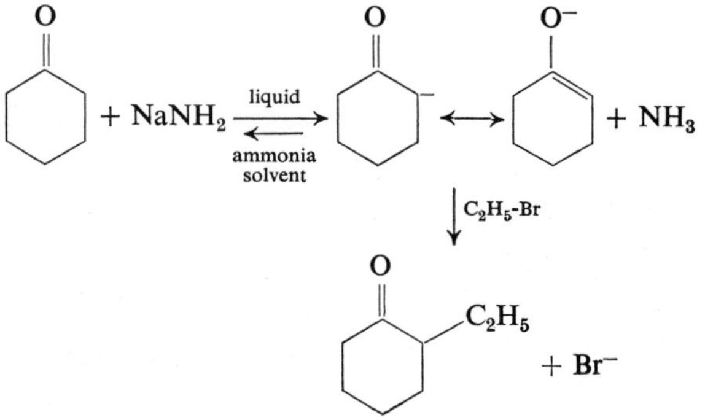

Sodium amide[3] is a sufficiently strong base to accomplish a satisfactory conversion of a simple ketone to the anion, and the anion may be alkylated by addition of a suitable alkyl halide.

In the type of alkylation shown in Eq. 18, the same principles apply as have been discussed for the di-unsaturated compounds such as malonic ester. Thus, a side reaction in monoalkylation is dialkylation (refer to Eqs. 4 and 5); however, the situation is further complicated by the fact that the monoalkylated ketone is unsymmetrical, therefore capable of forming two different enolate ions. Displacement by these respective enolate ions yields two ketones:

2,6-Diethylcyclohexanone   2,2-Diethylcyclohexanone

Indeed, alpha hydrogens remain in each of the dialkylated ketones, so further alkylation can occur, although in increasingly smaller amount on account of the multiple reactions required. The occurrence of polyalkylation, as well as the possibility of enolate condensation, lower the yields in the alkylation of simple ketones, so the process is ordinarily used only when a suitable more acidic structure is not readily available.

In practice, an α-alkylketone such as 2-ethylcyclohexanone is normally obtained in higher yield by alkylation of 2-ethoxycarbonylcyclohexanone, followed by the usual hydrolysis and decarboxylation. The required β-keto ester is readily available, for it results from Claisen ester condensation of a symmetrical di-ester (Eq. 19).

$$+ \text{HOEt} \qquad (19)$$

A similar condensation of diethyl adipate yields the ethoxycarbonylcyclopentanone. Of course ring sizes which require some strain in normal bond angles are not formed so readily as are the five- and six-membered rings.

---

[3] Although ammonia ordinarily functions as a base, on account of its ability to donate electrons, its hydrogen atoms are sufficiently "active" to be extracted by alkali metals under suitable conditions:

$$2NH_3 + 2Na \xrightarrow[\substack{\text{ammonia} \\ \text{solvent}}]{\text{liquid}} 2NaNH_2 + H_2$$

As might be predicted, the ion, $^-NH_2$, is a very powerful base. It is common practice to form the sodium amide by adding metallic sodium to liquid ammonia, then to add the ketone whose enolate ion is desired. At this stage, it is often desirable to remove ammonia by evaporation so as to displace the equilibrium in Eq. 18 forward, then carry out the alkylation in an inert solvent such as diethyl ether.

In case alkylation of an unsymmetrical ketone is carried out, there may be a preponderance of one of the two possible structures (such as the side reaction products shown above); however, there is usually a significant amount of each structure. Furthermore, it has proved quite difficult to gather sufficient data to make general predictions as to which of two structures will be favored. It is necessary to have specific experimental data for the structures involved. In spite of these difficulties, the most common use of the alkylation of mono-ketones has been for obtaining di- or tri-substituted compounds, for these structures are not available *via* β-keto esters. Considerable information is available on the conditions necessary to secure a desired isomer; however, few generalizations are possible, so consideration of these factors at this time is unprofitable.

The synthetic methods discussed in this chapter and the preceding one may be applied as key steps in synthesis of numerous complicated structures. More simple conversions, such as discussed in earlier chapters, are always necessary adjuncts in the multistep syntheses, however; so general methods and principles of synthesis should be reviewed in connection with study of the problems which follow.

EXERCISES

1. Write equations showing three side reactions that occur in the synthesis of diethyl *n*-butylmalonate by alkylation of diethyl malonate.

Which of these side reactions would you expect to become more serious if alkylation were with *sec*-butyl bromide rather than *n*-butyl bromide?

Explain why use of potassium *tert*-butoxide would be expected to reduce the side reactions which would become more serious with the secondary halide.

Which side reaction would become more serious if the halide were ethyl α-bromopropionate? (Cf. Chap. 16 concerning displacement reactions of α-bromo esters, and remember that the nucleophilicity of an enolate ion is reduced by its size.)

2. Let us suppose that the following compound is to be prepared:

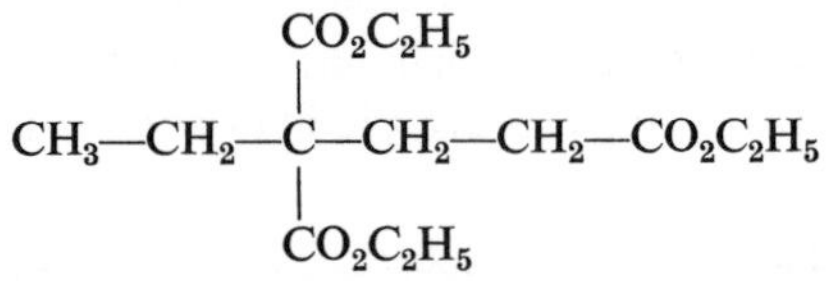

$$CH_3-CH_2-\underset{\underset{CO_2C_2H_5}{|}}{\overset{\overset{CO_2C_2H_5}{|}}{C}}-CH_2-CH_2-CO_2C_2H_5$$

Would it be best to alkylate first with ethyl bromide or with ethyl β-bromopropionate? What is the basis of your conclusion?

3. Which of the following compounds is easier to prepare:

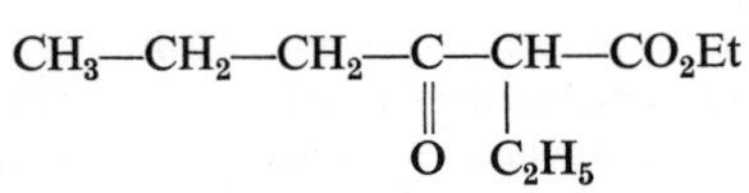

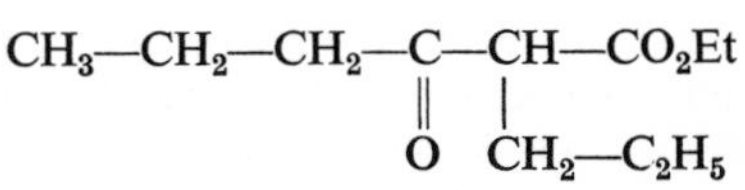

$$CH_3-CH_2-CH_2-\underset{\underset{O}{\|}}{C}-\underset{\underset{C_2H_5}{|}}{CH}-CO_2Et \qquad CH_3-CH_2-CH_2-\underset{\underset{O}{\|}}{C}-\underset{\underset{CH_2-C_2H_5}{|}}{CH}-CO_2Et$$

Justify your conclusion.

4. Write structures of the two cyclic β-keto esters that would result from Claisen ester condensation of the following di-ester:

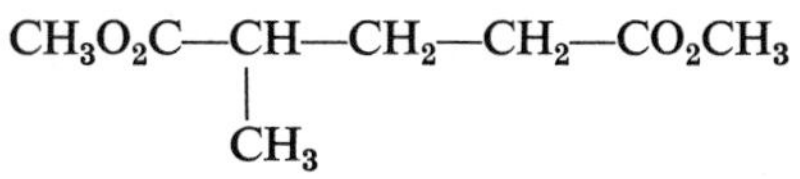

$$CH_3O_2C-CH-CH_2-CH_2-CO_2CH_3$$
$$\quad\quad\quad |$$
$$\quad\quad\quad CH_3$$

Explain why one of these products would be formed in considerably larger amount than the other.

5. Outline a synthesis of each of the following compounds, utilizing as one starting material in each case a straight-chain mono-ester or di-ester. Any other desired reactants or intermediates may be used for the synthesis, except that any bromo esters must also be synthesized from a mono- or di-ester.

(a) 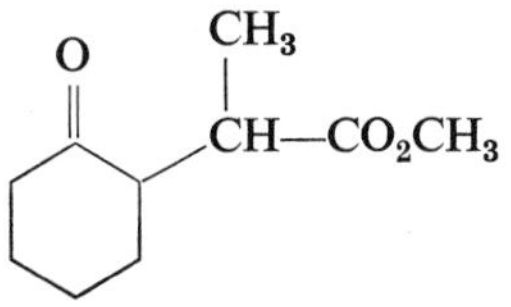
O   CH$_3$
‖ |
   CH—CO$_2$CH$_3$

(b) 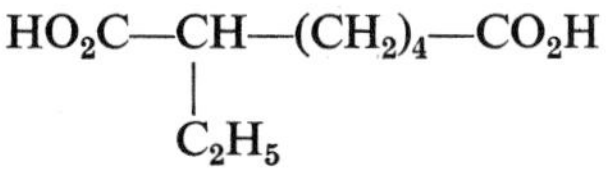 $HO_2C-CH-(CH_2)_4-CO_2H$
$\quad\quad\quad\quad |$
$\quad\quad\quad\quad C_2H_5$

(c) $HO_2C-CH_2-CH-CH_2-CH_2-CO_2H$
$\quad\quad\quad\quad\quad |$
$\quad\quad\quad\quad\quad CO_2H$

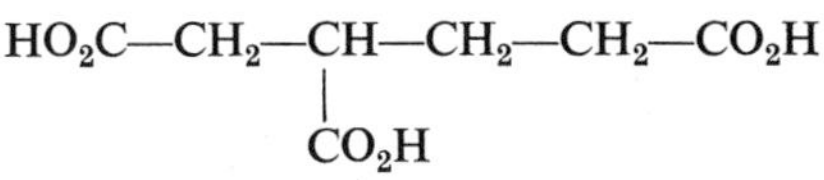

(d) 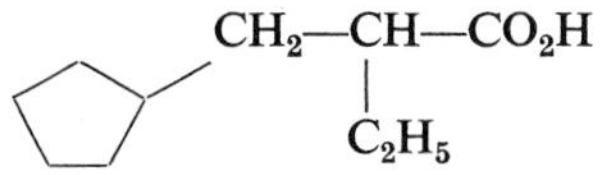
$CH_2-CH-CO_2H$
$\quad\quad\quad |$
$\quad\quad\quad C_2H_5$

(e) 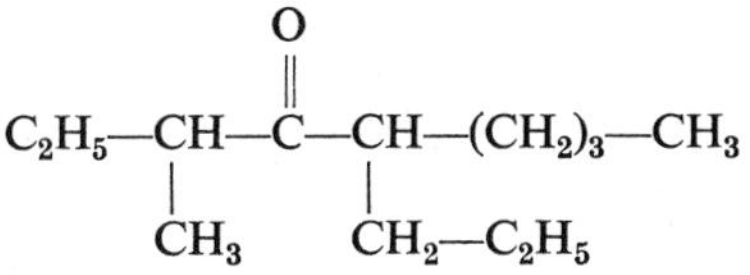 $C_2H_5-CH-\overset{\displaystyle O}{\overset{\|}{C}}-CH-(CH_2)_3-CH_3$
$\quad\quad |\quad\quad\quad\quad |$
$\quad\quad CH_3\quad\quad CH_2-C_2H_5$

(f) $CH_3-(CH_2)_4-\overset{\displaystyle O}{\overset{\|}{C}}-(CH_2)_6-CO_2H$

(g) 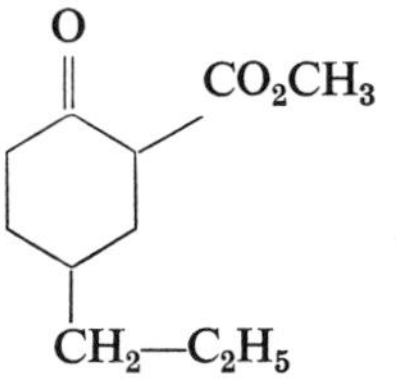
O   CO$_2$CH$_3$
‖
CH$_2$—C$_2$H$_5$

(h)
CH$_3$
CH$_2$—CH$_3$

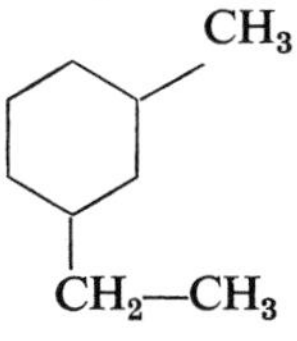

6. Give one correct name for each of the compounds whose synthesis is requested in the preceding exercise.

Biphenyl

Biphenyl, a white crystalline solid melting at 69–70°, consists of two benzene rings joined by a single bond, as has been mentioned in an earlier chapter. Although most of the chemical properties of biphenyl are entirely analogous to those of benzene, certain unique characteristics of biphenyl will be described in the present chapter. A study of these differences in the behavior of biphenyl affords an opportunity to review the chemistry of benzene.

Nomenclature

Since there are two rings in biphenyl, the positions in the two rings are distinguished by use of "prime" numbers and letters, as shown in the following formula:

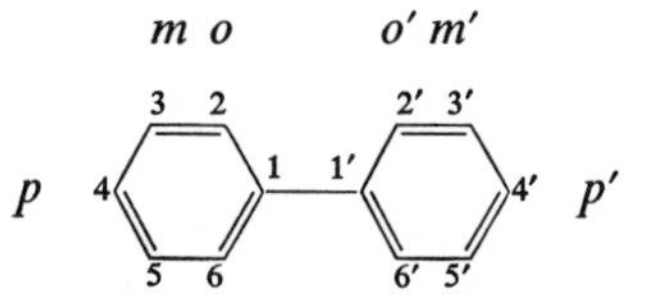

The prime numbers may be put in either ring so long as it be remembered that all prime numbers are in one ring. If only one ring is substituted, naturally unprimed numbers are used. Biphenyl derivatives are sometimes named as derivatives of benzene. Two examples of nomenclature follow:

Br

$\bigcirc$—$\bigcirc$—CO_2H

3-Bromobiphenyl-4-carboxylic acid
or 2-Bromo-4-phenylbenzoic acid

CH_3

$$CH_3—\overset{\overset{\textstyle O}{\|}}{C}—\bigcirc—\bigcirc$$

p-Acetyl-m′-methylbiphenyl

Among more commonly used trivial names in the biphenyl series are benzidine (p,p'-diaminobiphenyl) and diphenic acid (biphenyl-2,2′-dicarboxylic acid).

Stereoisomerism in Biphenyls

If distances between atoms (such as in Table 2, Chap. 3) and valence angles are considered, it becomes clear that adjacent o- and o′-substituents in biphenyl will tend to bump into each other if there occurs rotation about the bond joining the two phenyl rings. If the *ortho* groups are reasonably large groups, they will not be able to easily crowd past each other and allow complete rotation about the bond between the rings. If this is the case, a substance with large groups, such as 6,6′-dinitrodiphenic acid, should exist in two forms which are mirror images of each other. The forms are shown in Fig. 1. As discussed in Chapter 22, two molecules which are mirror images of each other are enantio-stereoisomers. The 6,6′-dinitrodiphenic acid molecule is capable of existing in

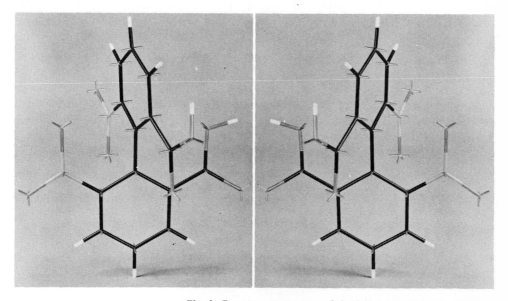

Fig. 1. Enantiostereoisomers of the 6,6′-dinitrodiphenic acid molecule. If a ring in one isomer is rotated 180° by crowding the adjacent groups past each other, the mirror image is formed.

forms which are mirror images, not because there is present an asymmetric carbon but because the molecule as a whole is asymmetric. There has been described in an earlier chapter (Chap. 22) another type of structure, the allene, in which asymmetry results from an asymmetric molecule not containing an asymmetric carbon. In the allene, asymmetry becomes possible because of restriction of rotation in double bonds, whereas the asymmetry in biphenyls results from steric interference with rotation about a single bond. Investigation has shown that a synthetic sample of 6,6'-dinitrodiphenic acid may actually be resolved into optical isomers by the use of an optically active base, according to the method described in Chapter 22. These isomers rotate the plane of polarization of polarized light in the same manner as molecules containing an asymmetric carbon. This experiment is an interesting support of the general theory of optical isomerism, also of the directional effect in valence bonds.

Valence directions may be distorted a certain amount by vibrational forces in the molecule, and this force naturally increases as the temperature is raised. As would follow from this consideration, heating of a pure optical isomer of the type shown in Fig. 1 will produce racemization. As the temperature is increased, the intensity of banging back and forth in the restricted positions increases until eventually the force is sufficient to bend the bonds enough to allow the groups to crowd past each other. This results in racemization. As might also be predicted, the larger the substituted groups (as determined from x-ray diffraction), the higher is the temperature required for racemization.

Inspection of Fig. 1 (better, molecular models) will show that one of the substituted groups may be replaced with hydrogen (sterically small) without relieving the restriction of rotation. The remaining large group in one ring is still caught between the two groups in the other ring. This conclusion, also, has been verified experimentally.

In conclusion to this topic, it should be mentioned that there have been investigated several other types of organic structures in which the molecule as a whole is asymmetric although no asymmetric carbon is present. In numerous such cases, optical resolution yielding isomers with an optical rotation has been possible.

Synthesis of Compounds in the Biphenyl Series

The synthesis of benzidine and substituted benzidines by the benzidine rearrangement has already been described (Eq. 18-15). This is an important source of diaminobiphenyls of use for coupling and synthesis of dyes.

The parent hydrocarbon, biphenyl, is not obtained from coal tar, but it is available in quantity by a special synthesis (Eq. 1).

$$2 \, C_6H_6 \xrightarrow[\substack{\text{molten lead} \\ \text{catalyst}}]{\text{high temp.}} C_6H_5 - C_6H_5 + H_2 \tag{1}$$

Synthesis of **substituted biphenyls** may be accomplished in several ways. Two of these are sufficient for present consideration.

Ullman reaction. Coupling of two molecules of an aryl halide may be accomplished by heating with any of several metals. Heating with copper (Eq. 2), which is known as the Ullman reaction, is the most useful procedure,

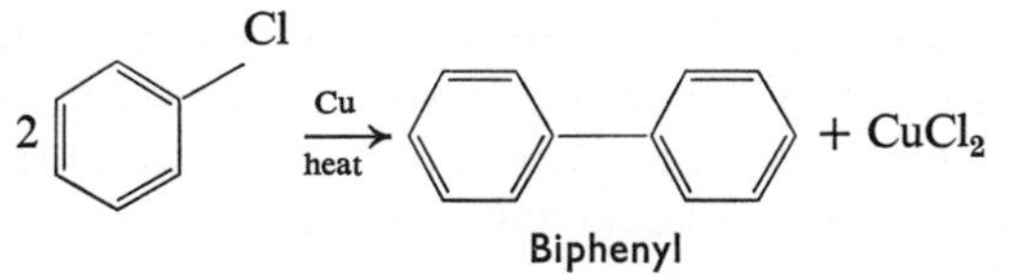

$$2 \quad \underset{}{\text{(structure with Cl)}} \quad \xrightarrow[\text{heat}]{\text{Cu}} \quad \text{(biphenyl structure)} + CuCl_2 \qquad (2)$$

Biphenyl

for copper does not attack various oxygen-containing functional groups such as nitro and carboxyl. Thus, substituted biphenyls may be prepared; however, satisfactory yields are ordinarily obtained only when a single aryl halide is used to give a symmetrical biphenyl. If two halides are used in the reaction, there result three different biphenyls (each halide may react with itself or with the other).

Diazotate coupling. One of the satisfactory methods for securing unsymmetrical biphenyls is coupling of a diazotate with benzene. As discussed in Chapter 19 (Eq. 19-41), the diazonium salt is converted to the diazotate in strong alkaline solution. A representative conversion is shown in Eq. 3.

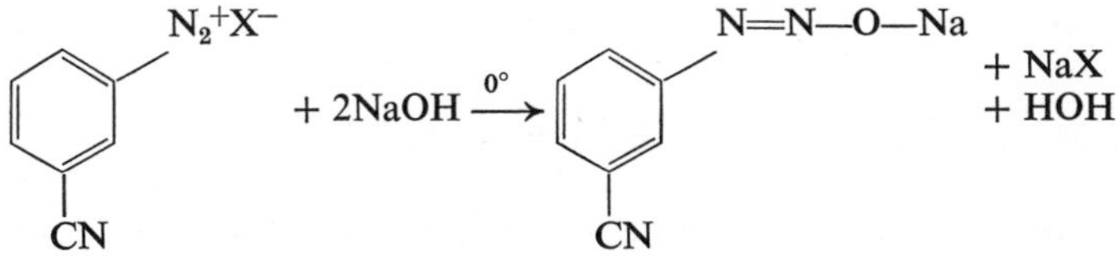

$$\underset{CN}{\text{(structure with } N_2^+X^-)} + 2NaOH \xrightarrow{0°} \underset{CN}{\text{(structure with } N=N-O-Na)} \begin{array}{c} + NaX \\ + HOH \end{array} \qquad (3)$$

The diazotate ion decomposes to furnish *free radicals* which attack benzene to give the coupling product, as shown in Eq. 4.

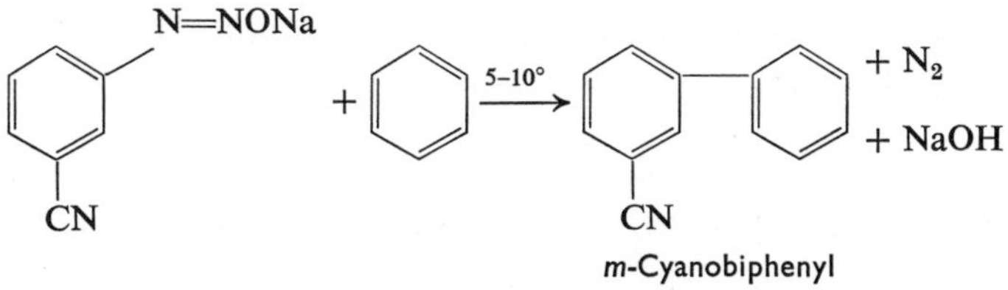

$$\underset{CN}{\text{(structure with } N=NONa)} + \text{(benzene)} \xrightarrow{5-10°} \underset{CN}{\text{(coupling product)}} \begin{array}{c} + N_2 \\ + NaOH \end{array} \qquad (4)$$

m-Cyanobiphenyl

Since the intermediate in this reaction is a free radical, and free radicals will attack nearly any type of compound including alkanes (cf. Chap. 11), it is difficult to find a solvent satisfactory for this reaction; so excess benzene is ordinarily used as solvent. The reaction is carried out just above the freezing point of benzene (5.5°).

The amine which is diazotized for coupling may be nearly any type of substituted aromatic amine; so a large variety of substituents may be introduced into one ring of the biphenyl. The component with which coupling occurs may be anything that is liquid at 5–10°; however, a rather unpredictable mixture of coupling products usually results from a substituted benzene. As discussed in Chapter 17, directing influence in the benzene ring depends on the entrance of a positive group. Since a free radical is neutral, usual directing influences do not hold.[1] Empirical knowledge of the specific reaction is necessary for any synthetic use where coupling is carried out with a substituted benzene. A reaction in which there may be secured a satisfactory yield of a single product is shown in Eq. 5, but p-nitrobiphenyl is prepared more conveniently by nitration of biphenyl (Eq. 7). A more usual result of coupling is shown in Eq. 6.

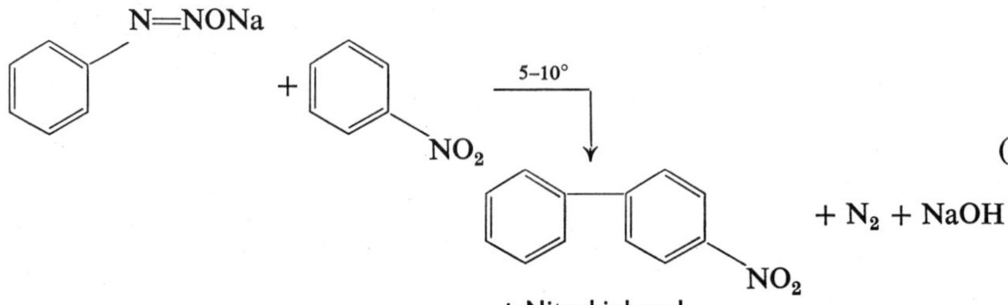

$$\text{(5)}$$

p-Nitrobiphenyl

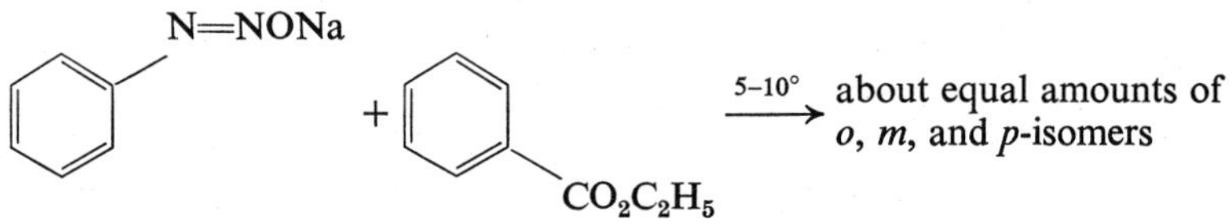

$$\text{(6)}$$

Chemical Reactions in the Biphenyl Series

Substitution occurs in the manner that would be expected in a benzene ring substituted with a moderately strong *ortho,para*-director. Indeed, substitution in biphenyl is so much faster than in benzene that benzene is not uncommonly used as a solvent for Friedel and Crafts reactions with biphenyl. This rapid substitution in biphenyl may reasonably be ascribed to the greater electron-delocalization which is possible in the transition state when the substituent enters the *ortho* or *para* position:

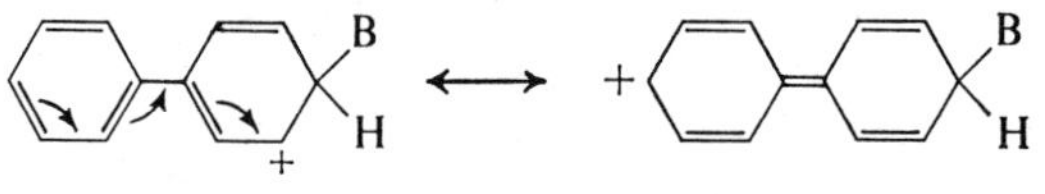

Additional resonance forms of the usual type may be written with the charge in alternate positions in the ring being substituted, as well as in either *ortho* position of the other ring. Such extensive delocalization should lower the energy of the transition state so that faster substitution will occur. It will be noted, if the trial is made, that inter-ring resonance forms cannot be written if the entering group attacks a *meta* position.

---

[1] A summary of the experimental observations concerning directing influence in free radical substitution has been presented by P. F. Nelson, *J. Chem. Educ.*, **32**, 606 (1955).

Halogenation, nitration, and sulfonation occur predominantly in the *para* position, with a minor substitution in the *ortho* position. The lower rate of substitution in the *ortho* position no doubt results from steric hindrance, for the inter-ring resonance stablization, as shown above, can occur only if the two phenyl rings are almost co-planar. Substitution in a biphenyl containing a *meta*-directing group occurs in the ring not containing the *meta*-director, as might be predicted. Even though the substitution is in the other ring, the rate is still greatly retarded (cf. following discussion of Friedel and Crafts reaction). Nitration is shown in Eq. 7. Substitution of the second nitro group also occurs

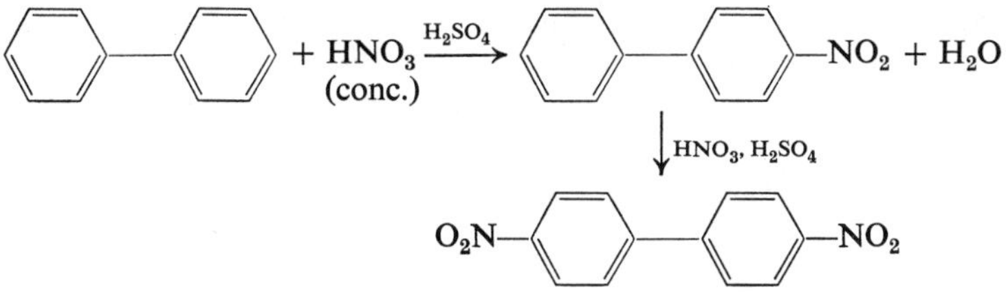

$$\text{(biphenyl)} + HNO_3 \xrightarrow[\text{(conc.)}]{H_2SO_4} \text{(biphenyl)}-NO_2 + H_2O$$

$$\downarrow HNO_3, H_2SO_4 \qquad (7)$$

$$O_2N-\text{(biphenyl)}-NO_2$$

4,4′-Dinitrobiphenyl

in the *para* position on account of the powerful directing effect of the inter-ring resonance stabilization in the transition state, as discussed above. Although a resonance form such as A below is no asset in lowering the energy of the transition state, the two forms of structure shown in B do provide inter-ring electron-delocalization without the positive charge being immediately adjacent to the meta-directing nitro group. Since this inter-ring resonance stabilization is not possible in the transition state for substitution *meta* to the ring juncture, substitution is predominantly *para*, although at a greatly reduced rate.

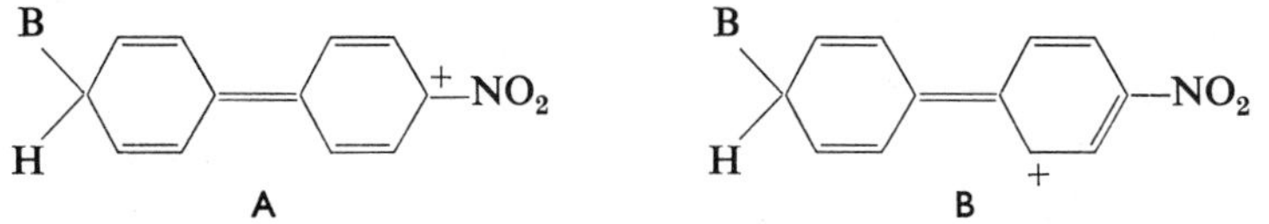

$$\text{B} \qquad \qquad \text{B}$$

$$A \qquad \qquad B$$

Friedel and Crafts reaction. Benzene is a very satisfactory solvent for Friedel and Crafts reactions on biphenyl (Eq. 8), as has been mentioned above.

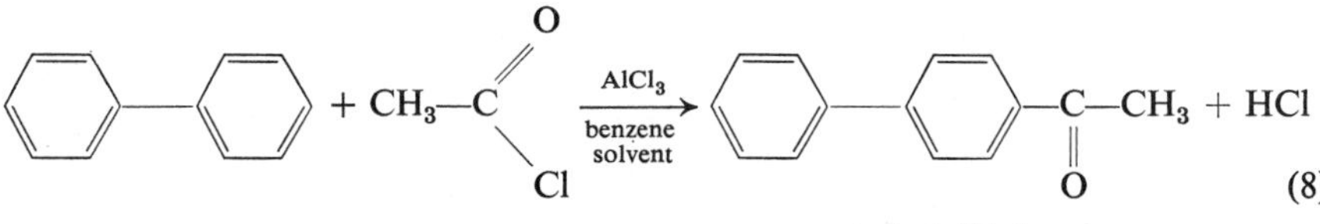

$$\text{(biphenyl)} + CH_3-C\overset{O}{\underset{Cl}{\diagdown}} \xrightarrow[\text{solvent}]{AlCl_3} \text{(biphenyl)}-\overset{O}{\underset{\|}{C}}-CH_3 + HCl \qquad (8)$$

p-Acetylbiphenyl

There is no difficulty with a side reaction in which the acylonium ion attacks benzene.

Substitution of a second acyl in biphenyl occurs in the 4-position in the second ring, as with other substitutions in biphenyls containing a *meta*-director;

however, *this reaction requires rather strenuous conditions*, prolonged reaction with excess of aluminum chloride. This follows from the possibility of inter-ring electron delocalization, to reduce electron density in the unsubstituted ring. Resonance forms of the following type would be involved:

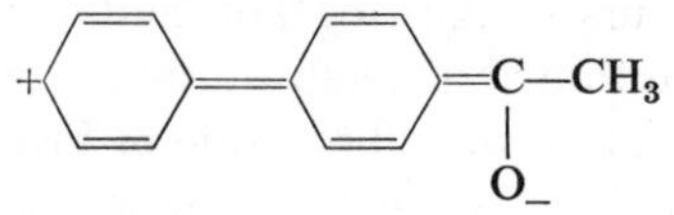

$$
+\langle \bigcirc \rangle = \langle \bigcirc \rangle = C\!-\!CH_3
$$
$$
\overset{|}{\underset{O_-}{}}
$$

Of course the *meta*-director will lower electron density in its own ring more than in the other ring, on account of the inductive effect being much stronger on the closer ring. It will be recalled that a second acylation in the benzene series is so difficult as to be of no practical value.

It is of interest that application of the hypohalite oxidation to 4-acetyl-biphenyl is the preferred method for preparing *p*-phenylbenzoic acid (Eq. 9).

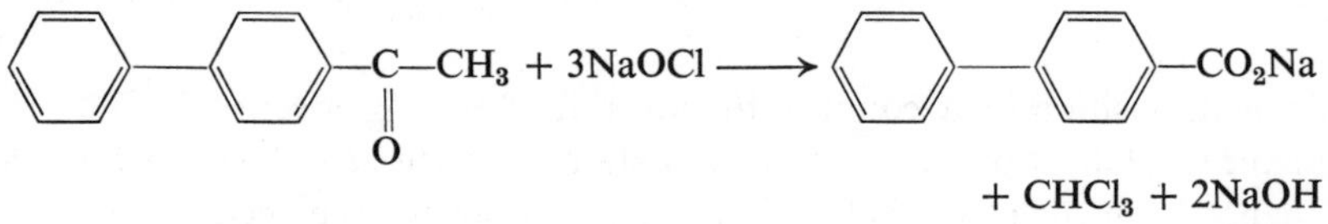

$$
\bigcirc\!-\!\bigcirc\!-\!\overset{O}{\underset{\|}{C}}\!-\!CH_3 + 3NaOCl \longrightarrow \bigcirc\!-\!\bigcirc\!-\!CO_2Na \tag{9}
$$

$$
+ \, CHCl_3 + 2NaOH
$$

Alternative routes are: (a) bromination of biphenyl, formation of Grignard reagent, carbonation of the Grignard reagent; (b) nitration of biphenyl, reduction, diazotization, nitrile by Sandmeyer reaction, hydrolysis. Neither of these methods is so satisfactory as that shown in Eq. 9. This should be contrasted with the situation in the benzene series.

Cyclization reactions. Cyclization to form a ring in the *o*- and *o'*-positions in biphenyl occurs with great facility. For example, such a cyclization occurs if distillation of *o*-phenylbenzoyl chloride is attempted, even at reduced pressure (Eq. 10).

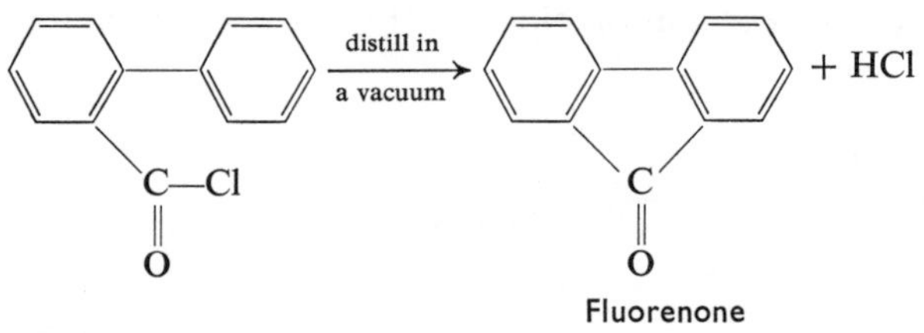

$$
\bigcirc\!-\!\bigcirc \quad \xrightarrow[\text{a vacuum}]{\text{distill in}} \quad \bigcirc\!-\!\bigcirc \quad + \, HCl \tag{10}
$$
$$
\underset{O}{\overset{|}{C}}\!-\!Cl \qquad\qquad\qquad \underset{O}{\overset{|}{C}}
$$

Fluorenone

With certain substituents in the rings, such a cyclization as shown in Eq. 10 will occur at room temperature. In all cases, reactions of the acid chlorides in the 2-position which require heating (such as the Rosenmund reduction) frequently cannot be secured. Cyclization occurs preferentially.

Synthesis of fluorene derivatives. The cyclization shown in Eq. 10 allows synthesis of the fluorene ring system. Reduction of the carbonyl leads to the parent hydrocarbon, fluorene, as shown in Eq. 11.

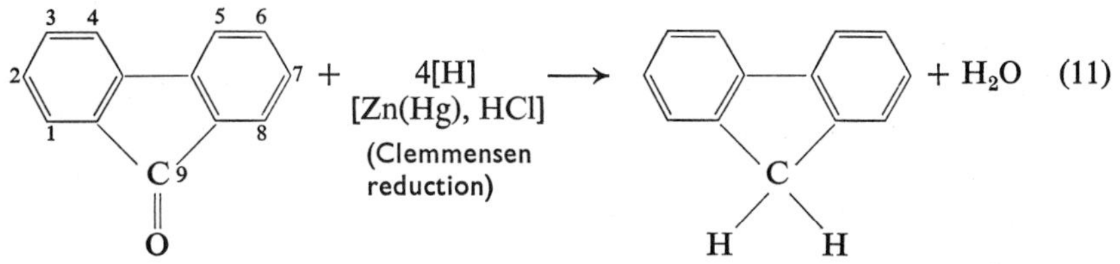

$$
\begin{array}{c}
\text{(biphenyl ketone structure, positions 3 4 5 6 7 8 1 2, } C_9 = O\text{)} + \begin{array}{c} 4[H] \\ [Zn(Hg), HCl] \\ \text{(Clemmensen} \\ \text{reduction)} \end{array} \longrightarrow \text{(Fluorene structure, C with H H)} + H_2O \quad (11)
\end{array}
$$

Fluorene

Reduction may also be carried out by the Wolff-Kishner method (Eq. 15-25). Fluorene itself occurs in coal tar; however, certain substituted fluorenes are profitably prepared via substituted biphenyls.

Aromatic substitution in fluorene occurs at position-2. This demonstrates the fact that inter-ring resonance stabilization in the transition state is a much more powerful *ortho,para*-director than is alkyl. It follows that 2-substituted fluorenes may be prepared by the usual aromatic substitution reactions. Other substituted fluorenes may be prepared from an appropriately substituted biphenyl. For example, 2-amino-3-methylbenzoic acid may be diazotized and coupled to give 2-phenyl-3-methylbenzoic acid. By appropriate steps, as described above, this acid may be converted to 4-methylfluorene.

EXERCISES

1. Cyclization of an *o*-phenylbenzoyl chloride, as in Eq. 10, may be regarded as a Friedel and Crafts reaction which goes so easily that no catalyst is needed. Would you expect ease of cyclization to be increased by an electron-donating group such as methoxyl in the position adjacent to the acid chloride?

2. How many stereoisomers are there of the following compound? Name this compound.

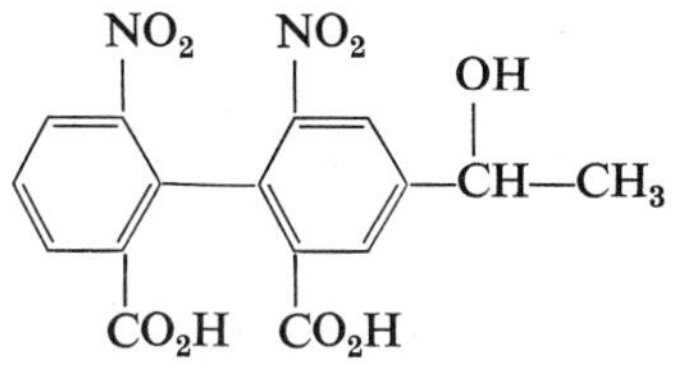

$$
\text{(biphenyl structure with substituents } NO_2 \text{, } NO_2 \text{, } OH, -CH-CH_3, CO_2H, CO_2H\text{)}
$$

3. Explain why nitration of nitrobenzene gives principally *m*-dinitrobenzene, whereas coupling of sodium benzenediazotate with nitrobenzene gives principally 4-nitrobiphenyl.

4. Explain why nitration of 4-nitrobiphenyl occurs in the 4′-position rather than *meta* to the nitro group already in the ring. Write any resonance forms appropriate to your explanation.

5. Starting with substances available from coal tar, and aliphatic compounds containing four carbons or less, indicate practical routes for synthesis of each of the following compounds.

(a)

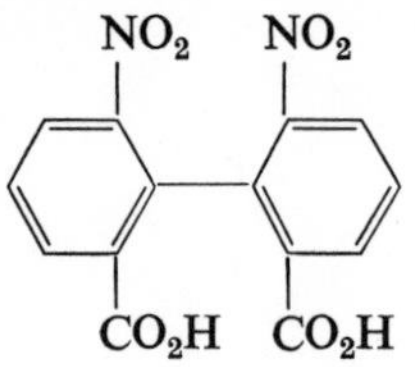

(b)

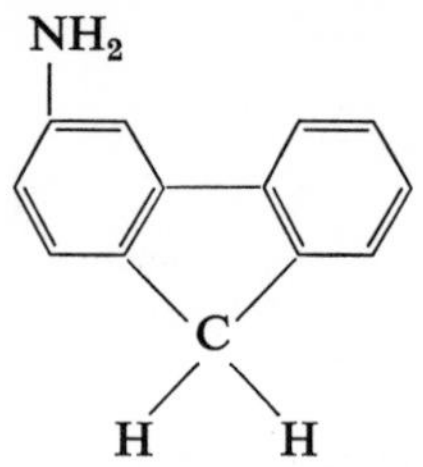

(Nitration of *p*-xylene is a good starting point to consider.)

(c)

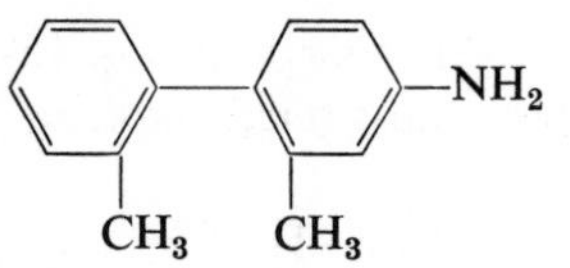

(d)

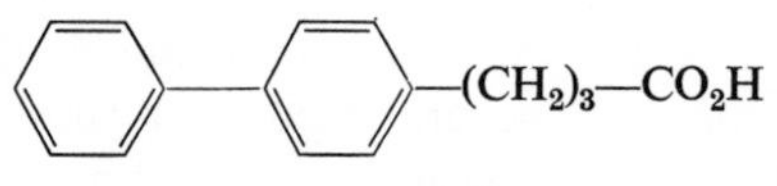

(e)

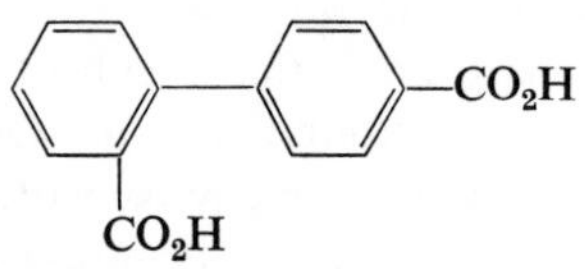

Naphthalene and Its Derivatives

Naphthalene is the most simple of the *condensed ring hydrocarbons.* Such hydrocarbons are those containing two or more aromatic rings fused together by virtue of sharing two carbon atoms. Naphthalene contains two fused aromatic rings, and its principal resonance forms are the following:

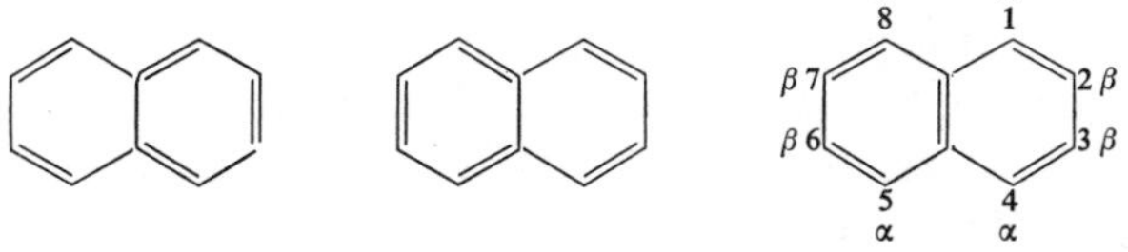

The numbering of the naphthalene ring and the use of Greek letters to designate positions are indicated on the right-hand formula. It will be noted that the four positions adjacent to another ring are termed alpha positions, while those not adjacent to another ring are termed beta positions. Thus there are two isomeric monosubstituted derivatives of naphthalene; the substituent may be either alpha or beta. If more than one substituent is present, numbers must be used in order to definitively locate the substituents. For example α,α-dibromonaphthalene might be the 1,4-, 1,5- or 1,8-dibromonaphthalene. Usual rules of nomenclature hold for naphthalene derivatives. Numbering is started on that α-carbon which gives the lowest numbers to the substituents. A few examples of nomenclature follow.

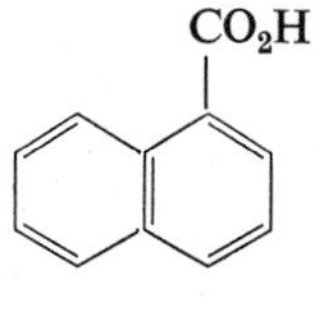

α-Naphthoic acid
or 1-Naphthoic acid

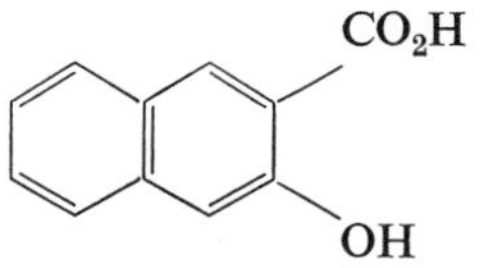

3-Hydroxy-2-
naphthoic acid

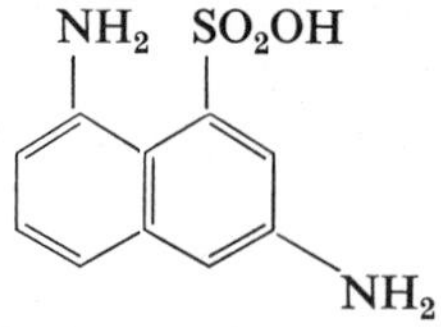

3,8-Diamino-1-
naphthalenesulfonic acid

In the above illustrations of nomenclature, it may be noted that the double bonds are indicated as in the position of the resonance form shown on the right previously. This is the usual practice in writing the naphthalene formula. If the three principal resonance forms are considered, it will be noted that each pair of adjacent alpha and beta carbons is joined by a double bond in two of these resonance forms, while each pair of adjacent beta carbons is joined by a double bond in only one of these forms. Since the double bonds must be placed somewhere in writing the formulas, according to the usual conventions, it seems best to put them between the carbons whose connecting bonds have more double bond character. It may be added that several of the reactions of naphthalene demonstrate that these bonds do have more double bond character than the others.

Sources and Characteristics of Naphthalene Derivatives

Naphthalene, the parent hydrocarbon, has the well-known characteristic odor of "moth flakes" (crude naphthalene), and is present in coal tar to a larger extent than any other substance. It constitutes about 10% of the average coal tar. This is fortunate, for naphthalene is the major source of naphthalene derivatives. As in the benzene series, several groups may be directly substituted, and these primary substitution derivatives may be converted to numerous other derivatives.

Naphthols and naphthylamines are not supplied from coal tar, but must be prepared from naphthalene. The α- and β-methylnaphthalenes are isolated from coal tar, however, and are available as starting materials for synthesis, In addition, the interesting compound, acenaphthene, is isolated from coal tar and serves as starting material for preparation of certain naphthalene derivatives.

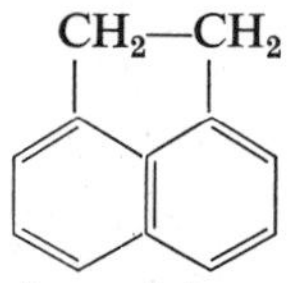

Acenaphthene

Most of the remaining derivatives of naphthalene must be prepared from these few starting materials. The only additional route to substituted naphthalene derivatives is by cyclization of aliphatic compounds. Syntheses of this latter variety will be studied after there have been discussed oxidation, reduction, and substitution of naphthalene, as well as certain characteristic reactions of substituent groups in naphthalene derivatives.

Many of the derivatives of naphthalene have been of great utility for manufacture of azo dyes (Chap. 19), and this has been a major impetus to the development of the chemistry of naphthalene.

A large fraction of the common derivatives of naphthalene are solids. Naphthalene melts at 80°, β-methylnaphthalene melts at 36°, and α-nitro-naphthalene melts at 60°. Among the few common liquid derivatives are α-methylnaphthalene, melting point $-22°$, and α-bromonaphthalene, melting point 6°. The two naphthols, the two naphthylamines, and β-bromonaphthalene are solids.

Oxidation of Naphthalene

Naphthalene proves to be oxidized more easily than is benzene, and the product of vigorous oxidation is a benzene derivative. This has been illustrated in connection with the preparation of phthalic acid (Eq. 21-5). The effect of electron-withdrawing groups in stabilizing the ring to oxidation, and of electron-donating groups in making the ring susceptible to oxidation may be well illustrated in the naphthalene series (Eq. 1).

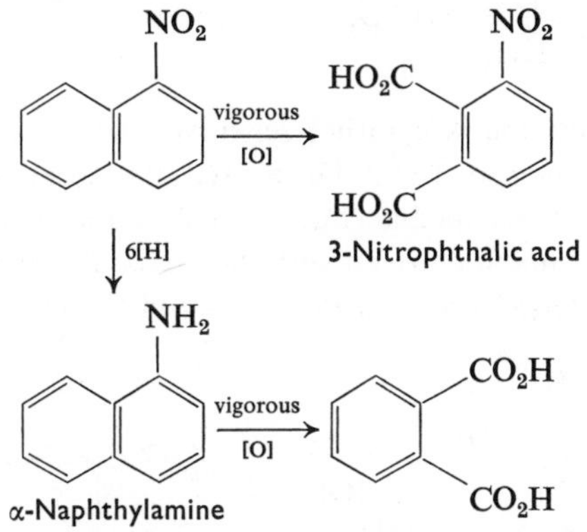

3-Nitrophthalic acid

(1)

α-Naphthylamine

Naphthoquinones. The relative ease of oxidation of naphthalene makes possible choice of conditions which will permit isolation of a very low yield of 1,4-naphthoquinone (Eq. 2).

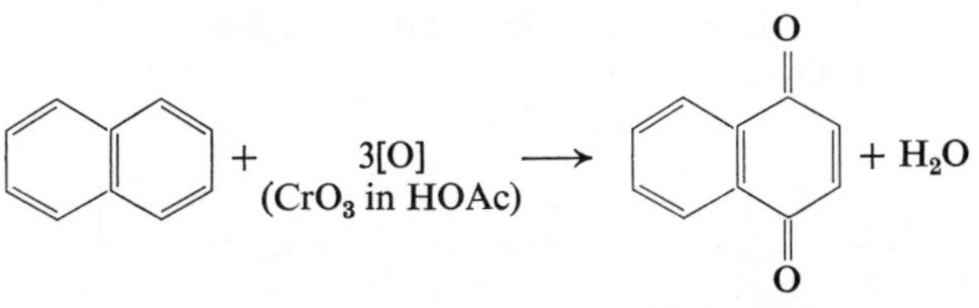

$$+ \quad \begin{array}{c} 3[O] \\ (CrO_3 \text{ in HOAc}) \end{array} \quad \longrightarrow \quad \quad + H_2O \qquad (2)$$

1,4-Naphthoquinone

In contrast with the benzene series, an alkyl substituent in naphthalene is more resistant to oxidation than is the ring. Thus β-methylnaphthalene may be oxidized to the corresponding quinone (Eq. 3); in fact, the yield is better than

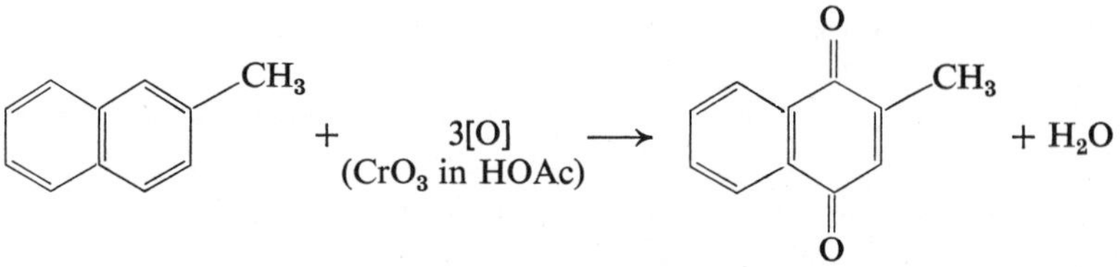

$$
\text{[naphthalene-CH}_3\text{]} + \underset{(CrO_3 \text{ in HOAc})}{3[O]} \longrightarrow \text{[2-Methyl-1,4-naphthoquinone]} + H_2O \quad (3)
$$

2-Methyl-1,4-naphthoquinone

in oxidation of naphthalene. It follows directly from Eq. 3 that *carboxylic acids cannot be prepared by oxidation of methylnaphthalenes* by usual methods. This is the first of several differences to be studied in the synthetic routes which are feasible in the naphthalene series, as contrasted to the benzene series.

As in the benzene series, best yields of quinones are secured by oxidation of compounds substituted with hydroxyl or amino in the positions oxidized (Eq. 4).

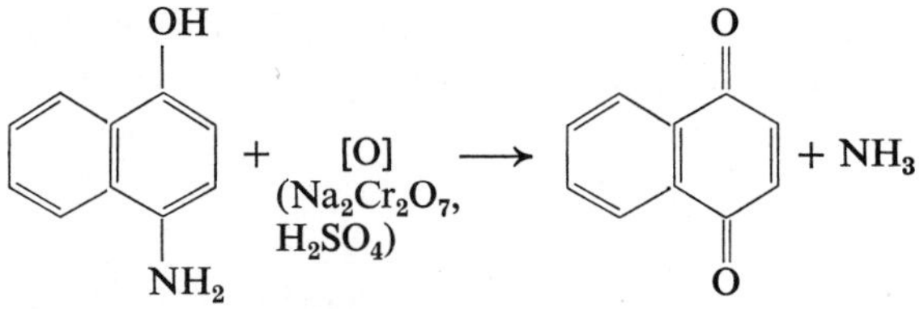

$$
\text{[1-OH, 4-NH}_2\text{ naphthalene]} + \underset{\substack{(Na_2Cr_2O_7, \\ H_2SO_4)}}{[O]} \longrightarrow \text{[1,4-naphthoquinone]} + NH_3 \quad (4)
$$

1,2-Naphthoquinone is a rather sensitive compound, but is more stable than 1,2-benzoquinone; so it may be secured by oxidation of the appropriate aminophenol in aqueous media (Eq. 5). The somewhat greater stability of 1,2-naphthoquinone, in comparison with the 1,2-benzoquinone, may be reasonably ascribed to presence of one aromatic ring in the naphthoquinone.

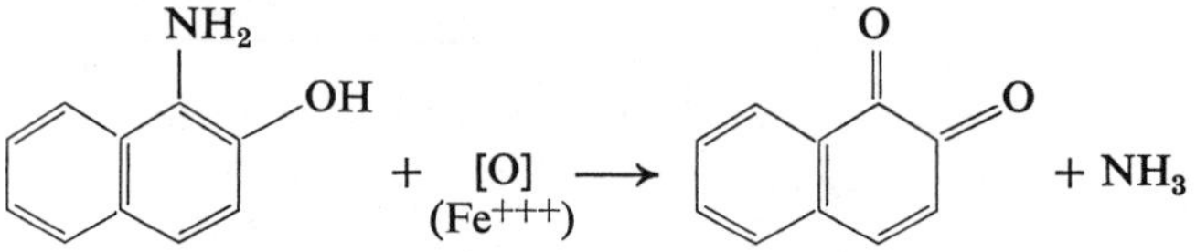

$$
\text{[1-NH}_2\text{, 2-OH naphthalene]} + \underset{(Fe^{+++})}{[O]} \longrightarrow \text{[1,2-naphthoquinone]} + NH_3 \quad (5)
$$

1,2-Naphthoquinone

A third naphthoquinone is known, the 2,6-naphthoquinone. It is rather unstable and obtained only on careful oxidation of the corresponding dihydroxy compound (Eq. 6). It will be noted that the 2,6-naphthoquinone does not contain an aromatic ring.

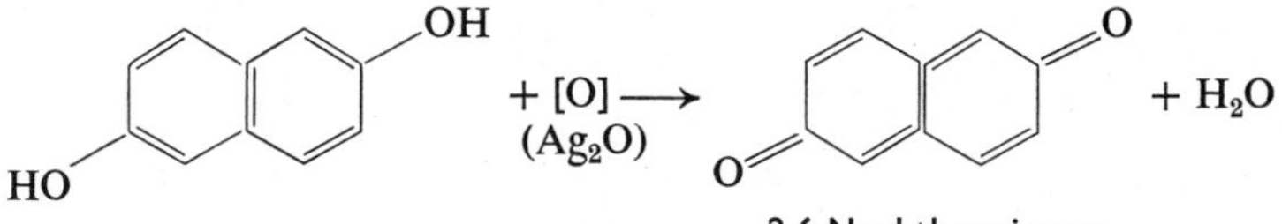

$$
\text{[2,6-dihydroxynaphthalene]} + \underset{(Ag_2O)}{[O]} \longrightarrow \text{[2,6-naphthoquinone]} + H_2O \quad (6)
$$

2,6-Naphthoquinone

Still another naphthoquinone is structurally possible, the 2,3-naphtho-quinone:

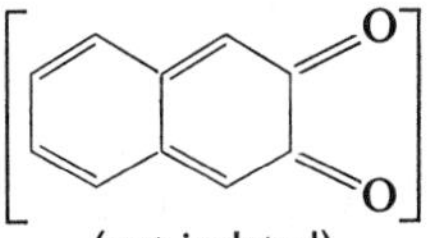

(not isolated)

This quinone has never been isolated, and is therefore a very unstabie compound. It may be noted that this structure contains the same bond system as the unstable 1,2-benzoquinone, but extended by an additional pair of double bonds. Such bond systems have proved to be unstable in various aromatic compounds.

Reduction of Naphthalene

Naphthalene is reduced considerably more readily than is benzene; so clean-cut reduction of one ring in naphthalene may be accomplished (Eq. 7).

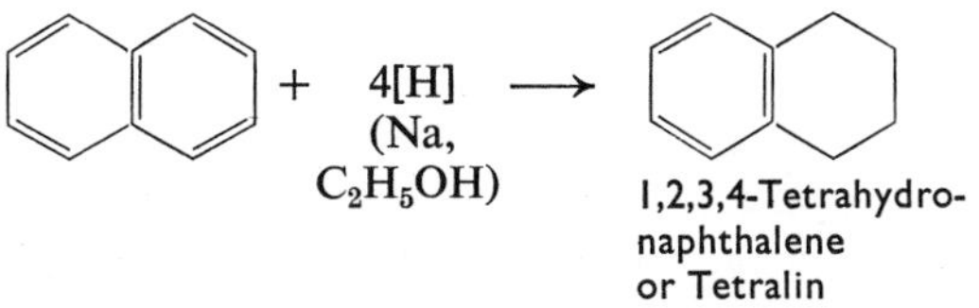

$$+ \quad 4[H] \quad \longrightarrow \tag{7}$$
(Na, C_2H_5OH)

1,2,3,4-Tetrahydro-naphthalene or Tetralin

If there are substituents in the naphthalene ring, one or the other ring may be reduced preferentially. The ring reduced more rapidly depends on the substituents present and the conditions used for reduction. Although numerous specific reductions have been worked out, no general principles have yet been formulated for prediction of the ring that will be attacked more rapidly in a specific instance.

Under strenuous conditions, sufficient to reduce benzene, both rings in naphthalene may be reduced. The best method is high-pressure catalytic hydrogenation (Eq. 8).

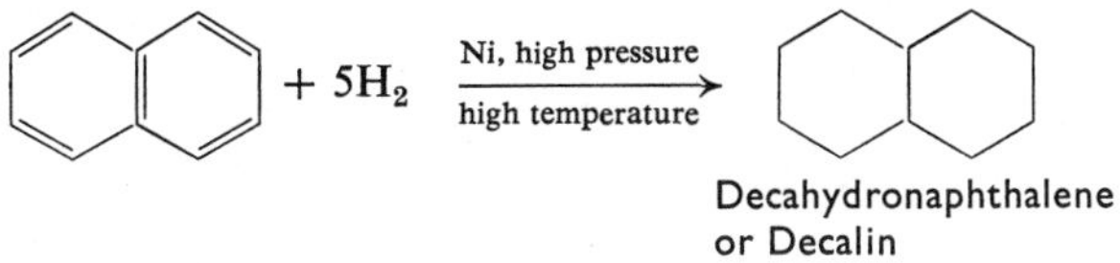

$$+ 5H_2 \quad \xrightarrow[\text{high temperature}]{\text{Ni, high pressure}} \tag{8}$$

Decahydronaphthalene or Decalin

Both tetralin and decalin are commercially available. Since the ring juncture in decalin may be either *cis* or *trans*, there are two geometric isomers of this substance. The stereochemistry of the decalin ring system, as discussed in Chapters 7 and 22, should be reviewed at this point. Of particular interest (Chap. 7) is the relatively linear, rather rigid structure in *trans*-decalin, resulting from ring juncture by two equatorial bonds, in contrast with the flexible, angular structure in *cis*-decalin.

Monosubstitution in Naphthalene

In general, the same substitution reactions applicable in the benzene series (Chap. 17) also apply in the naphthalene series; however, there must be considered in naphthalene the possibility of monosubstitution in either the alpha or beta position. The results obtained for each of the four principal substitution reactions in naphthalene will be discussed.

Halogenation. Halogenation of naphthalene is ordinarily limited to bromination and chlorination. The rate of substitution in naphthalene is much faster in the alpha position than in the beta position, so a non-reversible substitution such as halogenation (Eq. 9) goes almost exclusively in the alpha

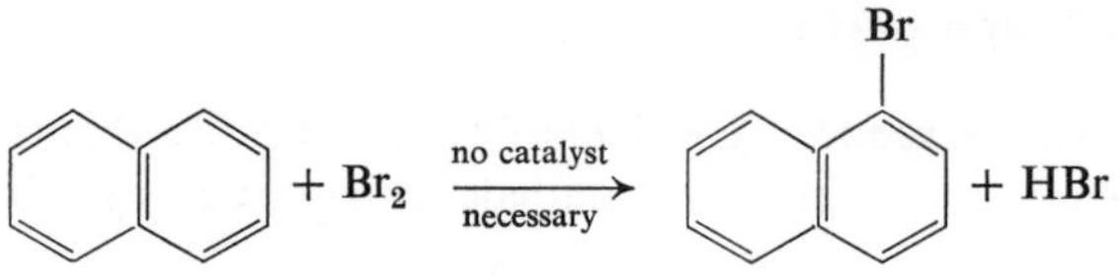

$$
\text{(naphthalene)} + Br_2 \xrightarrow[\text{necessary}]{\text{no catalyst}} \text{(1-bromonaphthalene)} + HBr \tag{9}
$$

1-Bromonaphthalene

position. In contrast with benzene, this substitution is so facile that no Lewis acid is necessary to take the halogen molecule apart and furnish a positive halogen for electrophilic attack on the aromatic system. The naphthalene ring system is able to displace bromide, or chloride, ion from the molecule. In the benzene series, only iodine is able to substitute without a Lewis acid as catalyst.

As usual in halogenation of aromatic compounds, some disubstitution in naphthalene is unavoidable; however, separation of a good yield of 1-bromo-naphthalene may be accomplished.

Nitration of naphthalene (Eq. 10) also occurs almost exclusively in the

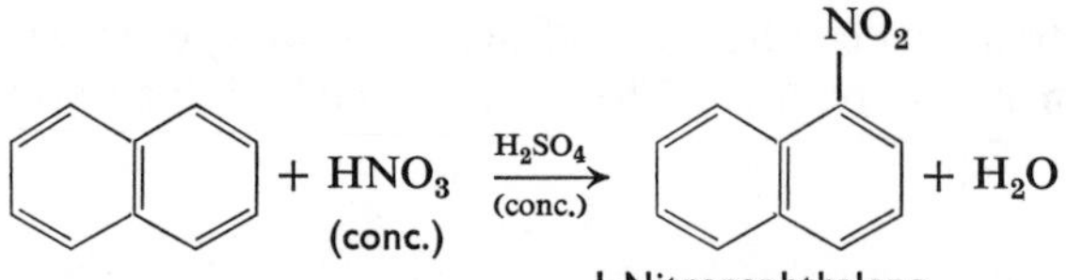

$$
\text{(naphthalene)} + HNO_3 \xrightarrow[\text{(conc.)}]{H_2SO_4} \text{(1-nitronaphthalene)} + H_2O \tag{10}
$$

1-Nitronaphthalene

1-position, for this reaction is non-reversible also. As in the other substitution reactions of naphthalene, a practical rate of reaction is realized under much milder conditions than required in the benzene series. The reaction in Eq. 10 proceeds readily at room temperature.

Sulfonation. As in the benzene series, sulfonation is reversible. Further-more, the initially formed 1-isomer is hydrolyzed more rapidly than is the 2-isomer. Thus sulfonation under mild conditions where the back reaction does not become significant gives principally the 1-isomer; but more strenuous conditions allow equilibration to be set up, so the slowly hydrolyzed 2-isomer accumulates. These reactions are presented in Eq. 11. As in the case of sulfonation of phenol (Eq. 20-2), the product obtained depends on whether the

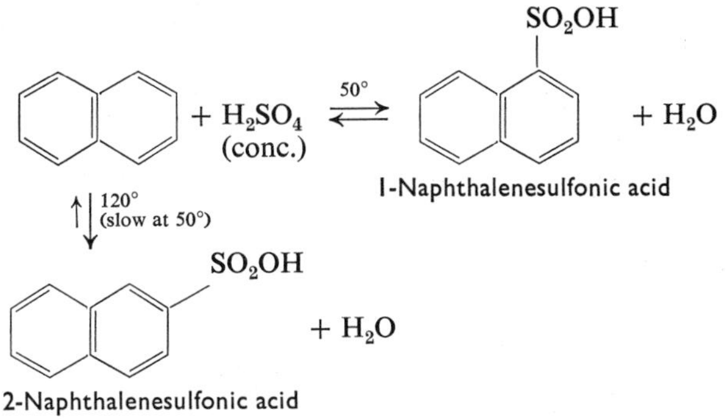

1-Naphthalenesulfonic acid (11)

2-Naphthalenesulfonic acid

process is carried out with *kinetic control* (product determined by relative rates of reaction) or *thermodynamic control* (product determined by relative positions of equilibria).

Although either the 1- or 2-sulfonic acid may be obtained, depending on conditions, the 1-isomer always contains some of the 2-isomer, which is separable with great difficulty. On account of the large size of the sulfo group, the rate of 1-substitution is slowed down by steric interference with the hydrogen at the adjacent 8-position, so there is a higher ratio of 2-substitution in sulfonation than is the case for bromination or nitration. There are many illustrations, including the Friedel and Crafts reaction to be discussed next, of the considerable steric interference between substituents at the 1- and 8-positions in naphthalene. These adjacent positions are known as *peri* **positions.**

The steric interference in *peri*-positions in naphthalene is probably responsible for the considerably lower energy of the 2-naphthalenesulfonic acid, relative to the 1-sulfonic acid. This energy difference is sufficient that the product of substitution with thermodynamic control is a relatively pure sample of the 2-isomer.

Friedel and Crafts reactions. Alkylation of naphthalene by the Friedel and Crafts procedure has found very limited utility; however, acylation is a very useful procedure. If the Friedel and Crafts acylation is carried out under usual conditions with carbon disulfide as solvent, a mixture of the alpha and beta isomers is secured; but if nitrobenzene is used as solvent, substitution occurs almost exclusively in the beta position. This is believed due to the fact

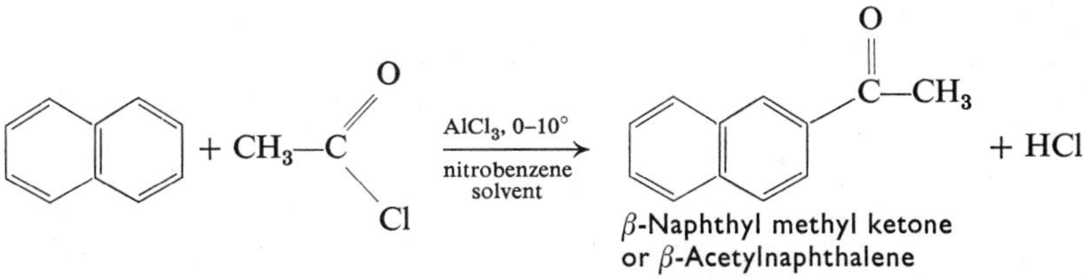

β-Naphthyl methyl ketone
or β-Acetylnaphthalene

that nitrobenzene forms a complex with aluminum chloride and the substituting group. Approach of this bulky complex to the ring is far easier in the position not hindered by being adjacent to the other ring. Acetylation to give the beta isomer is shown in Eq. 12.

The mixture obtained by acylation in carbon disulfide is ordinarily not separable on a practical basis; however, acylation with succinic anhydride does give a separable mixture. The acids shown in Eq. 13 can be separated

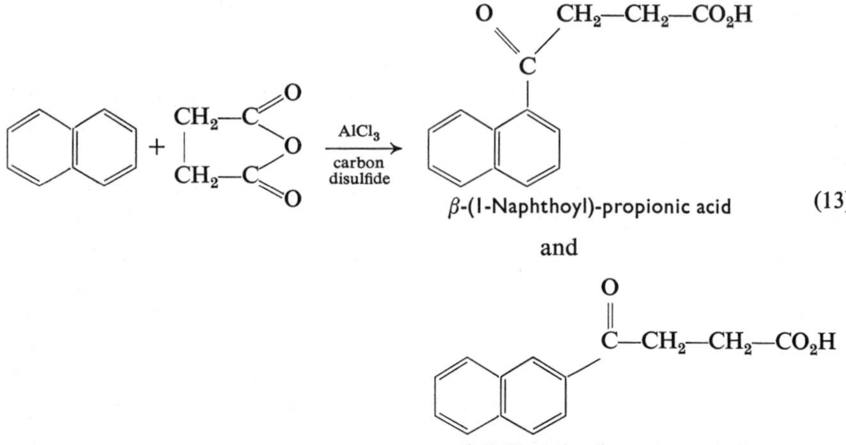

β-(1-Naphthoyl)-propionic acid   (13)

and

β-(2-Naphthoyl)-propionic acid

because of their significant difference in acid strength (ionization constant). This feature makes both of these isomers available in a pure condition for use in synthesis. Important applications of these compounds in synthesis of phenanthrenes will be discussed in Chapter 30.

Formation of Other Derivatives from the Primary Substitution Products

Consideration of the compounds obtainable by monosubstitution will reveal that many routes of synthesis must be different from those in the benzene series. For example, the β-substituted derivatives cannot be obtained from the nitro compound, the most common intermediate in the benzene series, but must be obtained from either the sulfonic acid or the acyl derivatives.

Study of conversions in the naphthalene series offers an excellent opportunity to review some of the chemistry discussed for benzene, as well as to learn certain new reactions which are not applicable or not useful in the benzene series.

Naphthylamines. The α-naphthylamine is obtained by reduction of the nitro compound, the same route applicable in benzene.

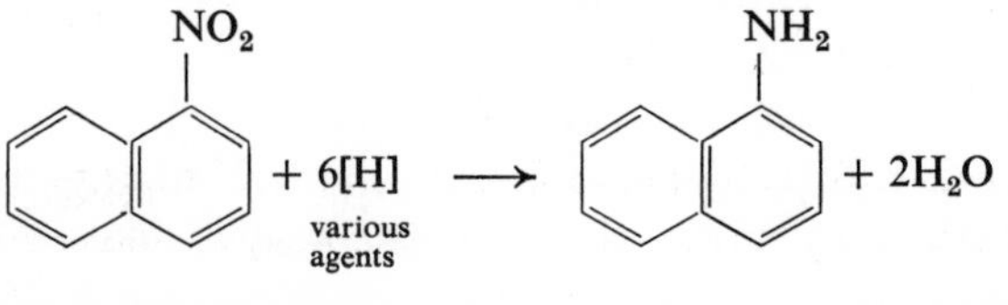

$+ 6[H] \longrightarrow$ various agents $+ 2H_2O$ (14)

Since the β-nitronaphthalene is not available, the β-naphthylamine must be secured by some other route. Fortunately, β-naphthol may be converted to the amine by the **Bucherer reaction** (Eq. 15), a reaction which is not successful in the benzene series but gives excellent yields in the naphthalene series.

$$\text{(naphthol-OH)} + NH_3 \xrightarrow[\substack{\text{pressure} \\ \text{heat}}]{(NH_4)_2SO_3} \text{(naphthyl-NH}_2) + H_2O \quad (15)$$

(aqueous)

Under other conditions, Eq. 15 can be run backwards (reverse Bucherer reaction), but in that direction the yields are usually not so good as may be secured by other methods (cf. Eq. 16).

The naphthylamines are important compounds, for they may be diazotized as in the benzene series, and converted to the large number of compounds obtainable from the diazonium salts (cf. Chap. 19). Also, coupling leads to numerous azo dyes of commercial importance. A Sandmeyer reaction on β-naphthyldiazonium bromide is the only practical source of β-**bromonaphthalene.** This diazonium reaction is beset by experimental difficulties, partly ascribed to the weak basicity of the β-naphthylamine and the insolubility of its salts with strong acids. This difficulty added to the number of steps involved makes β-bromonaphthalene much less accessible than the alpha isomer. Whereas 1-bromonaphthalene sells commercially for less than ten dollars per kilogram, the β-isomer is quoted at more than two hundred dollars per kilogram. It follows that any compound made from 2-bromonaphthalene is an expensive substance.

Naphthols. Both the alpha and beta naphthols are readily available from potassium hydroxide fusion of the corresponding sulfonic acids (cf. Eq. 18-18); however, this is not a source of pure α-naphthol. If the pure substance is desired, it must be made from the amine. Diazotization is a possible route, but in the naphthalene series an amine may be directly hydrolyzed in high yield under moderately strenuous conditions (Eq. 16). This process has found

$$\text{(naphthyl-NH}_3Cl) + H_2O \xrightarrow[220°, \text{ pressure}]{10\% \text{ aqueous HCl}} \text{(naphthol-OH)} + NH_4Cl \quad (16)$$

considerable use for conversion of substituted naphthylamines. Such a reaction is entirely impractical in the benzene series. The substituted naphthols are important as dye intermediates.

Naphthoic acids. 1-Naphthoic acid may be made satisfactorily from 1-bromonaphthalene by either of the routes used in the benzene series for conversion of a bromide to the carboxylic acids. These processes are outlined in Eq. 17.

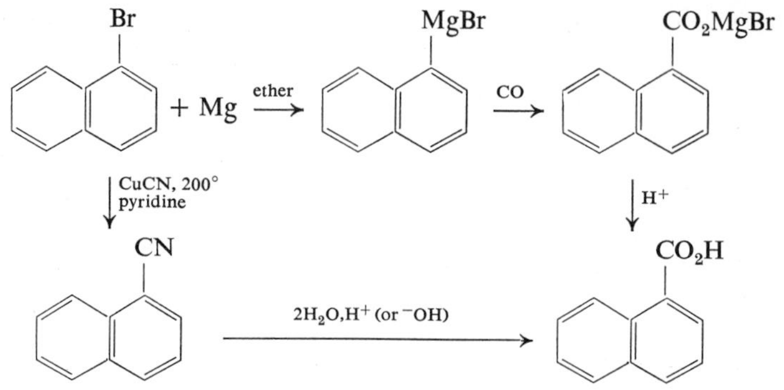

In this connection it should be mentioned that α-naphthylmagnesium bromide may also be used in the various other syntheses in which the Grignard reagent is useful. It is a source of many α-naphthyl derivatives.

2-Naphthoic acid can be made from 2-bromonaphthalene by the routes described for the 1-isomer, but these routes are not ordinarily used on account of the expense of 2-bromonaphthalene. Since 2-acetylnaphthalene is readily available (Eq. 12), the carboxylic acid is most conveniently obtained by hypohalite oxidation of this ketone, as shown in Eq. 18.

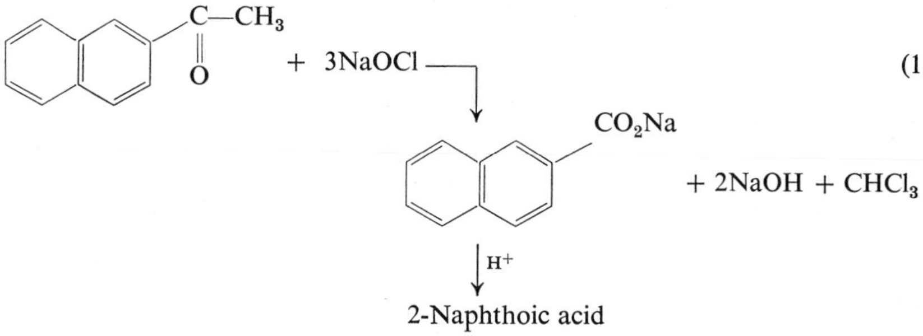

In polysubstituted naphthalenes obtained by cyclization reactions, β-bromo derivatives are sometimes available more readily than the acyl derivatives. In such instances, routes analogous to those shown in Eq. 17 become practical.

Nitriles and amides can be made by dehydration of the ammonium salts of the corresponding acids or via the acid chlorides. The amides are frequently obtained in this manner, but the nitriles are usually obtained by independent routes. Synthesis of α-naphthonitrile has already been indicated in Eq. 17. The β-isomer is usually obtained by potassium cyanide fusion of the salt of the sulfonic acid (Eq. 19).

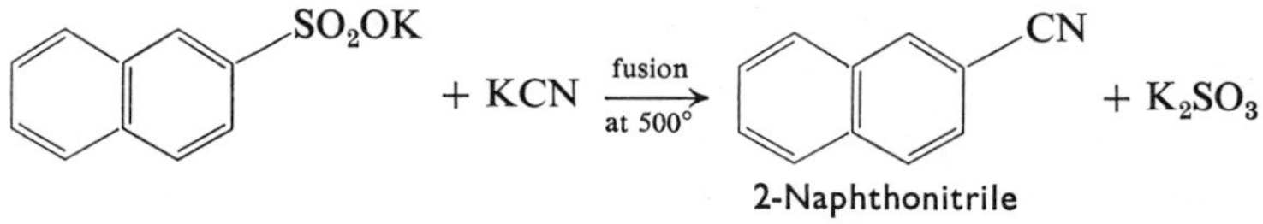

This is another illustration of a preparative scheme which is of little utility in the benzene series but is a preferred method in the naphthalene series.

Both nitriles may also be prepared from the corresponding amines via diazotization and the Sandmeyer reaction.

Naphthaldehydes are usually made from an acid derivative. The process previously discussed is the Rosenmund reduction of acid chlorides (Eq. 15-2).

Naphthyl ketones. The α-naphthyl ketones are usually made by a Grignard reaction with a nitrile (Eq. 14-21) or reaction of a cadmium reagent with an acid chloride (Eq. 18-36). The acid derivative may be attached either to the naphthalene nucleus or the alkyl group. For example, 1-propionylnaphthalene may be prepared: (a) from 1-naphthylmagnesium bromide and propionitrile, (b) from ethylmagnesium bromide and 1-naphtho-nitrile.

β-Naphthyl ketones are usually made by the Friedel and Crafts reaction (Eq. 12).

Monoalkylnaphthalenes. The methylnaphthalenes are obtained from coal tar, but the higher alkylnaphthalenes are usually obtained by Clemmensen (Eq. 15-24) or Wolff-Kishner reduction (Eq. 15-25) of the corresponding naphthyl ketone. For example, reduction of 2-acetylnaphthalene leads to 2-ethylnaphthalene. *sec*-Alkylnaphthalenes may be secured by way of the carbinol, as outlined in Eq. 20.

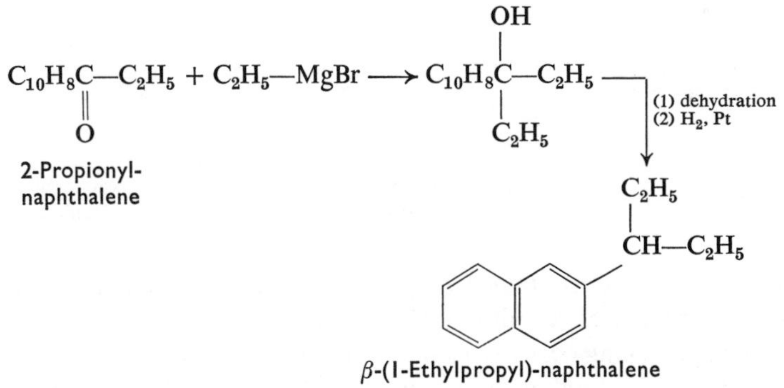

$$C_{10}H_8C\!\!-\!\!C_2H_5 + C_2H_5\!\!-\!\!MgBr \longrightarrow C_{10}H_8\overset{\overset{\displaystyle OH}{|}}{\underset{\underset{\displaystyle C_2H_5}{|}}{C}}\!\!-\!\!C_2H_5 \quad \begin{matrix}(1)\ \text{dehydration}\\(2)\ H_2,\ Pt\end{matrix}$$

2-Propionyl-
naphthalene

$$\overset{\displaystyle C_2H_5}{\underset{\displaystyle CH\!\!-\!\!C_2H_5}{|}}$$

(20)

β-(1-Ethylpropyl)-naphthalene

In conclusion of this discussion of conversions in the naphthalene series, a few generalizations may be presented:

1. Synthesis of naphthalene derivatives is complicated by the fact that there are two monosubstitution isomers.
2. Essentially all the reactions characteristic of the benzene series also occur satisfactorily in the naphthalene series; in addition, certain other reactions are useful in the naphthalene series.
3. Many of the useful reactions in the naphthalene series involve rather severe conditions, high temperatures and high pressures.

Polysubstitution Derivatives of Naphthalene

Polysubstitution in naphthalene can lead to a variety of isomers. When two of the same group are substituted in the naphthalene nucleus, there are ten possible isomers. With two different groups, the number of possible isomers becomes fourteen. In addition, disubstitution frequently gives three or four of these isomers, and only a relatively limited number of orientation rules are of general applicability. We will confine our attention to the few general rules concerning directive influence; however, it should be mentioned that a really large number of di- and tri-substituted naphthalene derivatives are commercially available. These are obtained by development of special methods for separating the complicated mixtures resulting from polysubstitution. Interest in this field has arisen from the importance of naphthalene derivatives as dye intermediates. When a chemist needs one of these derivatives, it is sometimes a minor project to discover whether it is commercially available, for most of them have trade names bearing no relationship to the chemical name. For example, Chicago Acid is 1-amino-8-naphthol-2,4-disulfonic acid. Various books and industrial catalogs are available as an aid in locating trade names and commercial sources of these dye intermediates.

An *ortho,para*-**director in the 1-position** directs to the 4-position, with minor substitution in the 2-position.

An illustration of this principle is found in sulfonation of 1-naphthol, Eq. 21.

$$\text{OH} + H_2SO_4 \longrightarrow \text{OH} \quad \text{and} \quad \text{OH} \qquad (21)$$

1-Naphthol-4-sulfonic acid   1-Naphthol-2-sulfonic acid

The two isomers are obtained in varying amounts, depending on conditions, but under appropriate conditions each is separable.

Diazo coupling occurs exclusively in the 4-position if this position is open; if it is occupied, coupling occurs in the 2-position. Thus 1-naphthol couples in the 4-position, and 1-naphthol-4-sulfonic acid couples in the 2-position. 4-Amino-1-naphthol may be obtained in good yield by way of coupling and reduction (cf. Eq. 19-55). This amine is useful for synthesis of 1,4-naphthoquinone (Eq. 4).

Heating of 1-naphthylamine sulfate gives dehydration and rearrangement to the 4-position in the manner previously described for the benzene series (cf. Eq. 19-37). This important reaction is illustrated in Eq. 22. Naphthionic acid is an important dye intermediate.

An *ortho,para*-**director in the 2-position** directs principally to the 1-position. The larger the entering group, sterically, the less clean-cut is the substitution

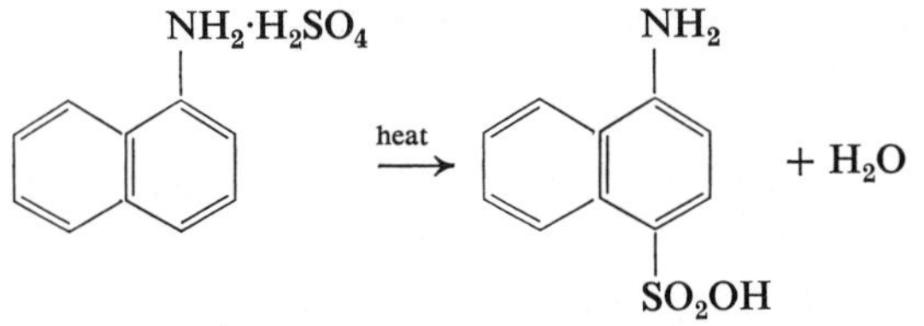

$$\text{(Naphthalene-}NH_2\cdot H_2SO_4) \xrightarrow{\text{heat}} \text{(Naphthionic acid, }NH_2, SO_2OH) + H_2O \qquad (22)$$

Naphthionic acid

in the 1-position. The secondary position of substitution is in the other ring; the location depends on the substituent and conditions.

Illustrations of substitutions in this category are shown in Eqs. 23 through 25.

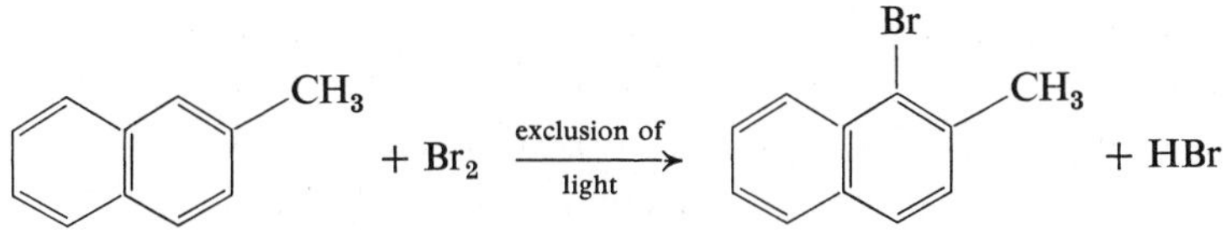

$$\text{(2-methylnaphthalene, }CH_3) + Br_2 \xrightarrow[\text{light}]{\text{exclusion of}} \text{(Br, }CH_3) + HBr \qquad (23)$$

(good yield of this isomer)

$$\text{(2-naphthol, }OH) + H_2SO_4 \xrightarrow[\text{perature}]{\text{low tem-}} \text{(}SO_2OH, OH) + H_2O \qquad (24)$$

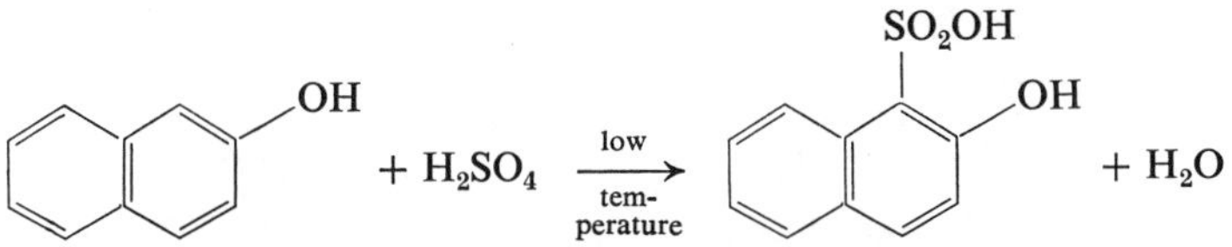

(moderate yield; more of other isomers at higher temperature)

$$\text{(2-naphthol, }OH) + \text{(}N_2^+X^-\text{)} \longrightarrow \text{(}N{=}N{-}C_6H_5, OH) + HX$$

(only isomer) $\qquad$ (25)

$\downarrow$ 4[H]

$$\text{(}NH_2, OH\text{)} + \text{(}NH_2\text{)}$$

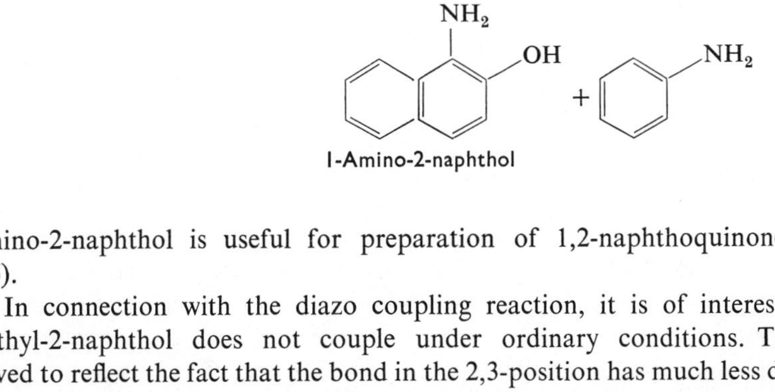

1-Amino-2-naphthol

1-Amino-2-naphthol is useful for preparation of 1,2-naphthoquinone (cf. Eq. 5).

In connection with the diazo coupling reaction, it is of interest that 1-methyl-2-naphthol does not couple under ordinary conditions. This is believed to reflect the fact that the bond in the 2,3-position has much less double bond character than does the bond in the 1,2-position. Another pertinent point is that the transition state for substitution in the 3-position would have the unstable system of double bonds characteristic of an *o*-quinone system, as shown on the right below.

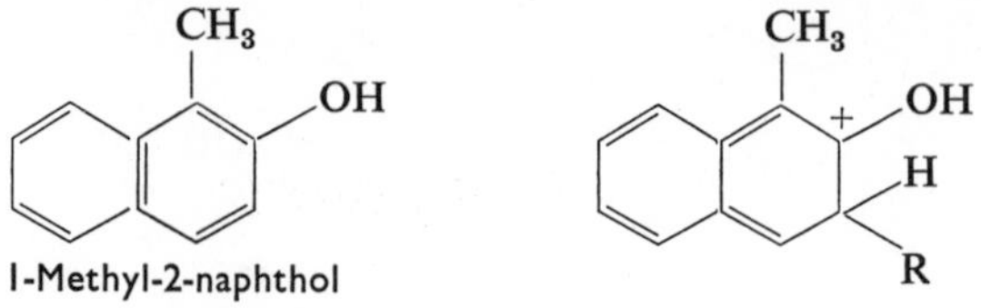

1-Methyl-2-naphthol

An illustration of the steric factor in 1-substitution is given by the Friedel and Crafts reaction in carbon disulfide and in the complex-forming nitrobenzene. A good yield of the respective products shown in Eq. 26 is obtained in each

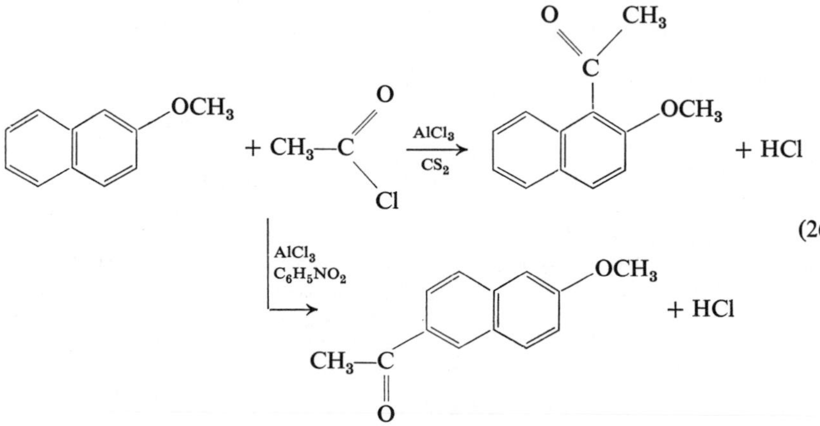

$$(26)$$

instance. Unfortunately, the rather clean-cut substitution in the 6-position in the lower line of Eq. 26 is *not* observed with other *o,p*-directors in the 2-position. In other cases, a majority of the substitution occurs in the 8-position.

Substitution in naphthalenes containing a *meta*-director leads to substitution in the other ring (i.e., ring not containing the *meta*-director), but in nearly all cases a mixture of isomers is obtained. Although many of these reactions are of great industrial significance, there appear to be no generalizations worthy of our attention.

Syntheses from Acenaphthene

Several of the 1,8-disubstituted naphthalenes may be obtained from acenaphthene. Two useful sequences are shown in Eqs. 27 and 28.

For use in synthesis, 1-acenaphthenol may be converted to the bromide or oxidized to 1-acenaphthenone. Lead tetraacetate is an oxidizing agent of considerable use for attacking specific structures. One structure selectively attacked by this agent is a rather reactive methylene group, as in acenaphthene or diethyl malonate.

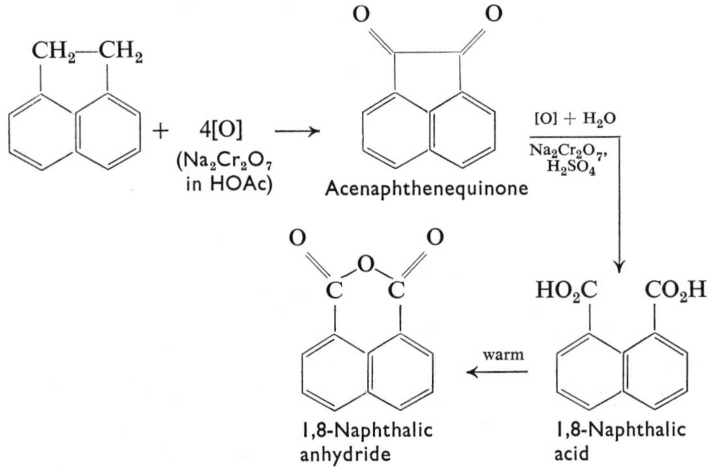
CH₂—CH₂
+ 4[O]
(Na₂Cr₂O₇ in HOAc)
Acenaphthenequinone
[O] + H₂O
Na₂Cr₂O₇, H₂SO₄
HO₂C
CO₂H
warm
1,8-Naphthalic anhydride
1,8-Naphthalic acid

(27)

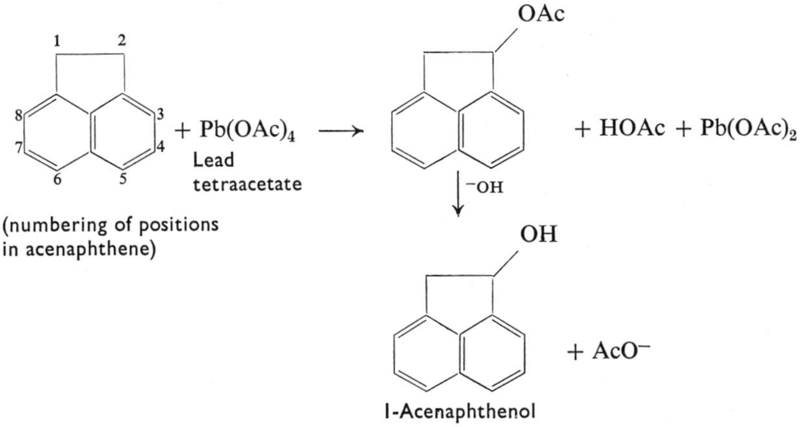
1
2
3
4
5
6
7
8
+ Pb(OAc)₄
Lead tetraacetate
OAc
+ HOAc + Pb(OAc)₂
⁻OH
OH
+ AcO⁻
1-Acenaphthenol

(numbering of positions in acenaphthene)

(28)

The remarkably low energy of the naphthalene derivatives with a six-membered ring attached at the *peri* positions is illustrated by the ease with which 1,8-naphthalic anhydride is formed. The conversion of 1,8-naphthalic acid to the anhydride, as in the lower line of Eq. 27, will occur if the acid is heated in boiling ethyl alcohol. This is in marked contrast to the normal energy relations for a cyclic anhydride. For example, if succinic anhydride is warmed with an alcohol (Eq. 14-7), the anhydride reacts with the alcohol to give a nearly quantitative yield of the half ester, ethyl hydrogen succinate. Indeed, the normal reaction of acid anhydrides with various nucleophiles gives acid derivatives (Chap. 14), but the very low energy of the *peri*-naphthalene ring prevents such reactions with 1,8-naphthalic anhydride.

Synthesis of Naphthalenes by Cyclization Reactions

Cyclization reactions are commonly used for synthesis of polyalkylnaphthalenes, as well as synthesis of various alkylnaphthalenes substituted with some other functional group. For such syntheses in the naphthalene series, as well as in the higher condensed ring series (Chap. 30), numerous methods have been developed. For illustration of these methods, we will study the **succinic anhydride synthesis,** which is probably the most versatile and useful of the procedures which have been applied. The sequence of reactions involved in synthesis of 1,7-dimethylnaphthalene is outlined below (entire sequence termed Eq. 29). It will be noted that all steps in this sequence except the last involve reactions studied on several previous occasions.

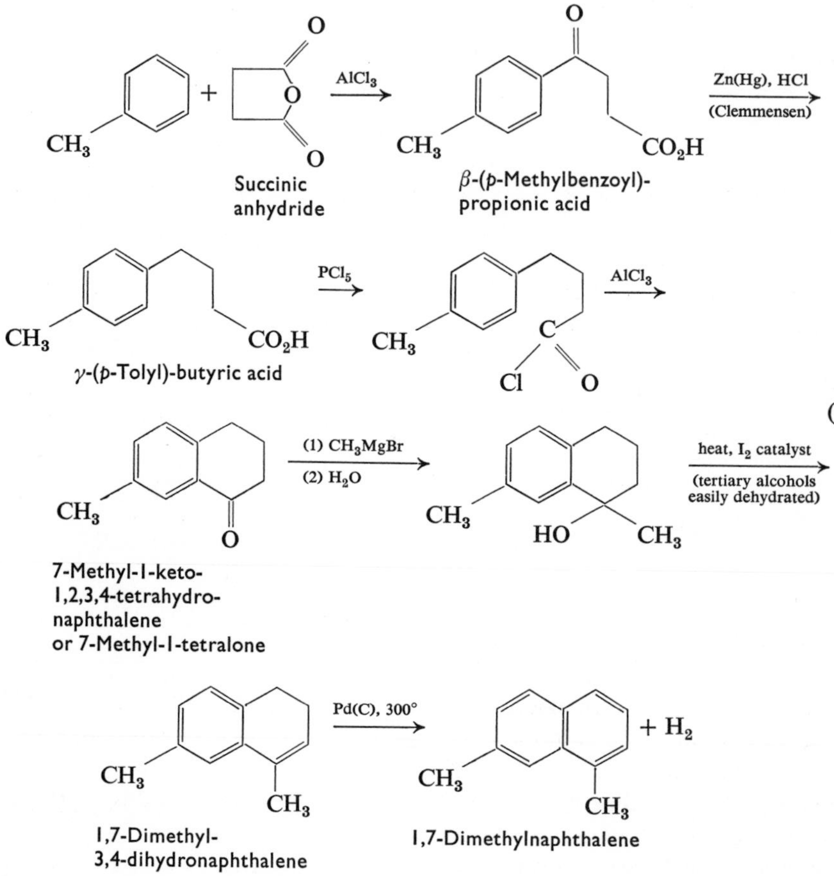

Succinic anhydride

β-(p-Methylbenzoyl)-propionic acid

γ-(p-Tolyl)-butyric acid

(29)

7-Methyl-1-keto-1,2,3,4-tetrahydro-naphthalene
or 7-Methyl-1-tetralone

1,7-Dimethyl-3,4-dihydronaphthalene

1,7-Dimethylnaphthalene

The last step is a dehydrogenation, the reverse of hydrogenation, and is actually a type of oxidation. It is ordinarily carried out with catalysts similar to or identical with those used for hydrogenation. In hydrogenation, hydrogen is applied under pressure; in dehydrogenation, hydrogen is allowed to escape and thus drive the reaction to completion in the desired direction.

Scope of the succinic anhydride synthesis. Since *ortho, para*-directors usually give a high percentage of *p*-substitution in the Friedel and Crafts acylation, various other substituents may be present in the starting benzene derivative, instead of methyl. Of particular use are other alkyls, halogen, and methoxyl. If a hydroxynaphthalene is desired, methoxyl is carried through the synthesis (to protect the hydroxyl group), then cleavage of the ether with hydriodic or hydrobromic acid is the final step in the synthesis.

After the naphthalene synthesis is completed, usual reactions of functional groups may be carried out, also substitution may be carried out in certain instances. In particular, conversion of bromine via the Grignard reagent to various other groups should be well remembered. The form of the naphthalene synthesized is as follows:

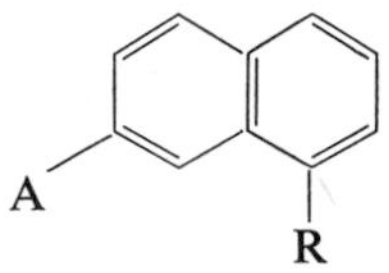

where A is the *ortho,para*-director originally present in the benzene derivative, and R is the alkyl (or aryl) introduced via the Grignard reagent during the synthesis. The positions of R— and A— are 1 and 7. If there is used as starting material a symmetrical benzene derivative such as *m*-xylene, there will also be a substituent at position-5. If A is hydroxyl, it should be noted that relatively clean-cut substitution at position-8 will occur, unless R— is sufficiently bulky to cause steric interference.

Additional variations of the synthesis are indicated in Eqs. 30 and 31.

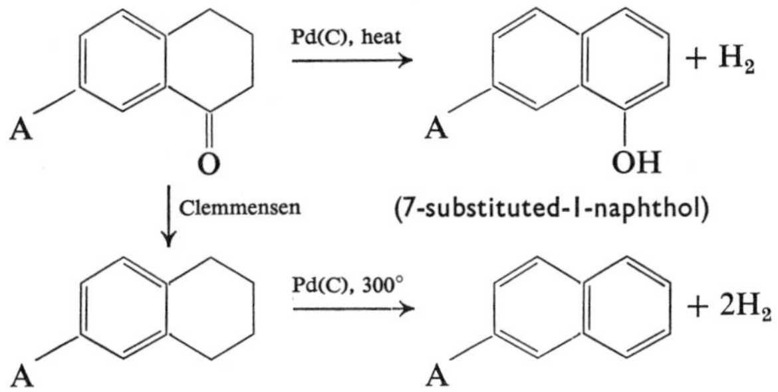

In the 1-naphthol shown in Eq. 30, if A— is alkyl or halogen, substitution may be secured satisfactorily at position-4.

There are actually several other possible variations and extensions of the succinic anhydride synthesis; however, the procedures discussed above give some idea of the scope and versatility of the method for synthesis of naphthalenes not obtainable by direct substitution in the parent hydrocarbon.

EXERCISES

1. Substitution in a naphthalene containing an *o,p*-director occurs mostly in the same ring as the directing group; therefore, it may be concluded that there is relatively little resonance stabilization in the transition state due to inter-ring electron delocalization. If there is minor substitution in the ring not containing the *o,p*-director, at what positions would you expect it to occur in 1-methylnaphthalene?

In Eq. 26 is shown a substitution where the substituent is driven by steric interference into the ring not containing the directing group. Is the position of substitution one of those predicted by consideration of the transition state?

2. If each of the following compounds were brominated under conditions suitable for giving monobromination in the ring, name the compound which would be expected in largest amount.

(a) 1-Bromonaphthalene.
(b) 2-Methylnaphthalene.
(c) 2,6-Dimethylnaphthalene.

(d) 2-Methyl-6-nitronaphthalene.
(e) Acenaphthene.
(f) 1,5-Dibromonaphthalene.

3. Indicate the best route for obtaining each of the following compounds in a pure condition, starting with naphthalene.

(a) 1-Naphthylamine.
(b) 1-Naphthol.
(c) 1-Naphthoic acid.
(d) 1-Acetylnaphthalene.
(e) 1-Naphthylmethylcarbinol.

(f) 2-Naphthylamine.
(g) 2-Naphthol.
(h) 2-Naphthoic acid.
(i) 2-Bromonaphthalene.
(j) 2-Naphthaldehyde.

4. If a succinic anhydride synthesis of a naphthalene derivative were attempted, using phenol as starting material, at what steps would presence of the hydroxyl interfere with the synthesis? Describe the specific difficulties that would be encountered.

5. Starting with substances available from coal tar, and aliphatic compounds containing four carbons or less, indicate practical syntheses of each of the following compounds by routes yielding compounds not contaminated with inseparable isomers.

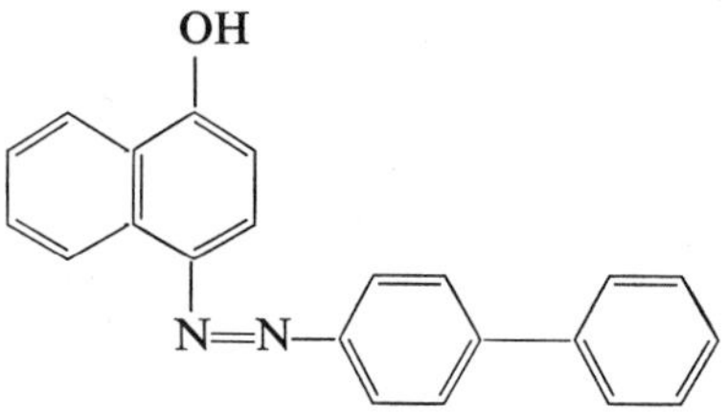

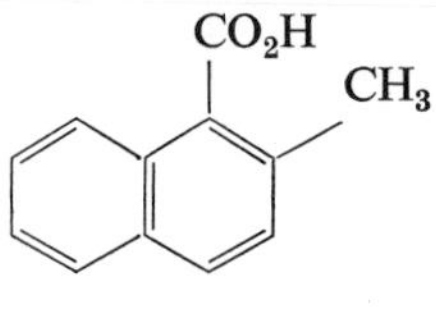

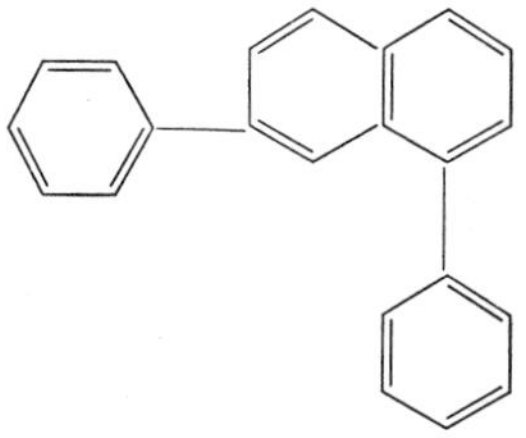

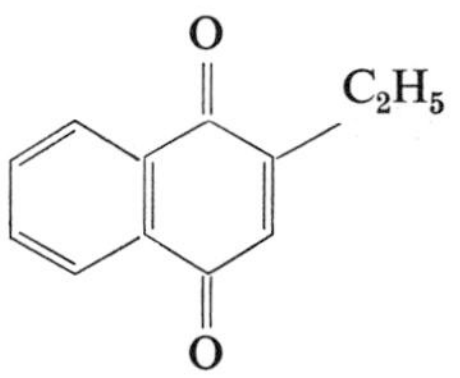

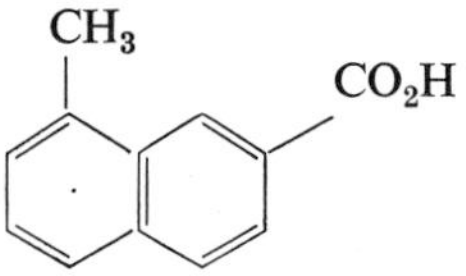

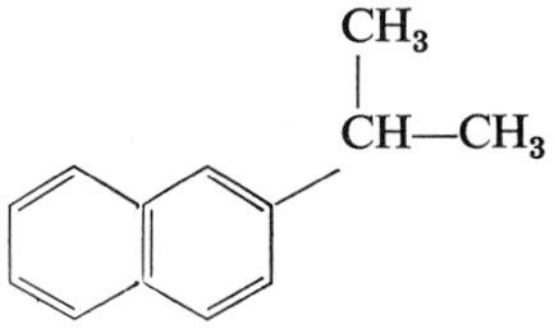

(g) 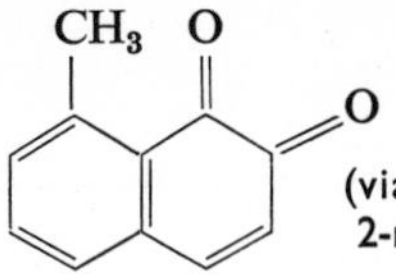 (via 8-methyl-2-naphthol)

(h) 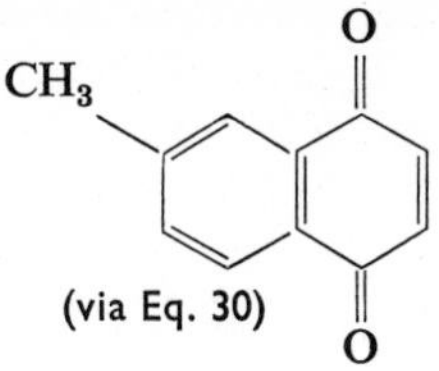 (via Eq. 30)

(i)

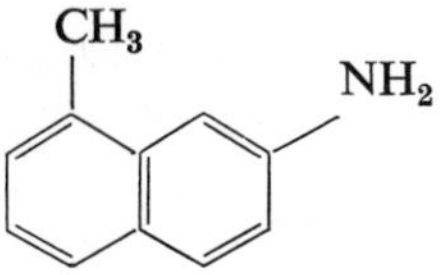

(j)

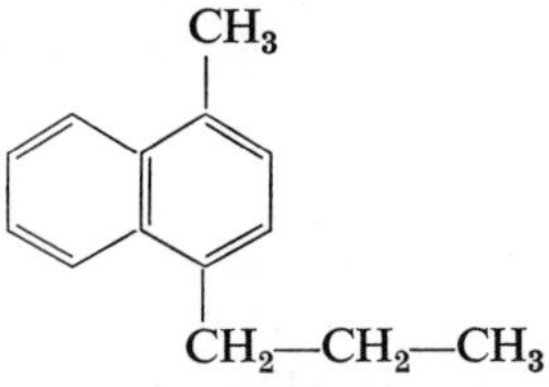

(k)

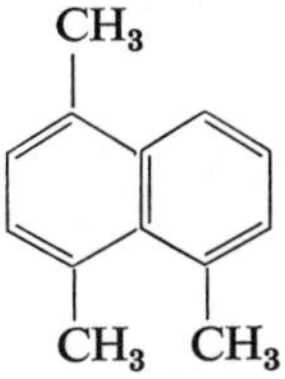

(l)

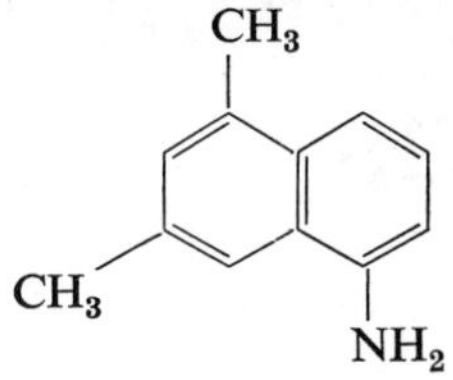

(m)

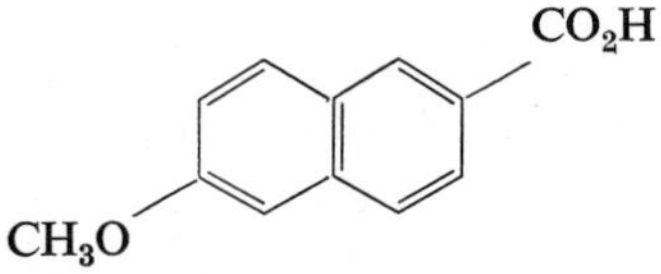

(n)

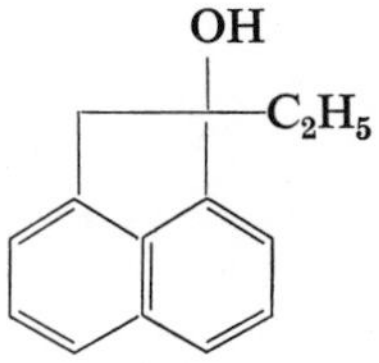

6. Name all the compounds whose formulas appear in Exercise 5, with the exception of that in part (a). Name all the intermediates encountered in synthesis of the compound in part (l).

30

Higher Condensed Ring Compounds

Several of the condensed ring compounds containing more than two rings are of either commercial or biological significance. Of these, anthracene and phenanthrene, containing three rings, are the most important; these ring systems will be the principal focus of attention in the present chapter. Other ring systems to be mentioned more briefly will include those of the carcinogenic (cancer-producing) hydrocarbons.

The parent hydrocarbons of most of the higher ring systems of interest are available from coal tar, and these parent hydrocarbons are the source of many of the derivatives. Synthesis of the higher ring systems is rather laborious, and a naphthalene derivative is nearly always used to contribute two of the rings.

Anthracene

Anthracene is the compound containing three benzene rings condensed in a linear fashion. The principal resonance forms are the following:

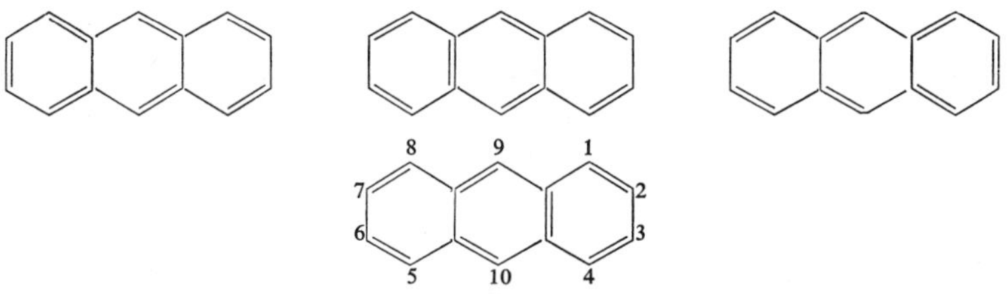

It should be noted that it is not possible to so arrange the bonds in anthracene that each ring has the bond structure of a benzene ring. This has an important effect on the reactions of anthracene which will be discussed in the next section.

Substituents are always located in anthracene by numbers, and it should be noted that the numbering is not continuous around the ring system. This system of numbering has certain advantages in that the end rings have the same numbers as the corresponding positions in naphthalene; in any case, it is the system used; so it should be carefully noted.

The symmetrical structure of anthracene is probably responsible for its rather high melting point of 218° and its rather low solubility in most solvents. The pure compound is colorless, but has such a strong blue fluorescence in the ultraviolet that it has a blue-violet appearance in daylight.

Reactions of Anthracene

Inspection of the anthracene formula reveals the fact that a 1,4-addition (cf. Chap. 12) at the 9- and 10-positions will yield a product containing two benzene rings. This type of structure is more stable than the *o*-quinonoid structure in anthracene; hence, such additions occur quite readily. Indeed, the additions at the 9- and 10-positions, known as the *meso* positions, occur so readily that little is known concerning orthodox electrophilic aromatic substitution in anthracene. Sulfonation gives a mixture of the 1- and 2-sulfonic acids, but the reaction has been of little use in synthesis.

Reduction and oxidation, as illustrated in Eqs. 1 and 2, are typical of reactions in which meso attack occurs in anthracene.

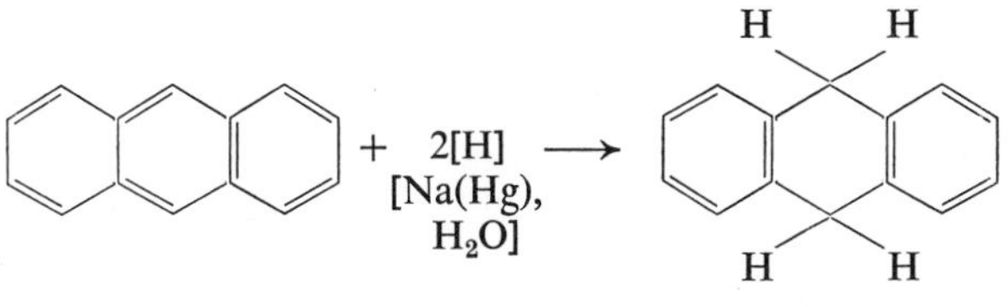

$$+ \quad 2[H] \longrightarrow \quad \quad \quad \quad (1)$$
$$[Na(Hg), H_2O]$$

9,10-Dihydroanthracene

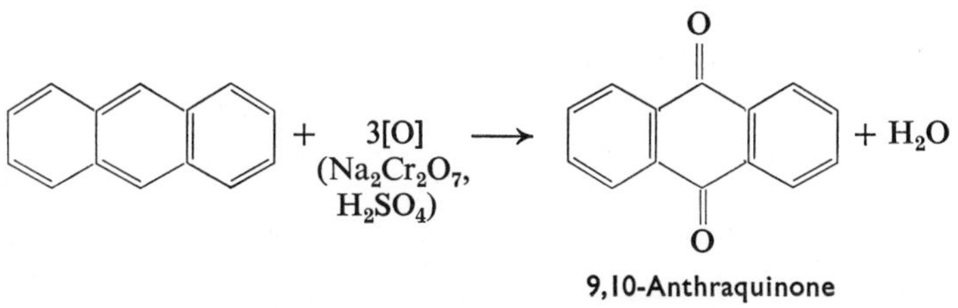

$$+ \quad 3[O] \longrightarrow \quad \quad \quad + H_2O \quad (2)$$
$$(Na_2Cr_2O_7, H_2SO_4)$$

9,10-Anthraquinone

9,10-Dihydroanthracene is very stable to further reduction, for any further reduction must attack a benzene ring. Anthraquinone is remarkably stable to further oxidation. This might be expected if it be noted that each benzene ring contains two electron-withdrawing groups. For this same reason, substitution in anthraquinone requires very vigorous conditions. The stability of anthraquinone, and the useful dyes that have been obtained with this ring system have combined to make the chemistry of the 9,10-anthraquinones of more interest than that of the parent hydrocarbon (cf. below).

Reactions under Friedel and Crafts conditions. When anthracene is treated with aluminum chloride under mild conditions, there may be a 9,10-addition, followed by elimination of a simple molecule; however, the over-all product of the reaction is substitution in the 9-position. Such reactions have been useful for obtaining the 9-acylanthracenes (Eq. 3), while a reaction of

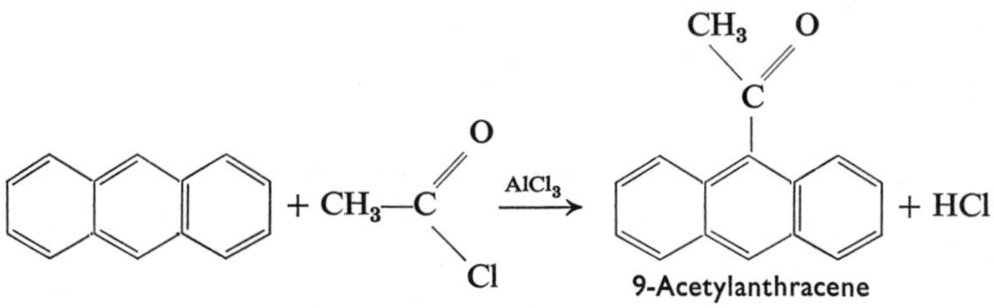

$$\text{anthracene} + CH_3-C\overset{O}{\underset{Cl}{\diagdown}} \xrightarrow{AlCl_3} \text{9-Acetylanthracene} + HCl \qquad (3)$$

the Gattermann type (cf. Eq. 17-33) is successful for forming 9-anthraldehyde (Eq. 4). A variety of 9-substituted anthracenes may be secured from these two derivatives.

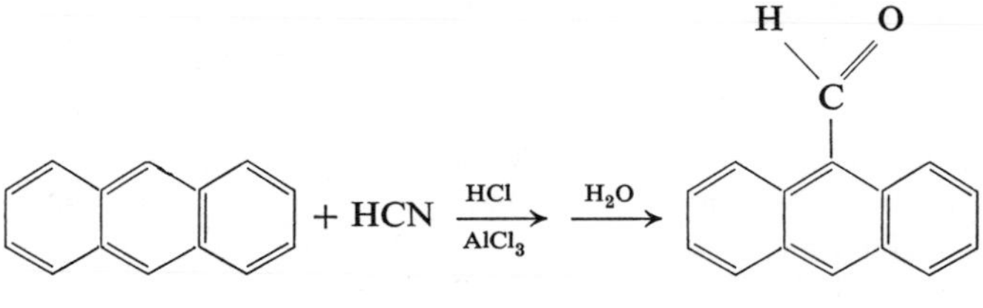

$$\text{anthracene} + HCN \xrightarrow[AlCl_3]{HCl} \xrightarrow{H_2O} \text{9-anthraldehyde} \qquad (4)$$

Diels-Alder reactions. The 1,4-addition of an alkene to a conjugated diene is known as a Diels-Alder reaction. If the alkene, which is called the **dienophile,** is activated by virtue of being conjugated with a polar unsaturated group such as an acid derivative, this addition to give a six-membered ring occurs on simply heating the reactants in a neutral solvent such as benzene. Maleic anhydride, whose double bond is conjugated with two polar unsaturated groups, is a particularly reactive dienophile. A typical reaction with the unsubstituted butadiene is shown in Eq. 5.

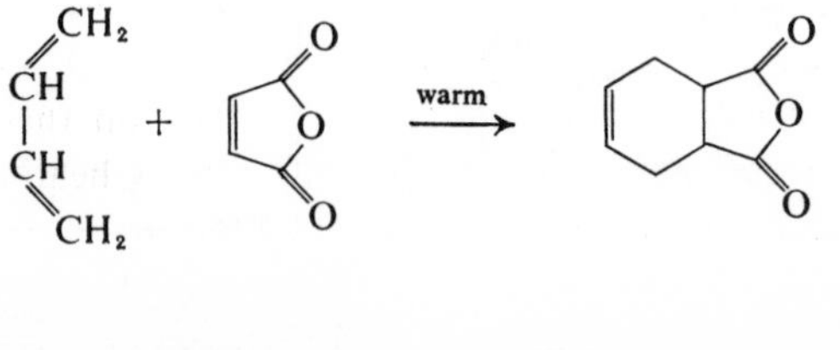

$$\begin{array}{c} CH_2 \\ \parallel \\ CH \\ | \\ CH \\ \parallel \\ CH_2 \end{array} + \text{maleic anhydride} \xrightarrow{\text{warm}} \text{product} \qquad (5)$$

It is of interest that anthracene readily gives the Diels-Alder reaction, which is a characteristic reaction of conjugated dienes. There results the interesting polycyclic system shown in Eq. 6.

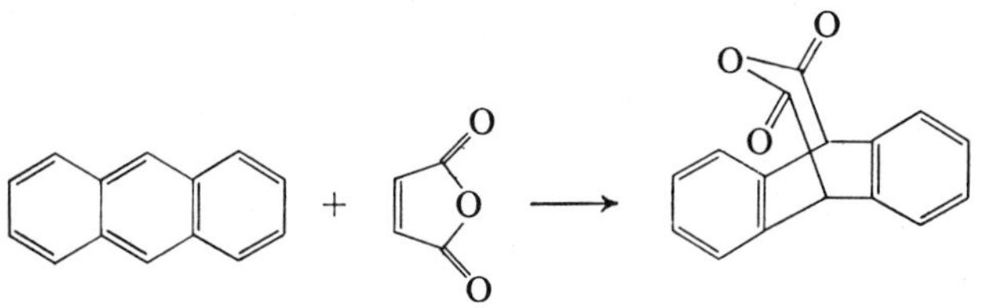

$$(6)$$

A compound such as the product of Eq. 6 may be named according to orthodox nomenclature, but the result is rather long, and these compounds are commonly called Diels-Alder adducts. Thus, the product in Eq. 6 is the Diels-Alder adduct of maleic anhydride and anthracene.

Synthesis of Anthraquinones by Cyclization Reactions

Anthraquinone is obtained by oxidation of anthracene from coal tar; however, substituted anthraquinones are often obtained by a synthetic route somewhat similar to the succinic anhydride synthesis described in the naphthalene series. The two steps involved in synthesis of 2-methylanthraquinone are shown in Eq. 7.

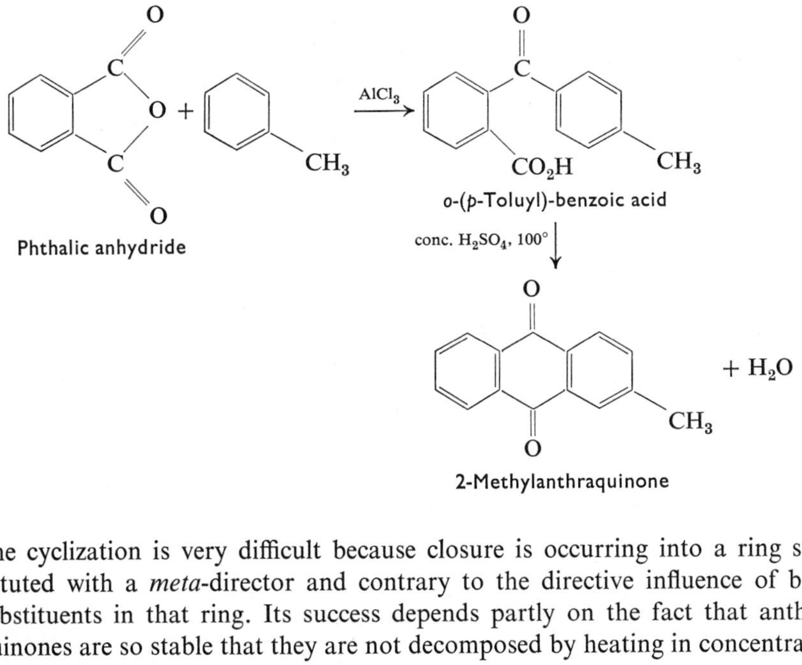

Phthalic anhydride

o-(p-Toluyl)-benzoic acid

conc. H_2SO_4, 100°

$$(7)$$

$+ H_2O$

2-Methylanthraquinone

The cyclization is very difficult because closure is occurring into a ring substituted with a *meta*-director and contrary to the directive influence of both substituents in that ring. Its success depends partly on the fact that anthraquinones are so stable that they are not decomposed by heating in concentrated sulfuric acid; hence, drastic conditions may be used.

Other 2-substituted anthraquinones may be made by the method shown in Eq. 7 if the starting material is a benzene derivative containing some other *ortho,para*-director in place of methyl. Furthermore, if the Friedel and Crafts reaction is carried out on benzene, a substituted phthalic anhydride may be used. A mixture of benzoylbenzoic acids will result but cyclization gives a single anthraquinone. For example, 3-nitrophthalic anhydride and benzene give the mixture shown in Eq. 8, but the mixture cyclizes to the single anthraquinone.

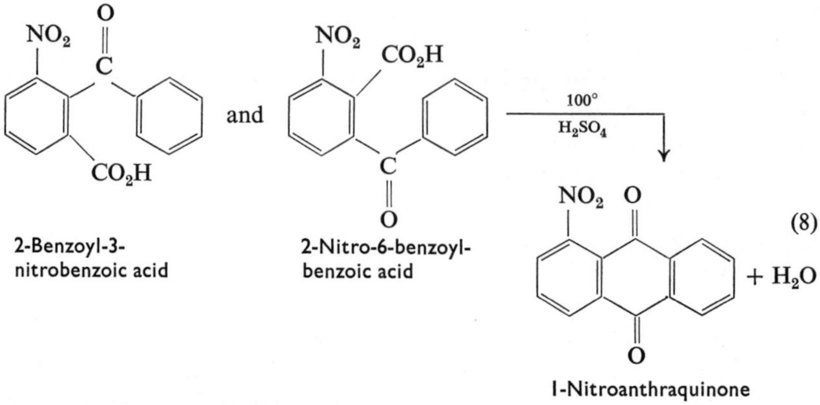

2-Benzoyl-3-nitrobenzoic acid

2-Nitro-6-benzoyl-benzoic acid

1-Nitroanthraquinone

$$+ H_2O \qquad (8)$$

Anthraquinone Dyes

A major interest in anthraquinones is for making dyes. The desired substances are made either by cyclization reactions or by substitutions in anthraquinone. Substitutions in anthraquinone are rather specialized reactions, and there is little of a general nature worthy of our attention. An illustration of the rather specialized chemistry involved is shown in the synthesis of alizarin, a bright red dye.

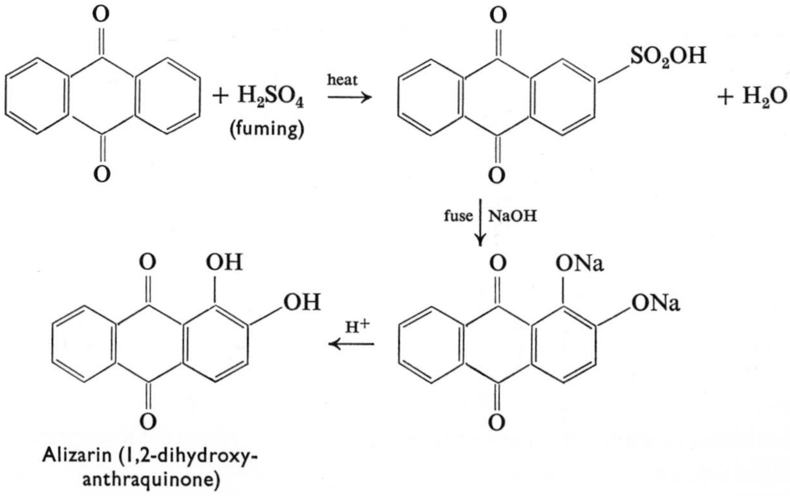

$$(9)$$

Alizarin (1,2-dihydroxy-anthraquinone)

Alizarin is a *mordant dye*. It will dye a cloth only if it is boiled in an aqueous solution containing a metallic hydroxide (the mordant). An aluminum mordant is frequently used with alizarin.

Most of the anthraquinone dyes are *vat dyes*. Such dyes are reduced to the colorless hydroquinone, which is soluble in alkali, and the cloth impregnated with this solution is exposed to air, whereupon the dye is formed on the cloth by oxidation. In Eq. 10 are shown the reduction and reoxidation of algol red, a scarlet red dye.

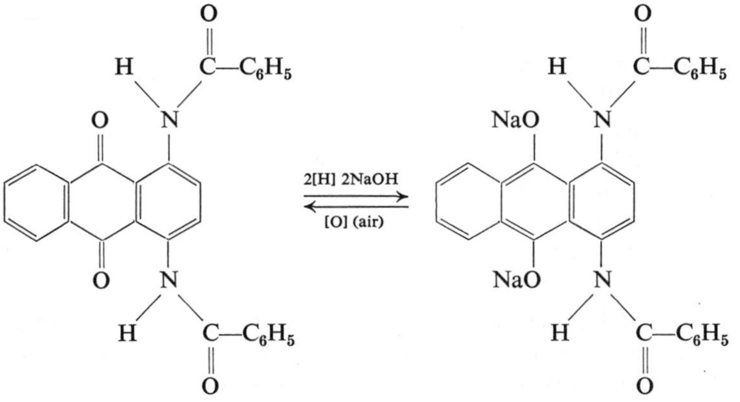

$$\text{Algol red} \quad \xrightarrow[\text{[O] (air)}]{\text{2[H] 2NaOH}} \quad \text{(water soluble)} \tag{10}$$

The anthraquinone dyes are relatively expensive but give fast colors.

A substantial number of naturally occurring dyes have proved to be highly substituted polyhydroxy anthraquinones. An illustration of the complicated substitution pattern in these dyes is found in carminic acid, the bright red coloring matter in cochineal, which consists of the dried bodies of the insect *Coccus cacti* L. The nature of the substituent, $C_6H_{11}O_5$, has not been fully

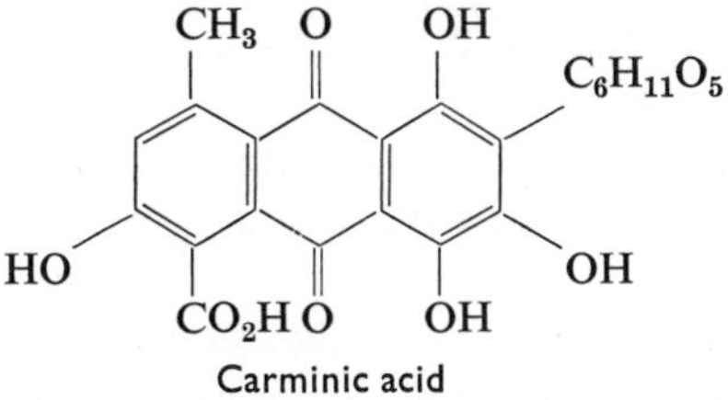

Carminic acid

elucidated; however, it contains four hydroxyl groups. Thus, this substituent is sugar-like, but the linkage to the aromatic ring is not a glycosidic linkage.

Phenanthrene

Phenanthrene is the three-ring hydrocarbon in which the rings are fused at an angle. As with anthracene, it has several resonance forms, but the formula is ordinarily written with the bonds as follows:

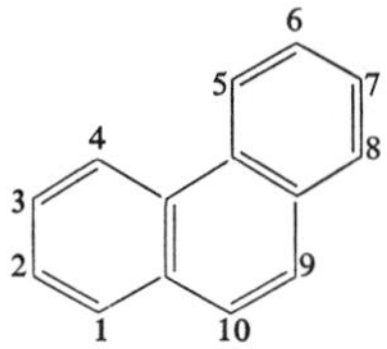

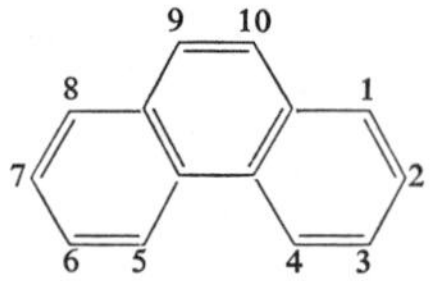

Since different chemists write the phenanthrene structure in different positions, two positions with numbers indicated are shown. It should be noted that carbons-9 and -10 are those in the middle ring.

Phenanthrene is a colorless compound and is obtained from coal tar. It is more soluble than the linear isomer, anthracene, and its melting point of about 100° is considerably lower than that of anthracene. Since anthracene is much the less soluble of the two hydrocarbons, removal of anthracene from the more soluble phenanthrene by crystallization is unsuccessful. For this reason, technical phenanthrene from coal tar always contains substantial quantities of anthracene. Pure phenanthrene can be obtained, however, by treating the technical material with maleic anhydride and thus converting anthracene to the Diels-Alder adduct (Eq. 6). The adduct is readily hydrolyzed to the di-acid which may be extracted with aqueous alkali. Since phenanthrene does not have a potential diene system it does not react with maleic anhydride and may be recovered in a pure condition after removal of the anthracene adduct.

An interesting feature of the anthracene-phenanthrene mixture concerns the shape of the binary melting point diagram for the mixture. The eutectic mixture contains only a few per cent of anthracene, and the melting point of this eutectic is only slightly below the melting point of pure phenanthrene. It follows that presence of a few per cent of anthracene in phenanthrene *raises* the melting point above that of pure phenanthrene. Thus, technical samples of phenanthrene always have a higher melting point than pure phenanthrene!

In contrast with anthracene, phenanthrene has hardly any commercial significance; however, various derivatives of phenanthrene have very great biological significance. At this time,[1] we will mention only that the natural products with a phenanthrene skeleton include such diverse substances as the sterols and bile acids, the male and female sex hormones (cf. Chap. 15 for formula of testosterone), heart poisons such as digitalis, and alkaloids such as morphine. Later in this chapter, a brief description will be made of the carcinogenic hydrocarbons, which contain additional rings fused to the phenanthrene nucleus.

The occurrence of the phenanthrene skeleton in so many different natural products has generated considerable interest in the rather complex fundamental

---

[1] A large book has been written by Professor and Mrs L. F. Fieser, of Harvard University, entitled *Natural Products Related to Phenanthrene*, Reinhold, New York, 1949.

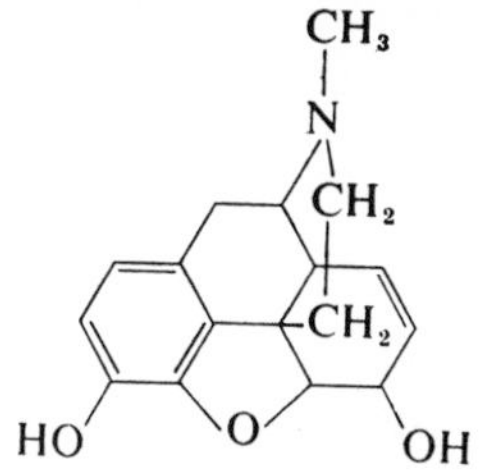

Morphine

chemistry of the phenanthrene ring system. The more basic principles involved will be discussed in this chapter with the intent that this will equip the reader with a foundation which will enable him to pursue further in the specialized literature any phase of this area of chemistry with which he may later become involved.

Chemical Reactions of Phenanthrene and Certain of Its Derivatives

Inspection of the formula for phenanthrene will reveal the fact that it may be written with a full component of double bonds for the benzene structure in each ring. If the double bond at the 9,10-position is saturated, however, there still remain two terminal benzene rings. One might expect, from these considerations, that oxidation and reduction would attack the 9,10-positions, as in anthracene, but less selectively than is the case in anthracene. This proves to be the fact; furthermore, halogen also adds to the 9,10-positions. In contrast with the situation in anthracene, however, oxidation and 9,10-addition reactions in phenanthrene are not so facile as to interfere with aromatic substitution in the molecule. As will be discussed below, the utility of aromatic substitution is rather severely limited by the large number of monosubstitution derivatives that are obtained.

Reduction. Phenanthrene may be reduced with various chemical agents and hydrogenated in the presence of several different catalysts; however, the most useful of these processes is the selective hydrogenation shown in Eq. 11.

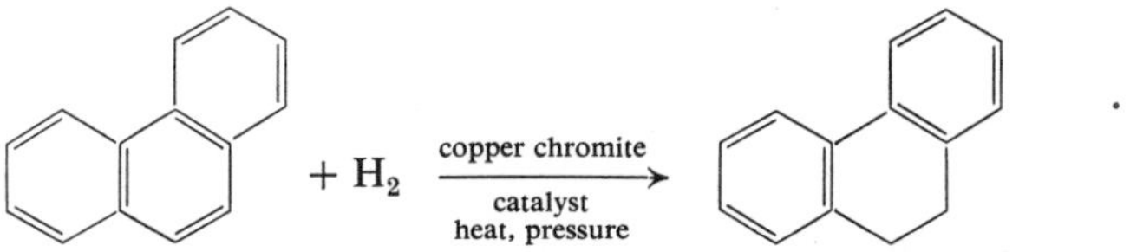

$$+ H_2 \xrightarrow[\substack{\text{catalyst} \\ \text{heat, pressure}}]{\text{copper chromite}} \qquad (11)$$

9,10-Dihydrophenanthrene

Utilization of 9,10-dihydrophenanthrene in synthesis of other derivatives will be discussed in a subsequent section.

Oxidation. Mild oxidation of phenanthrene gives the 9,10-quinone, while more vigorous oxidation cleaves the ring between the oxygen functions

(Eq. 12). If alkyl substituents are present in the phenanthrene ring, the quinone may be formed without oxidation of these substituents. In some instances,

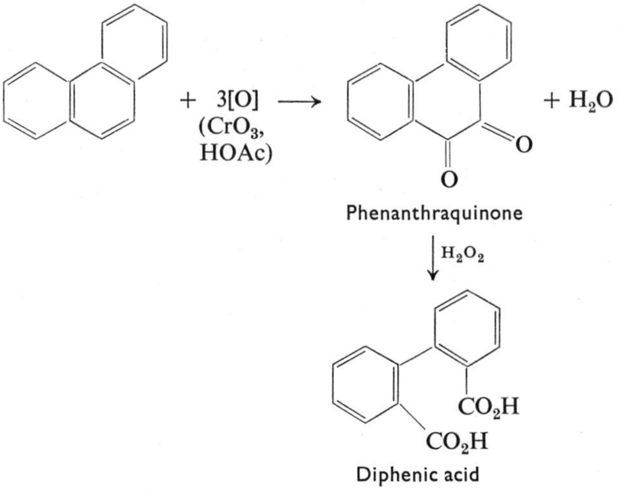

Phenanthraquinone

Diphenic acid

(12)

this route of synthesis has been used to make substituted diphenic acids, and it is the most common synthesis of diphenic acid itself. It should also be mentioned that oxidation to a diphenic acid has been used on various occasions to locate substituents in a phenanthrene of unknown structure. Identification of the diphenic acid locates the substituents in the phenanthrene ring system.

Bromination. Halogen adds readily to the double bond in the 9,10-position of phenanthrene. The most interesting thing about this reaction is that the dibromo compound loses hydrogen bromide on heating. The resultant 9-bromophenanthrene (Eq. 13) is the most important source of 9-

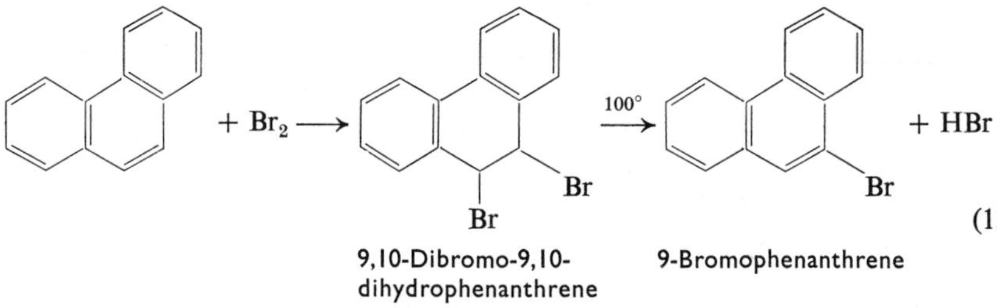

9,10-Dibromo-9,10-
dihydrophenanthrene

9-Bromophenanthrene

(13)

substituted phenanthrenes. It may be converted to other functional groups via the cyanide (using cuprous cyanide and pyridine, cf. Eq. 18-3) or the Grignard reagent.

Aromatic substitution reactions in phenanthrene. Although nitration and sulfonation of phenanthrene may be carried out in rather normal fashion for aromatic substitution, the reactions are of no value. The mixture of 1-, 2-, and 3-isomers cannot be separated on a practical basis to give a useful yield of a single compound. It is of interest that *essentially no substitution occurs in the 4-position*. This position is severely hindered by proximity of the other ring. Synthesis of a 4,5-disubstituted phenanthrene is very difficult indeed and was accomplished only after many years of painstaking effort. Indeed, construction of models shows that even groups as small as methyl overlap each other when substituted in the 4- and 5-positions; therefore, if the molecule is to exist, the groups must be pushed out of the plane of the aromatic rings, one on each side, by deformation of the normal bond directions. If this situation is the fact, then a phenanthrene such as 4,5-dimethyl-1-phenanthroic

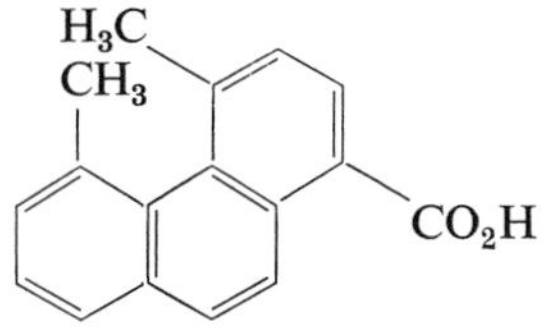

4,5-Dimethyl-1-phenanthroic acid

acid is an asymmetric molecule and should exist in optically active forms (optical antipodes). Professor M. S. Newman and co-workers, at The Ohio State University, have actually succeeded in resolving such a compound and obtaining the optical isomers. As would be predicted, heating racemizes the optical isomers at a temperature where molecular vibrations are sufficiently vigorous that the methyl groups can crowd past each other and thus shift from one side of the plane of the rings to the other. A related type of asymmetry in biphenyls has been described in Chapter 28.

The Friedel and Crafts reaction with acyl chlorides or anhydrides has proved to be the only substitution reaction of practical significance for preparation of pure substitution derivatives of phenanthrene. Other derivatives must be made from the acylphenanthrenes.

SUBSTITUTION IN THE 3-POSITION. The Friedel and Crafts reaction in nitrobenzene as solvent proves to give a preponderance of the 3-isomer (Eq. 14).

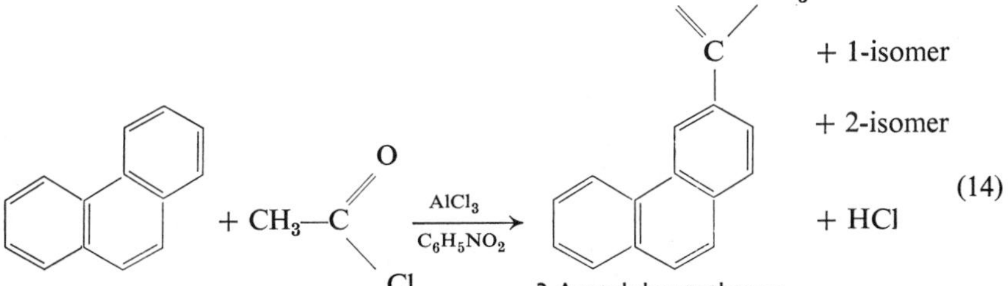

3-Acetylphenanthrene

The 3-acyl derivatives may be separated in yields below 50%, but in the phenanthrene series this is a good reaction. In some instances, the 1-isomer may be separated in low yield and with great difficulty (by handpicking of the crystals, for example).

Substitution in the 2-position is the best of all substitution reactions in the phenanthrene series, for 9,10-dihydrophenanthrene gives substitution exclusively in this position. This is entirely consistent with the fact that both biphenyl and fluorene give clean-cut substitution *para* to the phenyl ring. Substitution in 9,10-dihydrophenanthrene is shown in Eq. 15.

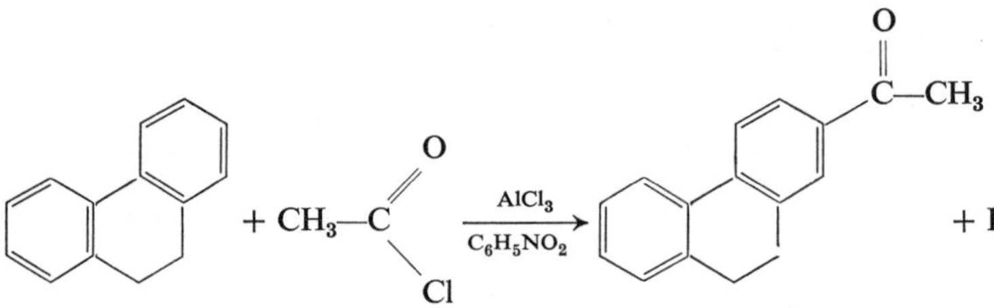

(for synthesis, cf. Eq. 11)   2-Acetyl-9,10-
                                            dihydrophenanthrene

After the desired synthetic sequences have been accomplished, or at a suitable intermediate stage, the 9,10-dihydrophenanthrene may be dehydrogenated with palladium on charcoal (cf. Eq. 17) to give the phenanthrene derivative. The only caution necessary in the dehydrogenation is that the hydrogen evolved may reduce some unsaturated substituent in the molecule. For example, dehydrogenation of the 2-acetyl-9,10-dihydrophenanthrene gives mainly the methyl-2-phenanthrylcarbinol. In such instances, reoxidation is usually feasible.

Derivatives obtainable from acylphenanthrenes. The 2- and 3-acylphenanthrenes may be converted to other derivatives by reactions already discussed, but this approach to functional derivatives is somewhat novel. The previous examples have been conversion of 4-acetylbiphenyl and 2-acetylnaphthalene to the corresponding carboxylic acids. Applicable conversions will be outlined for the phenanthrene series.

(1) CARBOXYLIC ACIDS. These are available by hypohalite oxidation of the corresponding acetylphenanthrenes (cf. Eqs. 15-11, 15-23, 29-18).

(2) PHENANTHRYLAMINES. The carboxylic acids may be converted to the amides and these subjected to the Hofmann hypobromite reaction (cf. Eq. 19-24). Although the phenanthrylamines have not been widely investigated, it may be presumed that they can be diazotized and converted to the compounds obtainable from diazonium salts (cf. Chap. 19).

(3) MONOALKYLPHENANTHRENES. These may be obtained by Clemmensen or Wolff-Kishner reduction of the acylphenanthrenes. This applies also to

keto acids, as shown in Eq. 16.

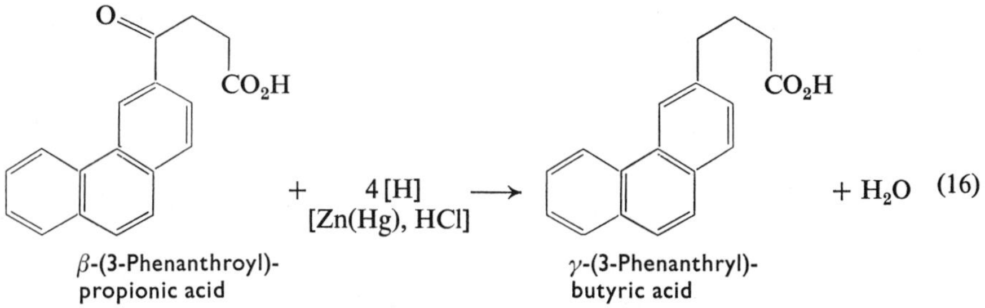

$$+ \quad \underset{[Zn(Hg),\ HCl]}{4\,[H]} \quad \longrightarrow \qquad\qquad\qquad + H_2O \quad (16)$$

β-(3-Phenanthroyl)-
propionic acid

γ-(3-Phenanthryl)-
butyric acid

Cyclization of the acid chloride of γ-(3-phenanthryl)-butyric acid gives closure in the unhindered 2-position. Continuation of the usual steps of the succinic anhydride synthesis of condensed ring compounds (cf. Chap. 29 and Eq. 17, this chapter) leads to 5-substituted benzanthracenes, such as the following:

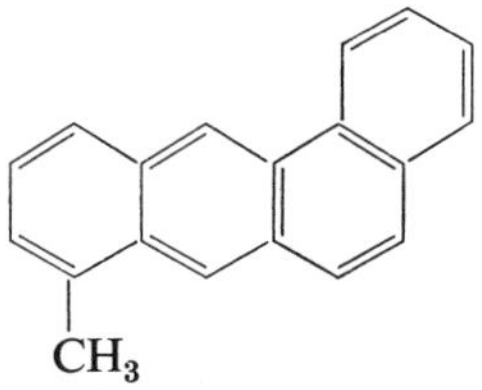

CH_3

5-Methyl-1,2-benzanthracene

The formula just above has been turned over from the position in which it occurs in Eq. 16, in order to create practice in visualization of condensed ring hydrocarbons in different positions. Such structures are ordinarily named as benzanthracenes, rather than benzphenanthrenes.

It should be noted that if the β-(9,10-dihydro-2-phenanthroyl)-propionic acid is reduced, then dehydrogenated, there will be formed the γ-(2-phenanthryl)-butyric acid:

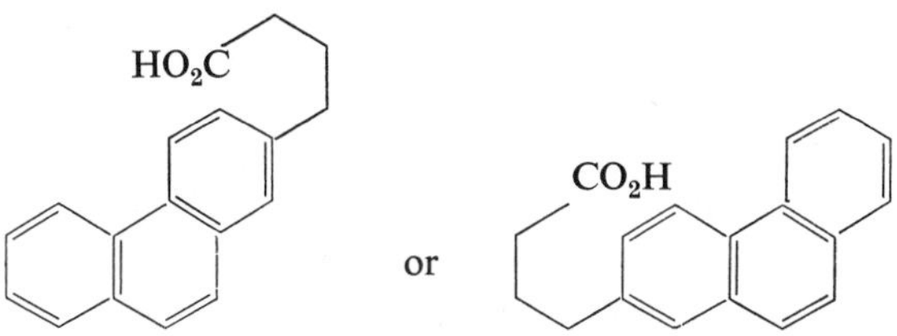

or

CO_2H

γ-(2-Phenanthryl)-butyric acid

This compound will lead to 8-substituted 1,2-benzanthracenes.

Synthesis of phenanthrenes by cyclization reactions. As with naphthalenes, various methods are available, but there will be discussed only application of the succinic anhydride route to the phenanthrene series. As described in Chapter 29 (Eq. 29-13), there may be synthesized and obtained in a pure condition both the 1- and 2-naphthoylpropionic acids. Reduction of the carbonyl, conversion to the acid chloride, and cyclization by the Friedel and Crafts route leads from these two acids to the following phenanthrene derivatives:

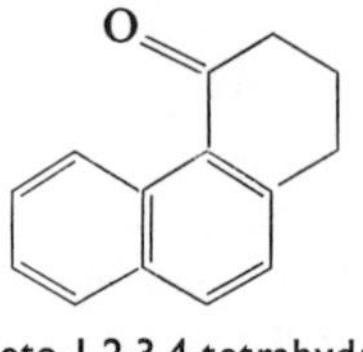

4-Keto-1,2,3,4-tetrahydro-
phenanthrene

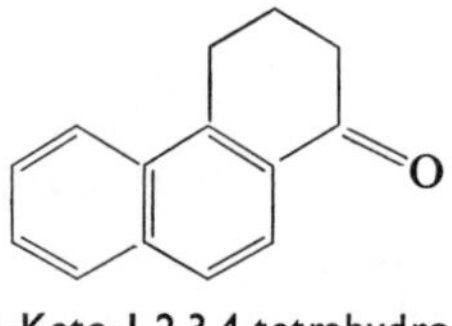

1-Keto-1,2,3,4-tetrahydro-
phenanthrene

Continuation of the usual steps of the succinic anhydride synthesis (cf. Chap. 29) yields either 1-substituted or 4-substituted phenanthrenes. Synthesis of 4-methylphenanthrene is illustrated in Eq. 17. Substitution in the other rings

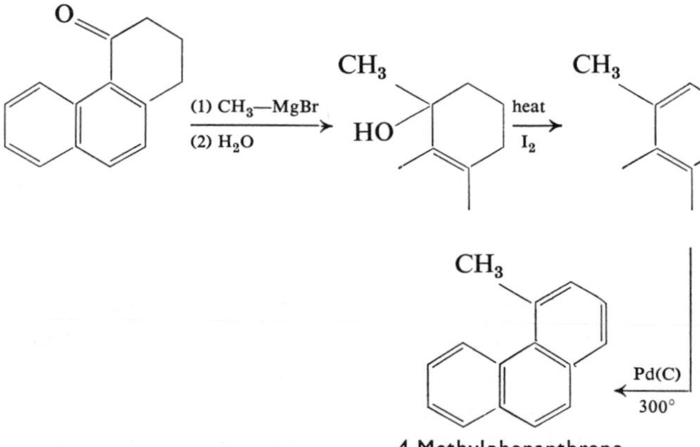

4-Methylphenanthrene

of phenanthrene by this route depends on what substituents may be secured in the naphthalene derivative used as starting material (cf. Chap. 29).

Carcinogenic Hydrocarbons

It was realized near the beginning of the twentieth century that workers in coal tar plants had a pronounced tendency to develop cancer of the skin, and by 1920 it had been shown that if crude coal tar is rubbed on the skin of mice for a prolonged period the mice develop tumors at the points where the tar had been applied. In about 1923, a large scale investigation of this problem was inaugurated at the Royal Cancer Hospital in London, with medical doctors, physicists, and chemists cooperating. The work was difficult and slow, but a climax was reached in 1933. From a laborious fractionation of several tons of coal tar, there was isolated a pure chemical compound shown to be very active in causing cancer. A single injection of half a milligram (0.0005 g.) was sufficient to cause a tumor in a mouse. Further work showed the active compound to be the substance known as 3,4-benzpyrene.

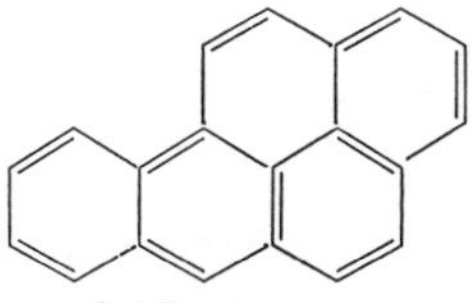

3,4-Benzpyrene

This discovery was of much significance for at least two reasons. First, the cause of the cancer among coal tar workers seemed definitely established, and its further incidence was prevented by measures taken to keep tar off the skin. Second, this was the first simple substance known to cause at least one type of cancer. Experimental tumors could be induced in test animals and used for investigation of causes and possible cure.

A large-scale synthetic program was inaugurated in this country and in England with the objective of discovering just what structural features are required in a hydrocarbon to make it carcinogenic. Hundreds of compounds were made by long and tedious syntheses and tested for carcinogenic activity in pure strains of mice bred for low incidence of tumors from natural causes. These investigations revealed that nearly all the carcinogenic hydrocarbons are derivatives of 1,2-benzanthracene, although the parent hydrocarbon itself is innocuous. Among the most active carcinogenic compounds are the following:

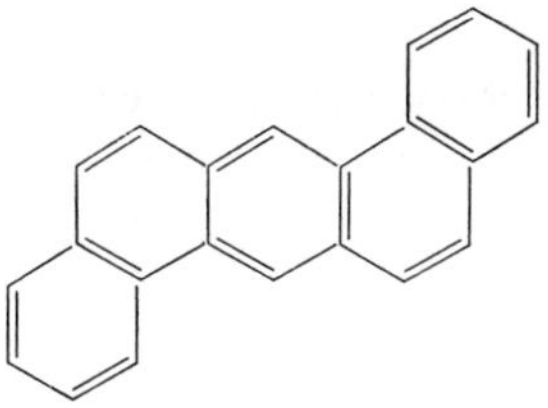

1,2,5,6,-Dibenzanthracene

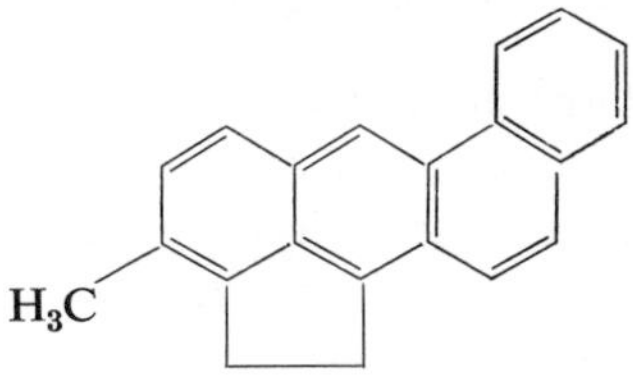

Methylcholanthrene

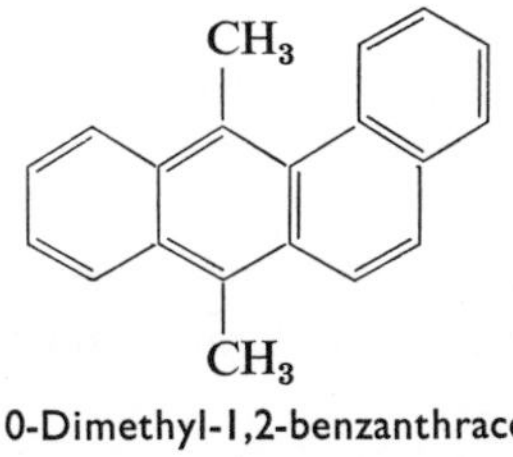

9,10-Dimethyl-1,2-benzanthracene

Except for 1,2,5,6-dibenzanthracene, the more active carcinogenic agents have been 1,2-benzanthracenes substituted in the 9-position or 10-position, or both.

Methylcholanthrene is of particular interest because it has been made in the laboratory from desoxycholic acid, one of the acids present in bile.

Although methylcholanthrene written as in Eq. 18 bears little resemblance, at first glance, to the formula written above, careful inspection shows them to be the same. In view of the fact that desoxycholic acid, a normal constituent

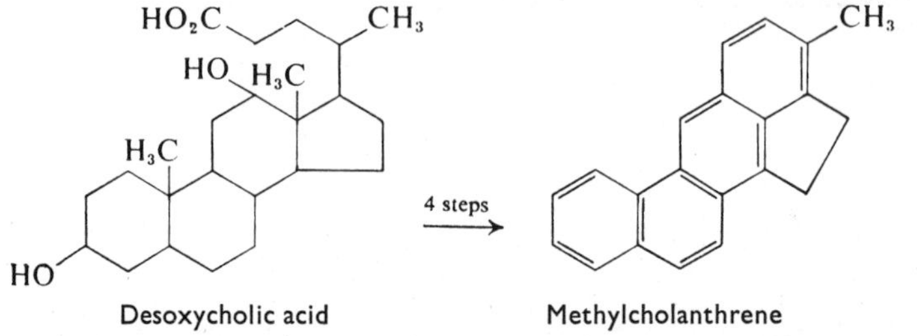

$$\text{(18)}$$

Desoxycholic acid   Methylcholanthrene

of human bile, may be converted in the laboratory to a very active carcinogenic hydrocarbon, there has naturally arisen speculation that spontaneous cancer may result from some metabolic aberration which results in formation of methylcholanthrene from normal body constituents. A large amount of research has failed to shed any light on whether this sequence should indeed be blamed for the occurrence of cancer. Another important, unsolved problem is the specific manner in which carcinogenic hydrocarbons are able to induce tumor formation. Among the more surprising features of the phenomenon is the fact that the tumor appears at the site of injection of the hydrocarbon (or site of application to the skin) several weeks or several months after the original application. The sooner a tumor appears, the more "active" the carcinogen is said to be.

Synthesis of Carcinogenic Hydrocarbons

A large number of methods have been devised for synthesis of benzanthracene derivatives. One of these is the succinic anhydride method, described earlier in this chapter in connection with the reactions of phenanthrene derivatives. This method has been especially useful for 5- or 8-substituted 1,2-benzanthracenes.

An anthracene synthesis which has been useful in some instances is the Elbs reaction, which depends on the pyrolysis of an *o*-methyl aromatic ketone. This procedure has been of particular use for making methylcholanthrene and 1,2,5,6-dibenzanthracene, desired in considerable quantity for biological experimentation. The over-all process for 1,2,5,6-dibenzanthracene is outlined in Eq. 19.

Although this synthetic process seems rather simple on paper, the resultant hydrocarbon sells at a price considerably higher than that charged for platinum.

The significant yield secured in the Elbs pyrolysis is a testimonial to the thermal stability of aromatic ketones and of condensed ring aromatic hydrocarbons. The temperature of the pyrolysis is only about 100° below red heat. The mechanism of this rather surprising reaction remains somewhat obscure.

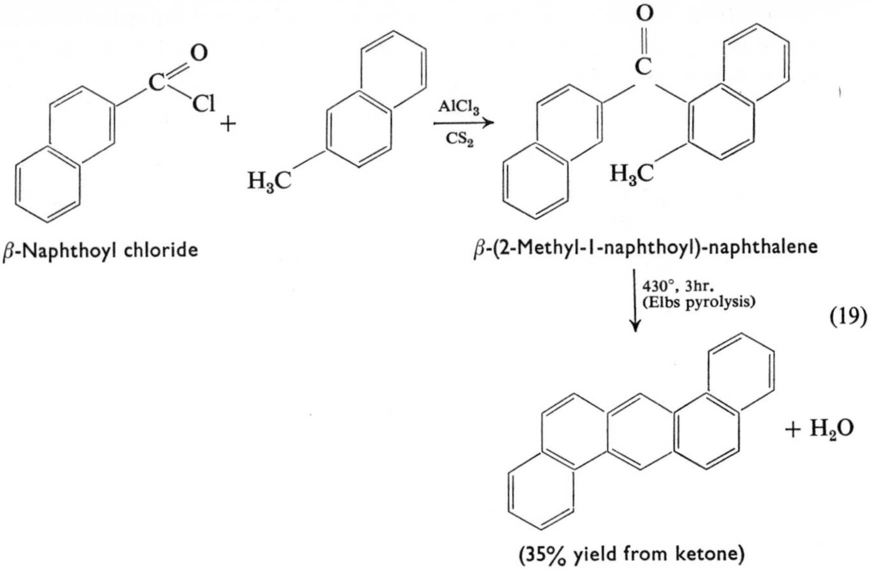
O
C
Cl
+
H$_3$C
AlCl$_3$
CS$_2$
O
C
H$_3$C
β-Naphthoyl chloride
β-(2-Methyl-1-naphthoyl)-naphthalene
430°, 3hr.
(Elbs pyrolysis)
+ H$_2$O
(35% yield from ketone)

(19)

EXERCISES

1. What compound would be obtained in each case if the following compounds were vigorously oxidized (hot permanganate)?

(a) Naphthalene.
(b) 2-Nitronaphthalene.
(c) Anthracene.
(d) Phenanthrene.
(e) 2-Aminonaphthalene.
(f) 2-Methylnaphthalene.

2. Among the dienophiles that are successful in the Diels-Alder reaction are the 1,4-benzoquinones. A single condensation occurs under mild conditions, while a second occurs under more strenuous conditions. Outline a synthesis of the compound shown on the left below, starting with benzene and 1,4-butanediol. Suggest conditions that might be expected to accomplish the conversion shown below.

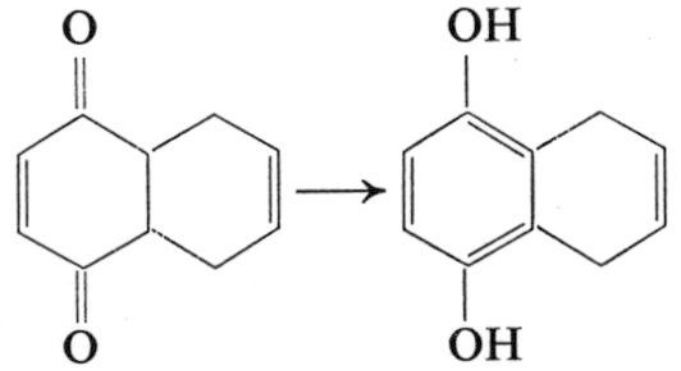
O
O
OH
OH

3. If the products of a Friedel and Crafts reaction between 3-nitrophthalic anhydride and bromobenzene were cyclized by heating with sulfuric acid, what anthraquinones would result?

4. Let us suppose that further investigation of the structure of the $C_6H_{11}O_5$ side chain in carminic acid should reveal that it has the β-*R*-glucose structure except that the aromatic nucleus is attached in place of the 1-hydroxyl in β-R-glucose. Write the formula of carminic acid, containing this additional structural feature, with the sugar unit in the proper conformation.

5. Outline a sequence that should be successful for resolution of 4,5-dimethyl-1-phenanthroic acid.

6. Starting with aliphatic compounds and materials available from coal tar, outline practical syntheses for each of the following compounds.

(a)

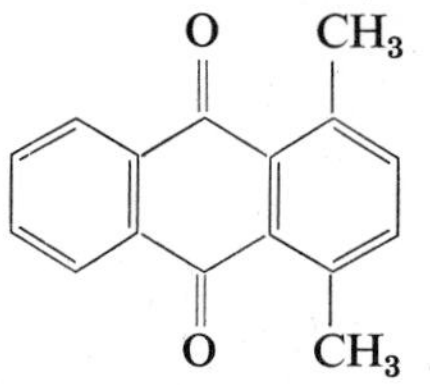

(b)

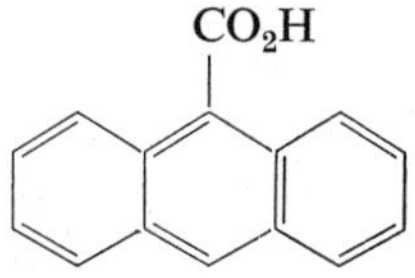

(c)

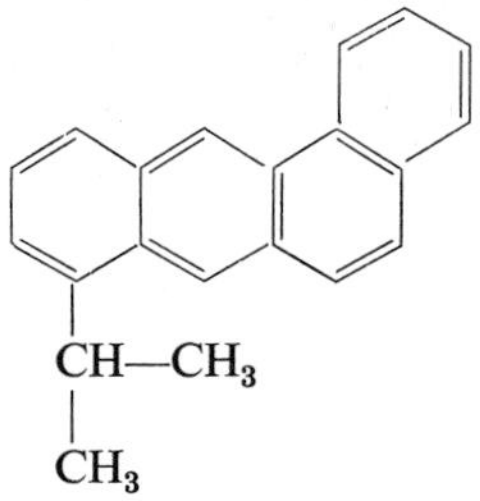

(d)

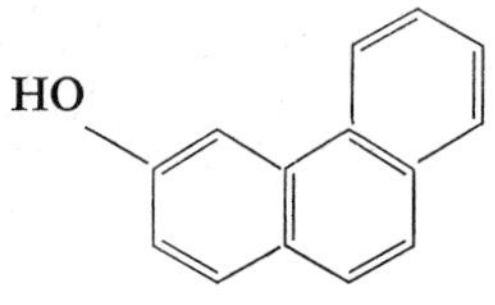

(e)

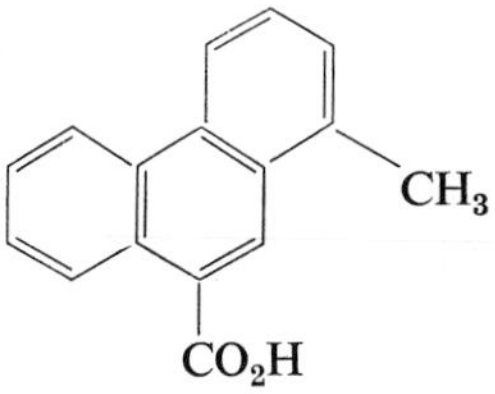

(f)

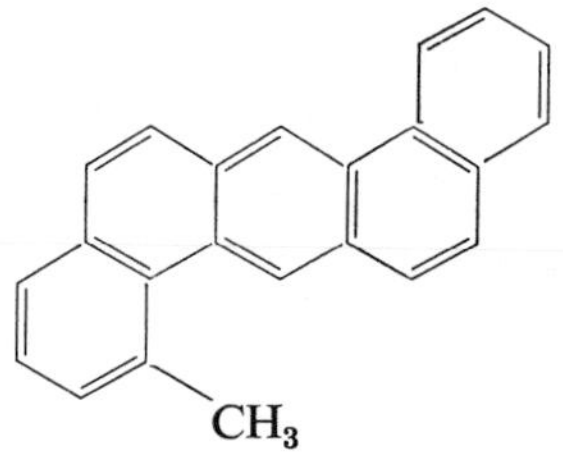

(via 8-methyl-2-naphthoic acid)

(g)

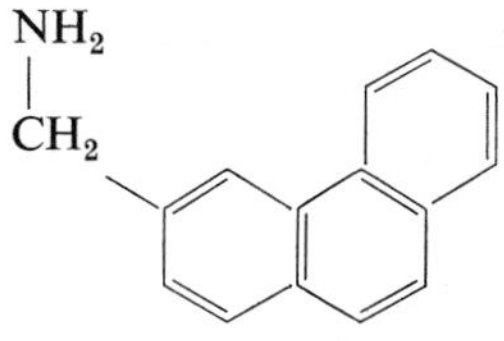

(h)

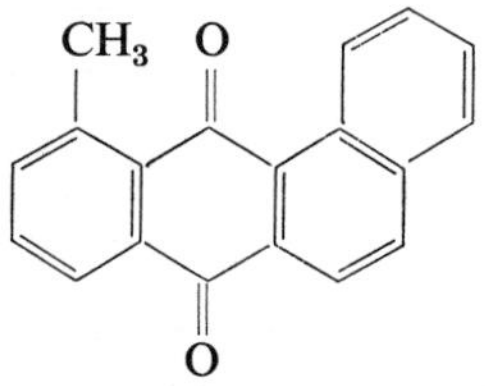

(via oxidation of 8-methyl-1,2-benzanthracene)

7. Name all the compounds whose formulas appear in Exercise 6, also all the intermediates encountered in the synthesis of 6(h).

Pyridine and Its Derivatives

The heterocyclic compounds, that is, compounds containing at least one atom other than carbon in a ring, have received increasing attention from organic chemists. A major incentive to this steady increase in interest has been the importance of the heterocyclic compounds in biochemistry (for example, cf. Chap. 25, **nucleic acids**) and in pharmaceutical chemistry (refer to Chap. 27 for discussion of barbiturates). A great majority of these compounds of biological interest are the nitrogen-containing heterocycles. The present chapter and the two following chapters are devoted to a study of three of the important nitrogen-containing heterocyclic ring systems.

Pyridine, the aromatic ring system consisting of six carbon atoms and one nitrogen atom, is probably second in importance only to the quinoline ring system (Chap. 32). Indeed, quinoline is 2,3-benzpyridine, and much of the basic chemistry of pyridine also applies to quinoline. In addition, the pyridine ring system occurs in numerous alkaloids.[1]

---

[1] An alkaloid is rather loosely defined as a naturally occurring nitrogen-containing compound possessing some physiological activity; however, an occasional physiologically active natural product not containing nitrogen is classed as an alkaloid. Most of the important alkaloids contain nitrogen in a ring, hence are heterocyclic compounds. An example is morphine, whose formula was given in the preceding chapter.

Pyridine, the parent compound, is a colorless liquid boiling at 115°. and possessing a characteristic disagreeable odor. It has a remarkably high solubility in water; in fact, at room temperature it is miscible with water in all proportions. With a pK_a for its cation of only 5.17, pyridine is only a slightly stronger base than aniline (pK_a 4.6, cf. Chap. 19). Although there is no entirely satisfactory theoretical basis for the low basicity of pyridine, it is a consistent phenomenon that multiply-bonded atoms have a low electron-donating capacity. One example of this phenomenon is the acidity of 1-alkynes (Chap. 10). When carbon is doubly-bonded to nitrogen the basicity of nitrogen is lowered by several powers of ten, as compared to compounds in which nitrogen is singly bonded to carbon. This trend continues to the case of the triple bond, for nitriles, with the $C \equiv N$ structure, are not basic compounds; they are neutral.

The source of pyridine, as well as the three methyl pyridines shown below, is coal tar. Numbering and Greek lettering of the positions in pyridine are illustrated.

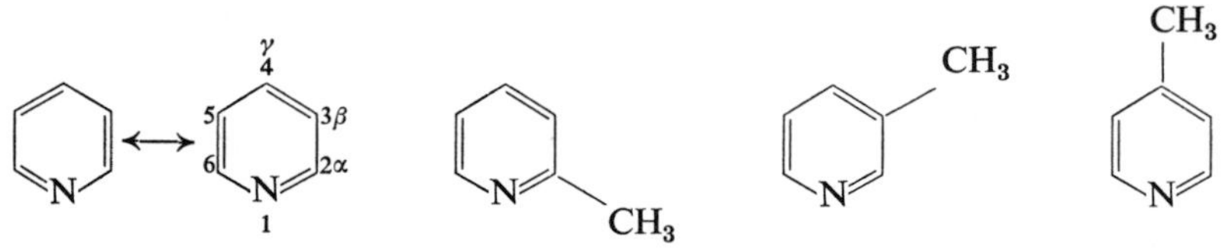

| Pyridine | α-Picoline | β-Picoline | γ-Picoline |

With rare exceptions, the hetero atom in heterocyclic compounds is numbered 1, and numbering proceeds around the ring in the direction to give the atoms bearing substituents the smaller numbers. A single substituent in pyridine may be located with a Greek letter, as illustrated for the picolines. The picolines also illustrate the fact that there are three monosubstitution positions in pyridine.

Resonance Stabilization in the Pyridine Ring System

The experimentally determined resonance energy of pyridine is 43 kilocalories per mole, about 7 kilocalories or 19% more than that of benzene. This higher resonance energy may reasonably be ascribed to the contribution of the charged forms in which nitrogen bears a negative charge:

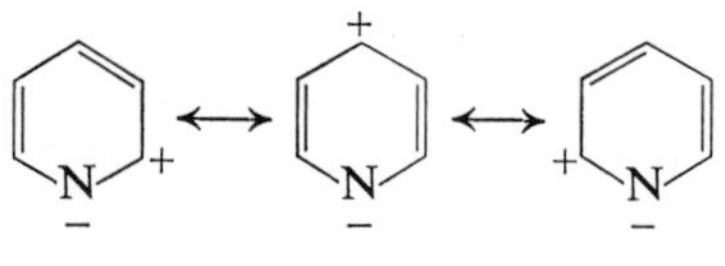

Such forms would be expected to contribute considerably more to resonance stabilization than corresponding forms in benzene in which charges are on carbon, for nitrogen is more prone to attract electrons than is carbon. This characteristic of nitrogen is supported by dipole moment measurements of such compounds as nitriles, whose polarity may be represented as follows: $C \equiv N \leftrightarrow {}^+C = N^-$.

There are several characteristics of pyridine which may be anticipated from consideration of the resonance possibilities just described. These characteristics will be discussed in connection with the reactions of pyridine to be presented in the following sections.

Chemical Reactions of the Pyridine Ring

Oxidation. The high resonance energy of pyridine would suggest an even greater stability to oxidation than encountered in benzene. This proves to be the case; in fact, unless the pyridine ring system is substituted with electron-donating groups, it resists nearly any oxidative conditions short of combustion. The greater stability of pyridine, in comparison with benzene, is illustrated by oxidation of quinoline (Eq. 1); however, fusion of the benz ring in the 3,4-position causes a decrease in the stability of the heterocyclic ring (cf. Eq. 33-1).

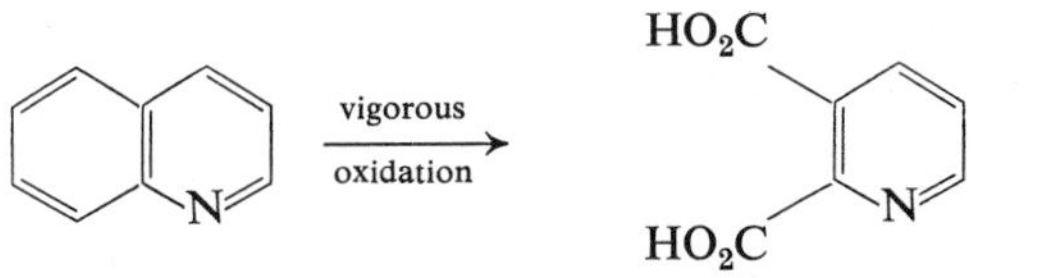

$$\text{(1)}$$

Quinoline → 2,3-Pyridinedicarboxylic acid or Quinolinic acid

Reduction. Pyridine is rather easily reduced, presumably on account of the polarity introduced by the nitrogen atom. A convenient method of reduction is shown in Eq. 2. Catalytic hydrogenation is also successful. As might be

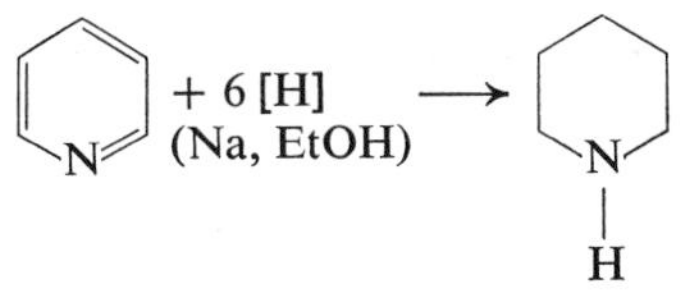

$$+ 6\,[\text{H}] \xrightarrow{\text{(Na, EtOH)}} \quad \text{(2)}$$

Piperidine (hexahydropyridine)

expected, piperidine is a much stronger base than pyridine, of about the basic strength of the usual aliphatic amines.

Substitution in pyridine. Since charged resonance forms reduce the electron density on the carbon atoms in the ring, substitution in pyridine might be expected to be rather difficult, comparable to a benzene ring substituted with a *meta*-director. Actually, the magnitude of this effect is even greater than might normally be expected to result from contribution of charged resonance forms. Substitution in pyridine is at least as difficult as substitution in a benzene ring containing two *meta*-directors.

In all reactions of pyridine with acidic reagents, which include all the normal reagents used in substitution reactions, the base would be converted more or less completely to the salt. Since pyridine is a very weak base, however, some of it would remain as free base even in concentrated acid solution. This small amount of free base is no doubt the species in which substitution occurs, for the salt would be expected to substitute much more slowly. The low concentration of the species being substituted is probably responsible for the unusually slow rate of substitution of pyridine. Furthermore, as the conditions for substitution are made more severe by use of stronger acid, this reduces still further the amount of free base present.

In spite of the importance of salt formation in reactions of pyridine, it is common practice not to indicate the salt in equations for substitution reactions. *This practice will be followed in this book,* for it is a considerable inconvenience to indicate in each equation the equilibria actually occurring with the salt.

As for position of substitution in pyridine, inspection of the charged resonance forms suggests that electron density on the alpha and gamma carbon atoms is especially low; therefore substitution in the beta positions would be expected. Furthermore, and probably more important, the beta position is the only one for which the transition state in substitution has no resonance form with a plus charge on trivalent nitrogen:

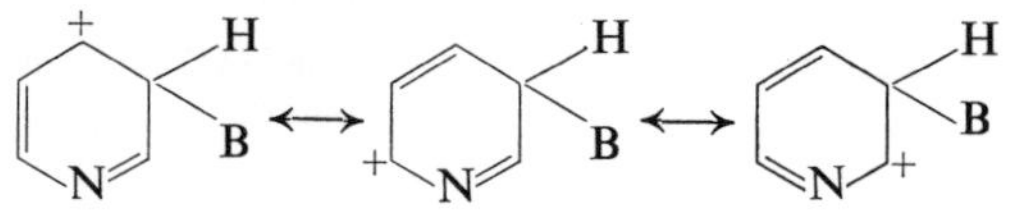

Beta substitution does prove to be the fact in all instances where the entering group is positive. In the case of free radical substitution, such directing influence naturally does not hold. In benzene, free radical substitution is similarly unaffected by directing influence dependent on electron density distribution (cf. Chap. 28).

Halogenation. Since bromination is more easily controlled than is chlorination, bromination is indicated in Eq. 3.

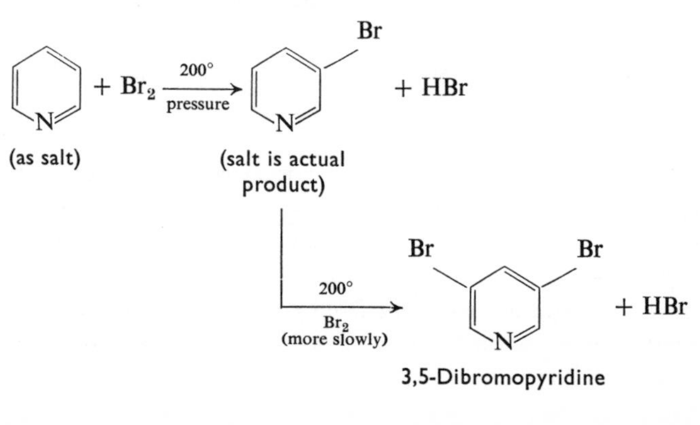

3,5-Dibromopyridine

This reaction is satisfactory for preparative purposes, for only the single mono-bromopyridine is formed, and this is readily separated from the dibromo-pyridine by distillation.

Pyridine is so stable that it may be heated to temperatures at which *bromine molecules dissociate into atomic bromine.* Under these conditions, attack is by the neutral bromine atoms; so usual directive influences do not hold. The 2-position proves to be the point of attack under these conditions.

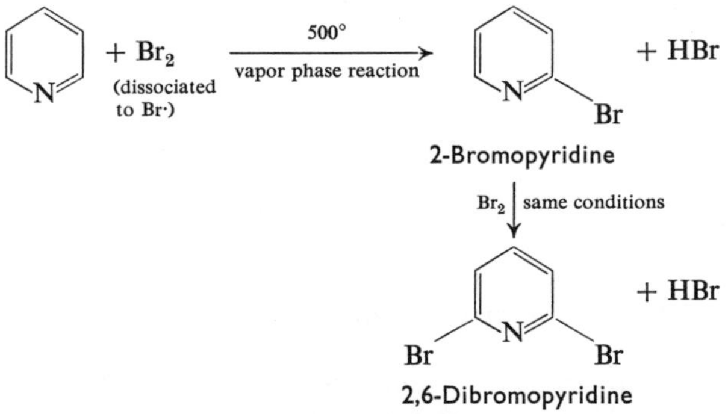

2-Bromopyridine

Br_2 | same conditions

2,6-Dibromopyridine

Although the processes shown in Eqs. 3 and 4 are reasonably satisfactory and entirely practical synthetic methods, their significance is not great, for the halogen derivatives prove to be of limited synthetic utility in the pyridine series. This should be noted as in marked contrast to the situation in the benzene series.

Nitration of pyridine is so difficult that it is not a practical reaction. The conditions required (Eq. 5) are so extreme that even pyridine is decomposed

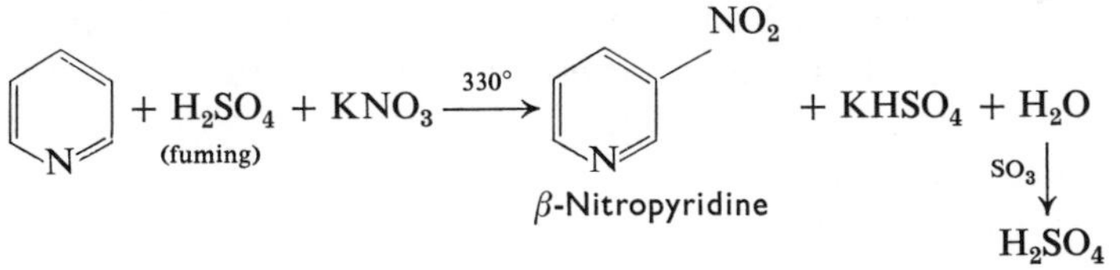

β-Nitropyridine

extensively. Again in marked contrast to the benzene series, the nitro compounds in pyridine are of little significance as intermediates in synthesis. The only pyridine derivatives in which nitration becomes practical are those containing amino or hydroxyl groups as substituents. Such reactions will be discussed in later sections.

Sulfonation. Pyridine may be sulfonated in moderately good yield by the process shown in Eq. 6.

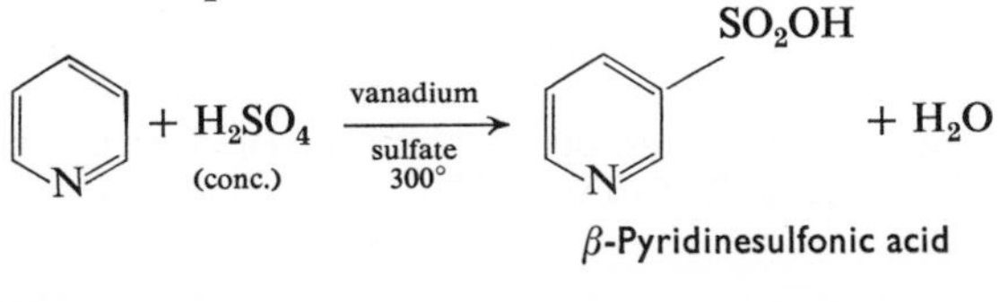

β-Pyridinesulfonic acid

This procedure renders the sulfonic acid a useful intermediate[2] for obtaining other 3-substituted pyridines (cf. later section).

Friedel and Crafts reaction. Since the Friedel and Crafts reaction will not occur satisfactorily in benzene derivatives containing a *meta*-director, it is not surprising that the reaction cannot be used to alkylate or acylate pyridine. It should be mentioned, however, that pyridinecarboxylic acid chlorides may be used to acylate other aromatic systems (Eq. 7).

$$\text{(pyridine-3-carbonyl chloride)} + \text{(benzene)} \xrightarrow{\text{AlCl}_3} \text{(phenyl 3-pyridyl ketone)} + \text{HCl} \qquad (7)$$

Synthesis and Reactions of Pyridine Derivatives

Fundamental to an understanding of the chemistry of substituent groups in pyridine is a realization of the fact that the reactivity of such groups is a function of the position of substitution. The empirical observations may be summarized as follows.

(a) A group substituted in a β-position (3- or 5-position) in pyridine behaves very much like the same group substituted in benzene. In other words, functional groups substituted in the β-position exhibit characteristic aromatic properties.

(b) A group substituted in an α- or γ-position (2-, 4-, or 6-position) in pyridine is much more reactive than normal for an aromatic substituent. The kinds of reactions exhibited by groups in these positions are similar to those characteristic of groups attached to a carbonyl although the rates of reaction of the groups in pyridine are less than those attached to carbonyl.

The reactivity of α- and γ-substituents in pyridine may well be regarded as entirely consistent with expectations. In Chapter 13, there was discussed the high reactivity of carbonyl compounds, and this reactivity was attributed primarily to two factors: polarity of the carbonyl group, resulting in a low electron density on carbon; presence of only four groups around the carbonyl carbon in the transition state, in comparison with five in displacement from a saturated carbon atom. The material in Chapter 13 should be reviewed at this time, but a typical reaction of an acid chloride will be included (Eq. 8) at this point in order to illustrate the type of reaction involved.

---

[2] It is also possible to obtain γ-pyridinesulfonic acid by a sequence of reactions starting with pyridine and thionyl chloride. Although the exact course of the intermediate steps is poorly understood, an experimental procedure has been developed which gives a modest yield of the sulfonic acid. Reference: R. R. Evans, H. C. Brown and H. C. van der Plas, *Org. Syntheses*, **43**, 97 (1963).

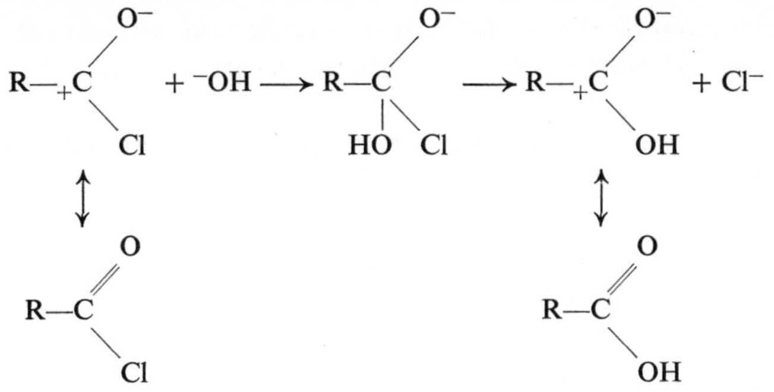

$$R-\overset{+}{\underset{Cl}{C}}\overset{O^-}{<} \;+\; {}^-OH \longrightarrow R-\underset{HO\;\;Cl}{C}\overset{O^-}{<} \longrightarrow R-\overset{+}{\underset{OH}{C}}\overset{O^-}{<} \;+\; Cl^-$$

$$R-\underset{Cl}{C}\overset{O}{\diagup} \qquad\qquad R-\underset{OH}{C}\overset{O}{\diagup} \qquad\qquad (8)$$

If we now consider charged resonance forms of pyridine, whose importance has already been discussed in connection with resonance stabilization of pyridine, we have the following:

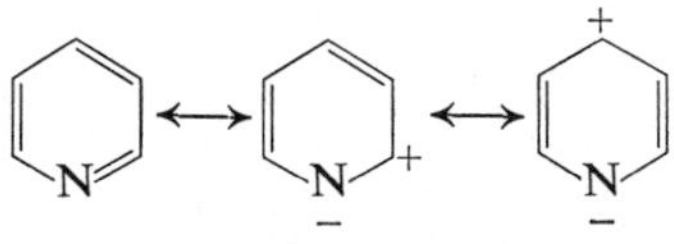

Contribution of these resonance forms might reasonably be expected to lead to the same type of reactions as illustrated in Eq. 8, and this proves to be the case. Displacement of one negative group by another is a relatively easy reaction in α- and γ-substituted pyridines, but is not an easy reaction in β-substituted pyridines. No major resonance form may be written which contributes a positive charge on the β-carbon. The aromatic character observed for β-substituents follows directly from this circumstance.

It may also be recalled that hydrogens on a carbon alpha to a carbonyl (cf. Chaps. 15, 26, and 27) have weakly acidic properties on account of resonance stabilization of the anion. It would follow that hydrogens on a carbon attached to the α- or γ-position in pyridine should have weakly acidic properties, on account of similar resonance stabilization of the anion:

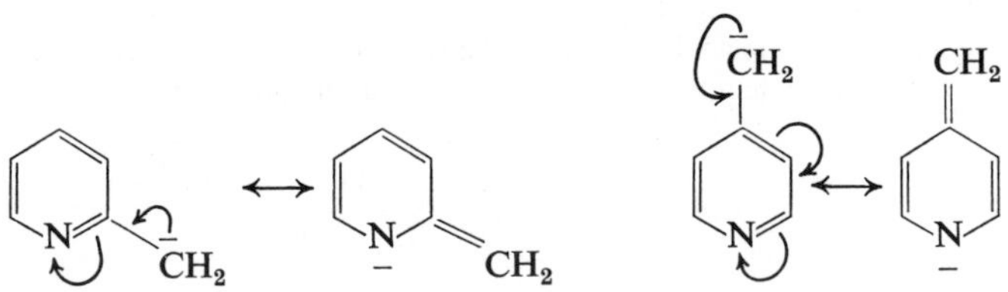

This also proves to be the fact, and such acidic properties are not associated with hydrogens on carbon attached to the β-position.

The following discussions of the chemistry of pyridine derivatives will prove to be easy to correlate if there be remembered the aromatic character of substituents in the β-position and the carbonyl character of the α- and γ-carbon atoms in pyridine.

Pyridinecarboxylic acids. The carboxylic acids are discussed first for they are useful as intermediates for securing other pyridine derivatives.

(1) PREPARATION FROM PICOLINES. Since all three of the picolines are available from coal tar, these serve as a source of *all three* of the pyridinecarboxylic acids.

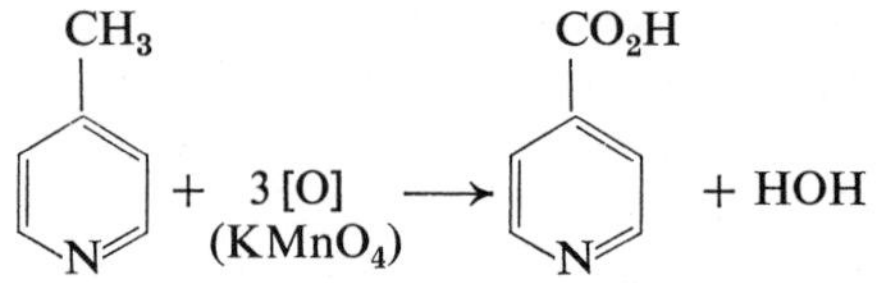

$$\text{CH}_3 \quad + \quad 3\,[\text{O}] \quad \longrightarrow \quad \text{CO}_2\text{H} \quad + \quad \text{HOH} \qquad (9)$$

$$\gamma\text{-Picoline} \qquad (\text{KMnO}_4) \qquad \text{Isonicotinic acid}$$

The β-pyridinecarboxylic acid has the common name *nicotinic acid*[3] while the α-pyridinecarboxylic acid is known as *picolinic acid*.

(2) COMMERCIAL SYNTHESIS OF NICOTINIC ACID. Since nicotinic acid is required in appreciable quantity for inclusion in vitamin preparations, its synthesis has been the subject of considerable study. The process shown in Eq. 10 has proved the most economical way of securing this acid. The yields

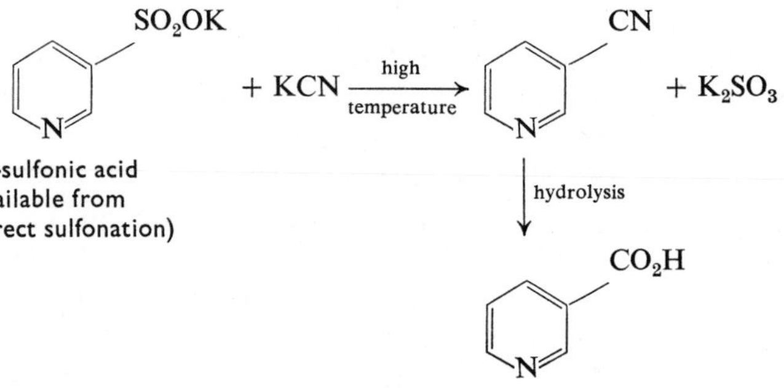

$$\text{SO}_2\text{OK} \quad + \text{ KCN} \xrightarrow[\text{temperature}]{\text{high}} \quad \text{CN} \quad + \text{ K}_2\text{SO}_3$$

(β-sulfonic acid available from direct sulfonation)

$$\Big\downarrow \text{hydrolysis} \qquad (10)$$

$$\text{CO}_2\text{H}$$

---

[3] The name nicotinic acid arose from the first isolation of this acid by oxidation of the alkaloid nicotine. Other than by this historical accident, nicotinic acid has no connection with

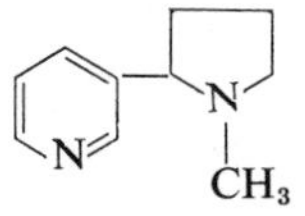

Nicotine

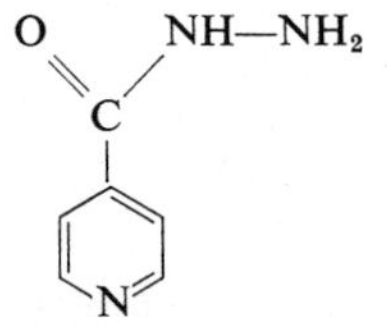

Isonicotinic acid hydrazide or "Isoniazide"

the highly toxic alkaloid, nicotine; in fact, nicotinic acid or its amide has the properties of a vitamin (it is one of the B vitamins). Isonicotinic acid is also of interest, for its hydrazide (amide from hydrazine rather than ammonia) has proved of value in chemotherapy of tuberculosis.

in this process are rather good, for pyridine is so stable that the high temperatures required in the cyanide fusion cause very little decomposition (compare with benzene, Eq. 18-19).

(3) PROPERTIES OF PYRIDINECARBOXYLIC ACIDS. As predicted from the general discussion of pyridine derivatives presented previously, nicotinic acid has the properties characteristic of an aromatic carboxylic acid. The α- and γ-isomers, however, behave somewhat like α-keto acids. The acids are relatively easily decarboxylated, and the α- and γ-acid chlorides decompose on standing or heating. These acid chlorides may be used in synthesis where no heating is required, provided they are prepared without heating and used immediately after preparation.

The acid chlorides of all the pyridinecarboxylic acids are *not satisfactorily prepared with phosphorus pentachloride or phosphorus trichloride, but may be prepared readily with thionyl chloride.*

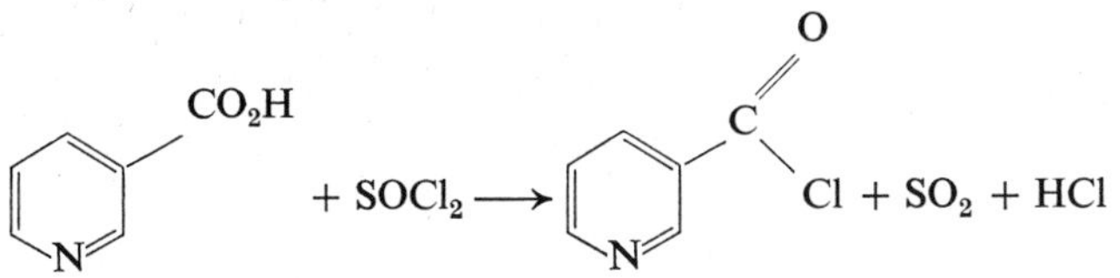

$$\text{(pyridine-3-CO}_2\text{H)} + \text{SOCl}_2 \longrightarrow \text{(pyridine-3-COCl)} + \text{SO}_2 + \text{HCl} \qquad (11)$$

Nicotinyl chloride

The acid chlorides give the usual useful reactions of carboxylic acid chlorides, except as limited by the instability of the α- and γ-isomers.

Aminopyridines. The aminopyridines may be obtained from the carboxylic acid amides by the Hofmann hypohalite reaction (Eq. 12); hence all three isomers are readily available.

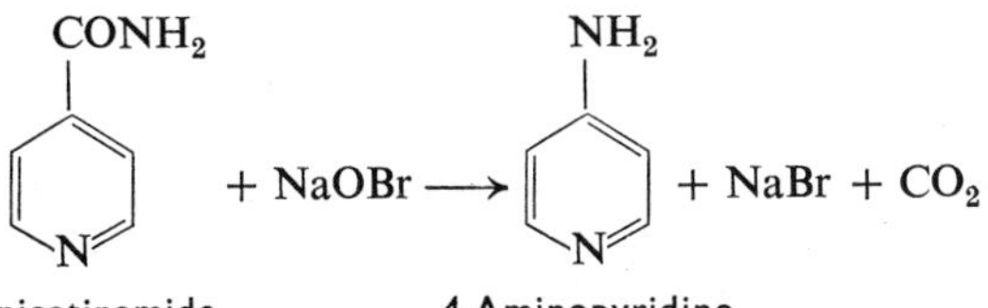

$$\text{(pyridine-4-CONH}_2\text{)} + \text{NaOBr} \longrightarrow \text{(pyridine-4-NH}_2\text{)} + \text{NaBr} + \text{CO}_2 \qquad (12)$$

Isonicotinamide   4-Aminopyridine

(1) CHICHIBABIN REACTION. 2-Aminopyridine, required as an intermediate for making sulfapyridine and several of the antihistamines, is prepared most conveniently by a special reaction which is useful only for the 2-isomer. This reaction, known as the Chichibabin reaction, employs sodium amide, which is able to displace a hydride ion from the 2-position in pyridine (Eq. 13). Since sodium hydride is a strong enough base to replace a hydrogen in an amine, the actual product of the Chichibabin reaction is the sodium derivative of 2-aminopyridine, as shown in Eq. 13. The 2-aminopyridine is freed by addition of water after completion of the reaction with sodium amide.

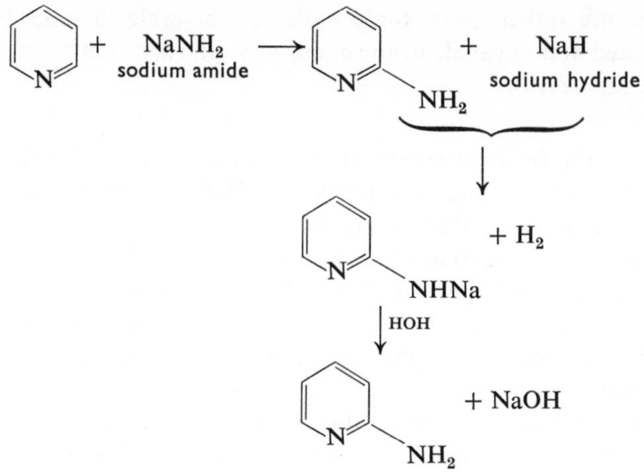

$$\text{(pyridine)} + \underset{\text{sodium amide}}{\text{NaNH}_2} \longrightarrow \text{(2-aminopyridine)}_{\text{NH}_2} + \underset{\text{sodium hydride}}{\text{NaH}}$$

$$\downarrow$$

$$\text{(pyridine)}_{\text{NHNa}} + \text{H}_2 \qquad (13)$$

$$\downarrow \text{HOH}$$

$$\text{(pyridine)}_{\text{NH}_2} + \text{NaOH}$$

For alkylsubstituted pyridines, the Chichibabin reaction has a relatively limited use, for the α- and γ-alkylpyridines are sufficiently acidic to give the reaction shown in Eq. 14 with the highly basic sodium amide.

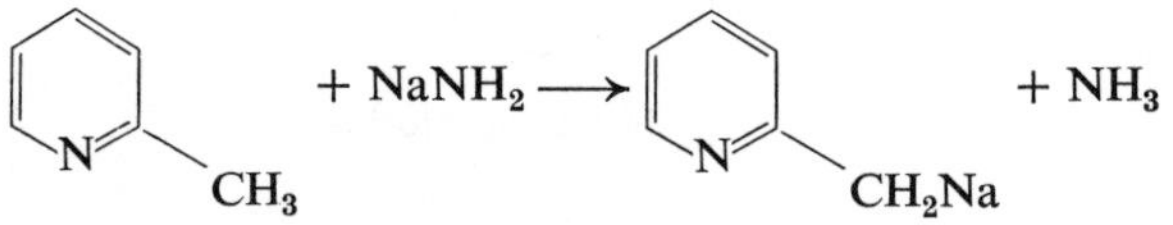

$$\text{(2-methylpyridine)}_{\text{CH}_3} + \text{NaNH}_2 \longrightarrow \text{(pyridine)}_{\text{CH}_2\text{Na}} + \text{NH}_3 \qquad (14)$$

The sodium derivative shown in Eq. 14 leads to numerous side reactions, and very little substitution of amino is secured.[4] With β-alkylpyridines, a reasonably satisfactory reaction occurs to substitute amino in the 2-position (Eq. 15), with a smaller amount of substitution in the 6-position.

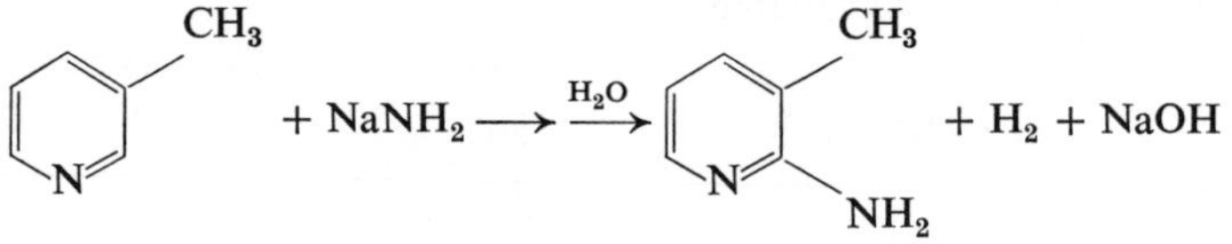

$$\underset{\text{CH}_3}{\text{(3-methylpyridine)}} + \text{NaNH}_2 \longrightarrow \overset{\text{H}_2\text{O}}{\longrightarrow} \underset{\text{CH}_3}{\text{(pyridine)}}_{\text{NH}_2} + \text{H}_2 + \text{NaOH} \qquad (15)$$

2-Amino-3-methylpyridine

(2) PYRIDINEDIAZONIUM SALTS. The β-pyridinediazonium salts are stable at low temperature, as are the corresponding benzene derivatives, and they may be utilized in the various reactions of the diazonium salts. Since the β-position

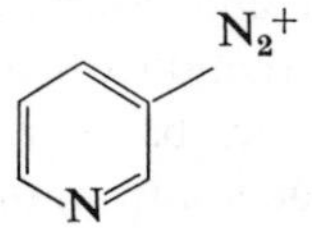

$$\text{(pyridine)}^{\text{N}_2^+}$$

---

[4] For the specific cases of the α- or γ-picolines, it has been possible to develop special conditions under which the Chichibabin reaction can be applied successfully, on an industrial scale.

is the position of direct substitution in pyridine, however, the diazonium salts find little application for introduction of substituents in this position.

The α- and γ-diazonium salts are not stable, but react rapidly with water, even at low temperature, as do aliphatic diazonium salts. Diazotization leads directly to the hydroxy compound (Eq. 16).

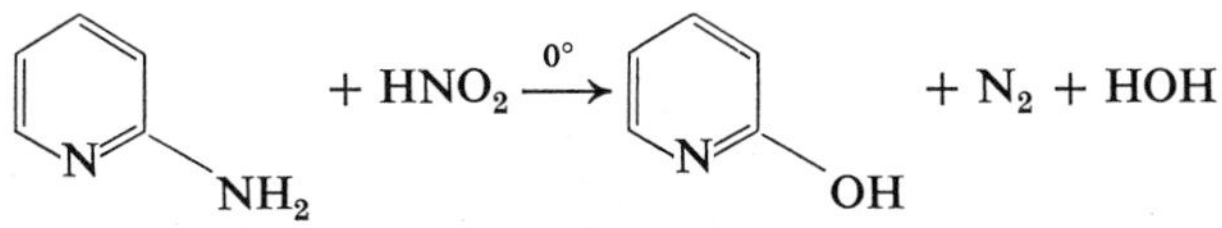

$$
\underset{\text{NH}_2}{\text{pyridine}} + \text{HNO}_2 \xrightarrow{0°} \underset{\text{OH}}{\text{pyridine}} + \text{N}_2 + \text{HOH} \qquad (16)
$$

This process is sometimes of value for synthesis of the hydroxypyridines; however, direct saponification of the amino group, as discussed in the next section, is also possible.

(3) PROPERTIES OF AMINOPYRIDINES. The β-aminopyridine acts like an aromatic amine. It cannot be hydrolyzed with alkali under ordinary conditions, and it is a di-acid base (forms a di-salt with two moles of acid).

The α- and γ-aminopyridines have the amino attached to the positive carbons, hence they might be expected to partake of the properties of an amidine, the nitrogen analog of an amide:

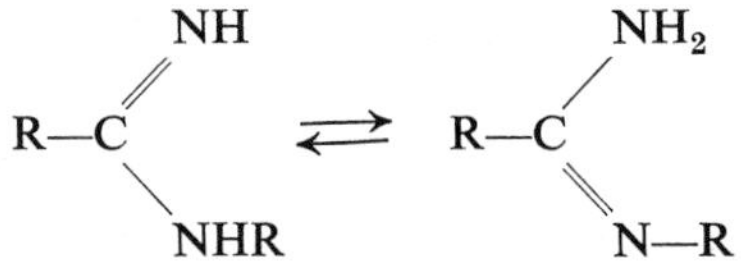

$$
\underset{\text{NHR}}{\overset{\text{NH}}{R\!-\!C}} \rightleftarrows \underset{\text{N}\!-\!R}{\overset{\text{NH}_2}{R\!-\!C}}
$$

If this is the case, the α- and γ-aminopyridines should behave as mono-acid bases (as do amidines), and they should be relatively easy to hydrolyze (as are all imino structures, $=$NH). These expectations are realized in fact, as shown in Eqs. 17 and 18 (similar reactions occur with the α-isomer). In the equilibrium

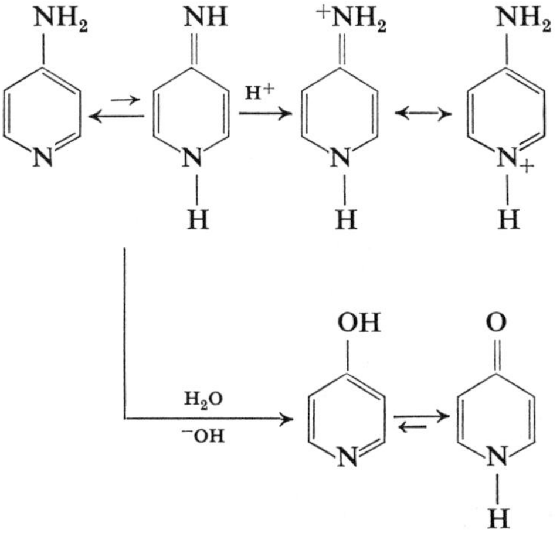

$$
(17)
$$

$$
(18)
$$

4-Hydroxypyridine

shown in Eq. 17, it has been found that the amino form is the dominant one, although the situation is reversed for the hydroxypyridines (Eq. 18). In Eqs. 17 and 18 there arises an opportunity to clearly distinguish between resonance and isomerism. The 4-aminopyridinium ion is a resonance hybrid, and this no doubt stabilizes the mono-ion sufficiently to inhibit reaction with a second mole of acid.

(4) NITRATION OF 2-AMINOPYRIDINE. The nitration of 2-aminopyridine (Eq. 19) furnishes another illustration that this substance has the properties of an amide. Rearrangement of a group from nitrogen into the ring has an analogy in the Fries rearrangement in the benzene series (cf. Eq. 20-5).

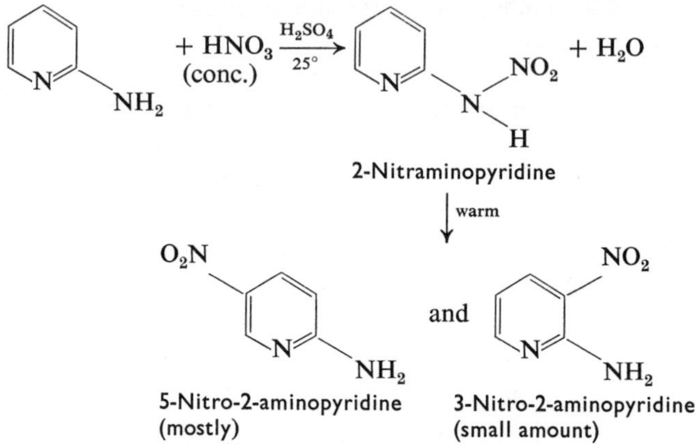

2-Nitraminopyridine

5-Nitro-2-aminopyridine (mostly)   and   3-Nitro-2-aminopyridine (small amount)

$$(19)$$

Separation of the 3- and 5-nitro-2-aminopyridines is simple, for the chelated isomer (cf. Chap. 17, nitration of phenol), 3-nitro-2-aminopyridine, is volatile with steam, while the 5-nitro isomer is nonvolatile with steam. Thus Eq. 19 represents a useful preparative procedure. So far as concerns the structure of 2-aminopyridine, the significant feature about Eq. 19 is initial formation of the nitramine. In simple aliphatic compounds, it has not been possible to convert a primary amine directly to the nitramine, whereas nitration of an amide (Eq. 20) is a simple reaction.

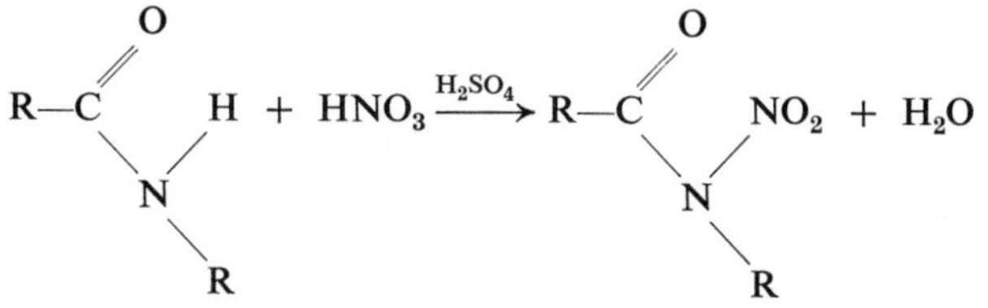

$$(20)$$

For preparative purposes, the aliphatic nitramine may be secured by hydrolysis of the nitramide.

Hydroxypyridines. The α- and γ-hydroxypyridines may be prepared from the corresponding amines, as described in the preceding sections (Eqs. 16 and 18).

The β-hydroxypyridine may be readily secured by potassium hydroxide fusion of the sulfonic acid, which is obtained by direct substitution.

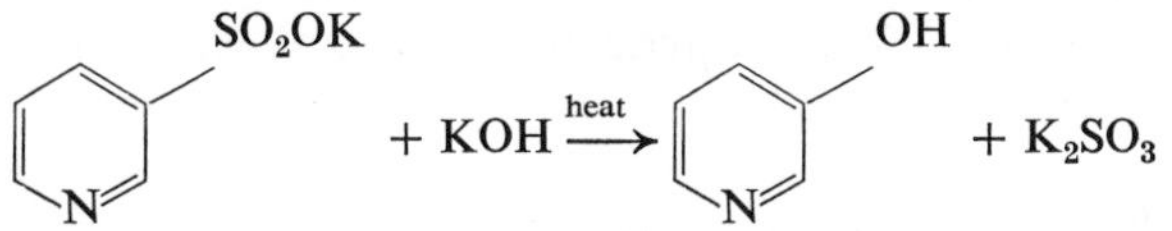

$$+ \text{KOH} \xrightarrow{\text{heat}} \qquad + \text{K}_2\text{SO}_3 \qquad (21)$$

(as salt in the reaction)

Properties of the hydroxypyridines are those to be expected from previous discussions of structure.

The β-hydroxypyridine has the properties of an aminophenol in the benzene series. It is amphoteric, and conversion to the ether (Eq. 22) gives the β-methoxypyridine.

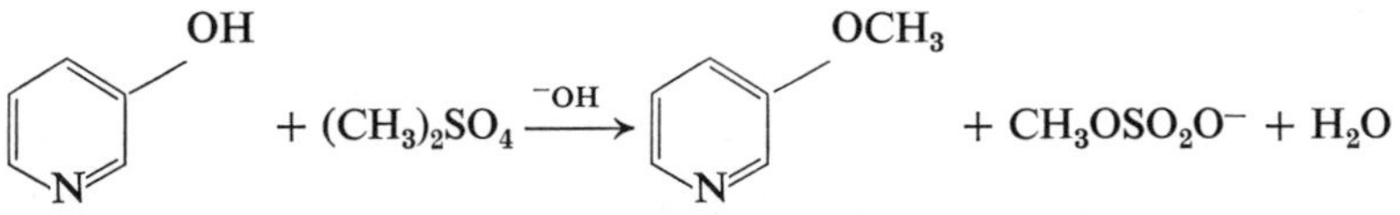

$$+ (\text{CH}_3)_2\text{SO}_4 \xrightarrow{-\text{OH}} \qquad + \text{CH}_3\text{OSO}_2\text{O}^- + \text{H}_2\text{O} \quad (22)$$

3-Methoxypyridine

In contrast, the α- and γ-hydroxypyridines do not have the properties of a phenol. The existence of the tautomeric equilibrium shown in Eq. 18 is demonstrated by formation of two methyl derivatives, as shown in Eq. 23.

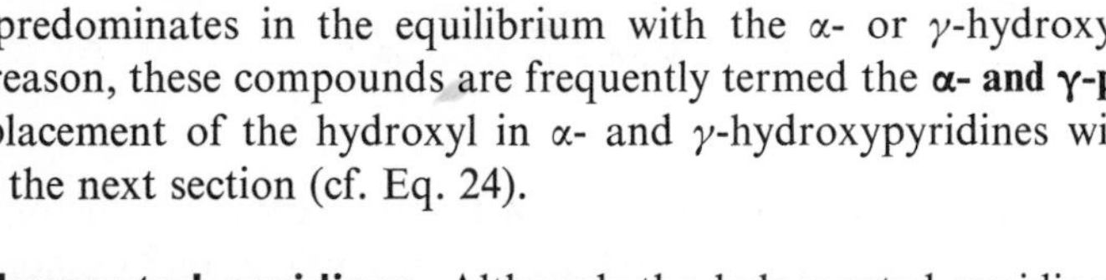

$$\xrightarrow{\text{ether formation}} \qquad \text{and} \qquad (23)$$

Considerable evidence has accumulated which indicates that the keto form actually predominates in the equilibrium with the α- or γ-hydroxypyridine. For this reason, these compounds are frequently termed the **α- and γ-pyridones**.

Replacement of the hydroxyl in α- and γ-hydroxypyridines will be discussed in the next section (cf. Eq. 24).

Halogenated pyridines. Although the halogenated pyridines are not very important intermediates in synthesis, substitution may be secured in any of the three positions. The direct substitution of bromine in the β-position (Eq. 3) or the α-position (Eq. 4) has already been discussed. The α- and γ-chloropyridines may be secured from the corresponding hydroxy compounds (Eq. 24).

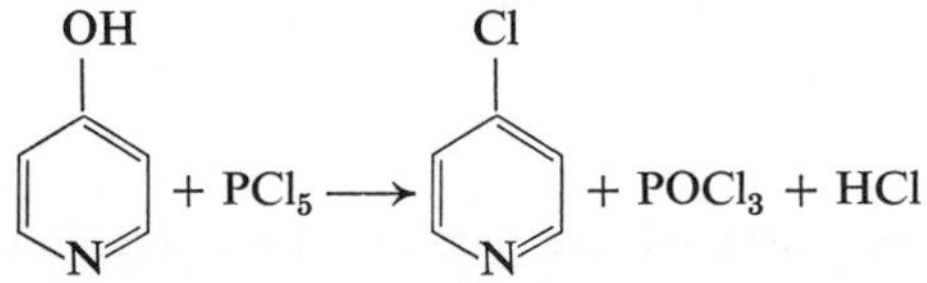

$$+ \text{PCl}_5 \longrightarrow \qquad + \text{POCl}_3 + \text{HCl} \qquad (24)$$

(2-isomer similarly)   γ-Chloropyridine

This conversion may be compared to conversion of an acid to an acid chloride; it should be recalled that in the benzene series a phenol cannot be converted to an aryl halide by the methods normally used for conversion of alcohols to alkyl halides. Similarly, 3-chloropyridine is not prepared satisfactorily from 3-hydroxypyridine.

PROPERTIES OF THE HALOGENATED PYRIDINES. The halopyridines fail to react with magnesium to give Grignard reagents, so one of the more useful reactions of aromatic halides is lost. A major utility of the 2- and 4-halogenated pyridines is removal of halogen by reduction (Eq. 25).

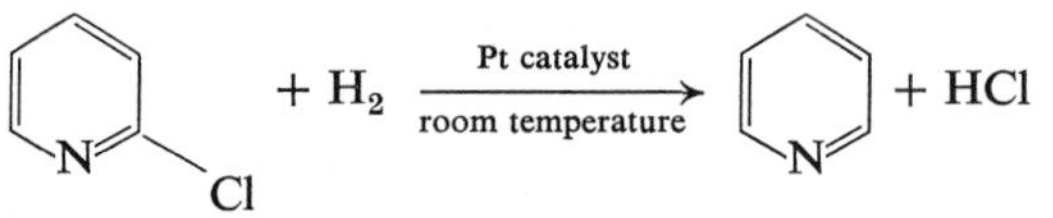

$$\text{(pyridine-Cl)} + H_2 \xrightarrow[\text{room temperature}]{\text{Pt catalyst}} \text{(pyridine)} + HCl \tag{25}$$

By combination of appropriate reactions discussed in this chapter, Eq. 25 may be utilized as the final step for removal from the ring of carboxyl, amino, or hydroxyl. The latter two groups are frequently put into the ring in order to facilitate substitution in pyridine, then removed via the chloride.

Pyridyl ketones. If the other group attached to carbonyl is an aromatic nucleus allowing Friedel and Crafts substitution, the ketone may be obtained from a pyridinecarboxylic acid chloride (Eq. 7); however, it should be remembered that substitution into the pyridine ring by means of the Friedel and Crafts reaction cannot be accomplished.

The 3-pyridyl ketones may be secured from the nitrile (Eq. 26).

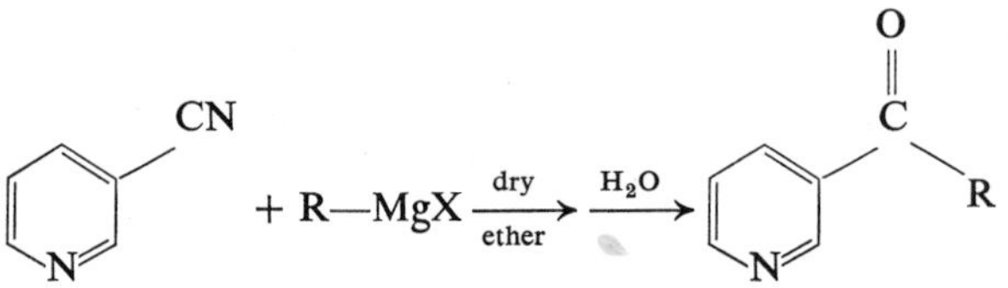

$$\text{(pyridine-CN)} + R\text{---}MgX \xrightarrow[\text{ether}]{\text{dry}} \xrightarrow{H_2O} \text{(pyridine-C(=O)R)} \tag{26}$$

The 2- and 4-pyridyl ketones are not readily secured via the nitriles, for the nitriles are not readily available (cf. Eq. 10 for synthesis of 3-cyanopyridine). The acid chlorides are accessible, however, and these give a good reaction with cadmium reagents (Eq. 27).

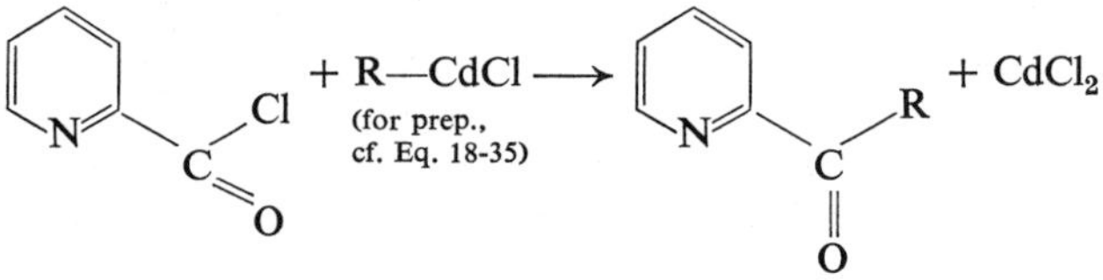

$$\text{(pyridine-C(=O)Cl)} + R\text{---}CdCl \xrightarrow{\text{(for prep., cf. Eq. 18-35)}} \text{(pyridine-C(=O)R)} + CdCl_2 \tag{27}$$

Alkylpyridines. Although the picolines are available from coal tar, the other alkylpyridines must be prepared.

(1) SYNTHESIS OF ALKYLPYRIDINES. Alkyl may be secured at any position in pyridine by reduction of the corresponding ketone (cf. preceding section); however, this method is most commonly used for securing the 3-alkylpyridines. For the 2- and 4-alkylpyridines, more direct routes are available.

The 2-alkylpyridines are conveniently obtained by a single direct reaction involving addition of a lithium reagent to pyridine (Eq. 28). The Grignard

$$\text{pyridine} + \text{R—Li} \xrightarrow{\text{heat}} \underset{\underset{\text{R}}{\overset{\text{H}}{|}}}{\text{intermediate}} \xrightarrow{\underset{\text{temp.}}{\text{higher}}} \text{2-R-pyridine} + \text{LiH} \qquad (28)$$

(from RX + 2Li)

reagent will not give addition to the C=N grouping in pyridine, but the more reactive lithium reagent will give the reaction under forcing conditions. In general, the lithium reagent gives reactions similar to those of the Grignard reagent but reacts at a higher rate. The process in Eq. 28 is illustrative of the fact that pyridine gives reactions characteristic of the carbonyl grouping, but has a reactivity less than that normal for carbonyl.

Another characteristic of pyridines, already discussed as illustrative of their carbonyl character, involves the acidity of hydrogens on carbon substituted at the 2- or 4-positions. The higher 4-alkylpyridines are conveniently prepared by taking advantage of the acidity of the hydrogens in a 4-methyl substituent. One of these hydrogens may be replaced by lithium as in Eq. 29.

$$\overset{\text{CH}_3}{\underset{N}{\bigcirc}} + \text{C}_6\text{H}_5\text{—Li} \longrightarrow \overset{\text{CH}_2\text{—Li}}{\underset{N}{\bigcirc}} + \text{C}_6\text{H}_6 \qquad (29)$$

(lithiumphenyl)

The resultant lithium reagent gives the normal reactions of lithium reagents. By coupling with an alkyl bromide (Eq. 30), higher alkylpyridines may be secured. This is another type of reaction in which the highly reactive lithium reagents are successful, whereas the Grignard reagent is not sufficiently reactive for coupling unless the halide is a reactive one such as a benzyl halide.

$$\overset{\text{CH}_2\text{—Li}}{\underset{N}{\bigcirc}} + \text{R—Br} \longrightarrow \overset{\text{CH}_2\text{—R}}{\underset{N}{\bigcirc}} + \text{LiBr} \qquad (30)$$

For a review of other functional derivatives which may be made from the above lithium reagent (or the 2-isomer), reactions of the Grignard reagent should be reviewed (utilize the index).

(2) REACTIONS OF 2- AND 4-ALKYLPYRIDINES. The reactions which become possible on account of the acidity of the α-hydrogens in these compounds will

be illustrated by use of the commercially available picolines. Replacement by lithium has already been cited (Eq. 29). In addition, rapid replacement of all α-hydrogens by bromine occurs, as in Eq. 31.

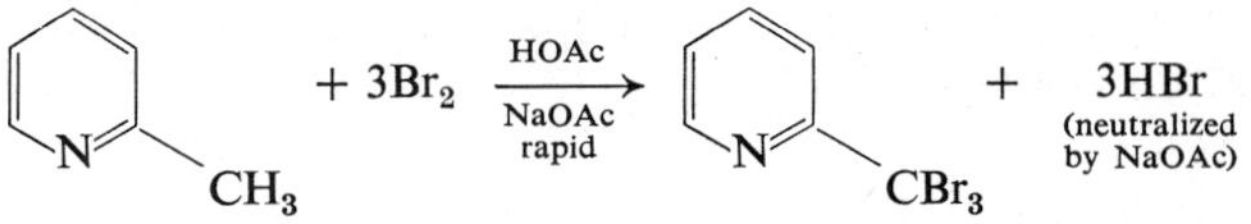

$$\text{(pyridine-}CH_3\text{)} + 3Br_2 \xrightarrow[\substack{NaOAc \\ rapid}]{HOAc} \text{(pyridine-}CBr_3\text{)} + \quad 3HBr \quad \text{(neutralized by NaOAc)} \tag{31}$$

Reactions of the aldol type also occur, and cross reactions are feasible because the pyridine derivatives are very inert to additions to the carbon-nitrogen bond. A representative reaction is shown in Eq. 32.

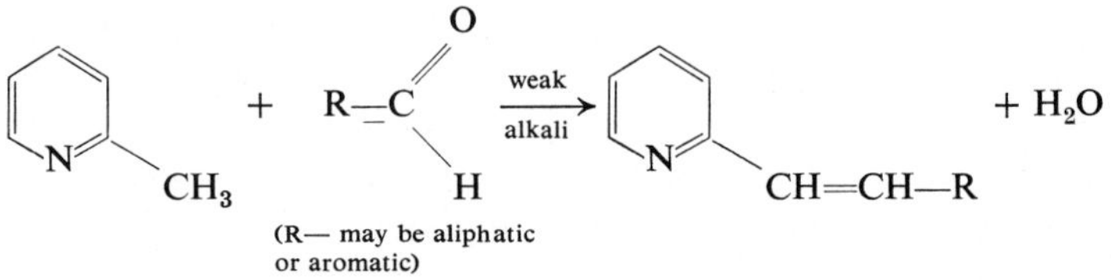

$$\text{(pyridine-}CH_3\text{)} + \quad R—C\overset{O}{\underset{H}{\diagdown}} \xrightarrow[\text{alkali}]{\text{weak}} \text{(pyridine-}CH{=}CH—R\text{)} + H_2O \tag{32}$$

(R— may be aliphatic or aromatic)

Water is lost as it is from condensations giving benzyl alcohols. Reduction of the unsaturated side chain in the product shown in Eq. 32 leads to higher alkylpyridines, and this is an *additional method of synthesis* of 2- and 4-alkyl-pyridines.

Various reagents may be added to the double bond in compounds obtained by condensations such as shown in Eq. 32. These reagents include hydrogen cyanide, which does not add to isolated carbon-carbon double bonds but does add to α,β-unsaturated carbonyl compounds. The addition probably occurs in a 1,4-manner, as shown in Eq. 33, for the negative group always adds to the

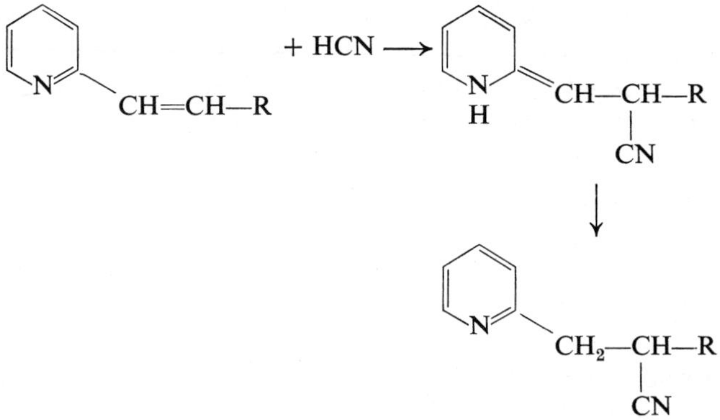

$$\text{(pyridine-}CH{=}CH—R\text{)} + HCN \longrightarrow \text{(pyridine-}N(H){=}CH—CH—R, CN\text{)}$$

$$\downarrow \tag{33}$$

$$\text{(pyridine-}CH_2—CH—R, CN\text{)}$$

carbon remote from the ring. The nitrile may be subjected to its usual reactions, such as hydrolysis and reduction.

An additional condensation of alkylpyridines is shown in the next section.

Pyridine aldehydes. The pyridine aldehydes give the usual reactions of aromatic aldehydes, in that they do not have alpha hydrogen atoms (review reactions of aromatic aldehydes, Chap. 18).

As usual, synthesis of the β-derivative is accomplished differently from that of the α- and γ-derivatives. The Rosenmund reduction in the pyridine series is less satisfactory than usual, but the 3-formylpyridine may be obtained by this procedure, Eq. 34. This method fails completely for the other isomers on account of the instability of the acid chlorides.

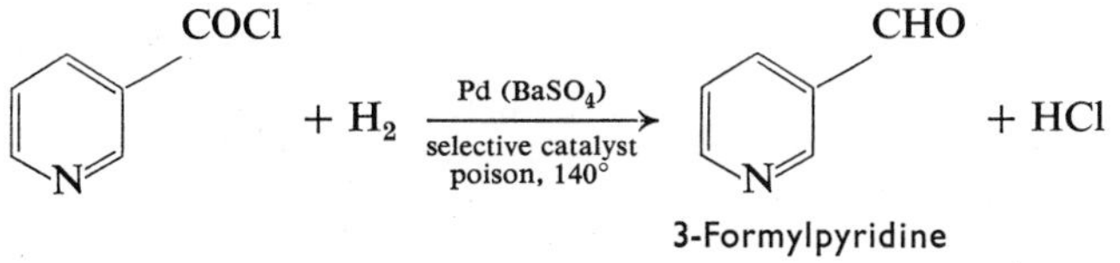

$$+ H_2 \xrightarrow[\substack{\text{selective catalyst} \\ \text{poison, } 140°}]{\text{Pd (BaSO}_4)} \qquad + HCl \qquad (34)$$

3-Formylpyridine

The 2- and 4-formylpyridines may be secured via condensation of the picolines with a nitrosobenzene, as is illustrated in Eq. 35. p-Dimethylamino-nitrosobenzene is used because it may be easily obtained by nitrosation of dimethylaniline (cf. Eq. 19-32).

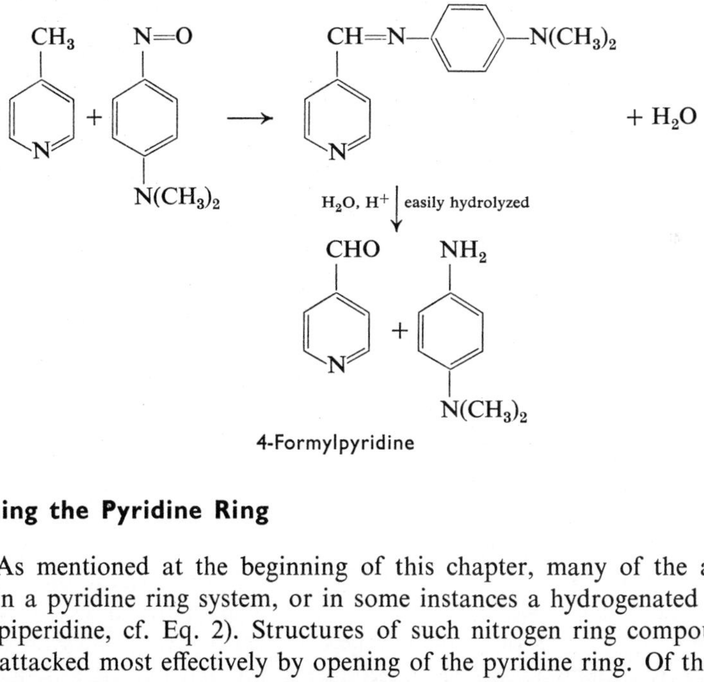

$$+ H_2O$$

$$\text{H}_2\text{O, H}^+ \Big| \text{ easily hydrolyzed} \qquad\qquad (35)$$

4-Formylpyridine

Opening the Pyridine Ring

As mentioned at the beginning of this chapter, many of the alkaloids contain a pyridine ring system, or in some instances a hydrogenated pyridine ring (piperidine, cf. Eq. 2). Structures of such nitrogen ring compounds are often attacked most effectively by opening of the pyridine ring. Of the several methods which have been used for opening nitrogen-containing rings, the one which has been most useful is the **Hofmann degradation,** and the application of this procedure is outlined in Eq. 36. This sequence is actually a combination of the quaternary ammonium salt synthesis discussed in Chapter 19 (Eqs. 19-13 to 19-16) with the Hofmann elimination reaction (Eq. 19-17).

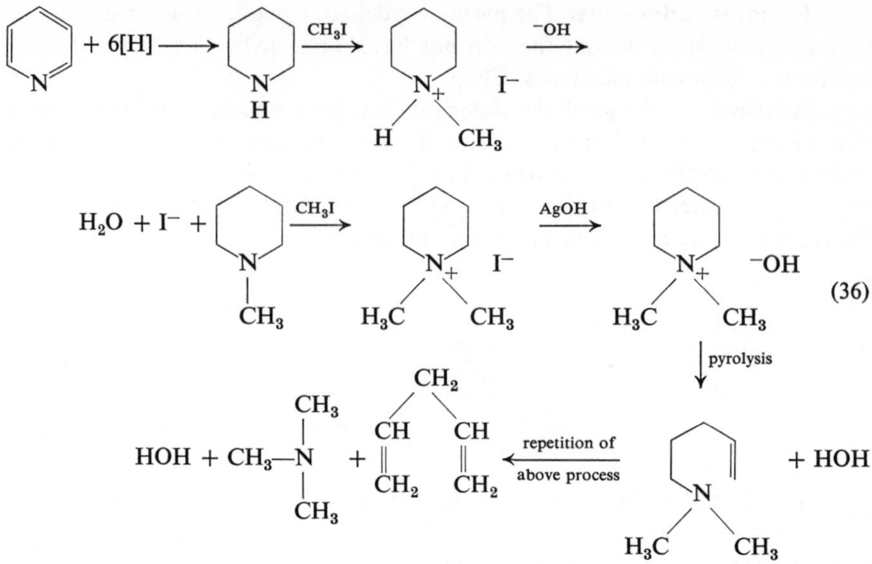

$$(36)$$

By identification of the degradation products from the series outlined in Eq. 36, substituents in the original ring may be located. For example, the different products eventually obtained from 2- and 3-alkylpyridines are shown:

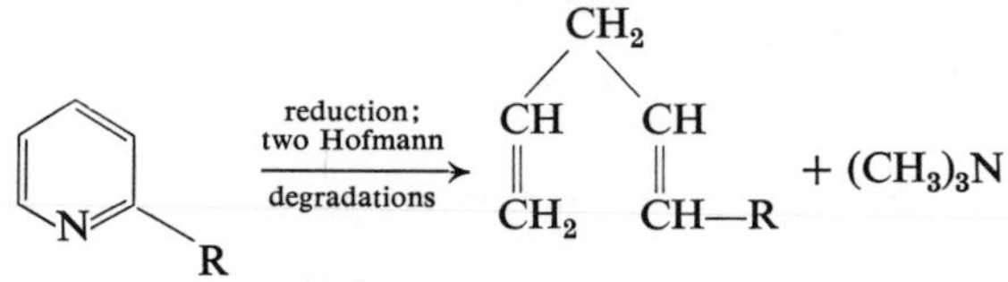

$$(37)$$

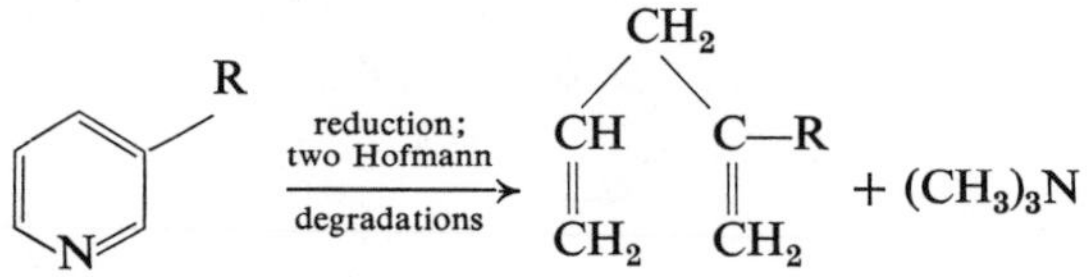

$$(38)$$

Sometimes the alkene may be oxidized after one degradation has opened the ring, but frequently a second degradation is used to eliminate nitrogen, as in the examples cited. The products of Eqs. 37 and 38 may be readily differentiated by oxidation. The product in Eq. 38 will, on oxidation, give formic acid as the only simple acid, while the product in Eq. 37 will give, in addition to formic acid, a higher carboxylic acid, $R—CO_2H$. Furthermore, oxidation of the product in Eq. 37 will yield malonic acid, which decarboxylates on heating above 150° (cf. Chap. 26), while the product in Eq. 38 will yield a β-keto acid, $R—\underset{\underset{O}{\|}}{C}—CH_2—CO_2H$, which decarboxylates quite readily, usually at room temperature (Chap. 26). Thus, a firm distinction between the two structures may be established by examination of the Hofmann degradation products.

In case a group other than hydrogen is substituted on nitrogen in a naturally occurring piperidine or other nitrogen ring (cf. nicotine formula, footnote 3), this may be detected by examining the tertiary amine finally eliminated. For example, an ethyl group would show up as in Eq. 39; also, much ethylene would be eliminated in each pyrolysis, for the less substituted alkene is formed preferentially in the Hofmann elimination.

$$
\underset{\underset{C_2H_5}{|}}{\overset{}{\bigcirc}}N \quad \xrightarrow[\substack{\text{degradations} \\ \text{(only one methylation} \\ \text{required for the first)}}]{\text{two Hofmann}} \quad \underset{}{\bigcirc} \!\!| + CH_3\!-\!\underset{\underset{C_2H_5}{|}}{\overset{\overset{CH_3}{|}}{N}} \tag{39}
$$

Since methyl groups are added to the nitrogen in all Hofmann degradations until the quaternary salt is finally secured, the process has occasionally been called "exhaustive methylation."

Synthesis of Pyridines by Cyclization Reactions

Although nearly any desired monosubstituted pyridine derivative can be secured by the reactions that have been discussed, the synthesis of poly-substituted pyridine derivatives often requires an initial sequence involving a cyclization procedure. The situation is not entirely dissimilar to that encountered in the various series of condensed ring hydrocarbons (Chaps. 29 and 30). As in the condensed ring compounds, the initial cyclization product in the pyridine series may be used for further substitution reactions or for alteration of functional groups.

Several methods have been used for synthesis of pyridines by cyclizations from appropriate carbonyl compounds, but we will discuss only one method which is probably the most versatile and useful of the various methods that have been reported.

The Hantzsch pyridine synthesis. The Hantzsch synthesis most frequently depends on condensation of a β-dicarbonyl compound and an aldehyde with ammonia. The path of the reaction depends on whether the aldehyde or the β-dicarbonyl compound is used in excess; so these two variations will be discussed separately.

(1) USE OF EXCESS DICARBONYL COMPOUND. The net condensation reaction of ammonia, acetaldehyde, and excess of ethyl acetoacetate is shown in Eq. 40. The net conversion shown in Eq. 40 involves a sequence of reactions which may be followed in a series of logical steps. In presence of the base, ammonia, the aldol condensation will occur, and the condensation occurring most rapidly should be that involving the most active carbonyl (the aldehyde) and the α-carbon bearing the most acidic hydrogens (those on carbon between two

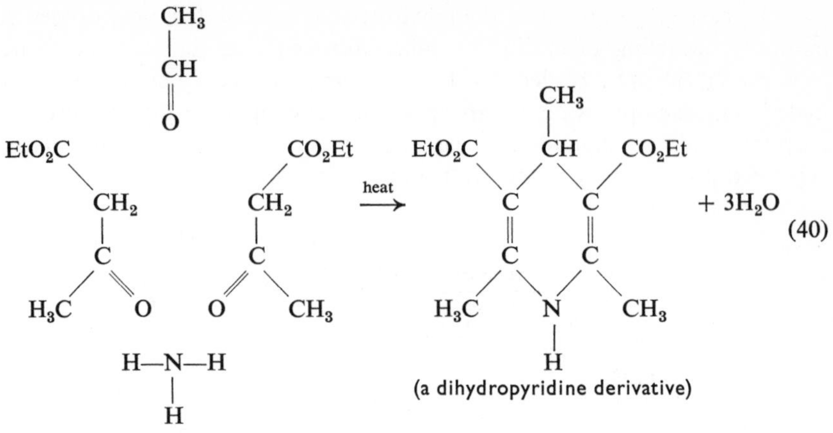

$$
\begin{array}{c}
CH_3 \\
| \\
CH \\
\| \\
O
\end{array}
$$

$$
\text{EtO}_2\text{C} \quad\quad \text{CO}_2\text{Et} \qquad \text{EtO}_2\text{C} \quad \overset{CH_3}{CH} \quad \text{CO}_2\text{Et}
$$

$$
\xrightarrow{\text{heat}} \qquad\qquad + 3H_2O \qquad (40)
$$

(a dihydropyridine derivative)

carbonyl groups). Thus the reaction that should go much faster than other possible aldol condensations is that shown in Eq. 40a.

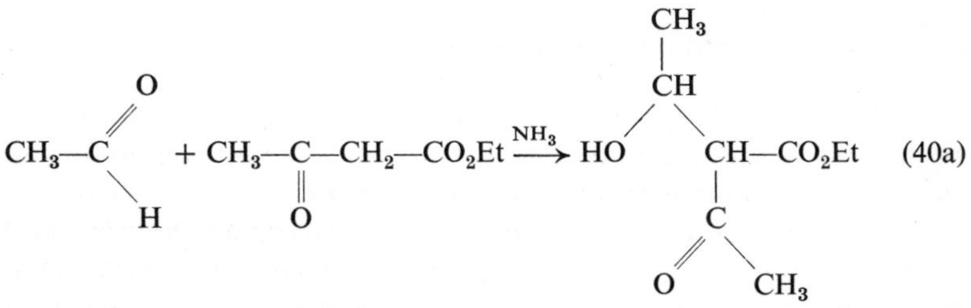

$$
CH_3-\overset{O}{\overset{\|}{C}}-H \;+\; CH_3-\overset{O}{\overset{\|}{C}}-CH_2-CO_2Et \xrightarrow{NH_3} \; HO \quad\quad CH-CO_2Et \qquad (40a)
$$

This initial reaction sets the pattern for the dihydropyridine that is eventually secured. If no β-dicarbonyl compound is used in order to favor a specific initial reaction, pyridines may still be obtained, but the yields are likely to be quite poor.[5]

The reaction shown in Eq. 40a is nothing more than the first step in a conventional Knoevenagel reaction. As discussed in Chapter 26, a hydroxyl beta to two carbonyl groups is eliminated even in basic solution (cf. Eq. 26-20), and the resultant unsaturated ester will undergo condensation of the Michael type (cf. Chap. 26). In the present instance, where excess of the dicarbonyl component is used, this subsequent Michael condensation will occur with the β-keto ester, as in the 1:2 Knoevenagel reaction. These next two steps are shown in Eq. 40b.

Reaction of ammonia or primary amines with 1,5-dicarbonyl compounds to give cyclic amines is a well-known reaction. This, no doubt, proceeds by way of attack of the base on the carbonyl carbons, followed by elimination of two moles of water. As shown in Eq. 40c, the cyclization product may be, in part

---

[5] In a very few instances, useful yields of pyridine derivatives have been obtained by condensation of an aldehyde with ammonia. A careful study of this reaction has been made by Frank and Seven and reported in *J. Am. Chem. Soc.*, **71**, 2633 (1949).

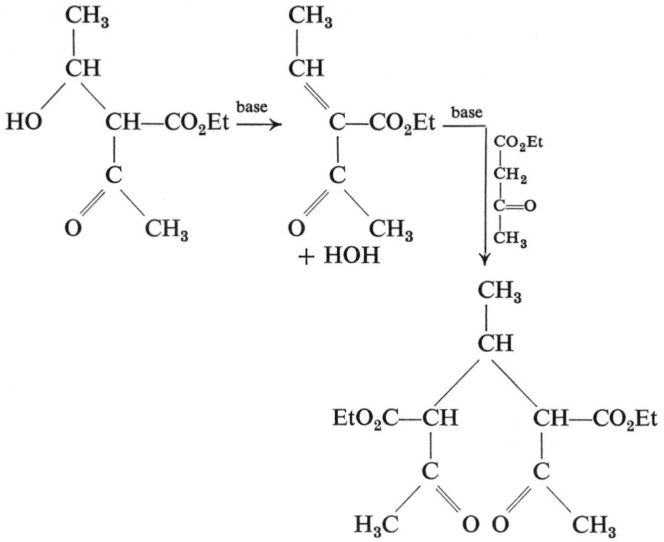

$$
\begin{array}{c}
CH_3 \\
| \\
CH \\
HO\diagup\quad\diagdown CH-CO_2Et \\
| \\
C \\
\diagup\!\!\diagdown \\
O \quad CH_3
\end{array}
\xrightarrow{\text{base}}
\begin{array}{c}
CH_3 \\
| \\
CH \\
\diagup\!\!\diagdown\quad\diagdown \\
C-CO_2Et \\
| \\
C \\
\diagup\!\!\diagdown \\
O \quad CH_3 \\
+ \; HOH
\end{array}
\xrightarrow[\substack{CO_2Et \\ | \\ CH_2 \\ | \\ C=O \\ | \\ CH_3}]{\text{base}}
$$

$$
\begin{array}{c}
CH_3 \\
| \\
CH \\
EtO_2C-CH\diagup\qquad\diagdown CH-CO_2Et \\
\quad| \qquad\qquad | \\
\quad C \qquad\qquad C \\
\diagup\!\!\diagdown\qquad\diagup\!\!\diagdown \\
H_3C \quad O\;O \quad CH_3
\end{array}
$$

(40b)

at least, a double-bond isomer of the product shown in Eq. 40. The second isomer would be expected if the first condensation product should lose water to

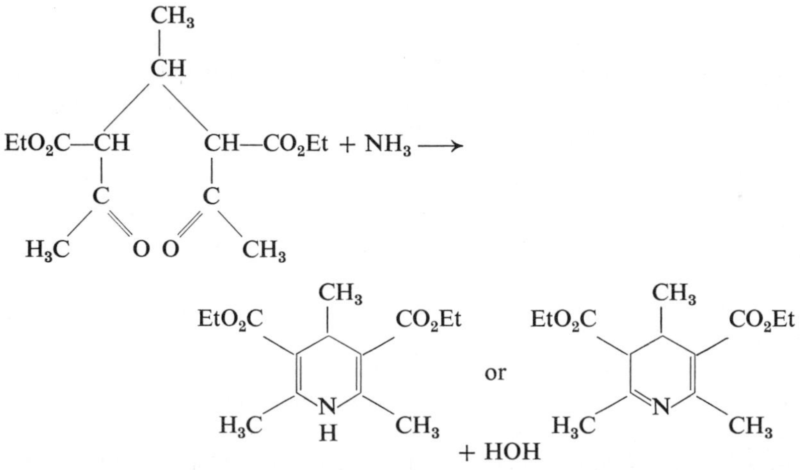

$$
\begin{array}{c}
CH_3 \\
| \\
CH \\
EtO_2C-CH\diagup\qquad\diagdown CH-CO_2Et \; + \; NH_3 \longrightarrow \\
\quad| \qquad\qquad | \\
\quad C \qquad\qquad C \\
\diagup\!\!\diagdown\qquad\diagup\!\!\diagdown \\
H_3C \quad O\;O \quad CH_3
\end{array}
$$

$$
\begin{array}{c}
CH_3 \\
EtO_2C\diagup\!|\diagdown CO_2Et \\
\diagdown\;\;\diagup \\
H_3C\diagdown N\diagup CH_3 \\
\quad H
\end{array}
\quad\text{or}\quad
\begin{array}{c}
CH_3 \\
EtO_2C\diagup\!|\diagdown CO_2Et \\
\diagdown\;\;\diagup \\
H_3C\diagdown N\diagup CH_3
\end{array}
\quad \text{(40c)}
$$

$$+ \; HOH$$

give the imine, as in the partial formulas in Eq. 40d, before attack of the nitrogen on the second carbonyl to close the ring.

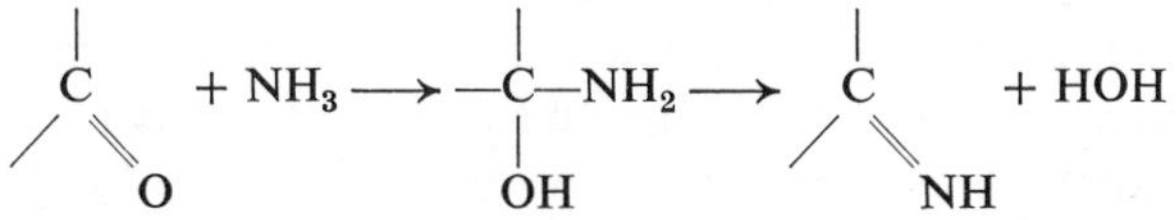

$$
\begin{array}{c}
| \\
C \\
\diagup\!\!\diagdown \\
O
\end{array}
+ NH_3 \longrightarrow
\begin{array}{c}
| \\
-C-NH_2 \\
| \\
OH
\end{array}
\longrightarrow
\begin{array}{c}
| \\
C \\
\diagup\!\!\diagdown \\
NH
\end{array}
+ \; HOH \qquad \text{(40d)}
$$

It should be pointed out at this time that the carbonyl group of a ketone is more reactive than is that in an ester; otherwise, alternative products could result from Eq. 40c. For example, if an unsymmetrical β-diketone were used, the carbonyl groups would usually be of approximately the same reactivity; so three products could result, as follows:

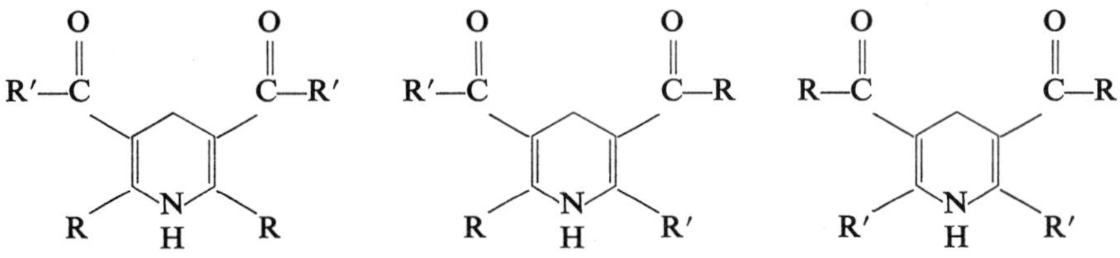

A symmetrical β-diketone will, of course, yield only one product.

The dihydropyridine, of either structure shown in Eq. 40c, is easily converted to the fully aromatic system by oxidation (Eq. 41).

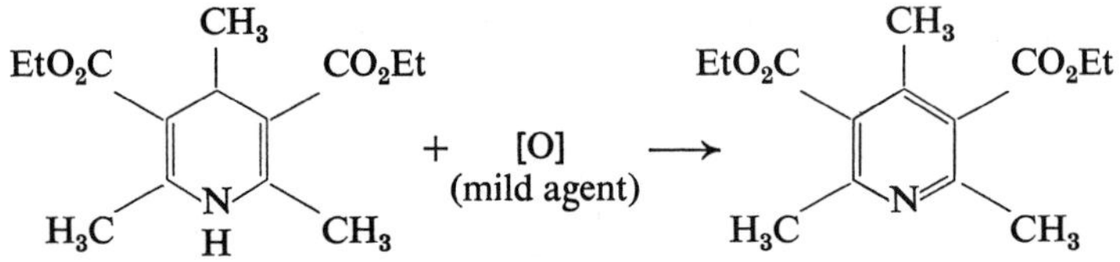

$$+ \quad [O] \quad \longrightarrow \qquad + H_2O \quad (41)$$
(mild agent)

Saponification of the ester gives the dicarboxylic acid, and this may be converted to the usual acid derivatives if desired. Since the carboxyls are in the β-positions in the pyridine ring, rather strenuous conditions are necessary for decarboxylation; however, the process shown in Eq. 42 gives a practical yield of the trimethylpyridine.

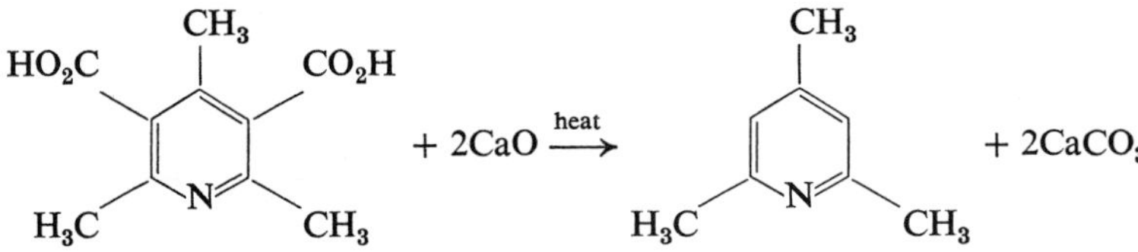

$$+ \, 2CaO \xrightarrow{\text{heat}} \qquad + \, 2CaCO_3 \quad (42)$$

2,4,6-Trimethylpyridine

The 2,4,6-trimethylpyridine obtained in Eq. 42, as well as other pyridines obtained via the Hantzsch procedure, may be subjected to the usual reactions giving substitution in the 3-position.

(2) HANTZSCH SYNTHESIS WITH EXCESS ALDEHYDE. If excess aldehyde be used in the Hantzsch synthesis, the reaction shown in Eq. 40b must occur with aldehyde, since no β-dicarbonyl compound will remain. The net condensation then, may be expressed as in Eq. 43. Conversion to the dimethylpyridine would follow the outline in Eq. 44.

Substitution in 2,4-dimethylpyridine would be expected to occur predominantly in the 5-position, on account of hindrance in the 3-position.

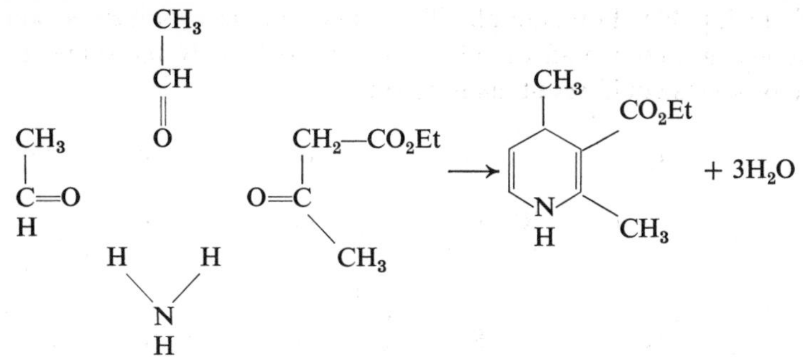

$$+ \ 3H_2O \qquad (43)$$

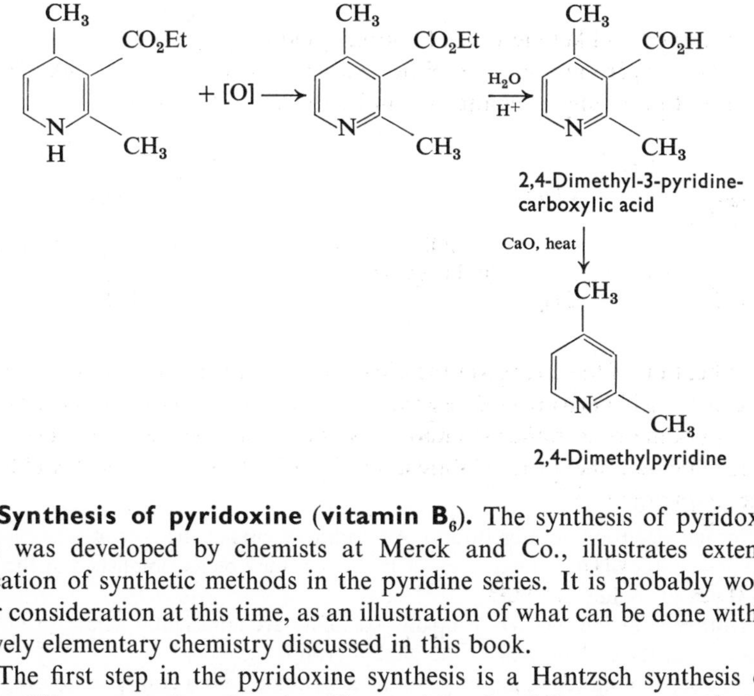

2,4-Dimethyl-3-pyridine-
carboxylic acid

$$(44)$$

2,4-Dimethylpyridine

Synthesis of pyridoxine (vitamin B$_6$). The synthesis of pyridoxine, which was developed by chemists at Merck and Co., illustrates extensive application of synthetic methods in the pyridine series. It is probably worthy of our consideration at this time, as an illustration of what can be done with the relatively elementary chemistry discussed in this book.

The first step in the pyridoxine synthesis is a Hantzsch synthesis of a slightly different type than those just discussed, but involving the same principles. The primary condensation, which sets the pattern of the synthesis, is between the carbonyl activated by the adjacent ethoxy group and the methylene activated by adjacent cyano and carbonyl groups (cyano renders adjacent hydrogens more acidic than does carbonyl). The entire sequence is outlined as Eq. 45.

Although all these reactions have been discussed, some elaboration on the multiple conversions in the next to last step may be in order. Diazotization with nitrous acid rapidly converts the side chain amine to the alcohol, as is the case with other aliphatic amines (cf. Eq. 19-30). Warming the aromatic diazonium salt (located at position-3) converts it to hydroxyl also, and conditions were found under which the ether group in the side chain was cleaved without conversion of the alcohols to bromides. This step gives the hydrobromide of the base, since hydrobromic acid was used; so a final step is necessary in order to form the hydrochloride, which is the natural vitamin.

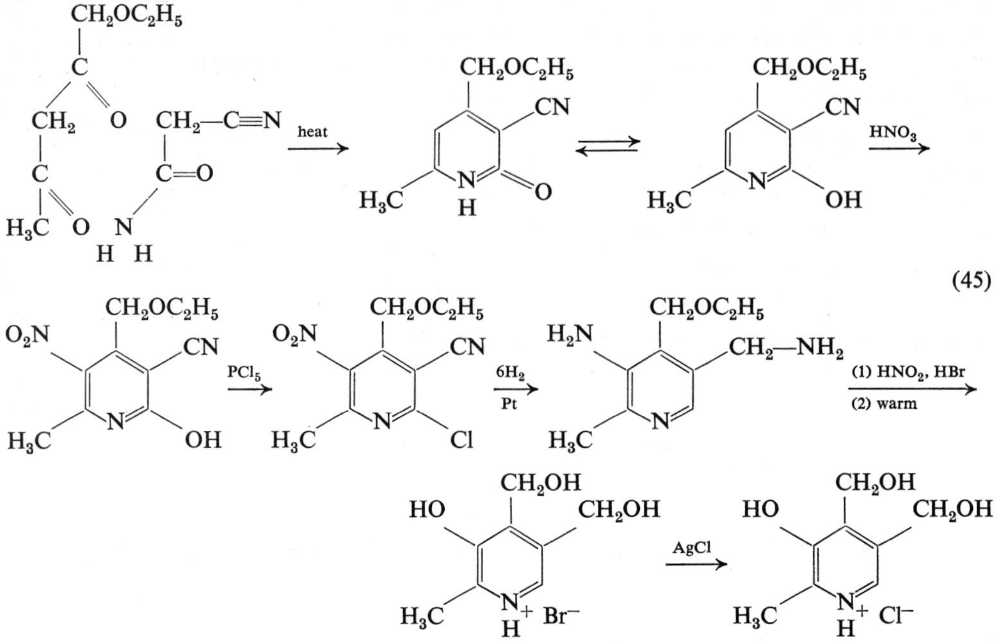

(45)

EXERCISES

1. On the basis of structural and electronic features in pyridine, offer a reasonable explanation or correlation of the following observations.

(a) Normal electrophilic substitution of pyridine occurs at the 3-position.

(b) Nucleophilic displacement, even of hydrogen, may be accomplished at the 2- and 4-positions of pyridine.

(c) Hydrogens in the methyl group in γ-picoline are sufficiently acidic to give condensations of the enolate type at the methyl group.

(d) The Rosenmund reduction of picolinic acid chloride is a complete failure.

(e) Electrophilic substitution in pyridine proceeds at an even slower rate than it does in nitrobenzene.

(f) Nitration of 2-aminopyridine gives substitution of the nitro group on nitrogen, in spite of the fact that it is normally not possible to directly substitute nitro on nitrogen in an amine.

(g) Treatment of 3-hydroxypyridine with phosphorus pentachloride gives little, if any, of the 3-chloropyridine; however, under the same conditions, 4-hydroxypyridine gives a satisfactory yield of 4-chloropyridine.

(h) 2-Aminopyridine is a mono-acid base, i.e., gives a salt with only one mole of acid, even when a strong mineral acid is used.

(i) As intermediates in synthesis of pyridine derivatives, the nitro compounds are of limited utility, whereas the pyridinecarboxylic acids are useful intermediates in synthesis.

(j) Substitution in the pyridine ring by use of the Friedel and Crafts reaction is of no value at all.

2. In the discussion of the synthesis outlined in Eq. 45, it was stated that the adjacent ethoxy group increases the reactivity of one carbonyl group to nucleophilic attack. Explain why this is a normal expectation, and refer in your explanation to the fact that ethoxyacetic acid is a stronger acid than is acetic acid.

3. Write the structure of the dihydropyridine you would expect in largest amount if a Hantzsch synthesis using ammonia were carried out with equimolar amounts of ethyl acetoacetate, propionaldehyde and acetone. Explain why you chose that particular product as the one expected in largest amount.

4. Write all the dihydropyridines that would be formed if a Hantzsch synthesis were carried out with ammonia, propionaldehyde, ethyl acetoacetate and 2,4-hexanedione.

5. Outline by equations practical schemes of accomplishing each of the following conversions.

(a) [pyridine with NH$_2$ at 2-position] $\longrightarrow$ [pyridine with NH$_2$ at 3-position]

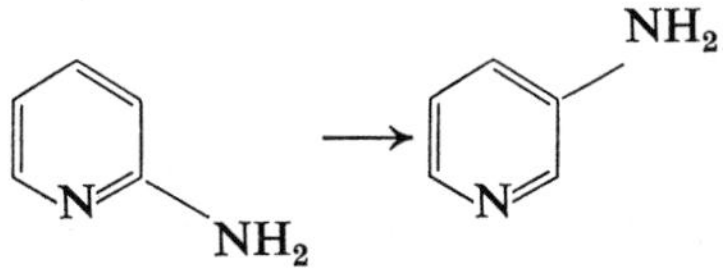

(b) [2-methylpyridine] $\longrightarrow$ [pyridine with CH$_3$ at 3-position and OH at 2-position]

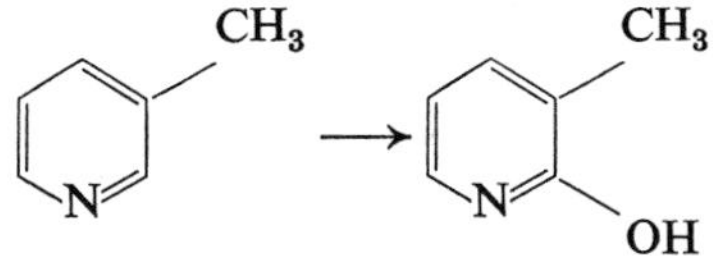

(c) [pyridine] $\longrightarrow$ [pyridine with CH(CH$_3$)OH group]

(d) [cyclohexene fragment] $\longrightarrow$ [pyridine with OH and CH—CH$_3$ groups]

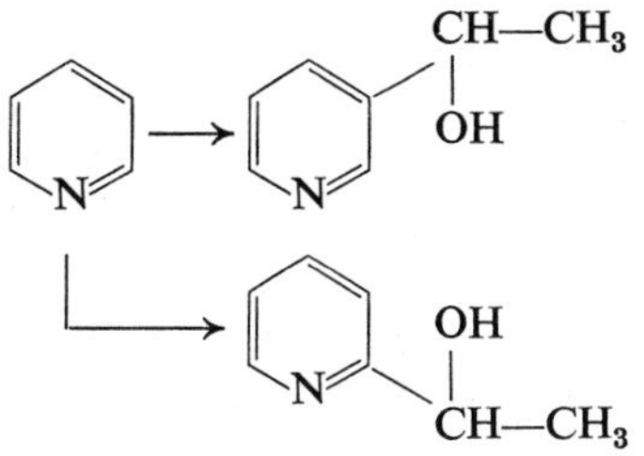

(e) [4-ethylpyridine] $\longrightarrow$ CH$_3$—N—CH$_2$—CH$_2$—CH(C$_2$H$_5$)—CO$_2$H with CH$_3$ groups on N

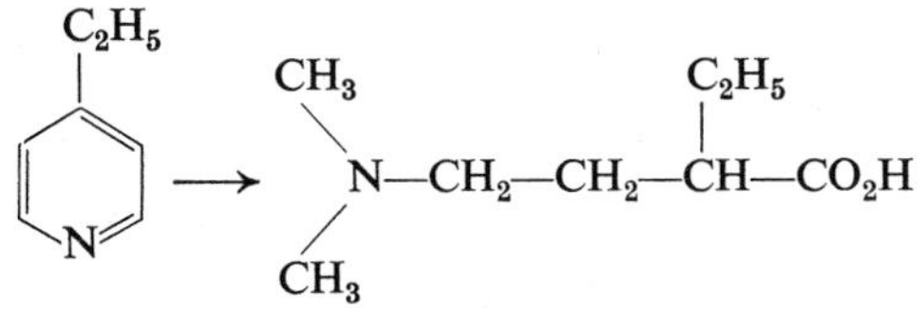

(f) [pyridine: HO$_2$C, C$_2$H$_5$, CO$_2$H, H$_3$C, CH$_3$] $\longrightarrow$ [pyridine: C$_2$H$_5$, C(=O)—CH$_3$, H$_3$C, CH$_3$]

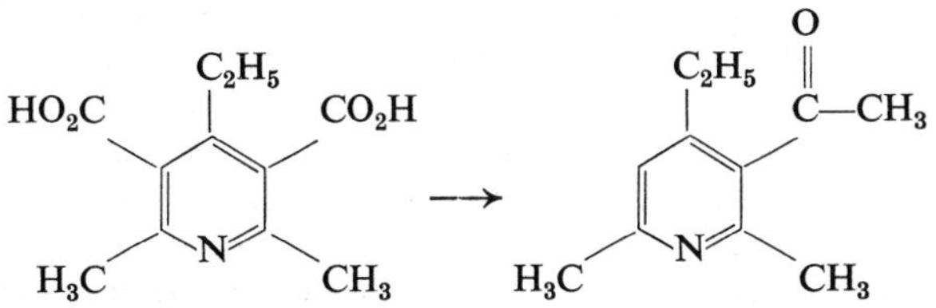

(g) [2,4-dimethylpyridine] $\longrightarrow$ [pyridine: H$_5$C$_2$, CH$_3$, CH$_3$]

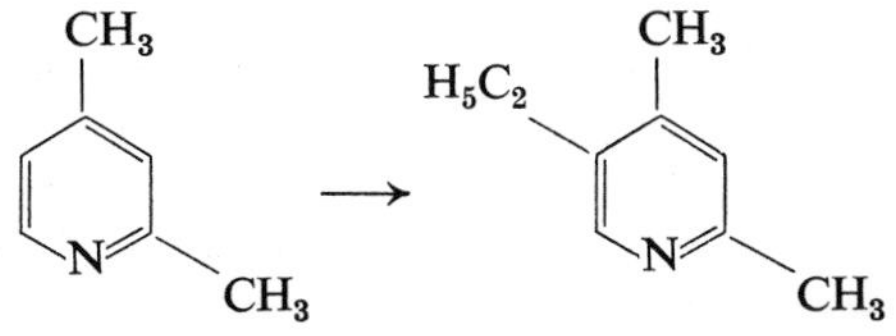

6. Name all the compounds whose formulas appear in Exercise 5.

7. Starting with compounds available from coal tar and aliphatic compounds with four or fewer carbons, outline by equations practical syntheses of each of the following compounds.

(a)

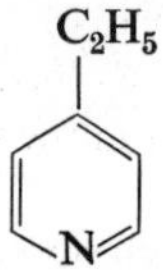

(b)

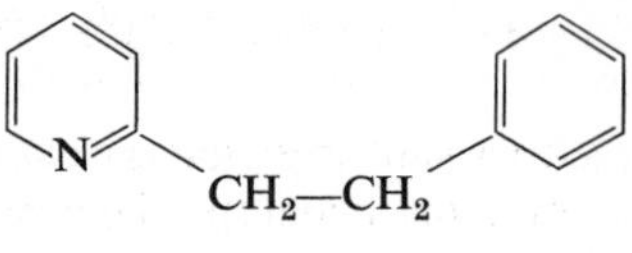

(c)

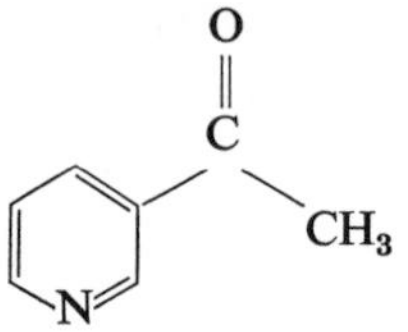

(d)

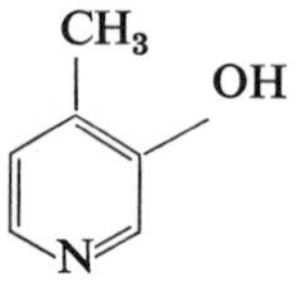

(e)

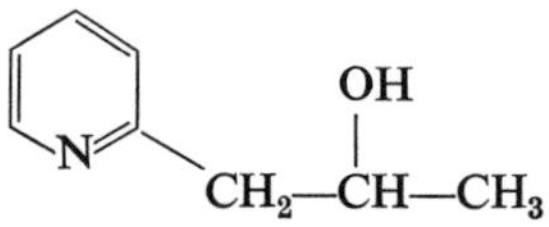

(f)

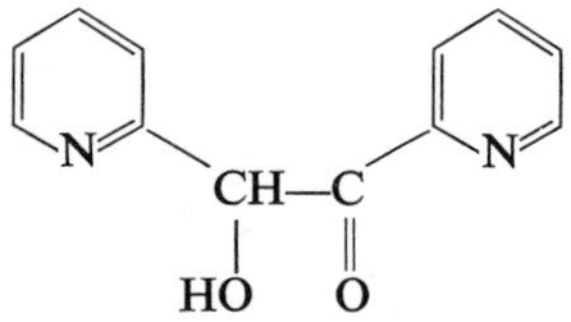

(via 2-formylpyridine; review benzoin condensation)

(g)

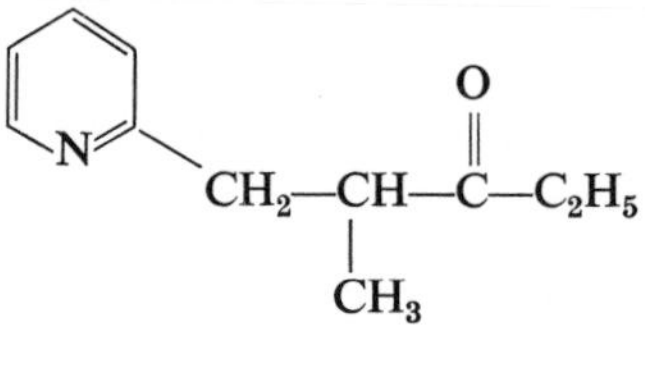

(h)

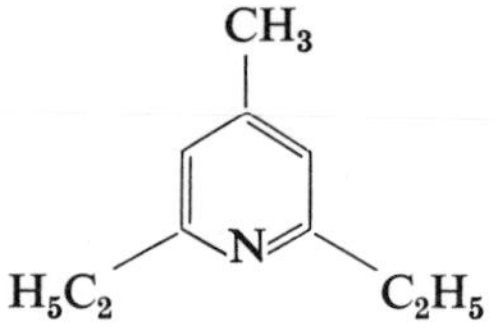

(i)

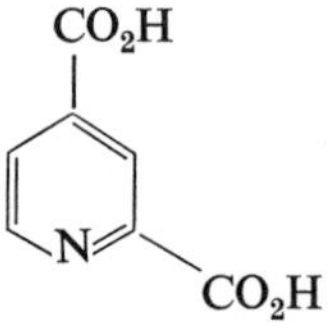

(j)

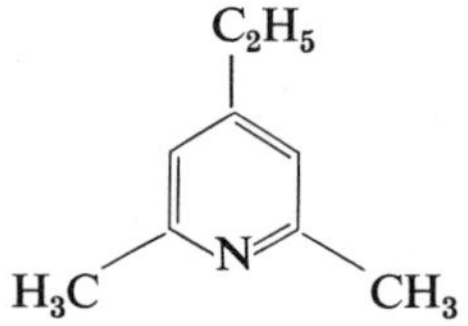

(k)

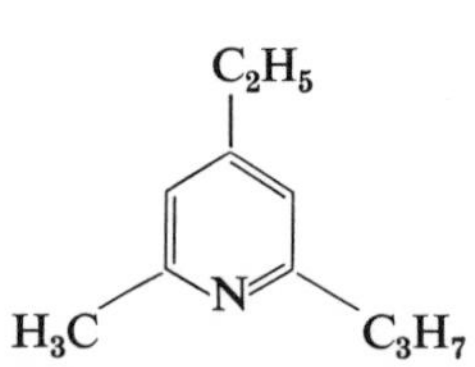

(l)

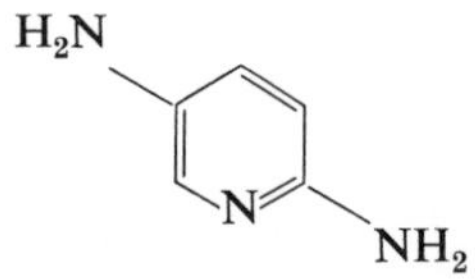

8. A basic compound isolated from natural sources did not react with benzenesulfonyl chloride. Quantitative analysis showed it to have the molecular formula $C_9H_{19}N$.

When subjected to the Hofmann degradation, it gave an unsaturated amine in poor yield, and a gas was evolved. When a second Hofmann degradation was applied to the unsaturated amine, there was isolated, again in poor yield, a tertiary amine ($C_4H_{11}N$) and a diene (C_7H_{12}).

When the diene was oxidized with permanganate there was obtained an acid which lost carbon dioxide so easily, in acid solution, that it was not isolated. The product obtained after decarboxylation of the acid was a ketone which was identified as butanone by conversion to the phenylhydrazone and comparison with an authentic sample.

On the basis of these data, what two structures are possible for the compound isolated from natural sources? How would you proceed further in order to decide which of these two possible structures is correct?

32

Quinoline
and Its Derivatives

Quinoline, which has the benzene ring fused to pyridine in the 2,3-position, is considerably more important than the isomer with the benzene ring fused at the 3,4-position. Isoquinoline, which has the latter structure, is discussed briefly in Chapter 33. Whereas interest in isoquinoline has derived largely from the occurrence of that nucleus in several alkaloids, quinoline occurs in numerous alkaloids and is also of importance in certain types of dyes and in a considerable number of drugs. On account of the commercial importance of quinoline derivatives, considerable research in this area has been carried out in industrial laboratories. Quinoline chemistry is of general interest in the study of organic chemistry because of the applicability of much basic aromatic and aliphatic chemistry. In particular, enolate condensations become of great importance in the synthesis of quinolines by cyclization reactions.

Quinoline is a colorless liquid of boiling point 239°, whose odor is considerably less potent and obnoxious than that of pyridine. Quinoline occurs in both coal tar and petroleum, and the technical product is obtained from coal tar; however, separation of pure quinoline from coal tar is quite difficult. The pure quinoline which is marketed is normally synthesized, usually by the Skraup method to be described later in this chapter. In contrast with the situation in the pyridine series, the methylquinolines are not available from coal tar, probably because of the near-impossibility of separating the seven isomeric monomethylquinolines.

Nomenclature

Numbering in the quinoline ring system follows the usual practice of starting the numbering with the hetero atom and proceeding first around the ring containing the hetero atom. This gives the same positions for the numbers

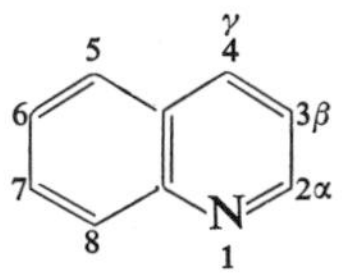

as in naphthalene. Greek letters, used only for locating a single substituent in the hetero ring, designate the same positions as in pyridine. Greek letters are used relatively infrequently in naming quinoline derivatives, probably because they apply only in one ring.

Numerous drugs and dyes in the quinoline series have common names; however, only a few of the simple derivatives have common names, in contrast with the pyridine series. The only methylquinoline with a common name is the 2-methylquinoline, known as **quinaldine.** Quinoline-2-carboxylic acid is logically named **quinaldinic acid.** The 4-carboxylic acid is termed **cinchoninic acid,** in reference to its early source from oxidation of the stereoisomeric alkaloids, cinchonidine and cinchonine.

Structural Characteristics

The basic structure of quinoline follows directly from its oxidation to quinolinic acid (pyridine-2,3-dicarboxylic acid), a reaction discussed in the preceding chapter. The quinoline formula is ordinarily written with the double bonds placed as shown above; however, the same resonance forms apply as discussed for naphthalene. In addition, charged resonance forms are of importance, as in pyridine, so substituents in the alpha and gamma positions exhibit the reactivity discussed in connection with pyridine chemistry. Inter-ring charged forms such as the following,

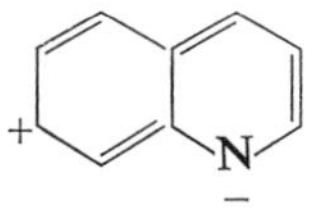

appear to be of such high energy as to make no significant contribution to the character of the molecule. Substituents in the 5- or 7-position have no unusual reactivity; they behave as normal aromatic substituents, similar to naphthalene derivatives. The bond structure shown in the inter-ring resonance form, with two double bonds at the ring juncture, appears to be of high energy, in general. It may be recalled (Chap. 29) that 2,6-naphthoquinone is a very unstable compound, and that 2,3-naphthoquinone has never been obtained.

Certain Important Compounds in the Quinoline Series

Among the several alkaloids containing the quinoline ring system, perhaps the most well-known is quinine, long used as a specific chemotherapeutic agent against malaria. Not only has the complex structure of quinine been worked out, but the compound has been synthesized, with the proper configuration for each of the four asymmetric carbon atoms.

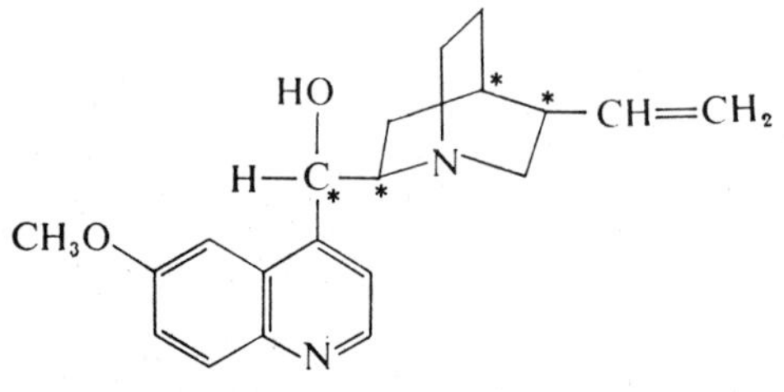

Quinine
(asymmetric carbons marked with *)

A feverish search was initiated in this country during World War II for synthetic substitutes for quinine. Although quinine was synthesized, the only practical source of the alkaloid in quantity is an Asiatic tree; so control of malaria during the war period depended entirely on synthetic drugs. The synthetic drug most widely used during the war was atabrine.[1] Another drug

---

[1] The initial production of atabrine in the United States proved to be so highly toxic to man that it was of no value in chemotherapy. After expenditure of considerable time and money, it was finally established that the high toxicity resulted from presence in the atabrine of an isomer in which attachment of the ring-substituted nitrogen was to the 3-position in the amyl group. This isomer was introduced in an intermediate synthetic step in which a secondary alcohol had been converted to the bromide by a process involving a significant percentage of carbonium ion intermediate (cf. Chap. 6, S_N1 mechanism). The reaction was the following:

$$CH_3—\underset{\underset{OH}{|}}{CH}—CH_2—CH_2—CH_2—\overset{+}{N}H(C_2H_5)_2 + HBr \longrightarrow$$

$$CH_3—\underset{\underset{Br}{|}}{CH}—CH_2—CH_2—CH_2—\overset{+}{N}H(C_2H_5)_2$$

and

$$CH_3—CH_2—\underset{\underset{Br}{|}}{CH}—CH_2—CH_2—\overset{+}{N}H(C_2H_5)_2$$

When there was employed a secondary bromide synthesis which eliminated, or greatly minimized, the S_N1 component in the reaction, the atabrine obtained as end-product showed the desired toxicity to the malaria parasite with a sufficiently low toxicity to man.

A particularly interesting feature of the experience with atabrine is that, during the early nineteen-forties, relatively few experienced research chemists were entirely familiar with reaction mechanisms now studied in elementary courses in organic chemistry.

for control of malaria is called chloroquine. It is of interest to note that both of these drugs contain a substituent grouping in the 4-position of the quinoline nucleus, as does quinine. Atabrine may be regarded as chloroquine with an additional benz ring fused to quinoline. The three-ring system in atabrine is the *acridine* ring system.

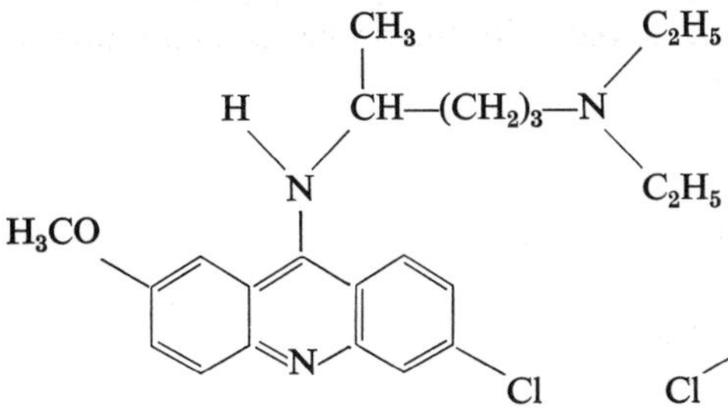

Atabrine 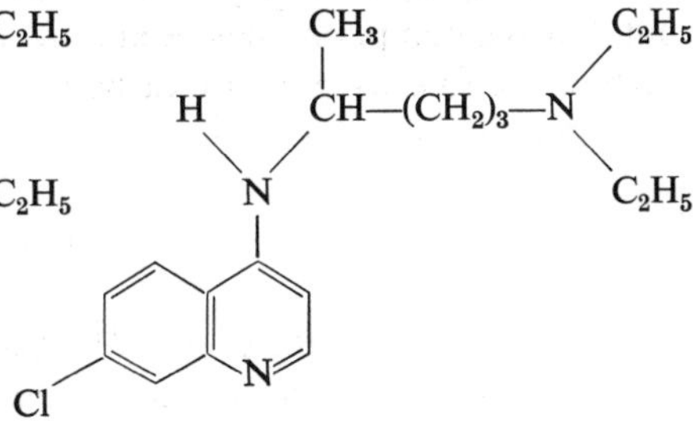   Chloroquine

The search for anti-malarial drugs has continued, on account of the facility of the malaria parasite for developing an acquired resistance to the drugs used against it. Chloroquine and atabrine have become virtually ineffective, and considerable resistance to quinine has been noted.

The remarkable **photosensitizing dyes** are usually quinoline derivatives. The silver halides used in photographic emulsions are sensitive chiefly to light of short wavelength, in the blue and ultraviolet. When a photosensitizing dye is included in the emulsion, the film becomes sensitized to longer wavelengths. A film sensitive as far as the yellow and green in the spectrum is known as an *orthochromatic* film, while film sensitized as far as the red is called *panchromatic*. Sensitivity may be secured even into the infrared. Apparently the photosensitizing dyes absorb light of longer wavelength and emit energy in the spectral region to which silver halides are sensitive.

A representative photosensitizing dye is **pinacyanole,** which is a panchromatic sensitizer. Two resonance forms of the cation of the ethiodide are shown:

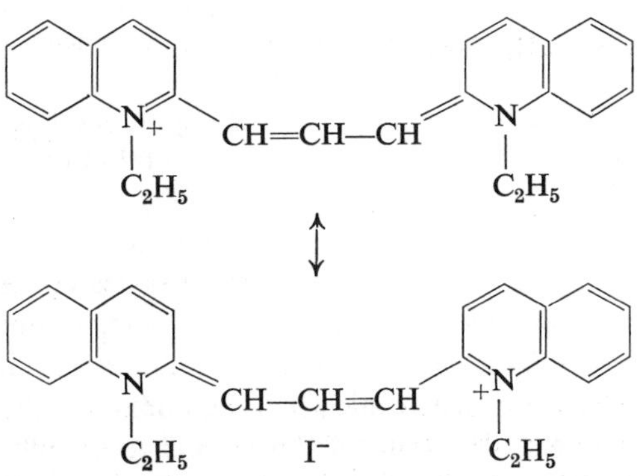

Pinacyanole

If the length of the resonance path in the cation is increased, light of longer wavelengths will be absorbed by the photosensitizing dye. A dye with one more vinyl group (—CH=CH—) than contained by pinacyanole will give sensitization to the infrared.

Reactions of the Quinoline Nucleus

In general, the reactions of quinoline may be predicted with some reliability from the reactions previously studied for benzene and for pyridine.

Oxidation. In the preceding chapter, it was pointed out (Eq. 31-1) that the pyridine ring is much more stable to oxidation than is the benzene ring; hence oxidation of quinoline gives the 2,3-pyridinedicarboxylic acid.

Reduction. Since chemical reduction of pyridine is relatively easy and chemical reduction of benzene is quite difficult, it would be expected that the hetero ring in quinoline would be more easily reduced. In the majority of quinoline derivatives, this is the fact (Eq. 1).

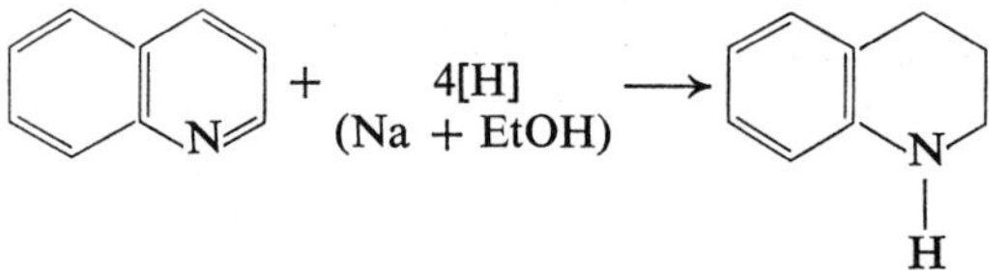

$$+ \quad \begin{array}{c} 4[\mathrm{H}] \\ (\mathrm{Na} + \mathrm{EtOH}) \end{array} \longrightarrow \qquad (1)$$

1,2,3,4-Tetrahydroquinoline

It should be mentioned that in certain highly substituted quinoline derivatives the benz ring is preferentially reduced (Eq. 2).

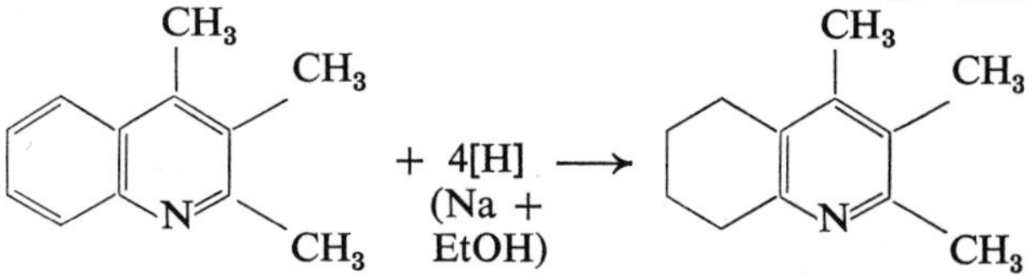

$$+ \begin{array}{c} 4[\mathrm{H}] \\ (\mathrm{Na} + \\ \mathrm{EtOH}) \end{array} \longrightarrow \qquad (2)$$

2,3,4-Trimethyl-5,6,7,8-
tetrahydroquinoline

Thus the direction of reduction in substituted quinolines may not always b predicted with confidence, in absence of experimental information.

Substitution. Since there are seven monosubstitution positions in quinoline, the situation is considerably more complicated than is the case in naphthalene. A relatively limited number of monosubstitution derivatives may be obtained in a pure condition, and polysubstitution is of minor utility. There will be mentioned the derivatives which may be obtained relatively readily.

Since the pyridine ring is substituted with such great difficulty, substitution in quinoline would be expected to occur in the benz ring, and this is the case for orthodox substitution involving nitration and sulfonation. Bromination, however, gives substitution in the hetero ring, and the reasons for this behavior are not understood. The rather unusual procedure used for bromination will be discussed.

(1) NITRATION. This occurs under the rather vigorous conditions shown in Eq. 3.

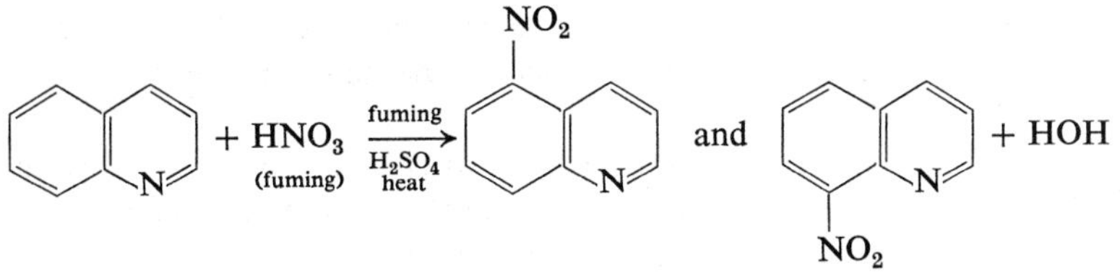

$$\text{quinoline} + HNO_3 \text{ (fuming)} \xrightarrow[\substack{H_2SO_4 \\ heat}]{fuming} \text{5-Nitroquinoline} \text{ and } \text{8-Nitroquinoline} + HOH \quad (3)$$

5-Nitroquinoline   8-Nitroquinoline

These two isomers can be separated, hence are available starting materials for synthesis.

(2) SULFONATION. This also occurs under rather extreme conditions. The isomers shown in Eq. 4 may be obtained under the conditions indicated, and they may be separated.

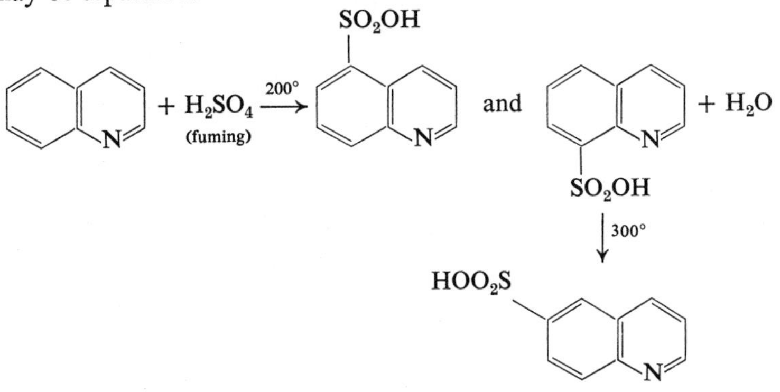

$$\text{quinoline} + H_2SO_4 \text{ (fuming)} \xrightarrow{200°} + H_2O$$

$$\downarrow 300° \quad (4)$$

6-Quinolinesulfonic acid

It may be noted that there is some parallel with naphthalene chemistry, in that nitration occurs adjacent to a ring and sulfonation occurs similarly, while rearrangement of the sulfo group to the lower-energy β-position occurs under conditions permitting thermodynamic control of the product. The preference of substitution for the 5-position is an additional indication that inter-ring resonance forms are of no significance in quinoline. If this were not the case, the 5-position would be relatively positive, hence unattractive in electrophilic substitution.

Under other conditions than those shown in Eq. 4, a small amount of 7-quinolinesulfonic acid is formed but isolation of an amount of this isomer sufficient to serve as a starting material in synthesis is not practical. In fact, it will be noted that substitution in the 7-position is not secured in either sulfonation or nitration.

(3) BROMINATION OF QUINOLINE IN THE 3-POSITION. This substitution may be secured in yields as high as 80% by the sequence shown in Eq. 5. The exact

$$
\text{quinoline} + Br_2 \xrightarrow[\text{solvent}]{CCl_4} \begin{array}{c} \text{Precipitate} \\ \text{of a complex} \\ \text{containing} \\ \text{quinoline and} \\ \text{bromine} \end{array} \xrightarrow[\substack{\text{in} \\ CCl_4}]{\text{reflux}} \text{3-bromoquinoline} \tag{5}
$$

nature of the complex containing quinoline and bromine has not been determined, and the reasons for the unexpected substitution in the hetero ring are not known.[2] This is an important entry to the 3-position in quinoline, however. The usefulness of the 3-bromoquinoline is considerably enhanced by the fact that it can be converted to the organolithium reagent, which gives reactions similar to those of the Grignard reagent (if necessary, use the index to review reactions of the Grignard reagent).

The substitution products shown in this section have typical aromatic character, and give such conversions as shown in outline form:

$$-NO_2 \longrightarrow -NH_2 \longrightarrow -N_2^+ \longrightarrow \text{various groups}$$

$$-SO_2OH \longrightarrow -OH$$

$$\longrightarrow -CN \longrightarrow -CO_2H \longrightarrow -COCl \longrightarrow \text{various groups}$$

$$-Br \longrightarrow$$

$$\longrightarrow -Li \longrightarrow \text{various groups}$$

If the reagents and conditions for these conversions cannot be recalled they should be reviewed by use of the index and reference to material in the chapters on the chemistry of benzene and the derivatives of carboxylic acids.

Synthesis and Reactions of 2- and 4-Substituted Quinoline Derivatives

In the preceding section have been discussed methods for securing 3-, 5-, 6-, and 8-substituted quinolines. The 7-position is not readily attacked, but substituents in the 2- and 4-positions can be secured by methods dependent in large measure on the reactivity of these positions. Entry into the 2-position may be secured by use of lithium alkyls or sodium amide, by reactions essentially identical with those discussed for pyridine (cf. Eqs. 31-13, 31-28). Entry into both the 2- and 4-positions can be secured by way of the carboxylic acids or the hydroxyquinolines; methods for securing these derivatives will be discussed below. Since substituents in the 2- and 4-positions are active in the manner of

---

[2] This interesting reaction has been investigated by J. J. Eisch, *J. Org. Chem.* **27,** 1318, 4682 (1962).

pyridine substituents in these positions, conversions such as the following can be accomplished (cf. Chap. 31):

$$-NH_2 \longrightarrow -OH \longrightarrow -Cl \longrightarrow -H$$

The 2- and 4-hydroxyquinolines (quinolones) are available by independent syntheses (see next sections and later syntheses from β-keto esters); therefore, it is sometimes convenient to proceed from hydroxyl to halogen (cf. Eq. 31-24), and thence to amino as in Eq. 6. Of course such reactions as this do not apply

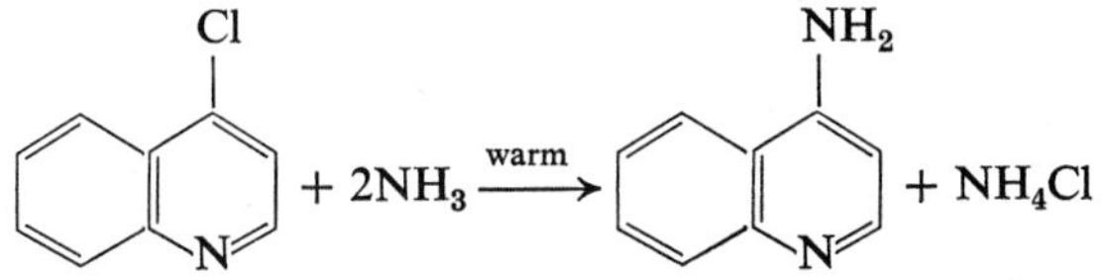

$$\qquad\qquad (6)$$

in the 3-position, as has been discussed for pyridine in Chapter 31.

Synthesis of quinolones. The 2- and 4-hydroxyquinolines are called quinolones because of the existence of tautomeric equilibrium of the sort discussed for the pyridine series:

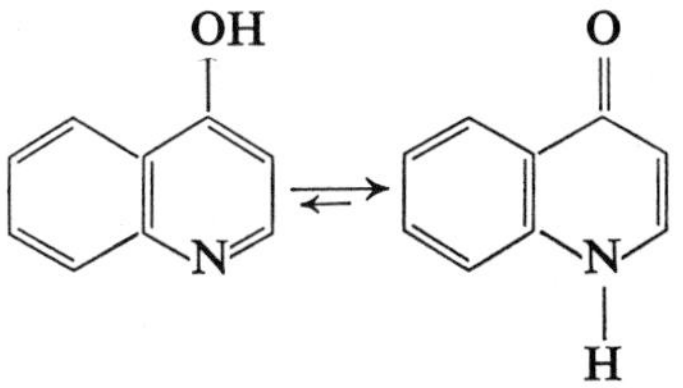

$$\qquad\qquad (7)$$

As in pyridine, equilibrium favors the keto form, hence use of the term quinolone.

2-Quinolone can be secured by the synthetic sequence in Eq. 8. Several features of the sequence in Eq. 8 are of interest. First may be mentioned the

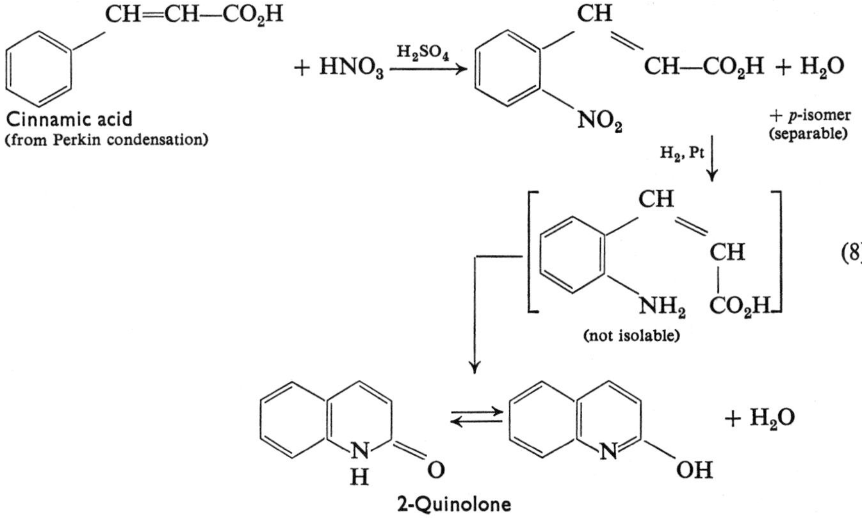

$$\qquad\qquad (8)$$

Cinnamic acid
(from Perkin condensation)

+ p-isomer
(separable)

(not isolable)

2-Quinolone

ortho,para-directing influence of the alkene group attached to the aromatic ring. Since *ortho,para*-directors are those with a relatively negative atom attached to the ring (cf. Chap. 12), this type of directing influence indicates that the alkene grouping is a relatively negative one, in contrast with the polar multiple bonds in which the carbon attached to the ring is relatively positive (hence, *meta*-directing). It will be recalled that normal attack of a reagent on a double bond (cf. Chap. 9) is an electrophilic attack, consistent with a relatively negative character for the double bond. Since the carbon-carbon double bond is ordinarily not highly polarized, this negative character would apply to both the carbon atoms and thus make the alkene grouping an *ortho,para*-director. In addition, energy of the transition state would be lowered to some extent by the electron delocalization indicated in the following resonance forms:

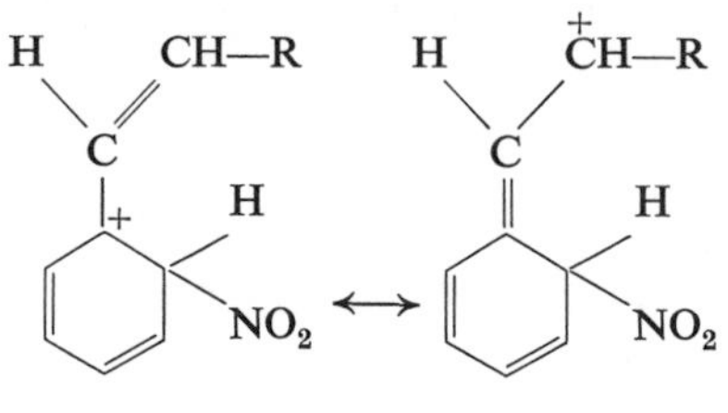

This is in contrast to the situation in a meta-director where a resonance form of the type shown on the right would have the positive charge on the normally negative atom, hence be of high energy.

A second point of interest in Eq. 8 is preferential hydrogenation of the nitro group in presence of the carbon-carbon double bond. This selective hydrogenation goes especially well with a platinum catalyst, for the amino group appears to poison this catalyst towards hydrogenation of the alkene linkage. Thus, preferential hydrogenation of a nitro group in unsaturated compounds has found considerable application in synthesis.

Finally, it should be noted that the cyclization, which amounts to amide formation, occurs spontaneously for the isomer with *cis* geometry at the alkene linkage. Amide formation ordinarily occurs slowly with heating, but the gain in resonance energy on going to the quinoline ring system makes this cyclization occur very readily. In the discussion of more general types of cyclization reactions in a later section of this chapter, there will appear other illustrations of the ease with which reactions occur when an aromatic system is being formed.

4-Quinolone can also be formed by a cyclization reaction, Eq. 9. This ready cyclization amounts to an aldol condensation, although the carbonyl

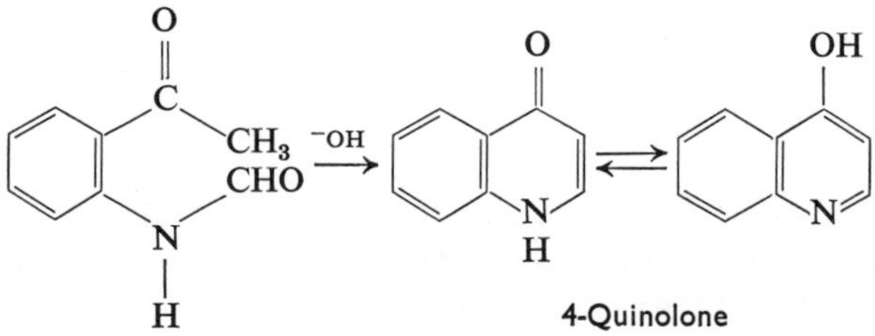

(9)

4-Quinolone

group involved is actually that in a formamide. The starting material for this cyclization may be secured by the reactions shown in Eq. 10. *o*-Nitroaceto-

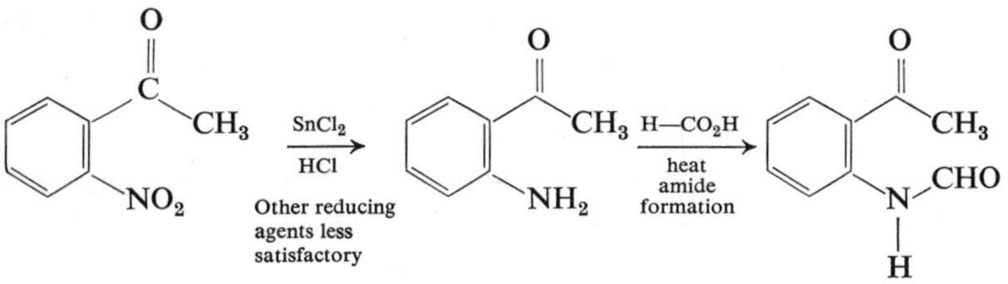

phenone, the starting material in Eq. 10, may be secured by the reactions shown in Eq. 11; however, it has also been found that the controlled oxidation shown

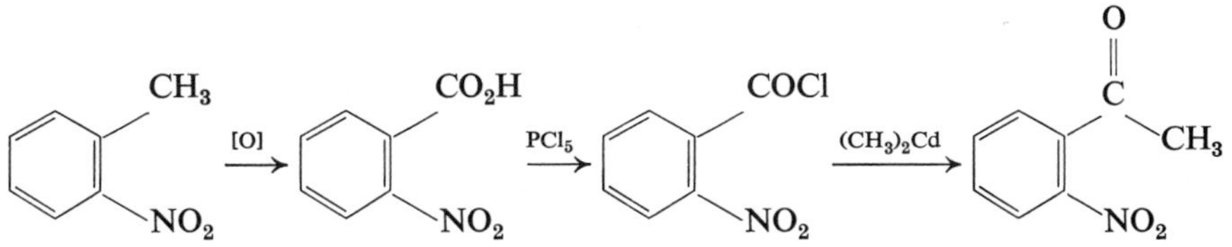

in Eq. 12 may be accomplished in yields as high as 55%. This furnishes *o*-nitroacetophenone after a single reaction on a compound which is cheaply available commercially, so 4-quinolone becomes only slightly less readily available than the 2-isomer. Quinolones substituted in the benz ring may be obtained if the appropriately substituted benzene derivative can be synthesized.

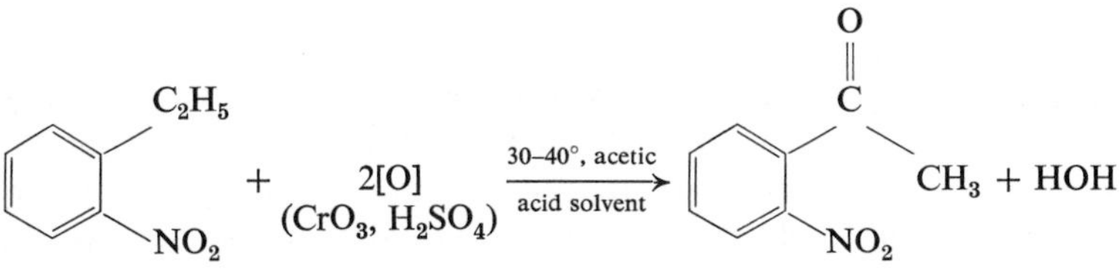

Another interesting source of 4-quinolone is from kynurenic acid, as shown in Eq. 13. Decarboxylation of the 2-carboxylic acid occurs on simply heating.

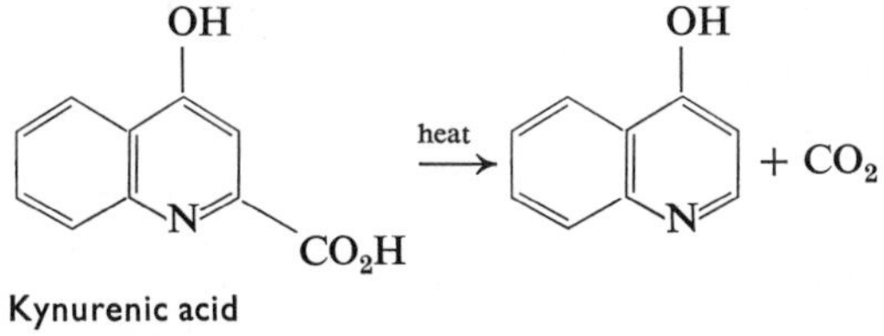

Kynurenic acid

Although most animals excrete urea and uric acid as end products of nitrogen metabolism, certain species of dogs excrete kynurenic acid instead. This can hardly be regarded as a practical source of large quantities of 4-quinolone.

Synthesis of 2- and 4-quinolinecarboxylic acids. Since the methyl-quinolines are not available from coal tar, the carboxylic acids are usually made by routes other than oxidation of the methylquinolines. The 2- and 4-carboxylic acids may be prepared from quinoline by rather unusual but effective sequences.

THE 2-CARBOXYLIC ACID is prepared by a sequence proceeding through the quaternary salt of quinoline and benzoyl chloride (an example of a quaternary salt with an acyl halide), as shown in Eq. 14.

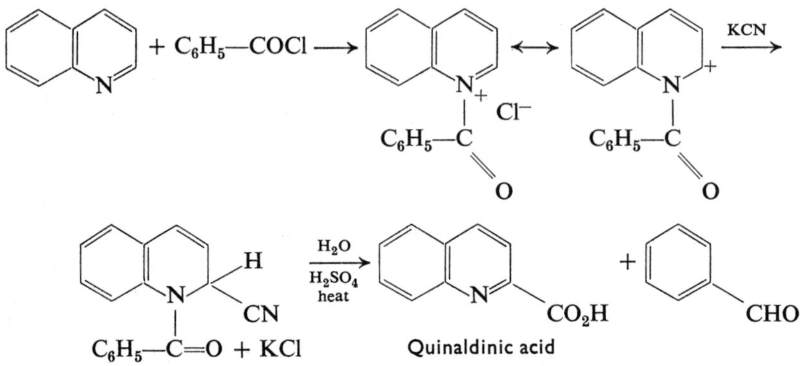

(14)

Quinaldinic acid

It will be noted in the last step that as cyano is hydrolyzed to acid, benzaldehyde is eliminated. The mechanism of this reaction is not well understood, but it constitutes the final step in a useful synthesis of quinaldinic acid. In certain rare instances, the process has been applied to synthesis of an aromatic aldehyde from the acid chloride, but other methods are usually superior (e.g., cf. Rosenmund reduction, Eq. 15-2).

A consideration of the resonance forms of the quaternary salt makes it clear that attack of the negative group at the 2-position is quite reasonable, but it is not clear why there is selective attack at the 2-position in preference to the 4-position. Indeed, with a different quaternary salt, selective attack at the 4-position occurs (cf. Eq. 15)! A possible influencing factor is inductive withdrawal of electrons from the adjacent 2-position by the benzoyl group; however, other less obvious effects are probably involved.

4-QUINOLINECARBOXYLIC ACID (cinchoninic acid) is available by way of the reactions outlined in Eq. 15. In this sequence it will be noted that the dihydroquinoline is oxidized with iodine to give the quaternary iodide. Pyrolysis of

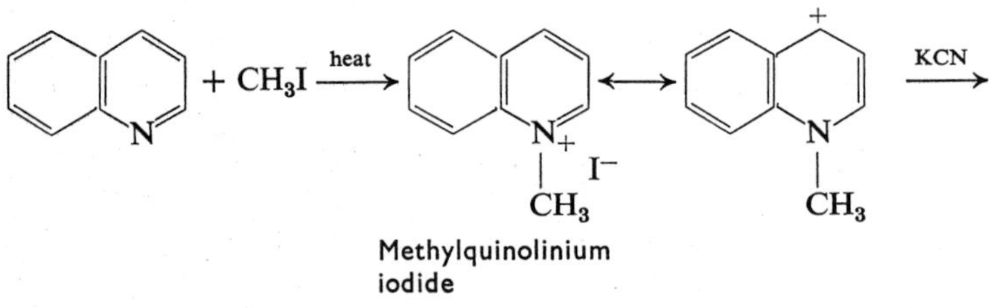

Methylquinolinium
iodide

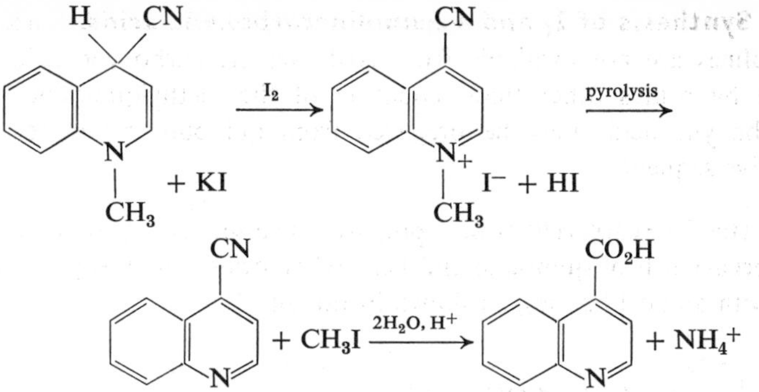

(15)

Cinchoninic acid

this iodide, allowing methyl iodide to escape, gives reversal of the reaction by which a quaternary salt is formed. As in synthesis of the 2-isomer, the final step involves hydrolysis of the nitrile.

General Syntheses of Quinolines by Cyclization Reactions

Since synthesis of monosubstitution derivatives of quinoline via substitution reactions is subject to some limitation, and pure disubstituted derivatives are rarely accessible by substitution, synthesis of quinolines by cyclization reactions becomes of considerable significance. More than thirty separate methods for synthesis of quinolines by cyclization have been developed, and we will study four of the more versatile methods. These will open up approaches to a large variety of substituted quinolines.

The Skraup synthesis. One of the best and most simple methods for preparation of quinolines substituted in the benz ring is the synthesis introduced by Skraup. The net result of this reaction is shown in Eq. 16. The route which

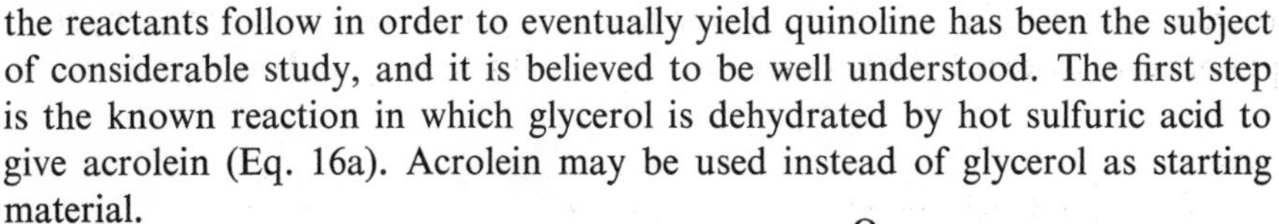

(or other aromatic amines) (or other mild oxidizing agent) (16)

the reactants follow in order to eventually yield quinoline has been the subject of considerable study, and it is believed to be well understood. The first step is the known reaction in which glycerol is dehydrated by hot sulfuric acid to give acrolein (Eq. 16a). Acrolein may be used instead of glycerol as starting material.

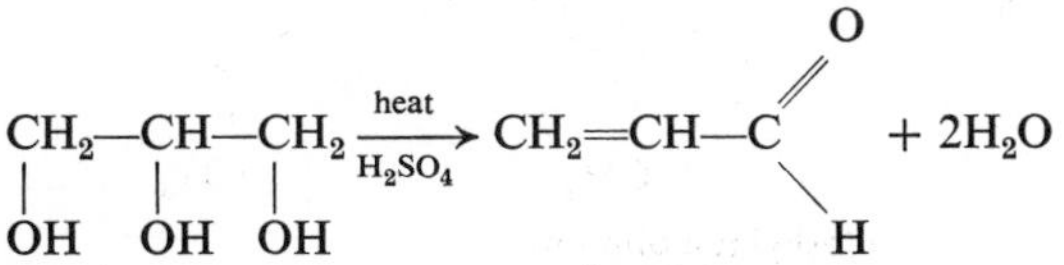

(16a)

Acrolein

The next step in the sequence is 1,4-addition of the amine to acrolein, Eq. 16b.

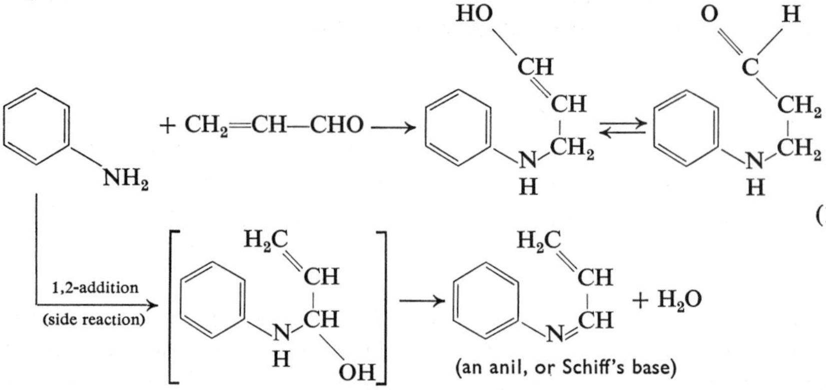

$$+ \ CH_2\!\!=\!\!CH\!\!-\!\!CHO \longrightarrow$$

(16b)

(an anil, or Schiff's base)

Cyclization[3] of the product formed in Eq. 16b leads to a dihydroquinoline, and the quinoline results from oxidation by nitrobenzene or other mild oxidizing agent included in the reaction mixture (Eq. 16c).

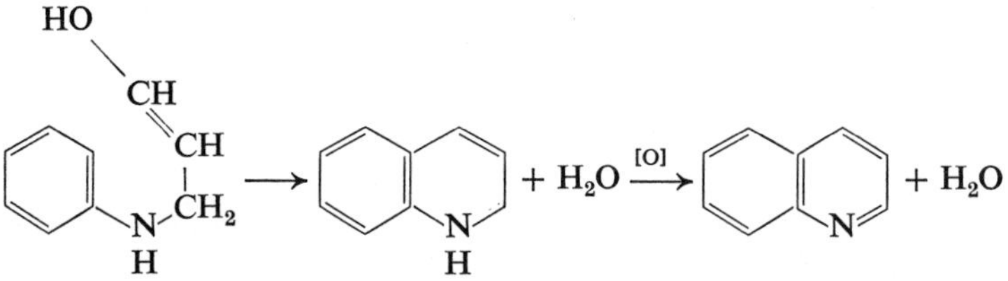

$$\xrightarrow{[O]} \qquad + \ H_2O \qquad (16c)$$

It is known that the quinoline does not arise from cyclization of the Schiff's base shown as a side reaction product in Eq. 16b, because substitution

---

[3] There is evidence that the product which actually cyclizes is the Schiff's base of the 3-anilinoaldehyde. As is shown in the sequence in Eq. 16d, the end result is the same as that of direct cyclization of the aldehyde.

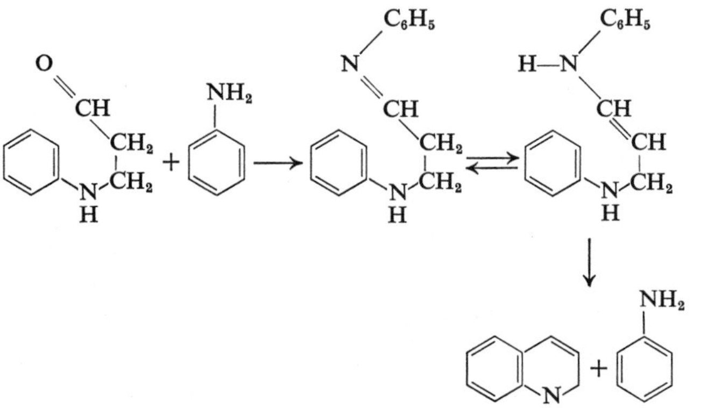

(16d)

of crotonaldehyde, CH_3—CH=CH—CHO, for acrolein leads to 2-methyl-quinoline, not 4-methylquinoline. This shows that the left-hand product below cyclizes to give the quinoline, not the right-hand product.

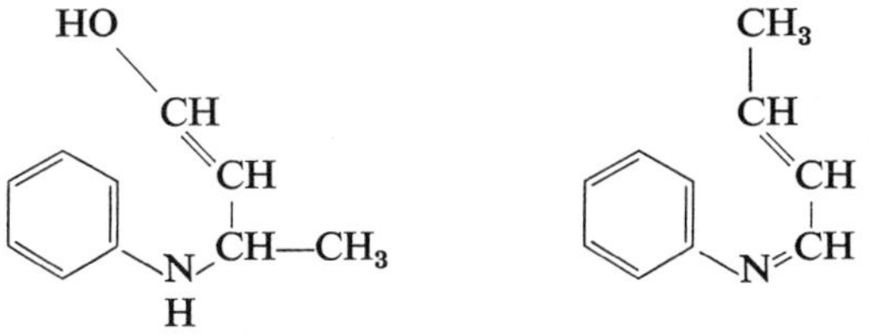

SCOPE AND LIMITATIONS OF THE SKRAUP SYNTHESIS. The Skraup method, using glycerol, cannot give any substitution in the hetero ring; however, varied substitution in the benz ring can be secured by use of a suitably substituted aniline. One of the few substituted anilines that has failed completely in the Skraup synthesis is *p*-acetylaniline.

An *ortho*- or *para*-substituted aniline gives a single quinoline in the Skraup synthesis:

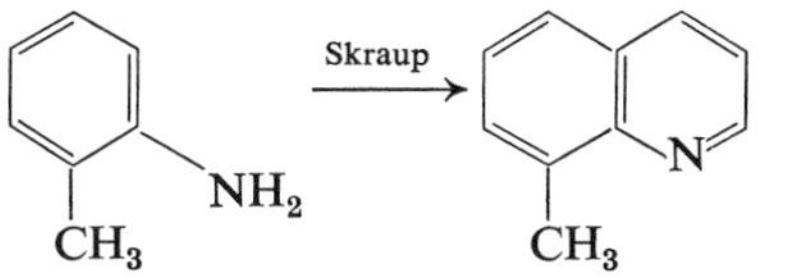

(17)

8-Methylquinoline

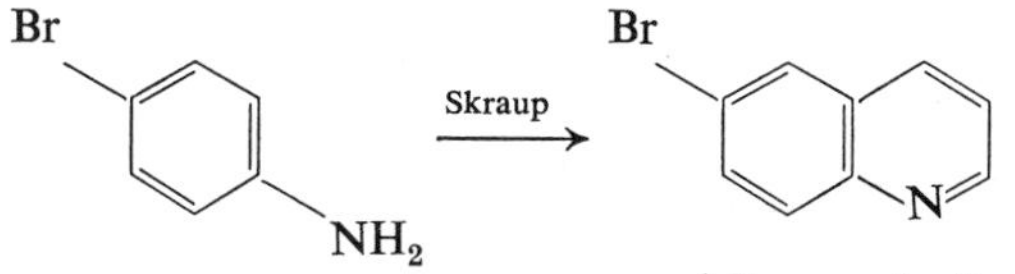

(18)

6-Bromoquinoline

On the other hand, if substitution in the difficultly accessible 7-position is sought, by use of a *m*-substituted aniline, a mixture results (Eq. 19).

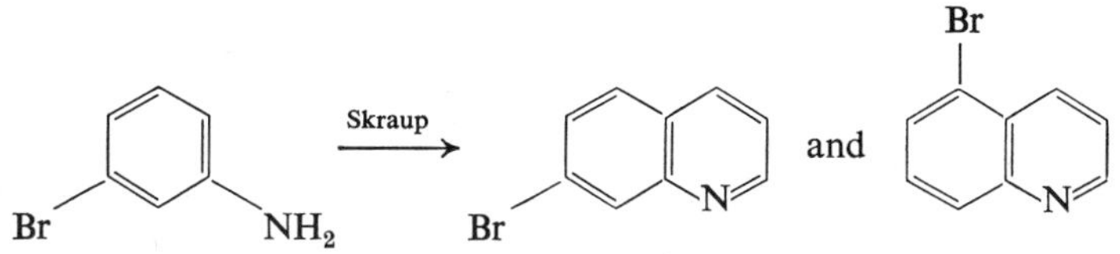

(19)

The possibility for closure in two directions naturally lowers the yield of the 7-isomer; however, the two isomers formed in a reaction such as Eq. 19 can often be separated, especially since many of the quinoline derivatives are solids. On account of the difficulty of securing 7-substituted quinolines, such reactions as in Eq. 19 are often employed for lack of a better approach. Hindrance to closure *ortho* to a substituent favors formation of the desired 7-isomer.

Disubstituted anilines of appropriate structure may be cyclized to yield only one product, as in Eq. 20.

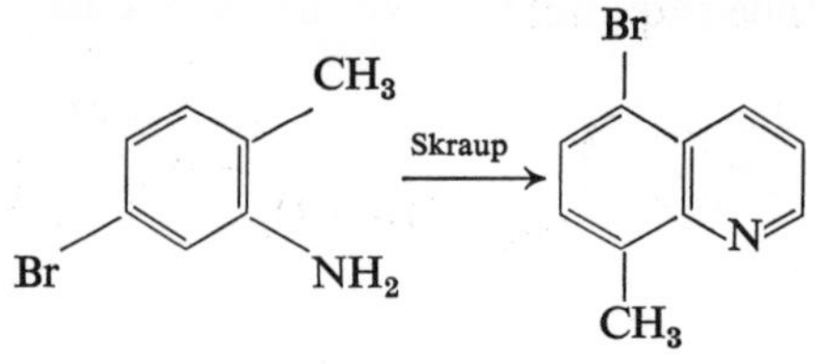

$$\text{(20)}$$

A symmetrically substituted aniline, such as 3,5-dimethylaniline, will also give only one product.

The Döbner–Miller synthesis. The yields in the Döbner-Miller synthesis are usually inferior to those secured in the Skraup synthesis; however, the starting materials are often rather cheap, and the Döbner-Miller method permits substitution in either or both rings. It is probably the most versatile of all quinoline syntheses, but the relatively poor yields limit it in practice to amines and carbonyl compounds which are cheaply available.

The over-all reaction in a simple Döbner-Miller synthesis is shown in Eq. 21.

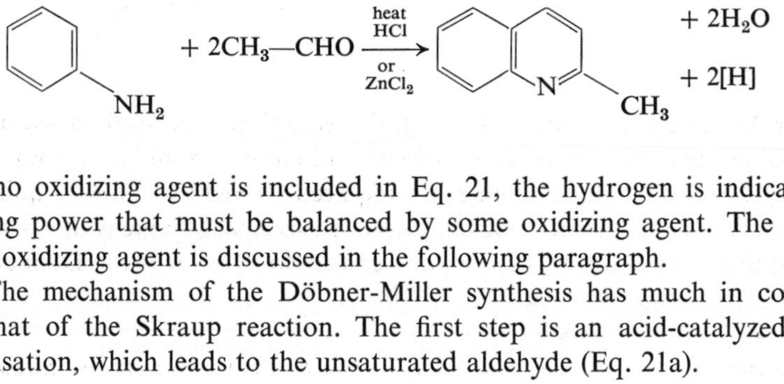

$$\text{(21)}$$

Since no oxidizing agent is included in Eq. 21, the hydrogen is indicated as reducing power that must be balanced by some oxidizing agent. The nature of this oxidizing agent is discussed in the following paragraph.

The mechanism of the Döbner-Miller synthesis has much in common with that of the Skraup reaction. The first step is an acid-catalyzed aldol condensation, which leads to the unsaturated aldehyde (Eq. 21a).

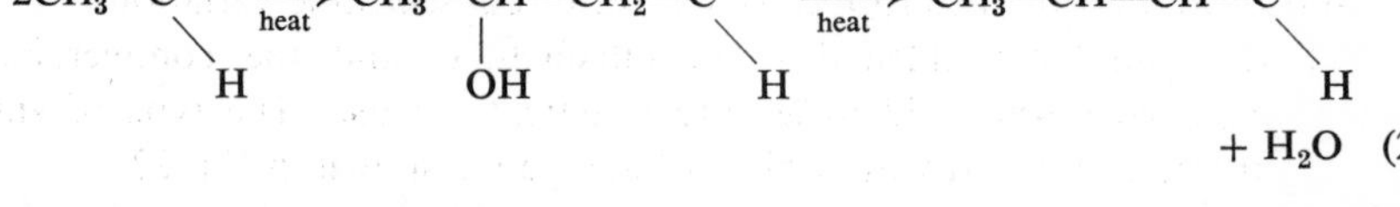

$$\text{(21a)}$$

The α,β-unsaturated aldehyde then proceeds to add 1,4- to the aniline just as shown in Eq. 16b, and this product cyclizes as shown in Eq. 16c or 16d. This sequence leads to the 1,2-dihydroquinoline, which is oxidized to yield the quinoline derivative. The identity of the oxidizing agent has been rather well established as the Schiff's base shown as a side reaction product in Eq. 16b and the similar Schiff's base from the starting aldehyde. In the preparation of quinaldine (as in Eq. 21), there have been isolated both ethylaniline (formed in Eq. 21b) and *n*-butylaniline (Eq. 21c).

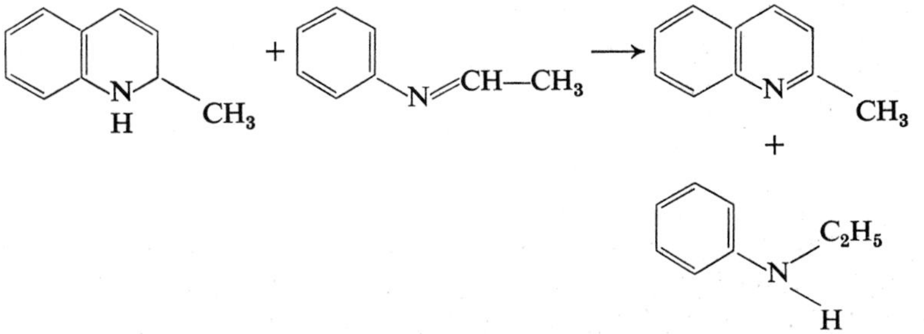

$$\text{(21b)}$$

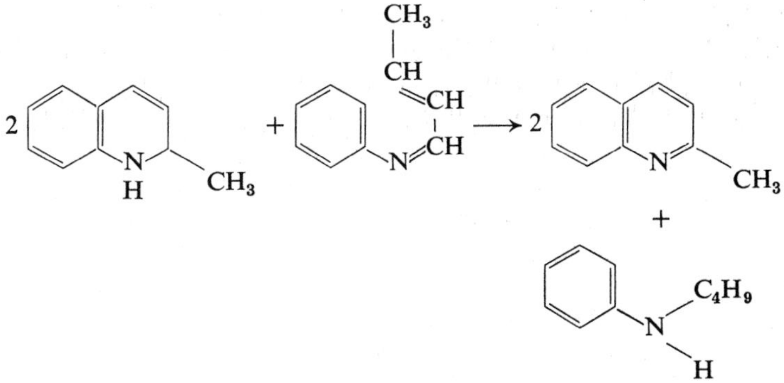

$$\text{(21c)}$$

It may be noted, by examination of the equations involved in synthesis of quinaldine, that 3 moles of acetaldehyde and either 1.5 moles (via Eq. 21c) or 2 moles (via Eq. 21b) of aniline are required to yield a mole of quinaldine. These ratios, coupled with linear polymerization of the aldehydes involved in the synthesis, lead to a relatively poor conversion factor in the Döbner-Miller process.

SCOPE AND LIMITATIONS OF THE DÖBNER-MILLER SYNTHESIS. Substitution in the benz ring is subject to considerations essentially identical to those elaborated in connection with the Skraup synthesis. Nearly any substituted aniline will give some yield, but certain of them will give two isomeric products.

Substitution in the hetero ring is subject to considerable variation.

(a) Most aliphatic aldehydes are satisfactory, and the commercially available normal aldehydes are practical for use. The type of substitution obtained with a higher aldehyde is shown in Eq. 22.

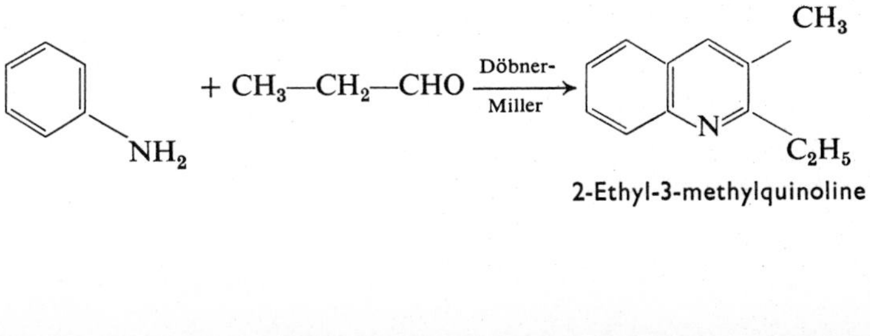

$$+ CH_3-CH_2-CHO \xrightarrow[\text{Miller}]{\text{Döbner-}} \qquad \text{(22)}$$

2-Ethyl-3-methylquinoline

The quinoline produced may be visualized by considering the initial aldol condensation product, as it fits into the quinoline:

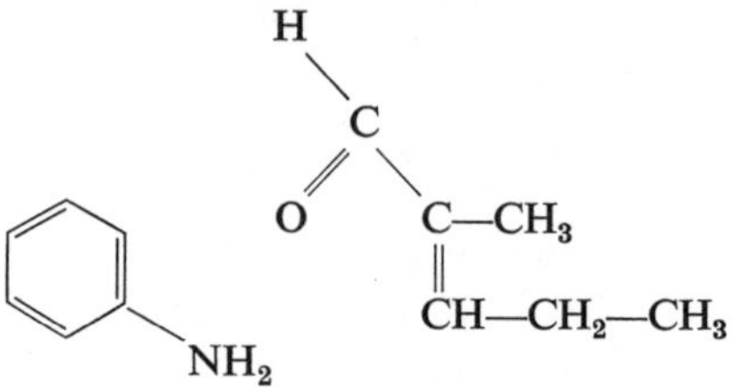

$$\text{(structure)}$$

$$\begin{array}{c} H \\ \diagdown \\ C \\ \diagup\diagup \qquad \diagdown \\ O \qquad C-CH_3 \\ \qquad \| \\ \qquad CH-CH_2-CH_3 \end{array}$$

(b) Two different aldehydes may often be used to give a practical amount of one quinoline resulting from a cross aldol condensation. Of course the yield is lowered still more by such a procedure, but the desired quinoline is separable in many instances. The predominant quinoline containing both aldehydes is determined by the aldol condensation that proceeds the fastest. This may be predicted from the fact that *the reactivity of the carbonyl group decreases significantly with increase in molecular weight, up to four carbons in the alkyl group.* Thus the favored aldol condensation will involve the carbonyl of the lower molecular weight aldehyde. For acetaldehyde and propional-dehyde, the favored cross aldol product would be

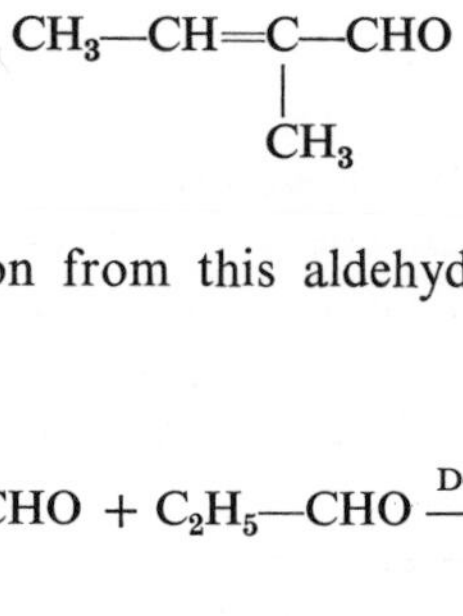

$$CH_3-CH=C-CHO$$
$$\qquad\qquad\quad |$$
$$\qquad\qquad\; CH_3$$

Quinoline formation from this aldehyde is shown in Eq. 23. The

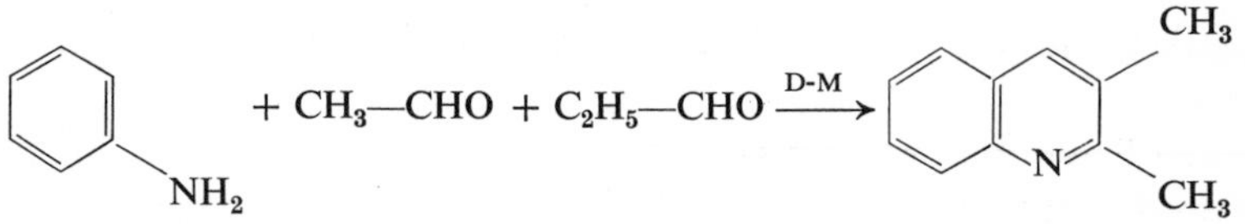

$$\text{(structure)} + CH_3-CHO + C_2H_5-CHO \xrightarrow{\text{D-M}} \text{(quinoline structure)} \qquad (23)$$

other quinoline formed in about equal amount would be quinaldine, resulting from the aldol condensation of acetaldehyde with itself. The other two possible quinolines would be formed in considerably lesser amounts.

  In planning syntheses of this type, it is helpful to remember that the carbonyl carbon of the lower molecular weight aldehyde becomes carbon-2 in the desired quinoline, while the α-carbon of the higher molecular weight aldehyde becomes carbon-3 in the quinoline.

(c) If one of two different aldehydes is aromatic, yields are improved considerably, for only two aldol condensations can result, and the carbonyl of the aromatic aldehyde is the more reactive. Such a synthesis is shown in Eq. 24.

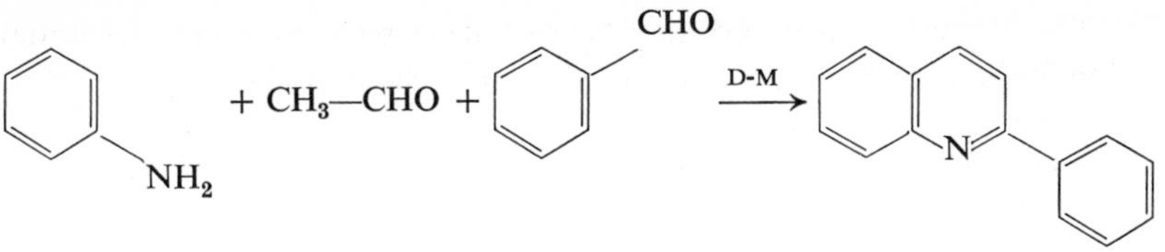

$$(24)$$

2-Phenylquinoline

The by-product would be quinaldine, easily separable by distillation on account of its lower molecular weight.

(d) Use of pyruvic acid with an aldehyde gives a rather favorable synthesis, for the carbonyl group in an aldehyde is much more reactive than that in a ketone, and the quinoline of the cross reaction is easily separated because it is an acid. The yield is especially good if the aldehyde is aromatic, as in Eq. 25. 2-Phenyl-4-quinolinecarboxylic

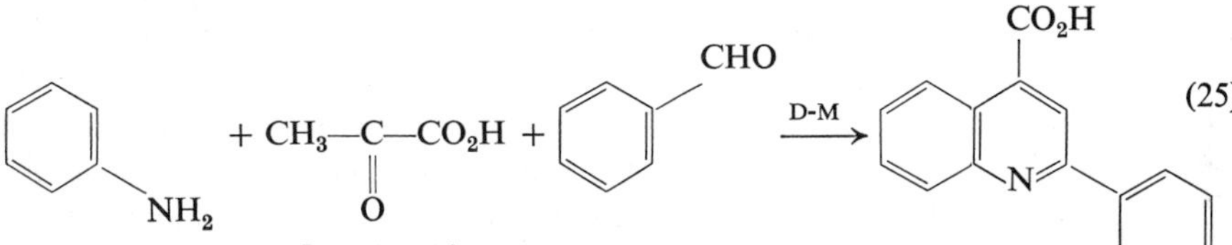

$$(25)$$

Pyruvic acid

2-Phenyl-4-quinoline-
carboxylic acid

acid, known as cinchophen, has been used as a drug for the treatment of gout.

Various other combinations can be successfully used to prepare quinolines by the Döbner-Miller synthesis; but the examples which have been discussed should be sufficient to indicate the considerable scope of this method of synthesis. Finally, it may be emphasized again that only relatively cheap starting materials are ordinarily used.

The Friedländer synthesis. This method is useful chiefly for quinolines substituted in the hetero ring, for the aromatic amine used in this process is a 2-aminobenzaldehyde, as shown in Eq. 26.

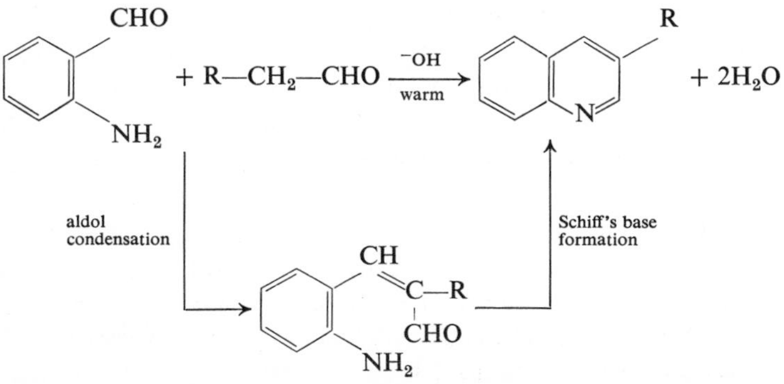

$$(26)$$

aldol
condensation

Schiff's base
formation

The reaction shown in Eq. 26 goes in good yield; it involves a base-catalyzed aldol condensation followed by Schiff's base formation. Frequently the condensation is carried out with *o*-nitrobenzaldehyde, then the nitro is reduced after the condensation. In this case, Schiff's base formation proceeds rapidly and the quinoline is obtained directly, as shown in Eq. 27.

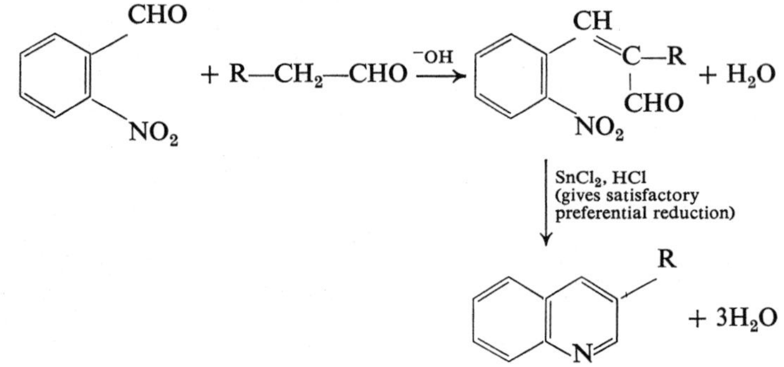

$$(27)$$

The advantage of the procedure in Eq. 27 is that it avoids use of *o*-amino-benzaldehyde, which is a rather unstable compound and difficult to isolate in good yield after reduction of *o*-nitrobenzaldehyde.

SCOPE AND LIMITATIONS OF THE FRIEDLÄNDER SYNTHESIS. The limitation to quinolines substituted in the hetero ring arises from the substantial difficulty in securing substituted *o*-aminobenzaldehydes. In fact, securing *o*-amino-benzaldehyde itself is rather troublesome, hence the use of the process shown in Eq. 27. Preparation of *o*-nitrobenzaldehydes also leaves something to be desired. The parent compound is probably secured best (although in only 20% yield) by the special oxidation procedure which was described in Eq. 18-34.

Substituted *o*-nitrotoluenes can be prepared, but any substituents must withstand the oxidation with chromic acid. Furthermore, the yield is sufficiently poor to make the Skraup or Döbner-Miller methods usually more attractive for quinolines substituted in the benz ring.

A *particular application* of the Friedländer method is for synthesis of quinolines substituted in the 3-position and not substituted in the 2-position. Synthesis of such types by the Döbner-Miller method requires a cross aldol with formaldehyde, a rather unpromising procedure.

(a) Ketones may be used in the Friedländer synthesis if they are low molecular weight and symmetrical. Unsymmetrical ketones have been used with some satisfaction, but use of ketones is usually confined to symmetrical ones, as illustrated in Eq. 28.

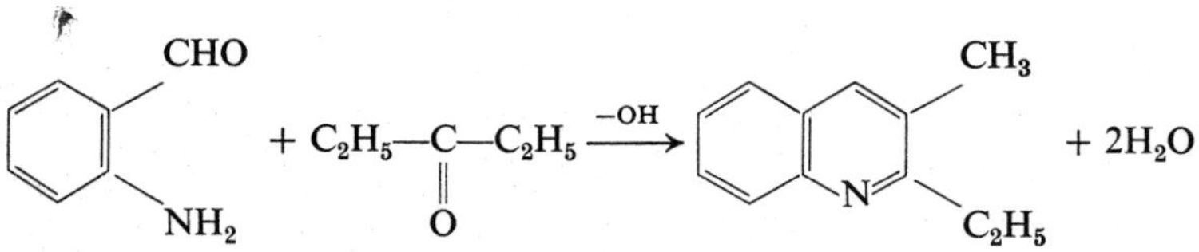

2-Ethyl-3-methylquinoline

It should be noted that the product of Eq. 28 is the same as that of Eq. 22. This type of quinoline is usually better obtained by the Döbner-Miller method, for the low yield by that route is usually less troublesome than securing the aminobenzaldehyde for use in the Friedländer synthesis.

(b) The Friedländer method is quite useful when applied to β-keto esters (Eq. 29).

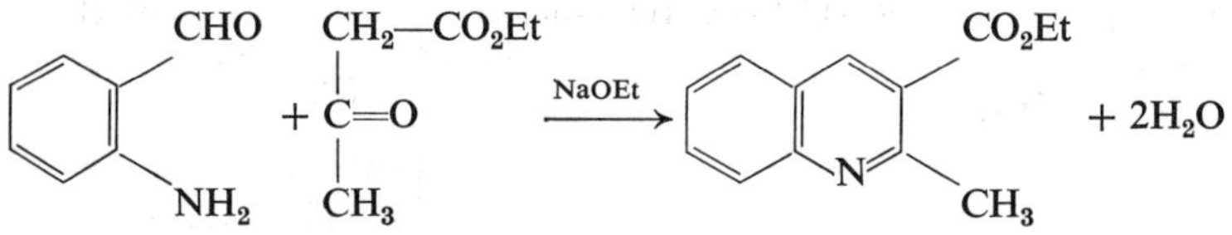

Quinolines of the type shown in Eq. 29 are not readily secured by other methods. Sodium ethoxide is used in order to avoid saponification of the β-keto ester.

Quinolines from an aromatic amine and a β–keto ester. The procedures described under this heading should not be confused with the modification of the Friedländer synthesis immediately preceding. Depending on the conditions used, an amine and β-keto ester may be eventually converted either to a **2-substituted-4-quinolone** or a **4-substituted-2-quinolone**. The alternative sequences are shown as Eq. 30.

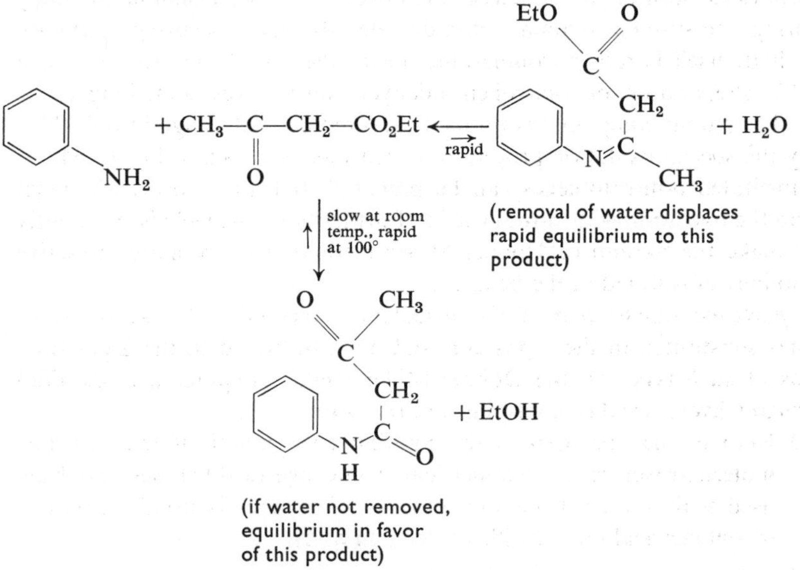

Equation 30 is an excellent illustration of a process in which a good yield of either of two products can be obtained, depending on the conditions that are applied. Although the normal positions of the two equilibria are such that a good yield of amide results, if water is removed as formed the equilibria can be shifted in the other direction.

The products of Eq. 30 can be used to secure quinolones as shown in Eqs. 31 and 32.

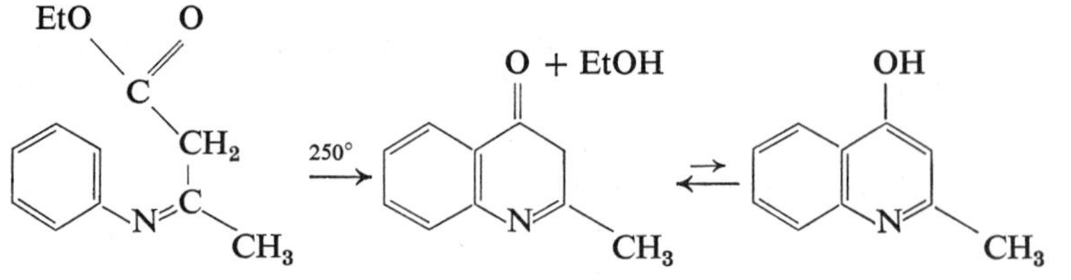

2-Methyl-4-quinolone

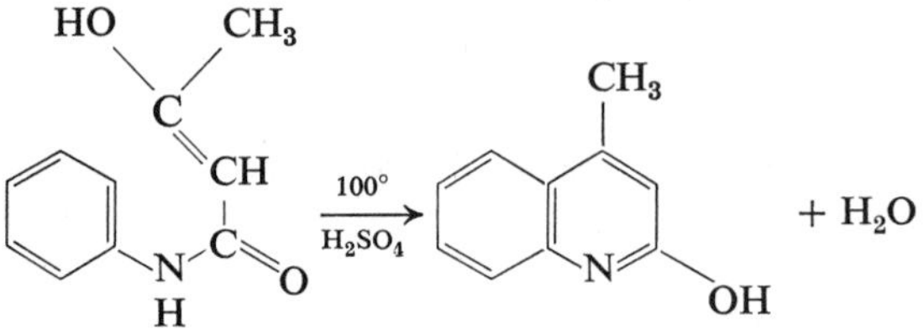

$$(31)$$

4-Methyl-2-quinolone

$$(32)$$

SCOPE AND LIMITATIONS OF SUBSTITUTED QUINOLONE SYNTHESES. The amine may be any of various substituted anilines. There apply the considerations discussed in detail in connection with the Skraup synthesis.

Substitution in the hetero ring is limited by the β-keto esters which can be synthesized (review Claisen ester condensation, Chap. 26; acylation of malonic ester, Chap. 27). In order to secure a fully aromatic system there must be at least one hydrogen on the alpha carbon of the β-keto ester.

If desired, hydroxyl may be removed from the quinolone by conversion to chloro with phosphorus pentachloride and removal of chlorine by hydrogenation.

Summary of quinoline syntheses by cyclization. As the initial step in solving problems by use of cyclization methods, it is useful to consider the following type of summary:

(a) Skraup synthesis: primarily for substitution in benz ring.
(b) Friedländer synthesis: primarily for substitution in hetero ring, especially 3-alkyl quinolines and 2-alkyl-3-carbethoxyquinolines.
(c) Amine plus β-keto ester: 4-substituted-2-quinolones and 2-substituted-4-quinolones, with or without substitution in benz ring.
(d) Döbner-Miller synthesis: substitution in either or both rings, usually best when substitution in both rings is desired or starting materials are cheap.
(e) The 4-quinolone synthesis (from o-nitroacylbenzenes) is well adapted to synthesis of many 7-substituted quinolines (via nitration of p-substituted alkylbenzenes). Use of acyl larger than acetyl gives alkyl substitution in the 3-position.

After a preliminary location of method by use of this sort of outline, the specific problem is solved by working backwards as usual; and the initial step often involves synthesis of a substituted aromatic amine.

EXERCISES

1. Using line formulas, write the five principal resonance forms for quinoline. Also write two inter-ring charged forms which contribute little, if anything, to the character of the molecule.

2. Illustrate or give an example of each of the following.

(a) Structural formula for a cyanine dye giving sensitization to the infrared.
(b) An isomer of atabrine which has proved highly toxic to man.
(c) A Schiff's base.
(d) Rate-controlled and thermodynamic-controlled reaction products.
(e) Tautomeric structures.

3. The quinoline required for synthesis of chloroquine is shown on the left below. Outline a practical synthesis of this compound, starting with ethylbenzene. Show how each of the two isomers obtained on nitration of ethylbenzene may be utilized in the synthesis.

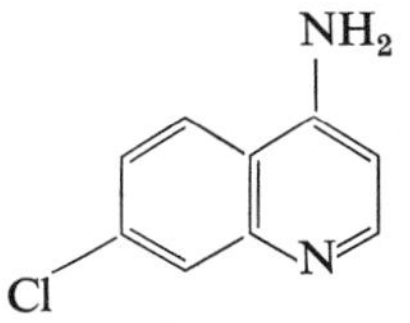

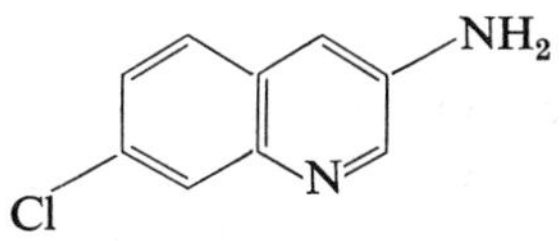

In pharmaceutical chemistry, isomeric compounds are nearly always checked for the possibility of improved drug action. The quinoline shown on the right above could be used to make an isomer of chloroquine. Outline a practical synthesis of the 3-amino-7-chloroquinoline, starting with n-propylbenzene.

4. Write the formulas for all the quinolines that would be formed if a Döbner-Miller synthesis were carried out with m-methoxyaniline, acetaldehyde, and butyraldehyde. Indicate which quinoline you would expect in largest amount and which in least amount (in case about equal amounts of two structures are expected, so indicate).

5. Write the structure of the quinoline expected in largest amount from a Döbner-Miller synthesis using 2-methylaniline, acetaldehyde, and acetone. How could the ratios of reagents be adjusted so that there would be very little of any other quinoline formed?

6. Outline by means of equations practical methods of accomplishing each of the following conversions. Any desired reagents may be used.

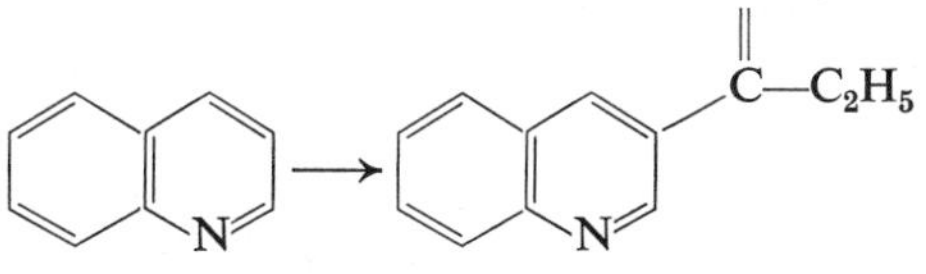

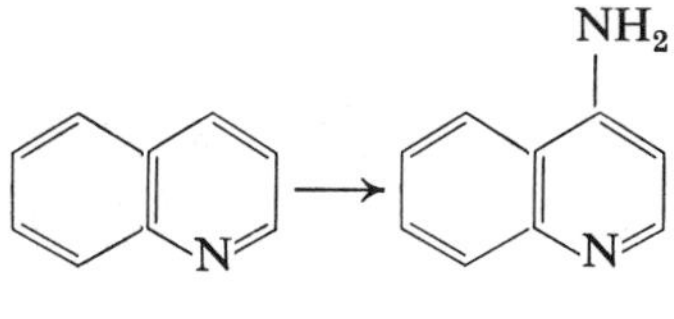

(c)

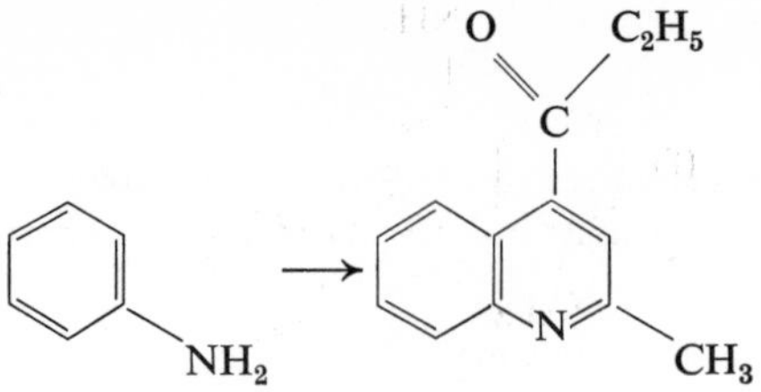

(d)

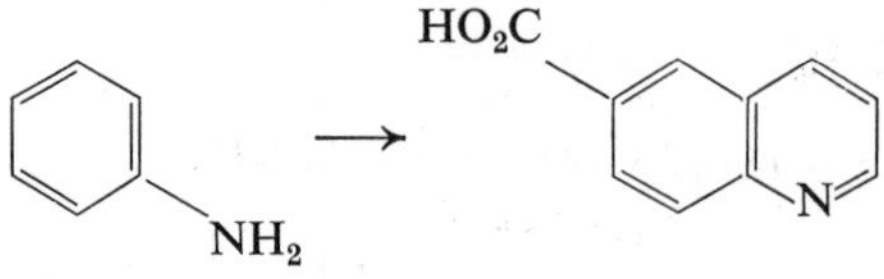

(e)

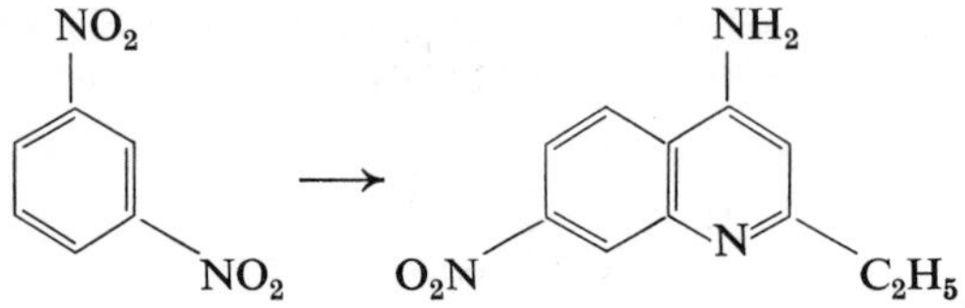

(f)

(g)

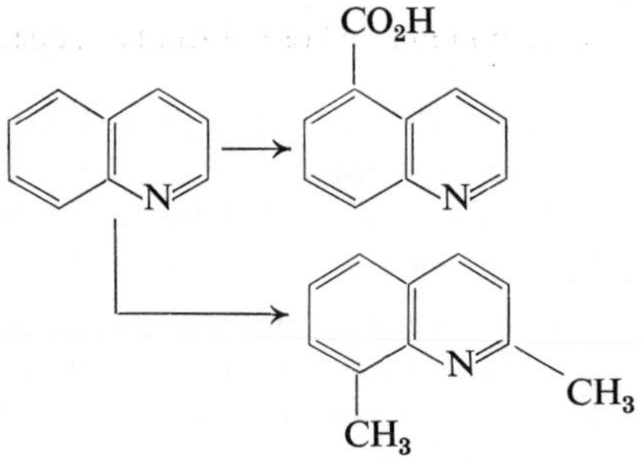

7. Using as starting materials compounds obtainable from coal tar and any desired aliphatic compounds containing four or less carbon atoms, outline practical syntheses of the following compounds.

(a)

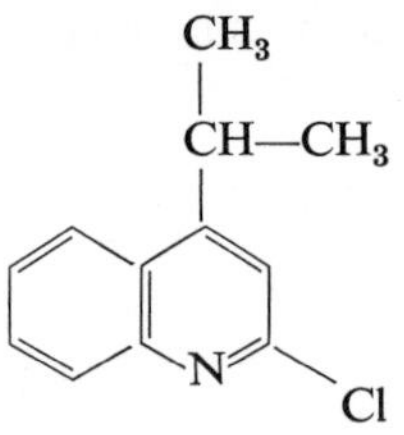

(b)

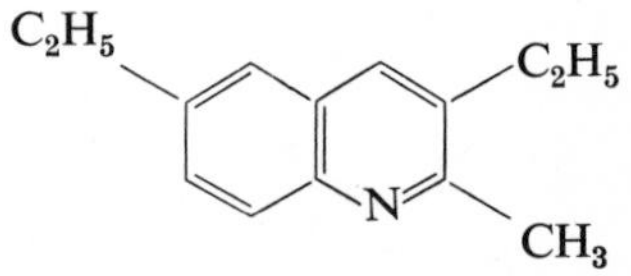

(c)

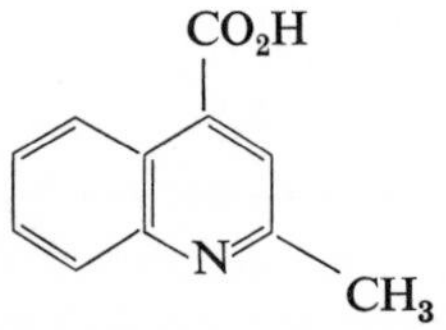

(d) 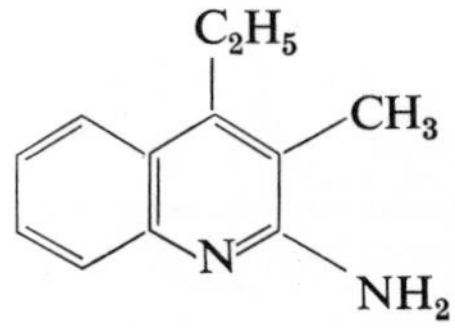   (via Claisen condensation of ethyl propionate)

(e)

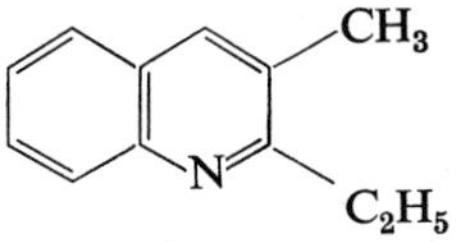

(f)

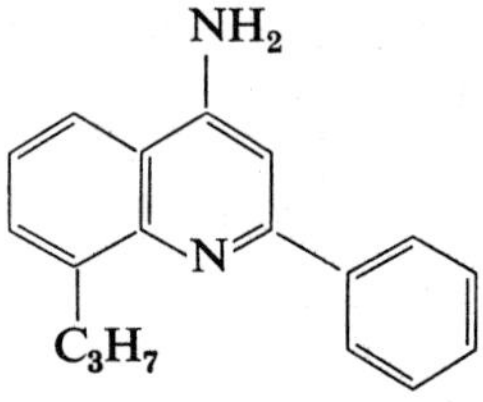

(g)

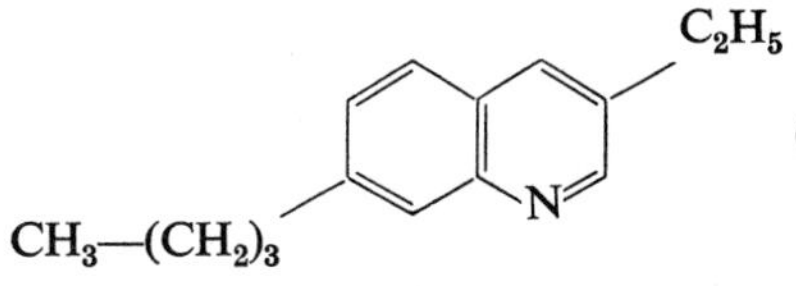

(h)

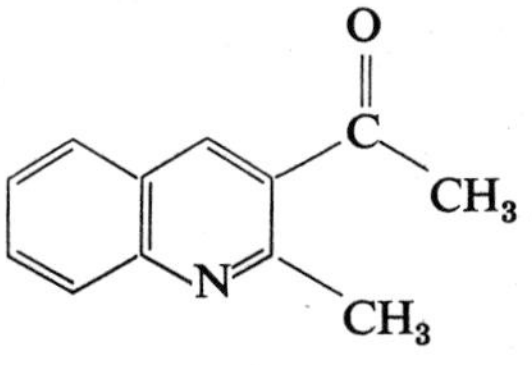

(i)

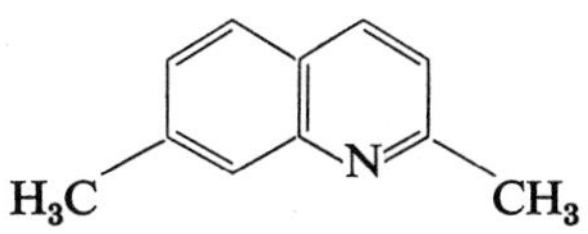

(j)

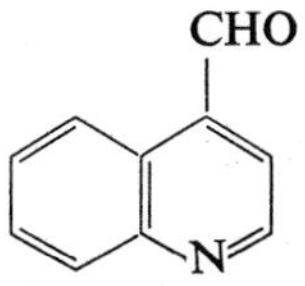

8. Give one correct name for each of the compounds whose formulas appear in Exercises 6 and 7.

Isoquinoline

Isoquinoline differs structurally from quinoline only in the position of fusion of the benzene and pyridine rings, and the differences in chemical behavior of the two compounds arise from this structural difference. The fact that the nitrogen atom is one atom removed from the benz ring changes the location of positions exhibiting "aliphatic reactivity." The consequences of this difference will be discussed in connection with the chemical properties of isoquinoline.

Isoquinoline is one of the very few heterocyclic compounds in which numbering of the ring atoms does not start on the hetero atom. As shown below, numbering starts adjacent to the benz ring.

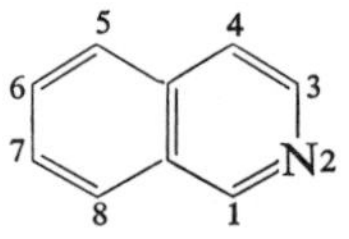

Presumably the objective of this exceptional feature of nomenclature is to make the numbering of substituents in the two rings in the same sequence as that in naphthalene and quinoline.

The commercial source of isoquinoline is coal tar. Since quinoline and isoquinoline have nearly identical boiling points, they must be separated by some means other than distillation. Several industrial methods have been developed for separation of these two coal tar bases. One procedure uses fractional extraction with limited quantities of acid. Since isoquinoline is a slightly stronger base, it becomes of higher concentration in the salt which is formed. The fractions rich in isoquinoline are then subjected to fractional freezing in order to secure the higher-melting isoquinoline in a pure condition. Isoquinoline melts at 25°, while quinoline melts at −17°. The higher melting point of isoquinoline makes possible the separation of a rather pure sample from coal tar. This is in contrast to the situation with quinoline, where the pure substance must be secured by synthesis.

Although there has been some investigation of isoquinoline derivatives as potential drugs, no really useful ones have been developed thus far. There is a limited application of isoquinolines in cyanine dyes, but in general we may say that this ring system has not become of significant commercial importance. The chemistry of isoquinoline has been developed largely because of the occurrence of this nucleus in several alkaloids; so our discussion of it will be rather brief. One method of synthesis by cyclization will be discussed.

Chemical Properties of Isoquinoline

Many of the chemical properties of isoquinoline are similar to those of quinoline; however, some interesting differences resulting from the location of the hetero atom are worthy of discussion.

Oxidation. The fusion of the benz ring to the 3,4-positions in pyridine de-stabilizes the pyridine ring to oxidation, as evidenced by oxidation of the hetero ring at about the same rate as the benz ring (Eq. 1). It will be recalled

$$
\text{isoquinoline} + [O] \xrightarrow{(KMnO_4)} \text{benzene-1,2-dicarboxylic acid} \quad \text{and} \quad \text{3,4-pyridinedicarboxylic acid} \tag{1}
$$

3,4-Pyridinedicarboxylic acid
(cinchomeronic acid)

(Eq. 31-1) that in quinoline the benz ring is oxidized at a much higher rate, as predicted from the higher resonance energy of pyridine. There appears to be no satisfactory theoretical basis for the experimental observation recorded in Eq. 1.

Reduction is similar to that of quinoline, in that the hetero ring is normally reduced at a considerably higher rate than the benz ring.

Activation in the 1-position. Since the 1- and 3-positions are adjacent to nitrogen in isoquinoline, the tentative expectation might be that these positions would exhibit the high order of reactivity shown by the 2- and 4-positions in quinoline. It is of considerable interest that experimentation has shown that **the 1-position is indeed reactive, but the 3-position is not.** This behavior may be related to similar phenomena in other ring systems. The resonance form that would contribute to activation of the 3-position would be the following charged form:

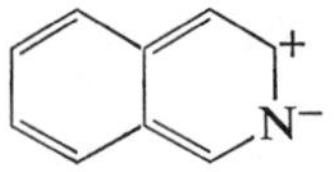

This form would be expected to be of very high energy, hence contribute very little to the resonance hybrid, for it will be noted to contain the unstable double *o*-quinone system. It may be recalled that the 2,3-naphthoquinone has never been isolated; furthermore, 1-methyl-2-naphthol does not couple readily with a

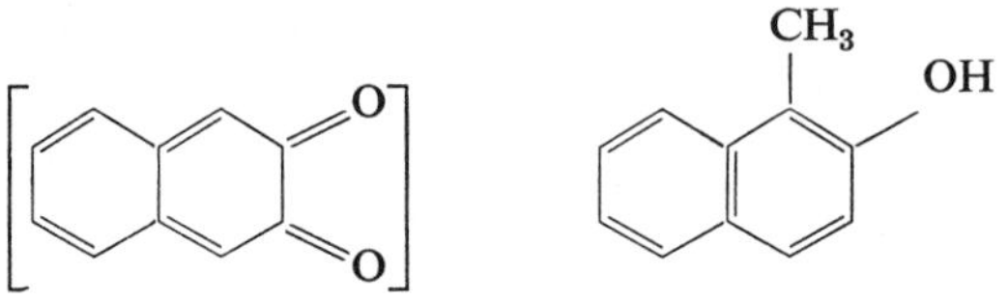

diazonium salt, in spite of having an open position adjacent to the hydroxyl. Another way of summarizing all these phenomena is to point out that there is very little double bond character to the bond between carbon-2 and carbon-3 in naphthalene and analogous ring systems. Only one of the three principal resonance forms in naphthalene has a double bond in this position, and this is a relatively high-energy resonance form (cf. Chap. 29).

Activation of the 1-position in isoquinoline makes possible reactions of the type occurring in the 2- and 4-positions in quinoline (cf. Chap. 32). Typical reactions are depicted in Eqs. 2 and 3.

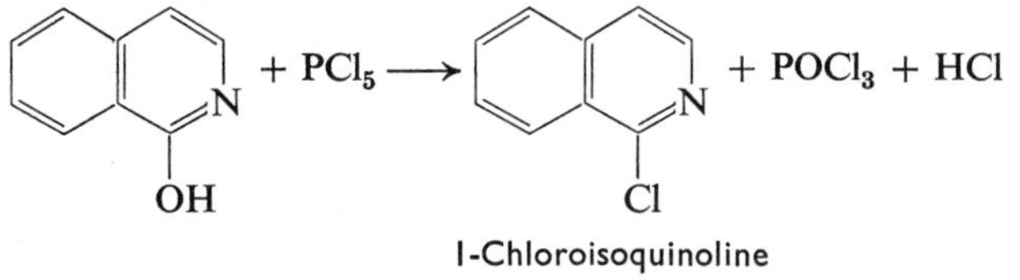

$$+ \text{PCl}_5 \longrightarrow \qquad + \text{POCl}_3 + \text{HCl} \qquad (2)$$

1-Chloroisoquinoline

$$+ 2\text{NH}_3 \longrightarrow \qquad \rightleftharpoons \qquad (3)$$

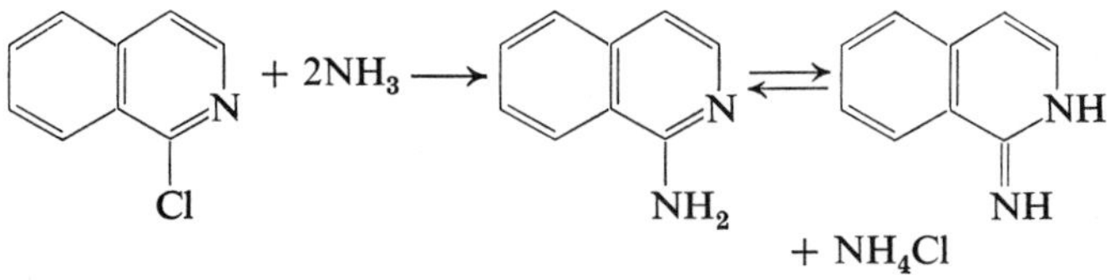

$$+ \text{NH}_4\text{Cl}$$

Synthesis of Isoquinolines by Cyclization Reactions

Cyclization reactions in this series ordinarily involve closures of three types of skeletal structures, as follows:

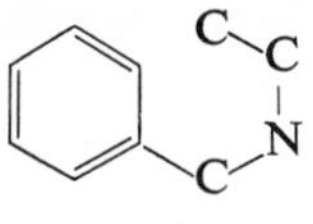

I 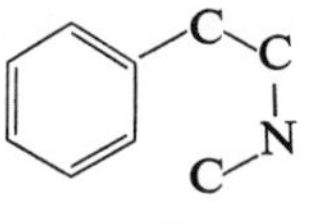   II 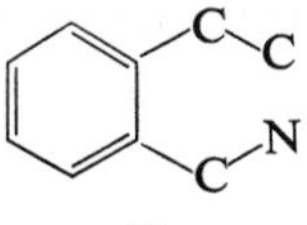   III

Of these skeletal structures suitable for closure to isoquinolines, type I is not well adapted to synthesis of isoquinolines containing substituents in the positions commonly substituted in natural alkaloids; type III is not readily synthesized. Type II is subject to neither of these limitations; so cyclization of a compound of this type will be discussed.

The Bischler–Napieralski synthesis. This reaction was actually not very satisfactory until Pictet and Decker introduced the method of closure shown in Eq. 5. The synthesis consists of formation of the amide from a β-phenylethylamine in orthodox manner (Eq. 4), followed by cyclization to a 3,4-dihydroisoquinoline (Eq. 5). This cyclization differs from the methods

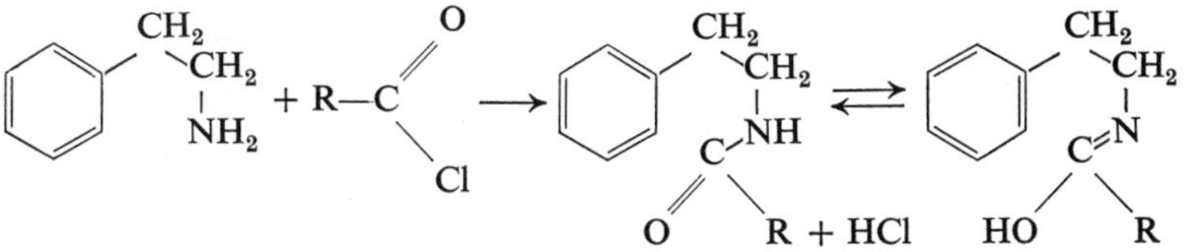

$$(4)$$

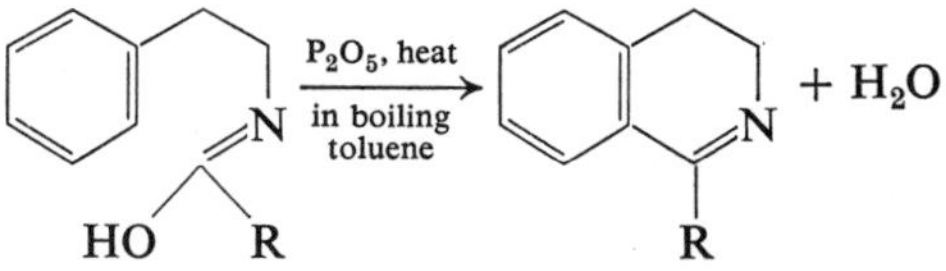

(a 1-substituted-3,4-
dihydroisoquinoline)

$$(5)$$

studied for making quinolines only in that the carbonyl of an amide is involved rather than that of an aldehyde, ketone, or ester.

The dihydroisoquinoline obtained from the cyclization may be either oxidized to an isoquinoline or reduced to a 1,2,3,4-tetrahydroisoquinoline (Eq. 6). Reduction becomes of some significance because of the occurrence of the tetrahydroisoquinoline structure in alkaloids.

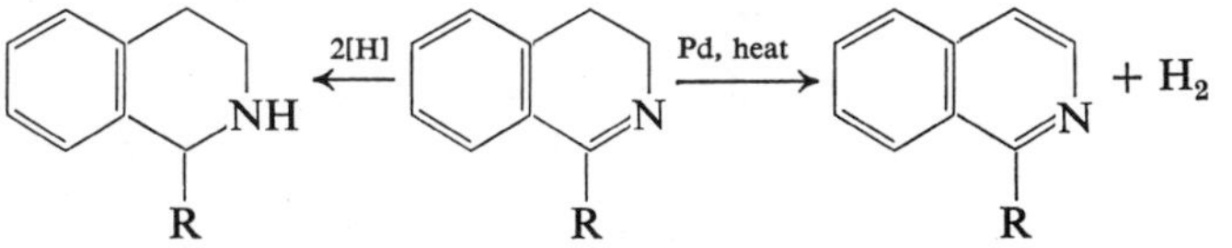

$$(6)$$

SCOPE AND LIMITATIONS OF THE BISCHLER-NAPIERALSKI SYNTHESIS. In general, the acid chloride of any available acid may be used, or amides may be prepared by other routes (cf. Chap. 14). The ring closure is not very satisfactory with formamides, but alkaloids containing the isoquinoline ring system are rather uniformly substituted in the 1-position, and the Bischler-Napieralski method is generally applicable for these types.

If a *meta*-substituted compound is used in the synthesis, closure occurs almost entirely in the *para* position, as in Eq. 7. This, also, is fortunate, for the natural products often have a substituent at the 6-position.

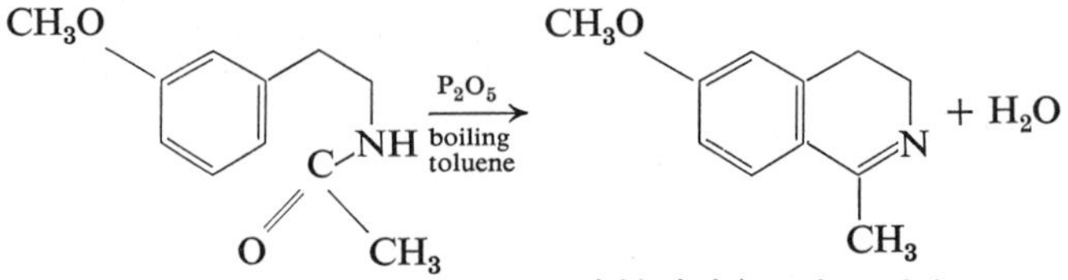

$$+ H_2O \qquad (7)$$

1-Methyl-6-methoxy-3,4-
dihydroisoquinoline

The amide from a secondary amine may also be closed successfully provided that the acylating group is phenylacetyl or a substituted phenylacetyl. An over-all sequence of this type is outlined in Eq. 8.

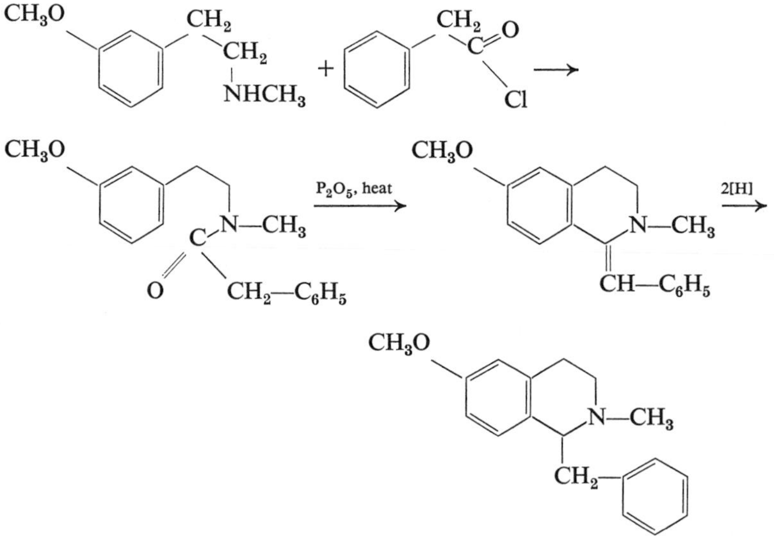

$$(8)$$

1-Benzyl-2-methyl-6-methoxy-
1,2,3,4-tetrahydroisoquinoline

The general structure synthesized in Eq. 8 is quite common in alkaloids and includes all the features which make the Bischler-Napieralski method of such general interest.

Phenylethylamines for use as starting materials in the Bischler-Napieralski method may be secured by the general methods discussed in Chapter 19 for synthesis of primary and secondary amines. A particularly useful method is nitrile reduction, for benzyl cyanides may be readily obtained from benzyl chlorides, secured in turn from benzyl alcohols. It follows that if a given

substituted benzyl alcohol may be secured, the route to an isoquinoline derivative can be completed. A variety of methods are available for making aromatic
acids (cf. Chap. 21); so a very useful route to benzyl alcohols is that outlined
in Eq. 9. Most other groups, even the nitro group, are not reduced by the special

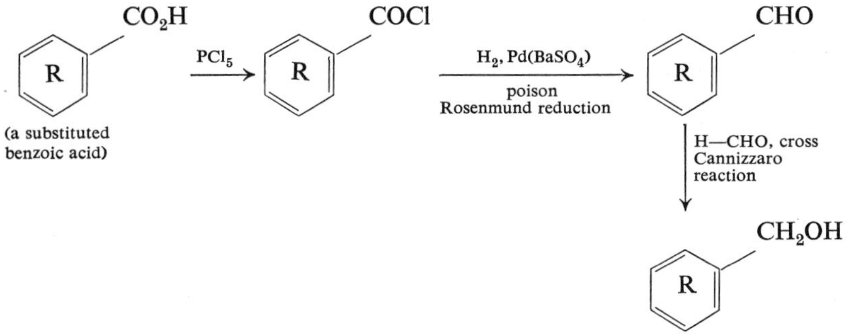

(a substituted
benzoic acid)

$$H_2, Pd(BaSO_4)$$

poison
Rosenmund reduction

H—CHO, cross
Cannizzaro
reaction

(9)

methods of reduction included in the sequence in Eq. 9, but selective reduction
of the nitrile or ester grouping is more difficult.

In connection with syntheses such as illustrated in Eq. 8, it should also
be mentioned that substituted phenylacetic acids can be prepared by hydrolysis
of the corresponding phenylacetonitriles.

EXERCISES

I. If it be assumed that isoquinoline gives the same reactions for the 1-position that
were discussed for the 2-position in quinoline, outline by equations satisfactory methods
for accomplishing the following conversions.

(a)

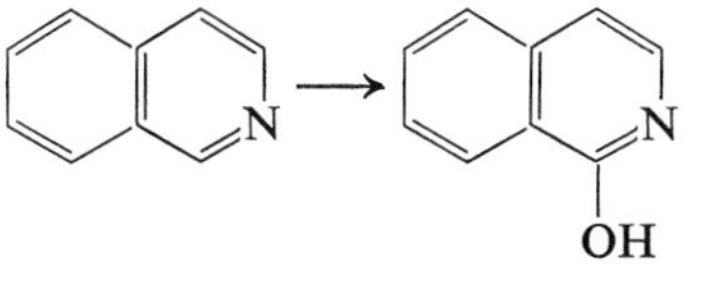

(b)

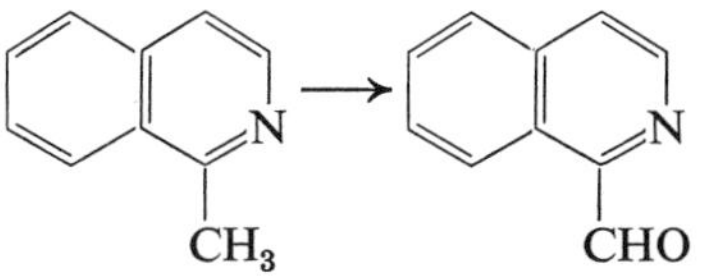

(c)

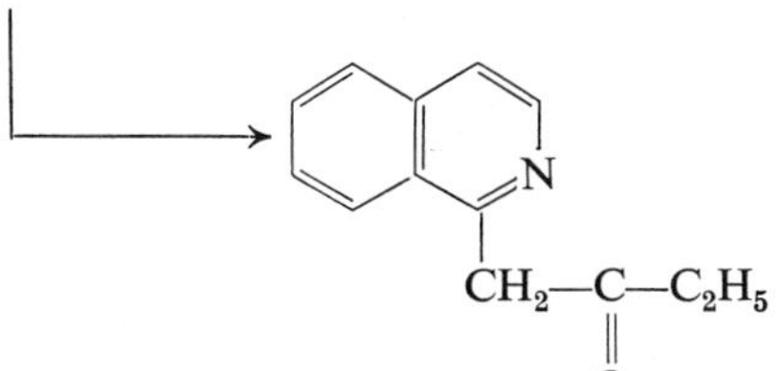

2. In view of the possibility of writing a resonance form of the following type for isoquinoline, explain why there is no activation of the 6-position in this molecule.

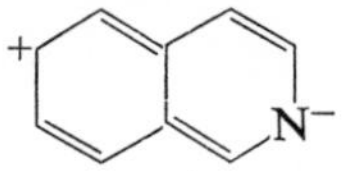

3. A substance obtained by degradation of a natural product was shown to be an isoquinoline with the molecular formula $C_{10}H_9N$. Vigorous oxidation of this substance yielded several products, of which one was identified as 2,3,4-pyridinetricarboxylic acid. Write the structural formula of the isoquinoline obtained as a degradation product.

4. Using as starting materials only aliphatic compounds or aromatic compounds available from coal tar, indicate practical syntheses of each of the following compounds.

(a)

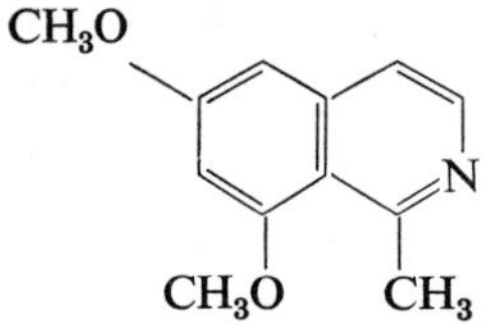

(b)

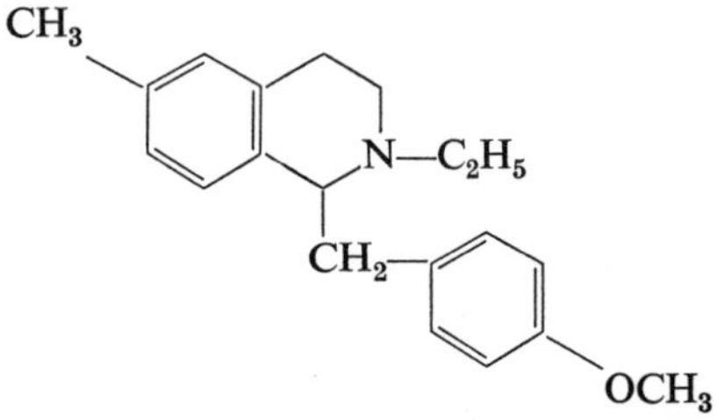

(c)

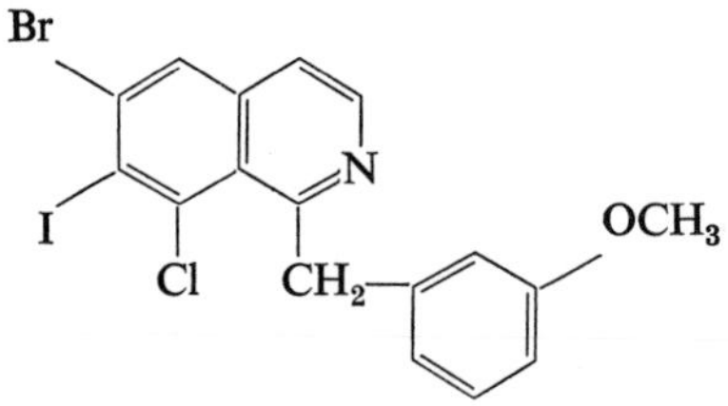

(d)

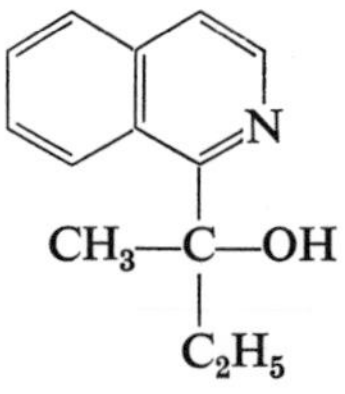

5. Name each of the compounds whose formulas appear in Exercise 4.

Survey of
Certain Additional Topics

The subjects discussed in this book have been treated in a basic or fundamental manner, rather than in great depth and detail. Advanced and highly sophisticated consideration of a few topics has been avoided in favor of a broad coverage which should serve as a basis for further study in the various areas of organic chemistry. Man has accumulated far more knowledge of each of these subjects than may be treated in a book of this size; in fact, the topics included in each chapter of this book could hardly be discussed fully in several books of this size. For example, at least twenty-five methods for synthesis of ketones have been developed. The mechanisms of organic reactions and the nature of chemical bonds have been the subject of intensive study during recent years; many hundreds of pages appear in chemical journals each month on these subjects alone.

In addition to the topics treated briefly in this book, there are numerous other topics, such as alkaloids, barely mentioned. There are still other important topics not mentioned at all thus far, and a few of these will be mentioned very briefly in the present chapter.

Such comments as included in the above paragraphs should not be regarded by a young chemist as discouraging. As one learns more about organic chemistry, he becomes more aware that no man can expect to accumulate any major percentage of what has been learned about organic chemistry.

One chemist may become an expert in a few fields; many chemists are expert in only one field. In order for a chemist to prosecute successful research it is not necessary for him to acquire all the knowledge that has been accumulated by his predecessors; those who attempt this find that the job is never finished, hence the time to contribute by doing research never arrives. The important thing is for the chemist to have sufficient fundamental knowledge to allow him to educate himself in whatever field he may choose for research. He may then proceed to advance to the frontiers of knowledge in that particular field. There have been included in this book topics believed to constitute the background essential for all chemists. More advanced courses will provide the essential information in broad fields of chemistry. Beyond this second tier of courses lies specialization in certain fields of research.

Additional Important Heterocyclic Ring Systems

The pyridine and quinoline ring systems have been discussed in some detail in this book, isoquinoline has been discussed more briefly, and pyrimidine has been mentioned. A few other heterocyclic ring systems have appeared as part of certain formulas. Several additional heterocyclic ring systems have sufficient importance that their chemistry has been investigated extensively. Among the more important of such ring systems are those for which the parent compounds, with positions numbered, appear in the following tabulation:

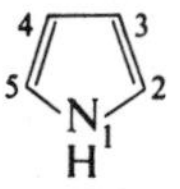

Pyrrole 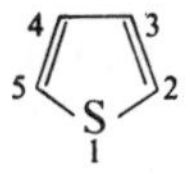   Thiophene    Furan 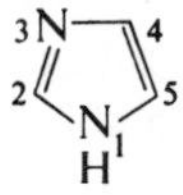   Imidazole 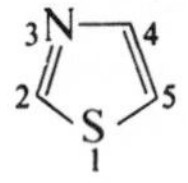   Thiazole

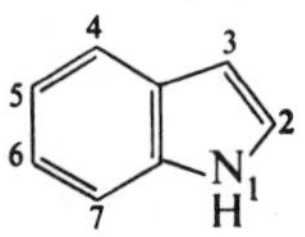

Indole 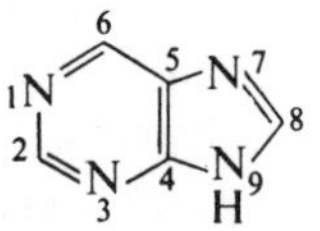   Purine 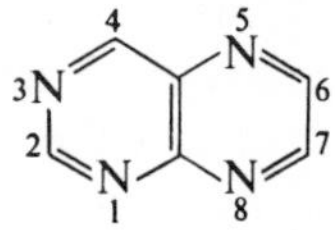   Pterin

The heterocyclic compounds containing nitrogen are especially important in biological chemistry. In Chapter 25 were mentioned the amino acids, proline and histidine, containing, respectively, the pyrrole and imidazole nuclei. It may be noted that indole consists of a benzene and a pyrrole ring, while purine consists of a pyrimidine and an imidazole ring. The pterin ring system contains a pyrimidine ring (nitrogens in 1,3-relationship) fused to a 1,4-diazabenzene

ring (pyrazine ring).[1] The purine and pterin ring systems are especially important in biological systems. Among many important purines found in nature
are uric acid, end product of nitrogen metabolism in most animals, and caffeine,
widely used and apparently harmless stimulant (coffee, tea, cola beverages).

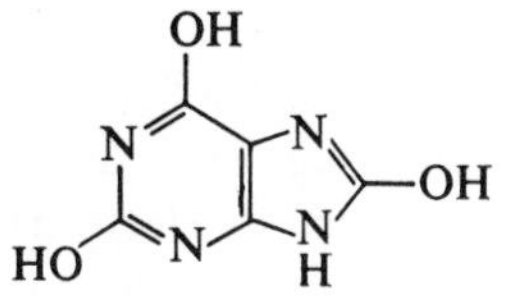

Uric acid

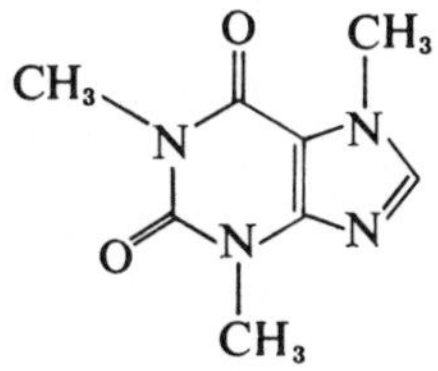

Caffeine
(1,3,7-trimethyl-2,6-dioxypurine)

The pterin ring system occurs in riboflavin (vitamin B_2), certain pigments
of butterfly wings, and in the growth and anti-anemia factor, folic acid.

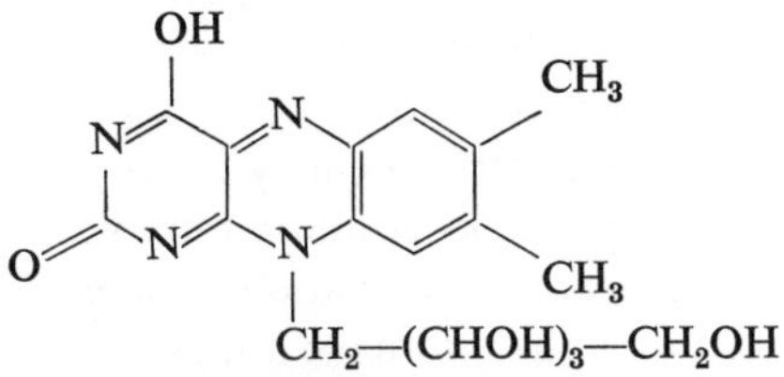

$CH_2—(CHOH)_3—CH_2OH$

Riboflavin
(sugar side chain has
the R-ribose structure)

The structure shown for caffeine points up the fact that the imidazole
ring may be written in tautomeric forms, depending on which nitrogen is
attached to hydrogen or a substituent. A 2-substituted imidazole is symmetrical,
but a 4-substituted imidazole may be either of two tautomeric forms:

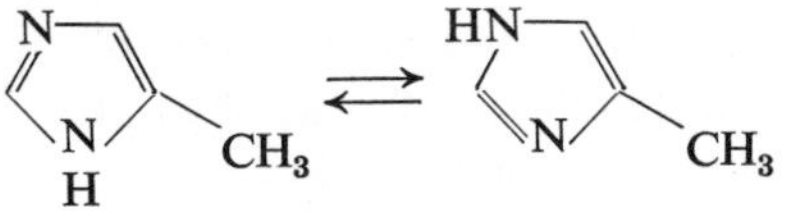

4-Methylimidazole

The heterocycles with 5-atom rings have considerably less resonance
energy than the ones with 6-atom rings, for resonance stabilization must

---

[1] Although many of the heterocyclic ring systems have common names which are
widely used, there is a growing tendency to avoid an unnecessary burden on the memory by
using a systematic nomenclature of the sort illustrated by the systematic name for pyrazine.
The hetero atoms are simply located by number, and the substance is named as a derivative of
the carbocyclic ring system. Nitrogen is designated as *aza-*, oxygen as *oxa-*, and sulfur as *thia-*.
In illustration, the systematic name for thiazole would be 1-thia-3-aza-2,4-cyclopentadiene.
Any substituents that may be in the ring are located by numbers in normal fashion.

depend on charged forms entirely:

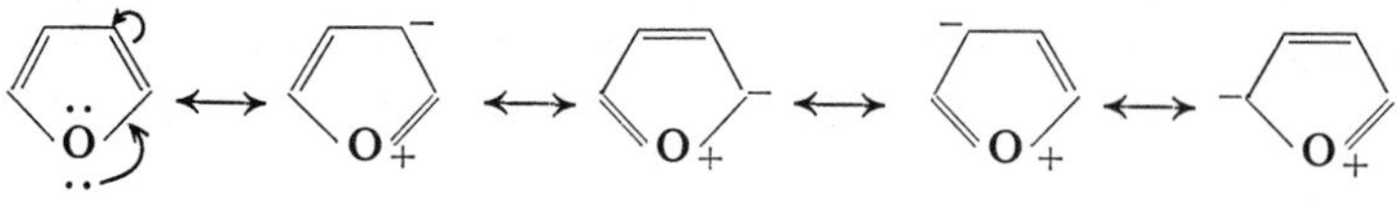

It should be noted that this type of electron delocalization differs sharply from that occurring in the charged forms of the 6-atom rings such as pyridine. In pyridine, charged resonance forms result in withdrawal of electrons from the ring, whereas in furan (and other 5-atom heterocyclic rings) charged resonance forms result in donation of electrons to the ring. This difference no doubt arises from the fact that resonance forms such as shown for furan may be considered for pyrrole (with pentavalent nitrogen in the charged forms); but such forms cannot be regarded as contributors to the resonance hybrid in pyridine, for two double bonds would be required on nitrogen. Such a structure would be of very high energy in a ring, for the normal angle between such bonds would be 180° (*sp* hybridized orbitals), and strain of this angle to that required in a six-membered ring would be very great.

The properties of the heterocycles with 5-atom rings are quite consistent with expectations from high electron density in the ring. Characteristic substitution reactions, such as the Friedel and Crafts reaction, occur very easily and the nucleus is quite unstable to oxidation. These properties may be compared with those of phenol, known to have a high electron density in the ring.

Phosphorus Compounds

There have already been mentioned two very important types of organic compounds which are esters of phosphoric acid. These are the phospholipids (Chap. 19) and the nucleic acids (Chap. 25). There are many other natural products of biological importance in which the phosphoric ester structure occurs. Among these are certain phosphoric esters of sugars, which are essential intermediates in the metabolism of carbohydrates. One important sugar phosphate is fructose-1,6-diphosphoric acid:

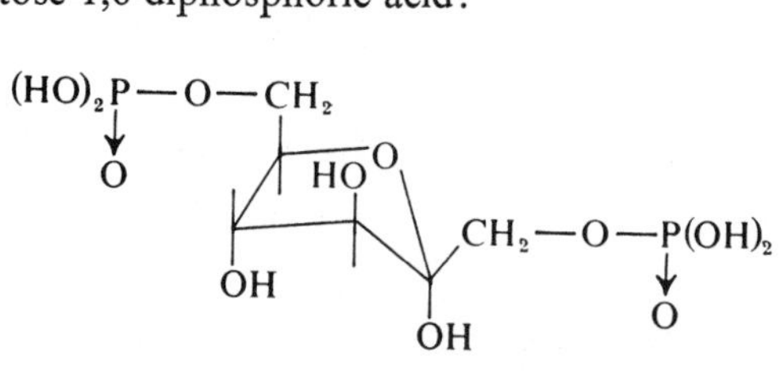

Fructose-1,6-diphosphoric acid

A principal device for transporting energy in animal organisms is by utilization of compounds containing the phosphoric anhydride structure. These compounds are derivatives of pyrophosphoric acid or of higher phosphoric acid anhydrides. The bond energy of the P—O—P sequence is quite low,[2] a general characteristic of acid anhydrides and acid chlorides (cf. Chap. 14 for carboxylic acid anhydrides and acid chlorides). Thus, reaction of this unstable,

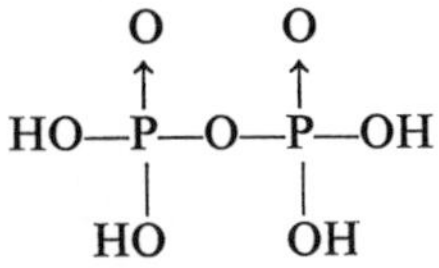

$$
\underset{\text{Pyrophosphoric acid}}{\overset{\displaystyle \overset{O}{\uparrow} \quad \overset{O}{\uparrow}}{\underset{\displaystyle HO \quad\; OH}{HO-P-O-P-OH}}}
\qquad\qquad
\underset{\text{Adenosine triphosphate}}{\overset{\displaystyle \overset{O}{\uparrow}\;\; \overset{O}{\uparrow}\;\; \overset{O}{\uparrow}}{\underset{\displaystyle HO \quad\; OH \quad\; OH}{Adenosine-O-P-O-P-O-P-OH}}}
$$

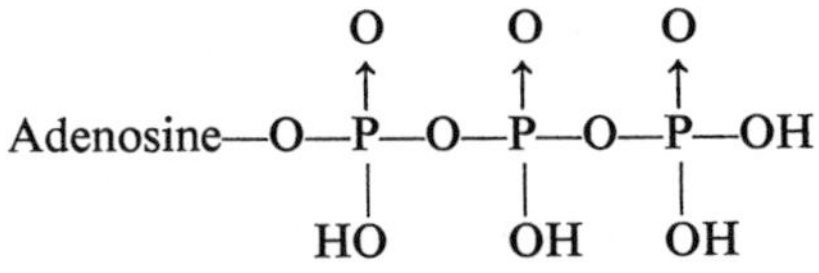

high-energy structure to yield other more stable structures, such as phosphoric esters or acids, results in the release of considerable energy (the difference in bond energy of the anhydride and ester or acid). It follows that energy may be consumed at one point in the organism where the phosphoric anhydride bond is formed; the compound so formed may be transported to another site in the organism; and the energy may then be released at a site distant from that at which the low-energy bond was formed. Perhaps the most important of these energy-transporting compounds is adenosine triphosphate, shown above. Adenosine is the purine, adenine, substituted with R-ribose as shown in the ribonucleic acid unit depicted in Chapter 25.

Synthesis of phosphate esters. On account of the importance of the phosphate esters in biochemistry, numerous methods for their synthesis have been developed.[3] A rather versatile method is reaction with phosphorus oxychloride, because the extent of reaction may be controlled surprisingly well by ratio of reagents and conditions. With a primary alcohol, the syntheses shown in Eqs. 1 through 3 may be carried out satisfactorily.

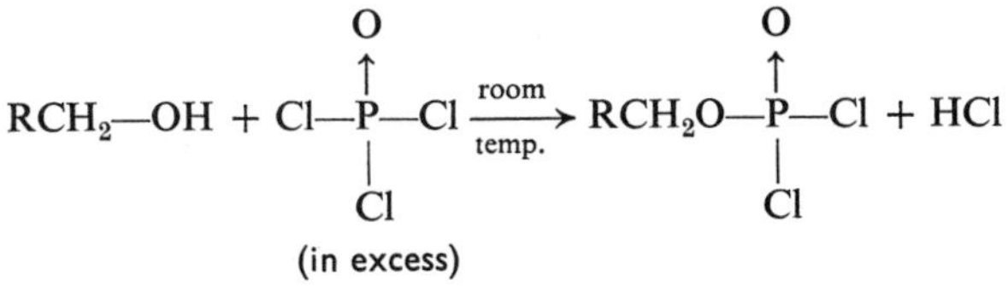

$$
RCH_2-OH + \underset{\underset{\text{(in excess)}}{\displaystyle Cl}}{\overset{\displaystyle \overset{O}{\uparrow}}{Cl-P-Cl}} \xrightarrow[\text{temp.}]{\text{room}} RCH_2O-\underset{\displaystyle Cl}{\overset{\displaystyle \overset{O}{\uparrow}}{P}}-Cl + HCl \tag{1}
$$

$$
2RCH_2-OH + POCl_3 \xrightarrow{\text{warm}} RCH_2O-\underset{\displaystyle Cl}{\overset{\displaystyle \overset{O}{\uparrow}}{P}}-OCH_2R + 2HCl \tag{2}
$$

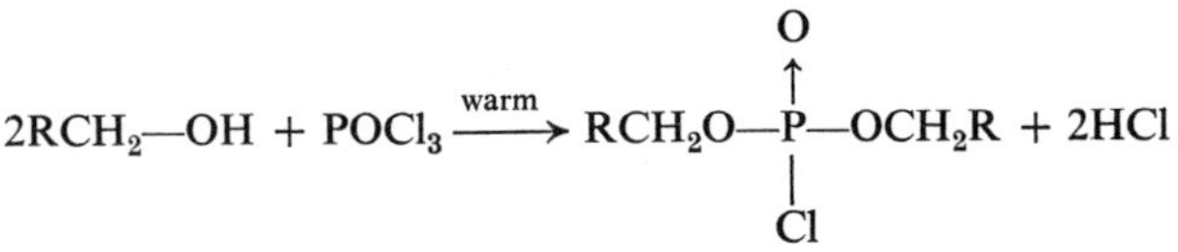

---

[2] It has been quite common in biochemistry to refer to this structure as the "high-energy phosphate bond," but this is actually a misnomer. It is the *compound which is of high energy* on account of the *low bond energy of the phosphoric anhydride structure*. Bond energy, which is the energy that must be supplied to the compound to break that bond, is in effect the energy the compound does not have on account of bond formation.

[3] The synthesis of phosphate derivatives, as well as numerous other types of organophosphorus compounds, has been described by Gennady M. Kosolapoff, *Organophosphorus Compounds*, Wiley, New York, 1950. Phosphate derivatives are presented in Chapter 9, while phosphonates are in Chapter 7.

$$3RCH_2—OH + POCl_3 \xrightarrow[\text{catalysis}]{\text{basic}} RCH_2O—\overset{\overset{\displaystyle O}{\uparrow}}{\underset{\displaystyle OCH_2R}{P}}—OCH_2R + 3HCl \xrightarrow{\text{base}} \text{salt} \quad (3)$$

Secondary or tertiary alcohols give very poor results. The mechanisms of these reactions are more complicated than appears from the over-all results, especially in the cases utilizing no base for removal of hydrogen chloride. There is probably an intermediate formed containing the phosphate chloride and hydrogen chloride. Reaction is frequently completed by a device such as removal of hydrogen chloride at reduced pressure.

The products of the reactions shown in Eqs. 1 and 2 may be hydrolyzed to the corresponding acids, or allowed to react with a different alcohol, so that mixed esters and acid esters of the types occurring in natural products may be secured. For example, the conversions in Eq. 4 are practical. It is worthy of

$$C_2H_5O—\overset{\overset{\displaystyle O}{\uparrow}}{\underset{\displaystyle Cl}{P}}—Cl + C_4H_9OH \longrightarrow C_2H_5O—\overset{\overset{\displaystyle O}{\uparrow}}{\underset{\displaystyle Cl}{P}}—OC_4H_9 + HCl$$

$$\xrightarrow[\substack{(1)\ HOH,\ ^-OH \\ (2)\ H^+}]{} C_2H_5O—\overset{\overset{\displaystyle O}{\uparrow}}{\underset{\displaystyle OH}{P}}—OC_4H_9 \quad (4)$$

note that a selective hydrolysis of a phosphoric ester acid chloride with water and base, as shown in Eq. 4, is quite effective; essentially no hydrolysis of the ester occurs under mild conditions. With acid catalysis, however, there is competing hydrolysis of the ester. Acid promotes hydrolysis of phosphoric esters (and other pentavalent phosphorus esters) by oxonium salt formation with the oxygen attached to alkyl. Base is ineffective in promoting hydrolysis of phosphorus esters, in marked contrast with the situation in carboxylic acid esters.

Another method for preparing phosphate esters consists of oxidizing phosphites with air, as in Eq. 5. This method is usually not so convenient as

$$2RO—\overset{}{\underset{\displaystyle OR}{P}}—OR + O_2 \xrightarrow{\text{(air)}} 2RO—\overset{\overset{\displaystyle O}{\uparrow}}{\underset{\displaystyle OR}{P}}—OR \quad (5)$$

that shown in Eqs. 1 through 4, for the reaction of alcohols with phosphorus oxychloride is normally more convenient and more subject to control than is the reaction with phosphorus trichloride (Eq. 7); however, use of sulfur is a rather convenient method for obtaining thiophosphates (Eq. 6). Both oxygen and sulfur oxidize phosphites quite readily. Phosphites not stored with careful exclusion of air become rapidly contaminated with phosphates. Addition of solid sulfur in the process shown in Eq. 6 must be carefully controlled in order to avoid an explosion or very violent reaction.

$$RO-P-OR + S \xrightarrow{\quad} RO-\overset{\overset{\displaystyle S}{\uparrow}}{P}-OR \tag{6}$$
$$\underset{\displaystyle OR}{\vert} \quad (solid) \qquad \underset{\displaystyle OR}{\vert}$$

Many thiophosphates have been used as insecticides, and some of these are remarkably effective. A chief limitation is their very high toxicity to man.

Phosphites

As has been mentioned in an earlier chapter, phosphorus trichloride reacts with alcohols to give phosphite esters, although phosphorus tribromide or phosphorus triiodide give alkyl halides by displacement of the phosphorus function by the more nucleophilic halogens. The trialkyl phosphite is best obtained by use of excess alcohol and a base for removal of halogen acid (Eq. 7).

$$PCl_3 + 3ROH \xrightarrow{\text{base}} (RO)_3P + 3HCl \tag{7}$$
$$\text{(excess)} \qquad \qquad \downarrow \text{base}$$
$$\text{salt}$$

Only the tri-esters of phosphorous acid are known. If only one hydroxyl remains unesterified, rearrangement to the pentavalent phosphorus compound occurs. For example, reaction of phosphorus trichloride with two equivalents of an alcohol, in absence of base, gives the dialkoxychlorophosphine (Eq. 8), and hydrolysis yields the dialkyl phosphonate.

$$PCl_3 + 2CH_3OH \longrightarrow (CH_3O)_2PCl + 2HCl$$
$$\text{Dimethoxychlorophosphine} \qquad \qquad O \qquad (8)$$
$$\underset{\displaystyle \xrightarrow[\text{HOH}]{}}{\vert} \qquad CH_3O-\overset{\overset{\displaystyle \uparrow}{}}{P}-OCH_3$$
$$\underset{\displaystyle H}{\vert}$$
$$\text{Dimethyl phosphonate}$$

Phosphonic Acids

Although most of the important naturally-occurring compounds of phosphorus are derivatives of phosphoric acid, many other types of organo-phosphorus compounds have been synthesized, and many of them have been of considerable interest. The phosphonic acids, containing the carbon-phos-phorus bond (except for the first member of the series; cf. above) have been notable for their remarkably high toxicity to animals and insects. In general, this toxicity appears to arise from interference with the enzyme system which destroys acetylcholine and thus keeps this toxic substance under control in the animal organism (cf. Chap. 19). Among the most toxic of the phosphonates is the substance called Sarin, one of the group of compounds known as "nerve

$$CH_3-\overset{\overset{\displaystyle O}{\uparrow}}{\underset{\underset{\displaystyle F}{|}}{P}}-O-\overset{}{\underset{\underset{\displaystyle CH_3}{|}}{CH}}-CH_3$$

Sarin

gases." Less than 5 mg. of this substance will kill a 150-lb. animal in a very few minutes.

Naming of phosphonic acid derivatives follows approximately the same principles used in naming sulfonic acids. Thus, Sarin is a derivative of methanephosphonic acid and would be named isopropyl methanephosphonyl fluoride.

Synthesis of phosphonic acids. Of the several methods for generating the carbon-phosphorus linkage in phosphonic acids, probably the most widely used and most versatile is the **Arbuzov synthesis.** In this reaction, a phosphonium salt is formed by mixing an alkyl halide and a trialkyl phosphite (usually the cheap methyl or ethyl ester), then the salt is heated to about 150° in order to secure displacement of the phosphorus function from alkyl by the halogen ion. Synthesis of an ethanephosphonic acid is shown in Eq. 9. The second step is an

$$(CH_3O)_3P + C_2H_5I \longrightarrow C_2H_5-\overset{\overset{\displaystyle OCH_3}{|}}{\underset{\underset{\displaystyle OCH_3}{|}}{\overset{+}{P}}}-O-CH_3 \ \ ^-I \xrightarrow{\text{heat}} C_2H_5-\overset{\overset{\displaystyle OCH_3}{|}}{\underset{\underset{\displaystyle OCH_3}{|}}{\overset{+}{P}}}-O^- + CH_3I \quad (9)$$

Dimethyl ethanephosphonate

S_N2 displacement reaction. This synthesis is most satisfactory with a primary halide, rather poor with a secondary halide. Acid chlorides are quite satisfactory and yield keto phosphonates, which have been of interest.

$$R-C-\overset{\overset{\displaystyle O}{\uparrow}}{\underset{\underset{\displaystyle OCH_3}{|}}{P}}-OCH_3$$
$$\underset{\displaystyle O}{\overset{\displaystyle \|}{}}$$

Wittig Synthesis of Alkenes

The most useful synthesis for securing unsymmetrically substituted alkenes, with no rearrangement of the double bond from the "expected" position, is that introduced by the German chemist, Georg Wittig. The starting material for this synthesis is the commercially available triphenylphosphine, which is allowed to react with an alkyl halide in a manner rather similar to the first step in the Arbuzov synthesis. As outlined in Eq. 10, this salt is dehydro-halogenated to give the interesting structure known as an **alkylidenephosphorane.** This type of compound contains carbon as the negative end of a semi-polar

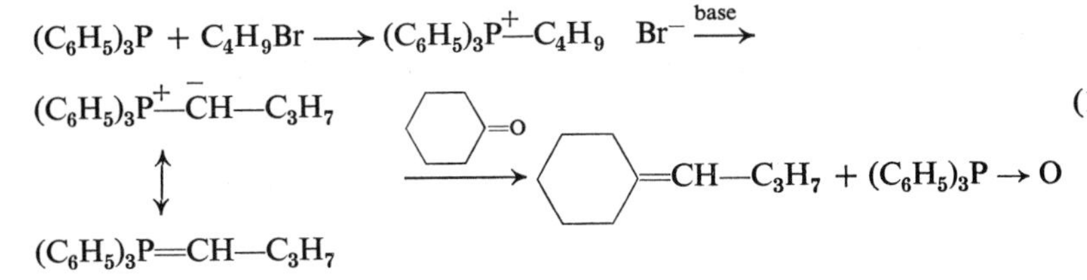

$$(C_6H_5)_3P + C_4H_9Br \longrightarrow (C_6H_5)_3\overset{+}{P}-C_4H_9 \quad Br^- \xrightarrow{\text{base}}$$

$$(C_6H_5)_3\overset{+}{P}-\overset{-}{C}H-C_3H_7 \qquad \qquad \qquad \qquad (10)$$

$$\updownarrow$$

$$(C_6H_5)_3P{=}CH{-}C_3H_7$$

double bond, a class of compounds known as **ylides.** Physical measurements indicate that this structure has a character similar to the structure containing the semi-polar double bond rather than that of the resonance form in which phosphorus is accommodating ten valence electrons.

Reaction of the phosphorane with an aldehyde or ketone gives an alkene in the manner shown in Eq. 10, and rearrangement has been noted only in very unusual structures. Cyclohexanone was used for the illustration, for the structure with the double bond in the ring (endo double bond) is of considerably lower energy than that with the double bond exo to the ring. The exo structure is quite difficult to secure by other methods.

The intermediate in the last step of the Wittig synthesis has commonly been assumed to be the following:

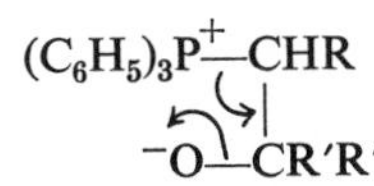

$$(C_6H_5)_3\overset{+}{P}-CHR$$
$$-O-CR'R''$$

Actually, there appears to be no evidence favoring this intermediate rather than the similar one containing two moles of the phosphorane in a quasi-ring structure similar to that of the intermediate in the Grignard reaction (cf. Eq. 13-17). Normally, a six-membered ring intermediate is likely to be favored rather than a four-membered ring. With the six-atom quasi-ring, products are the same except that a mole of phosphorane is regenerated:

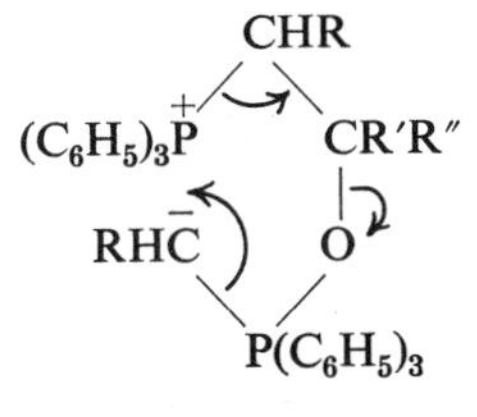

$$\begin{array}{ccc} & CHR & \\ (C_6H_5)_3\overset{+}{P} & & CR'R'' \\ RHC & & O \\ & P(C_6H_5)_3 & \end{array}$$

Sulfur Compounds

The only sulfur compounds that we have discussed in detail have been the sulfonic acids, but there have been mentioned the sulfinic acids (Eq. 18-20) and the thiols (Eq. 18-21). One amino acid containing the thiol grouping was mentioned in Chapter 25 (cysteine), and it was also mentioned that mild oxidation of cysteine would give the disulfide structure, —S—S—. This latter structure is one of the linkages holding proteins together. It may be noted that a thiol is the sulfur analog of a hydroxy compound, and a disulfide is the sulfur analog of a peroxide. There are also sulfur analogs of other functional groups containing oxygen. Thus there are the compounds thiourea (sulfur analog of urea, an amide), diethyl sulfide (sulfur analog of diethyl ether), carbon disulfide (sulfur analog of carbon dioxide), dithioacetic acid (analog of acetic acid), etc.

$$\underset{\text{Thiourea}}{\underset{\overset{\|}{S}}{H_2N-C-NH_2}} \qquad \underset{\substack{\text{Diethyl} \\ \text{sulfide}}}{C_2H_5-S-C_2H_5} \qquad \underset{\substack{\text{Carbon} \\ \text{disulfide}}}{S=C=S} \qquad \underset{\substack{\text{Dithioacetic} \\ \text{acid}}}{CH_3-\overset{\overset{\displaystyle S}{\|}}{C}\diagdown_{SH}}$$

The sulfur compounds are abundant in nature and of considerable significance. The thiol grouping appears important to the functioning of certain enzymes. Mustard gas, a toxic and corrosive compound used in chemical warfare, is bis-(β-chloroethyl)sulfide:

$$Cl-CH_2-CH_2-S-CH_2-CH_2-Cl$$
$$\text{Mustard gas}$$

Skunks use n-butyl mercaptan, C_4H_9—SH, as a chemical warfare agent. The mercaptans (aliphatic thiols, analogs of alcohols) have a particularly powerful and disagreeable odor. The sulfur analog of phosgene, thiophosgene, $Cl-\underset{\overset{\|}{S}}{C}-Cl$,

proves to be considerably less toxic than phosgene, probably because it is hydrolyzed too readily to persist for significant periods of time in the body fluids. Phosgene hydrolyzes at a surprisingly slow rate for a low molecular weight carboxylic acid chloride.

An interesting naturally-occurring cyclic disulfide is the compound first called α-lipoic acid, but more recently named thioctic acid. This substance is a factor required for normal growth of certain protozoa as well as various

$$(CH_2)_4-CO_2H$$
$$\underset{\text{Thioctic acid}}{S-S}$$

lactic acid-producing bacteria. It has been synthesized in the naturally-occurring (+)-form (asymmetric carbon marked with asterisk), as well as the (−)-form. The (−)-form exhibits no biological activity, and the RS-form has half the activity of the (+)-form, as would be expected.

The multitudinous colors found in plants result from a tremendous number of different organic compounds, and from a rather large variety of structural types. A few of the more important structural types will be cited here.

Indigo

The dyes used by men in the earliest times for which records have been discovered were of the indigo type. Ancient Egyptian mummies were wrapped in cloths dyed with indigo itself, and the substituted indigo, Tyrian purple, was also used more than 1000 years B.C. The ancient use of these dyes resulted

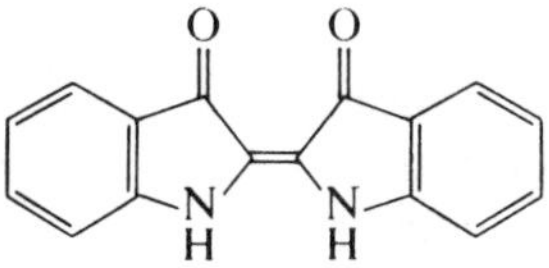

Indigo 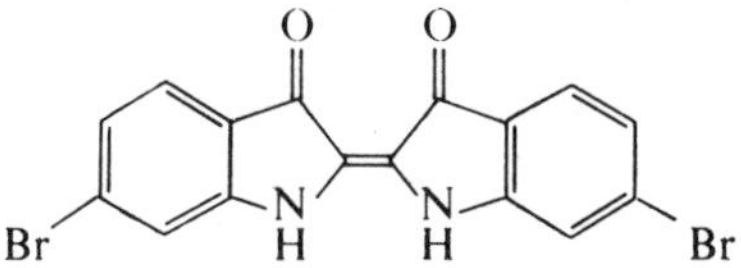   Tyrian purple

from their occurrence in natural products. Indigo was obtained from several species of European and Asiatic plants which contain a glucoside (cf. Chap. 23) of indoxyl. Hydrolysis yielded indoxyl, which gave indigo on exposure to air (Eq. 11).

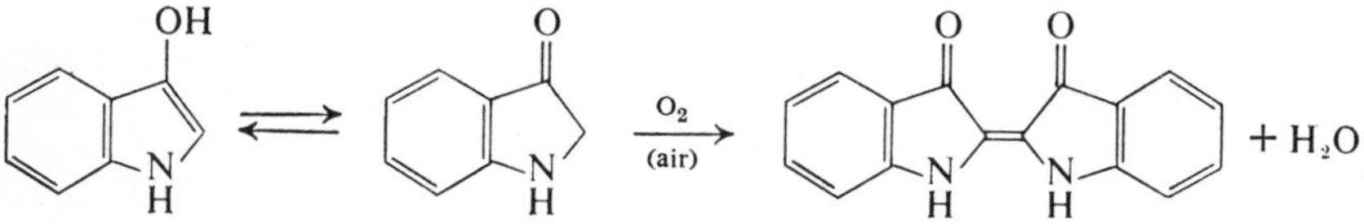

Indoxyl   Indigo

Tyrian purple was a very rare dye, for it was obtained from a species of mollusk native to the Mediterranean Sea, and a large number of mollusks were required to yield a little dye.

The growing of plants producing indigo became a large industry in Asia and in islands of the Pacific Ocean, but this source of livelihood was completely destroyed by the introduction of synthetic indigo near the end of the nineteenth century. Since that time several processes have been used to manufacture indoxyl, which gives indigo on oxidation (Eq. 11). The process which has probably been most widely used is shown in Eq. 12.

The first step in this process is an amino acid synthesis of the sort discussed in Chapter 25, and the second step is a cyclization similar to several discussed in Chapters 32 and 33. The use of substituted anilines leads to substituted indigos of different shades.

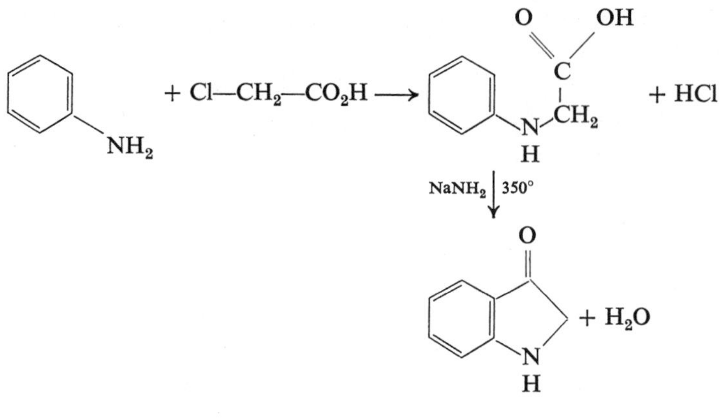

$$+ \text{HCl} \tag{12}$$

Flavones and Anthocyanidins

Many of the pigments in plants, including nearly all the red and blue pigments of flowers and fruits, are flavones or anthocyanidins. Both types of pigments are usually combined as glucosides in the plants. A representative flavone is **quercitin,** from the bark of the black oak, and a widely occurring anthocyanidin is **cyanidin chloride.**

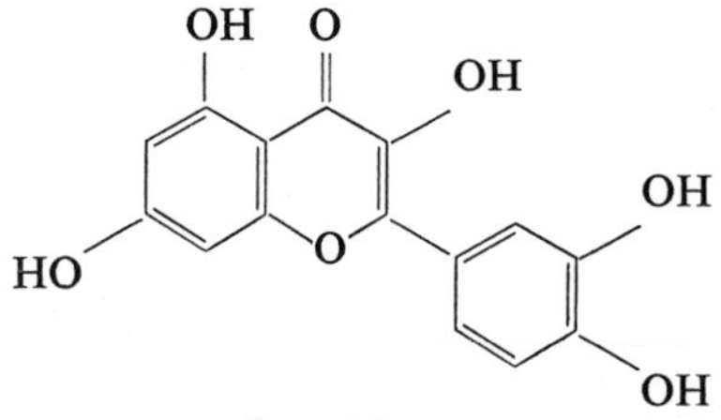

Quercitin

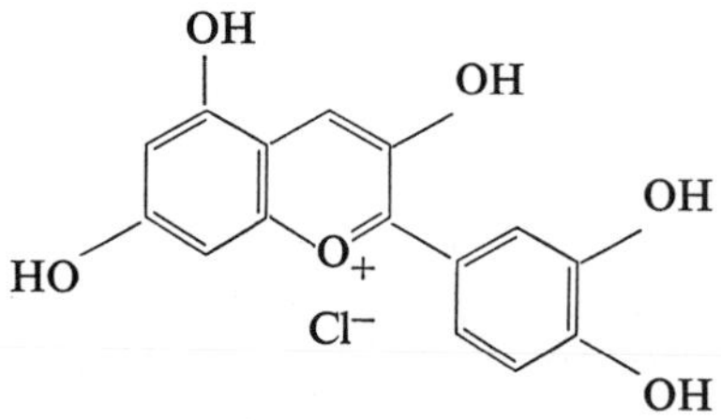

Cyanidin chloride

It will be noted that the skeletal structures of these two types of pigments are similar; the only skeletal difference is in the carbonyl group in the 4-position in the flavones. This carbonyl reduces the basicity of the cyclic ether structure so that the flavones do not form salts stable in water, as do the anthocyanidins. The salt structure in the anthocyanidins is of the oxonium type, but this particular structure is stabilized by electron delocalization in a full aromatic system. This greatly enhances the base strength of the cyclic ether.

Various shades of color result in these pigments from substitution of hydroxyl or methoxyl groups at various positions in the molecule. All the anthocyanidins have a minimum of three hydroxyls in the 3-, 5-, and 7-positions (numbering starts on the hetero atom and goes around the rings as in naphthalene).

Carotenoids

A type of pigment common in grains, fruits, and vegetables contains the carotenoid type of structure. The simplest of these pigments is probably the basic symmetrical structure found in β-**carotene,** present along with smaller amounts of α-**carotene** in carrots.

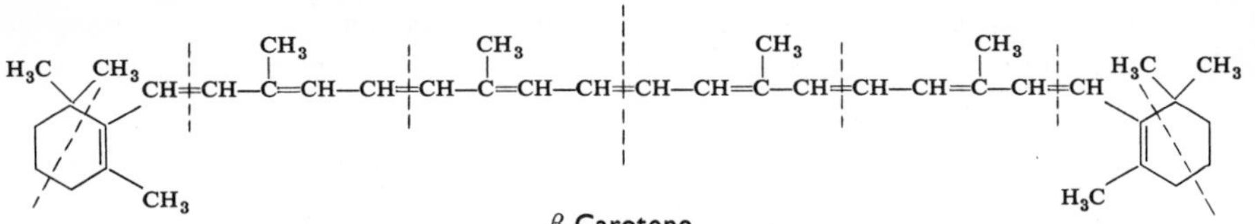

β-Carotene

Related pigments differ only in the parts shown in the formulas below:

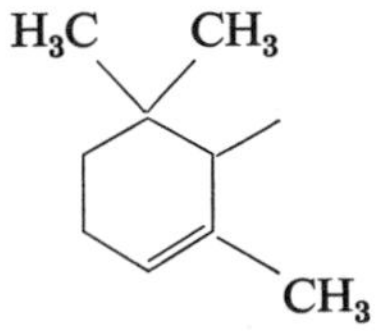

α-Carotene

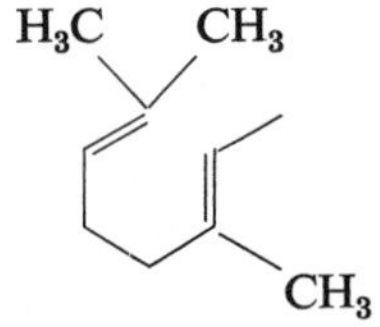

γ-Carotene

It may be noted that β-carotene is entirely symmetrical, with eleven double bonds all conjugated. In the formula, the longer dotted line indicates the center of the formula. It is of interest that it has been possible to secure terminal addition of one mole of hydrogen to the ends of this system of eleven conjugated double bonds.

α-Carotene differs from the beta isomer only in having the double bond in one terminal ring not conjugated with the remaining ten double bonds. In γ-carotene, one ring is open. Separation of these very similar compounds was accomplished by the technique of chromatography. A similar structure is **lycopene,** red pigment in tomatoes, which has both ends open in the manner of one end of γ-carotene.

It is of interest that vitamin A is the structure that would result from cleaving of β-carotene in the center and terminating the chain with addition of hydroxyl. Vitamin A is found largely in the oils of fish, and has not been

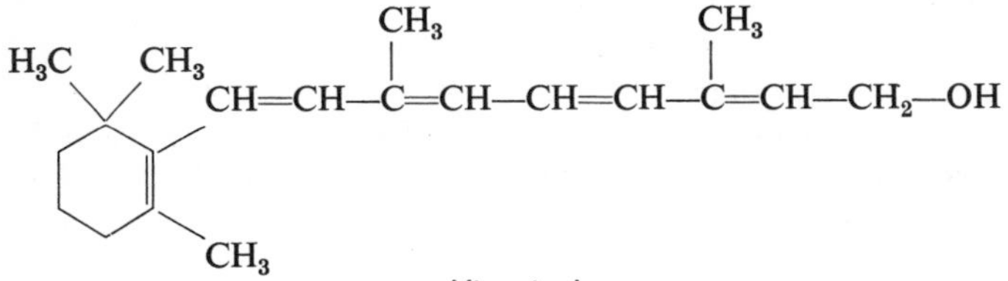

Vitamin A

found in plants, but fortunately enough, mammals are able to convert carotene to vitamin A in the liver.

Several plant pigments are hydroxyl derivatives of the carotenes. Well known ones are **zeaxanthin,** yellow pigment in corn, which has hydroxyl groups *para* to the chain in each ring of β-carotene; **xanthophyll,** partly responsible for the color of autumn leaves, which has similarly located hydroxyls in the α-carotene structure.

It is of interest that large numbers of compounds found in nature, including the carotenoids, appear to be built up from units of isoprene.

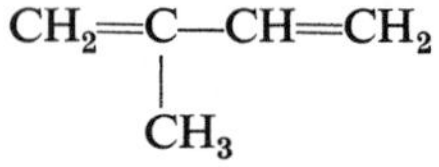

$$CH_2{=}C{-}CH{=}CH_2$$
$$|$$
$$CH_3$$

Isoprene
(2-methyl-1,3-butadiene)

The short dotted lines in the β-carotene formula indicate the manner in which the isoprene units may be blocked off. So many natural products have proved to be built of isoprene units that the "isoprene rule" has become of great value in guiding work on elucidation of the structure of natural products.

The carotenoids may be properly classed as **tetraterpenes** (cf. following section); however, they have been included in the present section because they are pigments, in contrast with most of the other terpenes.

Terpenes

A very large number of hydrocarbons occurring in the *volatile oils* of plants prove to be made up of isoprene units. As a class, these and related compounds have come to be known as **terpenes,** although one subdivision, the C_{10} compounds, is also known as terpenes. The C_{15} compounds (three isoprene units) are known as sesquiterpenes. Of the compounds containing larger numbers of isoprene units, the more important are the triterpenes, C_{30} compounds, and the polyterpenes of very high molecular weight.

In addition to the hydrocarbons made up of isoprene units, there also occur many compounds with similar skeletal structures but containing functional groups involving oxygen, usually carbonyl or hydroxyl. The terpene alcohols, ketones, and aldehydes also occur in the volatile oils of plants.

Terpenes

Most of the C_{10} compounds contain one or more rings, but a few open-chain oxygenated derivatives occur. A well-known one is **citronellal,** the chief component of oil of citronella.

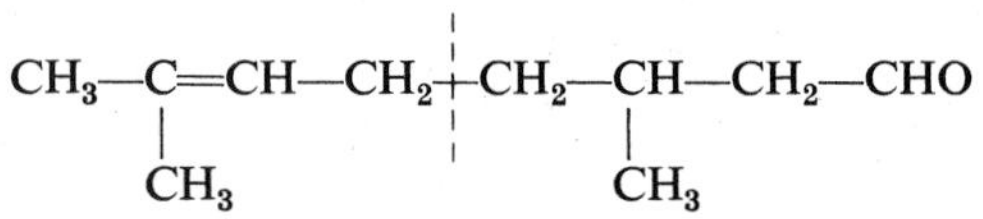

$$CH_3{-}C{=}CH{-}CH_2{+}CH_2{-}CH{-}CH_2{-}CHO$$
$$|\qquad\qquad\qquad\qquad |$$
$$CH_3\qquad\qquad\qquad\quad CH_3$$

Citronellal

The corresponding alcohol, **citronellol,** is the chief component of rose oil. In the citronellal formula, the division between the two isoprene units is indicated by the dashed line.

The monocyclic and dicyclic terpenes are quite numerous in volatile oils. Representative ones are **limonene,** chief constituent of many oils including orange oil and lemon oil, and α-**pinene,** principal component of the abundantly produced turpentine. The most common of the oxygen derivatives of this series is **camphor.** It may be noted that α-pinene is a bicyclo[3.1.1]heptene

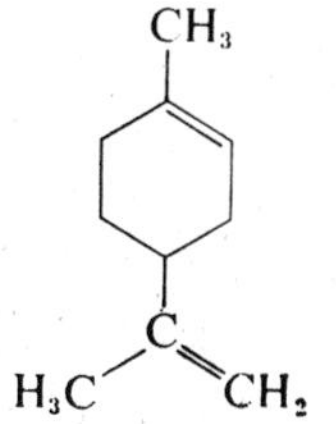

Limonene 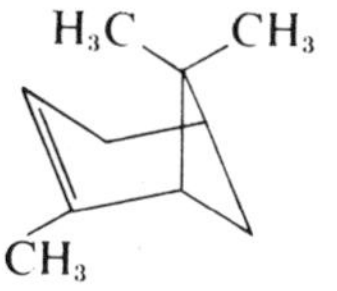   α-Pinene

which results from an additional cyclization of limonene. Camphor is a bicyclo[2.2.1]heptane whose formula has already been depicted in Chapter 7. It is quite instructive to examine molecular models of the bicyclic compounds. Some idea of the spatial arrangement of the atoms is gained from the photograph (Fig. 7-4) of the Framework Molecular Model of camphor.

Sesquiterpenes

Many of the C_{15} terpenes are hydrogenated naphthalene derivatives, and one incentive behind synthesis of alkylnaphthalenes by cyclization reactions (cf. Chap. 29) was for proof of structure of the naphthalenes obtained by dehydrogenation of sesquiterpenes. A representative dehydrogenation is that of **cadinene,** present in the oil of certain evergreen trees.

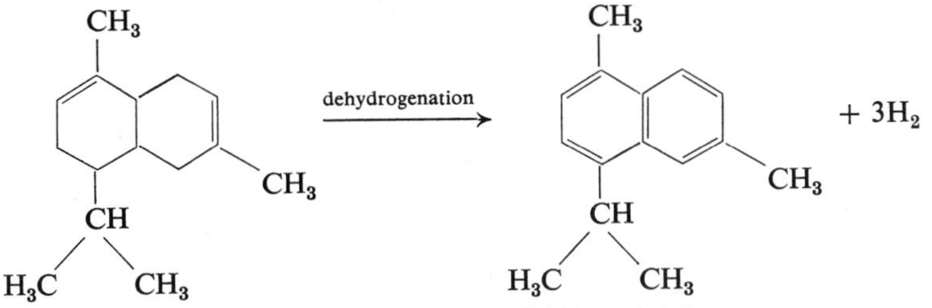

Cadinene

1,6-Dimethyl-4-
isopropylnaphthalene

$$+ 3H_2 \quad (13)$$

A particularly interesting group of sesquiterpenes are those containing fused 7-membered and 5-membered rings. Dehydrogenation of these compounds gives a ring structure containing a resonance-stabilized system of five double bonds. Illustrative is dehydrogenation of **guaiol** to give guaiazulene (Eq. 14). The parent hydrocarbon with the resonance-stabilized system of

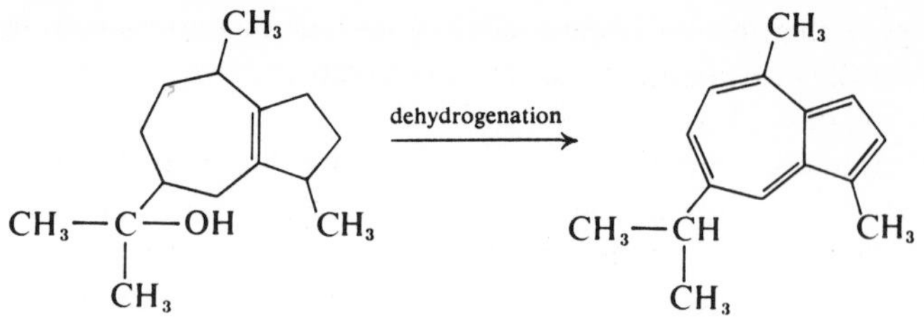

$$(14)$$

Guaiol → Guaiazulene

double bonds in the 5- and 7-membered rings is **azulene**. The two principal resonance forms may be represented as follows, although the significance of charged forms will be discussed below.

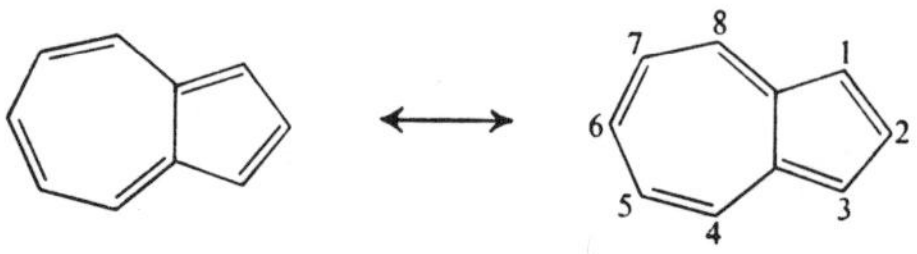

In addition to the interesting properties of azulenes discussed below, they also have a blue-violet color. Some essential oils (such as geranium oil, which contains guaiazulene) have the characteristic color of the fully dehydrogenated azulene system.

Properties of azulenes. Aromatic substitution in azulene has been studied, and initial substitution proves to be at the 1-position (note numbering in resonance structure above). Furthermore, the second substitution occurs at the 3-position, regardless of whether the first substituent is *ortho,para-* or *meta*-directing. This behavior indicates a more powerful directing influence than that normally exerted by substituents, as well as a higher electron density in the five-atom ring than in the seven-atom ring. Numerous correlations have been developed on the basis of the stability of a plus charge in a seven-atom ring (cf. tropolones, below) and a minus charge in a five-atom ring.[4] In addition, azulene proves to have a dipole moment, and this appears explicable only on the basis of an uneven charge distribution between the two rings. If charged resonance forms for the ground state of azulene are considered, it will be noted that the placement of the negative charge at the 1-position (or 3-position) gives the following resonance possibilities:

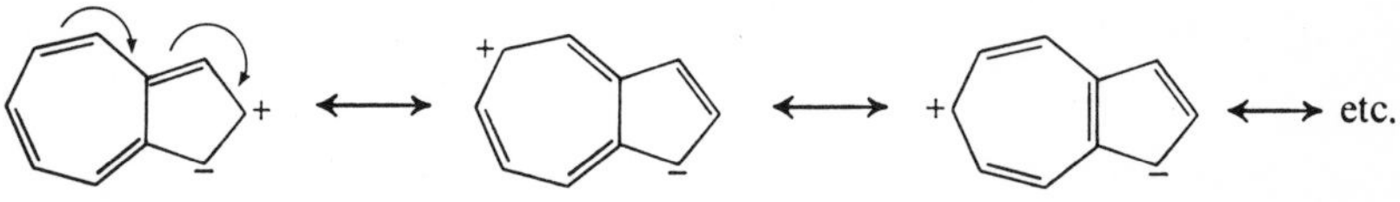

---

[4] According to the correlations first presented by the German chemist, Erich Hückel, a molecule is expected to have aromatic character and stability when the number of π-electrons in a cyclic system is equal to $4n + 2$, where n is an integer. Since azulene contains ten π-electrons ($4 \times 2 + 2$), aromatic character is predicted. For cycloheptatriene, the *cation* has six electrons ($4 \times 1 + 2$) in the π-system, while it is the *anion* of cyclopentadiene that has six electrons in the π-system.

Since the plus charge may appear on any carbon in the seven-atom ring, we may indicate the electron delocalization as follows:

If the negative charge is located at the 2-position, the positive charge may be accommodated at only certain positions (4-, 6-, 8-) in the seven-atom ring on account of the location of the double bonds in the five-atom ring:

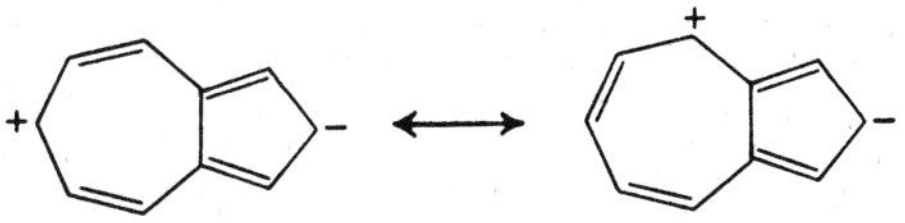

These considerations lead, then, to a prediction of substitution in the 1- and 3-positions.

If the transition state for the electrophilic substitution be considered, similar considerations are encountered, in that the following holds:

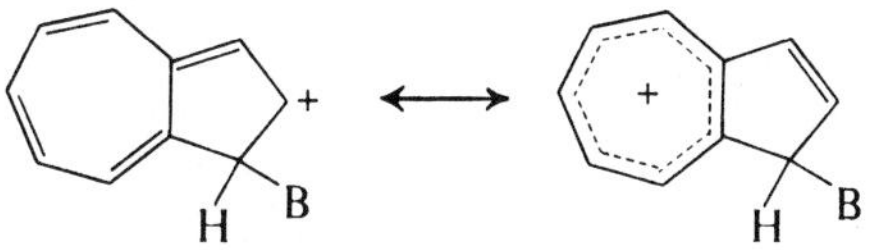

In similar fashion, the substituent in the 2-position allows only more limited electron delocalization. Thus, all considerations support substitution in the 1- and 3-positions, as observed.

An additional interesting characteristic of azulene concerns its basic properties. It will dissolve in strong acids by forming a salt (addition of a proton), which no doubt experiences resonance stabilization with the positive charge in the seven-atom ring:

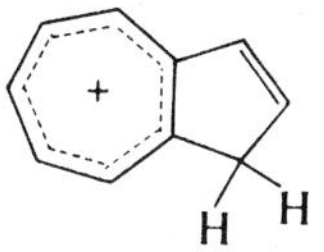

Unfortunately, the hydrocarbon azulene is available only by rather laborious syntheses, giving relatively low yields, so its chemistry has been studied largely in connection with its more novel aspects.[5]

---

[5] A paper reporting substitution reactions in azulene, and giving references to other work is that by Prof. A. G. Anderson and co-workers at the University of Washington in *J. Am. Chem. Soc.*, **75**, 4980 (1953).

Triterpenes

The C_{30} terpenes are numerous in nature, but only a few of them have structures which have been elucidated. They may have as many as five rings, and structure determination is usually very complicated.

An important open-chain triterpene is **squalene,** whose structure has been determined:

$$CH_3-\underset{\underset{CH_3}{|}}{C}=CH-CH_2-CH_2-\underset{\underset{CH_3}{|}}{C}=CH-CH_2-CH_2-\underset{\underset{CH_3}{|}}{C}=CH-CH_2 \vdots CH_2-CH=\underset{\underset{CH_3}{|}}{C}-CH_2-CH_2-CH=\underset{\underset{CH_3}{|}}{C}-CH_2-CH_2-CH=\underset{\underset{CH_3}{|}}{C}-CH_3$$

It will be noted that this structure is symmetrical about the dotted line in the center of the formula. Recent evidence has suggested that squalene may be the precursor of many of the cyclic compounds in the triterpene and sterol series. A series of fused rings may be formed in various patterns, depending on the size of the rings and the exact points of closure.

Squalene occurs very widely in nature, and is the principal component of the liver oil of certain sharks. Human skin oil appears to be more than one-fourth squalene, and the mechanics of transfer of this hydrocarbon in the body fluids seems obscure.

Polyterpenes

Several polyterpenes are found in nature, but the most useful and well-known of these is **natural rubber.** Rubber occurs in a colloidal suspension in a milky fluid known as *latex* which is found in many plants. The commercial source of this latex has been the rubber tree, native to Brazil but now grown extensively in cultivated plantations in southern Asia.

Natural rubber has been rather well established as a linear polymer of isoprene, a very high molecular weight structure similar to squalene. As is usual in such polymers, a large range of molecular weights is present in a given sample.

In **vulcanization** of rubber, it is heated with sulfur. This treatment is believed to give cross links of sulfur atoms between the hydrocarbon chains. This gives a material which is elastic over a wider range of temperatures than natural rubber, and is tougher and less prone to soften. Nearly all the rubber used for commercial purposes is vulcanized.

Steroids

Included among the steroids are a large number of compounds of extreme importance. Examples are the bile acids, the male and female sex hormones, oral contraceptives effective in the female, and many other types of compounds. Strangely enough, the exact function of the most widespread of the steroids, cholesterol, is not known. This compound is in particularly high concentration

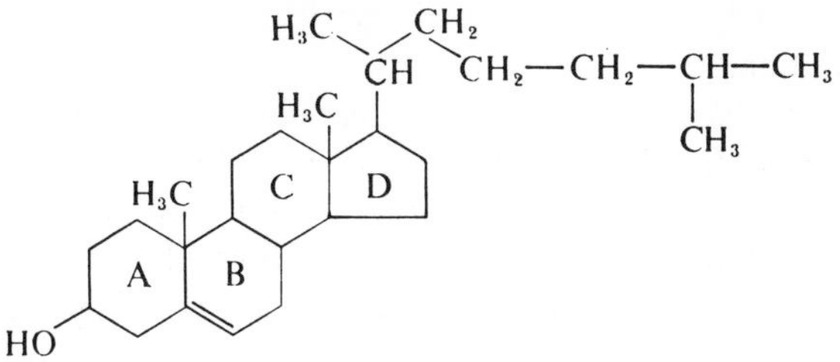

Cholesterol

in such strategic tissues as the spinal cord of mammals. The commercial source of cholesterol is the spinal cords of cattle. The basic sterol ring structure was worked out over a period of many years, and hundreds of investigators were involved. Several of the sterols were interrelated during this work so that the structures of many compounds became known as soon as the structure of one was completely elucidated. On account of its ready accessibility, cholesterol played a key role in this structural determination.

The essential characteristic of the steroid structure is the ring sequence A, B, C, and D, which may be recognized as a hydrogenated cyclopentenophenanthrene structure. This structural feature was originally established by degradation of sterol derivatives to the phenanthrene derivative known as the

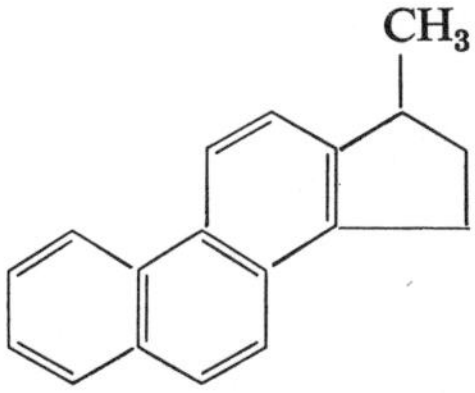

Diels hydrocarbon

Diels hydrocarbon. The structure of the Diels hydrocarbon was eventually established by synthesis. This hydrocarbon and other sterol degradation products were largely responsible for stimulation of investigation of the chemistry of phenanthrene (cf. Chap. 30).

In addition to the skeletal structure of the sterol system, another major problem has been presented by the large number of asymmetric carbons present in the molecule. A major effort was required before all important phases of the stereoisomerism of the sterols were worked out. The naturally occurring sterols have the ring junctures between B and C, as well as between C and D, *trans*. In cholesterol, there is a double bond, which eliminates the possibility of *cis* and *trans* junctures between rings A and B, but in many other sterol derivatives this double bond is absent, and members of both series of geometrical isomers are known. The compounds having rings A and B joined *trans* are said to belong to the *allo* series, while those having these rings joined *cis* are said to belong to the *normal* series. In each of these series, the hydroxyl may be on either side of the ring. From this brief account, it may be seen that there are many stereoisomers of each sterol skeletal structure. For synthesis of a naturally occurring sterol, each asymmetric carbon must be secured in the proper configuration.

Sterols in the *allo* series have an entirely linear arrangement of the rings, as shown in the conformational projections below, on account of the *trans* junctures between all rings. In the projections, the relative length of the ring is exaggerated; however, examination of a model will show the linear arrangement of the rings. In the *normal* series, the *cis*-fused end ring is at an angle.

Allo series

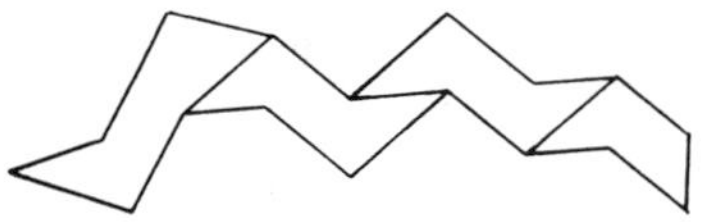

Normal series

Although the physiological function of cholesterol is not clear, many of the sterol derivatives do serve well-known functions. The several known male and female sex hormones include **estrone** (female) and **testosterone** (male). The hormone, **cortisone,** is also a sterol derivative.

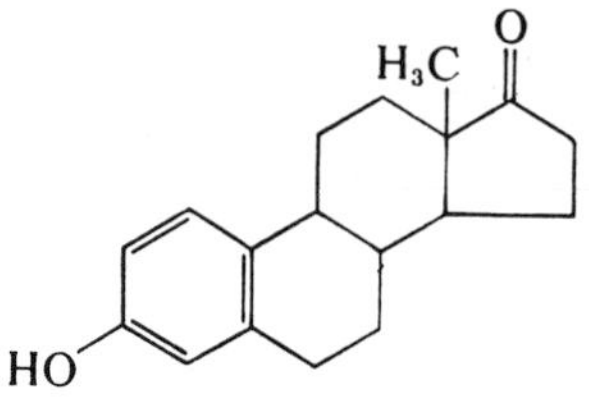

Estrone

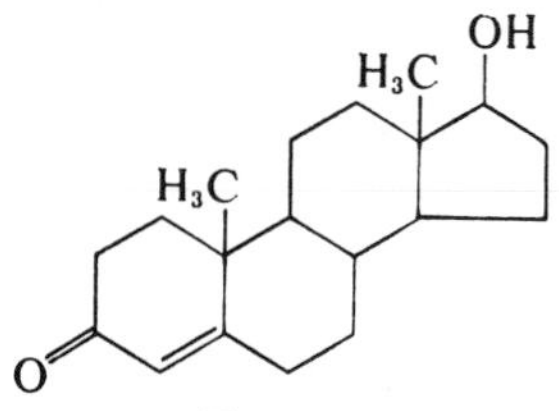

Testosterone

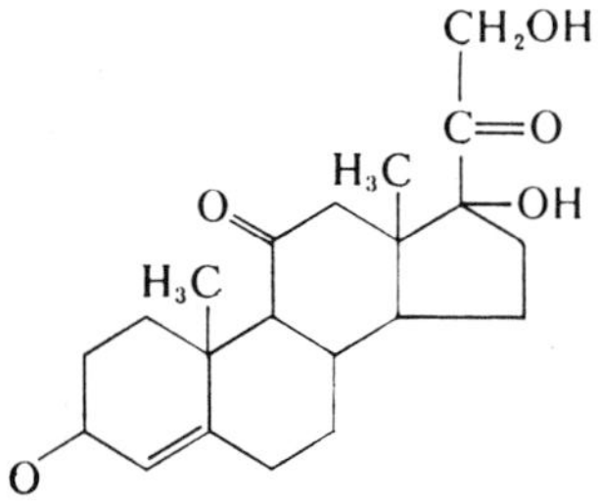

Cortisone

Investigation in the field of steroids continues to be very active, and a large volume of new material is published each month. An extensive and inclusive treatment of the literature prior to 1959 is available.[6]

---

[6] L. F. Fieser and M. Fieser, *Steroids*, Reinhold, New York, 1959.

The tropolone formula was predicted in 1945 by the British chemist M. J. S. Dewar (now at University of Texas) as a ring structure which should have the unusual properties that had been observed for certain natural products of then unknown structure. Subsequently, this brilliant deduction was shown to be accurate by the elucidation of the structures of the natural products in question. The tropolone structure cannot be properly represented in a simple formula, but for writing equations it is commonly depicted as in the following formula, in which the numbering and lettering of the ring are shown:

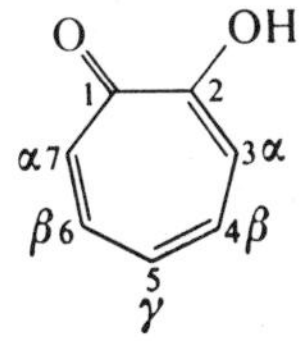

Difficulty in representing tropolone arises from the fact that there is a strong electron delocalization into the ring, evidenced in part by a high dipole moment, so that the molecule has essentially no ketonic character but is a resonance-stabilized aromatic compound. Studies by x-ray diffraction have shown that the carbon-carbon distances are all the same (1.39 Å.) and near that in benzene, but the two carbon-oxygen distances are different (1.26, 1.34 Å.). Thus, the hydrogen is not equally held between the two oxygens in the manner of a chelate ring, but is associated with one or the other oxygen. Nevertheless, it has never been possible to isolate two isomers of an α- or β-substituted tropolone; therefore it becomes necessary to assume that the hydrogen is in mobile equilibrium between the two oxygens. In view of the resonance energy of about 30 kcal., typical aromatic substitution in the α- and γ-positions, and the amphoteric nature of tropolone (discussed below), the substance is best represented as equilibrium between two resonance-stabilized tautomeric forms:

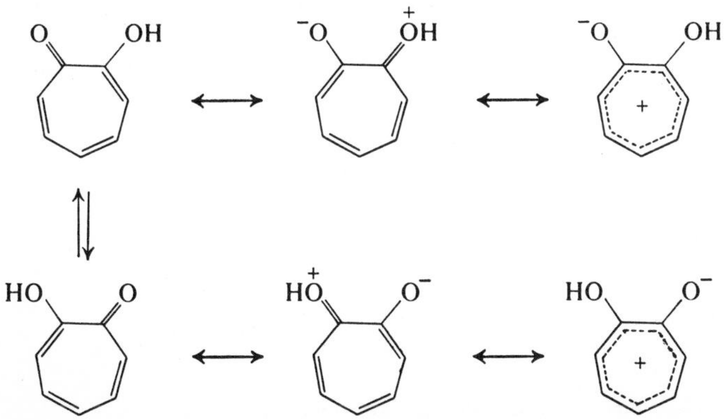

It should be emphasized that each of the resonance forms on the right actually represents seven different forms, one with the positive charge at each ring carbon.

The tropolone structure should possess significant acidity, for the anion would exhibit electron delocalization of the following type:

Not only is the resonance path large, but the two forms are equivalent. In actuality tropolone (pK_a 7) is a considerably stronger acid than is phenol. On the other hand, addition of a proton to tropolone gives a cation with a π-electron system of the $4n + 2$ type:

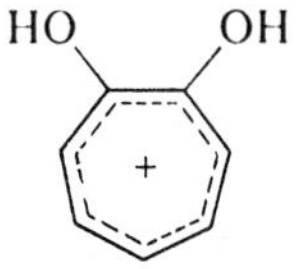

It is indeed the case that tropolone is basic. According to the theory involved, the structure without hydroxyl should be much more basic than a normal ketone, and this has proved to be the fact. Reaction of **tropone** with acid is shown in Eq. 15.

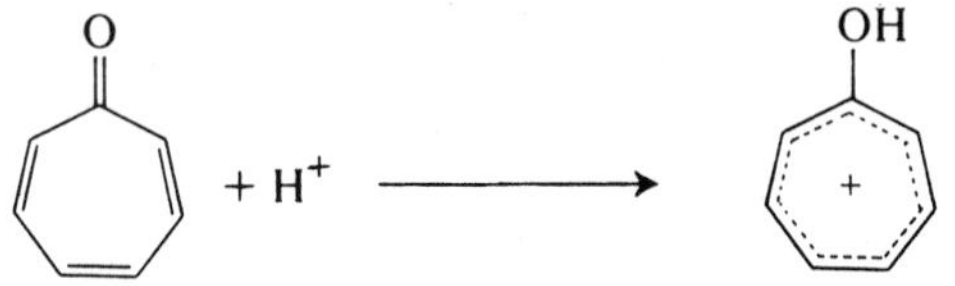

$$+ H^+ \longrightarrow \tag{15}$$

Synthesis of tropolones. Several methods have been developed for synthesis of tropolones, of which the most versatile involve synthesis of a 1,2-cycloheptanedione or a 2-hydroxycycloheptanone, followed by some type of oxidation to the aromatic system. The one that will be described uses the high-yield **acyloin condensation** to secure the hydroxyketone (Eq. 16), and this is oxidized in one net step to the tropolone. If an alkyl-substituted pimelic

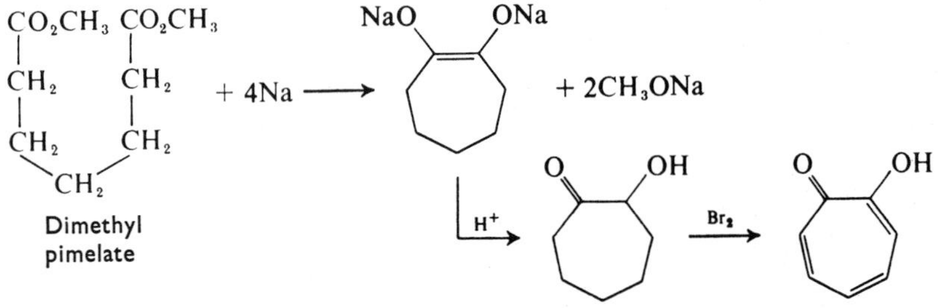

Dimethyl pimelate

$$+ 4Na \longrightarrow \qquad + 2CH_3ONa \tag{16}$$

acid be secured (cf. Chaps. 26 and 27), preparation of a substituted tropolone should be successful.

Natural products. Several natural products containing the tropolone structure have been isolated, including antibiotics and plant growth regulators. All three of the isopropyltropolones occur in the heartwood of the tree, *Thuja plicata*, and are called thujaplicins. The formula of the α-isomer is shown. Also depicted is the more highly substituted stipitatic acid, from *Penicillium stipitatum* Thom.

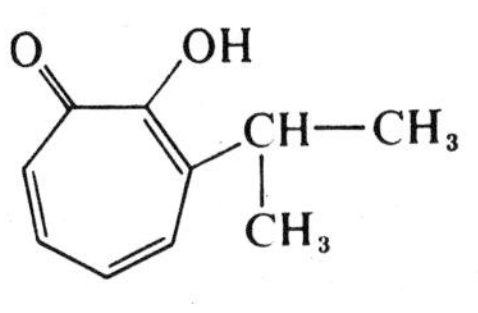

α-Thujaplicin 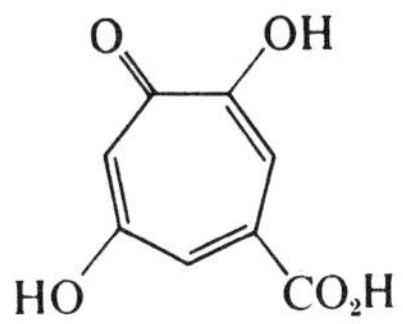   Stipitatic acid

Perhaps the most interesting of the naturally-occurring tropolones is colchicine, which has the remarkable property of affecting heredity in plants by doubling chromosomes. This molecule contains not only the tropolone ring but also an alicyclic seven-carbon ring.

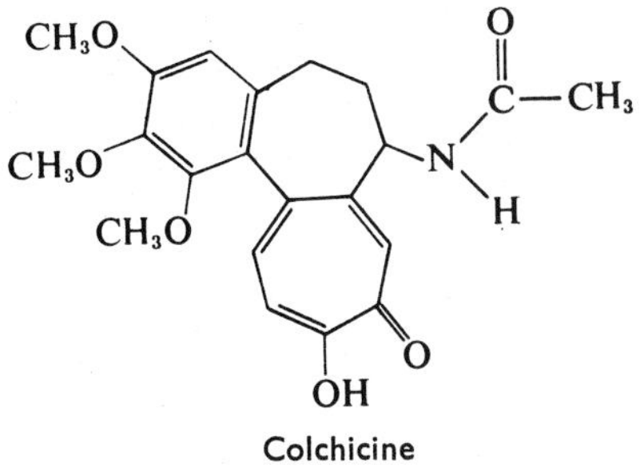

Colchicine

Large-Ring and Small-Ring Compounds

Although rings containing five or six atoms are of a size that form readily without undue strain of normal valence directions, and most organic compounds of both synthetic and natural origin contain rings of five or six atoms, there is considerable interest attached to "larger" and "smaller" rings.

Small Rings

We have already mentioned that four-membered rings may occur in nature (α-pinene), and such rings may also be synthesized in the laboratory. One method for readily securing such rings is by the alkylation of malonic ester with trimethylene dibromide (Eq. 17).

$$
\begin{array}{c}
\text{CO}_2\text{C}_2\text{H}_5 \\
| \\
^-\text{CH} \qquad + \ \text{Br—(CH}_2)_3\text{—Br} \ \longrightarrow \ \text{CH—(CH}_2)_3\text{—Br} + \text{Br}^- \\
| \qquad\qquad\qquad\qquad\qquad\qquad\quad | \\
\text{CO}_2\text{C}_2\text{H}_5 \qquad\qquad\qquad\qquad\qquad \text{CO}_2\text{C}_2\text{H}_5
\end{array}
$$

$$\downarrow \text{NaOC}_2\text{H}_5$$

$$
\begin{array}{c}
\text{CO}_2\text{C}_2\text{H}_5 \\
| \\
\text{CH}_2\text{—C—CO}_2\text{C}_2\text{H}_5 \\
| \qquad | \\
\text{CH}_2\text{—CH}_2 \qquad\qquad + \text{NaBr} + \text{C}_2\text{H}_5\text{OH}
\end{array}
$$

(17)

Diethyl 1,1-cyclobutane-
dicarboxylate

Formation of the open-chain tetra-ester is a side reaction, but under proper conditions a moderately good yield of the cyclobutane derivative may be obtained. The conclusion may be reached that although the valence angles in the four-atom ring are strained, the strain is not sufficient to seriously interfere with the stability of the molecule (cf. Chap. 7).

The diethyl cyclobutanedicarboxylate serves as a prominent source of cyclobutane derivatives by way of its conversion by normal procedures to cyclobutanecarboxylic acid (Eq. 18). This acid may be converted by orthodox

$$
\square\!\!<\!\begin{array}{c}\text{CO}_2\text{Et}\\ \text{CO}_2\text{Et}\end{array} \quad \xrightarrow[\ (2)\ \text{heat}\ ]{(1)\ \text{[HOH]}} \quad \square\!\!-\!\text{CO}_2\text{H}
$$

(18)

procedures (e.g., reduction of its ester with lithium aluminum hydride) to cyclobutylcarbinol; however, this carbinol is even more prone to rearrangement via a carbonium ion than are most *sec*-alkylcarbinols. Reaction of the alcohol with hydrogen bromide results in a large percentage of rearrangement (Eq. 19).

$$
\square\!\!-\!\text{CH}_2\text{OH} \quad + \text{HBr} \longrightarrow \quad \square\!\!-\!\text{CH}_2\text{Br} \quad \text{and} \quad \pentagon\!\!-\!\text{Br}
$$

(19)

An unusual feature of this rearrangement is that the carbonium ion with an adjacent tertiary hydrogen gives rearrangement predominantly by carbon migration to yield a secondary carbonium ion (Eq. 20) rather than by hydrogen

$$
\square\!\!-\!\overset{+}{\text{CH}_3} \quad \underset{\text{less}}{\longleftarrow} \quad \square\!\!-\!^+\text{CH}_2 \quad \underset{\text{more}}{\longrightarrow} \quad \pentagon^+
$$

(20)

migration to yield a tertiary carbonium ion. Apparently, strain in the cyclobutane ring is sufficient to make the tertiary ion in this ring size of higher energy than the secondary ion with the strain-free five-atom ring.

Cyclobutyl bromide, a useful intermediate for introducing the cyclobutyl ring via alkylation, may be obtained by use of the Hunsdiecker reaction (Eq. 21).

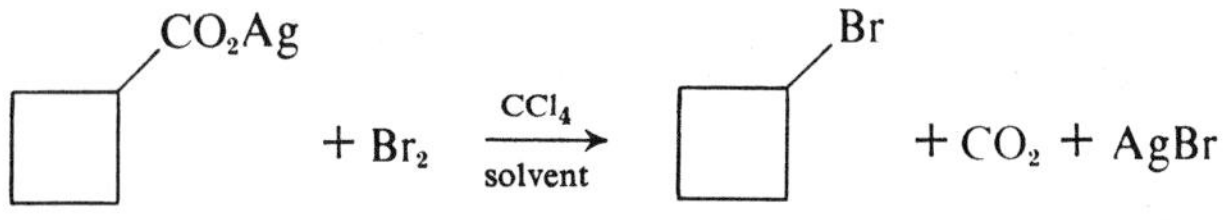

$$\underset{\text{CO}_2\text{Ag}}{\square} + Br_2 \xrightarrow[\text{solvent}]{CCl_4} \underset{\text{Br}}{\square} + CO_2 + AgBr \qquad (21)$$

Surprisingly enough, if a reaction such as shown in Eq. 17 is carried out with ethylene dibromide, **diethyl cyclopropanedicarboxylate** is formed in just as good yield as is the cyclobutane derivative formed from the three-carbon dibromide. Since it is clear that formation of a three-atom ring would strain the normal valence angles of carbon very much, it follows that the bond type in a three-membered ring must be different from that of the usual sp^3 bond with a normal valence angle of about 109°. An unusual bond structure becomes possible on account of the close proximity of the three atoms in the ring. Either of two alternate molecular orbital treatments of the bond type in the three-carbon ring suggests that the electron density should be highest at a point somewhat outside the direct line between the carbon atoms. Since the normal sp^3 bond gives highest electron density directly between the bonded atoms, the cyclopropane bond is termed a "bent bond" or a "partly unsaturated" bond. The latter designation follows from the fact that the electron density in the π-bond is highest outside the line directly connecting the two atoms (cf. Chap. 8). Furthermore, cyclopropane derivatives behave as if they were "partly unsaturated." Attempts to decarboxylate cyclopropane-1,1-dicarboxylic acid (analogous to the process in Eq. 18) give an extremely poor yield of the cyclopropanecarboxylic acid, presumably because of ring opening; therefore, the dicarboxylate is not a satisfactory source of cyclopropane derivatives. The cyclopropane ring is opened by catalytic hydrogenation somewhat less readily than an alkene is hydrogenated (Eq. 22).

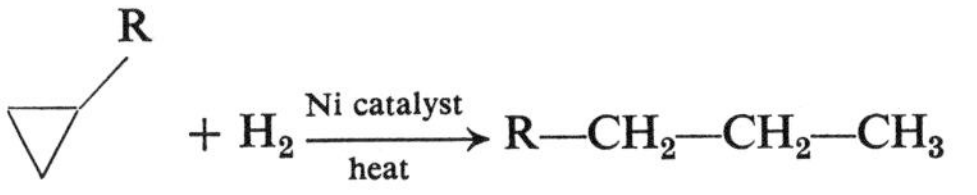

$$\underset{R}{\triangle} + H_2 \xrightarrow[\text{heat}]{\text{Ni catalyst}} R{-}CH_2{-}CH_2{-}CH_3 \qquad (22)$$

Of particular interest is the occurrence of a Michael reaction (cf. Chap. 26) which opens the cyclopropane ring (Eq. 23). It will be recalled that the

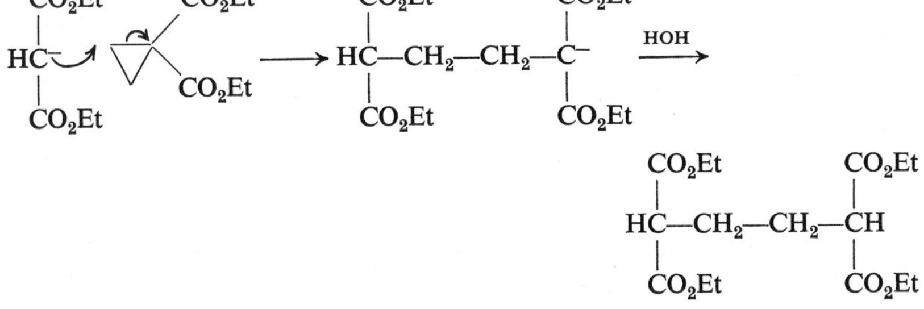

$$(23)$$

Michael reaction involves attack on the β-position in an α,β-unsaturated ester or other compound.

In recent years, cyclopropane derivatives have become readily accessible from nearly any type of alkene, by addition of methylene to the double bond. The process which accomplishes this conversion, known as the Simmons and Smith reaction, is illustrated in Eq. 24, which outlines the synthesis of the ester

$$CH_3\!-\!(CH_2)_5\!-\!CH\!=\!CH\!-\!(CH_2)_9\!-\!CO_2CH_3 + CH_2I_2 \xrightarrow[\text{couple}]{\text{Zn-Cu}}$$

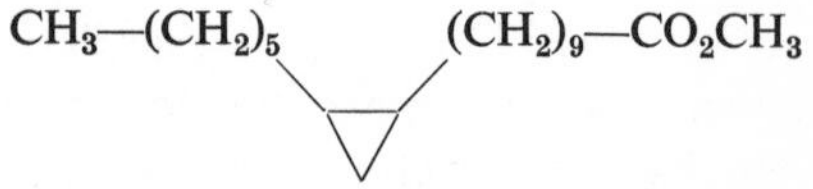

$$ \text{(24)} $$

of the interesting natural product **lactobacillic acid,** isolated from *Lactobacillus casei.* The mechanism of this useful reaction is somewhat uncertain, especially the exact function of the zinc-copper couple in converting the methylene diiodide to an organometallic reagent.

Other natural products are known which have the cyclopropane ring fused in a bicyclic system. An example is the terpene sabinene.

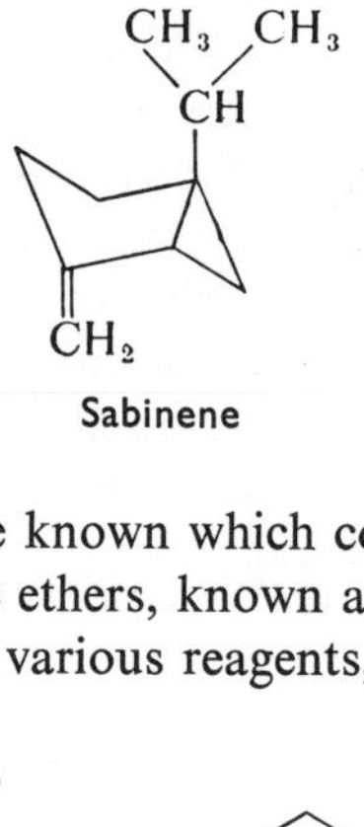

Sabinene

Numerous compounds are known which contain three-atom heterocyclic ring systems. Three-atom cyclic ethers, known as **epoxides,** are readily formed by oxidation of an alkene with various reagents, especially per-acids (Eq. 25).

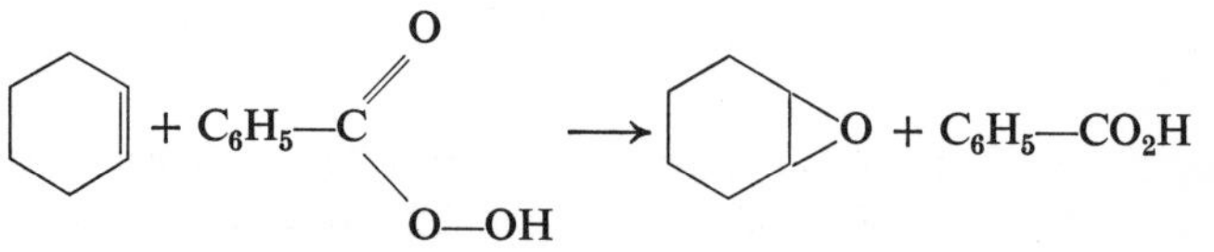

$$ \text{(25)} $$

Perbenzoic acid

The epoxide ring is readily opened with acidic catalysis to give vicinal disubstituted compounds. Hydrolysis to a *vic*-diol is shown in Eq. 26. Since the ring is opened by a backside nucleophilic attack on the protonated ether, the *trans* geometry results.

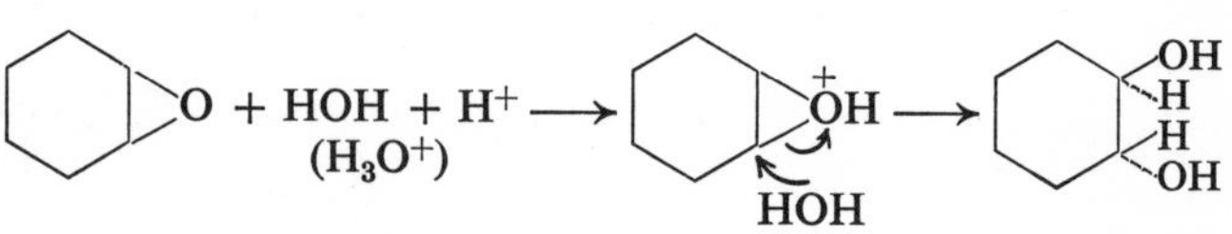

$$ \text{(26)} $$

Ethylene oxide, CH_2——CH_2, and ethyleneimine, CH_2——CH_2, which are

O

N
H

available commercially at a relatively modest price, are useful reagents for synthesis.

Highly strained small–ring systems. By means of reactions in which very high-energy transition states may be attained, it has been possible to secure polycyclic compounds whose structures involve a remarkable amount of strain.[7] A particularly successful method for securing such high-energy species is by irradiation with ultraviolet light. Absorption of a quantum of energy at these wavelengths can yield radical or bi-radical intermediates capable of passing to the highly strained systems.

Among the compounds whose existence appears improbable but which have been obtained by irradiation are bicyclobutane (Eq. 27) and quadricyclane (Eq. 28). The latter compound, in spite of its remarkable geometry, is relatively

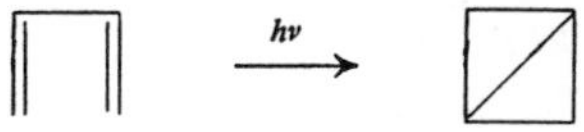

1,3-Butadiene   Bicyclobutane

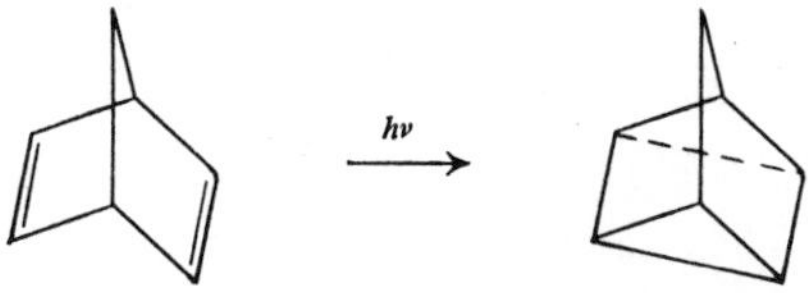

$$(27)$$

Norbornadiene   Quadricyclane

$$(28)$$

easily accessible, so some of its chemical properties have been investigated. Heating to about 200° gives the valence-bond isomer, norbornadiene, from which the quadricyclic compound had been obtained by irradiation. Catalytic hydrogenation of quadricyclane yields norbornane (hydrogenated norbonadiene) readily. The instability of the quadricyclane ring system is illustrated especially vividly by its reaction with as mild a reagent as acetic acid to give products with one or two of the rings opened (Eq. 29).

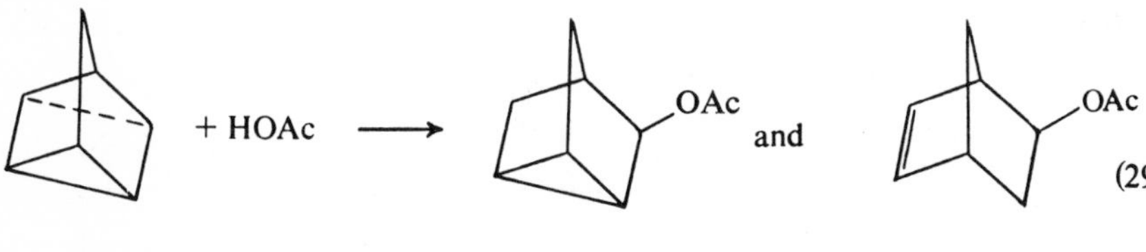

$$+ \text{ HOAc} \longrightarrow \quad \text{and} \qquad (29)$$

[7] The properties and methods of synthesis of strained polycyclic systems consisting of three- and four-membered rings have been reviewed by D. Seebach, *Angew. Chem. internat. edit.*, **4,** 121 (1965).

A rather complex sequence of reactions was used to arrive at the exotic structure of cubanedicarboxylic acid:

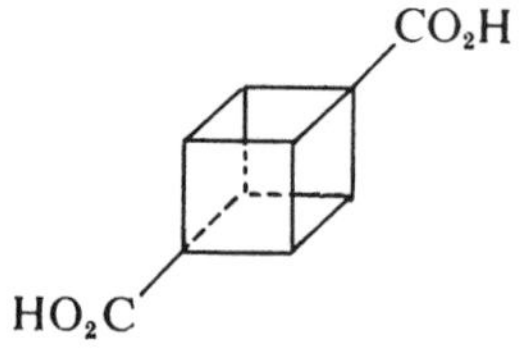

Cubane seems an appropriate name for a compound which is a cube.

Large Rings

We have discussed earlier in this chapter the occurrence of seven-membered aliphatic rings in nature, and have previously mentioned the occurrence of still larger rings (cf. Chap. 15, footnote 1). Rings of more than seven atoms are able to adopt various multiplanar conformations. Indeed, a cycloalkene with as many as eight carbons can be obtained in both *cis* and *trans* forms. The rings of eight to ten carbons, usually termed of "intermediate size" are especially difficult to secure by cyclization. The difficulty appears to involve the statistical improbability of the ends getting together when there is such a long flexible chain between them. After forming, the rings of intermediate size are able to adopt conformations involving little strain. The most successful method for securing the rings of intermediate size has been the acyloin condensation (cf. Eq. 16).

Numerous **transannular reactions** have been observed in the rings of medium or large size. These are reactions across the ring, which become possible because of the proximity in space of the atoms involved. A typical reaction of this sort is solvolysis of cyclooctene oxide with formic acid. After hydrolysis of the initially formed formate, the products consist of a mixture of the 1,2-

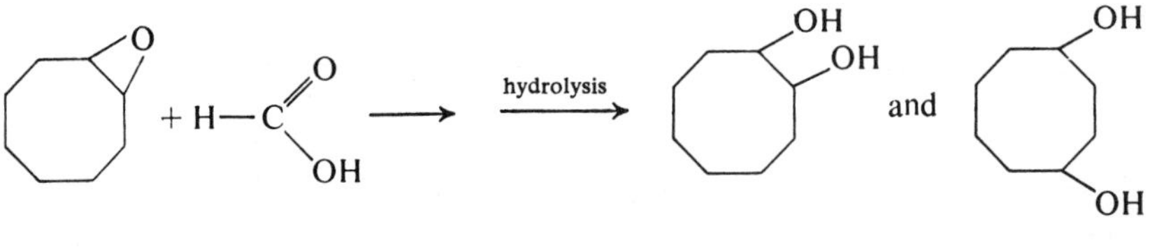

$$(30)$$

and 1,4-diols (Eq. 30). The transition state proposed for the transannular reaction leading to the 1,4-diol is as follows:

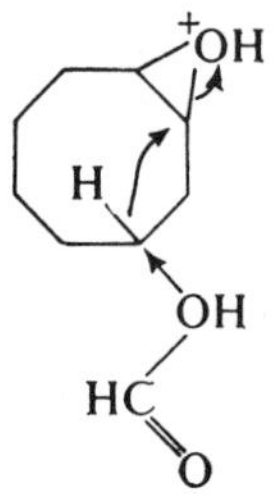

Cyclooctatetraene. Prior to World War II, an unequivocal synthesis of cyclooctatetraene had not been accomplished; however, the German chemist, Reppe, as a part of his war-time investigation of acetylene chemistry, accomplished the large scale polymerization of acetylene under very specific conditions to give the eight-atom ring with four double bonds (Eq. 31).

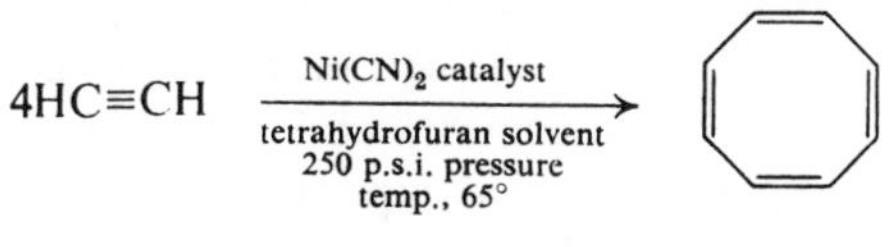

$$4HC\equiv CH \quad \xrightarrow[\substack{\text{tetrahydrofuran solvent} \\ 250 \text{ p.s.i. pressure} \\ \text{temp., } 65°}]{Ni(CN)_2 \text{ catalyst}} \quad \text{(octagon ring structure)} \qquad (31)$$

It might be assumed, at first consideration, that cyclooctatetraene would be a resonance-stabilized molecule, since one can write what appear to be resonance forms by placing the double bonds in alternate positions. For such forms to truly represent resonance forms, however, the ring must be planar, and this condition is not met. The cyclooctatetraene ring is multiplanar, and the molecule has no significant amount of resonance energy. It is of interest that this molecule also does not satisfy the Hückel rule, which predicts that either six or ten electrons $(4n + 2)$ must be in the π-system for the molecule to exhibit aromatic character.

In accord with its highly unsaturated nature, since there is no resonance stabilization, cyclooctatetraene is a very reactive substance, which polymerizes readily on standing. Many of its reactions result in rearrangement to a benzene derivative, as is illustrated by the reaction that occurs in presence of only a trace of acid (Eq. 32).

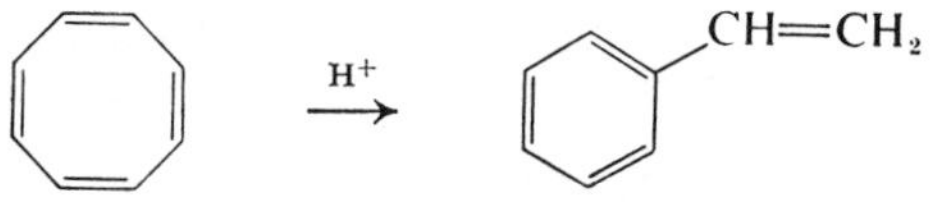

$$\text{(octagon ring structure)} \quad \xrightarrow{H^+} \quad \text{(styrene structure)} CH=CH_2 \qquad (32)$$

Styrene

The reaction shown in Eq. 32 was of considerable importance in Germany during World War II, for styrene was a component of the synthetic rubber which was manufactured at that time. This process, therefore, made possible the conversion of acetylene (from coal and limestone) to rubber.

Pharmaceutical Chemistry

In pharmaceutical chemistry, the search is for compounds which will have either a beneficial effect on man or a detrimental effect on microorganisms which have proved to be enemies of man. Since a particular physiological effect is desired, the type of chemical structure that will be encountered is unpredictable, and there is a powerful natural influence tending to make pharmaceutical chemists versatile. Mention has already been made of drugs of many types: carbohydrates, aromatic compounds, aliphatic compounds, pyridine derivatives, and quinoline derivatives. Of particular interest during the two decades following World War II have been the **antibiotics** produced by living organisms, often some strain of mold.

Antibiotic is a rather loosely defined term, but in general it applies to a compound made by a microorganism, which is destructive to microorganisms. Man has long searched for chemical compounds that will kill microorganisms which attack him but will not kill man. The closest to realization of this goal has come with the antibiotics. Several have been found which are lethal to certain types of bacteria, and sublethal to man in doses that are effective against the microorganisms. This is always a matter in delicate balance, however, so use of such drugs is most wisely reserved for a real emergency.

In general, the antibiotics have been of unusual and complicated structure, and synthetic methods have rarely been able to compete with molds in making them. Search for new antibiotics has consisted largely of hunting for new strains of molds, growing them, and investigating their metabolic products. In this field, the work of the chemist and bacteriologist meet.

The first of the antibiotics was **penicillin,** fabulously expensive during World War II, a few cents a dose by 1950. In the following formula, the R may be any of several groups; the effectiveness of the drug seems involved with the combination of reduced thiazole ring and four-atom lactam (cyclic amide) ring. The most common penicillin is **penicillin G,** which has R = benzyl.

Penicillin

The structure of penicillin was deduced only after an intensive program under great pressure had been directed at the problem for a period of years. Infrared spectroscopy furnished the key which broke the problem. The hope was that if the structure were known the compound could be synthesized at lower price, but a cheap synthesis has never been devised. Meanwhile, there have been discovered strains of the mold, *Penicillium*, which give such a high yield of the antibiotic that synthetic competition seems forever eliminated. The indigo growers did not fare so well.

Probably the most extensively utilized antibiotics are a group having the exceedingly complex structure known as **tetracycline.**

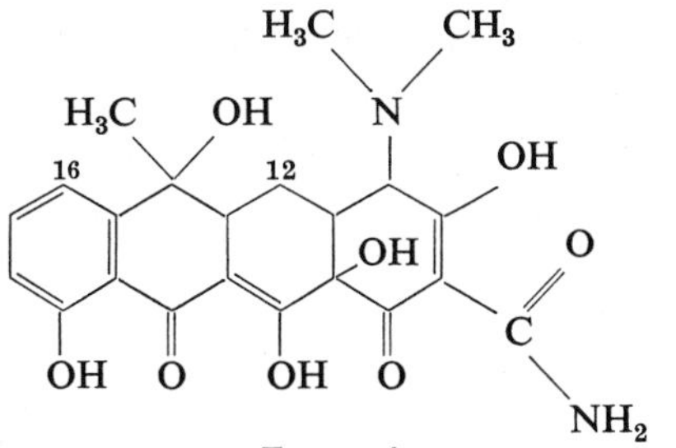

Tetracycline

Compounds with this basic structure have proved able to kill a "broad spectrum" of bacteria. Many infectious organisms not injured by penicillin, streptomycin, or other antibiotics, are destroyed by tetracycline. Two derivatives of tetra-cycline which have been useful are **aureomycin,** which has chlorine at the carbon marked 16 in the formula, and **terramycin,** which has hydroxyl at the carbon marked 12 in the formula.

Perhaps the sites of greatest activity in the drug industry during recent years have involved sterol chemistry (especially the search for oral contracep-tives), antibiotics, growth factors, drugs effective against mental illness, and alkaloids. Although the alkaloids include drugs of use against a variety of man's ailments, there has been a particularly intensive search for compounds having the pain-relieving properties of the narcotics (such as morphine) but not possessing the addicting action. This search has been rather frustrating, in that the analgesic properties and addiction liability seem intertwined. Nevertheless, the search in the above-mentioned areas, as well as others, continues; and the commercially employed research manpower in this field has become so large that forward strides are being made at an encouraging pace.

Mass Spectra of Organic Molecules

Mass spectra differ from other types of spectra in that there is not involved a distribution of energies but a distribution of ion masses. Vapor of the organic molecule at very low pressure is bombarded with electrons of sufficient velocity to knock electrons out of the valence orbitals of the molecule. This gives a positive ion of the same mass as the molecule, which is important; but of even more utility is the fact that a bond which has lost an electron usually ruptures to yield a radical and a positive ion. There has been a limited application of mass spectroscopy to negative ions, but very limited. The positive ions have yielded most of the useful information and are therefore the focus of major interest. These ions are accelerated with a voltage applied at the source of fragmentation, then deflected in a magnetic field. The amount of deflection in a given field is a function of the mass of the ion and the charge that it carries, so the mass of the ion may be determined from the amount of deflection. In the best instrument of this type,[8] there is no problem in securing unit resolution at masses as high as 800.

The molecular ion. In most compounds, the molecular ion (frequently termed M) is readily distinguished since it is the highest mass ion in significant abundance, and it is immediately followed by much less abundant ions in a definite ratio due to the natural ratio of deuterium and carbon-13 in organic compounds. If the ion which is most abundant in the spectrum, known as the **base peak,** is used as a reference of relative intensity, as is normally done, the intensity of the molecular ion is usually in the range of 2–25% of the base peak. In instances where the molecule is fragmented with unusual difficulty, the molecular ion may be of higher intensity; in other instances, an unusually easy reaction in the ion beam may make the intensity of the molecular ion very low or even zero.

In cases where the molecular ion[9] is of unusually high intensity, this generates no problem, indeed makes its location quite easy. In instances where the molecular ion is unusually low, or nearby ions are relatively high, serious uncertainty may arise as to the molecular weight, which is an important datum obtainable from the mass spectrum. Frequently, gaining of some chemical knowledge of the nature of the molecule helps identify the molecular ion. For example, alcohols are notorious for losing water (mass 18) so readily that the molecular ion becomes quite small, sometimes disappears. The ion at M − 18 for an alcohol is nearly always more intense than M. Indeed, this behavior of an alcohol in the electron beam is frequently of considerable diagnostic value for detection of an alcohol. The finding may then be confirmed by conversion of the alcohol to its acetate. This eliminates the M − 18 ion and gives a molecular ion at 42 units higher mass than M for the alcohol.

Another structure giving an unusual spectrum in the region of the molecular ion is a nitrile. Due to proton loss or capture in the ion beam, M − 1 and M + 1 are nearly always more intense than M. Again, this behavior can be turned to diagnostic value for detection of the cyano grouping. Alcoholysis to an ester can be used to confirm the presence of the cyano grouping.

As is already apparent, the mass spectrometer can be used in conjunction with simple "wet chemistry" to learn a great deal about structure in organic

---

[8] There is an increasing use of the "double-focussing" type of mass spectrometer, which is considerably more expensive; also the data can be reduced to usable form only with considerably more effort (preferably with use of a computer). In this type of machine, focussing is done with a magnetic field and also with an electric field. For some types of problem, the high-resolution machine (double-focussing) is able to contribute data not available from the single-focussing machine. In particular, molecular formulas of molecules containing several nitrogen and oxygen atoms may not be ascertainable without the ability of the high-resolution machine to assign masses to four decimal places. Other distinctions, as between ethylene and N_2, can also be accomplished.

[9] Although the ions of interest in mass spectra are nearly always singly-charged ions, and the doubly-charged ions give a recognizable type of signal in the recorder tracing of the ion beam, the ions are always described in terms of the mass divided by the charge, m/e. When the charge is unity, of course m/e is equal to the mass.

molecules; however, the greatest amount of information comes from a study of the pattern of fragmentation which occurs under electron impact.

Fragmentation patterns in mass spectrometry. Although mass spectrometry has been in wide use only since about 1960, it is such a powerful tool in determining structure that considerable research manpower has been channelled towards accumulating data necessary for more effective application of the device. The correlations possible from mass spectra are basically empirical in nature; however, a study of known compounds has made it possible to establish patterns of fragmentation characteristic of specific structures.[10] In order to illustrate the system used for this type of work, the esters of fatty acids will be considered. The methyl ester usually gives a fragmentation pattern more easily interpreted than that of other esters or the acid. The amide is frequently as useful as the methyl ester, and is a derivative that is frequently a solid, hence sometimes more amenable to purification. The only complication in the amide spectrum is that a second set of ions arising from the nitrile may also appear and make the spectrum more laborious to analyze. At the outset, it should be emphasized that principles analogous to those discussed below for methyl esters have been worked out for complicated polycyclic alkaloids and sterols.

In the **fragmentation pattern of a methyl ester** without an α-substituent a very prominent ion is at m/e 74; it is usually the base peak. This characteristic ion, of specific diagnostic value for identifying the ester function, has been shown (by use of compounds appropriately substituted with deuterium) to consist of the methoxycarbonyl group together with the α-carbon and substituent hydrogens *plus a hydrogen from the γ-carbon*. If the γ-carbon is substituted with deuteriums, the ion becomes of m/e 75. There is little doubt that this ion arises by way of a cyclic structure which transfers hydrogen to the oxygen which bears the charge from loss of an electron (Eq. 33). Since reactions

$$\tag{33}$$

[10] Several books and other types of review articles have been published which are a tremendous help in reducing the mass spectral data to useful applications. Of use as a general introduction to mass spectrometry is the book by Klaus Biemann, *Mass Spectrometry: Organic Chemical Applications*, McGraw-Hill, New York, 1962. A treatise containing chapters on various aspects of mass spectrometry, written by experts in the respective fields, has been edited by F. W. McLafferty, *Mass Spectrometry of Organic Ions*, Academic Press, London, 1963. A book giving extremely useful summaries of fragmentation of various structures, with emphasis on deduction of fragmentation patterns, is that by H. Budzikiewicz, C. Djerassi and D. H. Williams, *Interpretation of Mass Spectra of Organic Compounds*, Holden Day, San Francisco, 1964.

in the ion beam are those of radicals or radical ions, a single electron is normally transferred rather than a pair. This is indicated by an arrow with a single barb, as is the practice in discussions of radical chemistry (Chap. 11). Since the alkene that results from this fragmentation is neutral, it is not seen in the ion beam unless it is further fragmented to yield some recognizable ion (cf. illustration below); however, the m/e 74 fragment, known as the **rearrangement ion,** is observed as a highly diagnostic feature of ester fragmentation.

It follows directly from the fragmentation pattern in Eq. 33 that an alpha substituent in an ester is immediately recognized because the ion at m/e 74 is replaced by a higher mass ion. For example, a methyl substituent gives the base peak at m/e 88 (74 + 14), two methyls or one ethyl gives m/e 102, etc. Thus alpha substituents are immediately recognized with reliability.

In case there is a branch in a chain in any alkane, including the chain in an ester, there is a greater ease of rupturing the bond adjacent to the branch. In addition, an ester gives a facile rupture of the β,γ-bond even in a straight chain; therefore, a β-methyl in an ester causes a particularly large ion current for the mass 101 (in absence of another substituent in the α-position), which is due to $-CH-CH_2-CO_2CH_3$. Frequently 101 will be the base peak rather than
$\quad\quad\; |$
$\quad\;\; CH_3$
74, although 74 will remain quite large if there is no α-substituent. Of course a β-substituent larger than methyl gives a correspondingly heavier ion.

Substituents more remote from carboxyl than the beta position can also be located reliably on account of the tendency for a facile bond rupture adjacent to a branch. The ion containing the ester group is more abundant than those from the hydrocarbon end of the chain, presumably because of the ease with which an electron is knocked out of the oxygen-containing functional group. Thus, examination of the homologous ions containing oxygen reveals a characteristic "high-low-high" pattern for the reasons illustrated:

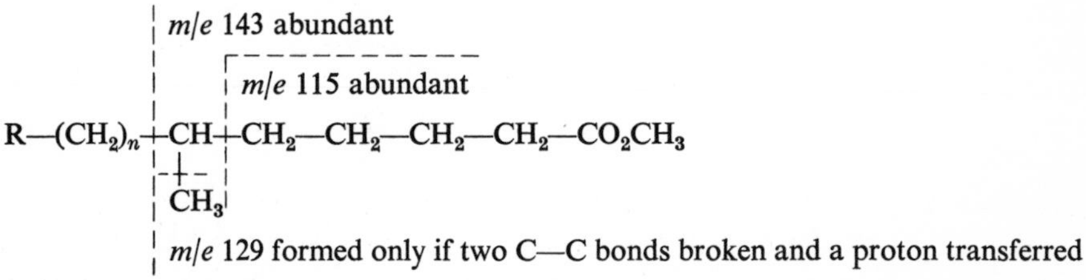

m/e 143 abundant

$\quad\quad$ m/e 115 abundant

$R-(CH_2)_n+CH+CH_2-CH_2-CH_2-CH_2-CO_2CH_3$
$\quad\quad\quad\quad | + |$
$\quad\quad\quad\; CH_3$

m/e 129 formed only if two C—C bonds broken and a proton transferred

The mass spectral features just discussed may be graphically illustrated by considering appropriate parts of the spectrum actually obtained from the ester of a branched-chain acid isolated from petroleum, as assembled in Table 1. It should be realized that large numbers of other ions are observed, especially those for alkyl (C_nH_{2n+1}), alkyl − 1 and alkyl − 2. It will be noted in Table 1 that the β-substituent is prominently revealed by the base peak at m/e 101. In addition, at m/e 143, 157, and 171 there occurs a conspicuous high-low-high pattern which reveals the branching methyl at the 7-position. The terminal isopropyl group is not reliably revealed by the mass spectrum, so it is fortunate that the infrared spectrum contains highly diagnostic absorption bands for the isopropyl group. Skeletal vibrations of the entire isopropyl group give a strong infrared band at 8.55 μ, while vibrations of the CH grouping give a characteristic doublet at 7.25 and 7.30 μ. Thus, use of spectra, especially the mass spectra, made possible determination of the structure of this acid with only a few milligrams available. Without the spectra, determination of such a structure, with branches remote from the functional groups, is difficult, if at all possible, even with large samples available.

Not all the details of the mass spectra of carboxylic acid esters have been included above, but some of the important ones have been mentioned. It is

Table I

**Diagnostic Features of the Mass Spectrum of
Methyl 3,7,11-trimethyldodecanoate**

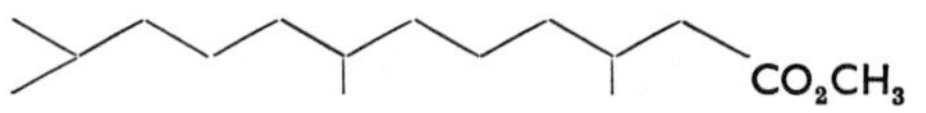

m/e	n in formula $-(CH_2)_n-CO_2CH_3$	Relative intensity
74	a	81.2%
87	2	5.3
101	3	100.
115	4	2.0
129	5	2.5
143	6	5.0
157	7	0.2
171	8	5.0
185	9	0.2
199	10	0.5
241	b	2.0
256	c	2.6

> [a] This is the rearrangement ion.
> [b] Ion for M — 15.
> [c] The molecular ion.

probably worthwhile to describe the behavior of one other structure as an illustration of the type of information that becomes available from the mass spectrum. It may be noted in Table 1 that the ion for M — 15 is not particularly prominent, in spite of the fact that the molecule being fragmented has four methyl groups in it. This results from the fact that M — 15 can be formed only if an electron is knocked out of the molecule and the methyl radical leaves (with a single electron) so as to give a positive ion from the remainder of the molecule. Since the methyl radical is of higher energy than larger alkyl radicals, this discourages fragmentation yielding the methyl radical. Similarly, the higher stability of *sec*-alkyl radicals encourages the fragmentation at a branch in a chain. In cases where the M — 15 ion is relatively abundant (more than 1–2% of the base peak), *there must be some structural feature present which gives an unusually low-energy ion.* Such a structure is a *gem*-dimethyl grouping,

CH_3—$\overset{\displaystyle |}{\underset{\displaystyle |}{C}}$—$CH_3$, for this gives the tertiary positive ion, which is a low-energy

type. Another variety of ion which is especially stable is an allylic ion, for it is resonance-stabilized. A striking illustration of this principle, and of certain other features of mass spectra, was encountered in establishing the structure of another acid from petroleum, 2,2,6-trimethylcyclohexylacetic acid, whose ester is shown below.

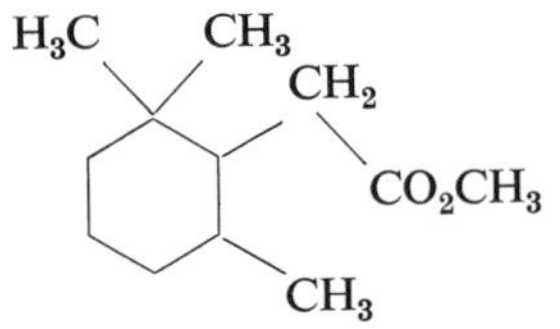

An unusual feature of the mass spectrum of this ester was an M — 15 ion of about 15%, very large indeed for this ion, while an initially puzzling feature was an even larger ion population (about 40%) at m/e 109. The large M — 15 ion population is reasonably explained by the tertiary carbonium ion resulting after loss of methyl at the *gem*-dimethyl structure. It was eventually realized that the m/e 109 ion arises from loss of methyl from the alkene resulting after loss of the rearrangement ion, as depicted in Eq. 34. The resultant ion is not only

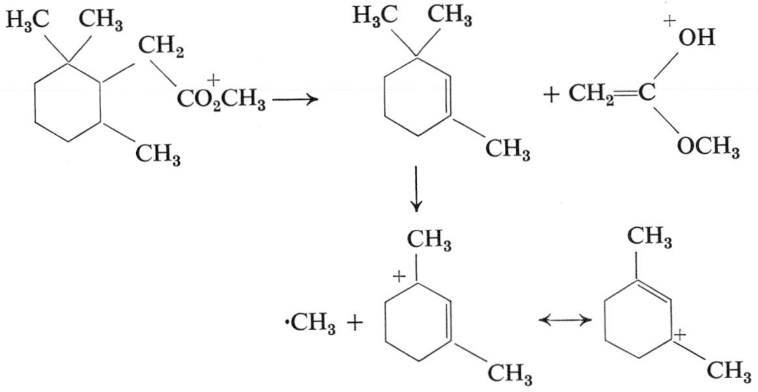

$$(34)$$

$(m/e\ 109)$

a tertiary allylic carbonium ion, but it is a di-tertiary ion whose resonance forms are equivalent. This should be a very stable ion indeed, and this is reflected by the highly favored fragmentation leading to the m/e 109 ion.

The discussion of some of the significant features of the mass spectra of the esters of carboxylic acids has been used to illustrate the manner in which this powerful tool may be applied to determination of structure. A relatively full discussion of this single phase of mass spectrometry is the subject of one section of the treatise edited by McLafferty (cf. footnote 10). Several additional books have already appeared, and much data appears in the research journals monthly. This method of structure determination, often supplemented by infrared, ultraviolet, and nuclear magnetic resonance spectroscopy, has already delegated methods of "wet chemistry" to a supplementary position in the determination of structure of organic molecules. In still more difficult problems, x-ray diffraction sometimes becomes necessary.

35

The Literature of Organic Chemistry

The extent of knowledge in organic chemistry is so great that no man can hope to carry in his head more than a minute fragment of this knowledge. As was developed in the preceding chapter, each investigator should learn the fundamentals of the science so that he may then proceed to accumulate the specific knowledge needed for his particular field of work. This makes especially important an understanding of the literature available to the organic chemist and the procedure to be used in locating the information desired.

Types of Literature

The chemical literature may be formally divided into two rather distinct classes:

1. Secondary literature: books and review journals.

2. Primary literature: chemical journals in which are published papers on original researches; occasionally, part of a book contains material of this nature.

References cited to the original literature ordinarily consist of the names of the authors, the abbreviation of the name of the journal (in *italics*), the volume number (in **boldface** type), the page number of the beginning of the article, and the year of the publication (in parentheses). For example, a reference to the Journal of the American Chemical Society is reported as follows:

N. L. Allinger, J. Allinger and M. A. DaRooge, *J. Am. Chem. Soc.*, **86**, 4061 (1964). Some journals do not have volume numbers, in which case this entry is of necessity omitted.

I. Secondary literature. There have been written large numbers of very useful books, each of which surveys a particular field, and additional ones are being written continually. Any mention of such books would be an arbitrary selection, so none will be mentioned; however, the value of such books should be emphasized. They are most commonly written by men who have devoted many years to study and experimentation in the particular field covered. There will be mentioned several books or series of books of a more general nature, which consist of sections or chapters, each devoted to a different topic and each contributed by an investigator in that particular field. The organization and over-all editing of such publications is usually in the hands of a board of editors, with an editor-in-chief.

Organic Reactions is a series of volumes which has been published at the approximate rate of one per year (after some delay in the early volumes during World War II). Volume 14 appeared in 1965. A volume consists of several chapters, each devoted to a particular organic reaction. For example, there have appeared chapters on the Reformatsky reaction, the Clemmensen reduction, etc. Each chapter follows a particular pattern, in which there is discussed the nature and scope of the reaction, what is known about its mechanism, and in particular the applications of the reaction in synthesis. Experimental procedures for typical preparations are included, and a major portion of each chapter consists of tables of all the compounds that have been prepared by this reaction (or all that the authors could find in the literature). The tremendous value of such tables may well be visualized. One should never run a particular reaction of a type described in *Organic Reactions* until he has first consulted original literature there cited. A full set of references is included in each chapter.

Organic Syntheses is a yearly publication in which are published detailed directions for the preparation of specific compounds. Yields obtained in other applications of the reaction are often included, and other preparations of the same compound are cited in the original literature. The unique feature of these books is that each preparation is submitted by any chemist desiring to do so, and the directions are checked by other chemists (including at least one member of the board of editors) who have had no personal contact with those submitting the directions. There are published only those procedures which can be checked as to yield, purity of product, and adequacy of procedure. This gives a much more reliable preparative procedure than those ordinarily found in the original literature. Any lack of detail in the directions or any subtle requirements not described by the submitters are very likely to be discovered by the independent checkers. An effort is also made to publish only preparative procedures which are the best available for the compounds involved; however, this cannot be assured. Also, better preparations may appear at a later date. The record for encore preparations is held by diazomethane, for which four successively improved procedures have been published after the original one. This compound is unusual, however, in that the objective of its preparation is to secure that specific compound, which is highly unstable (hence not obtainable commercially) but very valuable in synthesis. The principal objective of most preparations in *Organic Syntheses* is to supply reliable procedures representative of a *type of reaction* which is of extensive application. The particular compound is usually chosen because it is a convenient vehicle for illustrating a general method of organic synthesis. Relatively few compounds represented are of specific interest in themselves.

After ten years, the annual volumes of *Organic Syntheses* are collected and published in a "collective volume." In some instances, preparations in the collective volumes are improved and re-checked, or a new procedure is checked and included. Other useful additions to the collective volumes are several types of indexes and designation of compounds that have become commercially available. The fourth collective volume appeared in 1963, and the annual volume published in 1965 was Volume 45.

Chemistry of Carbon Compounds, edited by Dr. E. H. Rodd, is a series of volumes dealing with both theoretical and practical aspects of organic chemistry. They may be described as an advanced but rather condensed set of reference books. Volumes in this set are the following:

I A, *General Introduction and Aliphatic Compounds*

I B, *Aliphatic Compounds*

II A and II B, *Alicyclic Compounds*

III A and III B, *Aromatic Compounds*

IV A, IV B, and IV C, *Heterocyclic Compounds*

V, *Miscellaneous and Cumulative Index* (this final volume published in 1962). Publication of a second edition of this series was begun in 1965.

There are several series of annual reviews of various phases of chemistry, in which the more important developments of each year are summarized by a chemist especially competent in the particular field. A more general review of this type is the *Annual Reports,* published in England.

A rather unusual type of annual review, which is quite valuable, is *Synthetic Methods of Organic Chemistry,* by Theilheimer. This publication gives good yearly coverage of papers which contain useful new information on synthetic organic chemistry. It is one of the few places where one can find continually up-to-date information assembled according to type of reaction; and the coverage involves essentially the entire spectrum of organic synthesis. There is a five-year accumulative index in each fifth volume, as well as an index in the most recent volume which covers the volumes appearing since the last five-year index. Thus, Volume 18, which appeared in 1964, has an index covering Volumes 16–18.

In addition to annual books of a review nature, there are published in several countries *review journals,* and that published by the American Chemical Society is *Chemical Reviews.* Six issues appear each year, and they include reviews of topics of both a theoretical and practical nature, and in the various fields of chemistry. Ordinarily, original research is not published for the first time in *Chemical Reviews*. The review deals largely with a survey and correlation of papers which have appeared in the primary literature.

A rather special type of secondary literature is the *abstract journal*, which contains only abstracts of the articles appearing in the primary literature. The abstract journal published by the American Chemical Society is called **Chemical Abstracts,** and in it are abstracted all the original articles published in all the countries of the world. It is the research chemist's "key to the chemical literature." By its use, one has some chance of keeping abreast of the vast literature published each month. A research chemist ordinarily checks all the titles appearing in his general field (such as organic chemistry and biochemistry), reads the abstracts which appear of special interest to him, finally reads the original articles when the abstracts reveal that he is specifically interested. *Chemical Abstracts* appears twice monthly; each year there is published an author index, subject index, and formula index. A decennial index was published each ten years until appearance of that one covering 1947–1956. After that date, accumulative indexes have appeared at five-year intervals.

Chemisches Zentralblatt is the German abstract journal. It is often consulted by English-speaking chemists for any of several reasons: (a) to insure complete coverage by check of a second independent index (formula index is especially reliable), (b) to read a second abstract if the original article is in a language which he does not read, (c) to take advantage of the five-year indexes which have been a feature of this abstract journal since the inception of its publication.

Although much important secondary literature has not been specifically mentioned, the coverage above is sufficient to give a wide entry to the knowledge available.

2. Primary literature. At least one valuable chemical journal is published in each of a large number of countries, and in several countries many journals are published. There will be listed some of the more important, and the abbreviation of each will be italicized.

Journal of the *American Chemical Society* (U.S.) contains articles in all branches of chemistry.

Journal of *Organic Chemistry* (U.S.) contains articles dealing primarily with organic chemistry, defined as embracing the areas of organic reactions (both synthetic and mechanistic aspects), the structures of natural products, and spectroscopy applied to organic compounds.

Many other United States journals deal with narrower areas such as polymer chemistry, chemistry of oils and fats, heterocyclic chemistry, steroid chemistry, etc. A majority of the articles in the Journal of *Pharmaceutical Chemistry* deal with organic synthesis. Of interest to all teachers of chemistry is the Journal of *Chemical Education*.

The principal Canadian journal publishing articles on organic chemistry is the *Canadian Journal of Chemistry*.

Journal of the *Chemical Society* of London (British) contains articles in the various fields of chemistry

The *Biochemical Journal* (British) contains many articles of interest to organic chemists, especially in the field of natural products.

Tetrahedron, published in England, purports to be "The International Journal of Organic Chemistry." Most articles are in English, but articles submitted in German or French are published in those languages.

Berichte der deutsche chemische Gesellschaft (German) has continued with the same volume numbering since World War II, but since then has become known as *Chemische Berichte*. In the German language, this journal publishes articles in various fields, but more than half the articles deal with organic chemistry.

Zeitschrift für physiologische Chemie (German) probably has a larger number of papers of organic interest than any other biological journal.

Annalen der Chemie (German), founded by Justus Liebig and one of the oldest chemical journals, dates back to the beginning of the nineteenth century. It is devoted entirely to organic chemistry, and usually has more speculative discussion than other journals.

Helvetica Chimica Acta (Swiss) has papers in all fields of chemistry, but is usually more than three-fourths organic. The rising prominence of Swiss chemistry has steadily increased the prominence of this journal. It contains papers in German, French, Italian, and English, but German is most commonly encountered.

One of several Scandinavian journals publishing articles in the several fields of chemistry is *Acta Chemica Scandinavica*.

Bulletin de la société chimique de France (French) is the leading French journal and contains papers in all fields.

Bulletin de la sociétés chimiques Belges is the leading Belgian journal.

Recueil des travaux chimiques des Pays-Bas is the principal Dutch journal. It publishes papers in several languages.

Gazzetta chimica italiana is the Italian journal which contains many papers of interest to organic chemists. The Italian language is ordinarily used.

Several journals in Japan publish articles on organic chemistry, but the *Bulletin of the Chemical Society of Japan* is probably the one consulted most often. Articles may be in Japanese, English, German, or French, but there is included an abstract of each article in English or German.

There are also numerous Russian journals whose papers are abstracted by *Chemical Abstracts*. The major journal in this language appears to be the *Journal of General Chemistry* (U.S.S.R.) or *Zhurnal Obshcheĭ Khimii*, and this journal is translated into English in the United States. All Russian journals use only the Russian language.

Use of the Chemical Literature

The object of writing books and review articles is to assemble information in a form that makes it readily accessible to the reader. An author may spend several years collecting the material for a book, whereas the reader may digest it in a few days or few weeks, or may get from a part of the book what he wants, in a few minutes or few hours. Nevertheless, in chemical research of an experimental nature, it usually becomes necessary eventually to go back to the primary literature and learn what the investigators originally reported. The papers in this original literature are usually located by way of references found in books, review articles, abstract journals, or other original papers. The only other primary source of references is the current journals as they appear. An active research chemist is likely to follow the articles in his field which appear in a half dozen or more of the prominent journals.

The extent to which the literature search is carried naturally depends on how much information is desired, also on the type of information desired. If a topic, such as reduction of aldehydes, or theory of substitution in benzene, is being investigated, the principal routes to the literature are books such as cited under "secondary literature" or the subject index of *Chemical Abstracts*. Since it is quite difficult to make a subject index entirely satisfactory and inclusive of all the pertinent references, the publication of such books as *Organic Reactions* becomes of much importance.

If a particular compound is being searched, all the information on it may be secured with some certainty. The investigator may want to know only a boiling point or melting point; in other instances, he may want to know everything that has been published on the compound. If the compound in question has never been made, the investigator will be especially anxious to know this with certainty; so it becomes necessary for the system of searching to be so reliable that failure to find a compound constitutes reliable evidence that it has never been made or isolated. The various stages of search may be roughly classified.

I. Cursory look for physical constants, etc.

(a) Handbooks, the two most common being *Handbook of Chemistry*, edited by N. A. Lange, published by Handbook Publishers, Inc., and *Handbook of Chemistry and Physics*, published by the Chemical Rubber Company. These are commonly known as "Lange's Handbook" and "The Rubber Handbook." Each year, a new edition of each of these handbooks is published.

(b) *The Merck Index*, published by Merck and Co., differs from the handbooks mentioned above in that it contains only tabulated information on organic compounds. It also gives a brief summary of chemical and biological properties of each compound, as well as physical properties, and lists larger numbers of compounds.

(c) *Dictionary of Organic Compounds*, edited by Heilbron, Cook and Hey, commonly known as "Heilbron." The fourth edition of this publication, announced in 1965, is a set of five books which contains a much larger list than the above books. There is also more information on each compound, usually key references to recent literature. Annual supplements are planned, in order to keep the publication up to date.

2. More thorough search, including exhaustive search. Even if only physical constants are desired, this category of books must be consulted when the compound is not listed in the books described under Section 1.

(a) *Handbuch der organischen Chemie*, a "handbook" of some hundred large volumes, commonly called "Beilstein" after its first editor. This set of books is published in four series, the last of which covers the literature up to 1949. Additional series are in preparation; however, only five volumes of the fourth series (literature 1930–49) had been published by mid-1965. In these books are briefly abstracted the properties and reactions of *all compounds known and investigated during the period covered*, with references to *all* the original literature. Thus, by looking in four books, the investigator has before him all the information on the compound known up to 1949. A little training is required before one knows in which book to look and where; this topic will be discussed in the latter part of this chapter.

(b) Beyond 1949, except in certain areas (cf. Elsevier, end of chapter), the investigator has available to him only the subject and formula indexes of the abstract journals such as *Chemical Abstracts* and *Chemisches Zentralblatt*. They may be used for years prior to 1949, but Beilstein is much more convenient and reliable for searching specific compounds. As has been mentioned, each of these journals has yearly indexes, while a cumulative index is published by *Chemical Abstracts* each ten years (every five years after 1956), by *Chemisches Zentralblatt* each five years. The compounds are found by simply looking them up in the subject index, where they are listed alphabetically. Failing to find the compound in the subject index, one must consult the formula index to make sure, and sift through all compounds with the empirical formula of the compound being searched. Although searching for a compound in an alphabetical index appears simple at first glance, there prove to be some snares. In particular, a severe strain is thrown upon one's knowledge of nomenclature. Not only must one be able to name the compound, he must be able to name it in all ways known to man, for it is difficult to know just what name will be judged most convenient for indexing purposes. Sometimes, there is used a name which may be regarded as rather awkward by the practicing chemist.

Compounds are always listed as derivatives of parent compounds. For example, ethyl butyrate would be listed as "butyric acid, ethyl ester." If one is looking for 4-methyloctadecanoic acid, he must first learn by a process of elimination that the compound is listed as "γ-methylstearic acid"; so it is found by first locating stearic acid. After there are listed many properties of stearic acid with references, next are listed the substituted stearic acids and in alphabetical order among these will be found "γ-methyl." Frequently, much trickier instances are encountered, such as the following compound:

Ordinarily, this compound would be named γ-methyl-γ-caprolactone, γ-ethyl-γ-methylbutyrolactone, or 4-methyl-1,4-hexanolide (IUC system for naming lactones). The compound is listed in *Chemical Abstracts* under nothing resembling any of these names, but under the following heading and subheadings,

> Caproic acid,
>> γ-hydroxy-γ-methyl,
>>> lactone.

Each of the subheadings is, of course, located alphabetically in a list of subheadings. After one has struggled with a few examples of this sort, he may conclude that an alphabetical listing of organic compounds lacks some of being as simple as it sounds. He may even conclude that it is very much worth his time to learn how to use Beilstein efficiently (cf. below). The most serious problem in an alphabetical listing is that if one fails to find the compound, he is likely to be uncertain whether it was not there (no reference during period of the index) or he just didn't look under the right name. About the only recourse is to find the compound in one volume of the index or find one that would be named similarly. The name used for indexing is then known. If this fails, every formula index must be searched, and this can become laborious.

The Use of Beilstein

The problems of an alphabetical listing are completely avoided by the Beilstein system of listing because the compounds are arranged according to a highly systematic organization based on chemical structure.[1] If one understands the system of arrangement, he can positively find a compound of known structure if it is listed (that is, a reference occurs in the period covered), even though he may have no idea how to name the compound. If one does not find the compound in a given volume, then he knows with certainty that there was no reference during that period (the thoroughness and completeness of the Beilstein staff is well nigh infallible; extremely few references are missed). The only problem is learning the Beilstein system of listing. The Beilstein organization has published a rather large book in German which gives all the details of the system, of which there are many, and this is a last resort that can be consulted in dire need. Such an emergency is unlikely to develop for there is also a not-so-large book,[2] based on the original German book, which is a useful reference for solving various difficult problems of location or determining unusual details of the listing. Nearly all libraries have this book shelved with the volumes of Beilstein, and it can usually be used to resolve a problem in a few

---

[1] The only significant limitation to this system is that a certain amount must be known about the structure of a compound before it can be classified for listing. Compounds whose structures are unknown or highly uncertain may be omitted from Beilstein.

[2] E. H. Huntress, *A Brief Introduction to the Use of Beilstein's Handbuch der organischen Chemie,* Wiley, New York, 1938.

minutes. The following pages are a very brief survey of the major features of the Beilstein system of listing. If these are well understood, and if a little practice is secured by searching for several compounds, it is rarely indeed that one will need to spend more than a minute or two in finding a compound by following the beautifully developed system of listing used in Beilstein. This material is really all that one needs to carry in his memory in order to make adequate use of Beilstein. Even though one cannot read German, he can find a compound in Beilstein, although of course he will not be able to read what is said about the compound.

I. General organization. The most recent edition of Beilstein is the fourth edition, and the only one ordinarily shelved in libraries. It contains four sets of books, one of the *main series*, which covers all the literature from the earliest chemical journals up to 1910, a nice thing to have all in one volume. The *first supplementary series* is divided into the same number of volumes as the main series, and it covers the literature from 1910 to 1920. The next ten-year period is covered in the *second supplementary series*. On account of the major delay in publication during World War II, the decision was reached to include the twenty-year period, 1930–1949, in the *third supplementary series*. Five volumes (each bound in more than one book) of this last series had appeared by mid-1965.

In each volume of each supplementary series, at the center top of each page is a heavy black number, **which is the page number of the main series** on which occur the same compounds listed on the page of the supplementary series bearing that number at top **center**. For example, if one finds isobutyric acid on page 288 of Volume II of the main series, which he does, in order to find this compound in a supplementary series, he takes Volume II of the supplementary series, follows the heavy numbers at top center until he finds **288**. That page will have isobutyric acid listed on it. This is page 126 (numbered at the side of the page) in Volume II of the first supplementary series, but **288** is the black number listed at top center and is the cross reference to the main series. Thus, as soon as the compound is located in the main series, or there is located the page where it would be if listed, the location in the supplementary series becomes very rapid.

2. Fundamental divisions. There are three major divisions in Beilstein and a fourth rather minor division, as follows:

Acyclic compounds	Vols. I–IV
Isocyclic compounds	Vols. V–XVI
Heterocyclic compounds	Vols. XVII–XXVII
Carbohydrates, rubberlike compounds and carotenoids	Vols. XXX, XXXI

Volumes 28 and 29 are indexes (discussed later). It is of interest that although the open-chain compounds occupy only four volumes, the carbocyclic compounds occupy 12 volumes, and the heterocyclic compounds occupy 11 volumes.

In recent years, much interesting aliphatic chemistry has been developed, but much of this has been concerned with alicyclic compounds.

In the first two major groups, the compounds are listed in the same way, and listing in the third group differs only in having a prior classification according to type of hetero ring; so this fundamental system of listing will be discussed next.

3. Basic classes of compounds. The basic functional groups according to which classes are listed are the following, and *in the following order:*

1. Hydrocarbons (octane, benzene, etc.).
2. Hydroxy (oxy) compounds (ethyl alcohol, phenol).
3. Carbonyl (oxo) compounds (acetone, benzaldehyde).
4. Carboxylic acids (butyric acid, phenylacetic acid).
5. Sulfinic acids ($R—SO_2H$).
6. Sulfonic acids ($R—SO_2OH$).
7. Selenium compounds (rarely encountered).
8. Amines ($R—NH_2$, $R'NH—R$, etc.).
9. Hydroxylamines ($R—NHOH$).
10. Hydrazines (phenylhydrazine, etc.).
11. Azo compounds (azobenzene, etc.).

Several metal-containing relatively rare groups.

In the original binding of Beilstein, the classes of compounds in each volume are printed on the front of the book; however, these books receive so much use that those in most libraries have been rebound at least once; so the names of the classes may not appear on the front. After a little experience, one learns in which volumes the classes are located.

4. Polyfunctional compounds. There naturally arises the question of where to look for a polyfunctional compound. The situation is covered by the first of four rules which we will cite.

RULE 1. In polyfunctional compounds, the substance is listed under that class which occurs last in the order of listing.

This is the first of several illustrations of the importance of learning the order in which the classes are listed. Rule 1 may be best amplified by a few illustrations. Keto acids will be listed under carboxylic acids, since carboxyl occurs after keto. Similarly, hydroxy amines will be listed under amines. When more than two of the basic functional groups are present, the same rule applies; in fact, the whole scheme of listing polyfunctional compounds follows this rule. The following order will be found:

(a) Compounds with one functional group (that defining the class).
(b) Compounds with two of that functional group.
(c) Compounds with three of that group, etc.
(d) Compounds having the group defining the class and also one hydroxyl group.
(e) Similarly, with two hydroxyl groups, etc.

(f) Next the second group is keto, after that both hydroxyl and keto.

(g) Similarly for all groups.

Understanding this system of last in the order of listing is very important in several connections, including that presently being discussed. For example, amino acids occur in a different volume than do simple carboxylic acids or hydroxy acids.

5. Finding the specific compounds. Thus far we have discussed locating the major class in which a compound may belong, but we have not discussed locating the specific compound. Two additional rules are needed to proceed to this stage, and these will be considered one at a time.

RULE 2. Within a class, compounds are listed in order of decreasing saturation, i.e., increasing unsaturation.

The best way to follow the extent of saturation is by use of a general formula. Let us suppose that we are looking for levulinic acid,

$$CH_3—C—(CH_2)_2—CO_2H$$
$$\underset{O}{\overset{\|}{}}$$

Its molecular formula is $C_5H_8O_3$, and the general formula is $C_nH_{2n-2}O_3$. The general formula for the compound(s) on a pair of pages is always located at the top of the left-hand page. After the keto acids are located, the general formula at the top is noted. If the unsaturation is greater than H_{2n-2} one should turn back in the book, if the unsaturation is less than that (not possible in this particular illustration), one turns forward, for unsaturation increases as one turns forward in the book.

All compounds fitting one general formula belong to the same **system** in Beilstein, and have the same **system number.** The system numbers begin at unity and extend to many thousands. System numbers are at the top of each page, on the inside top next to the binding. Most cross references in Beilstein are not by page and volume, but by system number, and this appears to be the only significant use of the system numbers.

After we get the correct general formula located, we proceed according to the next rule.

RULE 3. Compounds in each system number are listed according to increasing molecular weight.

At the top of each right-hand page appears either the name of the compound(s) on that pair of pages or the molecular formula. The name is ordinarily used only for relatively common substances, but if one does not recognize the German name he can always glance down at the page to learn what the formula is. He then proceeds forward or backward until he arrives at the correct molecular weight.

At this stage, the only remaining step is locating the desired compound among all the isomers that may be listed. There is a completely worked-out system for the order of listing of isomers, beginning with the normal isomer, proceeding to those with one branch, etc. It is probably not profitable to attempt to memorize the system used for listing isomers, for it is so seldom needed. There are usually only a few isomers to be sorted through, and even two or three dozen can usually be run through in a few minutes, for each isomer is numbered and printed in black type, while derivatives (discussed next) are in lighter type and set in a secondary indentation.

6. Compounds classified as derivatives. Although we have discussed the detailed procedure for finding in Beilstein any compound with a functional group included in the list of "basic classes" of compounds, we have not yet considered compounds classified as derivatives of these basic classes. Brief consideration will reveal that the basic classes include only a relatively few functional groups. The remainder are classified as **derivatives.** These derivatives are listed immediately following the parent compounds. For example, after the description of butyric acid, there follow descriptions of the various derivatives of butyric acid, such as the amide, acyl halides, esters, etc. Next comes iso-butyric acid, then its derivatives, etc. These derivatives are grouped in three major classes which are listed in the following order:

(1) FUNCTIONAL DERIVATIVES. These are compounds resulting from alteration of the functional group and hydrolyzable to the parent compound. It is not profitable to remember all the functional groups included here, for the number is large, and the derivatives are different for each functional group. It is much more convenient to remember that this category includes all the derivatives except the substitution derivatives.

(2) SUBSTITUTION DERIVATIVES. These are few in number and should be remembered in the following order:
  1. Halogens: fluorine, chlorine, bromine, iodine.
  2. Nitroso: —NO.
  3. Nitro: —NO_2.
  4. Azido: —N_3 (rarely encountered).

(3) SULFUR COMPOUNDS. These are listed as derivatives of the oxygen analogs. For example, among the last type of derivative under *n*-butyl alcohol would be found *n*-butyl mercaptan; under propionic acid would be found dithiopropionic acid, C_2H_5—CS_2H.

7. Location of derivatives. Sulfur analogs are easily found at the end of the list of derivatives, but certain rules need be applied to locate a compound among the long lists of functional and substitution derivatives.

(1) FUNCTIONAL DERIVATIVES. Since the functional derivatives are different for each functional group, it is ordinarily not profitable to attempt to remember the order in which they are listed. There are usually not a sufficiently large

number of functional derivatives of a single compound to make the location laborious; however, such derivatives as esters of common acids may be quite numerous. In these instances, one should remember that the principles in Rules 2 and 3 apply here also; the esters are listed according to increase in unsaturation and increase in molecular weight. This makes a sufficiently rapid location possible.

When a substance may be regarded as a derivative of two or more compounds, such as the esters just mentioned, the rule of last in the order of listing applies, as stated in Rule 4.

RULE 4. When a functional derivative may be hydrolyzed into two or more organic molecules, the substance is listed as a derivative of that hydrolytic product listed last in the order of listing.

According to Rule 4, ethyl acetate is listed as a derivative of acetic acid, but N-methylacetamide is listed as a derivative of methylamine. Acetamide is listed as a derivative of acetic acid since only one organic product is formed on hydrolysis.

(2) SUBSTITUTION DERIVATIVES. Listing of monosubstitution derivatives follows the order given in section 6, paragraph 2. This list should be learned not only so that the order may be followed, but also because it makes it possible to locate all other derivatives among the substitution derivatives.

In the case of **polysubstitution derivatives,** the principle of last in the order of listing (Rule 1) applies. For example, a chlorobromobenzene would be listed after all the polybromobenzenes, and a chloroiodobenzene would be listed after the iodobenzenes. Similarly, a bromonitrobenzene would be listed after the chloronitrobenzenes, which would all be listed after the nitrobenzenes. In the aromatic series, especially, there are so many of the polysubstitution derivatives that it is imperative to understand the order in which they are listed.

8. Second–order derivatives. A second-order derivative (derivative of a derivative) is again listed according to the principle of last in the order of listing. For example, let us consider a compound such as chloroacetyl chloride,

$$Cl-CH_2-C\overset{\displaystyle O}{\underset{\displaystyle Cl}{\Big\langle}}$$

This is a functional derivative of chloroacetic acid, and a substitution derivative of acetyl chloride. Since substitution derivatives occur after functional derivatives in the order of listing of derivatives, chloroacetyl chloride is regarded first as a substitution derivative of acetic acid. Among the functional derivatives of chloroacetic acid will be found the acid chloride. An understanding of this sort of listing is important, for a large number of pages will be found devoted to functional derivatives of acetic acid, and the substitution derivatives are found after these pages.

Numerous other sorts of second-order derivatives may be located by similarly applying the rule of last in the order of listing; for example, we may consider the following acetamino acid:

$$C_2H_5\text{---}CH\text{---}CO_2H$$
$$|$$
$$HN\text{---}C\text{---}CH_3$$
$$\|$$
$$O$$

Hydrolytic products would be acetic acid and 2-aminobutanoic acid. The latter is listed as a polyfunctional compound following amines; so the acetyl derivative would be listed among the functional derivatives of the amino acid. These derivatives would also include the ethyl ester of this acetamino acid.

9. Special problems and special rules. Certain special situations require exceptions to the general system which has been described. For example, the acetyl derivatives of complicated alcohols will be listed as derivatives of the alcohol, in spite of the fact that acids are last in the order of listing. Similarly, hydrazones will be listed under the carbonyl compound, not under the hydrazine. These exceptions are instituted in order to prevent a very inconveniently large accumulation of derivatives under such substances as acetic acid and phenylhydrazine. One soon becomes acquainted with such exceptions which apply in his particular field of activity. When encountered for the first time, they can be resolved either by reference to Huntress' Beilstein guide or by use of the indexes in the manner described below.

Certain types of derivatives tend to be deceptive because the Beilstein system does not follow usual chemical methods of preparation. Halogen derivatives can be especially deceptive. One would normally look for bromobenzene as a substitution derivative of benzene, but he might forget to look for *n*-butyl bromide as a derivative of butane. One tends to think of *n*-butyl bromide as a derivative of *n*-butyl alcohol, but this is not the case in the Beilstein system.

Certain derivatives of open-chain compounds become heterocyclic compounds, and these sometimes tend to catch one unaware. Since acetic anhydride is located as a functional derivative of acetic acid, it seems natural to look for succinic anhydride as a functional derivative of succinic acid; but succinic anhydride happens to be a heterocyclic compound that will be found about fifteen volumes later on in the series. Similar considerations apply to lactones.

10. Heterocyclic compounds. Any compound with one or more atoms other than carbon in a ring is a heterocyclic compound, even if it is a derivative of an open-chain compound. Each heterocyclic system is given a **hetero number,** which applies only to one size of ring and one hetero atom or one combination of hetero atoms. For example, furan will have one hetero number, pyran will have another, and imidazole will have another. Succinic anhydride is under the same hetero number as furan, because each has a five-membered ring with one oxygen atom in the ring. δ-Valerolactone will have the same hetero number as pyran, and glutaric anhydride will also fall under this hetero number.

The hetero number may be found by consulting the Beilstein guide, but a method which is usually faster is to locate in the index a very simple compound with the same ring system. The selected simple compound can then be located in the appropriate volume and its hetero number noted. The desired compound will also be listed under the hetero number.

Within a given hetero number, compounds are listed by the system which has been described for the other classes of compounds. Certain additional complications arise in listing some kinds of heterocyclic compounds, but these problems are best resolved when and if the need arises.

II. The Beilstein indexes. Each volume of Beilstein has an index to that volume; in addition, Volumes 28 and 29 are cumulative indexes to the series. It should be stated at once, however, that these indexes do not contain all the compounds in Beilstein, nor do they contain a major fraction of these compounds. The indexes are intended to supplement the system of arrangement, not substitute for it. As a matter of fact, these indexes are subject to the disadvantages previously mentioned for an alphabetical index; furthermore, one must know the German word for the compound he is searching. A reasonable knowledge of German will eliminate much of the language difficulty, but only if one has had occasion to refer to the specific substance will he know that Bernsteinsäure is succinic acid.

The indexes have several important uses, one of which is for rapid determination of hetero numbers, as mentioned in the previous section. Three additional applications of the indexes will serve to illustrate the sorts of things for which they are useful.

(a) Simple and very common substances which are derivatives are often most easily located by consulting the index of the appropriate volume. For example, one is likely to thumb through many pages in locating ethyl acetate among the many pages of derivatives of acetic acid. Time is likely to be saved by use of the index.

(b) If one has encountered a problem not covered by the relatively condensed amount of information he carries in his memory, or if he has become confused on the functioning of the system, the difficulty may often be resolved more rapidly by the use of indexes than by use of the Beilstein guide. For example, suppose that one is looking for the following acid:

$$HO_2C-CH_2-CH-CH-CO_2H$$
$$\underset{\displaystyle CH_3}{\overset{\displaystyle |}{\underset{\displaystyle |}{CH_2}}}\quad \overset{\displaystyle |}{CH_3}$$

He is very unlikely to find this in the index, even if he could decide what name to search; it is not the sort of key compound listed in the

Beilstein indexes. The normal isomer will be listed. This is the C_8 dibasic acid, suberic acid; so locating Korksäure in the index will immediately locate one in the correct system number and at the desired molecular weight. Looking through the isomers listed will reveal whether the isomer of interest is among those to which there is a reference. Similarly, one might be uncertain how to look up a substance such as the following:

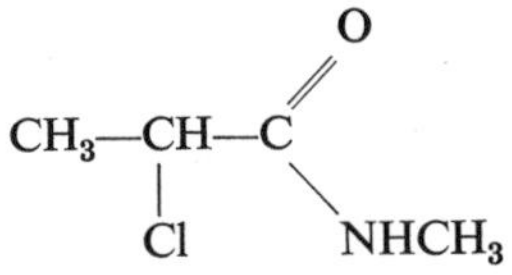

$$CH_3-CH-C\begin{matrix}O\\ \\NHCH_3\end{matrix}$$
$$\underset{Cl}{|}$$

This could be resolved by locating methylamine by use of the indexes, then looking for the desired compound among the derivatives of methylamine.

(c) It sometimes happens that a compound has such structural features that application of the Beilstein system becomes complicated, even with help from the guide. Such a compound is the following well-known industrial chemical:

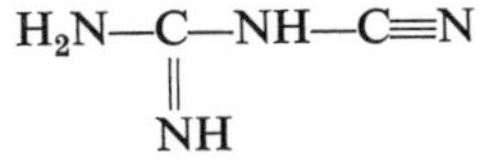

$$H_2N-C-NH-C\equiv N$$
$$\underset{NH}{\|}$$

Dicyandiamide

For a structure of this kind, it is probably better to try and resolve the difficulties of an alphabetical listing in German rather than to apply the Beilstein system. For such difficult problems, there is also available the cumulative **formula index.** The use of the formula index is usually rather laborious, but it is reliable, frequently the best and most rapid solution for difficult problems.

Elsevier's Encyclopaedia of Organic Chemistry

Since 1946, the Elsevier Publishing Company, of Amsterdam, Holland, has begun publication of an English language *Encyclopaedia of Organic Chemistry*, which was initially projected with a scope comparable to that of Beilstein. The initial plan was as follows:

Series I. *Aliphatic Compounds* (3 volumes).
Series II. *Carboisocyclic Non-Condensed Compounds* (Vols. 4–11).
Series III. *Carboisocyclic Condensed Compounds* (Vols. 12–14).
Series IV. *Heterocyclic Compounds* (Vols. 15–18).
Subject and formula indexes (Vols. 19 and 20).

Fortunately, Series III was selected for initial publication, on the grounds that developments in these areas (especially sterols) had become so rapid that it was especially desirable to have a compendium more current with the literature than Beilstein. Eventually, it became apparent that the volume of the chemical literature had become such that realization of the initial ambitious plan for Elsevier was quite impossible. The only publication has been in Series III, and cooperative publication with Beilstein has now been developed so that more manpower may be utilized in keeping these valuable publications from falling excessively far behind current literature.

Series III of Elsevier includes not only the condensed ring aromatic compounds such as naphthalene and the carcinogenic hydrocarbons, but also the sesquiterpenes and sterols. These fields have developed so actively that a "volume" in Elsevier has become merely an organizational unit; a "volume" may consist of many books. The general content of the Elsevier publications is as follows:

Vol. 12 A, Non-naphthalenic compounds, 1262 pp., literature covered through 1941.

12 B, Naphthalene and derivatives, 4840 pp., eight books, literature covered through 1944.

13, Tricyclic compounds, one book, literature covered through 1936.

14, Tetracyclic and higher ring compounds, 611 pp., one book, literature covered through 1936.

14, Supplements 1–6, 3672 pp., six books.

The most important of the Elsevier books are no doubt the six supplements to Volume 14. The last four of these concern steroids. The literature on structure and conformation is covered to various dates, of which the latest is 1961 for Supplement 6. Continuing publication in Series III of Elsevier is anticipated.

The **arrangement in Elsevier** bears some similarity to that in Beilstein; however, *in Elsevier the major dependence for location of compounds is the indexes*. Each book has a complete alphabetical index which includes *all the compounds* in that book. Coverage of the literature in Elsevier seems quite good, although perhaps not at the near-infallible level so characteristic of Beilstein.

EXERCISES

1. Give the names and abbreviations for eight different chemical journals published in eight different countries.

2. List in order the following:

(a) The 10 major classes of compounds in the Beilstein classification.
(b) The substitution derivatives in the Beilstein system.

3. Give four rules used in locating compounds in Beilstein.

4. According to the Beilstein classification, the following compounds are classed as derivatives. Give the formula for the parent compound under which they would be listed.

(a)

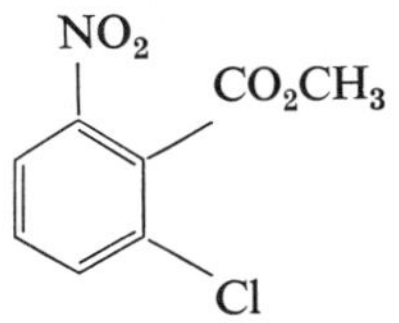

$$\underset{\text{(NO}_2\text{ ring with CO}_2\text{CH}_3\text{ and Cl})}{}$$

(b)

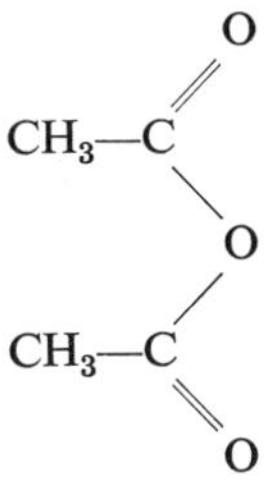

$$\underset{\text{CH}_3-\text{C}}{\overset{\text{O}}{}}\text{O}\quad\underset{\text{CH}_3-\text{C}}{\overset{\text{O}}{}}$$

(c) CH$_3$—CH—CH$_2$—$\overset{\text{O}}{\overset{\|}{\text{C}}}$—N$\overset{\text{H}}{\underset{\text{C}_2\text{H}_5}{}}$

  OH

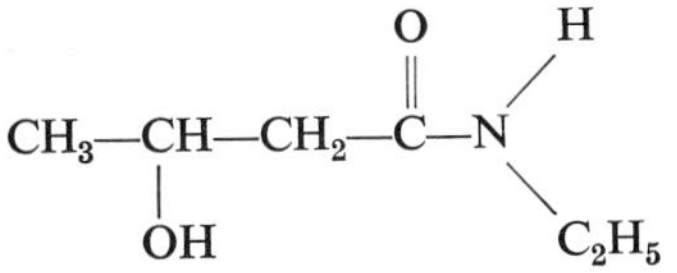

(d) Br—CH$_2$—CH$_2$—Br

(e)

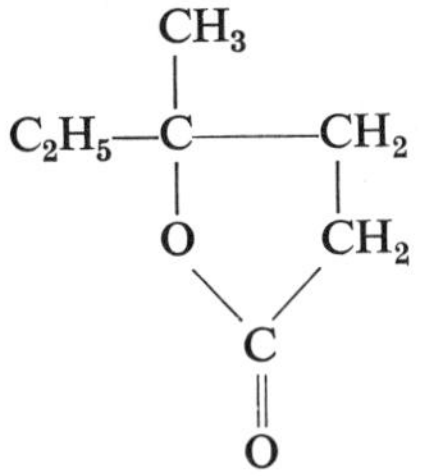

$$\text{C}_2\text{H}_5-\overset{\text{CH}_3}{\underset{\text{O}}{\overset{|}{\text{C}}}}-\overset{}{\underset{}{\text{CH}_2}}$$
$$\text{O}\quad\text{CH}_2$$
$$\overset{}{\underset{\|}{\text{C}}}$$
$$\text{O}$$

(f)

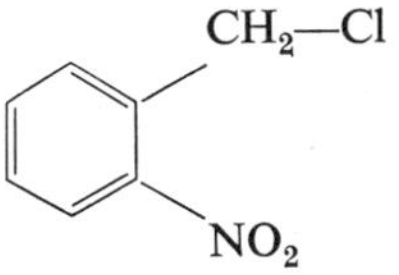

$$\underset{\text{(ring with CH}_2-\text{Cl and NO}_2\text{)}}{}$$

(g) CH$_3$—O—C$_2$H$_5$

(h) 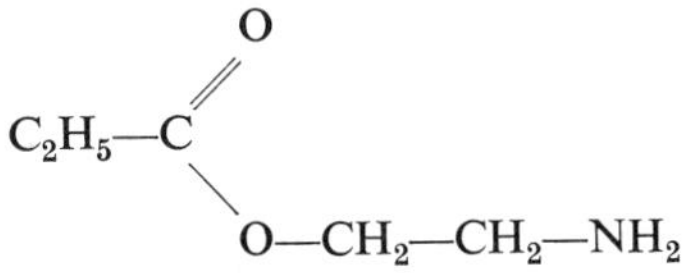 C$_2$H$_5$—$\overset{\text{O}}{\overset{\|}{\text{C}}}$

  O—CH$_2$—CH$_2$—NH$_2$

5. Find each of the following compounds in Beilstein, checking the main series and all supplementary series.

(a)

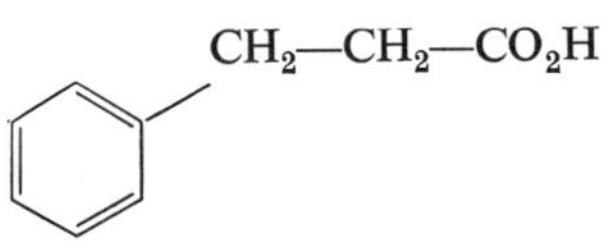

$$\underset{\text{(ring with CH}_2-\text{CH}_2-\text{CO}_2\text{H)}}{}$$

(b)

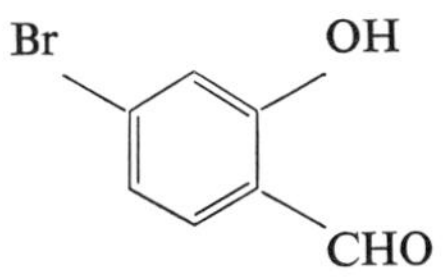

$$\underset{\text{(ring with Br, OH, CHO)}}{}$$

(c)

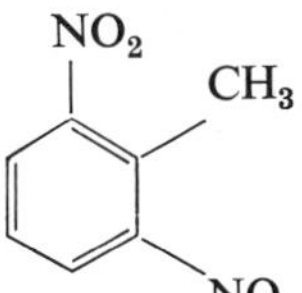

$$\underset{\text{(ring with NO}_2\text{, CH}_3\text{, NO}_2\text{)}}{}$$

(d) 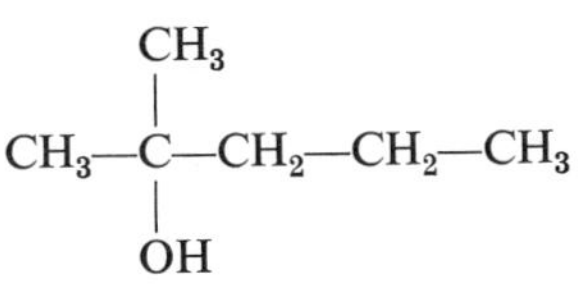 CH$_3$—$\overset{\text{CH}_3}{\overset{|}{\underset{|}{\text{C}}}}$—CH$_2$—CH$_2$—CH$_3$

  OH

(e) 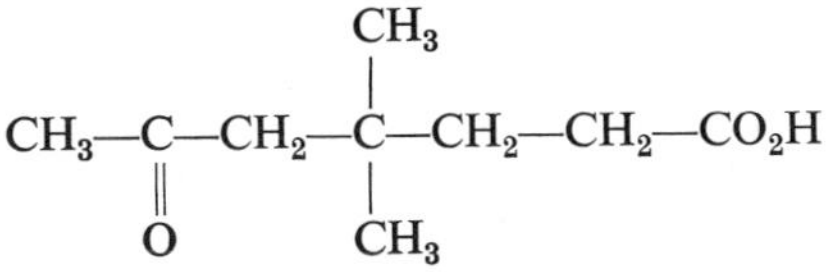 CH$_3$—$\overset{}{\underset{\|}{\text{C}}}$—CH$_2$—$\overset{\text{CH}_3}{\overset{|}{\underset{|}{\text{C}}}}$—CH$_2$—CH$_2$—CO$_2$H

  O   CH$_3$

(f) H$_2$N—(CH$_2$)$_5$—NH$_2$

(g) CH_3
$C_2H_5-\overset{|}{CH}-CH_2-CH_2-CO_2C_2H_5$

(h)

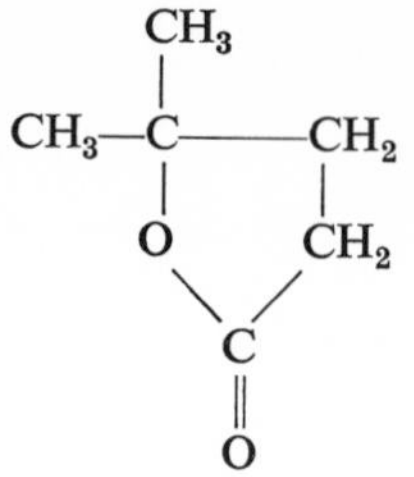

(i)

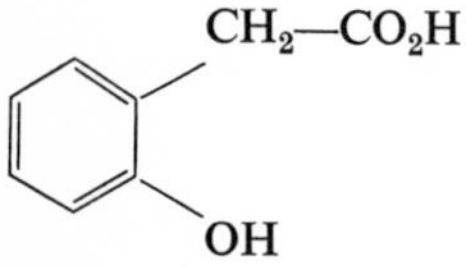

(j)

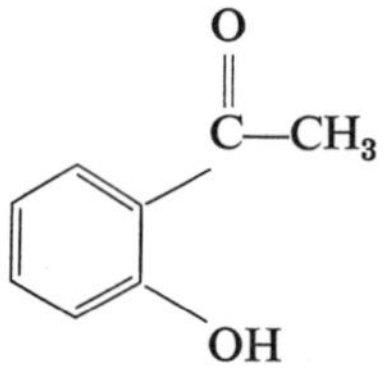

(k) $CH_3-\overset{|}{\underset{OH}{CH}}-CO_2H$

(l) $CH_3-(CH_2)_5-CH_2-SH$

(m) $CH_3-\overset{|}{\underset{NH_2}{CH}}-CO_2H$

(n)

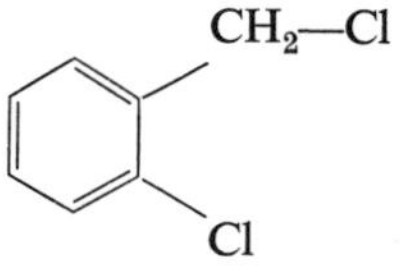

(o) $HO-CH_2-CH_2-SH$

(p) $HO_2C-\overset{|}{\underset{Cl}{CH}}-CO_2H$

(q)

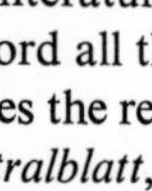

(r)

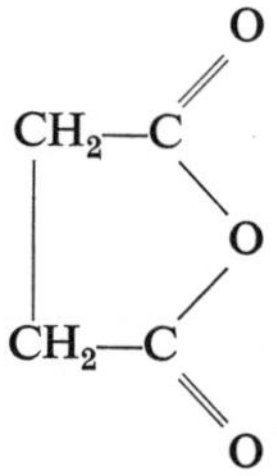

6. Select six compounds from Exercise 5, and make a systematic search of them in all the literature up to the last index that has been published by *Chemical Abstracts*. Record all the references found in Beilstein and in *Chemical Abstracts*, and record the places the references were found. Search two of the selected compounds in *Chemisches Zentralblatt*, and check the references so found against those found in *Chemical Abstracts*.

Index

The index has been organized with particular attention to its utility for study or review. Thus, extensive sub-headings are assembled under such entries as "Mechanism of:" or "Nomenclature:". Also listed are entries such as common names for compounds whose structure may be sought, as well as the names of "Name reactions."

Many chemists, especially contemporary ones, are mentioned in the book, but a separate index is not included; these names are listed in normal alphabetical order in this index.